The Safety Professionals Handbook
Management Applications

Second Edition

Joel M. Haight, Editor

American Society of Safety Engineers
DES PLAINES, ILLINOIS, USA

Library of Congress Cataloging-in-Publication Data

The safety professionals handbook : management applications / Joel M. Haight, editor.
    p. cm.
  Includes bibliographical references and index.
  ISBN 978-1-885581-60-0 (alk. paper)
    1. Industrial safety--Management--Handbooks, manuals, etc. I. Haight, Joel M. II.
    American Society of Safety Engineers.

T55.S21578.2012
658.4'08--dc23

          2011053318

Revision Editor: Jeri Ann Stucka, ASSE

Text Editing, Page Design, and Composition: Cathy Lombardi, Liberty NY

Proofreading: Adept Concept Solutions

Cover Design: Stephanie Johnson, ASSE

Managing Editor: Michael F. Burditt, ASSE

Printed in the United States of America

18 17 16 15 14 13 12 7 6 5 4 3 2 1

THE SAFETY PROFESSIONALS HANDBOOK

Management Applications

Contents

FOREWORD

WHILE THIS SECOND EDITION of this important book, written by EH&S professionals, remains unique in both its approach and the scope of information provided on the most important EH&S programs at most companies, it is now even more than that. The format has remained the same and presents each topic area from five or more points of view: regulatory, science and engineering, cost analysis and budgeting, benchmarking and performance criteria, and best practices. We have incorporated the results of new research, published in peer-reviewed journals, on subjects ranging from resource allocation modeling to improved hazardous materials handling to work physiology improvements. All of the chapters were reviewed, and many were significantly updated. While, in some cases, that meant just updating the references used, many chapters have undergone a nearly complete re-write. The hazardous materials chapter and the appendix of conversions, constants, frequently used calculations, and so on, are two of those. We've added new chapters on sustainability and best practices in industrial hygiene. Many of the chapters have been expanded to include new approaches and updated regulatory requirements.

The contributions of a number of new authors helped to make this new edition possible. It was and continues to be the goal of ASSE, in producing this book, to bring together the vast body of knowledge available in the safety, health, and environmental arena into one source that should be found in the office of every safety professional and be easily accessed, read, and understood. You, the reader, will find this second edition as informative and detailed as the first edition and will also find that the coverage is more extensive and goes into even greater depth in many cases.

All of the chapters were peer reviewed, most by three qualified technical reviewers. The authors added their own insights, experiences, opinions, and interpretations of this extensive body of literature for their individual field of expertise. In my experience as a contributor to other peer-reviewed publications, the peer-review process is never easy on authors or reviewers and, quite frankly, most of the time that goes into such a peer-reviewed publication is spent on these reviews and on making the corrections, revisions, additions, and adjustments to the first drafts. This was the case for our book. It was peer reviewed to ensure that our readers can have confidence in the technical accuracy and the depth and breadth of coverage in the book and are able to gauge their own experience and measure it against both the summary of the existing, well-known, time-honored, published literature and the validated experience and insight of our authors.

While the publishing of a new edition of such an important book is an exciting and happy event, we are all saddened by the passing of one of our authors and colleagues, Craig Schroll. Craig was a significant contributor to this book as both an author and a topic coordinator. He was able to finish his chapter before he passed, but that is of little consolation. We will at least get to read his final contribution to the profession in which he was so active. We will miss Craig.

The safety field is such a diverse, multidisciplinary, and widely applied field that the only way this type of book could be successfully put together was to involve the input of a large segment of this diverse safety profession. The second edition, just as with the first edition, was written by practitioners, researchers, and academics, and it represents nearly two thousand years of work experience, as our authors average roughly twenty years of experience in the field. It is our goal for you, our reader, to both learn something when you read the book and also to aid you in performing your very valuable role of protecting people, property, and the environment. We invite your input as you read the book and wish you well in your quest to "Protect People, Property, and the Environment."

Joel M. Haight

PREFACE

THIS NEW SECOND EDITION retains the focus of the first edition on working environmental, health, and safety professionals, and follows its original intended purpose as a reference handbook. All of the chapters were reviewed and revised under peer review. Two new chapters have been added, one on sustainability and a second on best practices in industrial hygiene. Whether you need to develop and implement a new safety, health, or environmental program or want to improve one of your existing programs, *The Safety Professionals Handbook* provides EH&S professionals a complete resource for: standards and regulations, applied science and engineering, cost analysis and budgeting, benchmarking and performance criteria, and best practices.

The Safety Professionals Handbook, Second Edition, continues the American Society of Safety Engineers' commitment to providing a unique resource to practicing professionals and students preparing to enter professional practice. No other EH&S publication offers the breadth of information from so many experienced safety professionals, providing the peer-reviewed, proven, information necessary to develop, benchmark, and improve the many safety programs essential to business operations.

A revised Instructor's Guide will be available in 2012 to instructors who adopt the Handbook. And, ASSE is evaluating various, but appropriate electronic media as a way to get this material out there and in the hands of the students of safety, health, and the environment. Since the first edition came out in 2008, the rapid rise in availability of new and better ways to access the written material through smartphones and other electronic media and reduce impact on the environment by minimizing paper usage will have us reading this book in other formats.

Attention Instructors: An instructor's guide containing questions and answers for each of the chapters in *The Safety Professionals Handbook* will be available at no cost to instructors who have adopted the Handbook for a course. You must provide the title and number of the course, the semester/term offered, and the expected enrollment. Please contact ASSE's Customer Service Department for information on how to request a free copy (847-699-2929; CustomerServiceDept@asse.org).

ACKNOWLEDGMENTS

As WE PUBLISH a second edition of ASSE's *Safety Professionals Handbook*, such an enormous undertaking would not be possible if it were not for the extensive input and countless hours of effort put in by many, many experts and professionals to keep the material current and useful to our readers. To our authors, I offer my appreciation for volunteering for this, at times, frustrating but worthwhile experience. Your contribution to the book is recognized and appreciated by ASSE, and its technical value will be recognized and appreciated by our profession as the book makes its way into the hands of professionals in the safety field and students studying to begin a career in the safety field. I would also like to thank those new authors who submitted new chapters or revised chapters where the previous author was unable to participate in this revision. We are grateful to you for "stepping in" to keep the chapter up to date with new developments in these areas. I emphasize the word "volunteering," so that our readers recognize that you gave of your personal time for the good of the Society and for the good of the profession. Thank you, authors.

Because the handbook content is so widely varied, no one person is expert enough in the field to know and manage all of what is being written in such a book. For this reason, we enlisted the help of 11 additional topic area coordinators. Each one of these experts managed an individual topic area that most matched their expertise. Without their input and support, this book would not have been possible. Additionally, each one of these topic coordinators authored a chapter themselves. They are recognized in the book with a short biographical sketch, but I also would like to thank each one of them here by name: Thank you Adele Abrams, Magdy Akladios, Dennis Andrews, Mike Behm, Mike Blayney, Jeff Camplin, Dick Decker, Gayla McCluskey, John Mroszczyk, Jim Ramsay, and Pam Walaski. In 2011, we lost one of our coordinators and authors, Craig Schroll. He will be missed for his expertise and guidance.

Of course, it goes without saying that the authors will be most recognized in the book, as they are the ones who developed the content; however, if it were not for the reviewers and editors providing valuable technical and editorial feedback to our authors, there could be no book. We recognize, in the book, the valuable contribution made by all of our technical and editorial reviewers by name, but I also offer my personal thank you here to this very important group of experts.

To the patient spouses, family, and friends of our authors, I offer my thanks for providing valuable feedback to our authors through informal means, as well as for giving up time that you could have been spending with your loved one, but couldn't because they were working on their chapter. Your contribution did not go without notice. Thank you.

I would like to offer a special thanks to our Manager of Technical Publications, Mike Burditt, for his professionalism, his patience, his administrative and editorial expertise, and his extensive, knowledgeable input to the writing as well as to the publishing process. Without Mike and the efforts of his very capable and dedicated Publishing Associate, Jeri Stucka, it would not have been possible to publish this book. Her input and continuous effort were absolutely invaluable for this second edition, and I am extremely grateful for all of that effort and stick-to-itiveness! Our authors are technical experts, but many are not professional writers, so Mike and Jeri's input was critical in the process of putting together such a significant work where professional writer quality is demanded and necessary. While this book is part of their regular job, they had to do their job while enduring countless delays, many author changes, frequent missed deadlines, as well as sometimes providing a calming influence for many frustrated authors who also had multiple other priorities pulling at their available time. They have helped our authors and I make this book one that we can be proud of. Thank you, Mike and Jeri.

Lastly, I would like to thank my wife Janet for her patience in enduring many months of long work weeks while I reviewed all of our chapters and for enduring my many frustrations in managing this endeavor that has finally become the second edition of this book. I believe that without her support, I would not have been able to continue with this process all the way to successful publication. Thank you, Janet.

I think all of our authors and I have learned much through this process and I hope all of you, our readers, learn just as much through reading and using this important ASSE book.

Joel M. Haight, Ph.D., P.E.

ABOUT THE EDITOR

In 2009, Joel M. Haight, Ph.D., P.E., was named Branch Chief of the Human Factors Branch at the Centers for Disease Control and Prevention (CDC)—National Institute of Occupational Safety and Health (NIOSH) at their Pittsburgh Office of Mine Safety and Health Research. He continues in this role. In 2000, Dr. Haight received a faculty appointment and served as Associate Professor of Energy and Mineral Engineering at the Pennsylvania State University. He also worked as a manager and engineer for the Chevron Corporation domestically and internationally for eighteen years prior to joining the faculty at Penn State. He has a Ph.D. (1999) and Master's degree (1994) in Industrial and System Engineering, both from Auburn University. Dr. Haight does human error, process optimization, and intervention effectiveness research. He is a professional member of the American Society of Safety Engineers (where he serves as Federal Liaison to the Board of Trustees and the ASSE Foundation Research Committee Chair), the American Industrial Hygiene Association (AIHA), and the Human Factors and Ergonomics Society (HFES). He has published more than 30 peer-reviewed scientific journal articles and book chapters and is a co-author and the editor-in-chief of ASSE's *The Safety Professionals Handbook* and the John Wiley and Sons, *Handbook of Loss Prevention Engineering*.

ABOUT THE SECTION COORDINATORS

Adele L. Abrams, Esq., CMSP is President, Law Office of Adele L. Abrams PC, and an Adjunct Professor at Catholic University of America. She received a Juris Doctor degree from George Washington University National Law Center. She was previously an attorney in practice with the law firm of Patton Boggs LLP. Prior to joining Patton Boggs, LLP, Ms. Abrams was Director of Government Affairs for the National Stone Association. She is a member of two National Standards Committees, ASTM E34 and ASTM D22, and is chair of the National Safety Council's Standards, Regulatory, and Legal Affairs Committee.

Dennis R. Andrews, Ph.D., PSP, CECD, is Principal of Accident & Safety Consultants. His B.S. and M.S. are in Safety and Health, and his Ph.D. is in Biomechanics. He has been a safety, injury, and accident consultant for over 30 years and testifies in court as an expert. He has published several books, as well as many articles, and has taught at several universities. He has also been chair of several safety and standards committees for international organizations, including ASSE.

Michael Behm, Ph.D., M.A., CSP, is an Associate Professor in the Occupational Safety Program at East Carolina University. Mike holds a Bachelor of Science in Occupational Safety and Hygiene (1991) from Millersville University, a Master of Science in Environmental Health (1998) from Temple University, and a Ph.D. in Public Health from Oregon State University (2004). Previously, Mike worked for ten years in the private sector, holding environment, safety, and health positions with Lenox China and Saint-Gobain Corporation. He is an active member of NIOSH's NORA Construction Sector and Prevention through Design Councils. In 2009, he was awarded ASSE's President's Award for service to the Society. His research interests include safety through design, demonstrating business value for occupational safety, and incident causality. In 2011, he was awarded a Research Fellowship with the Singapore National Parks Board and Centre for Urban Greenery and Ecology to study safe design aspects of rooftop and vertical greenery systems.

Jeffery C. Camplin, M.S., CSP, CPEA, obtained a Safety degree in Industry and Technology from Northern Illinois University and a Master's degree in Safety and Emergency Management from Eastern Kentucky University. He is President of Camplin Environmental Services, Inc., a safety and environmental consulting firm he founded in 1991.

James D. Ramsay, Ph.D., M.A., CSP, received his Ph.D. from the University of Wisconsin in 1994 as a joint degree in Preventive Medicine and Industrial Engineering. He is currently the coordinator for the homeland security program at Embry-Riddle Aeronautical University in Daytona Beach, Florida. He currently serves on the CDC/NIOSH Board of Scientific Counselors, is an ABET Board member, and the Chair of the ASSE Education Standards Committee. Prior to his coming to Embry-Riddle, he was a professor of safety sciences at the Indiana University of Pennsylvania for one year; before that, he was a professor of safety and health protection at the University of Wisconsin–Stevens Point for ten years.

ABOUT THE AUTHORS

Brent A. Altemose, M.S., CIH, CSP, is President and Principal Consultant, SABRE Health & Safety LLC, Easton, PA.

Nancy J. Bendickson, CSP, CDS, ARM, ALCM, is a Senior Consultant, Casualty Risk Control, with Aon Global Risk Consulting, Minneapolis, MN.

James V. 'Jim' Bradshaw, CRM, IPMA-CP, CIC, ARM, is Risk Manager for the City of Little Rock, AR.

Thomas S. Butler, Ph.D., CSP, CHMM, is a principal of Butler Health and Safety Inc., San Pedro, CA.

Salvatore Caccavale, B.S., CPE, CHMM, serves as the Vice President of Safety and Health for First Group America (passenger transportation) based in Cincinnati, OH.

Sharon Lynn Campbell, M.A., CSP, is President of S.L.C. Communications. She is an expert of disability safety.

David F. Coble, M.S., CSP, is President of Coble, Taylor & Jones Safety Associates in Cary, NC.

Ben D. Cranor, Ph.D., MPH, CSP, CIH, is a Graduate Faculty Member in the Department of Industrial Engineering & Technology at Texas A&M University–Commerce, in Commerce, TX.

Fred Drennan is a President of Team Safety, Inc. and has been a professional safety consultant, speaker, and author for more than thirty years.

Katina Drennan is a professional author and technical writer, specializing in safety, fitness, and health.

Matthew E. Elam, Ph.D., ASQ, CQE, is Associate Professor of Industrial Engineering at Texas A&M University–Commerce, in Commerce, TX.

Fred E. Fanning, M.Ed., M.A., is the Director, Program Integration and Logistics Operations for the U.S. Department of Energy in Washington, D.C.

David L. Fender, Ed.D., CSP, CSHM, is an Associate Professor in the Department of Occupational Safety and Health at Murray State University.

Lon Ferguson is a Professor in the Safety Sciences Department at Indiana University of Pennsylvania (IUP). Dr. Ferguson has both his B.S. and M.S. in Safety Sciences from IUP, and his doctorate is from the University of Pittsburgh.

William S. Fink, CIH, CSP, CHMM, is the Corporate EHS Manager for Oneida Total Integrated Enterprises (OTIE).

Judy Freeman is President, of Green SEED Energy, a company that develops and markets integrated solutions for bio-energy production. She is also Special Projects Manager with Gabriel Environmental Services, Inc., of Chicago, IL. She has been involved in the environmental and waste industries for over 26 years. She is past administrator of ASSE's Environmental Practice Specialty.

Hamid Fonooni, Ph.D., CPE, is an Associate Professor and Coordinator of the Master of Science in Occupational Safety Program (MSOS) at East Carolina University, Greenville, NC. He holds a B.S. in Mechanical Engineering Technology from Indiana State University, and M.S. and Ph.D. degrees from the University of Cincinnati. He is a Professional Member of ASSE and has published numerous articles and book chapters related to occupational safety and health.

Jubal D. Hamernik, Ph.D., P.E., is President/CEO of Hamernik & Associates, Inc., as well as a nationally qualified expert in many areas of engineering and accident reconstruction.

Peter M. Himpsel, holds a B.S. in Mechanical Engineering from the University of Colorado at

Boulder and was project lead of Formula SAE (Society of Automotive Engineers).

Christopher A. Janicak, Ph.D., CSP, CEA, ARM, is Professor and Doctoral Program Coordinator for the Department of Safety Sciences at Indiana University of Pennsylvania (IUP).

Anthony J. Joseph, Ph.D., was Professor and Director of Environmental, Health and Safety programs at the University of Connecticut.

Anjan K. Majumder, M.S., CHMM, EIT, CSP, is a Safety Engineer with the Federal Aviation Administration.

James M. Miller, P.E., Ph.D., is President of Miller Engineering Associates of Ann Arbor Michigan and an Emeritus Professor of Industrial and Operations Engineering at the University of Michigan.

Phil Moser is National Sales Manager for Advanced Driver Training Services, Inc. (ADTS) in Trooper, Pennsylvania, and is certified in Pennsylvania courts in the field of accident investigation and reconstruction.

Edward A. Musal, M.A., M.S., CSP, CPEA is the Environmental Health & Safety Officer for the State University of New York College at Purchase and adjunct faculty at Manhattan College School of Engineering.

Tyler Nguyen, CSP, REP, is the Principal Safety and Environmental Compliance Specialist for Santa Clara County, California. He is also Past President of the American Society of Safety Engineers, Greater San Jose chapter.

Linda S. Rowley, M.B.A., CSP, is the Safety and Health Manager for the U.S. Bureau of Reclamation.

Kathy A. Seabrook, CSP, CMIOSH (UK), is President Global Solutions, Inc., which she founded in 1996. She holds professional safety and health certifications in the US and UK and graduated with a B.S. in Chemistry from James Madison University. She is a published author in the field of global safety, health, and environmental management, a member of the ANSI Z10 Standards Development Committee,

and served on the working party for OHSAS 18002. Kathy has been a member of the ASSE National Faculty since 1996, teaching Global SHE Management and Sustainability & the Safety Professional. She currently serves on the ASSE Board of Directors and is an advisory committee member to the ASSE International Practice Specialty and Women in Safety Engineering, as well as the British Institution of Occupational Safety and Health's International Group.

Francis P. Sehn, M.S., CSP, ARM, is Assistant Vice President–Casualty Risk Control Services for Willis of PA, of Pittsburgh, Pennsylvania.

Phyllis A. Simmons, M.A., CSP, is a safety consultant and President of Creative Safety Designs in San Leandro, CA.

Gregory L. Smith, CSP, is President of Construction Safety & Health, Inc., in Austin, Texas.

C. Keith Stalnaker, Ph.D., is Professor in the Department of Occupational Safety and Health at Columbia Southern University in Orange Beach, AL.

Charles V. Stanfill, Jr., is Safety Director at the North Carolina Department of Environment and Natural Resources.

Richard A. Stempniak, CMfgE, is an Associate Professor of Technology (Industrial) at the State University of New York College at Buffalo.

Amy Stewart, CSP, has more than twenty years' experience designing, implementing, and conducting safety and training programs. Specializing in transportation, she holds a current, fully endorsed Ohio Commercial Driving License (CDL), and is published with the ASSE among numerous other publications.

Robert Stewart, M.S., CIH, CSP, is EHS Director for Oldcastle Building Products, Atlanta, GA.

Linda M. Tapp, M.S., ALCM, CSP, is President of Crown Safety LLC.

Michael Taubitz, B.S.M.E., M.A., is currently cochair of the Lean and Safe Network, Secretary for the Michigan Lean Consortium Board of Directors, and manages issues related to the integration of safety with sustainability for FDR Safety LLC. Prior to this, he spent 43 years at General Motors, holding every safety position in the company.

T. Michael Toole, Ph.D., P.E., is Associate Professor of Civil and Environmental Engineering at Bucknell University.

Anthony Veltri is an Associate Professor of environment, safety, and health in the College of Health and Human Sciences at Oregon State University. Dr. Veltri's current research is aimed at making the business case for environment, safety, and health.

Cherie C. Walton, CSP, is co-owner and Vice President of Reactives Management Corporation.

George C. Walton, M.S., CHMM, is founder and co-owner of Reactives Management Corporation.

Barry R. Weissman, REM, CHMM, CHS-IV, CIPS, CSP, is Corporate Manager—Health & Safety with Benjamin Moore and Company in Flanders, NJ.

TECHNICAL REVIEWERS

The following individuals reviewed one or more chapters in the *Safety Professionals Handbook—Management Applications*. ASSE and the Editor, Dr. Joel Haight, gratefully acknowledge their contributions.

Michael Belcher
Elyce Biddle
Peter Bowen
Tracey Cekada
Randy DeVaul
Brenda Franklin
Ken Fries
Julie Griffin
Jody Grizz
Matthew Hallowell
Vladislav Kecovic
Sharon Kemerer
Fred Lang
Mark Lehto
Bruce Main

Charles McGlothlin
Jim McKown
John McNeel
Samuel Oyewole
Helmut Paschold
Eli Paster
Bonnie Rogers
Craig Schilders
Ron Scholtz
Bernard Silverstein
Paul Specht
Steven Strayer
Albert Stutz
Tamie Webber
Bram Weiser

FOUNDATION PRINCIPLES AND APPLICATIONS

BASIC ECONOMIC ANALYSIS AND ENGINEERING ECONOMICS

Anthony Veltri and James D. Ramsay

LEARNING OBJECTIVES

- Describe the main motivation for applying economic analysis to occupational safety, health, and environmental affairs.

- Articulate the rationale that supports and the logic that is behind incorporating economic analysis findings into safety, health, and environmental investment proposals.

- Describe the safety, health, and environmental investment strategies available to firms and currently being practiced by firms.

- Characterize what is needed to construct a safety, health, and environmental economic analysis model.

- Describe what will be needed for economic analysis to become an on-going practice within the occupational safety and health profession.

THE ECONOMIC ASPECTS of occupational safety, health, and environmental (SH&E) issues and practices are a timely subject to explore, study, and comprehend. Today, SH&E needs are affecting how business decisions are made, and the needs of business are affecting how SH&E decisions are made. This perspective is expected to dramatically change how proposals for investment in SH&E practices will be put together and presented within an organization's overall investment-allocation process. The primary motivation for applying economic analysis to SH&E investment proposals is to become more competitive when the firm makes decisions about which projects to fund. This indicates that investment allocators will make SH&E investments for the same reasons they make other strategic investments within a firm—because they expect those investments to contribute to economic performance. The desire to understand and use SH&E financial analysis has been attracting increasing attention. There are various descriptions of what an SH&E financial accounting system looks like, but essentially all definitions describe the system as a way of enhancing SH&E financial performance.

Economic analysis was defined by Friedman (1987) as the study of trends, phenomena, and information that are economic in nature. While it is understood that the principles of economic analysis will not change much over time, many aspects of how they are applied and under what context they are applied do occur. For example, developments in SHE economic analysis have moved to making the business case covering the social/community/ people component of sustainability, supply-chain management, and the lean operation movement. Economic analysis has been used extensively by other internal organizational specialists (i.e., research and development, purchasing, design and process engineering, quality assurance, facility maintenance, operations management, transportation/distribution, and information management). So far, however, SH&E professionals have lagged behind in this effort. The significance of incorporating SH&E elements in the economic analysis of investment proposals was first recognized over a quarter century ago by Professor C. Everett Marcum, founder and curriculum designer of the West Virginia University graduate degree in SH&E Management Studies. Marcum reasoned in his course lectures that "The design intent (i.e., functionality and form) of a firm's products and technologies, and its operational processes and services, are first expressed by their economic attractiveness; and foremost judged from an economic point of view; and any other features are secondary to the initial economic review."

Bird (1996), in his book entitled *Safety and the Bottom Line*, expressed a similar reasoning in his concept concerning the Axiom of Economic Association. Bird stated that "A manager will usually pay more attention to information when expressed or associated with cost terminology."

These crucial lines of reasoning have generally evaded the practitioners, professors, and students in SH&E management. While they may be well read in the strategic management practices, technical principles, and regulatory aspects that guide decision making and operating actions for the field, practitioners seldom have studied and used the concepts and methods that underlie their economic logic and attractiveness. Most commonly, books, journal articles, and lectures merely mention these in passing.

Concern about analyzing the economic aspects of SH&E issues and practices initially surfaced in the early 1990s and continues today (Henn 1993, Cohan and Gess 1994, Warren and Weitz 1994, Cobas et al. 1995, Brouwers and Stevels 1995, Mizuki et al. 1996, Van Mier et al. 1996, Lashbrook et al. 1997, Hart et al. 1998, Timmons 1999, Nagel 2000, Warburg 2001, Adams 2002, Behm et al. 2004, Asche and Aven 2004, Oxenburgh and Merlin 2004, Markku Aaltonen et al. 2006, Santos et al. 2007, Marelli and Vitali 2009). During the last fifteen years, there has been a growing need to understand the economic impact that SH&E issues and practices have on competitive performance. Yet the economics of those issues is one of the least-understood

subjects in the industry (Tipnis 1994). Increasingly, U.S. firms have taken steps toward better understanding their competitive impact. This trend is evidenced by the development of SH&E sections of national technology roadmaps (Semiconductor Industry Association 1997–1999, The Microelectronics and Computer Technology Industry Environmental Roadmap 1996, and The United States Green Building Council 2003) that incorporate initiatives to reform the way costs linked to SH&E issues and practices are profiled and by the construction and use of various cost-of-ownership (CoO) models (Venkatesh and Phillips 1992, Dance and Jimenez 1995) that have been developed.

Each unit in this volume will have a chapter on cost analysis and budgeting. Therefore, this chapter was developed to advance these efforts by presenting economic analysis as a useful tool for changing how proposals for investment in practices to confront and manage SH&E issues are put together and presented within a firm's overall investment decision-making process. Specifically, this chapter provides (1) a rationale that supports economic analysis and the logic behind incorporating its findings into SH&E affairs and investments, (2) a catalog of SH&E investment strategies available to firms and some currently being used by firms, (3) a blueprint recommended for constructing and using an SH&E economic analysis model, and (4) a summary of elements necessary for economic analysis to become a regular practice in the safety, health, and environmental management profession.

A RATIONALE FOR INCORPORATING ECONOMIC ANALYSIS FINDINGS INTO SAFETY, HEALTH, AND ENVIRONMENTAL INVESTMENT PROPOSALS

Showing a relationship between investments in SH&E practices and economic performance can be an elusive undertaking (Behm et al. 2004). The question that continues to challenge internal organizational stakeholders is "Do investments in practices intended to confront and manage SH&E issues contribute to economic performance?" Many SH&E field practitioners and academics have answered yes (Goetzel 2005, The

European Agency for Safety and Health at Work 2004, American Society of Safety Engineers 2002, Jervis and Collins 2001, Smallman and John 2001); however, there is no compelling research that provides a *definitive* financial answer. Many internal stakeholders say no (Asche and Aven 2004, Dorman 2000, Shapiro 1998). They are very skeptical about how SH&E economic analyses are conducted; specifically, they question how cost and potential profitability data are collected, calculated, analyzed, interpreted, and reported. The reality may be that SH&E investments do not routinely set up opportunities to make money. At the same time, the opposite stance that SH&E investments seldom provide a financial payoff is also inaccurate. There should be no denying that investing in practices to confront and manage SH&E issues has always been a complicated proposition with very real methodological issues and economic implications. Even so, most firms invest in SH&E practices despite their economic impact, but they should do so knowingly.

Typically, concern for SH&E performance and economic performance have been viewed as separate lines of attack operating independent of and usually in opposition to one another. However, the actual *interdependence* between these concerns increasingly highlights the need for showing some type of an economic relationship. Generally, SH&E professionals have not incorporated economic analysis as a way of showing how investments in these practices contribute to economic performance (Behm et al. 2004). As a result, left out of the firm's competitive business strategy and excused from internal stakeholder expectations that this function justify its internal and external affairs with an economic perspective, SH&E practices tend to be looked at as a necessary cost of doing business, with little economic payback expected (Veltri et al. 2003a). To say the least, this is not a viable perception for internal stakeholders to bring and hold onto during the investment-allocation process. Only a focus on the results of economic analysis can provide internal stakeholders with the necessary information to set investment-allocation priorities. The emphasis on the results of economic analysis should not be interpreted to mean there is any intention to deemphasize the importance of ensuring compliance with regulatory

mandates. Concern for compliance surely exists, as it rightly should, and employing economic analysis is not intended to replace compliance applications. However, to focus *only* on maintaining compliance with SH&E regulations should not be expected to yield positive financial returns. Alternatively, what one attempts to accomplish with economic analysis is to go beyond compliance in ways that provide pertinent quantitative and qualitative economic information about how a firm's organizational activities (i.e., products, technologies, processes, services) tend to create SH&E issues and how strategic investments in innovative practices to confront and manage these issues might offer financial opportunities and reduce liability.

As a rule, the investment decision-making process hinges on a firm's competitive strategy, its research and development capability, its technology wherewithal, and the human means to productively use and protect organizational resources. The analysis used to reach investment-allocation decisions tends to be heavily slanted toward economic aspects. How well economic analyses are conducted and how well analysis findings support a firm's competitive strategy will usually affect how investments are allocated within a firm. During the last 25 years, existing and emerging SH&E issues (e.g., occupational injuries and illnesses, environmental incidents, natural and man-made hazardous exposures, tough government regulatory requirements, pressure from nongovernment interest groups concerning sustainable resource development and use, and long-term contingent liabilities as a result of past operations) are also increasingly affecting how decisions to fund projects are made within a firm. The real dilemma facing financial decision makers is how investment choices to confront and manage SH&E issues can be made in the absence of sound quantitative economic information. Without economic analysis results that detail the estimated cost and potential profitability of investments, even the most zealous SH&E internal stakeholders are left without a means to objectively make fiscally prudent investment-allocation decisions.

The following are beneficial outcomes that should be expected and leveraged when SH&E economic analyses are effectively conducted (Veltri 1997):

1. A refined understanding of the products, technologies, processes, and services that tend to drive SH&E life-cycle costs.
2. A more complete and objective data set on life-cycle costs and profitability potential of SH&E investments, enabling improvements to product, technology, process, and service designs.
3. An enhanced way of determining which SH&E management strategies and technical tactics to pursue and what level of investment will be required.
4. A new investment analysis structure in which fashioning SH&E issues and practices affects how business decisions are made, and in which business needs affect how SH&E decisions are made.

Despite these leveraging opportunities, usually there are internal organizational barriers to overcome when applying economic analysis to SH&E investments. The following are a sample of internal perceptions that SH&E professionals should be expected to confront:

1. An operations-level perspective that SH&E issues linked to the firm's processes are primarily regulatory-compliance-based and play a very small part in the investment-allocation process of the firm.
2. A design engineering-level perspective that sees the existing strategy and methodology for performing economic analysis of SH&E issues and practices that affect new product, technology, and process designs as qualitatively and quantitatively immaterial for enhancing design changes.
3. A senior-level executive perspective that proposals for investments in practices to counteract SH&E issues affecting the firm are not financially structured and reported in a manner that allows them to compete with other investment-allocation alternatives.

Such internal organizational barriers can be significant and must be overcome so that SH&E proposals can compete for the firm's investment dollars. The strategy considered most effective in overcoming these barriers is to employ economic analysis in a manner that discloses both the internal and external SH&E-related costs throughout the productive/economic life cycle of a firm's existing, new, and upgraded organizational activities and reveals the financial impact that investments in SH&E practices have on these organizational activity designs.

AVAILABLE SH&E INVESTMENT STRATEGIES

SH&E professionals who wanted to better understand how investment allocation decisions are made have had to satisfy themselves with professional literature that is nonobjective and fragmented with piecemeal approaches, causing them to be disadvantaged during the investment-allocation process. It is imperative that the forward-thinking SH&E specialist, who is interested in making his/her firm more competitive and in advancing his/her own career, understand how the firm makes strategic investment decisions and how it views investment utilization. However, to accomplish this, the SH&E specialist has to first understand the type of investment strategy being used by his/her firm. Figure 1 offers such a framework by providing a catalog of typical SH&E investment strategies that are available to firms or that are already being practiced by firms. The framework is a derivative work and borrows heavily from other strategy typologies (Miles and Snow 1978, Porter 1980, Adler et al. 1992, Roome 1992, Schot and Fischer 1993, Welford 1994, Chatterji 1995, Ward and Bickford 1996, Epstein 1995, Day 1998, Brockhoff et al. 1999, Stead and Stead 2000, and Coglianese and Nash 2001).

Each of these levels represents a distinct strategy for how a firm typically makes strategic SH&E investment decisions and how they tend to view investment utilization. Together they represent a way of thinking about SH&E investments that goes beyond existing investment strategies, which are at a distinct disadvantage when competing with the firm's other investment options. Investment allocators are usually reluctant to accept qualitative estimates (i.e., compliance audits performed, behavior-based training provided, perception surveys) when deciding to invest in SH&E investment proposals. They prefer quantitative estimates (i.e., cost and profitability potential).

Levels of Investment Strategy

Level 1 Reactive: Posture is to invest only when required, with attention to responding to government directives or insurance carrier mandates

Level 2 Static: Posture is to invest cautiously, with specific attention on preventing occupational injuries, illnesses, and environmental incidents from occurring

Level 3 Active: Posture is to invest assertively, with major emphasis on reducing risk to existing operations, and to lower contingent liability resulting from past operations

Level 4 Dynamic: Posture is to invest strategically, with major emphasis on counteracting the life-cycle risk and cost burdens linked to the firm's organizational activities

Level 1 Reactive

Strategy for financing the firm's SH&E investments at this level can be characterized as a reactive and resistive arrangement. Access to financial resources is based solely on correcting violations cited by government regulatory agencies and mandates from insurance carriers. Additional financial resources needed for providing technical day-to-day SH&E services are provided when it financially suits the company. Tools for performing economic analysis of SH&E issues do not exist because the firm does not want to, does not think it needs to, or is not aware of the potential cost impact of failing to counteract these issues.

Level 2 Static

Strategy for financing the firm's SH&E investments at this level can be characterized as an informal arrangement. A mentality of funding only as much as others in their industry sector is strongly adhered to. An informal pay-as-you-go funding mentality exists; invest to counteract issues only when trying to reduce the outlays associated with injury/illness and environmental incidents. Investments undertaken for preventing occupational injuries, illnesses, and environmental incidents and to meet compliance with regulations generally do not compete for access to financial resources. However, access to financial resources needed to confront and manage more technically discriminating SH&E issues depends upon the capabilities of the firm's SH&E professionals to assemble internal coalitions of support in order to compete for funding. These technically discriminating prevention initiatives tend to have no clear criteria and pattern of funding, thus subjecting them to unpredictable funding outcomes. Tools for performing economic analysis of SH&E investments are considered by internal organizational stakeholders to be qualitatively and quantitatively immaterial for competing with other investment allocation decision alternatives. SH&E cost accounting practices focus on aggregating cost data, causing costs to be hidden in general overhead accounts rather than included throughout the life cycle of the product, service, technology, or process responsible for their generation. As a result, integrated and concurrent design engineering decision-making capabilities required for aggressively controlling SH&E costs are limited and incomplete.

Level 3 Active

Strategy for financing the firm's SH&E investments at this level can be characterized as an applied arrangement. Access to financial resources tends to be allocated when investment requests are intended to reduce risk to products, technologies, processes, and services; enhance compliance with regulatory standards; reduce contingent liability caused by past operations; and minimize outlays associated with accidents, environmental incidents, lawsuits, and boycotts. The funding level tends to be above others in their industry sector and included in the overall budget of the core business units obtaining the services. Tools for performing economic analysis of SH&E investments are chiefly focused on cost-benefit analysis and payback, and sometimes internal rate of return. Costs are accumulated either through the use of cost accounting systems or through the use of cost-finding techniques and are reported on a regular basis for management information purposes. The cost of incidents are charted and charged back to core business units and incorporated into the firm's budget process. However, profiling the cost and profitability of SH&E issues affecting the organizations products, technologies, processes, and services, and integrating cost information into decision-making, does not occur. This condition results in senior-level executives looking at SH&E issues as nonbusiness issues.

Level 4 Dynamic

Strategy for financing the firm's SH&E investments at this level can be characterized as being self-sustaining and a down-to-business arrangement. A strategically opportunistic funding position is taken; this means having sufficient funding for the long-term, while having the financial wherewithal to remain flexible enough to solve new issues and support research and development and other opportunities for innovation that, over time, will lead to significant SH&E performance gains while advancing measurable business goals. Business strategies and SH&E changes are tightly interwoven; changes in products, technologies, processes, and services affect SH&E, and changes in SH&E issues and practices in turn force product, technology, process, and service changes. Access to financial resources and capital is approved for 3 years (typically related to potential business contribution over the long and short term) and is based on factors and circumstances that are causing the firm to fail in its efforts to protect and use resources productively and on conditions/circumstances under which SH&E pays. Senior-level financial executives desire SH&E strategy and activities to become financially self-sustaining and contribute measurably to company competitiveness. Tools for performing economic analysis of SH&E investments provide reliable and timely information on the full cost burdens associated with the firm's products, technologies, processes, and services over their productive and economic life cycle. Major thinking is performed on how to enhance the efficiency and effectiveness of SH&E spending.

FIGURE 1. Available safety, health, and environmental investment strategies (*Source:* Veltri and Maxwell 2008)

Internal organizational stakeholders constantly face investment choices among alternatives that are linked specifically to changes in the firm's organizational activities. They may have to decide whether to continue or drop a product or service, acquire certain technologies, or reengineer a process. Generally, making these decisions requires conducting economic analyses that provide cost and profitability comparisons among mutually exclusive alternatives (i.e., accepting one alternative means not accepting others). Likewise, investment decisions about SH&E practices require choosing among alternatives that are mutually exclusive and linked to the changes in the firm's organizational activities (e.g., products—substituting regulated occupational safety and health resource inputs with unregulated and perhaps less harmful ones, technologies—employing new environmental toxicity monitoring and detection systems, processes—reengineering to eliminate process waste from resource outputs, or services—modifying supply-chain relationships related to SH&E practices). This results in investment-allocation decisions that are usually based on the direct result of the projected economic impact of the mutually exclusive alternatives under analysis. Economic analysis, then, provides a recommended approach to how one might best present proposals for SH&E investments where economic aspects dominate and drive decision making and where economic effectiveness and efficiency are the criteria for choosing which SH&E issues to confront and manage and in which alternative solutions to make selected investments.

An abridged life-cycle costing method, which features net-present-value financial analysis, is the recommended tool for constructing a SH&E economic analysis model. The rationale for this abridged approach is that internal stakeholders have questioned both the relevance of the full life-cycle costing methodology for the actual business decisions they must make and the efficacy of the full methodology for making business decisions in real time. As a result, most firms are encouraging their SH&E professionals to develop and use a more streamlined method that focuses on internal private costs (i.e., costs incurred from organizational activities that result in

product-yield quality and process logistical performance problems, injury/illness and environmental incidents, and liability) rather than on external societal costs (i.e., costs incurred as a result of organizational activities that cause pollution of air, water, or soil; natural resource depletion or degradation; chronic or acute health effects; alteration of environmental habitats; and social/economic welfare effects) to make the economic analysis more relevant and useful for business decision making.

Several abridged life-cycle assessment methods have been described in the literature (Graedel et al. 1995), ranging from primarily qualitative approaches to quantitative ones in which expert judgment, a limited scope, and a system boundary keep the life-cycle assessment effort manageable. Experience demonstrates that life-cycle assessment for a complex manufactured product or an industrial manufacturing process works most effectively when it is done semiquantitatively and in modest depth. Unlike the full life-cycle assessment method, an abridged method is less quantifiable and less thorough. It is also quicker and more practical to implement. An abridged assessment will identify approximately 80 percent of the useful SH&E actions that could be taken in connection with corporate activities, and the amounts of time and money consumed will be small enough that the assessment has a good chance of being carried out and its recommendations implemented. The foundation for the abridged architecture was based on the unabridged life-cycle framework developed by the Society of Environmental Toxicology and Chemistry (SETAC 1991).

Present-value financial analysis provides the final link in the architecture. As a dollar today is always preferable to a dollar tomorrow, the sheer nature of SH&E initiatives at the work site often take multiple fiscal years to become fully realized. That is, dollars spent today on SH&E programs and activities may not reap or return benefits to the firm for several years. Hence, present-value financial analysis provides the most reliable means of comparing the financial performance of mutually exclusive alternatives when said alternatives fully mature in subsequent fiscal years (Newman 1983). In this way, present-value financial analysis helps to delineate the long-term financial impact of SH&E investments by presenting the after-tax cash flow and the present-cost value of the investment over a sufficient time horizon. The rationale for using net-present-value financial analysis is that many of the traditional financial analysis techniques employed by SH&E professionals, such as payback and rate of return on investment, fail to take the time value of money into consideration. Although useful tools in the financial analysis of investment decisions, exclusive use of these methods can result in making incorrect decisions, such as accepting SH&E project proposals that lose money, or, conversely, rejecting SH&E project proposals that may represent

financial opportunities and may reduce contingent liability.

Figure 2 provides an architecture for the SH&E economic analysis model. This architecture is built around three stages: (1) defining and setting all the boundaries necessary for managing the economic analysis; (2) conducting an abridged life-cycle inventory analysis and impact assessment of existing SH&E issues and proposed alternatives, from upfront analyses and the acquisition of capital and the permits through resource and material use, disposal, and closure; and (3) conducting postimplementation reviews that will ensure that the results of implemented

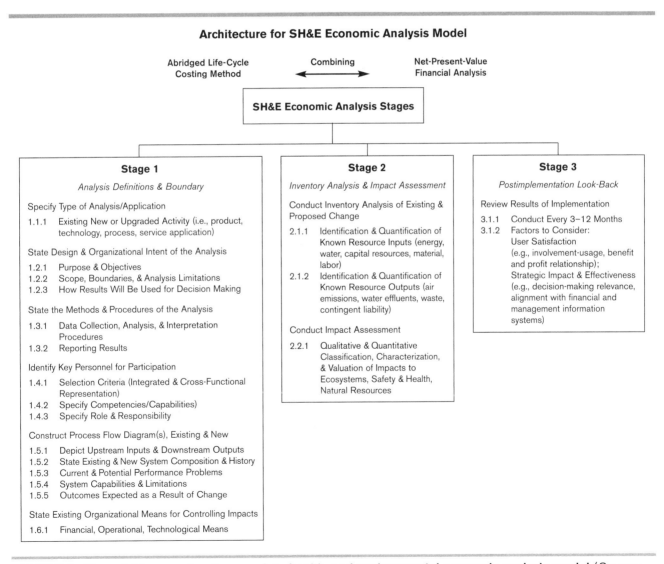

Architecture for SH&E Economic Analysis Model

Abridged Life-Cycle Costing Method ⟷ Combining   Net-Present-Value Financial Analysis

SH&E Economic Analysis Stages

Stage 1

Analysis Definitions & Boundary

Specify Type of Analysis/Application

1.1.1 Existing New or Upgraded Activity (i.e., product, technology, process, service application)

State Design & Organizational Intent of the Analysis

1.2.1 Purpose & Objectives
1.2.2 Scope, Boundaries, & Analysis Limitations
1.2.3 How Results Will Be Used for Decision Making

State the Methods & Procedures of the Analysis

1.3.1 Data Collection, Analysis, & Interpretation Procedures
1.3.2 Reporting Results

Identify Key Personnel for Participation

1.4.1 Selection Criteria (Integrated & Cross-Functional Representation)
1.4.2 Specify Competencies/Capabilities)
1.4.3 Specify Role & Responsibility

Construct Process Flow Diagram(s), Existing & New

1.5.1 Depict Upstream Inputs & Downstream Outputs
1.5.2 State Existing & New System Composition & History
1.5.3 Current & Potential Performance Problems
1.5.4 System Capabilities & Limitations
1.5.5 Outcomes Expected as a Result of Change

State Existing Organizational Means for Controlling Impacts

1.6.1 Financial, Operational, Technological Means

Stage 2

Inventory Analysis & Impact Assessment

Conduct Inventory Analysis of Existing & Proposed Change

2.1.1 Identification & Quantification of Known Resource Inputs (energy, water, capital resources, material, labor)
2.1.2 Identification & Quantification of Known Resource Outputs (air emissions, water effluents, waste, contingent liability)

Conduct Impact Assessment

2.2.1 Qualitative & Quantitative Classification, Characterization, & Valuation of Impacts to Ecosystems, Safety & Health, Natural Resources

Stage 3

Postimplementation Look-Back

Review Results of Implementation

3.1.1 Conduct Every 3–12 Months
3.1.2 Factors to Consider: User Satisfaction (e.g., involvement-usage, benefit and profit relationship); Strategic Impact & Effectiveness (e.g., decision-making relevance, alignment with financial and management information systems)

FIGURE 2. Blueprint for constructing a safety, health, and environmental economic analysis model (*Source:* Veltri and Ramsay 2009)

solutions are deemed to be in reasonable agreement with the estimated projections.

Stage I: Defining SH&E Economic Analysis Strategy and Boundaries

Defining the SH&E economic analysis strategy and setting its structural boundaries are key aspects of the economic analysis. As outlined in Figure 2, this initial stage should be accomplished through the following five steps. First, the SH&E professional should consider specifying the type of analysis to be conducted, specifically attending to the following components: (a) a description of the existing, upgraded, or new product, technology, process, or service system; (b) the system's expected economic life (i.e., the equivalent of the estimated amount of time that investments in the system can be expected to have economic value or productive uses and the estimated amount of time recurrent savings and reduced contingent liability can be achieved without having to reinvest as the initial investment ages); (c) the firm's hurdle rate (i.e., the required rate of return in a discounted cash-flow analysis that the firm is using for judging investment proposals); and (d) the existing and potential SH&E issues and impacts (e.g., musculoskeletal disorders resulting in workers' compensation claims, CO_2–NOX emissions resulting in global warming potential acidification) that are linked to the firm's activity under analysis.

The second step is to keep the analysis on course and focused. This requires that the design and organizational intent be stated up front. Possible components include: purpose and objectives, key assumptions and analysis limitations, and how information will be used to drive decision-making capabilities.

The third step is to specify the methodology suggested for performing the analysis (i.e., data collection, analysis and interpretation, and reporting procedures). These should be transparent and stated at the outset.

The fourth step is to identify and empower an integrated SH&E economic analysis project team and assist them in carrying out the study. Individuals on this team must be utilized as supportive personnel in order to carry out the project. Note that it is absolutely essential that their assistance be requested and used. Of course, they must be provided with the advisement and encouragement they will need to perform as expected. The team should be cross-functional in makeup and possess skills in finance, design and process engineering, operations, facility management, procurement, legalities, SH&E affairs, and community relations.

The fifth component of this stage is to construct process flow diagrams of the existing organizational activity and the proposed solution change. The process flow diagram should depict upstream inputs and downstream outputs, the existing and new system composition and history, current and potential performance problems, existing and new system capabilities and limitations, and any beneficial outcomes expected as a result of the change.

Stage II: Inventory Analysis and Impact Assessment

Figure 2 shows that the main function of stage two is to conduct an inventory analysis (i.e., the identification and quantification of known resource inputs such as energy, water, capital, resources, materials, and labor, and known outputs such as air emissions, water effluents, waste, and contingent liability) and an impact assessment (i.e., qualitative and quantitative classification, characterization, and valuation of impacts to ecosystems, human safety and health, and natural resources based on the results of the inventory). It is also sensible to provide investment-allocation decision makers with estimates of the firm's ability and means to control or improve the existing SH&E issue. This will add an additional level of robustness to the analysis. Chief factors to assess should include the firm's (1) financial funding capability (i.e., the existing level of funding available to control or improve the SH&E issue: a high level of funding suggests the firm has the financial means to effectively control or improve the issue, whereas a low level of funding suggests the firm has little financial means to affect the issue in the immediate future); (2) human operational capability (i.e., the existing level of human operational wherewithal to control or improve the SH&E issue: a high level of wherewithal suggests the firm has the human means and capability to control or improve the issue, whereas a low level suggests the firm has little human operational means to affect the issue in the immediate future); and (3) available technology (i.e., the existing level of technology that is to control or improve the SH&E issue: a high level of available technology suggests the firm can utilize technology as a way to control or improve the issue, whereas a low level suggests the firm has little technological means to affect the issue in the immediate future).

The use of impact models (e.g., risk and economic) helps guide the decision making and the operating actions that are necessary for keeping the inventory analysis and impact assessment structured and gives a picture of the life-cycle process-flow inputs and outputs linked to the organizational activity under analysis. In addition, it provides investment-allocation decision makers with an understanding of the extent and magnitude of the issue. A large number of risk assessment and analysis models and documents are available for profiling risk impacts and contingent liability linked to the firm's organizational activities.

Stage III: Postimplementation Review

After investing in SH&E practices, it is very important to determine the degree to which the results of the implemented changes are in reasonable agreement with the estimated projections. For example, if a new technology was purchased because of potential reductions in cost and contingent liability, it is important to see if those benefits are actually being realized. If they are, then the economic analysis projections would seem to be accurate. If the benefits are not being obtained, a review to discover what has been overlooked should be performed. A post-implementation assessment helps uncover the reasons why targets were not met. One possible reason could be that economic projections may have been overly optimistic. Knowing this can help analyzers avoid mistakes in economic cost projections in the future. In order to ensure that economic calculations and cost projections are realistic, everyone involved must know that a review of results will take place.

Therefore, three to twelve months after a mutually exclusive alternative has become operational, and regularly thereafter, a postimplementation review should be conducted. Factors to be considered in the look-back should include: user satisfaction (i.e., involvement/usage or cost/profit relationship) and strategic impact and effectiveness (i.e., decision-making relevance, alignment with financial and management information technology systems, and organizational objectives).

An economic analysis of a SH&E investment proposal collects cost information associated with the inventory analysis and impact assessment and uses a financial analysis measure for understanding economic impact. The SH&E professional is cautioned that an economic impact analysis of a SH&E investment proposal is only as accurate as the cost information that it collects—quite literally, the euphemism "garbage in, garbage out" applies. In this sense, SH&E professionals are encouraged to work with their finance and accounting colleagues as estimates for necessary costs are obtained. Therefore, a major component of an economic analysis is gathering data to make reasonable estimates of cost. Appendix A provides an outline of usual as well as potentially hidden SH&E life-cycle cost factors and activity drivers that are typically linked to a firm's organizational activities. Estimated costs are referred to in SH&E economic analysis as incremental costs; they are the difference between the after-tax cash flow of the mutually exclusive alternative(s). Net present value (NPV) analysis is the most applicable financial measure for understanding economic impact because it provides the most reliable method for comparing the financial performance of mutually exclusive alternatives on the basis of their projected after-tax cash flows. Net present value analysis can be thought of as the present value of an investment's future cash flows minus the initial investments required to initiate a particular program (or set of programs). Conventional NPV decision-making rules indicate that projects with profitability indices (PI) of greater than 1.0 should be pursued. When comparing multiple project alternatives, those with higher PIs are understood to be financially more attractive than those with lower, albeit positive, PIs. Alternatively, projects with a PI of 0 will recuperate only the cost of the resources required to make the investment, and, conversely, projects with a negative PI represent a financial loss for the investment. Because investment decisions in SH&E are important, proposals should also be supplemented with qualitative information, such as how the investment is expected to maximize sustainable resource development and use practices, enrich the quality of management information, develop human competency and capability, lower contingent liability, maintain regulatory compliance, reduce nongovernment special interest group concerns, and enhance organizational reputation. This type of qualitative information is sufficiently important that it could influence a decision to fund the investment proposal, in spite of the fact that the proposal may not meet the firm's established hurdle rate (i.e., the required return on a discounted investment).

Many firms discontinue their economic analysis after identifying and quantifying resource inputs and outputs. They simply decide to reduce the amount of resource inputs and outputs, taking on a "less is best" strategy rather than investing in the effort necessary for assessing the estimated economic impact. At times, because of the data requirements of impact assessments, it is difficult to relate inventories to an impact analysis and to provide cost and profitability estimates necessary for advancing investment-allocation decision making beyond what has already been collected in the inventory analysis. On the other hand, making an effort to conduct at least a relative impact assessment should provide investment allocators with information that is more meaningful for decision making. For instance, stating the firm's contingent liability (i.e., an estimate of the firm's probability of an accident/incident occurring and the range of cost and economic impact) resulting from increased use and disposal of toxic chemicals is just as easy to understand and assess as providing the change in the reduced level of a chemical input use and/or output waste that was identified and quantified in the inventory analysis. Also, when determining the relative impacts using only inventory analysis, the information provided is limiting when investment-allocation de-

cisions must be made. For example, when the exposure to gases emitted is estimated to be higher for the existing process technology, and the exposure to gases of a different pollutant is also estimated to be higher, which mutually exclusive alternative is preferable for reducing contingent liability and what is the economic impact in terms of cost and profitability potential for making a change? An impact assessment provides investment decision makers with additional information to make such choices. This can be best accomplished by identifying the high risk and cost factors that were linked to the existing situation and performing sensitivity analysis so that the effects of certain changes can be studied and forecast. Using this strategy, benefits and costs are reported in monetary terms and can be estimated over the full life cycle of the product, technology, process, or service under analysis. In addition, a risk and cost impact analysis should be conducted on the countermeasure options to ensure that they do not create additional risk and cost impacts that negate their estimated improvement.

One can readily see that constructing an architecture that is reliably gauging costs and profitability potential can be a complicated and time-consuming process with many aspects to consider. The most essential aspect to consider in constructing an SH&E cost model is assuring that the cost-driver information is reliable. Is there sufficient usable, accurate, and timely information from a good data source to make a determination about its usefulness? A peer-reviewed list of cost drivers that should prove useful can be found in the Appendix.

SUMMARY

Questions and uncertainties related to SH&E issues, practices, and investments tend to create business challenges for a firm's internal stakeholders. It is crucial to understand the existing circumstances that drive these issues, their impacts, and their costs. Knowing how to allocate the investment outlays necessary for confronting and managing these issues and how to evaluate the efficacy of those investment outlays is imperative. In fact, an emerging area of research evolving from SH&E economic analysis is that of SH&E

performance measurement, which is concerned with discovering ways to assess the financial benefits of improved SH&E performance. For example, there have been numerous calls in the previous five years for incorporating safety, health, and environmental life-cycle costing in operational settings (DOL 2006, ASSE 2008, and RoSPA 2011). Most organizations do not understand which products, technologies, processes, or services provide more or less value comparative to their existing SH&E costs. Traditional SH&E costing systems tend to suffer from imprecise cost collection, poor analysis and interpretation procedures, and distorted cost reporting. They offer little transparency of what comprises their costs, fail to consider the financial returns that can be expected later from the investment, and thus lose their decision relevance. However, it is interesting that, despite these deficiencies, many organizations continue to invest in SH&E practices, in the authors' experience. It is now time that traditional approaches for justifying SH&E investments yield to a newly fashioned and more economically valued way of thinking.

The last 25 years have shown that changes in a firm's products, technologies, processes, and services are interconnected with its SH&E practices: changes in the firm's products, technologies, processes, and services affect SH&E, and SH&E issues in turn force design changes in the firm's products, technologies, processes, and services. When internal stakeholders are first presented with this connection, many refuse to think about it as an economic opportunity. Viewing it as an additional annoying cost or another regulatory threat, they see it as a move to negotiate a trade-off between operations-related costs and costs related to SH&E practices. This is not the case. In fact, what the safety manager will be able to show internal organizational specialists is that one can set acceptable SH&E performance criteria and then compare the life-cycle cost of ownership for mutually exclusive alternatives that meet or exceed those criteria. The comparative approach will provide them with an improved way of deciding between alternative methods for meeting a specific set of criteria. By looking at investments through the SH&E lens, and looking at SH&E issues and practices through a business lens, internal organizational specialists can derive insights that would otherwise go unnoticed.

The use of economic analysis techniques on SH&E issues is really in its infancy. Economic analysis is not a core accreditation requirement of the Applied Sciences Commission of the Accreditation Board of Engineering and Technology (ABET), which accredits safety programs (ABET 2006). Indeed, the use of economic analysis as applied to SH&E investments currently has reached a point somewhere between the stage of understanding the factors that drive SH&E costs and the stage of using that information to assess economic impact. Any continued developments in this area will require that SH&E professionals put together investment proposals that are based on sound economic analysis and creatively use the results of the analysis for estimating how countermeasure strategies offer opportunities for reducing costs and enhancing revenues. Like any new concept, economic analysis in SH&E areas will go through a predictable life cycle. First, the concept will become increasingly appealing to SH&E professionals as a way to enhance the acceptance of investment proposals and make the business case for SH&E issues and practices. Next, firms will tend to hire outside "experts" with SH&E economic analysis backgrounds to help their internal specialists design an SH&E economic analysis model that is congruent with the way they operate their business and to help pave the way for and steer the use of the model. When the model and its use become functional, SH&E specialists will take over. As the SH&E economic model continues to mature, firms will integrate it into their investment-allocation process. At this point, a firm's ability to respond to SH&E issues associated with its products, technologies, processes, and services with appropriate and economically justified SH&E countermeasures may well become a leading indicator of its competitive advantage in the marketplace.

REFERENCES

Adams, S. "Financial Management Concepts: Making the Bottom Line Case for Safety." *Professional Safety*, August 2002, pp. 23–26.

Adler, P. S., D. W. McDonald, and F. MacDonald. 1992. "Strategic Management of Technical Functions." *Sloan Management Review* 33(2):19–37.

American Society of Safety Engineers (ASSE). 2002. *White Paper Addressing the Return on Investment for Safety, Health, and Environmental (SH&E) Programs* (retrieved September 1, 2010). www.asse.org/professional affairs/govtaffairs/ngposi10.php

Applied Sciences Commission of the Accreditation Board of Engineering and Technology (ABET). 2006 (accessed 4/03/06). www.abet.org

Asche, F., and Terje Aven. "On the Economic Value of Safety." *Risk, Decision and Policy* (July–Sept. 2004) 9(3):283–267.

Behm, M., A. Veltri, and I. Kleinsorge. "The Cost of Safety." *Professional Safety*, April 2004, pp. 22–29.

Bird, F. E. 1996. *Safety and the Bottom Line*. Logansville, GA: Febco.

Brockhoff, K., A. K. Chakrabarti, and M. Kirchgeorg. 1999. "Corporate Strategies in Environmental Management." *Research Technology Management* 42(4):26–30.

Brouwers, W., and A. Stevels. 1995. "Cost Model for the End of Life Stage of Electronic Goods for Consumers." Proceedings of the 3rd International Symposium on Electronics and the Environment, Dallas, Texas, pp. 279–284.

Chatterji, D. 1995. "Achieving Leadership in Environmental R&D." *Research Technology Management* 38(2):37–42.

Cobas, E., C. Hendrickson, L. Lave, and F. McMichael. 1995. "Economic Input/Output Analysis to Aid Life Cycle Assessment of Electronics Products." Proceedings of the 3rd International Symposium on Electronics and the Environment, Dallas, Texas, pp. 273–278.

Coglianese, C., and J. Nash. 2001. "Bolstering Private Sector Environmental Management." *Issues in Science and Technology* 17(3):69–74.

Cohan, D., and D. Gess. 1994. "Integrated Life-Cycle Management." Proceedings of the 2nd International Symposium on Electronics and the Environment, San Francisco, California, pp. 149–154.

Dance, D., and D. Jimenez. "Cost of Ownership: A Tool for Environment, Safety and Health Improvements." *Semiconductor International*, September 1995, pp. 6–8.

Day, R. 1998. "The Business Case for Sustainable Development." *Greener Management International* 23:69–92.

Dorman, P. Three Preliminary Papers on the Economics of Occupational Safety and Health, Chapter 3, "Investments in Occupational Safety and Health." April 2000, International Labour Organization, Geneva.

Environmental Protection Agency (EPA). 1995. *An Introduction to Environmental Accounting As A Business Management Tool: Key Concepts and Terms*. Washington D.C.: Office of Pollution Prevention and Toxics.

Epstein, M. J. 1995. *Measuring Corporate Environmental Performance*. New York: McGraw-Hill.

European Agency for Safety and Health at Work. 2004. *Quality of the Working Environment and Productivity – Research Findings and Case Studies*. Belgium: European Agency for Safety and Health at Work.

Friedman, J. 1987. *Dictionary of Business Terms*. Hauppage, NY: Barron's Educational Series, Inc.

Goetzel, R. Z. Policy and Practice Working Group Background Paper. "Examining the Value of Integrating Occupational Health and Safety and Health Promotion Programs in the Workplace." Steps to a Healthier U.S. Workforce Symposium. NIOSH, October 26, 2004, Washington, D.C.

Graedel, T., B. Allenby, and R. Comrie. "Matrix Approaches to Abridged Life-Cycle Assessments." *Environmental Science and Technology* (March 1995) 29(3):134A–139A.

Harrington, J., and A. Knight. 1999. *ISO Implementation*. New York: McGraw-Hill.

Hart, J., I. Hunt, D. Lidgate, and V. Shankararaman. 1998. "Environmental Accounting and Management: A Knowledge-Based Systems Approach." Proceedings of the 6th International Symposium on Electronics and the Environment, Oak Brook, Illinois, pp. 225–230.

Henn, C. L. 1993. "The New Economics of Life-Cycle Thinking." Proceedings of the 1st International Symposium on Electronics and the Environment, Arlington, Virginia, pp. 184–188.

Jervis, S., and T. R. Collins. 2001. "Measuring Safety's Return on Investment." *Professional Safety* 46(9):18–23.

Kliendorfer et.al. 2005. "Sustainable Operations Management." *Production and Operations Management* vol. 14, no. 4, Winter 2005, pp. 482–492.

Lashbrook, W., P. O'Hara, D. Dance, and A. Veltri. 1997. "Design for Environment Tools for Management Decision Making: A Selected Case Study." Proceedings of the 5th International Symposium on Electronics and the Environment, San Francisco, California, pp. 99–104.

Marelli, A., and M. Vitalli. 2009. "Environmental Accounting in Italy: A Research Note" (retrieved September 1, 2010). www.ssrn.com/sol3/papers.cfm? abstract_id=1480608&CFID=150896418&CFTOKEN= 12252547.

Markku Aaltonen, Kimmo Oinonen, Jari-Pekka Kitinoja, Jorma Saari, Mika Tynkkynen, Henriikka Virta. 2006. "Costs of occupational accidents—effects of occupational safety on company business—a research and development project." Scientific Proceedings of the European Productivity Conference in Finland, 30 August to 1 Sept 2006, pp. 47–51.

Microelectronics and Computer Technology Corporation (MCC). 1996. Report MCC-ECESM001-99, *Environmental Roadmap*. 1st ed. Austin, TX: MCC.

Miles, R., and C. Snow. 1978. *Organizational Strategy Structure and Processes*. New York: McGraw-Hill.

Mizuki, C., P. Sandborn, and G. Pitts. 1996. "Design for Environment—A Survey of Current Practices and

Tools." Proceedings of the 4th International Symposium on Electronics and the Environment, Dallas, Texas, pp. 66–72.

Nagle, M. "Environmental Supply-Chain Management versus Green Procurement in the Scope of a Business and Leadership Perspective." Proceedings of the 8th International Symposium on Electronics and the Environment, May 2000, San Francisco, California, pp. 219–224.

Newman, Donald. 1983. *Engineering Economic Analysis.* San Jose, California: Engineering Press, Inc.

Occupational Safety and Health Administration (OSHA). *Making the Business Case for Safety and Health.* www.cdc.gov/niosh/blog/nsb092109_businesscase.html

Oxenburgh, M., P. Merlin, and A. Oxenburgh. 2004. *Increasing Productivity and Profit Through Health and Safety: The Financial Returns from a Safe Working Environment.* 2d ed. Boca Raton, FL: CRC Press.

Porter, M. 1980. *Competitive Strategy.* New York: The Free Press.

Roome, N. 1992. "Developing Environmental Management Strategies." *Business Strategy and the Environment* 1(1):11–24.

The Royal Society for the Prevention of Accidents (RoSPA). 2011. "Making the Business Case for Safety and Health" (accessed December 20, 2011). www.rospa.com/occupationalsafety/advice and information/business-case.aspx

Santos, A., T. Bourbon, A. Soeiro, J. Taufer, and L. Bazant, 2007. "Economic analysis of safety risks in construction." *WIT Transactions on the Built Environment*, Vol. I, pp. 13–17.

Schot, J., and K. Fischer. 1993. "Introduction: The Greening of the Industrial Firm." *Environmental Strategies for Industry.* Washington, D.C.: Island Press.

Semiconductor Industry Association (SIA). 1997 and 1999. *The National Technology Roadmap for Semiconductors Technology Needs.* San Jose, California: SIA.

Shapiro, S. A. 1998. "The Necessity of OSHA." *Kansas Journal of Law and Public Policy* 3(3):22–31.

Smallman, C., and G. John. 2001. "British Directors Perspectives on the Impact of Health and Safety on Corporate Performance." *Safety Science* 38:727–739.

Society of Environmental Toxicology and Chemistry. 1991. *A Technical Framework for Life Cycle Assessments.* Washington D.C.: Society of Environmental Toxicology and SETAC Foundation for Environmental Education, Inc.

Stead, J., and E. Stead. 2000. "Eco-Enterprise Strategy: Standing for Sustainability." *Journal of Business Ethics* 24(4):313–329.

Suhejla, H., M. McAleer, and Laurent Pawels. 2005. "Modeling Environmental Risk." *Environmental Modeling and Software* 20(10):1289–1298.

Timmons, D. M. 1999. "Building an Eco-Design Toolkit at Kodak." Proceedings of the 7th International Symposium on Electronics and the Environment, Danvers, Massachusetts, pp. 122–127.

Tipnis, V. 1994. "Towards a Comprehensive Methodology for Competing on Ecology." Proceedings of the 2nd International Symposium on Electronics and the Environment, San Francisco, California, pp. 139–145.

Torres, Katherine. 2008. *Making the Business Case for Safety* (retrieved November 9, 2011). www.ehs.com/mag/making_business_case

Van Mier, G., C. Sterke, and A. Stevels. 1996. "Life Cycle Cost Calculations and Green Design Options." Proceedings of the 4th International Symposium on Electronics and the Environment, Dallas, Texas, pp. 191–196.

Veltri, A. 1997. "Environment, Safety and Health Cost Modeling," Technology Transfer Report #97093350A-ENG. Austin, Texas: SEMATECH, Inc.

Veltri, A., and E. Maxwell. 2008. "Safety, Health and Environmental Strategies Available to Firms and Being Used by Firms: A Conceptual Framework for Formulating Strategy." *Journal of Safety, Health and Environmental Research*, vol. 5, no.2.

Veltri, A., and J. Ramsay. 2009. "Economic Analysis of Environment, Safety and Health Investments." *Professional Safety* 48(7):30–36.

Veltri, A., D. Dance, and M. Nave. 2003a. "Safety, Health and Environmental Cost Model: An Internal Study from the Semiconductor Manufacturing Industry, Part 1." *Professional Safety* 48(7):30–36.

———. 2003b. "Safety, Health and Environmental Cost Model: An Internal Study from the Semiconductor Manufacturing Industry, Part 2." *Professional Safety* 48(6):23–32.

Venkatesh, S., and T. Phillips. 1992. "The SEMATECH Cost of Ownership Model: An Analysis and Critique." SEMATECH/SRC Contract No. 91-MC-506 Final Report, Texas SCOE, Texas A&M University.

Warburg, N. 2001. "Accompanying the (re) Design of Products with Environmental Assessment (DfE) On the Example of ADSM." Proceedings of the 9th International Symposium on Electronics and the Environment, Denver, Colorado, pp. 202–207.

Ward, P., and D. Bickford. 1996. "Configurations of Manufacturing Strategy, Business Strategy, Environment, and Structure." *Journal of Management* 22(4):597–626.

Warren, J., and K. Weitz. 1994. "Development of an Integrated Life Cycle Cost Assessment Model." Proceedings of the 2nd International Symposium on Electronics and the Environment, San Francisco, California, pp. 155–163.

Welford, R. 1994. "Barriers to the Implementation of Environmental Performance: The Case of the SME Sector." *Cases in Environmental Management and Business Strategy.* London: Pittman.

Wieber, M. 2008. "The Business Case for Corporate Social Responsibility: A Company-Level Measurement Approach for CSR." *European Management Journal*, Volume 26, Issue 4, pp. 247–261.

Appendix: Life-Cycle Phases, Cost Factors, and Activities

I. UPFRONT. The phase concerned with profiling the SH&E risk and cost burdens associated with an existing, new, or upgraded product, technology, process, or service over its productive/economic life cycle and designing improvement options that maintain a balance between SH&E priorities and other competing business performance factors. The cost of upfront analysis includes all early-stage studies of risk and cost burdens to bring it to a form for decision making.

Note: Activities performed during the upfront phase are considered one-time costs.

Designing for Safety, Health, and Environment. Consideration of SH&E concerns at an early stage in the design engineering of products, technologies, processes, or services to prevent later risk and cost burdens.

Stage I.   Concept Development - Specification Setting
Stage II.   Detail Design – Design of Components, Parts, Subassemblies, Process Steps
Stage III. Prototype Manufacture and Testing

II. ACQUISITION. The phase concerned with profiling the costs associated with obtaining SH&E permits and procuring capital equipment necessary for controlling hazardous exposures, preventing/controlling pollution, maintaining regulatory compliance, and enhancing business performance. The costs of acquiring a capital asset or permit include both its purchase price and all other costs incurred to bring it to a form and location suitable for its intended use.

Note: Activity performed and capital costs incurred during the acquisition phase are considered one-time costs.

Obtaining Permits. One-time costs associated with obtaining permits (i.e., wastewater discharge; air emissions; handling, storing, and transporting hazardous substances and associated wastes) for the product, technology, process or service. Examples include:

1. **Permit Review/Approval.** Activities performed to study the procedural and performance requirements of the permit, conduct environmental impact studies, make application, lobby for gaining community approval, and sign off on the permit contract.

2. **Permit Fee.** The direct cost associated with the permit.

3. **Process Reengineering.** Activities performed for reengineering and remodeling the process infrastructure to comply with the procedural and performance requirements of the permit, including capital-related equipment and installation and utility hook-up expenses.

Procuring Capital. One-time costs associated with acquiring capital equipment/areas/structures for the product, technology, process, or service (e.g., emission/effluent control equipment for reducing, neutralizing, and minimizing the volume, toxicity, or hazardous properties of process waste; emission/effluent monitoring devices for providing periodic or continuous surveillance, detection, and recording of exposures to process hazards; reclaim equipment for separating process waste for reuse; treatment/storage/disposal facility equipment for the treatment, storage, recycling, or disposal of waste generated by the process, including the consolidation of waste until shipping.

1. **Equipment Review/Signoff.** Activities performed to study capital equipment alternatives; to qualify suppliers; to develop, negotiate, and sign off on equipment contracts; and to make ready the process to receive equipment.

2. **Equipment Cost.** The direct costs associated with capital equipment, including spare parts.

3. **Process Reengineering.** Activities performed for reengineering and remodeling the process infrastructure to accommodate capital, including equipment installation and utility hook-up expenses.

III. USE/DISPOSAL. The phase concerned with profiling the cost burdens associated with protecting and productively using and disposing of process resources in a manner that prevents injury/illness and environmental incidents and that reduces pollution and waste.

Note: Activity costs incurred in the operational phase are considered annual costs.

Operating Capital (CoO). Annual costs associated with operating/owning capital (i.e., equipment, areas, structures). Examples of costs include: utilities, labor, supplies/materials, maintenance, and preventative maintenance.

Resources Consumed. Annual cost of resources consumed by the product, technology, process, or service that has SH&E life-cycle concerns (e.g., effects on natural resource depletion; reduction of raw material; chemical/gas, energy, and water use).

Consumables Used. Annual cost of consumables used by the product, technology, process, or service (e.g., safety, industrial hygiene, ergonomics equipment or supplies for providing employee protection against exposure to process hazards; environmental protection supplies for preventing and controlling environmental incidents; environmental packaging equipment and supplies for consolidating/protecting/improving the handling of waste; hazardous material management equipment and supplies for providing environmental incident response and recovery services; fire-protection equipment and supplies for providing fire prevention and incident-control services; security equipment and supplies for providing process and factory site-monitoring and surveillance; license/certificates for complying with ESH regulations).

Providing Strategic/Technical Support. Annual costs associated with providing strategic and technical support (e.g., strategic management activities such as process strategic planning, reengineering, auditing-process implementation, and managing contracts); technical support activities (e.g., identifying, evaluating, and controlling exposures to hazards; providing training, environmental emission monitoring, and process, safety, and industrial hygiene inspections; advising on regulatory compliance matters; and assisting in manifesting and record-keeping procedures); research/development activities (e.g., testing, conducting studies, and creating innovative ways to protect and use process resources productively).

Training. Annual costs associated with providing training support in areas such as (1) SH&E law required for maintaining compliance with regulatory laws and standards, and (2) SH&E process specific for developing special competencies and capabilities.

Environmental Processing. Annual costs associated with implementing pollution prevention, reuse, and treatment and disposal strategies (e.g., source reduction by process-optimization activities used for limiting pollution before it occurs, including methods for modification of end product to eliminate a waste; revised operating practices; process-modification changes in raw materials, technology, and equipment; reclaim activities used for reusing and recycling a waste based on a closed and open loop system).

> Closed Loop: Implies no further processing of a waste material; it is fed directly into the process step.

> Open Loop: Implies the material must be processed (e.g., separating a particular component) prior to being reused.

Abatement activities used to control the physical and/or chemical characteristics of a waste; dilution activities used to change the physical and/or chemical characteristics of a waste after its use to reduce the material's volume and toxicity; waste treatment prior to disposal activities used to change the physical and/or chemical characteristics of a waste after its use to reduce the material's volume and toxicity and to improve handling and storage; waste consolidation/packaging activities used to consolidate and store waste before shipping; waste exchange activities used to transfer or sell waste to a brokerage that could use the waste as a raw material; waste shipping and disposal activities for transporting and disposing of a waste.

IV. POSTDISPOSAL. The phase concerned with profiling the cost burdens associated with monitoring the disposal of waste after the waste has left the control of the process and internal factory site and has been transferred to another company for management.

> *Note: Activity costs incurred during the postdisposal phase are considered to go beyond the productive life of the product, technology, process, or service.*

Managing Waste-Site Compliance. Annual costs associated with assuring that waste-site disposal procedures are managed in a manner that maintains compliance with the waste-site disposal contract agreements and federal and state regulations. Examples include:

1. **Waste-Site Review/Selection.** Activities performed to review and select disposal-site alternatives and to develop, negotiate, and sign off on waste disposal contract agreements.

2. **Compliance Monitoring.** Activities performed to assure that the procedural and performance requirements of the contract agreement and federal and state regulations are in compliance.

V. CLOSURE. The phase concerned with profiling the cost burdens associated with retiring the product, technology, process, or service at the end of its useful life and preparing the area for other productive uses.

> *Note: Activity costs incurred during the closure phase are considered one-time costs.*

Decommissioning. One-time costs associated with retiring the product, technology, process, or service following its useful life. Examples include:

1. **Decommissioning Review.** Activities performed for profiling the risk and cost burdens associated with retiring the manufacturing process or factory site.

2. **Dismantling/Cleanup.** Activities required for disassembling components used in the manufacturing process, arranging for disposal, and conducting clean-up procedures.

3. **Component Shipping and Disposal.** Costs incurred for transporting and disposing of dismantled components.

Remediation. One-time costs associated with remediation and preparing the area for other productive uses.

1. **Remediation Plan.** Activities required for developing ways to prepare the area for other productive uses.

VI. INCIDENTS. The area concerned with profiling the cost burdens associated with environmental contamination, pollution, alteration, occupational injury/illness, and noncompliance fines that adversely affect the product, technology, process, or service. Examples include:

Internalities. Incidents that only affect the internal manufacturing process and tend to result in (1) an adversity or disablement to a resource, (2) incurred direct and indirect costs, and (3) production interruption to the process. Examples of costs include:

> **Direct Costs.** Those costs that can be easily identified and calculated or directly assigned to the incident with a high degree of accuracy (e.g., employee financial compensation (both current and reserved), damaged manufacturing property resources, capital replacement expenditures, incident fines, and legal expenses).

> **Indirect Costs.** Those costs that can be intangible and difficult to calculate in the short term (e.g., incident investigation, production delays, loss of training investment, loss of future contribution of employee, replacement of resources, claims management, incident response/recovery/remediation, and business resumption).

Externalities. Internal incidents that affect the outside environment and tend to result in (1) air, water, soil pollution, (2) resource depletion/degradation, (3) chronic/acute health effects, (4) environmental habitat alteration, and (5) social/economic welfare effects.

> **Direct Costs.** Those costs that can be easily identified and calculated or directly assigned to the incident with a high degree of accuracy (e.g., financial compensation for damaged environmental resources, fines, and legal expenses).

> **Indirect Costs.** Those costs that can be intangible and difficult to calculate in the short term (e.g., incident investigation, incident recovery/remediation costs, and claims management).

Noncompliance Fine Facilitation. Citations issued for failing to comply with federal, state, or local environmental, safety, and health agencies.

> **Direct Costs.** Those costs that can be easily identified and calculated or directly assigned to the fine with a high degree of accuracy (e.g., financial payment for the citation; making the facility and the process ready to comply, including any capital expenditures, materials, labor, legal fees, and research).

> **Indirect Costs.** Those costs that can be intangible and difficult to calculate in the short term (e.g., activities needed to study and contest the fine).

FOUNDATION PRINCIPLES AND APPLICATIONS

LEARNING OBJECTIVES

- Understand what sustainability is and what is driving this business strategy.

- Learn about the Global Reporting Initiative (GRI).

- Be able to clarify the relationship between sustainability and social responsibility.

- Recognize the value of the integration model: safety and continuous improvement within sustainability.

- Discuss legislation, standards, and market influences on sustainability.

- Learn about ISO 26000, *Guidance on Social Responsibility*, and its relationship to occupational safety and health.

- Discover from case studies how companies are integrating safety into their sustainability strategies and reporting.

SUSTAINABILITY AND THE SAFETY, HEALTH, AND ENVIRONMENTAL PROFESSIONAL

Kathy A. Seabrook, Robert Stewart, Jeffrey Camplin, and Mike Taubitz

IN TODAY'S WORKPLACE, an EHS professional can expect to hear or read about sustainability; Global Reporting Initiative (GRI); corporate social responsibility; lean, continuous improvement; and "green." These terms and conditions, while related to each other, can often cause confusion. This chapter puts various strategic issues into context to help readers better understand the big picture of sustainability. Employee safety is currently viewed as one small part of the overall equation, but it should be viewed as a more important ingredient for long-term success in any organization.

The first part of this chapter provides an historical overview of topics related to sustainability. Later sections will describe these topics and present case studies to demonstrate the link between safety and sustainability.

SUSTAINABILITY

Sustainability embodies *stewardship* and *design with nature*—well-established goals of design professionals—and *carrying capacity*, a highly developed modeling technique used by scientists and planners.

The most popular definition of sustainability can be traced to a 1987 UN conference. It defined sustainable developments as those that "meet present needs without compromising the ability of future generations to meet their needs" (WECD 1987). Gilman extends this goal-oriented definition by stating that "sustainability refers to a very old concept (the Golden Rule) . . . do [unto] future generations as you would have them do [unto] you" (Gilman 1990, 1996).

These well-established definitions set an ideal premise but do not clarify specific human and environmental parameters in modeling and measuring sustainable developments. The following definitions are more specific:

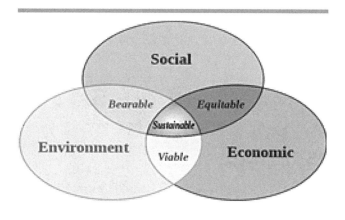

FIGURE 1. Confluence of sustainability
(*Source:* Dréo 2006/2007; adapted by Mike Taubitz)

- Sustainable means using methods, systems, and materials that will not deplete resources or harm natural cycles (Rosenbaum 1993).
- Sustainability "identifies a concept and attitude in development that looks at a site's natural land, water, and energy resources as integral aspects of the development" (Viera 1993).
- Sustainability integrates natural systems with human patterns and celebrates continuity, uniqueness, and placemaking (Early 1993).

The 1970 National Environmental Policy Act (NEPA) formally established as a national goal the creation and maintenance of conditions under which humans and nature "can exist in productive harmony, and fulfill the social, economic and other requirements of *present and future generations of Americans*" [emphasis added] (EPA 1970).

The concept of sustainable development was described in a 1981 White House Council on Environmental Quality (CEQ) report: "The key concept here is sustainable development. If economic development is to be successful over the long term, it must proceed in a way that protects the natural resource base of developing countries" (White House 1981).

A later concept of sustainability that took root in the global arena was an outgrowth of the 1987 Brundtland Commission (named for the chair) for the United Nations (UN WCED 1987). This concept of sustainability was based upon the concept of the *triple bottom line*—balancing environmental concerns and social needs with economic issues. Sustainability may be envisioned,

as depicted in Figure 1, as the confluence of the three pillars (3 Ps): social (people), economic (profit), and environmental (planet). Sustainability is a very complex subject that includes biodiversity, climate change, carbon footprint, and so on. For purposes of discussion in the safety, health, and environmental (SHE) community, it seems best to deal with the practical aspects of the 3 Ps that safety, health, and environmental professionals may impact or influence.

Sustainable growth is not possible without a culture of continuous improvement. This chapter will demonstrate how continuous improvement provides the foundation for an organizational culture capable of attaining the triple bottom line. First of all, there must be an introduction to the current guidelines for organizations that choose to report their progress on sustainable growth. These guidelines are contained in the Global Reporting Initiative (GRI).

GLOBAL REPORTING INITIATIVE (GRI)

The GRI provides the framework for voluntary reporting of initiatives related to sustainable growth. Table 1 presents definitions that pertain to sustainability, including their sources, Web sites, and a discussion of each. It generally addresses the elements of waste from the business process, including time and effort.

GRI Vision

The vision of the GRI is that disclosure on economic, environmental, and social performance becomes as commonplace and comparable as financial reporting, and as important to organizational success.

GRI Mission

GRI's mission is to create conditions for the transparent and reliable exchange of sustainability information through the development and continuous improvement of the GRI sustainability reporting framework.

The GRI is a network-based organization that has pioneered the development of the world's most widely used sustainability reporting framework and is committed to its continuous improvement and application worldwide (GRI 2007).

In an effort to ensure technical quality, credibility, and relevance, the reporting framework was devel-

TABLE 1

Definitions and Discussion

Term	Definition/Source	Discussion
Carbon market	The carbon market grew out of carbon reduction and trading schemes as a result of the Kyoto Protocol and other carbon reduction commitments and regulations. The market tracks and trades carbon (in units of 1 ton CO_2 emissions) like other commodities (UNFCC 2010).	One of the ways organizations are meeting their commitments to their overall carbon emissions targets (locally, nationally and internationally).
Continuous improvement (CI)	Continuous improvement (CI) or continuous improvement processes (CIP) ccs.mit.edu/21c/iokey.html	Ongoing efforts to improve products, processes, and services.
Corporate social responsibility	A firm's sense of responsibility toward the community and environment (both ecological and social) in which it operates and draws resources and sustenance from. www.businessdictionary.com/definition/corporate-citizenship.html	Firms express this citizenship (1) through their waste and pollution reduction processes, (2) by contributing educational and social programs, and (3) by earning adequate returns on the employed resources.
Global reporting initiative (GRI)	A network-based organization that has developed the world's most widely used sustainability reporting framework and is committed to its continuous improvement and application worldwide. www.globalreporting.org/Home	The global reporting initiative (GRI) is a network-based organization that has pioneered the development of the world's most widely used sustainability reporting framework.
Green/Environment	Green is typically associated with any form of environmental initiative that reduces adverse impacts to the planet. www.epa.gov/greenpower	It is sometimes used interchangeably with sustainability. However, green is but one of three legs of sustainable growth.
Greenhouse gases	Gases that trap heat in the atmosphere. www.epa.gov/climatechange/emissions/index.html	Common greenhouse gases derived from human activity are: • Carbon dioxide (CO_2) • Methane (CH_4) • Nitrous oxide (N_2O) • Fluorinated gases
Lean	The suite of tools and thinking employed by companies following the teachings of W. Edwards Deming.	The term lean was first introduced in 1990 with the book, *The Machine That Changed the World*. It generally addresses the elements of waste from the business process, including time and effort.
LEED®	Leadership in Energy and Environmental Design. www.usgbc.org	An internationally recognized green building certification system that provides third-party verification that a building or community was designed and built using strategies intended to improve performance; it is headed by the U.S. Green Building Council.
Kaizen	Incremental efforts driving continuous improvement.	A Japanese term [the translation of *kai* ("change") and *zen* ("good") is "improvement"].
PDCA	Plan-Do-Check-Act en.wikipedia.org/wiki/PDCA	Often referred to as the Deming Cycle, PDCA is an iterative four-step problem-solving process typically used in management systems that drive continuous improvement.
Sustainability	Development that meets the needs of the present without compromising the ability of future generations to meet their own needs. www.sustainabilitydictionary.com	An outgrowth of the 1987 UN Commission; referenced as the Brundtland Report and named for the Commission's Chair.
Triple bottom line	Financial, social, and environmental effects of a firm's policies and actions that determine its viability as a sustainable organization. www.businessdictionary.com/definition/triple-bottom-line.html	Sometimes referred to as the "3 Ps" for people, planet, and profit; the triple bottom line strategically balances competing requirements for long-term sustainable growth.

(Adapted by Taubitz from various sources)

oped through a consensus-seeking process with global participants drawn from business, society, labor, and professional institutions. The cornerstone of the framework is the sustainability reporting guidelines. The third version of the guidelines, known as the *G3 Guidelines*, was published in 2006 and is available free to the public (GRI 2007).

Health and safety is but one small aspect of GRI under the heading of the International Labour Organization's (ILO) decent work agenda for labor practices

(GRI 2007). Reporting guidelines from the ILO include the following:

- percentage of total workforce represented in formal joint management: worker health and safety committees that help monitor and advise on occupational health and safety programs
- rates of injury, occupational diseases, lost days and absenteeism, and total number of work-related fatalities by region
- education, training, counseling, prevention, and risk-control programs in place to assist workforce members, their families, or community members regarding serious diseases
- health and safety topics covered in formal agreements with trade unions

To put things into context, the GRI labor practices section is twenty pages and is only a small part of the overall GRI guidelines. The guidelines are comprised of the following major sections (GRI 2007):

- application levels
- G3 guidelines
- the environment
- economics
- human rights
- labor practices
- product responsibility
- society

Considering Dr. Peter Drucker's statement, "What gets measured, gets managed" (Aaron 2008), it would seem that employee safety would not garner much management attention if one relies only on the areas emphasized by the GRI. It is incumbent upon SHE to find ways to integrate with GRI, not the other way around.

Let us turn to how corporate social responsibility fits into the picture.

SOCIAL RESPONSIBILITY (SR) AND CORPORATE SOCIAL RESPONSIBILITY (CSR)

Social responsibility (SR) and *corporate social responsibility* (CSR) are interrelated, and can best be defined through the ISO 2600 standard on social responsibility (ISO 2010). *Social responsibility* refers to any organization's need to preserve resources for future generations and complements the traditional view that only private corporations have a duty to make products and provide services responsibly.

Although these terms are different and are driven by different organizations, they all point in the same general direction. Throughout the industrialized world and in many developing countries, there has been a sharp escalation in the social roles corporations are expected to play. Companies are facing new demands to engage in public/private partnerships and are under growing pressure to be accountable not only to shareholders, but also to stakeholders, such as employees, consumers, suppliers, local communities, policymakers, and the society at large (Noer et al. 2008).

Also known as corporate responsibility, corporate citizenship, responsible business, sustainable responsible business, or corporate social performance, *corporate social responsibility* is a form of corporate self-regulation integrated into a business model. CSR policy is intended to function as a built-in, self-regulating mechanism where the inclusion of public interest into corporate decision making facilitates achievement of a triple bottom line that benefits people, planet, and profit (BNET n.d.). The term corporate social responsibility has been used interchangeably with corporate responsibility, corporate citizenship, social enterprise, sustainability, sustainable development, triple bottom line, corporate ethics, and, in some cases, corporate governance. Social responsibility is used to suggest that all organizations, including government, nongovernmental organizations (NGOs), and professional organizations, need to be socially responsible.

ISO 26000

The International Organization for Standardization (ISO) finds that sustainability and social responsibility are closely related but different (ISO 2010). Sustainable development from the ISO perspective is about meeting the needs of society while living within the planet's ecological limits, without jeopardizing the ability of future generations to meet their needs. Social responsibility, on the other hand, has the organization as its focus and concerns an organization's responsibilities to society and the environment. Social responsibility is closely linked to sustainable development. Essentially, the main objective of an organization's social responsibility should be to contribute to sustainable development (ISO 2010).

ISO 26000, *Guidance on Social Responsibility*, is an international standard that helps organizations achieve the benefits of implementing policies on social responsibility (SR). Ninety-nine countries and 42 public- and private-sector organizations with liaison status were involved in the ISO working group on social responsibility under the joint leadership of the ISO members for Brazil (ABNT) and Sweden (SIS). The group included a geographical and gender-based balance of participants. Main stakeholder groups represented include: industry; government; labor; consumers; nongovernmental organizations; service, support, and research; and others. The American Society for Quality (ASQ) is the administrator of the U.S. Technical Advisory Group for development of ISO 26000 (ASQ 2010). Published in November 2010, ISO 26000 contains voluntary guidance, not requirements, and therefore is not for use as a certification standard, such as ISO 9001:2008 and ISO 14001:2004. ISO 26000 seeks to help all types of organizations, regardless of their size, activity, or location, to operate in a socially responsible manner by providing guidance on:

- concepts, terms, and definitions relating to social responsibility
- the background, trends, and characteristics of social responsibility
- principles and practices relating to social responsibility
- core subjects and issues relating to social responsibility
- integrating, implementing, and promoting socially responsible behavior throughout the organization
- its sphere of influence on various stakeholders
- identifying and engaging with stakeholders
- communicating commitments and performance related to social responsibility

The SH&E professional can benefit from a general understanding of social responsibility by obtaining a copy of ISO 26000. A review of the new ISO 26000, *Guidance on Social Responsibility*, will help the SH&E professional demonstrate the value safety management contributes to achieving organizational sustainability and social responsibility goals (ASQ 2010).

Whereas sustainability evolved from the United Nations, it is the ISO that has been driving efforts on social responsibility. In October 2010, ISO 26000:2010, *Guidance on Social Responsibility*, was published as a guidance standard for social responsibility (ISO 2010).

It does not matter whether an organization has a foundation based upon sustainability or social responsibility; what is important is to understand that both are similar strategies, often with overlapping goals. By virtue of its seniority and its United Nation's origin, sustainability is probably best thought of as the umbrella for all succeeding initiatives, making CSR one part of an overall approach for attaining sustainable growth.

If sustainability or CSR is not important in your organization, it is safe to assume that the concept of continuous improvement is. Any organization desiring to meet strategic future challenges must have a culture and systems that drive improvement in all facets of the business.

SIDEBAR

ISO 26000 Content List
(ISO 2010)

The content of ISO 26000 is structured as follows:

Foreword
Introduction
1 Scope
2 Terms and definitions
3 Understanding social responsibility
4 Principles of social responsibility
5 Recognizing social responsibility and engaging stakeholders
6 Guidance on social responsibility core subjects
7 Guidance on integrating social responsibility throughout an organization
Annex A – Voluntary initiatives and tools for social responsibility
Annex B – Abbreviated terms
Bibliography

GREEN ENVIRONMENT

Green is typically associated with any form of environmental initiative to reduce adverse impacts to the planet. It is sometimes used interchangeably with sustainability. However, green is only one of the three legs of sustainable growth. A significant amount of work and effort is required to link environmental efforts with sustainability. For that reason, this chapter will not repeat what is widely available in publications and on the Internet. However, lean and green are aligning with little mention of safety (Taubitz et al. 2010).

INTEGRATION OF SAFETY AND CONTINUOUS IMPROVEMENT WITH SUSTAINABILITY

Safety

It has already been noted that safety is seen as a small part of sustainability and GRI. Because CSR is also a broad initiative emulating sustainability, safety is therefore viewed as a small part of social responsibility. Social responsibility efforts are often focused *outside* the workplace. Employee safety is rarely, if ever, mentioned in articles and publications that deal with sustainability and corporate social responsibility.

Without safety, the people part of sustainability is missing its core, but this is not well recognized. Baxter International, Inc., is an example of a company that has integrated safety into its sustainability strategies. The case study on Baxter International, Inc., outlines the safety and health performance metrics reported in the Baxter "2009 Sustainability Priorities Report" (Baxter 2010a).

Continuous Improvement: The Bridge

The bridge between dealing with the tactical issue of employee safety and the strategic goal of sustainable growth is depicted in Figure 2.

Continuous improvement (CI) or *continuous improvement processes* (CIP) are ongoing efforts to improve products, processes, and services. Process management, project management, and quality management are all tools that businesses use to drive continuous im-

provement. The following section of this chapter provides more detail on comparing strategic and tactical continuous improvement.

Many companies, large and small, are working on the somewhat nebulous issue of sustainability. Even if the term itself is not used, the concept of balancing people, the planet, and profit to achieve long-term success makes sense. Concurrently, leaders everywhere are faced with creating an organizational culture and processes that drive continuous improvement and the opportunity to stay in business for the long term.

Strategic and Tactical Continuous Improvement

Strategic continuous improvement is an ongoing effort to improve products, services, or processes. These efforts can seek *incremental* improvement over time or *breakthrough* improvement all at once. Delivery (customer-valued) processes are constantly evaluated and improved in the light of their effectiveness, efficiency, and flexibility.

In the experience of author Taubitz, five key criteria for continuous improvement processes include:

1. A core principle of CIP is the (self) reflection of processes (*feedback*).
2. The purpose of CIP is the identification, reduction, and elimination of suboptimal processes (*efficiency*).
3. The emphasis of CIP is on incremental, continuous steps rather than giant leaps (*evolution*).
4. Respect for people is the basis for including everyone in continuous improvement efforts (*empowerment and engagement*).

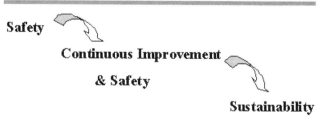

FIGURE 2. Bridge from safety to sustainability with continuous growth (*Source:* Adapted from model by Taubitz)

CASE STUDY

Baxter International, Inc.

Baxter International, Inc., is working to integrate worker safety performance into its overall sustainability strategies and priorities. With approximately 49,700 employees in 27 countries and gross sales of $12.6 billion in 2009, Baxter International, Inc., and its subsidiary companies manufacture and distribute medical devices, pharmaceuticals, and biotechnology products in 100 countries (Baxter 2010a).

Robert L. Parkinson, Jr., Baxter's Chairman and Chief Executive Officer (June 2010) highlights workplace safety and health, injury, and illness performance, as well as environmental achievements, in Baxter's "2009 Sustainability Priorities Report." The report states that one of Baxter's priorities is to "promote a safe and healthy workplace" (Baxter 2010c). To do this, Baxter has set a 2015 goal to "implement best-in-class programs designed to protect the safety and improve the health of employees that result in performance in the top three industry peers" (Baxter 2010a). This demonstrates Baxter's recognition that occupational safety and health performance is integral to its sustainability strategy and is reflected in its commitment to performance reporting and peer benchmarking. A 2008 ORC benchmarking study ranked Baxter fourth among twelve reporting healthcare companies in days-lost rate performance (Baxter 2010a).

For worker safety and health performance, Baxter primarily reports in the area of injury/illness incident statistics: recordable case rate, cases with days-lost rate, days-lost rate, and restricted days rate as shown in the following table (Baxter International, Inc. 2010a, 2010b).

Lost-day case rate	0.15 (21% improvement)
Days-lost rate	4.16 (2% Improvement)
Restricted days rate	12.68 (35% improvement)
Recordable case rate	1.07 (17% improvement)
Employee/contractor serious incidents*	12/2
Employee/contractor fatalities	0/0

*A serious workplace incident case "results in an employee or contractor being hospitalized overnight, sustaining an amputation or dying."

According to Baxter, it has realized improvements in its incident rates over the previous year in all areas, with the exception of serious incident cases. According to the ORC report, the company proactively recognized this exception and is assessing the root causes of these serious incidents to prevent potential reoccurrence in the future (Baxter 2010a).

In addition to injury/illness incident statistics, Baxter is also focused on two areas of leading performance metrics: hazard identification and risk assessment (HIRA) and near-miss reporting. Baxter has identified ergonomic risk as a key focus area for its operations globally. To that end, the company has used a risk-based approach (HIRA) to reduce its manual handling-related injuries— 11 percent in one year at its Castlebar, Ireland, facility (Baxter 2010a).

The second leading performance indicator used by Baxter is adoption and implementation of a near-miss reporting initiative. By the end of 2009, Baxter reported that 64 percent of its manufacturing, research and development, and distribution sites (more than 100 employees) had implemented this initiative. Baxter's manufacturing site in Cleveland, Mississippi, has seen an 89 percent increase in near-miss reporting since the initiative was implemented there in 2006 (Baxter 2010a). Near-miss reporting allows for incident investigation, root cause analysis, and implementation of control methodologies to prevent reoccurrence of a future near-miss incident or potential injury or illness as a result of the same incident root cause. According to Baxter, this will be an ongoing leading indicator of sustainability performance (Baxter 2010a).

For their 2009 sustainability performance, Baxter International, Inc., was ranked 20th out of America's "100 Best Corporate Citizens" by *Corporate Responsibility (CR) Magazine* (*CR Magazine* 2010). The company has also been recognized as one of the "Global 100 Most Sustainable Corporations" since the list was first published in 2005, has been listed on the Dow Jones Sustainability Index since its launch in 1999, and has been named Medical Products Industry Leader for nine years (Baxter 2010b).

5. The more strategic elements include deciding how to increase the value of the delivery-process output to the customer (*effectiveness*) and how much flexibility is valuable in the process to meet changing needs.

Examples of continuous improvement tools and processes include the following (Taubitz):

- problem solving
- brainstorming
- cause-and-effect diagrams
- check sheets
- flow diagrams

Lean thinking and Kaizen events are developed around the concept of identifying and eliminating waste. The seven forms of lean waste are:

1. Correction
2. Overproduction
3. Motion (people)
4. Material movement
5. Waiting
6. Inventory
7. Process

These make up the acronym COMMWIP, which is a useful way of remembering wastes that negatively impact operational performance. When considered with the wastes of safety (injury and illness) and environmental wastes (air, water, solids, energy, and so on), it is possible to view things in a new light, one that allows the best approach for achieving sustainable growth. A new goal of achieving acceptable risk (safety and environment) with minimized (lean) operational waste fosters daily decisions that contribute to the triple bottom line.

The Kaizen approach from lean manufacturing is another tactical CI tool. Kaizen efforts are small, incremental steps that employ other tools in addition to those cited above. Based upon the experience of author M. Taubitz, Kaizen tools (often associated with lean tools and thinking) are simple and designed to empower and engage the entire workforce, including:

- 5S
- value-stream mapping
- A3 and one-page reports
- knowledge folders
- standardized work

NOTE: 5S is a simple five-step process to sustain the workplace as clean and organized. A3 reports are a standardized approach used for communication and problem solving.

CASE STUDY

COMAU Inc.: Coping Machine Project Summary—X-Mation Facility (Megan Raines 2009)

This situation involved a metalworking machine which did not have a guard to protect operators from hand/finger injury during machine operation. (*Note:* thankfully, no such injuries had been sustained.) The machine could perform various functions, including coping, and was being used for coping various sizes of angle iron stock. It was actuated using a guarded foot pedal. Upon actuation, the top portion of the machine moved downward to cope the stock. When the point of operation of the machine was opened, it exposed a gap approximately two inches high and several inches wide and deep under the moving area (Figure 3).

In the past, a guard had been added, but it blocked the point of operation, which prevented the machine from being used. Thus, the guard was only in place when the machine was not in use and did not protect the operators. Other protections had been discussed but were not feasible due to the design of the machine. For example, two-hand controls could not be installed because the operator needed to hold the stock in place during operation for safety and quality reasons. The guard the manufacturer could provide was a sliding guard that had to be moved to expose the point of operation prior to using the machine, which was determined to provide inadequate protection for this task.

On both sides, the machine had a guide to help properly position the stock. The guide was adjustable to allow for different stock sizes. The guide did not have preset locations for the different stock sizes—the operator would have to know exactly where to position the guide during adjustment. Changeover required use of hand tools and four different adjustments. Total changeover time was approximately fifteen minutes.

During operation, the operator had to firmly hold the stock close to the point of operation, to ensure that the stock did not move during machine operation (Figure 4). When the stock moved, it caused quality problems with burrs on the stock, which required rework to correct and thus added cost. If the stock was not held, it could be ejected from the machine, thereby expos-

ing the machine operator to injury. Repetitive holding of the stock in this manner introduced ergonomic risk factors.

The main goal of the project was to design appropriate guarding for the machine to prevent risk of an injury. A requirement of the design was that it would not negatively impact the productivity or quality of the operation. Operator input for the design was sought to ensure compliance and satisfaction with the result.

With support from management and safety personnel, the machine operator personally developed a design for a guard that met all of the project goals. The guard was manufactured in-house for very little cost. Photos of the new guard were sent to the machine manufacturer, who approved Comau's use of the guard.

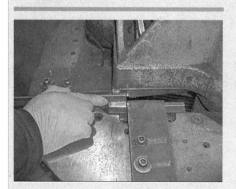

FIGURE 3. Before: point of operation configuration creates injury risk (*Source:* COMAU Inc. 2009)

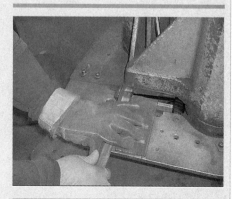

FIGURE 4. Before: operator has to hold stock (*Source:* COMAU Inc. 2009)

The two-piece guard was permanently installed in front of the point-of-operation area. The guard completely prevented the operator's hands/fingers from entering the hazardous gap area, virtually eliminating the risk of a finger/hand injury (Figure 5). The guard allowed the edge of the stock to slide underneath it to enter the machine.

The new guard had two preset settings for stock of different sizes. Changeover required a simple hand adjustment in two locations, which took 30 seconds or less in total. During operation, the operator would slide the stock into the guard. Because of the design allowing the two sections of guard to work together, the guards would guide the stock into proper position each time without the operator needing to make adjustments. The stock was held in place by the guards and no longer needed to be held by hand during operation, which eliminated an ergonomic risk factor (Figure 6). Because

FIGURE 5. After: point of operation no longer exposed (*Source:* COMAU Inc. 2009)

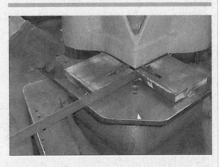

FIGURE 6. After: operator no longer holds stock during operation (*Source:* COMAU Inc. 2009)

of the ease of use and stock positioning, productivity improved by over 15 percent. Because the stock cannot move around during operation, quality was improved and the need for rework was eliminated.

All of the goals were accomplished and exceeded during this project. The risk of injury due to the gap was virtually eliminated, while productivity, quality, ergonomics, and changeover time were also significantly improved. The machine operators were fully involved in the solution and are very happy with the result. Projects such as this demonstrate and uphold Comau's commitment to the health and safety of its workers.

According to Taubitz, examples of a Kaizen approach include:

- Improvements are based on many small changes rather than on radical changes that might arise from research and development (R&D) and project efforts.
- Since the ideas come from the workers themselves, they are less likely to be radically different, and therefore easier to implement.
- Small improvements are less likely to require major capital investment than major process changes.
- The ideas come from the talents of the existing workforce, as opposed to using R&D, consultants, or equipment, any of which may be very expensive.
- All employees continually seek ways to improve their own performance.
- Workers are encouraged to take ownership for their work and can help reinforce working in a team, thereby improving overall worker motivation.

Particular attention should be paid to problems associated with process, including:

- too many steps/unnecessarily bureaucratic
- no process, allowing work to be performed that may not be safe or in line with best practice
- process not understood by those who perform the work
- not inclusive of all issues

This latter point is key for safety, health, and environmental professionals. Risk assessment that does not balance safety, environment, and operational performance is likely to suboptimize one leg of the triple bottom line at the expense of the others. Case studies will prove that overall performance is negatively impacted in such instances.

Some see continuous improvement inherently intertwined with management systems. Processes, such as business process management, quality management, and project management, are all part of the strategic toolkit. Deming saw it as part of the system whereby feedback from the process and the customer were evaluated against organizational goals (Deming 1982). W. Edwards Deming's Plan-Do-Check-Act (PDCA) is the foundation for management systems and continuous improvement (Deming 1982):

- *Plan*: Identify and analyze the problem
- *Do*: Pilot/implement the planned change
- *Check*: Analyze results and modify or plan for full implementation
- *Act*: Introduce systemic changes and training

The fact that this can be called a management process does not mean that it needs to be executed by management, merely that it makes decisions about the implementation of the delivery process and the design of the delivery process itself. Plan-Do-Check-Act (PDCA) is the foundation for ANSI/AIHA Z10:2005, *Occupational Health and Safety Management Systems* (ANSI 2005) and is also central to ISO 9000:2008 (ISO 2008), ISO 14000 (ISO 2004), and OSHA's Voluntary Protection Program (VPP) (OSHA 2009) are other examples of management systems that will drive continuous improvement.

A Management System

Though continuous improvement (CI) comes in many forms for different organizations, it is often associated with a management system to drive continuous improvement. CI can provide a foundation for the organizational culture and the goal of zero injuries—identical to the goal of zero defects—and it includes everyone in the desired transformation. Achievement of zero defects and zero injuries demands both responsibility and accountability, which is where a management system based on PDCA comes into play (see Figure 7).

A management system is nothing more than a tool for leaders to drive continuous improvement. Goals and objectives are established to accomplish or achieve improvements. Planning and implementation allow for integration into the day-to-day business. Audits, metrics, and evaluation are part of the checking processes that indicate where system adjustments should be made (act) to further reduce injuries (defects). A management system is a series of processes that allows leaders to define responsibility and hold people accountable.

The philosophy of continuous improvement, driven by root-cause analysis of problems, fits perfectly with safety. Use of continuous improvement tools and thinking paves the way for continuously improving safety on and off the job.

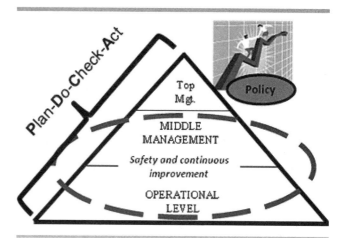

FIGURE 7. Management system based on Plan-Do-Check-Act (*Source:* M. Taubitz, adapted from the Lean & Safe Network 2008)

Learning to associate integrating safety into continuous improvement will lead the organization to a new way of thinking. Attitudes improve and behaviors change accordingly.

LEGISLATION, STANDARDS, AND MARKET INFLUENCES

International Influences and Regulations

There are several influences that are driving organizations and governments to reduce their greenhouse gas (GHG) emissions and focus on their sustainability strategies. These include international protocols; United Nations Conventions; European Union GHG regulations; carbon trading markets; and instruments used by the investment community that reports on an organization's environmental, social, and governance (ESG) sustainability performance. These instruments include, but are not limited to, the *Carbon Disclosure Market*, *Dow Jones Sustainability Index* (DJSI), and *MSCI Inc*. These factors have a global reach and impact U.S. organizations. Safety professionals who understand the external financial, voluntary, and regulatory forces that are driving sustainability within their organizations are better able to align safety and health management within the context of the greater dialogue on sustainability. The following provides a brief overview of some of these influences to familiarize the reader with terminology and concepts.

Kyoto Protocol

The Kyoto Protocol is an international agreement that, among other things, sets out binding targets for 37 countries and the European Union to reduce greenhouse gas emissions. Adopted on December 11, 1997, in Kyoto, Japan, it became effective in February 2005, and is linked to the United Nations Framework Convention on Climate Change (UNFCCC). These targets amount to an average of 5 percent reductions from the 1990 emission levels over a 5-year period from 2008–2012 (UNFCCC 2010b).

There is a significant distinction between a *protocol* (e.g., Kyoto) and a *convention* (e.g., UNFCCC or UN labor conventions). In the case of GHG emissions, the UNFCCC convention *encourages* industrialized countries to stabilize their GHG emissions, while the Kyoto Protocol *commits* them to do so.

Under the Kyoto Protocol, countries are expected to meet their targets through GHG emission-reduction strategies; however, the Protocol also offers countries an ability to meet their targets through three market-based mechanisms (UNFCCC 2010b):

- *Emissions trading:* Known as "the carbon market," this allows countries with emission units (permitted to them) they have not used to sell their excess emission units to countries that are over their emission targets (UNFCCC 2010a).
- *Clean development mechanism (CDM):* Allows a country to implement an emission-reduction project in developing countries to earn saleable, certified emission-reduction (CER) credits (equivalent to one ton of CO_2). This can be counted toward meeting their Kyoto targets.
- *Joint implementation (JI):* Allows a country to earn emission-reduction units (ERUs) from a joint emission-reduction or emission-removal project with another country also covered by the Kyoto Protocol. The ERU is equivalent to one ton of CO_2, which can be counted toward meeting the first country's Kyoto target. The rationale is that the CO_2 emissions overall are being reduced globally, and this mechanism benefits the developing country through foreign investment and technology transfer.

Safety professionals who understand the overall business of carbon trading and what influences their country and organization's decisions in the United States and around the world are better positioned to influence their organization's sustainability strategies for energy and CO_2 reductions. Reducing GHG emissions, whether by implementing processes to reduce energy consumption or reducing CO_2 emissions directly, often impacts safety and health (OSH and product end users) and should to be considered in the design and implementation of these new reduction strategies.

Copenhagen Accord

Representatives from over 190 nations met in Copenhagen to discuss the future of global climate change. The meeting, which produced the *Copenhagen Accord*, was held in conjunction with the United Nations Framework Convention on Climate Change (UNFCCC 2009c). Signing the Copenhagen Accord did not impose any legal requirements or targets on a country, but the country agrees to work to achieve its GHG emissions goals. The signatories of the Accord included countries such as the United States, China, India, Brazil, the European Union (27 countries) and others, accounting for 86 percent of global emissions according to the Climate Action Network's calculations (Broder 2010). The next global climate summit, known as the Conference of Parties (COP) was held in November 2010 in Cancun, Mexico.

European Union Emissions Trading System (EU ETS)

The *EU Greenhouse Gas Emissions Trading System* (EU ETS) is a worldwide system that began in January 2005. The EU ETS is based on the requirements set out in the EU Emissions Trading Directive (Directive 2003/87/EC), which became effective in October 2003 (EU Commission 2010). The system tracks GHG emissions by country and the individual entity owning the emission unit.

The EU ETS is overseen by a central administrator at the EU level, but the accounts in electronic registries are set up by each EU member state. The registry system tracks the ownership of emission allowances in the same way the banking system tracks the ownership of money (EU Commission 2010). This trading system is one of the first carbon markets.

CARBON DISCLOSURE PROJECT (CDP)

The Carbon Disclosure Project (CDP) is a UK-based, global climate-change reporting system. Over 3000 organizations in approximately 60 countries measure their greenhouse gas emissions and disclose their climate-change strategies through the CDP (CDP 2010). This disclosed information is used by institutional investors, corporations, policymakers and their advisors, public-sector organizations, government bodies, academics, and the public. CDP has shaped the harmonization of climate-change data and has significantly influenced the development of international carbon-reporting standards.

According to their Web site, CDP acts on behalf of 534 institutional investors, holding $64 trillion in assets under management, and some 60 purchasing organizations, such as Cadbury, PepsiCo, and Walmart (CDP 2010).

It is important to understand that these socially responsible investors are influencing organizations around the world to develop CO_2 reduction strategies. The designing of processes to implement these strategies can have a direct impact on the work of the safety professional, whose job it is to assure the safety and health of the workforce involved in these processes. Additionally, understanding and anticipating how these various influences are impacting business decisions in an organization, the safety professional is better able to proactively identify new business opportunities, such as new products and services, process improvements, and mitigating OSH and CO_2 implications for product end users, which enhances the marketability of the product.

Dow Jones Sustainability Index (DJSI)

The Dow Jones Sustainability Index (DJSI), derived from the Dow Jones Global Index (DJGI), benchmarks and tracks the financial performance of the leading sustainability-driven companies on a global basis. The DJSI is used by the investment community to identify and select companies for investment purposes based upon their sustainability performance.

The DJSI tracks the financial performance of 57 sectors out of the 2500 in the DJGI, and reports on the top 10 percent in those sectors in the areas of social, economic, and environmental performance (DJSI and SAM 2010); specifically, it defines what a company's business strategy is and how it identifies its risks and opportunities around sustainability.

Sustainability asset management (SAM) is the investment group that manages the DJSI. It provides assessment information on a company's corporate sustainability performance based upon a set of questions. The results of the assessment determine whether the company will be listed on the index. According to the DJSI Web site, SAM measures a company's strategy, financials, customer relationships, product sustainability, corporate governance, stakeholder engagement, and human resource management (DJSI and SAM 2010).

MSCI Inc.

MSCI USA Broad Environmental, Social, and Governance (ESG) Index provides ESG performance information for the investment community, including asset managers, banks, hedge funds, and pension funds (MSCI Inc. 2010). According to the MSCI Inc., the following criteria are used to rate companies: management of environmental challenges; impacts on communities, employees, contractors, and suppliers (antidiscrimination, labor-management, employee safety, and labor rights) throughout the supply chain; product quality; regulatory compliance; investor relations; board accountability; business ethics; and governance around management, financial, and sustainability reporting practices (MSCI Research 2010).

National Regulations and Initiatives

With sustainability, waste reduction, and energy efficiency becoming more desirable characteristics within communities, national and local initiatives have been developed to address this need and to promote the changes necessary to foster responsible use of natural resources.

The first U.S. government legal initiative toward promoting sustainability was the National Environmental Policy Act (NEPA) of 1970, which laid out the national goal of creating and maintaining sustainable conditions for future generations of Americans (EPA 1970).

The U.S. Environmental Protection Agency (EPA) oversees a number of sustainability regulatory programs, including those involving transportation fuels, fuel economy, and greenhouse gas emissions.

Transportation Fuels

The Energy Policy Act of 2005 (EPA 2010c) and the Energy Independence and Security Act of 2007 (EPA 2010c) authorized the EPA to create standards requiring transportation fuels to contain a minimum amount of renewable fuel content, and to encourage production and use of renewable fuels while reducing dependence on foreign energy sources. The resultant renewable fuels standard (RFS) sets minimum volumes of renewable fuels, such as ethanol, to be incorporated into the nation's transportation fuel supply (EPA 2010c).

Fuel-Economy Standards

The EPA provides annual automotive fuel-economy data for several federal agencies, including the Internal Revenue Service (IRS), the U.S. Department of Transportation (DOT), and the U.S. Department of Energy (DOE) (EPA 2010a). Among its many uses, the data is displayed on stickers for new vehicles sold in the United States, informing potential consumers about a vehicle's fuel efficiency. Fuel-economy standards for cars and light trucks are continually updated, driving increased efficiency and reduction in fuel use in the U.S. economy.

In January 2007, President Bush signed Executive Order 13423, "Strengthening Federal Environmental, Energy, and Transportation Management" (EPA 2007). The order requires all federal agencies to carry out their missions in a sustainable and energy-efficient manner and to set goals for continuous improvement (EPA 2007).

Greenhouse Gas Emissions Standards

On May 7, 2010, the EPA, in cooperation with the National Highway Traffic Safety Administration (NHTSA), issued the first greenhouse gas emissions standards for manufacturers of light-duty vehicles (EPA 2010g). The standards, which establish limits for carbon emissions in cars and light trucks, start in 2012 and extend through 2016 (EPA 2010g). Similar standards for heavy vehicles are proposed.

Economy, Energy, and Environment (E3) Sustainability Efforts in Manufacturing

Those safety, health, and environmental (SH&E) professionals looking for ways to capitalize on linking lean manufacturing principles with sustainability initiatives will benefit from the EPA's *Economy, Energy, and Environment (E3) Initiative*. E3 is a coordinated federal and local technical assistance initiative to help manufacturers adapt and thrive in a new business era focused on sustainability. According to the EPA (EPA 2010d), the program provides technical assessments of production processes and training in four key areas:

- lean
- clean
- energy
- greenhouse gas emissions

Depending on the processes of a company, large or small, there are assessments and training target opportunities to:

- maximize energy efficiency
- reduce environmental wastes
- identify opportunities for reducing carbon emissions
- promote sustainable manufacturing practices and growth
- reduce business costs

The EPA offers support to interested companies by providing assistance with:

- a *lean review* that leads to increased productivity and reduced costs
- an *energy audit* that provides tools and insights for reducing energy demand and costs
- a *greenhouse gas evaluation* that teaches manufacturers how to calculate GHG emissions and evaluate reduction strategies
- a clean review that results in water and energy conservation, reduced emissions, and additional cost savings

- *postassessment recommendations* that guide each facility toward improvements in overall efficiency; reduced waste; more efficient use of resources, including energy and water; and cost savings

PILOT PROJECTS

In Columbus, Ohio, six companies participated in an E3 pilot that identified energy savings of $1.7 million and environmental savings of $2.6 million, avoided over 250,000 pounds of water pollutants, and reduced solid waste by 24,000 pounds (EPA 2010d).

E3 is currently completing two pilot projects. In Columbus, Ohio, federal partner agencies are coordinating to conduct technical assessments and provide training by working with six manufacturers, the city government, the Solid Waste Authority of Central Ohio, and American Electric Power. In San Antonio, Texas, the EPA, the Department of Commerce, CPS Energy, and the city government are working with six manufacturers.

The E3 partnership in San Antonio, Texas, resulted in a local manufacturer of detention equipment realizing increased energy efficiency that included $85,000 in energy savings, reduced annual electric consumption of 159,000 kwh, reduced monthly electric demand of 48 kW, and reduced annual natural gas usage of 36,000 CCF.

State and Local Sustainability Initiatives

A number of U.S. states have initiated sustainability programs and requirements without prompting from the federal government. For example, the state of California was granted a waiver of Clean Air Act preemption in 2009 to establish its own light-duty vehicle GHG emission standards. The standards were scheduled to start with model year 2009, but are currently undergoing a regulatory review process (Cal EPA 2007).

The Oregon Sustainability Board works to promote sustainable business practices within Oregon state government. One example is statewide Policy 107-011-140, also known as Sustainable Procurement and Internal Operations. The policy sets high sustainability standards for purchases and the disposal of electronics and related office waste; it also includes guidance for electronic distribution of meeting minutes, telecommuting, and audio/video conferencing instead of travel (Oregon DAS, 2009).

The state of Washington has adopted a number of policies aimed at reducing GHG emissions from transportation, industry, use of buildings, and other sources (ECY 2010). A target of returning to 1990 GHG emission levels by the year 2020 is in place. Facilities emitting over 10,000 metric tons of greenhouse gases must submit an annual emission inventory report to the State Department of Ecology. Certain large employers must have a commute trip-reduction program in place to reduce energy use. A Green Economy Jobs Initiative looks to approximately triple the number of green jobs in Washington by 2020, as compared to a 2004 baseline (ECY 2010).

Sustainable Jersey®, a voluntary New Jersey initiative, was started in 2006 by a group of town mayors. It encourages local municipalities to become certified by implementing a series of sustainable management practices (SJ n.d.). The certification process involves implementing a series of environmental, cultural, and energy-efficiency improvements in accordance with a set of standardized best practices. Certification benefits include cost savings, access to ongoing state and local grant funding for sustainability programs, and a positive public image (SJ n.d.).

Similar to many U.S. states, local municipalities are establishing their own environmental and sustainability programs. For example, within New Jersey, the Princeton Environmental Commission provides counsel and guidance to its host municipalities, Princeton Township, and the Borough of Princeton. Made up of eleven voting community members from various backgrounds and professions, the commission drafts and reviews sustainability-based ordinances for its local governing officials and provides community educational opportunities in accordance with the Princeton Environmental Commission Mission Statement: "To inform local government and residents on environmental issues, laws, and programs" (Wasserman 2010).

Several of the commission's key projects include:

- proposing updates to land-use ordinances to include land preservation provisions
- drafting proposed green building provisions to local construction projects
- encouraging further local recycling efforts

Since its inception in 1977, the commission has provided progressive sustainability guidance to the Princeton community (Wasserman 2010).

U.S. Green Building Council (USGBC)

Prompted by the growing trend toward more efficient and sustainable building design, the U.S. Green Building Council (USGBC) was formed in 1993 as a means to provide measurable criteria for green construction. The organization has grown steadily to its current level of 30,000 members, united across 80 U.S. chapters (USGBC 2010a). The broad spectrum of professional members includes building owners, real estate developers, architects, and engineers (USGBC 2010a).

The USGBC has developed a number of tools to assess and promote green building: educational materials, outreach programs, national and local membership chapters, and the LEED® (Leadership in Energy and Environmental Design) Green Building Certification Program and LEED Green Building Rating System™ (USGBC 2010b). The Council also hosts the Greenbuild International Conference and Expo (Greenbuild 2010).

LEED® GREEN BUILDING CERTIFICATION PROGRAM

In 2000, the LEED® Green Building Certification Program was initiated. Under the program, architects and building owners can apply for and receive LEED® certification for the design and functionality of their green building project. The building project must take into account the entire life cycle of the building, from initial design through construction and end use (USGBC 2010f). The LEED® logo is shown in Figure 8.

Under the program, certification credits are awarded to a building project based on a number of critical areas, including (USBCG 2010f):

- sustainable sites
- water efficiency
- energy and atmosphere
- materials and resources
- indoor environmental quality

Point values for materials and other criteria are contained in a series of tables available from USGBC. From the maximum of 100 possible points (plus up to

10 bonus points for a combination of innovative design and regional priority, where earned) for certain types of LEED® projects, a building project is rated (USGBC 2010f). Based on the cumulative total points earned, a project will be awarded one of the following LEED® certifications (USBGC 2010e):

- LEED® Certified
- LEED® Silver
- LEED® Gold
- LEED® Platinum

LEED® green building-certification rating systems include: homes, neighborhood development, commercial interiors (including core and shell for applicants responsible for a portion of a building project—their portion can become LEED® Certified), existing buildings, operations and maintenance facilities, schools, and healthcare and retail sales facilities (see Figure 9).

FIGURE 8. LEED® logo (*Source:* USBGC 2010b. "LEED" and related logo is a trademark owned by the U.S. Green Building Council and is used with permission.)

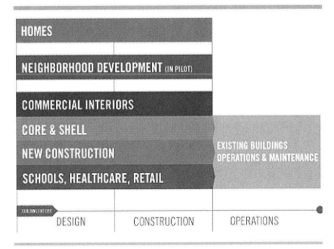

FIGURE 9. LEED® green building-certification rating systems (USGBC 2010f)

Applying for LEED® Building Certification

Once an individual or project team decides to pursue LEED® certification, a comprehensive registration package is sent to the Green Building Certification Institute (GBCI), the certification body of USGBC (USGBC 2010e). The decision to pursue LEED® certification should be made early in a project, preferably in the design phase, to allow material procurement, site selection and preparation, and waste handling to be managed for the maximum number of LEED® rating points.

Over 35,000 projects are LEED®-registered as of August 2010 (USGBC 2010f). Government agencies, such as the EPA, have set up green building programs for their new acquisitions or for agency remodeling projects based on LEED® registration. The program has resulted in the registration of a number of EPA buildings, including the EPA's Region I office (Boston, MA), Region IX office (San Francisco, CA), and Region X office (Seattle, WA) (EPA 2010e).

Individual LEED® Certification

Architects, engineers, environmental specialists, and other professionals can obtain certification in the administration of LEED® criteria through the LEED® professional certification program, administered by the GBCI (USGBC 2010f). Certification levels include:

- LEED® Accredited Professional (AP): This is the highest individual LEED® coordinator certification, representing a combination of experience, education, and successful written examination. Successful candidates are awarded the LEED® AP designation for use on individual promotional materials as an indicator of attained professional expertise in green building management. The certification is intended for technical professionals.

  Several specialty LEED® AP certifications are available, including ND (neighborhood development), Homes, O&M (operations and maintenance), ID+C (interior design and construction), and BD+C (building design and construction) (USGBC 2010c).

- LEED® Green Associate: This certification is for nontechnical individuals interested in documenting an attained knowledge of green building concepts, including building design and use (UGBC 2010d).

California Green Building Standards Code®

California is the first U.S. state to adopt sustainability-based building code requirements. The *California Green Building Standards Code®*, known as the CALGreen Code, with its final form appearing first in 2010, became effective in January 2011 (CALGreen Code 2010). The code is made up of the following chapters, each of which contains minimum building requirements for California establishments that meet certain defined criteria (CALGreen Code 2010, vii):

> Chapter 1: Administration
> Chapter 2: Definitions
> Chapter 3: Green Building
> Chapter 4: Residential Mandatory Measures
> Chapter 5: Nonresidential Mandatory Measures
> Chapter 6: Referenced Organizations and Standards
> Chapter 7: Installer and Special Inspector Qualifications
> Chapter 8: Compliance Forms and Worksheets
> Appendices of Residential and Nonresidential Measures are also included

The code provides specific construction and renovation requirements for building owners once the applicable occupancy and governing state agency or agencies are determined. It regulates every newly constructed building in California (CALGreen Code 101.3).

Among the code's sustainability requirements are minimum standards for utility use and waste minimization. For example, during residential construction, water use must be reduced by 20 percent through installation of plumbing fixtures or fittings meeting code requirements (CALGreen Code 4.303.1). To minimize waste during residential construction, at least 50 percent of nonhazardous construction or demolition waste must be recycled or salvaged for reuse (CALGreen Code 4.408.1). Similar requirements exist for nonresidential construction.

Linking Safety to Social Responsibility

ISO 26000 outlines key principles for recognizing social responsibility efforts and engaging stakeholders in the process (see the sidebar above on page 21). The SH&E professional can use the structure of ISO 26000 to demonstrate the strategic role SH&E management plays in social responsibility. There are several areas where SH&E issues are directly and indirectly connected to social responsibility principles found in ISO 26000 (Knott 2010). These are discussed in the sections below.

Recognizing Unique Needs of Members of the Organization

Safety management often involves addressing the unique issues related to ergonomics, disabled workers, language barriers, cultural differences, young workers, and an aging workforce. These programs should be highlighted by the safety professional when demonstrating an organization's social responsibility efforts toward recognizing the unique needs of its workforce.

Employee Participation in Safety and Health Efforts

The need for employee participation is highlighted by several safety management systems, including ANSI Z10 (ANSI/AIHA 2005), OHSAS 18000 (2007–2008), and OSHA. According to OSHA (n.d.), employee participation can take several forms:

- participating on joint labor-management committees and other advisory or specific-purpose committees
- conducting site inspections
- analyzing routine hazards in each step of a job or process, and preparing safe work practices or controls to eliminate or reduce exposure
- developing and revising the site safety and health rules
- training both current and newly hired employees
- providing programs and presentations at safety and health meetings
- conducting accident/incident investigations
- reporting hazards to upper management and/or responsible parties
- fixing hazards within your control
- supporting your fellow workers by providing feedback on risks and assisting them in eliminating hazards
- participating in accident/incident investigations
- performing a pre-use or change analysis for new equipment or processes in order to identify hazards up front before use

EMPLOYEE PARTICIPATION IN HEALTH AND SAFETY MANAGEMENT SYSTEMS

ANSI Z10, *Health and Safety Management Systems* (2005) also specifically itemizes effective employee participation, including a role in activities such as incident investigations, procedure development, health- and safety-related audits, training development, job safety analysis, and all aspects of the planning process. In organizations where social responsibility is already a goal of the organization, the SH&E professional should already be able to identify several activities within the organization that address employee involvement. Areas where employee involvement is lacking or hampered can be more easily implemented by demonstrating that they add value to the organization's social responsibility goals. Examples of obstacles or barriers to employee involvement include: lack of response to employee input or suggestions, reprisals (supervisory and/or peer), or any other forms of discrimination (ANSI/AIHA 2005).

Guidelines for Safety Committee Development

Social responsibility is part of sustainability, involves employees in an organization, and gives them a voice on safety issues. Safety committee development is another way to demonstrate direct employee involvement in the safety program while also satisfying another component of good social responsibility. Safety committees are voluntary in many organizations but may be required by company policy or local regulations. The state of Oregon requires safety committees for most employers. A checklist provided by Oregon OSHA is found in Figure 10 for those SH&E professionals interested in developing, implementing, and/or auditing a safety committee (OR-OSHA 2010).

Eliminating Workplace Hazards, Including Psychosocial Issues

There is broad recognition that the psychosocial environment at work can affect physical and mental health as well as organizational outcomes, such as work performance and effectiveness (NIOSH 2004). Psychosocial issues can include stress, posttraumatic stress, workplace violence, bullying, substance abuse, absenteeism, racism and racial/ethnic prejudice, sexism

**Occupational Safety and Health
Safety Committee Evaluation Checklist**

To Do	Done	Item
☐	☐	The safety committee is composed of an equal number of employer and employee representatives.
☐	☐	Employee representatives are volunteers or elected by their peers.
☐	☐	There are at least four representatives on the committee if the workplace has more than 20 employees–at least two representatives if the workplace has 20 or fewer employees.
☐	☐	The representatives elect the committee chairperson.
☐	☐	Representatives are paid their regular wages during safety committee training and meetings.
☐	☐	Employee representatives serve on the committee for at least one year.
☐	☐	Representatives' terms of service are staggered so that at least one experienced representative is always on the committee.
☐	☐	Reasonable efforts are made to ensure that committee representatives represent the company's major work activities.
☐	☐	The committee meets monthly except when representatives schedule quarterly workplace inspections.
☐	☐	Committee meetings follow a written agenda.
☐	☐	The minutes for each meeting are maintained for at least three years.
☐	☐	Minutes are available to all employees.
☐	☐	All reports, evaluations, and recommendations are included in the minutes.
☐	☐	Management has a reasonable time to respond in writing to the committee's recommendations.
☐	☐	The committee has a method for collecting and reviewing employees' safety-related suggestions and reports of hazards.
☐	☐	The committee assists management in evaluating and improving the workplace safety and health program.
☐	☐	The committee's quarterly inspection team follows a standard procedure for identifying safety and health hazards during its inspections.
☐	☐	The inspection team includes employer and employee representatives.
☐	☐	The inspection team documents the location and identity of workplace hazards.
☐	☐	The inspection team–or other persons designated by the committee–inspects satellite locations quarterly.
☐	☐	The committee has a procedure for reviewing the team's quarterly inspection reports.
☐	☐	The committee recommends to management ways to control hazards and unsafe work practices.
☐	☐	The committee makes recommendations to ensure all employees are accountable for following safe work practices.
☐	☐	The committee has a procedure for investigating workplace accidents, illnesses, and deaths.
☐	☐	Representatives understand the purpose of their safety committee and know how it functions.
☐	☐	Representatives have access to applicable occupational safety and health rules.
☐	☐	Representatives have received safety training for identifying workplace hazards and investigating accidents.

FIGURE 10. Oregon OSHA's sample safety and health checklist (OR-OSHA 2010)

and sexual harassment, gender and racial discrimination, work-family integration and balance, and support for diversity in the workplace/workforce. A questionnaire developed to assess psychosocial issues within an organization is available online (Pejtersen 2010). The safety professional may be directly or indirectly involved with one or more psychosocial programs within an organization, yet all safety programs will address workplace hazard identification and abatement methodologies that can be correlated to sound socially responsible actions of the organization. There are many hazard identification methods, which are discussed in greater detail in the "General Safety Management" chapter of this handbook.

Two-Way Communication Regarding Safety and Health

Sound SH&E management requires commitment from all levels of an organization but, most importantly, from top management. Management leadership and employee involvement go hand in hand for safety success. In fact, top-management leadership and effective employee participation are crucial for the success of a safety management system (ANSI/AIHA 2005). Management provides the leadership for organizing and controlling activities within an organization. It provides the motivating force, resources, and influence necessary to embed safety as a fundamental value within the organization. In an effective program, management involvement also provides the means through which employees express their own commitment to safety and health for themselves and their fellow workers (OSHA 1989). The ANSI Z10 standard identifies management leadership as the first step toward a successful safety management system (ANSI/AIHA 2005). Since employee involvement is crucial, it is important to establish communication and trust between management and workers.

According to Manuele (2003), an organization's culture consists of its values, beliefs, legends, rituals, mission, goals, and performance measures, and its sense of responsibility to its employees, customers, and its community, all of which are translated into a system of expected behavior. The culture of an organization dictates the effectiveness of a safety management system. Petersen found that the culture of the organization sets the tone for everything in safety. "In a positive safety culture, it says that everything you do about safety is important" (Petersen 1966, 66). Consider this statement by OSHA: "The best Safety and Health Programs involve every level of the organization, instilling a safety culture that reduces accidents for workers and improves the bottom line for managers. When safety and health are part of the organization and a way of life, everyone wins" (OSHA 2002). A simple survey to measure the culture gap between upper management, middle management, and the workforce is found in the "General Safety Management" chapter of the handbook.

Worker's Rights Regarding the Economics of Safety

In 1986, OSHA issued a program evaluation profile (PEP) for their compliance officers to use when evaluating an employer's safety program (OSHA 1998). Although this compliance directive was rescinded, it serves as guidance in the evaluation of a sound employee training program. The OSHA PEP is available on the OSHA Web site. According to PEP, key indicators include (OSHA 2010):

- Knowledgeable persons conduct safety and health training.
- Training is properly scheduled, assessed, and documented.
- Training covers all necessary topics and situations, and includes all persons working at the site (hourly employees, supervisors, managers, contractors, part-time and temporary employees).
- Employees participate in creating site-specific training methods and materials.
- Employees are trained to recognize inadequate responses to reported program violations.
- A retrievable record-keeping system provides for appropriate retraining, makeup training, and modifications to training as the result of evaluations.

OSHA regulations contain more than 100 standards that include training requirements. OSHA has developed some voluntary training guidelines to assist employers in providing safety and health information, which are available on its Web site (OSHA 1998). These guidelines also provide employers with instructions needed for employees to work at minimal risk to themselves, to fellow employees, and to the public. A summary of the training guidelines (OSHA 1998) lists areas designed to help employers:

(1) Determine whether a work-site problem can be solved by training
(2) Determine what training, if any, is needed
(3) Identify goals and objectives for the training
(4) Design learning activities
(5) Conduct training
(6) Determine the effectiveness of the training
(7) Revise the training program, based on feedback from employees, supervisors, and other workers

A more in-depth discussion of effective safety training can be found in the "Safety and Health Training" section of the handbook.

Social responsibility requires a balance among the three Ps: people, profit, and the planet. Social responsibility should impact the balance between economic decisions and issues related to worker safety and health from the perspective of the workforce. This starts with the SH&E professional linking safety initiatives with profits or demonstrating the business value of safety. ANSI Z10 states that (ANSI/AIHA 2005, 6):

Organizations and the community may see additional benefits of implementing an OHSMS beyond the reduction of injury and illnesses. Some of these benefits may include: lowered workers' compensation costs, reduced turnover of personnel, reduced lost workdays, compliance with laws and regulations, increased productivity, improved employee health status, improved product quality, higher morale of employees, reduction or elimination of property damage due to incidents, reduced business interruption costs, and reduced impact on the environment due to incidents.

The benefits discussed above are the positive outcomes of an effective safety management system that senior management can see. The job of the SH&E professional is to paint the picture of success and obtain a commitment from management while the vision is fresh. This salesmanship is a means to achieve commitment to safety from management. A little salesman-

ship can integrate safety into the business model by illustrating incident and accident effects on production and profitability. Integrating the costs of safety into the business and demonstrating a return on investment has been identified and is still a major goal of the SH&E professional (ASSE 2007, ASSE/AIHA 2005). This puts safety into a language to which management, front-line supervisors, and even employees can relate. Unfortunately, many safety initiatives have a negative impact on the bottom line of an organization. In these circumstances, a safety initiative may lose priority within an organization due to its economic impact. Socially responsible organizations will weigh the benefits of an SH&E initiative based on its social and environmental impacts in addition to its effect on the bottom line. The savvy SH&E professional will utilize social responsibility principles involving employee rights in economic decisions as value added to the organization when a profit-based business case for a safety initiative is lacking. The SH&E professional must be able to make a case for safety when there is not a direct positive effect on the bottom line. Various aspects of social responsibility help demonstrate value to an organization interested in sustainability and social responsibility. Active SH&E programs that routinely involve employees in the decision-making process on workplace hazard reduction should be highlighted as examples of meeting this social responsibility initiative.

Health and Safety in an Organization's Value Chain

ISO 26000 (2010) defines a *value chain* as the entire sequence of activities or parties that provide (suppliers, outsourced workers, contractors) or receive (customers, consumers, clients, members, and other users) value in the form of products or services. Organizations have found that sustainability can be reached only through people (Nestle 2009). No other asset in an organization is as important as the people that contribute with their work to the organizational culture and goals. These organizations devote all the necessary energy and attention to protect employees, contractors, and any other people along the value chain, including suppliers, customers, and the public. Organizations can highlight social responsibility by requiring suppliers to meet minimum SH&E program requirements. This can include the procurement of products and services that have a reduced environmental impact, often referred to as *green supply chain*. Organizations can also mandate SH&E compliance to standards higher than what is mandated by local regulations. Serious organizations will also perform audits of their supply chain's SH&E commitment.

Consumer, Product, and Product Life-Cycle Safety

Organizations often work to address environmental and social issues across a product's life cycle. For instance, Baxter International, Inc., (2010d) incorporates these issues from sustainable design and bioethics during research and development to efficient use of energy and materials during manufacturing and transport, appropriate product advertising and promotion, and, finally, responsible repair, refurbishment, and recycling at product end of life. The SH&E professional should be aware of how his or her organization addresses consumer alerts and product recall information as part of its overall social responsibility goals. This awareness should also extend to products used within one's own organization. Social responsibility should also include a system to make management and employees aware of product defects and recalls on products utilized by the organization.

Personal Protective Equipment

The use of personal protective equipment (PPE) is an important aspect of an organization's social responsibility obligations. However, regulations and best practices require organizations to address workplace hazards using a hierarchy of controls. The use of PPE must be a last resort for protecting workers from workplace hazards. Protective equipment is acceptable as a hazard control method under the following circumstances (ANSI/ASSE 2005):

- when engineering controls are not feasible or do not totally eliminate the hazard
- while engineering controls are being developed

SIDEBAR

The organization shall implement and maintain a process for achieving feasible risk reduction based upon the following preferred order of controls (ANSI/ASSE 2005):

- A. Elimination
- B. Substitution of less hazardous materials, processes, operations, or equipment
- C. Engineering controls
- D. Warnings
- E. Administrative control
- F. Personal protective equipment (PPE)

Feasible application of this hierarchy of controls shall take into account:

- The nature and extent of risks being controlled
- The degree of risk reduction desired
- The requirements of applicable local, federal, and state statutes, standards, and regulations
- Recognized best practices in industry
- Available technology
- Cost-effectiveness
- Internal organization standards

- when safe work practices do not provide sufficient additional protection
- during emergencies when engineering controls may not be feasible

The ANSI Z10 standard expands upon the traditional hazard-abatement hierarchy of engineering controls, administrative controls, and personal protective equipment. The sidebar outlines the hazard-abatement hierarchy that is provided by the Z10 standard (ANSI/AIHA 2005, 16).

Use of PPE should address workplace hazards. Good social responsibility should include the use of PPE as part of the hierarchy of controls to protect workers.

CASE STUDIES

Following are five case studies, showing how safety and sustainability principles are implemented in the business community.

CASE STUDY 1

Sustainability in Action at BMW Group

The Munich, Germany-based BMW Group encompasses 24 manufacturing facilities in 13 countries. The company traces its roots to the 1917 Bayerische Motoren Werke G.M.B.H., originally producing aircraft engines, and later motorcycles. Several acquisitions and management decisions led to the current focus on individual mobility, primarily through the production and marketing of premier luxury automobiles that include BMW, Rolls Royce, and MINI brands. The group continues to manufacture quality motorcycles and the Husqvarna brand of power equipment.

Sustainability Management

The BMW Group embraces sustainability in all of its operations and publicizes its commitment through the group's Sustainability Strategy Objective: to be the most sustainable company in the automotive industry. BMW Group's Chairman of the Board of Management, Dr. Norbert Reithofer, succinctly states the group's commitment to sustainability: ". . . Our aim is to actively shape the future. To achieve this, we are making sustainability an increasingly integral part of our value chain. Sustainability should be a defining principle of how we design our processes and procedures."

To manage its sustainability objective, the group developed three core units (see Figure 11).

The *Sustainability Board* is an internal advisory committee comprised of the Group's entire Board of Management. The Board meets regularly to set future benchmarks and to discuss progress on current sustainability initiatives.

The *Sustainability Circle*, comprised of one representative per division, develops opportunities and enhances cross-communication throughout the Group. The Circle reports directly to the Sustainability Board.

Each functioning department works with the Sustainability Circle to imple-

ment the appropriate waste reduction and conservation initiatives needed to advance the program and to meet the Group's objective.

All BMW Group employees play a key role in implementing the sustainability program. Each has a responsibility to manage resources with the company's sustainability stakeholders and the Group's goals and objectives in mind.

Strategy and Organization

The BMW Group Sustainability Strategy covers all group operations and is a corporate principle of the organization (see Figure 12).

In 2009, the Group set a sustainability target and measures progress

through a corporate scorecard. Sustainability in the supply chain is managed through a system of procurement procedures that are managed by specially trained employees. Potential suppliers are carefully screened and audited for environmental and social responsibility. Suppliers and potential suppliers are provided with assistance as necessary to comply with the Group's policy.

The overall sustainability strategy of the BMW Group is demonstrated through reduced environmental impact and increased efficiency in all areas of production, their positive contributions to the surrounding communities, and the uncompromising quality and innovation provided to customers.

BMW Group sustainability organisation

Sustainability Board
composed of the entire Board of Management
chaired by: Chairman of the Board of Management
responsible for strategic alignment

Sustainability Circle
composed of one representative per division
chaired by: Group Representative for Sustainability and
Environmental Protection – responsible for drafting proposals

Departments
implement the sustainability targets
by initiating appropriate activities and
processes

FIGURE 11. BMW Group Sustainability Organization (BMW 2008)

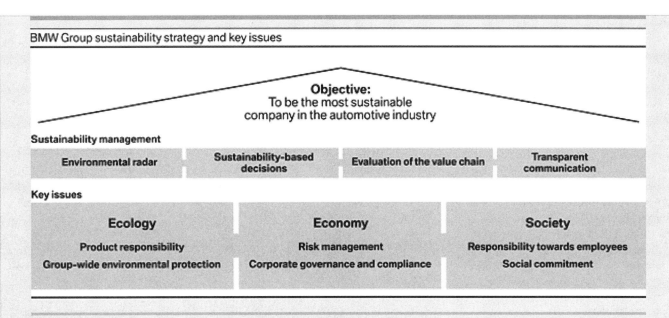

FIGURE 12. BMW Group Sustainability Strategy (BMW 2008)

Environmental Impact of Its Products

More efficient vehicle emissions and fuel consumption are among the Group's top priorities in its mission to provide value to its stakeholders. The Group is currently conducting the largest field-test of electric vehicles worldwide, with the near-term goal of putting a sustainable, fully electric vehicle into production and distribution. A hydrogen concept car has also been tested in Europe and worldwide; the test scenario in Europe included 100 test vehicles and a series of hydrogen filling stations. Research is ongoing, with focus on liquid hydrogen storage.

With reduction in CO_2 emissions as a long-held corporate objective, BMW has also been successful in engineering vehicles that emit less CO_2.

Also important are the life cycle of the vehicle itself and production efficiency. Approximately 95% of a new BMW vehicle can be recycled. Water use in the production process has decreased, as has the volume of waste, and volatile organic compounds per vehicle produced. Additionally, in 2009 the Group's Spartanburg, SC, plant recycled 85% of plant-generated waste. Details of the Spartanburg plant's waste-handling in 2009 are shown in the table.

All of these innovations are done with the goal of minimizing the Group's use of resources in providing a valuable product to its customers.

2009 Waste (lb)	
Metal	5,030,731
Wood	2,441,280
Cardboard	4,199,280
Plastic	752,787
Glass	107,338
E-waste	34,528
Chemical	1,064,365
Hazardous	226,627
Special	17,970
Waste to landfill	2,433,220
Total 2009 Waste	16,308,126
Total recycled	85%
Total disposed	15%

(*Source:* www.bmwusfactory.com – Environmental Responsibility)

Sustainability and Safety

An integral part of the Group's sustainability initiative is the concept of employee health and safety. As with any safety-minded organization, a safe workforce is essential to the Group's success. To further improve performance, the Group has undertaken the goal of establishing occupational health and safety management systems at all locations. At the time of this writing, 50% of locations representing 80% of employees had fully operational systems in place in conformance with internationally accepted guidelines, such as OHSAS. The remaining sites are scheduled to have systems in place by 2010. The focus on safety has improved the Group's accident frequency to 2.7 accidents per million hours worked, 33 percent less than the industry average of 4.0.

Initiatives for older workers, those with families or elderly relatives, as well as those with financial difficulties, are in place to enhance the overall well-being of BMW Group employees. The investment in these initiatives allows BMW employees to focus their efforts on efficient achievement of the Group's goals through outstanding performance.

Summary

Environmental and social responsibility simply governs the way the BMW Group conducts business. They do not consider sustainable operations as an option, but rather as a guiding principle that is integral to BMW's future success. In partnership with employees, customers, neighbors, and government, the Group is positioned to lead the automotive industry in sustainability and to succeed in its objective: to be the most sustainable company in the automotive industry.

CASE STUDY 2

Integration Failure: When Safety, Lean and Green Are Not Integrated (Bruce Main, September 2010)

Situation

A machine tool was cutting a metal part when the operator working adjacent to the machine heard a whooshing sound, flames shot out the finished parts' exit ports, the guard doors burst open, and he felt a sudden burning sensation on his arm and face. A flash of fire had erupted from ports of the machine. The operator suffered significant burns, resulting in severe pain, lost work time, and residual scarring.

Background

An investigation into the incident revealed a causal chain of factors. The flash fire was caused by a spark from the tooling. During the course of operation, heat and, occasionally, sparks are generated. The machining oil used to cool and lubricate the cutting operation was relatively benign in liquid form but flammable in a mist above a minimum concentration. During operation, an excessive concentration of airborne cutting fluid, which was in mist form, ignited. The mist concentration exceeded the machine tool supplier's recommendations at the time of the incident because the ventilation system did not provide adequate air flow. The air flow was inadequate because the machine user had installed a third machine on a two-machine system and tapped into the existing ventilation system without making adjustments for increasing the air flow. As a result, the ventilation system, designed for two machines, was inadequate to accommodate the requirements of a three-machine system.

Further investigation revealed that the machine was originally manufactured and sold in the 1980s. The machine supplier offered a fire suppression and mist control system with the machine proposal in the 1980s, but the customer "thrifted out" the fire suppression system at the purchase. The customer also opted to install the machine itself rather than pay for installation by the machine supplier. Historically, such systems and services are often resisted by some customers seeking to minimize the machine purchase price.

The machine was manufactured in Europe, shipped to the United States, and installed at the machine-user facility. The machine was rebuilt in the United States by the machine supplier in the early 2000s with updated control and ventilation systems. Prior to the incident, the customer installed the mist collection system.

Following the refurbishment, the machine supplier performed the startup and qualifying run of the machine at the customer's facility. The qualifying run evaluated the ability of the machine to perform the necessary cutting operations within specifications and general operations of the machine.

More recent evolutions of this type of machine include fire suppression systems, ventilation systems, and interlock door switches on the doors. Following the incident, three new systems were installed on the machines: a retrofit ventilation system, a fire suppression system, and a mist collection system.

Hazards

A task-based, risk assessment of the system identified 145 task-hazard pairs. These hazards include both safety and environmental potential sources of harm, including the following hazards:

- cutting/severing from sharp edges of parts during normal operation
- slip and fall from cutting fluid dripping on the floor
- noise hazards
- environmental/industrial hygiene hazards of oil getting on parts and hands and airborne emissions from the enclosure
- a chemical allergen or irritant from the cutting fluid or, while reaching into the machine, cutting fluid dripping on neck or arms
- ergonomic hazards of posture when reaching into the machine with the doors
- hot surface temperatures from machined parts or motor surface temperatures

- pinch points between tooling in the machine or drive system
- fire from sparks from tool collision if the tooling is misinstalled or incorrectly moved or if the machine is not reset to accommodate new tooling
- crushing hazards during tool change or parts replacement
- fall hazards during parts replacements or filter changes while accessing the top of the machine
- pressurized lines if not locked out and energy released
- electrical hazards from energized equipment if not locked out during servicing
- fire hazard from heightened oil mist concentration; if fluid gets too low, the impeller can create an ignitable mist
- ergonomic hazards of lifting assemblies out of the machine
- environmental or fire hazards from hazardous waste of grease oils in rags
- environmental hazards of cleaning compounds and chemicals
- unexpected startup or motion if not locked out during servicing
- material movement hazards related to fork-truck delivery and removal of product
- hazards related to installation, hook up, and start up of machinery
- fire hazard of ignitable mist if the concentration exceeds the recommended maximum or the air flow is insufficient, or if the air intake is improperly located

Analysis

This case study highlights safety, environmental, fire, and operational hazards. The connection of a third machine to a ventilation system designed for two machines resulted in an unidentified hazard of inadequate ventilation and mist control. The ensuing fire and injury caused the company significant loss of production because the machines were unserviceable and required extensive repairs. The machines had to be sent to the U.S.-based service operations for repairs and updates.

Operational wastes that resulted from this incident include added:

- delay/waiting
- motion movement
- process

Additionally, several weeks' delay and significant costs were incurred by both maintenance operations and management personnel in dealing with the incident.

In addition, this case study highlights the challenges the machine supplier can encounter when a legacy machine it built many years ago is involved in injury incident, particularly if the residual risks associated with the older machine differ from those of the current product offerings.

Conclusion

The drive for the triple bottom line of sustainable growth requires that risk assessment concurrently address production, safety, and environmental risks. In this case, failure to address the environmental issue resulted in a significant safety issue, fire damage to equipment, and the consequence of lost production. All of the lean (operational) wastes (correction, motion/movement, and waiting), safety wastes (injury) and environmental waste (air contaminant) could be attributed to the seventh form of lean waste, process. Lack of a process that employed a fully integrated risk assessment overlooked a condition that caused pain, injury, and significant production and attendant costs.

CASE STUDY 3

Safety and Sustainability

A manufacturing company utilizes large vertical and horizontal boring mills to bore complex hole patterns into steel work pieces. Boring mills operate using "ways," which are essentially tracks that allow the body of the mill to move in three dimensions as needed based on the desired hole pattern. The ways are protected from metal chips by way covers, which adjust to the position of the body of the mill. The way covers require oil as a lubricant to ensure they slide correctly when the machine is moving. This oil drips off the ways over time, and this oil drip is inherent to the design of the machine.

At this company, the large boring mills are located in pits. In the original process, the excess oil would drip into the pit. Boring mill operators would then soak up the oil using oil absorbent, which was kitty litter. The absorbent would build up over time until it was several inches deep in the bottom of the pit. Several times per year, the operators would scoop the absorbent out of the pit into collection drums using shovels. Once the absorbent was drained of all free liquids, the absorbent was placed into the general trash which would be sent to a landfill. The drained liquid would be reclaimed.

This process created a number of problems for both safety and sustainability:

- The amount of absorbent used greatly increased the amount of waste generated.
- Nearly all of the waste was being sent to the landfill, which did not support the company's sustainability goals.
- Operators who had to enter the pit to lubricate the machine would be subject to slip and fall hazards because of the unstable absorbent surface, as well as the oil, which would get into the soles of their shoes when inside the pit.
- The soaked kitty litter buildup resulted in an odor near the machine.

Additionally, the process of cleaning the pit was not lean and resulted in significant downtime, the absorbent buildup lowered employee morale, and its appearance did not impress visiting customers.

Therefore, machine maintenance personnel partnered with the safety/environmental department and machine operators to resolve these issues. A temporary fix was put in place as follows. First, the pit was completely emptied and cleaned. Then, absorbent socks were placed along the length of the way covers to contain the oil close to the machine. During this time, the oil in the socks could be squeezed out into drums and reclaimed. This eliminated the landfill waste. It also kept the pit much cleaner and ensured a stable walking surface when operators entered the pit. Additionally, it resulted in much less downtime for cleaning, and was visibly cleaner. However, the downside is that the socks needed to be replaced from time to time, and if they were not emptied soon enough the oil could leak into other areas of the pit.

Ultimately, a long-term solution was developed by the group. A small containment berm was built near the machine in a location that would not pose a trip hazard. When the oil builds up in the containment area, it can easily be pumped out for reclamation. The oil cannot leak into other areas of the pit. The only waste generated is the oil, which is reclaimed. This process significantly improved safety and sustainability for the machine. Productivity improved, while cleaning times decreased. The area looks visibly cleaner, and the employees working in the area are very appreciative. An added benefit is that the pit can now be swept with a broom to pick up metal chips generated by the boring process, and the chips can be recycled, which further improves sustainability. In the original process, the chips would mix with the kitty litter and be sent to the landfill.

The lesson learned is that safety and sustainability can often produce synergistic effects when both are considered together. Also, lean principles can also be applied when implementing safety and sustainability initiatives to improve other business priorities, such as productivity, while simultaneously improving safety and sustainability.

CASE STUDY 4

Safety and Sustainability

The challenge: Reduce safety and ergonomic risks along with cost and environmental impact of using disposable plastic wrapping material to protect parts shipped from a local supplier.

The previous method of wrapping and shipping the covers required annually:

- thousands of square feet of bubble wrap
- over a mile of tape to secure the wrap

- estimated labor and material costs exceeding $10,000

Cuts and complaints of sore wrists and hands were part of the process, along with significant amounts of material waste. Using lean tools and thinking, a team considered modifying the carts used to transport the parts. However, closer analysis suggested that every other part covered with a plastic sleeve would provide necessary protection while using half the material. The bubble wrap was eliminated.

Once removed, the plastic sleeves are returned to the supplier for reuse.

Injuries from cuts and repetitive trauma problems were eliminated, and the environmental waste from scrap material was also eliminated. Operational costs were significantly reduced due to reusing the plastic sleeves, and faster performance of the task was achieved.

This real-life case study was driven by a desire to reduce injuries, which led to actions where people, the planet, and profit all won. These tactical steps in today's world are part of the journey to sustainable growth.

CASE STUDY 5

Safety and Sustainability

An automotive company had a significant amount of waste that was being sent to a landfill. The plant assembled a team to investigate methods to reduce the amount of waste being sent to the landfill and increase the amount of waste being recycled. This team included representation from the safety department.

One waste type the team identified for potential recycling was the wooden pallets and "pallet boxes" (pallets with corrugated cardboard containers stapled on the top). Previously, the pallets and pallet boxes had been crushed in a compactor and sent to a landfill. Not only was this very expensive, but it negatively impacted the environment and did not support the company's sustainability goals.

The plant began a process where the pallets were gathered and sent to a third party for reuse/recycling. The cardboard was removed from the pallet boxes by hand to allow the attached pallets to be sent to the third party. The safety department reviewed and approved the pallet box process based on the fact that packaging specifications required the cardboard on the pallet boxes to incorporate

a "breakaway" feature to make it fairly easy to remove the cardboard by hand. Overall, the pallet recycling program saved the plant over $25,000 in the first year and significantly increased the overall percentage of recycled waste.

However, the process of removing the cardboard from the pallet boxes by hand was starting to cause ergonomic injuries to employees performing this task because of the amount of upper-extremity force necessary to pull the cardboard from the pallets. Additionally, it was a time-consuming process and negatively impacted productivity. Although packaging specifications required specific "breakaway" features for the cardboard, some pallet boxes did not have this feature, and others were still too difficult to remove by hand, even with the breakaway feature. Various methods to alleviate the ergonomic risk factors were tested, such as using a powered hand saw and removing the cardboard using the forks of a forklift. However, these options presented other hazards.

Finally, a solution was developed that would alleviate or eliminate the ergonomic risk while still allowing the pallet box pallets to be recycled. First, the suppliers

for all nonconforming pallet boxes were contacted to ensure the breakaway features were incorporated. Where possible, employees were allowed to manually pull off the cardboard from breakaway pallet boxes as long as the cardboard came off easily. For nonconforming boxes, and larger boxes where the cardboard was not easy to pull off, a different removal method was developed. A steel "shear plate" was installed directly above the compactor (and with the compactor manufacturer's approval). A forklift would pull the top of a pallet box across the shear plate to easily and quickly shear the cardboard from the pallet. The cardboard would then fall into the compactor and would be recycled. The pallet would be sent to the third party for recycling.

This new process resulted in a 100% reduction of injuries for this process and significantly improved productivity, while still allowing both components of the pallet boxes to be recycled. The lesson learned is that all potential safety hazards must be fully investigated prior to making a change to improve sustainability (or any other business priority).

REFERENCES

Aaron, William. 2008. "What Gets Measured Sometimes Gets Managed." *Entrepreneur* (retrieved October 23, 2010). www.entrepreneur.com/tradejournals/article/185487705.html

American National Standards Institute (ANSI) and American Industrial Hygiene Association (AIHA). 2005. Standard Z10-2005, *Occupational Health and Safety Management Systems*. Fairfax, VA: AIHA.

Baxter International, Inc. 2010a. "Baxter 2009 Sustainability Priorities Report" (retrieved September 22, 2010). www.baxter.com/documents/sustainability_report_2009.pdf

_____. 2010b. *Baxter's Sustainability Efforts Support Education, Sustainable Product Design; Earn Dow Jones Sustainability Index Recognition* (retrieved September 22, 2010). www.baxter.com/press_room/press_releases/2010/09_16_10_sustainability.html

_____. 2010c. *Baxter will promote a safety and health workplace: 2015 Goal* (retrieved September 22, 2010). www.sustainability.baxter.com/sustainability_at_baxter/priorities_goals/safe_workplace.html

_____. 2010d. *Baxter 2009 Sustainability Report: Health and Safety Approach* (retrieved September 22, 2010). www.sustainability.baxter.com/EHS/health_and_safety_approach/index.html

Bayerische Motoren Werke, Aktiengesellschaft (BMW). 2008. "BMW Sustainable Value Report 2008." 80788, Munich, Germany: BMW.

BNET. *Business Definition for Corporate Social Responsibility* (retrieved October 23, 2010). dictionary.bnet.definition/Corporate+Social+Responsibility.html

Broder, John M. 2010. *Remember the Copenhagen Accord?* (retrieved October 8, 2010). www.green.blogs.nytimes.com/2010/06/08/remember-the-copenhagen-accord/

California Building Standards Commission. 2010. California Code of Federal Regulations, Title 24, Part 11. 2010. *2010 California Green Building Standards Code* (CALGreen Code). Sacramento, CA: California Building Standards Commission.

California EPA Air Resources Board (Cal OSH ARB). 2007. "Climate Change Emissions Standards for Vehicles." Fact Sheet (retrieved November 22, 2010). www.arb.ca.gov/cc/factsheet.ccfaq.pdf

Carbon Disclosure Project (CDP). 2010. *Overview* (retrieved October 8, 2010). www.cdproject.net/en-US/WhatWeDo/Pages/overview.aspx

CR Magazine. 2010. "100 Best Corporate Citizens" (retrieved October 5, 2010). www.thecro.com/content/100-best-corporate-citizens

Deming, W. Edwards. 1982. *Out of the Crisis*. Cambridge, MA: The MIT Press.

Dow Jones Sustainability Indexes (DJSI) and SAM. 2010. *Corporate Sustainability* (retrieved October 5, 2010). www.sustainability-index.com/07_htmle/sustainability/corpsustainability.html

Dréo, Johann. 2006/2007. *Corporate Social Responsibility* (retrieved October 23, 2010). www.en.wikipedia.org/wiki/File:Sustainable_development.svg

Environmental Protection Agency (EPA). 1970. *National Environmental Policy Act of 1970 (NEPA)* (retrieved November 19, 2010) www.epa.gov/compliance/nepa

_____. 2007. *Strengthening Federal Environmental, Energy and Transportation Management* (retrieved November 18, 2010). www.epa.gov/oaintrtn/practices/eo13424.htm

_____. 2010a. *Fuel Economy: Data & Testing/Fuel Economy* (retrieved October 4, 2010). www.epa.gov/fuel economy/data.htm

_____. 2010b. *Fuel Economy: EPA's Fuel Economy Programs* (retrieved October 1, 2010). www.epa.gov/fuel economy/420f09067.htm

_____. 2010c. *Fuel and Fuel Additives/Renewable Fuel Standard (RFS)* (retrieved October 1, 2010). www.epa.gov/otaq/fuels/renewablefuels/

_____. 2010d. *Green Suppliers Network: E3: Economy, Energy and Environment* (retrieved October 29, 2010). www.epa.gov/greensuppliers/e3.html

_____. 2010e. *Greening EPA: Green Buildings* (retrieved November 4, 2010). www.epa.gov/oaintrnt/projects/

_____. 2010f. *Sustainability: Basic Information: What Is Sustainability?* (retrieved September 30, 2010). www.epa.gov/sustainability/basicinfo.htm

_____. 2010g. *Transportation and Climate: Regulations & Standards* (retrieved November 11, 2010). www.epa.gov/otaq/climate/regulations.htm

European Commission (EU), Directorate for Environment. 2010. *Emission Trading System (EU ETS)* (retrieved November 7, 2011). ec.europa.eu/environment/clima/emission/index_en.htm

Federal Energy Management Program. 2007. Executive Order 13423, "Strengthening Federal Environmental, Energy and Transportation Management" (retrieved November 15, 2010). www.edocket.access.gpo.gov/2007/pdf/07-374.pdf

Global Reporting Initiative (GRI). 2007. *About GRI* (retrieved October 23, 2010). www.globalreporting.org/AboutGRI/

Greenbuild International Conference and Expo. 2010. (retrieved November 22, 2010). www.greenbuild expo.org/expo/internationalexpo.asp

International Organization for Standardization (ISO). 2010. ISO/FDIS 26000:2010(E), *Guidance on Social Responsibility*. Geneva, Switzerland: ISO.

Knott, M. Personal Correspondence "Summary extracted from Lines 1671 through 1705 of ISO/FDIS 26000:2010(E)" by Michael G. Knott, CSP, member of the Industry Group for U.S. TAG TO ISO/TC SR 26000. Email dated September 5, 2010.

Manuele, F. A. 2003. *On the Practice of Safety*. 3d ed. Hoboken, NJ: John Wiley & Sons.

MSCI Research. 2010. *MSCI USA Broad ESG Index* (retrieved October 8, 2010). www.mscibarra.com/ products/indices/thematic_and_strategy/esg_indices/ MSCI_USA_Broad_ESG_Index_Methodology_Jul10.pdf

National Institute for Occupational Health and Safety (NIOSH). 2004. NIOSH Publication #2004-135, *How to Evaluate Safety and Health Changes in the Workplace*. Cincinnati, OH: NIOSH.

Nestle, USA. 2009. *Creating Shared Value in the United States* (accessed November 15, 2011). www.nestleusa.com/ Creating_Shared_Value/~/Media/Files/PDFs/NUS ACS/Brochure.asx

Noer, Michael, David M. Ewalt, and Tara Weiss. 2008. "Corporate Social Responsibility: Can Companies Save the World? Should They Try?" *Forbes Magazine* (retrieved October 23, 2010). www.forbes.com/2008/ 10/16/corporate-social-responsibility-corprespons08- lead-cx_mn_de_tw_1016csr_land.html

Occupational Safety and Health Administration (OSHA). 1989. *Safety and Health Program Management Guidelines; Issuance of Voluntary Guidelines*. Federal Register Notice 54:3904-3916.

_____. 1998 (revised). OSHA 2254, *Training Requirements in OSHA Standards and Training Guidelines*. Washington, D.C.: OSHA.

_____. 2002 (revised). OSHA 3071, *Job Hazard Analysis*. Washington, D.C.: OSHA.

_____. 2009. *OSHA Fact Sheet: Voluntary Protection Programs* (retrieved November 15, 2010). www.osha. gov/OshDoc/data_General_Facts/factsheet-vpp.pdf

_____. n.d. *Safety and Health Management System E-tool* (retrieved November 15, 2010). www.osha.gov/SLTC/ etools/safetyhealth/index.html

Oregon Department of Administrative Services (DAS). 2009. *Sustainable Procurement and Internal Operations* (retrieved September 30, 2010). www.oregon.gov/ DAS/OP/docs/policy/107-011-140.pdf?ga=t

Oregon OSHA (OR-OSHA). 2010. "Occupational Safety and Health Safety Committee Evaluation Checklist." www.cbs.state.or.us/external/osha/pdf/pubs/forms/ eval_checklist.doc)

Pejtersen, J. H. et al. 2010. "The Second Version of the Copenhagen Psychosocial Questionnaire." *Scand J Public Health* 2010 38: 8 (retrieved October 10, 2010). www.sjp.sagepub.com/content/38/3_suppl/8

Petersen, Dan. 2003. *Techniques of Safety Management: A Systems Approach*. Des Plaines, IL: American Society of Safety Engineers.

Sustainable Jersey. n.d. *Certification Benefits* (retrieved October 1, 2010). www.sustainablejersey.com/ about.php

_____. n.d.. *History and Mission* (retrieved October 1, 2010). www.sustainablejersey.com/about.php

United Nations Framework Convention on Climate Change (UNFCCC). 2010a. *Emissions Trading* (retrieved October 8, 2010). www.unfccc.int/kyoto_ protocol/mechanisms/emissions_trading/items/ 2731.php

_____. 2010b. *Kyoto Protocol* (retrieved October 8, 2010). www.unfccc.int/kyoto_protocol/items/2830.php

_____. 2010c. *Copenhagen Accord* (retrieved November 23, 2010). www.unfccc.int/home.items/5262.php

United Nations World Commission on Environment and Development (UN WCED) (also known as the Brundtland Commission). 1987. *Our Common Future: Report of the World Commission on Environment and Development* (retrieved November 18, 2010). www.un-documents.net/wced_ocf.htm

U.S. Green Building Council. 2010a. *About USGBC* (retrieved October 5, 2010). www.usgbc.org/Display Page.aspx?CMSPageID=124

_____. 2010b. *What LEED Is: LEED Rating System* (retrieved October 5, 2010). www.usgbc.org/Display Page.aspx?CMSPageID=222

_____. 2010c. *LEED AP BD+C* (retrieved October 3, 2010). www.usgbc.org/DisplayPage.aspx?CMSPage ID=2192

_____. 2010d. *LEED Green Associate* (retrieved November 22, 2010). www.usgbc.org/DisplayPage.asp? CMSPageID=2191

_____. 2010e. "The LEED Green Building Program at a Glance" (fact sheet) (retrieved October 3, 2010). www.usgbc.org/DisplayPage.aspx?CMSPageID=97

_____. 2010f. *LEED Project Certifications* (retrieved November 22, 2010). www.usgbc.org/DisplayPage. asp?CMSPage=2191

_____. 2010g. *LEED Rating Systems* (retrieved November 22, 2010). www.usgbc.org/DisplayPage/aspx?CMS PageID=222

Taubitz, Michael A. 2010. *Lean, Green & Safe: Integrating Safety into the Leans, Green and Sustainability Movement* (Appendix) (retrieved November 22, 2010). www.asse.org/professionalsafety/docs/Lean- Taubitz_0510.pdf

Washington Department of Ecology (ECY). 2010. *Sustainability Laws and Executive Orders* (retrieved September 30, 2010). www.ecy.wa.gov/sustainability/ exeorders.html

White House. 1981. "Annual Report of the Council on Environmental Quality (CEQ)" (accessed December 21, 2011). www.slideshare.net/whitehouse/august- 1981-the-12th-annual-report-of-the-council-on- environmental-quality

ADDITIONAL RESOURCES

Manuele, F. A. 2005. "Risk Assessment & Hierarchies of Control" *Professional Safety* 50(5):33-39.

Muller, S, and Braun, C. 1998. *Safety Culture: A Reflection on Risk Awareness*. Zurich: Swiss Reinsurance Company.

Occupational Safety and Health Administration (OSHA). 2009. *Accident Prevention* (retrieved November 15, 2010). www.osha.gov/SLTC/accidentinvestigation/index.html

Telephone interview with Matthew Wasserman, Chair, Princeton Environmental Commission, October 4, 2010.

Value Based Management. 2010. *The Deming Cycle* (retrieved October 23, 2010). www.valuebased management.net/methods_demingcycle.html

Womack, J. P., and D. T. Jones. 2003. *Lean Thinking: Banish Waste and Create Wealth in Your Corporations*. 2d ed. Northampton, MA: Free Press.

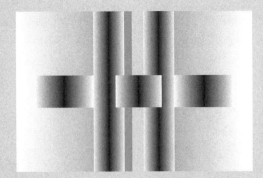

SECTION 1
MANAGEMENT
OF SAFETY
ENGINEERING WORK

Regulatory Issues

Applied Science and Engineering

General Safety Management

Managing a Safety Engineering Project

Global Issues

Cost Analysis and Budgeting

Benchmarking and Performance Criteria

Best Practices

LEARNING OBJECTIVES

- Be able to define safety engineering management.

- Understand the purpose and goal of safety engineering and management.

- Be aware of regulations applicable to workplaces: mandatory requirements, consensus standards, codes and standards (including international standards), best management practices adopted by private or public entities, occupational safety and health standards applicable to private industry as well as federal agencies (including environmental laws and regulations).

- Explain the two main functions of OSHA under the Occupational Safety and Health Act (OSH Act).

- Be aware of voluntary programs that help businesses and organizations to proactively attain and maintain safe work environments.

REGULATORY ISSUES

Anjan K. Majumder

THIS CHAPTER IS a summary of some of the regulations and voluntary and consensus standards associated with managing safety engineering work. It is not an exhaustive list, nor does it contain exact wording from the regulations. It is meant to inform the reader of some of the more important regulations and standards that guide safety engineering work and to provide the reader with a pathway to find this regulatory and consensus information. It is expected that once the reader determines the need to gather regulatory information, he or she will refer to the regulations and standards themselves. This chapter provides an informative background and summary upon which the reader can build a foundation of regulatory and consensus standards' knowledge.

SAFETY ENGINEERING AND MANAGEMENT

Safety engineering management is a part of the general management system. It is a combination of risk identification, risk mitigation, and balancing among levels of acceptable risk, cost, and availability of technology. Safety engineering management includes system safety, occupational safety in the workplace, and behavioral safety. It requires implementation of regulatory requirements, consensus standards, and best management practices in the policies and procedures of safety engineering management. The regulatory requirement is the mandatory part, while the level and extent of consensus standards or best management practices can vary according to company policies.

A goal of safety engineering management is the efficient implementation of safety, reliability, quality, and cost-effectiveness. Some compliance policies applicable to specific establishments may be more stringent than others, based on the requirements of a federal agency, state or local authority having jurisdiction (AHJ), or company policy. This chapter discusses government regulations as well as codes and standards that can become mandatory for a company, agency, or AHJ if their policy has been established that way. By the end of the chapter, the reader should be familiar with the laws, regulations, codes, and standards that might need to be applied in any workplace when implementing safety engineering management.

Requirements that may apply to safety engineering and management are of the following types:

1. Executive orders
2. *Code of Federal Regulations* (CFR)
3. Federal agency orders and standards
4. State and local regulations
5. Consensus standards
6. International Organization for Standardization (ISO) standards
7. Best management practices

Executive Orders

An *executive order* is a formal or authoritative proclamation issued by a member of the executive branch of government, usually the head of the branch. Most executive orders are issued by the president of the United States. For example, Executive Order 12196 of February 26, 1980, Occupational Safety and Health Programs for Federal Employees (Federal Register 1980), orders all heads of agencies to furnish to employees places and conditions of employment that are free from recognized hazards that are causing or are likely to cause death or serious physical harm. Executive Order 13148, of April 21, 2000, Part 4, Sec 401 (EPA 2000), states that each federal agency, within eighteen months of the date of that order, must conduct an agency-level environmental management system (EMS) self-assessment— based on the Code of Environmental Management Principles for Federal Agencies, which has been developed by the Environmental Protection Agency (EPA) or another appropriate EMS framework.

Executive orders are found in sequential editions of Title 3 of the CFR. Each executive order is signed by the president of the United States and received by the Office of the Federal Register. The National Archives and Records Administration (NARA) of the Office of the Federal Register publishes the *Federal Register*, an official daily publication containing rules, proposed rules, and any notices created by federal agencies and organizations, as well as executive orders and other presidential documents.

Code of Federal Regulations (CFR)

The CFR is an annual codification of general and permanent rules. It is divided into 50 titles representing the broad areas that are subject to federal regulation. Each title is divided into chapters that are assigned to agencies issuing regulations pertaining to that broad subject area. Each chapter is divided into parts, and each part is divided into sections. The CFR provides the official and complete text of agency regulations in one organized publication. Each volume of the CFR is updated once each calendar year and and is issued quarterly (for example, the volume containing titles 1–16 is issued on January 1, the volume containing titles 17–27 is issued on April 1, and so on). The CFR is available electronically (free of charge) as well as in paper publication (by full set subscription or individual copy purchase). It can be obtained from the superintendent of documents or at any federal depository library. Among the 50 titles, some of the following may be required to deal with issues of safety engineering and management in some work environments.

Title 10: Energy
Title 21: Food and Drugs
Title 23: Highways
Title 29: Labor
Title 40: Protection of Environment
Title 42: Public Health
Title 44: Emergency Management and Assistance
Title 49: Transportation

Federal Agency Orders and Standards

Apart from executive orders and federal regulations, federal agencies have their own orders and standards.

All federal agencies have developed orders and standards for their own agency, but some have orders or standards that are applicable to other industries or workplaces as well. For example, the Department of Energy (DOE) has orders and technical standards that are applicable to DOE facilities, but the Department of Transportation's (DOT) classifications and placards for dangerous goods are applicable to any company that transports items by air, water, rail, public road, or private vehicle that qualifies under DOT regulations. The following government agencies have safety and health regulations that may be applicable to safety engineering management in other workplaces:

- Department of Energy (DOE)
- Defense Nuclear Facilities Safety Board (DNFSB)
- Environmental Protection Agency (EPA)
- Department of Transportation (DOT)
- Occupational Safety and Health Administration (OSHA) under Department of Labor (DOL)
- Mine Safety and Health Administration (MSHA) under Department of Labor (DOL)
- Department of Defense (DOD)
- Nuclear Regulatory Commission (NRC)

Among the above, OSHA's mission to prevent work-related injuries, illnesses, and deaths is the driving force behind safety engineering and management for workplaces in the United States.

State and Local Regulations

Section 18 of the Occupational Safety and Health Act of 1970 encourages states to develop and operate their own job safety and health programs to establish safe work environments (OSHA 1970). However, states operating their own state safety and health programs under plans approved by the DOL cover most private-sector workers and are also required to extend their coverage to public-sector (state and local government) workers in the state.

OSHA approves and monitors the state plans. Currently 27 states and other jurisdictions operate approved state plans that cover both private-sector and state and local government employees. Five jurisdictions—Connecticut, Illinois, New Jersey, New York, and the Virgin Islands—cover public employees only.

In addition, the AHJ may use other standards, such as consensus standards (discussed below), as mandatory requirements. For example, many areas have adopted the ASME *Boiler and Pressure Vessel Code* as the mandatory requirement for boiler operations.

Consensus Standards

A *standard* is a practice or a product that is widely recognized or employed because it has been proven best by repeated or common use. A *consensus standard*, similarly, is a practice, procedure, technique, or product that has been widely accepted or applied in a particular area. Consensus standards are developed by technical or professional societies or by national or international standards-setting organizations for consensus agreement among representatives of various interested or affected individuals, companies, organizations, and countries.

Standards developed or adopted by voluntary consensus standards bodies, both domestic and international, are also a basis for safety engineering management. When they are adopted by an AHJ, they become mandatory. Some of these standards are also published in the *Federal Register* and the CFR through a process called *incorporation by reference*.

Incorporation by reference allows federal agencies to comply with the requirement to publish rules in the *Federal Register* by referring to materials already published elsewhere. The legal effect of incorporation by reference is that the material is treated as if it had been published in the *Federal Register* and the CFR. Incorporation by reference is used primarily to make privately developed technical standards federally enforceable. Only the mandatory provisions (i.e., provisions containing the word "shall" or other mandatory language) of standards incorporated by reference are adopted as standards under the Occupational Safety and Health Act (OSHA 1970).

Some commonly used consensus standards are those developed by the American National Standards Institute (ANSI), the National Fire Protection Association (NFPA), the Compressed Gas Association (CGA), the American Society of Mechanical Engineers (ASME), the Institute of Electrical and Electronics Engineers (IEEE), and the Underwriters Laboratory (UL).

International Organizations' Standards

The International Organization for Standardization (ISO) is an international standards-setting body that was founded on February 23, 1947. (*Note:* To eliminate different abbreviations due to the translation of "International Organization for Standardization" into various languages, the short form "ISO" is used universally.) It is a network of the national standards institutes of 159 countries, one member per country, with a central secretariat in Geneva, Switzerland, that coordinates the system. It provides worldwide industrial and commercial standards called ISO standards (ISO 2011).

ISO is a nongovernmental organization. Its members are not delegates of national governments. Many of its member institutes, however, are part of the governmental structure of their countries or are mandated by their governments. Other members have their roots in the private sector. Adoption of ISO standards is voluntary. As a nongovernmental organization, ISO has no legal authority to enforce their implementation, but companies adopting ISO standards help to make international standardization of products or services possible. Companies that adhere to ISO standards assure the quality and reliability of their products and services and also the safety of people and the environment. The most widely accepted standards are ISO 9000 and ISO 14000. ISO 9000 deals with quality management standards (ISO 2005) and ISO 14000 with environmental management standards (ISO 2004). The president of ISO, usually a recognized industry figure, is elected to a two-year term. The secretary general of ISO manages the operations. An ISO council forms the members that develop the proposals. ISO members make the decisions in an annual General Assembly. Detailed information about ISO may be obtained online at www.iso.org.

Other international organizations and foreign governments have rules and regulations that address environmental, safety, and health issues. Some are:

1. International Atomic Energy Agency (IAEA)
2. International Radiation Related Agencies
3. International Environmental Programs Information & Compliance Services
4. The Global Network for Environment & Technology

Best Management Practices

Best management practices are practices or techniques or a combination of practices, procedures, or controls that are *not* required by law or mandatory requirement but have proven to be useful to companies or organizations. Management implements best practices to provide a safe work environment or to safeguard people, property, and the environment. Adopting these policies, procedures, or techniques is considered as adopting best management practices.

The primary elements of the above-mentioned requirements and practices can be summarized in four groups:

1. OSHA program-management regulations
2. OSHA cooperative programs
3. ISO standards
4. EPA program-management regulations

OSHA Program-Management Regulations

Congress created the Occupational Safety and Health Act of 1970 (OSH Act) to prevent work-related injuries, illnesses, and deaths in workplaces and to assign employers the responsibility of providing a safe work environment for their employees. The act applies to employers and their employees in all states, the District of Columbia, Puerto Rico, and all other territories under the federal government. Self-employed persons, family farms that employ family members, workplaces owned and regulated by federal agencies operated under other federal statutes, and state and local governments with their own health and safety programs are not covered by this act. President Richard M. Nixon signed the OSH Act on December 29, 1970, and it became effective in April 1971. It was coauthored by Senator Harrison A. Williams (Dem.-NJ) and Congressman William Steiger (Rep.-WI), so it is also called the Williams-Steiger Act (OSHA 1970).

Before its enactment in the United States, safety and health laws had primarily been left up to the states. Section 5 of the OSH Act mandates the duties of employers and employees and thus sets the main goal of safety engineering management as providing a safe working environment. One of the several functions of the Department of Labor is to improve the work environment of all workplaces in the Unites States. OSHA, which is under the Department of Labor, fulfills that function by the power of the OSH Act of 1970. OSHA sets and enforces standards by providing education, consultation, and partnership for continual improvement in workplaces. OSHA is directed by an assistant secretary of labor who reports to the secretary of labor. The act assigns OSHA two main functions: (1) setting workplace standards, and (2) conducting workplace inspections to ensure that employers provide employees with a safe and healthful workplace and that they comply with occupational safety and health standards. OSHA standards are published in the CFR, Title 29. Federal occupational safety and health standards cover general industry, construction, maritime operations (shipyards, marine terminals, longshoring), and agriculture.

OSHA maintains 29 CFR 1910, Occupational Safety and Health Standards for General Industry, and 29 CFR 1926, Safety and Health Regulations for Construction, and enforces them to ensure the safety and health of the workforces in all workplaces except those that are in states with approved state plans.

A *state plan* is an occupational safety and health program developed by a state that has received the ultimate accreditation from OSHA. The job safety and health standards in state programs have to be "at least as effective as" federal standards. Section 18 of the OSH Act of 1970 encourages states to develop their own programs. Details regarding the process for creating a state plan are available online at www.osha.gov.

All federal agencies of the executive branch of the U.S. government conform to Executive Order 12196 and 29 CFR 1960, Basic Program Elements for Federal Employees OSHA. Section 19 of the act has special provisions for federal employees' safe working conditions. Executive Order 12196 prescribes additional responsibilities for the heads of agencies, the secretary, and the general services administrator (Federal Register 1980). As a requirement, the secretary of labor issues basic program elements for the heads of the agencies according to which they must operate their safety and health programs. These are called Basic Program Elements for Federal Employees OSHA and are available in Title 29, Chapter XVII, Part 1960.

Under the Department of Labor, the Mine Safety and Health Administration (MSHA) ensures mine safety for coal and other mines. Every operator of such a mine and every miner is required to follow the provisions of the Federal Mine Safety and Health Act of 1977. MSHA enforces the mandatory safety and health standards that eliminate accidents and reduce the frequency and severity of accidents or near-misses (MSHA 1977).

Under the heading of OSHA program-management regulations, AHJs, like companies or federal agencies, can include all or some of the federal agency orders, best management practices, and consensus standards such as those created by ASME, ANSI, NFPA, and CGA in addition to the OSHA regulations mentioned above as mandatory requirements in their safety engineering and management policies.

Cooperative Programs

Section 2(b)(1) of the OSH Act encourages employers and employees to reduce the number of occupational safety and health hazards at their places of employment. It also stimulates employers and employees to institute new programs and to perfect existing programs that provide safe and healthful working conditions. Following this section, OSHA created cooperative programs through which businesses and organizations can work with the agency to improve safety and health in workplaces. These initiatives include alliance programs, on-site consultations, Safety and Health Achievement Recognition Programs (SHARP), Voluntary Protection Programs (VPP), and strategic partnerships (OSHA 2011a).

Alliance Program

Alliance programs provide professional and labor organizations, employers, and other groups with tools that help them work together to build relationships with the agency, utilize resources, establish a network with other organizations with the same goal, and obtain recognition for using proactive approaches toward safety and health.

Through alliance programs, OSHA offers help in the areas of training, education, and communication as well as sharing of safety- and health-related information. It helps with the formation of forums and groups to improve workplace safety and health. It addresses occupational trends, emerging issues, and the agency's priorities. In doing so, it emphasizes OSHA's strategic areas to the public by working with businesses, trade and professional organizations, and groups that are involved with safety and health. In an alliance program, OSHA and the participating organization sign a formal document with goals. This program does not relieve the participant organization from OSHA programmed inspections (OSHA 2011b).

On-site Consultation Program

OSHA's On-site Consultation Program primarily helps small businesses, but other businesses may use this program as well. The program consists of free consultation to help identify workplace hazards and improve safety and health. By participating in this program, businesses may even qualify for a one-year exemption from routine OSHA inspections. Most importantly, OSHA will not issue any citation or penalty if hazards are identified and addressed as part of this program. Trained professionals will help to identify hazards and suggest mitigation on site, but the name and any other information provided by the organization is kept confidential. The only commitment requested is for organizations to correct the deficiencies in a timely manner (OSHA 2011c).

Safety and Health Achievement Recognition Program (SHARP)

The Safety and Health Achievement Recognition Program (SHARP) provides useful incentives to employers who have used OSHA's On-site Consultation Program. Employers may seek recognition for their safety and health programs and become models among their peers. SHARP allows workplaces to be exempt from OSHA inspections during the period of SHARP certification. To get into the SHARP program, first an on-site OSHA consultation request has to be made. During this consultation, all hazards are identified and mitigated, as suggested by OSHA professionals. A safety and health program involving employees must be implemented to address at least OSHA's 1989 Safety and Health Program Management Guidelines. Also, the days away, restricted, or transferred (DART) rate and total recordable case (TRC) rate must be below the national average, and the company has to agree to notify the state Consultation Project Office before making any change in working conditions or introducing a new hazard (OSHA 2011c).

OSHA Strategic Partnership Program (OSPP)

The OSHA Strategic Partnership Program (OSPP) partners companies with OSHA to address specific safety and health issues. This partnership can be with one or more organizations, employees, and employee representatives. Instead of the usual role as the enforcer of safety and health standards, here OSHA serves as a technical resource and facilitator to employers, employees, unions, trade associations, state on-site consultation projects, and other interested parties. It helps them to use its resources to train employees and develop site-specific safety and health management systems. The OSHA Strategic Partnership (OSPP) is also a voluntary program. Each partnership prepares its own formal agreement with specific goals, strategies, and performance measures. This program is available to private as well as government agencies (OSHA 2011d).

Voluntary Protection Program (VPP)

The Voluntary Protection Program (VPP) is the most important program in this category. This program promotes safety and health excellence through cooperative efforts among employees, management, unions, and OSHA. VPP has performance-based criteria, and any safety and health system of a workplace may qualify for one of three programs: Star, Merit, or Star Demonstration. Interested sites must apply. OSHA reviews the application and then conducts a thorough on-site evaluation of the safety and health program and its implementation. As a VPP-certified site, the establishment will not receive OSHA compliance inspections unless it fails to maintain its VPP status or other significant safety and health issues arise.

Along with this benefit, statistical evidence shows fewer injuries and illnesses for organizations that have implemented the program. The success is impressive: reductions in injuries and illnesses begin when the site commits to the VPP approach to safety and health management and in the middle of application process.

Fewer injuries and illnesses also mean greater profits as workers' compensation premiums and other costs are reduced. The reductions in injuries and illnesses are achieved by the principles of VPP: management leadership, employee involvement, work-site analysis, hazard prevention and control, and safety and health training (OSHA 2011a).

OSHA Challenge Program

Any employee, company, or government agency can take a proactive approach toward going through the OSHA Challenge Program to prepare for the Voluntary Protection Program's Star, Merit, or Star Demonstration status. The OSHA Challenge Program is applicable for general industry as well as construction work activities. There are three stages that a participant has to go through in this program, and an online road map guides the company to improve its safety and health program.

Each participant company has to be associated with an administrator of this program. Some companies may qualify to be an administrator for their own facilities, but administrators may not be private safety or health consultants or for-profit associations. The OSHA Challenge Program will be in operation for at least two years; at that time, OSHA will evaluate the participant's safety and health program. Based on that evaluation, the participant will graduate, continue, or terminate the program. The program benefits a participant company by substantially improving its safety and health program (OSHA 2011e).

International Organization for Standardization (ISO) Standards

ISO produces voluntary standards that are considered useful to industrial and business organizations of all types, to governments and other regulatory bodies, to the suppliers and customers of products and services in both public and private sectors, and, ultimately, to people in general in their roles as consumers and end users. ISO standards contribute to making the development, manufacturing, and supplying of products and services more efficient, safer, and cleaner. They make trade between countries easier and fairer. They provide governments with a technical base for health, safety, and environmental legislation, which is why they are used in safety engineering and management along with other requirements. ISO 9000 and ISO 14000 are international references for quality management and environmental management, respectively. Industries and businesses in many countries are making these standards mandatory, along with regulations and laws in the safety engineering and management arena, to achieve consistency in quality, safety, and environmental areas.

EPA Program-Management Regulations

More than a dozen major statutes or laws form the legal basis for the programs of the Environmental Protection Agency (EPA).

National Environmental Policy Act of 1969 (NEPA)

The purpose of this act is to prevent or eliminate damage to the environment and biosphere by considering the impact of any proposed action and reasonable alternatives. The act requires federal agencies to include the understanding of ecological systems and natural resources in their decision-making process and to establish the Council on Environmental Quality (CEQ). Federal agencies must prepare detailed reports, known as environmental impact statements (EISs). The Environmental Protection Agency (EPA) confirms that it complies with NEPA and reviews and provides comments on EISs prepared by other federal agencies. EPA also maintains a national filing system for all EISs. Title II of NEPA asks the Council on Environmental Quality (CEQ) to gather environmental quality information, evaluate federal programs according to Title I of NEPA, develop and promote national policies, and conduct studies and research on ecosystems and environmental quality (EPA 2011a).

The Clean Air Act of 1970 (CAA), Amended in 1990

The Clean Air Act is a comprehensive federal law that regulates air emissions from area, stationary, and mobile sources. This law authorizes the EPA to establish National Ambient Air Quality Standards (NAAQS) to protect public health and the environment. The act prevents significant deterioration of air quality in the country by setting limits on how much of a pollutant can be in the air anywhere in the United States. States must develop state implementation plans (SIPs), which must be at least as stringent as the CAA, and the EPA must approve each SIP after review. The 1990 CAA amendments provide control over interstate air pollution, international air pollution that originates in Mexico and Canada and drifts into the United States, and pollution that travels from the United States to Mexico and Canada. It also has a permit program and gives authority to the EPA for enforcement of the law. The details of the act are in 40 CFR Parts 50–99 (EPA 2011b).

Federal Insecticide, Fungicide and Rodenticide Act of 1972 (FIFRA)

The Federal Insecticide, Fungicide and Rodenticide Act (FIFRA) provides federal control of the distribution, sale, and use of pesticides. All pesticides used in the entire country must be registered by the EPA. They must be properly labeled and used according to the specifications. Under FIFRA, the EPA was given authority to study the consequences of pesticide usage and to require users (farmers, utility companies, and others) to register when purchasing pesticides to protect applicators and consumers of pesticides and insecticides and also to protect the environment. Users, if applying the regulated material, also must take examinations for

certification as pesticide applicators. The details of the act are available in 40 CFR Parts 150–189 (EPA 2011c).

The Endangered Species Act of 1973 (ESA)

The Endangered Species Act (ESA) provides a program for the conservation of threatened and endangered plants and animals and the habitats in which they are found by conserving their ecosystems. The U.S. Fish and Wildlife Service of the Department of Interior maintains a list of 632 endangered species and 190 threatened species. The details are available in 50 CFR Part 17 (EPA 2011d).

The Safe Drinking Water Act of 1974 (SDWA), Amended in 1986 and 1996

The Safe Drinking Water Act (SDWA) authorizes the EPA to establish safe standards of purity for all water actually or potentially designed for drinking use from aboveground and underground sources. The SDWA authorizes EPA to create combined federal, state, and tribal systems to comply with the standard. It requires all owners or operators of public water systems to comply with primary (health-related) standards. State governments, which assume this power from the EPA, also encourage the attainment of secondary standards that are nuisance-related. The amendments in 1986 and 1996 extended the law to cover protection at the source through the control of underground injection of liquid waste, operator training, and information for the public.

The EPA developed two water-quality standards—primary and secondary. The primary standard is legally enforceable and applies to public water systems. It protects drinking water quality by limiting the levels of specific contaminants that can adversely affect public health and are known or anticipated to occur in water. The primary standard lists a maximum containment level (MCL)—the amount of a contaminant allowed in water delivered to a user of any public water system—or a treatment technique (TT), a procedure or level of technological performance set when there is no reliable method to measure a contaminant at very low levels.

Secondary standards are nonenforceable guidelines regarding contaminants that may cause cosmetic effects (such as skin or tooth discoloration) or aesthetic effects (such as changes in taste, odor, or color) in drinking water. The EPA recommends secondary standards to water systems but does not require systems to comply. However, states may choose to adopt them as enforceable standards.

Secondary standards are based on nonenforceable maximum containment-level goals (MCLGs). The MCLG of a drinking water contaminant is the level below which there is no known or expected health risk. MCLGs allow for a margin of safety. They are based on the risks of exposure to infants, the elderly, and persons with compromised immune systems. Drinking water standards apply to public water systems (PWSs) that provide water for human consumption through at least fifteen service connections or that regularly serve at least 25 individuals. Public water systems include municipal water companies, homeowner associations, businesses, campgrounds, schools, and shopping malls.

The details of this act are available in 40 CFR Parts 141–149 (EPA 2011e).

The Resource Conservation and Recovery Act of 1976 (RCRA)

The Resource Conservation and Recovery Act (RCRA), also known as the "cradle to grave" rule, gives the EPA the authority to control hazardous waste from its generation through transportation, treatment, storage, and ultimately disposal. The RCRA also sets forth a framework for the management of nonhazardous wastes. The goal of this act is to protect people and the environment from the harmful effects of disposed waste; to clean up leaked, spilled, or improperly stored waste; and to advocate reuse, reduction, and recycling.

The 1986 amendments to the RCRA enable the EPA to address environmental problems that could result from underground tanks storing petroleum and other hazardous substances. The RCRA focuses only on active and future facilities and does not address abandoned or historical sites. The details of this act are available in 40 CFR Parts 261–299 (EPA 2011f).

The Toxic Substances Control Act of 1976 (TSCA)

The Toxic Substances Control Act (TSCA) gives the EPA broad authority to regulate the manufacture, use, distribution in commerce, and disposal of chemical substances. It requires the EPA to review the health and environmental effects of existing chemical substances and all new chemicals before they are manufactured for commercial purposes and to control some substances that have been identified as potentially high risks to the public. The TSCA is a federally managed law and is not delegated to states. It is overseen by the EPA Office of Pollution Prevention and Toxics (OPPT). The TSCA became law on October 11, 1976, but Congress later added more titles. The original part remained as Title I, Control of Hazardous Substances and Asbestos; Hazard Emergency Response was added as Title II; Indoor Air Radon Abatement was added as Title III; and Lead-Based Paint Exposure became Title IV (EPA 2011g).

The Clean Water Act of 1977 (CWA)

This is officially the federal Water Pollution Control Act, but it is commonly known as the Clean Water Act (CWA). It regulates both direct and indirect discharges of water. The goal of this act is to "restore and maintain the chemical, physical, and biological integrity of the nation's waters by preventing point and nonpoint sources, providing assistance to publicly owned treatment works (POTWs) for the improvement of wastewater treatment, and maintaining the integrity of wetlands." The act employs a variety of regulatory and nonregulatory tools to reduce direct pollutant discharges into waterways, finance municipal wastewater treatment facilities, and manage polluted runoff. It does not deal directly with groundwater or with water quantity issues. The details of this act are available in 40 CFR, Parts 100–149 (EPA 2011h).

Comprehensive Environmental Response, Compensation, and Liability Act of 1980 (CERCLA)

The Comprehensive Environmental Response, Compensation, and Liability Act (CERCLA), commonly known as Superfund,

1. establishes prohibitions and requirements concerning closed and abandoned hazardous waste sites
2. provides for liability of persons responsible for releases of hazardous waste at these sites

3. establishes a trust fund to provide for clean up when no responsible party can be identified.

The law authorizes the EPA to enforce clean up by the responsible parties or to force responsible parties to reimburse the Superfund for clean up. The EPA implements the act in all 50 states and U.S. territories. State environmental protection or waste management agencies coordinate all Superfund site identification, monitoring, and response activities (EPA 2011i).

The Emergency Planning & Community Right to Know Act of 1986 (EPCRA)

After two accidents related to chemicals, one in Bhopal, India, (1984) and the other in Institute, West Virginia, (1985), Congress enacted the Emergency Planning & Community Right to Know Act (EPCRA) of 1986 to protect communities. It contains requirements regarding emergency planning programs, emergency release notification, community right-to-know reporting, and toxic chemical release reporting.

EPCRA requires each state to appoint a state emergency response commission (SERC). The SERCs are required to divide their states into emergency planning districts and to name a local emergency planning committee (LEPC) for each district. To ensure that all necessary elements of the planning process are covered, committee members include health officials, government and media representatives, community groups, industrial facilities, fire fighters, and emergency managers. This law helps local communities protect public health, safety, and the environment from chemical hazards. It is also known as SARA, Title III, and is commonly referred to as the Community Right to Know law. Details of the act are available in 40 CFR, Part 355 (EPA 2011j).

Federal Food, Drug, and Cosmetic Act (FFDCA)

FFDCA is the basic authority intended to ensure that:

- foods are safe to eat and produced under sanitary conditions
- drugs and devices are safe and effective for their intended uses
- cosmetics are safe and made from appropriate ingredients

- all labeling and packaging is truthful, informative, and not deceptive

The Food and Drug Administration (FDA) is primarily responsible for enforcing the FFDCA, although the USDA also has some enforcement responsibility. The EPA establishes limits for concentrations of pesticide residues on food under this act. This act is known for naming certified food color additives like Brilliant Blue FCF (FD&C Blue No. 1), Erythrosine (FD&C Red No. 3), and so on (EPA 2011k).

The Superfund Amendments and Reauthorization Act of 1986 (SARA)

The Superfund Amendments and Reauthorization Act (SARA) amended the Comprehensive Environmental Response, Compensation, and Liability Act (CERCLA) on October 17, 1986.

This act has several key features:

- It increases the size of the Superfund.
- It expands the response authority of the EPA.
- It strengthens enforcement activities at Superfund sites.
- It broadens the law to include federal facilities.
- It adds a citizen suit provision.
- It allows the EPA to condemn property.
- It provides deadlines for response action.

Also, SARA requires the EPA to revise the Hazard Ranking System (HRS) to ensure that it accurately assesses the relative degree of risk to human health and to the environment posed by hazardous waste sites and disposal facilities.

In addition, SARA authorizes states to participate in clean-up processes, from initial site assessment to selecting and carrying out the remedial action and negotiating with responsible parties. To encourage states to establish new hazardous waste treatment and disposal facilities, SARA requires that states assure that they will have adequate disposal capacity for all hazardous wastes expected to be generated within the state for the next twenty years. This requirement went into effect in November 1989 (EPA 2011l).

The Pollution Prevention Act of 1990 (PPA)

The Pollution Prevention Act (PPA) requires that:

- pollution should be prevented or reduced at the source whenever feasible
- pollution that cannot be prevented should be recycled in an environmentally safe manner whenever feasible
- pollution that cannot be prevented or recycled should be treated in an environmentally safe manner whenever feasible
- disposal or other release of pollution into the environment should be used only as a last resort and conducted in an environmentally safe manner (EPA 2011m)

The Oil Pollution Act of 1990 (OPA)

The Oil Pollution Act became a law in August 1990. It provides the EPA the ability to prevent and respond to catastrophic oil spills. A trust fund financed by a tax on oil is available to clean up spills when the responsible party is incapable of doing so or unwilling to do so. The federal government directs response efforts for certain types of spills. Area committees are formed of federal, state, and local government officials, and the committees develop site-specific area contingency plans. Certain oil storage facilities and vessels that may cause serious damage to the environment are required to submit their own plans to the federal government giving details of how they will respond to large discharges. Details are available in 33 U.S.C. 2701–2761 (EPA 2011n).

Chemical Safety Information, Site Security and Fuels Regulatory Relief Act (CSISSFRRA), January 6, 1999

This is an amendment to Section 112(r) of the Clean Air Act.

Under section 112(r), facilities handling large quantities of extremely hazardous chemicals are required to include information about handling the chemicals in a risk management plan (RMP) submitted to the EPA. As required by CSISSFRRA, this provides members of the public and government officials with access to that information in ways designed to minimize the likelihood of accidental releases, the risk to national security associated with posting the information on the Internet, and the likelihood of harm to public health and welfare (EPA 2011o).

There are several other laws in the environmental safety area, such as the Lead-Based Paint Poisoning Prevention Act, 1971; the Hazardous Materials Transportation Act, 1975; and the Asbestos Hazard Emergency Response Act, 1986.

CONCLUSION

The regulatory requirements applicable to the management of safety engineering work depend on the scope of the work, identification of the hazards associated with the scope of the work, the applicable hazard control and mitigation process, and the location and responsibility/ownership of the process, project, or facility. Location and ownership will be determining factors with regard to which rules, regulations, codes, or standards are applicable for that process, project, or facility. Depending on the level of acceptable risk and the level of protection set by the management, the above-mentioned requirements may be incorporated into the appropriate policies and procedures of a company or agency using a process that balances risk, cost, and availability of technology.

In the author's opinion, for the management of any safety engineering work, six elements should be considered:

1. development of strategy and policy
2. implementation of procedures, including roles and responsibilities
3. identification of controls and requirements according to the scope of work
4. training
5. audits and inspections
6. continual improvement based on feedback and lessons learned from audits and inspections

The following are steps organizations may consider adopting in order to establish necessary controls and requirements for managing safety engineering work:

1. Identify the total scope of work. This will provide information about the laws and regulations that must be applied. For example, if the scope of work includes environmental or waste management work, identify which environmental laws and regulations are applicable.

2. Identify the location of the work. This will define whether it falls under federal agency, private industry, state, or local authority.

3. Identify the authority having jurisdiction (AHJ). This is over and above what is identified in the previous step. For example, an electrical safety committee set up by any one company's management is the AHJ that will decide whether the company will adopt NFPA 70E *Standard for Electrical Safety in the Workplace* as mandatory.

4. Ascertain whether federal OSHA or a state plan will apply. This will be based on the ownership of the workplace.

5. Determine whether work falls under operations and maintenance or construction and then decide whether 29 CFR 1910, General Industry, or 29 CFR 1926, Construction, or both, apply. This decision is based on the type and scope of work.

6. Decide which environmental law shall apply. This is based on the work involved.

7. Ascertain the acceptable risk level using probability and consequence as the basis of risk assessment. This will depend on management policy.

8. Identify which consensus standards and best management practices should be adopted. This depends on management policy.

9. Review whether any specific federal agency orders, such as DOT orders, are applicable.

10. Determine whether ISO standards must be applied.

REFERENCES

Centers for Disease Control (CDC) (last accessed on November 21, 2006). www.cdc.gov/niosh/homepage.html

Environmental Protection Agency (EPA). 2000. Executive Order 13148, *Greening the Government Through Leadership in Environmental Management* (accessed October 18, 2011). www.epa.gov/epa/pubs/eo13148.pdf

_____. 2011a. *National Environmental Policy Act* (accessed October 21, 2011). www.epa.gov/compliance/nepa

_____. 2011b. *Summary of the Clean Air Act* (Accessed October 21, 2011). www.epa.gov/lawsregs/laws/caa.html

_____. 2011c. *Summary of the Federal Insecticide, Fungicide, and Rodenticide Act* (accessed October 21. 2011). www.epa.gov/lawsregs/laws/fifra.html

_____. 2011d. *Summary of the Endangered Species Act* (accessed October 21, 2011). www.epa.gov/lawsregs/laws/esa.html

_____. 2011e. *Summary of the Safe Drinking Water Act* (accessed October 21, 2011). www.epa.gov/lawsregs/laws/sdwa.html

_____. 2011f. *Summary of the Resource Conservation and Recovery Act* (accessed October 21. 2011). www.epa.gov/lawsregs/laws/rcra.html

_____. 2011g. *Summary of the Toxic Substances Act* (accessed October 21, 2011). www.epa.gov/lawsregs/laws/tsca.html

_____. 2011h. *Summary of the Clean Water Act* (accessed October 21, 2011). www.epa.gov/lawsregs/laws/cwa.html

_____. 2011i. *Summary of the Comprehensive Environmental Response, Compensation and Liability Act* (accessed October 21.2011). www.epa.gov/lawsregs/laws/cercla.html

_____. 2011j. *Summary of the Emergency Planning and Community Right-to-Know Act* (accessed October 21, 2011). www.epa.gov/lawsregs/laws/epcra.html

_____. 2001k. *Summary of the Federal Food, Drug and Cosmetic Act* (accessed October 21, 2011). www.epa.gov/lawsregs/laws/ffdca.html

_____. 2011l. *SARA Overview* (accessed October 21, 2011). www.epa.gov/superfund/policy/sara.html

_____. 2011m. *Summary of the Pollution Prevention Act* (accessed October 21, 2011). www.epa.gov/lawsregs/laws/ppa.html

_____. 2011n. *Summary of the Oil Pollution Act* (accessed October 21. 2011). www.epa.gov/lawsregs/laws/opa.html

_____. 2011o. *Summary of the Chemical Safety Information, Site Security, and Fuels Regulatory Relief Act* (accessed October 21, 2011). www.epa.gov/lawsregs/laws/csissfrra.html

Federal Register. 1980. Executive Order 12196, *Occupational Safety and Health Programs for Federal Employees* (accessed October 18, 2011). www.archives.gov/federal-register/codification/executive-order/12196.htm

International Organization for Standardization (ISO). 2004. ISO 14001-2004, *Environmental Management—Environ-*

mental Communication—Guidelines and Examples (accessed October 17, 2011). www.iso.org/iso/iso_14000_essentials

_____. 2005. ISO 9000-2005, *Quality Management Systems--Fundamentals and Vocabulary* (accessed October 17, 2011). www.iso.org/iso/iso_9000_essentials

_____. 2011. *About ISO* (accessed October 18, 2011). www.iso.org

Mine Safety and Health Administration (MSHA). *MSHA Statutory Functions* (accessed October 21, 2011). www.msha.gov/MSHAINFO/MSHAINF1.HTM

Occupational Safety and Health Administration (OSHA). 1970. *Occupational Safety and Health Act* (accessed October 17, 2011). www.osha.gov/pls/oshaweb/owasrch.search_form?p_doc_type=oshact

_____. 2011a. *The OSHA Alliance Program* (accessed October 17, 2011). www.osha.gov/dcsp/alliances/whatis.html

_____. 2011b *OSHA Challenge: A Roadmap to Safety and Excellence* (accessed October 17, 2011). www.osha.gov/dcsp/vpp/challenge.html

_____. 2011c. *On-Site Consultation Program: Safety and Health Achievement Recognition Program (SHARP)* (accessed October 17, 2011). www.osha.gov/dcsp/sharp.index.html

_____. 2011d. *OSHA Strategic Partnership Program* (accessed October 17, 2011). www.osha.gov/dcsp/partnerships.index.html

_____. 2011e. *Voluntary Protection Program* (accessed October 17, 2011). www.osha.gov/dcsp/vpp/index.html

APPENDIX: ADDITIONAL RESOURCES

Chemical Safety Information, Site Security and Fuels Regulatory Relief Act of 1999 (CSISSFRRA), 42 U.S.C. Section 7410 et seq. (accessed October 20, 2011). www.dotcr.ost.dot.gov/documents/ycr/PL106-40.pdf

Clean Air Act of 1990 (CAA), 42 U.S.C. Section 7401 et seq. (accessed October 18, 2011). www.epa.gov/air/caa

Clean Water Act of 1977 (CWA), 33 U.S.C. Section 1251 et seq. (accessed October 20, 2011). epa.senate.gov/water.pdf

Comprehensive Environmental Response, Compensation and Liability Act of 1980 (CERCLA), 42 U.S.C. Section 9601 et seq. (accessed October 20, 2011). epa.senate.gov/cercla.pdf

Emergency Planning and Community Right-to-Know Act of 1986 (EPCRA), 42 U.S.C. Section 11001 et seq. (accessed October 18, 2011). frwebgate.access.gpo.gov/cgibin/usc.cgi?ACTION=BROWSE&TITLE=42USCC116

Endangered Species Act of 1973 (ESA), 16 U.S. S. 1531 et seq. (accessed October 18, 2011). epa.senate.gov/esa1973.pdf

Federal Food, Drug and Cosmetic Act (FFDCA), 21 U.S.C. 301 et seq. (accessed October 20, 2011). epa.senate.gov/FDA_001.pdf

Federal Insecticide, Fungicide and Rodenticide Act of 1972 (FIFRA), 7 U.S.C. 136 et seq. (accessed October 20, 2011). www.epa.gov/opp00001/regulating/fifra/pdf

Mine Safety and Health Administration (MSHA). *Federal Mine Safety and Health Act of 1977* (accessed October 17, 2011). www.msha.gov/regs/act/acttc.html

National Environmental Policy Act of 1969 (NEPA) (accessed October 17, 2011). ceq.hss.doe.gov/laws=and_exec_orders/the_nepa_statute.html

Oil Pollution Act of 1990 (OPA), 33 U.S.C. Section 2701 et seq. (accessed October 20, 2011). epa.senate.gov/opa90.pdf

Pollution Prevention Act of 1990 (PPA), 42 U.S.C. Section 13101 et seq. (accessed October 21, 2011). epa.senate.gov/PPA90.pdf

Resource Conservation and Recovery Act of 1976 (RCRA), 42 U.S.C. Section 6901 et seq. (accessed October 20, 2011). epa.senate.gov/rcra.pdf

Safe Drinking Water Act of 1974 (SDWA), 42 U.S.C. Section 300f et seq. (accessed October 21, 2011). epa.senate.gov/sdwa.pdf

Toxic Substances Control Act of 1976 (TSCA), 15 U.S.C. Section 2601 et seq. (accessed October 21, 2011). epa.senate.gov/tsca.pdf

MANAGEMENT OF SAFETY ENGINEERING WORK

LEARNING OBJECTIVES

- Recognize relevant concepts and components of an effective safety management system.

- Express voluntary safety management concept models developed by OSHA and ANSI for effective safety management.

- Analyze safety management system needs and integrate safety management into the business culture of an organization.

- Express the relevant concepts of an effective safety professional including education, experience, and certification.

APPLIED SCIENCE AND ENGINEERING: GENERAL SAFETY MANAGEMENT

Jeffery C. Camplin

DEFINING AN EFFECTIVE safety management system first requires a definition of the function of safety. Defining safety is easy. Petersen states, "The function of safety is to locate and define the operational errors that allow accidents to occur. This function can be carried out in two ways: (1) by asking why accidents happen—searching for their root causes—and (2) by asking whether certain known effective controls are being utilized" (Petersen 2003).

Although the specific job descriptions and titles of those delegated with the safety function may vary among organizations, the goal of safety professionals is to safeguard the entities' assets. First and foremost, they protect the human assets; second, they manage the tangible and intangible assets in a cost-effective manner (Schneid 2000).

Defining a safety management system can be more difficult. Most safety management systems are unique, differing in structure, definition, and/or implementation (Colvin 1992). Addressing safety and health issues in the workplace saves the employer money and adds value to the business. Recent estimates place the business costs associated with occupational injuries at close to $170 billion—expenditures that come straight out of company profits (OSHA 2005). When workers stay whole and healthy, OSHA found that the direct cost savings to businesses can include:

- lower workers' compensation insurance costs
- reduced medical expenditures
- smaller expenditures for return-to-work programs
- fewer faulty products
- lower costs for job accommodations for injured workers
- less money spent for overtime benefits

Safety and health can also make big reductions in indirect costs, due to:

- increased productivity
- higher-quality products
- increased morale
- better labor/management relations
- reduced turnover
- better use of human resources

Employees and their families benefit from safety and health because

- their incomes are protected
- their family lives are not hindered by injury
- their stress is not increased

Most successful safety management systems share common elements. This chapter will discuss: (1) the common elements of any safety management system; (2) tools of the trade to develop and implement these system elements; and (3) an overview of competencies and resources for improving the safety, health, and environmental (SHE) professional.

DEFINING AN EFFECTIVE SAFETY AND HEALTH MANAGEMENT SYSTEM

What is a safety and health program or management system? There are many ways to answer this question. Below are some definitions.

> An effective safety and health program depends on the credibility of management's involvement in the program, inclusion of employees in safety and health decisions, rigorous worksite analysis to identify hazards and potential hazards, including those which could result from a change in worksite conditions or practices, stringent prevention and control measures, and thorough training. It addresses hazards whether or not they are regulated by government standards. (OSHA 1998a, 3905)

> Measures for the prevention and control of occupational hazards in the workplace should be based upon a clear, implementable and well-defined policy at the level of the enterprise. The occupational health and safety policy represents the foundation from which occupational health and safety goals and objectives, performance measures, and other system components are developed. It should be concise, easily understood, approved by the highest level of management, and known by all employees in the organizations. (IOHA 1998, B-1)

There are several themes that emerge from effective safety management systems. The first is the involvement by all employees in a company, including top management. There must be buy-in by all employees at all levels of the organization. Ownership of safety management is not the sole charge of the SHE professional. Ownership of a company's safety management system should emanate from the senior management team as part of the overall business plan "inseparable from productivity and profitability" (Barfield 2004, 8). Management must clearly define realistic goals and expectations that hold all levels of the organization accountable for the program's success. The seamless integration of safety management throughout an organization involves assessing its overall business culture. "An organization's culture determines the probability of success of its hazard management endeavors" (Manuele 2003, 1). To improve safety awareness, it is also important to assess how the view of workplace safety by an organization's management might be removed "from those on the shop floor" (Petersen 2004, 29). The SHE professional will need a strategy for providing senior management with the tools and guidance for safety management system success. These tools and guidance include establishing reasonable and achievable goals, objectives, and performance measures that are easily understood throughout all levels of an organization. Attaining management's understanding of safety management requires that the SHE professional talk the language of business. Safety should not be seen as a cost for compliance, but more like a return on investment, in the form of savings to a company's bottom line. The SHE professional's role in providing tools and guidance to an organization's safety management system are discussed further in this chapter.

A second theme found in the definitions of a safety management system involves work-site analysis and hazard recognition. The OSHA definition provided earlier in the chapter discusses a "rigorous worksite analysis to identify hazards and potential hazards, including those which could result from a change in worksite conditions or practices." The SHE professional cannot provide guidance on preventing and controlling workplace hazards unless the hazards are identified and analyzed with an evaluation of the significance of risks derived from them. (Manuele 2005). Hazard identification and analysis involves a variety of work-site examinations to identify not only existing hazards, but also conditions and operations in which changes might create hazards. Effective management actively analyzes the work and the work site to anticipate and prevent harmful occurrences (OSHA 2002). There are several techniques used to analyze workplace hazards and associated risks. Manuele found commonly used techniques include preliminary hazard analysis, safety reviews, operations analysis, what-if analysis, hazard and operability analysis (HAZOP), failure modes and effects analysis, fault tree analysis, and management oversight and risk tree (Manuele 2005).

A third theme in safety management is effective hazard control and prevention. The SHE professional often is in the position of recommending or providing guidance on solving workplace hazards. These recommendations must address specific hazards and associated risks if the intended risk reduction is to be achieved. Figure 1 illustrates the safety decision hierarchy that will help the SHE professional and an organization's management understand how to evaluate and effectively resolve unacceptable hazardous situations (Manuele 2005).

Manuele provides a simple hazard/risk problem-solving methodology: (1) identify and analyze the problem, (2) consider actions in order of effectiveness, (3) decide and take action, and (4) measure for effectiveness and reanalyze as needed. Effective hazard control and prevention requires ensuring that actions selected to solve workplace hazards accomplish their intended purpose of risk reduction. The final theme in safety management is the development of effective training to provide the knowledge and skills necessary for all employees to understand workplace hazards and safe procedures.

Structuring the safety management system can be accomplished in many ways. A management systems approach has been developed by OSHA as a guideline and a consensus standard safety management system has been developed by industry stakeholders. The American National Standards Institute (ANSI) has developed a voluntary consensus stan-

dard for occupational safety and health management to help organizations minimize workplace risks and reduce the occurrence and cost of occupational injuries, illnesses, and fatalities. The Z10 standard (ANSI/AIHA 2005) is designed to continually improve safety and health performance and is aligned with the traditional Plan—Do—Check—Act approach for improving the workplace (Walton 1986).

The consensus standard provides basic requirements for occupational health and safety management systems rather than detailed specifications to provide flexibility in a manner appropriate to each organization and corresponding with its occupational health and safety risks. The standard defines *what* has to be accomplished in generic performance terms, but it leaves the *how* to each organization to develop. The standard recognizes that the risks, organizational structure, culture, and other characteristics of each organization are unique, and that each organization has to define its own specific measures of performance. An apparent theme throughout the standard is that hazards are to be identified and evaluated; risks are to be assessed and prioritized; and risk elimination, reduction, or control measures are to be taken to assure that an acceptable risk level is attained.

To properly understand and implement the Z10 standard, the SHE professional should know the ANSI definitions of hazard and risk. A *hazard* is defined as a condition, set of circumstances, or inherent property that can cause injury, illness, or death. *Risk* is defined as

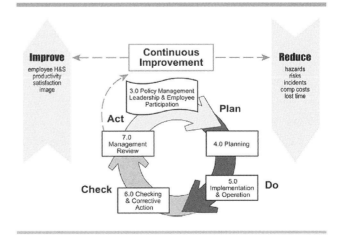

FIGURE 1. Continuous improvement diagram
(*Source:* ANSI/AIHA 2005)

an estimate of the combination of the likelihood of an occurrence of a hazardous event or exposure(s) and the severity of injury or illness that may be caused by the event or exposures (ANSI/AIHA 2005). Additional information on the Z10 standard will be discussed throughout the chapter.

OSHA has also developed a management approach to merge the themes discussed above into a system for building an effective safety management system. This OSHA management system has four elements:

1. Management, leadership, and employee involvement
2. Work-site analysis
3. Hazard prevention
4. Safety and health training

This chapter next looks at each of these elements and other resources available from OSHA. Then some tools of the trade are provided to assist the SHE professional in the implementation of an effective safety management system.

OSHA's Role in Safety Management

Section 5(a)(1) of the OSH Act, often referred to as the General Duty Clause, requires an employer to "furnish to each of his employees employment and a place of employment, which are free from recognized hazards that are causing or are likely to cause death or serious physical harm to his employees." Section 5(a)(2) requires employers to "comply with occupational safety and health standards" promulgated under this Act (OSHA 1970). However, OSHA compliance does not necessarily mean an employer has a complete and effective safety management system. In 1998, OSHA published a draft rule for safety management systems based upon their General Duty clause (see Sidebar 1).

OSHA has recognized that regulatory compliance is only one factor in the implementation of a successful safety system. Over their years of experience with enforcing the provisions of the Occupational Safety and Health Act of 1970 (OSH Act 1970), OSHA representatives have noted a strong correlation between the application of sound management

SIDEBAR 1

DRAFT PROPOSED SAFETY AND HEALTH PROGRAM RULE (OSHA 1998a)
29 CFR 1900.1
Docket No. S&H-0027

What is the purpose of this rule? The purpose of this rule is to reduce the number of job-related fatalities, illnesses, and injuries. The rule will accomplish this by requiring employers to establish a workplace safety and health program to ensure compliance with OSHA standards and the General Duty Clause of the Act (Section 5(a)(1)).

(a) Scope.

(a)(1) Who is covered by this rule? All employers covered by the Act, except employers engaged in construction and agriculture, are covered by this rule.
(a)(2) To what hazards does this rule apply? This rule applies to hazards covered by the General Duty Clause and by OSHA standards.

(b) Basic obligation.

(b)(1) What are the employer's basic obligations under the rule? Each employer must set up a safety and health program to manage workplace safety and health to reduce injuries, illnesses, and fatalities by systematically achieving compliance with OSHA standards and the General Duty Clause. The program must be appropriate to conditions in the workplace, such as the hazards to which employees are exposed and the number of employees there.

(b)(2) What core elements must the program have? The program must have the following core elements:

(i) Management leadership and employee participation;
(ii) Hazard identification and assessment;
(iii) Hazard prevention and control;
(iv) Information and training; and
(v) Evaluation of program effectiveness.

(b)(3) Does the rule have a grandfather clause? Yes. Employers who have implemented a safety and health program before the effective date of this rule may continue to implement that program if:

(i) The program satisfies the basic obligation for each core element; and
(ii) The employer can demonstrate the effectiveness of any provision of the employer's program that differs from the other requirements included under the core elements of this rule.

(c) Management leadership and employee participation.

(c)(1) Management leadership.

(c)(1)(i) What is the employer's basic obligation? The employer must demonstrate management leadership of the safety and health program.

(c)(1)(ii) What must an employer do to demonstrate management leadership of the program? An employer must:

(A) Establish the program responsibilities of managers, supervisors, and employees for safety and health in the workplace and hold them accountable for carrying out those responsibilities;

(B) Provide managers, supervisors, and employees with the authority, access to relevant information, training, and resources they need to carry out their safety and health responsibilities; and

(C) Identify at least one manager, supervisor, or employee to receive and respond to reports about workplace safety and health conditions and, where appropriate, to initiate corrective action.

(c)(2) Employee participation.

(c)(2)(i) What is the employer's basic obligation? The employer must provide employees with opportunities for participation in establishing, implementing, and evaluating the program.

(c)(2)(ii) What must the employer do to ensure that employees have opportunities for participation? The employer must:

(A) Regularly communicate with employees about workplace safety and health matters;

(B) Provide employees with access to information relevant to the program;

(C) Provide ways for employees to become involved in hazard identification and assessment, prioritizing hazards, training, and program evaluation;

(D) Establish a way for employees to report job-related fatalities, injuries, illnesses, incidents, and hazards promptly and to make recommendations about appropriate ways to control those hazards; and

(E) Provide prompt responses to such reports and recommendations.

(c)(2)(iii) What must the employer do to safeguard employee participation in the program? The employer must not discourage employees from making reports and recommendations about fatalities, injuries, illnesses, incidents, or hazards in the workplace, or from otherwise participating in the workplace safety and health program.

Note: In carrying out this paragraph (c)(2), the employer must comply with the National Labor Relations Act.

(d) Hazard identification and assessment.

(d)(1) What is the employer's basic obligation? The employer must systematically identify and assess hazards to which employees are exposed and assess compliance with the General Duty Clause and OSHA standards.

(d)(2) What must the employer do to systematically identify and assess hazards and assess compliance? The employer must:

(i) Conduct inspections of the workplace;

(ii) Review safety and health information;

(iii) Evaluate new equipment, materials, and processes for hazards before they are introduced into the workplace; and

(iv) Assess the severity of identified hazards and rank those that cannot be corrected immediately according to their severity.

Note: Some OSHA standards impose additional, more specific requirements for hazard identification and assessment. This rule does not displace those requirements.

(d)(3) How often must the employer carry out the hazard identification and assessment process? The employer must carry it out:

(i) Initially;

(ii) As often thereafter as necessary to ensure compliance with the General Duty Clause and OSHA standards and at least every two years; and

(iii) When safety and health information or a change in workplace conditions indicates that a new or increased hazard may be present.

(d)(4) When must the employer investigate safety and health events in the workplace? The employer must investigate each work-related death, serious injury or illness, or incident (near-miss) having the potential to cause death or serious physical harm.

(d)(5) What records of safety and health program activities must the employer keep? The employer must keep records of the hazards identified and their assessment and the actions the employer has taken or plans to take to control those hazards.

Exemption: Employers with fewer than 10 employees are exempt from the recordkeeping requirements of this rule.

(e) Hazard prevention and control.

(e)(1) What is the employer's basic obligation? The employer's basic obligation is to systematically comply with the hazard prevention and control requirements of the General Duty Clause and OSHA standards.

(e)(2) If it is not possible for the employer to comply immediately, what must the employer do? The employer must develop a plan for coming into compliance as promptly as possible, which includes setting priorities and deadlines and tracking progress in controlling hazards.

Note: Any hazard identified by the employer's hazard identification and assessment process that is covered by an OSHA standard or the General Duty Clause must be controlled as required by that standard or that clause, as appropriate.

(f) Information and training.

(f)(1) What is the employer's basic obligation? The employer must ensure that:

(i) Each employee is provided with information and training in the safety and health program; and
(ii) Each employee exposed to a hazard is provided with information and training in that hazard.

Note: Some OSHA standards impose additional, more specific requirements for information and training. This rule does not displace those requirements.

(f)(2) What information and training must the employer provide to exposed employees? The employer must provide information and training in the following subjects:

(i) The nature of the hazards to which the employee is exposed and how to recognize them;
(ii) What is being done to control these hazards;
(iii) What protective measures the employee must follow to prevent or minimize exposure to these hazards; and
(iv) The provisions of applicable standards.

(f)(3) When must the employer provide the information and training required by this rule?

(f)(3)(i) The employer must provide initial information and training as follows:

(A) For current employees, before the compliance date specified in paragraph (i) for this paragraph (f); and
(B) For new employees, before initial assignment to a job involving exposure to a hazard.

Note: The employer is not required to provide initial information and training in any subject in paragraph

(f)(2) for which the employer can demonstrate that the employee has already been adequately trained.

(f)(3)(ii) The employer must provide periodic information and training:

(A) As often as necessary to ensure that employees are adequately informed and trained; and
(B) When safety and health information or a change in workplace conditions indicates that a new or increased hazard exists.

(f)(4) What training must the employer provide to employees who have program responsibilities? The employer must provide all employees who have program responsibilities with the information and training necessary for them to carry out their safety and health responsibilities.

(g) Evaluation of program effectiveness.

(g)(1) What is the employer's basic obligation? The employer's basic obligation is to evaluate the safety and health program to ensure that it is effective and appropriate to workplace conditions.

(g)(2) How often must the employer evaluate the effectiveness of the program? The employer must evaluate the effectiveness of the program:

(i) As often as necessary to ensure program effectiveness;
(ii) At least once within the 12 months following the final compliance date specified in paragraph (i); and
(iv) Thereafter at least once every two years.

(g)(3) When is the employer required to revise the program? The employer must revise the program in a timely manner to correct deficiencies identified by the program evaluation.

(h) Multi-employer workplaces.

(h)(1) What are the host employer's responsibilities? The host employer's responsibilities are to:

(i) Provide information about hazards, controls, safety and health rules, and emergency procedures to all employers at the workplace; and
(ii) Ensure that safety and health responsibilities are assigned as appropriate to other employers at the workplace.

(h)(2) What are the responsibilities of the contract employer? The responsibilities of a contract employer are to:

(i) Ensure that the host employer is aware of the hazards associated with the contract employer's work and what the contract employer is doing to address them; and

(ii) Advise the host employer of any previously unidentified hazards that the contract employer identifies at the workplace.

practices in the operation of safety and health systems and a low incidence of occupational injuries and illnesses (OSHA 1998b). Where effective safety and health management is practiced, injury and illness rates are significantly less than rates at comparable work sites where safety and health management is weak or nonexistent. OSHA has developed several guidance documents, tools, and training to assist employers and safety professionals in the development and implementation of effective safety management systems. Sidebar 2 discusses a brief history of the OSHA consultative program.

In 1989, OSHA issued guidance that consists of safety and health management practices that are used by employers who are successful in protecting the safety and health of employees. The four major elements of an employer safety and health program identified by OSHA include (1) management, leadership, and employee involvement, (2) work-site analysis, (3) hazard prevention, and (4) safety and health training (OSHA). In January 2001 OSHA developed an eTool, a stand-alone, interactive, Web-based training tool on occupational safety and health payoffs (OSHA 2007b). The tool is highly illustrated and uses interactive graphical menus. OSHA also provides expert advisor software to employers and safety professionals to evaluate the financial impact of sound safety management programs. OSHA's *$AFETY PAYS* program is interactive software developed by OSHA to assist employers in assessing the impact of occupational injuries and illnesses (with lost work days) on their profitability (OSHA 1998c). It uses a company's profit margin, the average costs of an injury or illness, and an indirect cost multiplier to project the amount of sales a company would need to generate in order to cover those costs.

In 1982, OSHA began recognizing those employers that voluntarily participated in promoting effective

SIDEBAR 2

(Source: OSHA 2001a. Directive 00-01 (CSP 02), TED 3.6, *Consultation Policies and Procedures Manual*, Chapter 1, Section IX: *A Brief History of the OSHA Consultation Program.* (August 6, 2001).

A Brief History of the OSHA Consultation Program.

Section 21(c) of the Occupational Safety and Health Act of 1970 (the Act) requires the Secretary of Labor to establish programs for the education and training of employers and employees in recognizing, avoiding, and preventing unsafe or unhealthful working conditions covered under the Act. Many States began providing onsite consultation services to employers as part of their State plan under Section 18(b) of the Act. OSHA soon recognized that employers needed help in understanding and complying with the sometimes complex regulations applying to their workplaces. In addition, small employers often lack the financial resources to hire private consultants to aid them in meeting their obligations under the Act. In response to the demand for similar onsite consultation in Federal enforcement States, in 1975, the Secretary of Labor set forth the regulation at 29 CFR Part 1908 (FR 40: 21935), which authorized Federal funding of onsite consultation activity by States under Federal OSHA's jurisdiction. This activity was funded through Cooperative Agreements under the authority of Sections 21(c) and 7(c)(1) of the Act.

In 1977, the level of Federal funding for State run consultation projects was increased to ninety percent, a level that provided a strong incentive for all States to enter into the program. Forty-eight States, the District of Columbia, and Guam operate OSHA onsite consultative programs under Section 21(d) agreements with Federal OSHA. Two States and two U.S. territories operate programs as part of their approved State plans, for which fifty percent funding is received from Federal OSHA through 23(g) grants.

Part 1908 has been amended several times in the intervening years. In 1983, OSHA published a proposed change to the consultation regulation to clarify a number of provisions and to change the focus of services provided to an employer during an OSHA consultative visit. The proposal raised a number of new issues, including the Agency's desire to shift the focus of the consultation visit from simply the identification and correction of specific workplace hazards to the broader and more comprehensive goal of addressing the employer's overall management system for ensuring a safe and healthful workplace. In addition, the proposal allowed for offsite consultation services, including training and education services, to be made available to employers. It also provided for an exemption from Programmed OSHA Inspections for employers who met specific criteria. A final rule including these provisions was published in the Federal Register on June 19, 1984 (FR 49: 25082).

The Occupational Safety and Health Compliance Assistance Authorization Act of 1998, Public Law 105-197, codified OSHA's Consultation Program and amended Section 21 of the OSH Act by adding a new subsection, (d). On October 26, 2000, 29 CFR Part 1908 was amended to ensure that employees would be allowed to participate in site visits, that employees would be informed of the results of site visits, that site visits would be conducted according to updated procedures, and that information obtained during site visits would be treated as confidential.

I. *How the Consultation Program Works.*

A. The consultation program is designed to assist employers in identifying and correcting serious hazards in the workplace. Priority in scheduling visits is generally given to small employers in high hazard industries. Consultation projects also provide assistance to employers in developing safety and health management systems. However, this assistance must be linked to a hazard evaluation visit by either the consultation project, by OSHA enforcement, or by a private consultant. The consultation project must have access to the report of the visit before providing program assistance. In the case of offsite technical training, the Consultation Project Manager may provide specific training services that are not directly related to an onsite visit.

B. Because consultation services are voluntary, an employer must request service and agree to certain obligations, the principal one being that the employer agrees to correct all serious hazards found during the consultation visit within an agreed-upon timeframe.

work-site-based safety and health management programs through their Voluntary Protection Programs (VPP). In the VPP, management, labor, and OSHA establish cooperative relationships at workplaces that have implemented a comprehensive safety and health management system. Acceptance into VPP is OSHA's official recognition of the outstanding efforts of employers and employees who have achieved exemplary occupational safety and health (OSHA 2004). The legislative underpinning for VPP is found in Section (2)(b)(1) of the Occupational Safety and Health Act of 1970, which declares the Congress's intent "to assure so far as possible every working man and woman in the Nation safe and healthful working conditions and to preserve our human resources—(1) by encouraging employers and employees in their efforts to reduce the number of occupational safety and health hazards at their places of employment, and to stimulate employers and employees to institute new and to perfect existing programs for providing safe and healthful working conditions" (OSHA 2004).

In practice, VPP sets performance-based criteria for a managed safety and health system, invites sites to apply, and then assesses applicants against these criteria. OSHA's verification includes an application review and a rigorous on-site evaluation by a team of OSHA safety and health experts. OSHA approves admission of qualified sites to one of three programs: Star, Merit, and Star Demonstration. Star Demonstration recognizes work sites that address unique safety and health issues. As of February 2005, there were over 1250 participants in both state and federal VVP plans. OSHA has also developed a 4-day training course to increase the understanding of safety and health management principles for all OSHA enforcement personnel, State Plan consultants, and other interested stakeholders. This course emphasizes the VPP culture, philosophy, and criteria as the basis for students to understand and evaluate any safety and health management systems. Currently this course is offered at the OSHA Training Institute four times a year.

Elements of an Effective Safety Management System

Effective safety management involves developing and implementing several operational elements and integrating them into the organization's management

SIDEBAR 3

Safety and Health Program Management Guidelines; Issuance of Voluntary Guidelines OSHA Federal Register Notice 54:3904-3916, January 26, 1989

The Guidelines

(A) General. (1) Employers are advised and encouraged to institute and maintain in their establishments a program which provides systematic policies, procedures, and practices that are adequate to recognize and protect their employees from occupational safety and health hazards.

(2) An effective program includes provisions for the systematic identification, evaluation, and prevention or control of general workplace hazards, specific job hazards, and potential hazards which may arise from foreseeable conditions.

(3) Although compliance with the law, including specific OSHA standards, is an important objective, an effective program looks beyond specific requirements of law to address all hazards. It will seek to prevent injuries and illnesses, whether or not compliance is at issue.

(4) The extent to which the program is described in writing is less important then how effective it is in practice. As the size of a worksite or the complexity of a hazardous operation increases, however, the need for written guidance increases to ensure clear communications of policies and priorities and consistent and fair application of rules.

(B) Major Elements. An effective occupational safety and health program will include the following four elements. To implement these elements, it will include the actions described in paragraph (C).

(1) Management commitment and employee involvement are complementary. Management commitment provides the motivating force and the resources for organizing and controlling activities within an organization. In an effective program, management regards workers safety and health as a fundamental value of the organization and applies its commitment to safety and health protection with as much vigor as to other organizational purposes. Employee involvement provides the means through which workers develop and/or express their own commitment to safety and health protection, for themselves and for their fellow workers.

(2) Worksite analysis involves a variety of worksite examinations, to identify not only existing hazards but also conditions and operations in which changes might occur to create hazards. Unawareness of a hazard which stems from failure to examine the worksite is a sure sign that safety and health policies and/or practices are ineffective. Effective management actively analyzes the work and worksite, to anticipate and prevent harmful occurrences.

(3) Hazard prevention and controls are triggered by a determination that a hazard or potential hazard exists. Where feasible, hazards are prevented by effective design of the jobsite or job. Where it is not feasible to eliminate them, they are controlled to prevent unsafe and unhealthful exposure. Elimination or controls is accomplished in a timely manner, once a hazard or potential hazard is recognized.

(4) Safety and health training addresses the safety and health responsibilities of all personnel concerned with the site, whether salaried or hourly. If is often most effective when incorporated into other training about performance requirements and job practices. Its complexity depends on the size and complexity of the worksite, and the nature of the hazards and potential hazards at the site.

(C) Recommended Actions

(1) Management Commitment and Employee Involvement.

(i) State clearly a worksite policy on safe and healthful work and working conditions, so that all personnel with responsibility at the site and personnel at other locations with responsibility for the site understand the priority of safety and health protection in relation to other organizational values.

(ii) Establish and communicate a clear goal for the safety and health program and objectives for meeting that goal, so that all members of the organization understand the results desired and the measures planned for achieving them.

(iii) Provide visible top management involvement in implementing the program, so that all will understand that management's commitment is serious.

(iv) Provide for encouragement of employee involvement in the structure and operation of the program and in decisions that affect their safety and health, so that they will commit their insight and energy to achieving the safety and health program's goal and objectives.

(v) Assign and communicate responsibility for all aspects of the program so that managers, supervisors, and employees in all parts of the organization know what performance is expected of them.

(vi) Provide adequate authority and resources to responsible parties, so that assigned responsibilities can be met.

(vii) Hold managers, supervisors, and employees accountable for meeting their responsibilities, so that essential tasks will be performed.

(viii) Review program operations at least annually to evaluate their success in meeting the goal and objectives, so that deficiencies can be identified and the program and/or the objectives can be revised when they do not meet the goal of effective safety and health protection.

(2) Worksite Analysis. (i) So that all hazards are identified:

(a) Conduct comprehensive baseline worksite surveys for safety and health and periodic comprehensive update surveys;

(b) Analyze planned and new facilities, processes, materials, and equipment; and

(c) Perform routine job hazard analyses.

(ii) Provide for regular site safety and health inspection, so that new or previously missed hazards and failures in hazard controls are identified.

(iii) So that employee insight and experience in safety and health protection may be utilized and employee concerns may be addressed, provide a reliable system for employees, without fear of reprisal, to notify management personnel about conditions that appear hazardous and to receive timely and appropriate responses; and encourage employees to use the system.

(iv) Provide for investigation of accidents and "near miss" incidents, so that their causes and means for their prevention are identified.

(v) Analyze injury and illness trends over time, so that patterns with common causes can be identified and prevented.

(3) Hazard Prevention and Control. (i) So that all current and potential hazards, however detected, are corrected or controlled in a timely manner, establish procedures for that purpose, using the following measures:

(a) Engineering techniques where feasible and appropriate;

(b) Procedures for safe work which are understood and followed by all affected parties, as a result of training, positive reinforcement, correction of unsafe performance, and, if necessary, enforcement through a clearly communicated disciplinary system;

(c) Provision of personal protective equipment; and

(d) Administrative controls, such as reducing the duration of exposure.

(ii) Provide for facility and equipment maintenance, so that hazardous breakdown is prevented.

(iii) Plan and prepare for emergencies, and conduct training and drills as needed, so that the response of all parties to emergencies will be "second nature."

(iv) Establish a medical program which includes availability of first aid on site and of physician and emergency medical care nearby, so that harm will be minimized if any injury or illness does occur.

(4) Safety and Health Training. (i) Ensure that all employees understand the hazards to which they may be exposed and how to prevent harm to themselves and others from exposure to these hazards, so that employees accept and follow established safety and health protections.

(ii) So that supervisors will carry out their safety and health responsibilities effectively, ensure that they understand those responsibilities and the reasons for them, including:

(a) Analyzing the work under their supervision to identify unrecognized potential hazards;

(b) Maintaining physical protections in their work areas; and

(c) Reinforcing employee training on the nature of potential hazards in their work and on needed protective measures, through continual performance feedback and, if necessary, through enforcement of safe work practices.

(iii) Ensure that managers understand their safety and health responsibilities, as described under (C)(1). "Management Commitment and Employee Involvement," so that the managers will effectively carry out those responsibilities.

structure. The safety management system should go beyond mere regulatory compliance. Sidebar 3 presents OSHA's proposed safety and health program rule from 1989. This proposed compliance document was geared toward addressing OSHA's general duty clause.

Sidebar 4 presents an outline of the ANSI Standard Z10-2005, *Occupational Health and Safety Management Systems*. A review of each program will illustrate the major differences between a safety compliance program and a safety management system. This section addresses how to develop and implement each of these elements of a successful and effective safety management system.

SIDEBAR 4

ANSI Z10, Occupational Health and Safety Management Systems Table of Contents

(ANSI/AIHA 2005)

1.0 Scope, Purpose, and Application
1.1 Scope
1.2 Purpose
1.3 Application
2.0 Definitions
3.0 Management Leadership and Employee Participation
3.1 Management Leadership
3.1.1 Occupational Health and Safety Management system
3.1.2 Policy
3.1.3 Responsibility and Authority
3.2 Employee Participation
4.0 Planning
4.1 Initial and Ongoing Review
4.1.1 Initial Review
4.1.2 Ongoing Review
4.2 Assessment and Prioritization
4.3 Objectives
4.4 Implementation Plans and Allocation of Resources
5.0 Implementation and Operation
5.1 OHSMS Operation Elements
5.1.1 Hierarchy of Controls
5.1.2 Design Review and Management of Change
5.1.3 Procurement
5.1.4 Contractors
5.1.5 Emergency Preparedness
5.2 Education, Training, and Awareness
5.3 Communication
5.4 Documentation and Record Control Process
6.0 Evaluation and Corrective Action
6.1 Monitoring and Measurement
6.2 Incident Investigation
6.3 Audits
6.4 Corrective and Preventive Actions
6.5 Feedback to the Planning Process
7.0 Management Review
7.1 Management Review Process
7.2 Management Review Outcomes and Follow Up

Annexes

A Policy Statements (Section 3.1.2)
B Roles and Responsibilities (Section 3.1.3)
C Employee Participation (Section 3.2)
D Initial/Ongoing Review (Section 4.1)
E Assessment and Prioritization (Section 4.2)
F Objectives/Implementation Plans (Section 4.3 and 4.4)
G Hierarchy of Control (Section 5.1.1)
H Incident Investigation Guidelines (Section 6.2)
I Audit (Section 6.3)
J Management Review Process (Section 7.1 and 7.2)
K Bibliography and References

The 11 annexes provide explanatory comments, examples of forms and procedures, and reference sources for many of the major sections. While information in the annexes is not part of the standard, it will be helpful to those assigned responsibility to implement the standard.

Management Leadership and Employee Involvement

Management leadership and employee involvement go hand in hand for safety success. In fact, top management leadership and effective employee participation are crucial for the success of a safety management system (ANSI/AIHA 2005). Management provides the leadership for organizing and controlling activities within an organization. They provide the motivating force, resources, and influence necessary to place safety as a fundamental value within the organization. In an effective program, management involvement also provides the means through which workers express their own commitment to safety and health for themselves and their fellow workers (OSHA 1989).

The ANSI Z10 standard identifies management leadership as the first step of a successful safety management system (ANSI/AIHA 2005). The voluntary consensus standard identifies management's involvement as follows:

- Top management shall direct the organization to establish, implement, and maintain an Occupational Health and Safety Management System (OHSMS).
- The organization's top management shall establish a documented occupational health and safety policy.

- Top management shall provide leadership and assume overall responsibility.
- The organization shall establish and implement processes to ensure effective participation in the OHSMS by its employees at all levels.

The ANSI Z10 standard also addresses employee involvement in an effective safety management system by stating, "Employees shall assume responsibility for aspects of health and safety over which they have control, including adherence to the organization's health and safety rules and requirements (ANSI/AIHA 2005).

Petersen (2003) developed a list of principles of safety management that illustrates the roles of the employee and management in effective safety management. First, the safety system should fit into the culture of the organization. Next, safety should be managed like any other company function, with strong leadership. In most cases, unsafe behavior is normal human behavior, and an unsafe act, unforeseen condition, or an accident are all symptoms that something is wrong with the organization's management system. It is therefore management's job to change the environment that leads to the unsafe behavior or hazard present (Petersen 2003). The safety professional must facilitate this process by identifying the root causes of accidents or occupational hazards so that the solutions work toward changing the organization's management culture. This requires a flexible process involving the visibility of top management, involvement of middle management, accountability of supervisors, and employee involvement. The SHE professional should also implement these programs so that they are perceived as a positive impact to the culture of the organization. This ambitious undertaking begins very simply with an assessment of the organization's culture.

Management, Culture, and Safety

The leadership of an organization influences its overall culture. The organization's culture in turn "determines what will—and will not—work in SHE efforts"

(Petersen 2004, 28). The culture of an organization influences the attention paid to job-site hazards, risks, and the safety attitudes of the employees. This safety culture must be evaluated so the SHE professional can develop a strategy for: (1) improving management commitment to safety, (2) establishing realistic goals of where the organization needs to be, (3) preparing achievable objectives to effectively meet those goals, and (4) developing metrics to measure the safety management system's success toward achieving the stated goals.

Several surveys of the SHE community have consistently cited integrating safety into the company culture as a top priority for safety professionals (Hintch 2005, ASSE and BCSP 2007a). Integrating safety into the culture of an organization requires leadership from management. However, management must be committed to safety before they can lead. Obtaining the commitment of upper management to safety management requires the SHE professional to evaluate the existing culture of the organization and its attitude toward safety. SHE professionals may find that management's attitude toward safety falls into one of the following categories:

- Management is already committed to safety. Safety is an investment with a measurable return.
- Management is aware of some of the benefits of safety but does not lead. Safety pays for itself or is an acceptable cost.
- Management is aware of safety compliance but does not understand safety benefits. Safety is compliance-driven. Safety is a cost to the organization.
- Management is not committed to safety. Production and profits take precedence over workplace safety and health. Safety negatively impacts production. Hazards and accidents are part of doing business.

These are but a few of the attitudes held by management that affect the safety culture in an organization. There are many other variations in an organization's culture and how it impacts on safety.

The key for the SHE professional is to use appropriate tools to determine where the current culture of the organization is, compared to where it needs to be.

The SHE professional should not underestimate management's understanding and commitment to safety. A recent survey of 500 CEOs on awareness of safety benefits by the American Society of Safety Engineers (ASSE 2003) found:

- 60 percent said safety contributes to profits
- 22 percent said safety pays for itself
- 10 percent called safety a minor expense
- 5 percent called safety a major expense
- 3 percent did not respond

Although this study was limited, it provides anecdotal findings that four out of five CEOs see safety as breaking even or contributing to profits. Another recent publication provided insight into the successful companies that "get" safety (Colford 2005b). One key issue found in successful companies was that they embrace safety as a core value. These companies also found safety is nonnegotiable, uncompromising, and permanent. Finally, the cultures of these successful companies indicated that providing a safe workplace is the right thing to do regardless of financial payback.

The SHE professional will have to use a variety of tools to evaluate where their company's culture is to achieve the goals of successful companies such as those cited above.

The SHE professional must use other tools to continue to demonstrate to management that safety provides a return on investment for the company and should be incorporated into the business plan like all other departments in the organization. Tools of the trade for a successful safety management system will be discussed later in this chapter.

Employee Involvement

Employee involvement in the safety management system is essential for its success. We often hear the phrase, "Safety is everyone's responsibility." Of course,

safety is everyone's responsibility, but what does this responsibility mean?

First, everyone is responsible for safety to some degree, including employees. Employees who are accountable for everyday safety must be able to contribute to reasonable and achievable safety program elements. Teamwork has a lot to do with a company's culture. It is hard to have teamwork when you are not part of the team. Therefore, it is essential for employees to be involved in the safety management system and to effect a positive change in workplace culture.

Secondly, employees provide critical insight into workplace- and job task-related hazards. Employees see the implementation and effectiveness of safety objectives firsthand. This awareness and feedback is also important to the safety program's success. Special emphasis should be given to participation by nonsupervisory employees because they are often those closest to the hazard, and often have the most intimate knowledge of workplace hazards. In addition, nonsupervisory employees are a valuable but often overlooked resource for improving health and safety (ANSI/AIHA 2005).

Third, management and the SHE professional cannot observe all operations all of the time. Developing a strong culture with employee involvement provides peer observation and self-observation to follow established safety principles "when no one is looking."

Fourth, employees have legal and regulatory obligations to act in a safe manner. Employers' actions can affect legal and regulatory obligations of the company as well.

Finally, employees are generally involved with contributing to accidents and injuries and/or suffering the consequences of them. Employees are involved in the safety management system and the organization's culture, whether it is acknowledged by management or not. The key is whether employee involvement contributes positively or negatively to the overall culture of an organization. The SHE professional must involve employees so that there is a positive effect on the overall safety culture of the organization.

There are multiple ways to get employees involved in the safety management system. Many authors (Anton 1989, Della-Giustina 2000, Petersen 2003, Reese 2003) suggest examples of employee participation, including:

- participating on safety committees
- conducting work-site safety inspections
- performing a job-site hazard analysis identifying routine hazards in each step of a job or process
- preparing safe work practices or controls to eliminate or reduce exposure to job hazards
- suggesting revisions and improvements to safety and health rules
- participating during safety training
- providing programs and presentations at safety and health meetings
- participating in or assisting with incident investigations
- reporting recognized workplace hazards and unsafe work practices
- recommending corrective actions to fix hazards within one's control
- supporting fellow workers by providing feedback on risks and assisting them in eliminating hazards
- suggesting or performing a pre-use or change analysis for new equipment or processes in order to identify hazards before use

Employees' active involvement is mandatory if safety is to be integrated into an organization's culture. Leadership from management is the other component for a successful management system. The success of the safety management system is a sum of how both of these two groups communicate as a whole. The SHE professional plays a critical role in facilitating management leadership and employee involvement and buy-in to the values and benefits of workplace safety (see Sidebar 5).

Work-Site Analysis

As previously discussed, a primary goal for the safety management system is to prevent and minimize job-

SIDEBAR 5

Evaluating Management Leadership and Employee Involvement (OSHA 1996)

According to OSHA, an organization will have successfully established management leadership and employee involvement when it can demonstrate:

Work Site Safety and Health Program

- There is a written policy supported by senior management that promotes safety and health.
- The policy is straightforward and absolutely clear.
- The policy can be easily explained or paraphrased by the entire workforce.
- The policy is expressed in the context of other organizational values. It goes beyond compliance to address the safety behavior of all members of the organization and guides them in making
- Decisions in favor of safety and health when apparent conflicts arise with other values and priorities.

Setting and Communicating Clear Goals and Objectives

- A safety and health goal directly related to the safety and health policy exists in writing.
- The goal incorporates the essence of a positive and supportive safety system integrated into the workplace culture.
- An assessment tool is used to identify deficiencies that relate to objectives that are designed to achieve the goal, and they are assigned to responsible individuals.
- A measurement system is consistently used to manage work on objectives and indicate progress towards the goal.
- The goal and objectives are supported by senior management and can be paraphrased by the entire workforce.
- Measures used to track objective progress are known to the workforce and members of the workforce are active participants in the objective process.

Management Leadership

- The positive influence of management is evident in all elements of the safety and health program.

- All members of the workforce perceive management to be exercising positive leadership.
- All members of the workforce can give examples of management's positive leadership.

Management Sets Examples

- All managers know and understand the safety and health rules of the organization and the safe behaviors they expect from others.
- Managers throughout the organization consistently follow the rules and behavioral expectations set for others in the workforce as a matter of personal practice.
- Members of the workforce perceive management to be consistently setting positive examples and can illustrate why they hold these positive perceptions.
- A majority of members of management at all levels consistently address the safety behavior of others by coaching and correcting poor behavior and positively reinforcing good behavior.
- Members of the workforce credit management with establishing and maintaining positive safety values in the organization through their personal example and attention to the behavior of others.

Employee Involvement

- Employees accept personal responsibility for ensuring a safe and healthy workplace.
- The employer provides opportunities and mechanisms for employees to influence safety and health program design and operation.
- There is evidence of management support of employee safety and health interventions.
- All employees have a substantial impact on the design and operation of the safety and health program.
- There are multiple avenues for employee participation.
- The avenues are well known, understood, and used by all employees.
- The avenues and mechanisms for involvement are effective at reducing accidents and enhancing safe behaviors.

uele 2005). A work-site analysis means that managers and employees analyze all work-site conditions to identify and eliminate any existing or potential hazards.

There should be a comprehensive baseline survey, with a system in place for periodic updates. However, the SHE professional should ensure that the staff and resources are available to address any identified hazards promptly before initiating the program.

To help in conducting a work-site analysis, OSHA suggests the following:

- Request a free OSHA consultation visit.
- Become aware of hazards in your industry.
- Create safety teams.
- Encourage employees to report hazards.
- Provide an adequate system for reporting hazards.
- Encourage trained personnel to conduct inspections of the work site and correct hazards.
- Ensure that any changes in process or new hazards are reviewed.
- Seek assistance from safety and health experts.

There are many ways to conduct a work-site analysis. OSHA suggests the following plan to identify work-site hazards (see Figure 2):

- Conduct a comprehensive, baseline survey for safety and health and periodic, comprehensive update surveys.
- Change analysis of planned and new facilities, processes, materials, and equipment.
- Perform routine job-hazard analyses.
- Conduct periodic and daily safety and health inspections of the workplace.

These analytical tools are used to identify not only existing hazards, but also conditions and operations in which changes might create new hazards. An organization's management team can demonstrate its commitment to safety through leadership that actively analyzes job tasks and the work site to anticipate, prevent, or address workplace hazards before they occur.

site hazards. Therefore, the hazards must be identified and subsequent risks assessed in order to select appropriate control options to address them (Man-

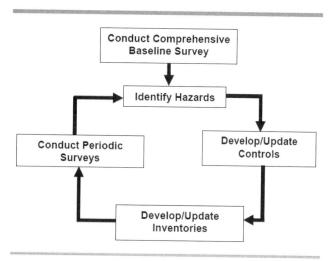

FIGURE 2. OSHA work-site analysis chart (*Source: OSHA 2001a*)

There are many hazards in a workplace that the SHE professional should make sure are evaluated during any analysis of the workplace. Some of the more common workplace hazards include chemicals (toxic, flammable, corrosive), explosions (chemical reactions, over-pressurizations), electricity (shock, short circuit, static discharge, loss of power, fire), ergonomics (human errors, strains), excavation (collapse/cave-in), falls (slips, trips, from heights), fire, heat, vibration (chaffing, fatigue), machinery (failure, crushing, caught between), noise, radiation (ionizing, nonionizing), struck by or against, temperature extremes, poor visibility, and weather (OSHA 2005). The ANSI Z10 standard discusses hazards and risk by stating, "Hazards and risks may include health, medical and weather-related emergencies, as well as emergency events that may arise from the characteristics of the materials, processes and activities of the workplace" (ANSI/AIHA 2005, 15).

There are also certain situations that can contribute to the severity of accidents and injuries. Petersen (2004) found that a number of recent studies suggested that severe injuries are fairly predictable in certain situations, including:

- unusual nonroutine work, including unique, one-of-a-kind projects where normal routine controls have little effect
- nonproduction activities, including maintenance functions and research and development activities that may not be carried out by

standardized procedures or receive little safety attention

- sources of high energy, including electricity, steam, compressed gases, and flammable liquids
- unique construction activities, including steel erection, tunneling, and work over water where unusual risks are present
- various lifting situations that result in the large and costly problem of severe strains and injuries, primarily to workers' backs
- repetitive motion activities that lead to chronic conditions and costly surgeries involving tendonitis and carpal tunnel syndrome
- psychological stress situations resulting from employee exposures to stressful environments
- exposure to toxic materials that can have acute or chronic health problems that may become problems for decades, as in the example of asbestos

Hazard Prevention

It is important to take steps to eliminate or control the uncontrolled hazards that were identified during workplace surveillance and reduce them to an acceptable risk level. Therefore, these hazard prevention methods are only going to be as effective as the hazard-assessment *and* risk-evaluation process. Once hazards are identified, the SHE professional must perform some type of risk evaluation of each hazard to define its relationship to worker exposure (including frequency and duration), severity of consequences, and probability of occurrences. Then the SHE professional can rank the risks, develop a hazard remediation strategy, and take action.

The ANSI Z10, *Standard for Occupational Health and Safety Management Systems*, discusses hazard assessment and prioritization by stating, "The assessment of risks should include factors such as identification of potential hazards, exposure, measurement data, sources and frequency of exposure, types of measures used to control hazards, and potential severity of hazards. Assessing risks can be done using quantitative (numeric) or qualitative (descriptive) methods.

There are many methods of risk assessment" (ANSI/AIHA 2005). Some of these risk-assessment methods include:

- Preliminary Hazard Analysis (PHA)
- Safety Reviews—Operations Analyses
- What-If Analysis
- Checklist Analysis
- What-If/Checklist Analysis
- Hazard and Operability Analysis (HAZOP)
- Failure Modes and Effects Analysis (FMEA)
- Fault Tree Analysis (FTA)

Risk-assessment methodologies are discussed in later chapters of this manual.

The SHE professional should also be aware that since any actual knowledge of hazards that constitute OSHA violations can be discovered in the course of a compliance investigation or the litigation process, documenting proper control of identified hazards is important. This actual or imputed knowledge can be the basis for willful violations, which can carry significant penalties and—if a fatality was involved—form the basis for a criminal referral by OSHA to the U.S. Department of Justice under Section 17 of the OSH Act. If a nonemployee is harmed, the OSHA citations will come in as "negligence per se" (considered intrinsically negligent) to substantiate the plaintiff's tort injury or wrongful death action. In some states, a high negligence (willful) OSHA citation permits an employee to get around the workers' compensation shield (Abrams 2005). A proactive safety hazard-analysis program will address identified hazards immediately. Figure 3 displays the four major actions that form the basis from which good hazard prevention and control can develop.

The SHE professional should ensure that the staff and resources are available to address any identified hazards promptly before initiating the hazard recognition program. It is impracticable to attempt to achieve an immediately hazard-free environment due to the excessive costs and resources that would be necessary. However, the total abatement of all identified hazards does result in total compliance, regardless of the costs. There will have to be some decisions made on what hazards to address, then prioritize their importance. What resources should be allocated and what is the return on investment or cost savings to be achieved? Financial and management decisions that address hazards will be prioritized along with all other organizational business decisions.

The following is a summary of a hazard-analysis and risk-assessment guide developed by Fred A. Manuele (2005):

1. Establish analysis parameters. Select a manageable task, system, process, or product to be analyzed, and establish its boundaries and operating phase. Determine the scope of analysis in terms of what can be harmed or damaged: people, property, equipment, productivity, and the environment.

2. Identify the hazards. The frame of thinking adopted should get to the root of causal factors, which are hazards. These questions need to be asked: What are the characteristics of things or the actions or inactions of people that present a potential for harm?

3. Consider the failure modes. Define possible failure modes that would result in the realization of the potential of the hazards. Consider how an undesirable event could occur and what controls are in place to mitigate its occurrence.

4. Determine exposure frequency and duration. For each harm or damage category selected in Step 1 for the scope of the analysis, estimate the frequency and duration of exposure to the hazard.

5. Assess the severity of consequences. What is the magnitude of harm or damage that could result? Learned speculations must be made regarding the consequences of occurrence: the number of resulting injuries and illnesses or fatalities, the value of property or equipment damaged, the duration of lost productivity, or the extent of environmental damage. Historical data can establish a baseline. When severity of consequences is determined, the hazard analysis is complete.

These four major actions form the basis from which good hazard prevention and control can develop.

Comprehensive surveys

For small businesses, OSHA-funded, state-run consultation services can conduct a comprehensive survey at no cost. Many workers' compensation carriers and other insurance companies offer expert services to help their clients evaluate safety and health hazards. Numerous private consultants provide a variety of safety and health expert services. Larger businesses may find the needed expertise at the company or corporate level.

For the industrial hygiene survey, at a minimum, all chemicals and hazardous materials in the plant should be inventoried, the hazard communication program should be reviewed, and air samples analyzed. For many industries, a survey of noise levels, a review of the respirator program, and a review of ergonomic risk factors are needed.

Change Analysis

Anytime something new is brought into the workplace, whether it be a piece of equipment, different materials, a new process, or an entirely new building, new hazards may unintentionally be introduced. Before considering a change for a worksite, it should be analyzed thoroughly beforehand. Change analysis helps in heading off a problem before it develops.

You may find change analysis useful when:

• Building or leasing a new facility.
• Installing new equipment.
• Using new materials.
• Starting up new processes.
• Staffing changes occur.

Hazard Analysis

Hazard analysis techniques can be quite complex. While this is necessary in some cases, frequently a basic, step-by-step review of the operation is sufficient. One of the most commonly used techniques is the Job Hazard Analysis (JHA). Jobs that were initially designed with safety in mind may now include hazards or improper operations. When done for every job, this analysis periodically puts processes back on the safety track.

Other, more sophisticated techniques are called for when there are complex risks involved. These techniques include: WHAT-IF Checklist, Hazard and Operability Study, Failure Mode and Effect Analysis, and Fault Tree Analysis.

Safety and Health Inspections

Routine site safety and health inspections are designed to catch hazards missed at other stages. This type of inspection should be done at regular intervals, generally on a weekly basis. In addition, procedures should be established that provide a daily inspection of the work area.

You can use a checklist already developed or make your own, based on:

• Past problems.
• Standards that apply to your industry.
• Input from everyone involved.
• Your company's safety practices or rules.

Important things to remember about inspections are:

• Inspections should cover every part of the worksite.
• They should be done at regular intervals.
• In-house inspectors should be trained to recognize and control hazards.
• Identified hazards should be tracked to correction.

Information from inspections should be used to improve the hazard prevention and control program.

FIGURE 3. Four major actions from which good hazard prevention and control develop (*Source:* OSHA 2001a)

6. Determine occurrence probability. Consider the likelihood that a hazardous event will occur. This process is also subjective. Probability must be related to an interval base of some sort, such as a unit of time, an activity, events, units produced, or the life cycle of a facility, equipment, process, or product.

7. Define the risk. Conclude with a statement that addresses both the probability of an incident occurring and the expected severity of harm or damage. Categorize each risk in accord with agreed-upon terms, such as high, serious, moderate, or low.

8. Rank risks in priority order. Risks should be ranked in order to establish priorities. Since the hazard-analysis and risk-assessment exercise is subjective, the risk-ranking system will also be subjective.

9. Develop remediation proposals. When required by the results of the risk assessment, alternate proposals for design and operational changes that are needed to achieve an acceptable risk level would be recommended.

10. Actions and follow-up activities. Actions should be taken as necessary, as should follow-up activities to determine whether the action was effective.

Although each organization will address hazard abatement differently, certain steps should be considered to handle them in a prioritized manner. Petersen outlines four general principles for conducting hazard-abatement activities (Petersen 2003).

1. Set priorities. Most organizations cannot do everything at once, so decisions must be made about what comes first. Priorities can be determined based upon cost, severity of the hazard, risk, regulatory violations, or other ranking systems.

2. Schedule and assign tasks. Without planning and assigning responsibilities, nothing very significant will happen. Establishing deadlines for completing assigned corrective actions will create accountability for addressing identified hazards.

3. Follow up to ensure that things are being done. Hazard-abatement activities should be evaluated to ensure that the hazard reduction assignment has been performed correctly and in a timely manner. The hazard can be reevaluated to determine if the fix actually resulted in a reduction or elimination of the hazard. Also, a reevaluation can determine if a new hazard was created by the fix.

4. Document everything that is done, if not for internal reasons, certainly for OSHA. Documentation provides a written record that hazards are identified and that corrective actions are taken to abate the hazard.

Prioritizing hazard-abatement activities will vary based upon the types of hazards present, abatement costs (direct and indirect), complexity of the abatement method selected, and risk tolerance of the organization. For instance, replacing a burnt-out light bulb in an exit sign is a fairly simple and inexpensive hazard-abatement choice that can be implemented quite easily. The bulb replacement can be scheduled through daily work orders. A quick follow-up inspection will verify the exit light is properly illuminated. Finally, documenting the corrective action demonstrates the effectiveness of the employer's safety management system to find and abate workplace hazards. More expensive hazard abatement, such as designing and installing a guard system on machinery, might be a high priority if an insurance premium increases as long as the hazard exists. In this case, prompt scheduling, along with documented hazard abatement provided to the insurance carrier, may result in reduced premiums. However, if after prioritization an identified hazard cannot be fixed immediately, it should be isolated through securing the hazard area, tagging out the hazardous equipment, training employees on hazard avoidance, or using other remedial actions that are available. Most importantly, the SHE professional should document all interim actions in order to show that all reasonable steps were taken to protect workers until a permanent fix is completed.

It is critical that the SHE professional also ensure that the hazard prevention methods selected actually eliminate or reduce hazards and associated risks to acceptable levels. Judging the amount of risk deemed as acceptable will have an impact on defining the extent of injury and incident reduction. Judgment can be quantified if criteria are developed with values placed upon them.

Reese (2003, 106) suggests that one way to develop quantifiable judgments of risk is to calculate them using the following formula:

$$\text{Risk-Assessment Factor} = \\ \text{Consequence} \times \text{Exposure} \times \text{Probability} \qquad (1)$$

A point system is assigned to each of the subchoices in each of the three areas used to calculate the risk-assessment factor.

- Consequences could be listed as multiple deaths (10 points), single death (9 points), multiple injuries (7 points), disabling injuries (6 points), serious injuries (5 points), other injuries (3 points), or first aid (1 point).
- Exposure could be defined as continuous (10 points), hourly (8 points), daily (6 points), weekly (4 points), and so on.
- Probability is expressed as a percentage, such as 100 percent (10 points), 75 percent (8 points), 50 percent (6 points), 25 percent (4 points), and 0 percent (2 points).

A risk-assessment factor can be developed based upon multiplying the values selected in consequences, exposures, and probability. A range of 801–1000 points might be deemed the highest risk. A range of 601–800 might be a high risk, and so on. This method can be customized for specific hazards or specific situations. The results can be used, not used, or combined with other risk-assessment tools. Cost justifications can then be performed to determine if the cost is worth the amount of hazard that is abated. This includes a determination of whether the cost of the hazard prevention activity had complete, partial, or no effect on resolving the intended hazards.

Good judgment for assessing risks of hazards involves understanding that the total human and eco-nomic burdens of occupational injuries and illnesses is crucial to setting priorities and shaping other components of the safety management plan. Furthermore, determining the magnitude of these economic burdens is essential to the assessment of the financial effectiveness of safety and health interventions designed to reduce the number of occupational injuries and illnesses. Such evaluations provide decision makers in organizations with necessary information to assess whether the outcomes of interventions justify the expenditures relative to other choices. Economic analysis is vital in preventing and controlling occupational injury and illness (NIOSH 2005). There should also be an evaluation of whether the hazard-prevention actions actually created new hazards during the process (Manuele 2005).

The selection of hazard abatement must follow an order of precedence to be effective in addressing and controlling the hazard. Figure 4 depicts the safety decision hierarchy.

The hierarchy of addressing hazards is summarized as follows:

1. Engineering Controls. The most effective control is by engineering out the hazard through physically changing a machine or work environment to prevent employee exposure to the hazard. Examples include:

A) Problem Identification & Analysis
1) Identify and analyze hazards.
2) Assess risks.

B) Consider These Actions in Order of Effectiveness

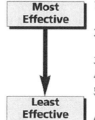

1) Eliminate hazards and risks through system design and redesign.
2) Reduce risks by substituting less-hazardous methods or materials.
3) Incorporate safety devices.
4) Provide warning systems.
5) Apply administrative controls (e.g., work methods, training).
6) Provide PPE.

C) Decide & Take Action

D) Measure for Effectiveness: Reanalyze as Needed

FIGURE 4. ANSI Z10: Hierarchy of health and safety controls (*Source:* Manuele 2005)

- elimination/minimization of the hazard through designing the facility, equipment, or process to remove the hazard, or substituting processes, equipment, materials, or other factors to lessen the hazard
- enclosing the hazard using cabs, enclosures for noisy equipment, or other means
- isolating the hazard with interlocks, machine guards, blast shields, welding curtains, or other means
- removing or redirecting the hazard with local and exhaust ventilation

2. Administrative controls. This involves changing how the employee performs workplace tasks. Examples include:

- writing operating procedures, work permits, and safe work practices
- limiting exposure times to the hazards, such as exposure to temperature extremes or ergonomic-related hazards
- monitoring highly hazardous materials used by employees
- use of alarms, signs, and warnings
- use of a buddy system
- effective use of training

3. Personal Protective Equipment. Examples include:

- respiratory protection
- hearing protection
- protective clothing
- safety glasses
- gloves
- hard hats

Protective equipment is acceptable as a hazard-control method under the following circumstances:

- when engineering controls are not feasible or do not totally eliminate the hazard
- while engineering controls are being developed
- when safe work practices do not provide sufficient additional protection
- during emergencies when engineering controls may not be feasible

The ANSI Z10 standard on occupational health and safety management systems expands upon the traditional hazard-abatement hierarchy of engineering controls, administrative controls, and personal protective equipment. The Z10 standard provides the following hazard-abatement hierarchy (ANSI/AIHA 2005, 16):

The organization shall implement and maintain a process for achieving feasible risk reduction based upon the following preferred order of controls:

A. Elimination
B. Substitution of less hazardous materials, processes, operations, or equipment
C. Engineering controls
D. Warnings
E. Administrative control
F. Personal protective equipment

Feasible application of this hierarchy of controls shall take into account:

a. The nature and extent of the risks being controlled
b. The degree of risk reduction desired
c. The requirements of applicable local, federal, and state statutes, standards, and regulations
d. Recognized best practices in industry
e. Available technology
f. Cost-effectiveness
g. Internal organization standards

This standard prescribes a hierarchy of controls that contains six elements instead of the three mandated by OSHA. The ANSI Z10 hierarchy's first priority is to design out or otherwise eliminate the hazard. If the hazard is eliminated, the overall risk associated with that specific hazard is either eliminated or reduced. Also, in ANSI Z10, the substitution element is separate from the elimination element. The additional number of elements and the separation of substitution from elimination are important changes to the prioritized hierarchy of work-site hazard-abatement activities (ANSI/AIHA 2005).

The SHE professional may use one of the control methods in the ANSI Z10 hierarchy over another control higher in the precedence when providing appropriate interim protection until the hazard is abated by a more appropriate permanent control. More likely, the selected hazard-abatement measures will be a combination of two or three items implemented simultaneously. Once the abatement measures are selected, the SHE professional should discuss these measures with all affected employees who perform the job. Employee input and feedback on hazard-control measures is important, so their responses should be carefully considered. When the hazard-control measure involves the introduction of a new or modified job procedure, the SHE professional should ensure that the employees understand the reasons for the modifications. The employees must also receive appropriate training that addresses new procedures or actions to be taken by the employee.

Training

In establishing training programs, employers must clearly define the employees to be trained and what subjects are to be covered by training. In setting up training programs, employers will need to clearly establish the goals and objectives they wish to achieve with the training that they provide to employees. The learning goals or objectives should be written in clear, measurable terms before the training begins (Reese 2003; Manuele 2003; Anton 1989; Easter, Hegney, and Taylor 2004). These goals and objectives need to be tailored to each of the specific training modules or segments. Employers should describe the important actions and conditions under which the employee will demonstrate competence or knowledge, as well as what are acceptable performance outcomes.

In 1986, OSHA issued a program evaluation profile (PEP) for their compliance officers to use when evaluating an employer's safety program (OSHA 1996). Although this compliance directive was rescinded, it serves as guidance in the evaluation of a sound employee training program. The OSHA PEP is available on the OSHA Web site. Highlights of this OSHA guidance state:

- Knowledgeable persons conduct safety and health training.
- Training is properly scheduled, assessed, and documented.
- Training covers all necessary topics and situations, and includes all persons working at the site (hourly employees, supervisors, managers, contractors, part-time and temporary employees).
- Employees participate in creating site-specific training methods and materials.
- Employees are trained to recognize inadequate responses to reported program violations.
- A retrievable record-keeping system provides for appropriate retraining, make-up training, and modifications to training as the result of evaluations.

OSHA regulations consist of more than 100 standards that contain training requirements.

OSHA has developed some voluntary training guidelines to assist employers in providing safety and health information, which are available on their Web site. These guidelines also provide employers with instructions needed for employees to work at minimal risk to themselves, to fellow employees, and to the public. A summary of the training guidelines (OSHA 2006a) lists areas designed to help employers accomplish the following:

(1) Determine whether a work-site problem can be solved by training.
(2) Determine what training, if any, is needed.
(3) Identify goals and objectives for the training.
(4) Design learning activities.
(5) Conduct training.
(6) Determine the effectiveness of the training.
(7) Revise the training program based on feedback from employees, supervisors, and other workers.

More in-depth discussion of effective safety training can be found in the "Safety and Health Training" section of this Handbook.

INCIDENT INVESTIGATIONS

Thousands of workplace incidents occur throughout the United States every day. Manuele (2003, 190) defines the term *incident* as encompassing "all hazards-related events that have been referred to as accidents, mishaps, near misses, occupational illnesses, environmental spills, losses, fires, explosions, et cetera." Incident investigations are more accurately defined as a hazard-related incident. Hazards include the characteristics of things, and actions or inactions of persons that result in a potential harm. A hazard-related incident can be an unplanned, unexpected process of multiple and interacting events, deriving from the realization of uncontrolled hazards occurring in sequence or in parallel, which most likely could result in harm or damage to people, property, and/or the environment (Manuele 2003, 192).

The failure of people, equipment, supplies, or surroundings to behave or react as expected causes most of the incidents (OSHA 2005). Incidents indicate a failure by the management system of an organization, which makes it very important to investigate the root cause of an incident. Some of these reasons provided by the Indiana University of Pennsylvania Safety Department (IUP 2006, 4) include:

- Identify and correct root causes to prevent recurrence in order to reduce costs and increase profits.
- Identify trends in incident experience.
- Comply with standards and regulations.
- Satisfy public concern.
- Litigate incident claims.

Incident investigations determine how and why these management-system failures occur. By using the information gained through an investigation, a similar or perhaps more disastrous incident may be prevented. It is important to conduct incident investigations with future incident prevention in mind. The incident investigation process provides the accurate, timely information needed to prevent these recurrences (Colvin 1992).

Management's commitment to safety includes a strong visibility once incidents occur. An organization's commitment to safety can be measured by its efforts to investigate the root causes of incidents (including near misses) that cause injury to people, property, or the environment. Most occurrences of incidents are due to a failure of the management system to be able to control acts and conditions in the workplace. Once an incident occurs, management has the obligation to ensure that proper control measures are implemented to prevent them from happening again (Della-Giustina 2000). Thorough incident investigation and follow-through with remedial actions support a culture that gives importance to safety. Poor response to incident investigations give the employees reasons to doubt management's sincerity with respect to safety (Manuele 2003).

Sources of Fatal and Nonfatal Occupational Injury Statistics

The SHE professional should be familiar with national statistics on occupational injuries as part of the overall incident investigation process. National statistics on the sources of occupational injuries (fatal and nonfatal) provides the safety professional with insightful information on workplace hazards that may require evaluation. This information can be combined with internal incident investigations to identify root causes of incidents and selection of appropriate hazard abatement.

According to the National Safety Council, floors and ground surfaces were the source of 255,548 out of 1.4 million occupational injuries in 2002. Many of these injuries typically involved slips, trips, and falls with an average cost per injury in 2002 of $18,838 (Parker 2005).

Identifying the Root Cause of Incidents

The primary goal of conducting an incident investigation is to determine its root cause. Proper investigation of incidents provides information about root causes that can then be adequately corrected to prevent future occurrences. Manuele (2003, 83) defines an incident as "a term encompassing all hazards-related events that have been referred to as accidents, mishaps, near-misses, occupational illnesses, environmental spills, losses, fire, explosions, et cetera." All of the incidents Manuele defines above are derived from hazards.

The effective safety professional must break away from traditional theories of hazard reduction and accident causation and identify the root cause of the accident (Petersen 2003, 27). This point is illustrated by Petersen, using a traditional incident investigation form, in the following passage:

If we investigate a person falling off a step ladder using our present investigation forms, we identify one act and/or one condition:

> The unsafe act: Climbing a defective ladder.
> The unsafe condition: A defective ladder.
> The correction: Getting rid of the defective ladder.

Let us look at the same accident in terms of multiple causation. Under the multiple-causation theory, we would ask what were some of the contributing factors surrounding the incident:

1. Why was the defective ladder not found during normal inspections?
2. Why did the supervisor allow its use?
3. Didn't the injured employee know it should not be used?
4. Was the employee properly trained?
5. Was the employee reminded not to use the ladder?
6. Did the supervisor examine the job first?

The answers to these and other questions would lead to the following corrections:

1. An improved inspection procedure
2. Improved training
3. A better definition of responsibility
4. Pre-job planning by supervisors.

Effective safety management requires that the hazards and events that contribute to the incident process be identified, evaluated, and eliminated or controlled (Manuele 2003). There are several pro-grams available to assist the SHE professional with performing evaluations of the root cause of an accident or incident. A few sources of these programs include:

- *Cause and Effect Diagrams.* A cause-and-effect diagram is a tool that helps identify, sort, and display possible causes of a specific problem. It graphically illustrates the relationship between a given outcome and all the factors that influence the outcome. This type of diagram is sometimes called an Ishikawa diagram because it was invented by Dr. Kaoru Ishikawa (Ishikawa 1968), or a fishbone diagram because of the way it looks. Dr. Ishikawa developed this technique to improve quality within an organization. Additional information on cause-and-effect diagrams can be found at the American Society for Quality (ASQ 2004).
- *5 Whys.* The 5 Whys is a method of solving a problem by repeatedly asking why the problem occurred, then why did that cause occur, at least five times so the layers of symptoms are peeled away until you get to the root cause of a problem. Shigeo Shingo (1981) developed this process for getting to the root cause of a problem. Very often the ostensible reason for a problem will lead to another question. Although this technique is called "5 Whys," one may find that the question will need to be asked fewer or more than five times before one finds the issue related to a problem. This process has been incorporated into the Six Sigma process of quality management. Additional information on the 5 Whys can be obtained from the iSix Sigma Web site located at www.isixsigma.com.
- *TapRooT®.* TapRooT® is a system (which includes a book, training, and software) for root-cause analysis of problems (Paradies and Unger 2000). This system assists SHE professionals in solving problems by finding and correcting root causes so that problems do not

recur. The system is based on theories of human performance and equipment performance, which are built into the TapRooT® system so that they can easily be applied. Additional information about the system is available on the TapRooT® Web site at www.taproot.com.

- *Apollo.* The Apollo process (Apollo Associated Servcies 2007) is a four-step method for facilitating a thorough incident investigation. The steps are:

  1. Define the problem. What do we want to prevent from recurring? When and where did it occur? What is the significance of the problem?
  2. Analyze cause and effect relationships. Once the problem is defined, one needs to understand the causes and how they interact with one another.
  3. Identify solutions. Solutions are specific actions that control causes.
  4. Implement the best solutions. The best solutions are those that prevent problem recurrence, are within our control, and meet our goals and objectives.

Additional information can be obtained from the Apollo Associated Services LLC Web site at www.apollorca.com.

- *Kepner-Tregoe (KT).* Kepner-Tregoe (KT 2007) helps people consciously learn and use four basic thinking patterns to answer four basic questions:

  - What's going on?
  - Why did this happen?
  - Which course of action should we take?
  - What lies ahead?

The Kepner-Tregoe system uses four rational processes for applying critical thinking to information, data, and experience in the process of identifying the root cause of an incident. Additional information can be obtained from their Web site at www.kepner-tregoe.com.

Investigating Incidents

Incident investigation should also be a fact-finding process, not a fault or blame-assessing process. Incidents include near-misses and accidents. Accidents result in loss, while near-misses do not (Friend 2006). As previously discussed, these incidents should be investigated to determine their root cause. The events that result in a near-miss rather than an accident may be pure chance. If our goal is to prevent future incidents, then all incidents should be investigated.

The goal of an effective safety management system should be to control or eliminate occupational hazards before there is injury or damage to people, property, or the environment. However, some hazards may not be recognized or addressed until an incident occurs. Incident investigation can be an important tool for workplace hazard identification, even though it is after the fact (Reese 2003). Identified hazards from incident investigations can be incorporated into the hazard identification and assessment process of an effective safety management system.

The investigation should be documented in writing and should adequately identify the causes of the incident and even the close-call or near-miss occurrences (ACGIH 2007).

Accident Rates Used by OSHA

OSHA tracks injury and illnesses throughout the nation. Statistics are available from OSHA on "Lost Workday Injury and Illness Rates and Total Recordable Case Rates" (BLS 2009). These rates can be computed for an organization for comparison with like organizations in a given industry. These rates are calculated as follows:

Lost-Workday Injury and Illness (LWDII) Rate

The annual LWDII rate is calculated according to the following formula, with an example and calculation provided by OSHA (2009, A-1):

LWDII Rate =

$$\frac{\text{Lost-workday injuries and illnesses} \times 200{,}000}{\text{Employee hours worked}}$$

(2)

where:

- lost-workday injuries and illnesses = sum of column 2 and column 9 from the OSHA log in the reference year
- employee hours worked = sum of employee hours worked in the reference year
- 200,000 = base for 100 full-time workers working 40 hours per week, 50 weeks per year

Sample One-Year LWDII Rate Calculation

In calculating the LWDII rate of an establishment scheduled for inspection in October 2005, injury and illness cases and employment data for the preceding calendar year are used.

In this example:

- the number of LWDIIs in 2004 = 5
- the number of workers employed in 2004 = 54
- the number of employee hours worked in 2004 = 54 workers × 50 weeks = 108,000

$$\text{LWDRII Rate} = \frac{5 \times 200,000}{108,000} = \frac{1,000,000}{108,000}$$

$$= 9.26 \text{ (rounded to 9.3)}$$

Sample Two-Year LWDII Rate Calculation

An establishment scheduled for inspection in October 2006 employed an average of 50 workers in 2005 and 54 workers in 2004. The injury and illness cases and employment data for the two preceding calendar years are used.

The two-year LWDII rate can be calculated using the following equation.

$$\text{LWDII Rate} =$$

$$\frac{(\text{Year 1 LWDIIs} + \text{Year 2 LWDIIs}) \times 200,000}{\text{Yr 1 employee hrs worked} + \text{Yr 2 employee hrs worked}}$$

$$(3)$$

In this example:

- the number of LWDIIs in 2004 = 5
- the number of LWDIIs in 2005 = 6
- the number of employee hours worked in 2004 = 108,000
- the number of employee hours worked in 2005 = 100,000

$$\text{LWDRII Rate} = \frac{(5 + 6) \times 200,000}{108,000 + 100,000}$$

$$= \frac{2,200,000}{208,000} = 10.58 \text{ (rounded to 10.6)}$$

Three-Year LWDII Rate Calculation

When determining the rate for an employer who has been in OSHA's Safety and Health Achievement Recognition Program (SHARP) for two or more years, calculate the LWDII rate in the same way as for the two-year rate, but include the third year's data.

Total Recordable Case Rate (TRCR)

The Total Recordable Case Rate (TRCR) is the rate of total nonfatal injuries and illnesses for the calendar year reviewed. The TRCR is compared to the rate in the Total Cases column that most precisely corresponds to the Standard Industrial Classification (SIC) code of the site under review. The Total Cases column is found in the Incidence Rates table reported in the annual Bureau of Labor Statistics Data on Occupational Injuries and Illnesses.

The annual TRCR is calculated according to the following formula:

$$\text{TRCR} =$$

$$\frac{(\text{Recordable injuries} + \text{Recordable illnesses}) \times 200,000}{\text{Employee hours worked}}$$

$$(4)$$

where:

- recordable injuries = sum of column 2 and column 6 from the OSHA log in the reference years
- recordable illnesses = sum of column 9 and column 13 from the OSHA log in the reference year

- number of employee hours worked = sum of employee hours worked in the reference year
- 200,000 = base for 100 full-time workers working 40 hours per week, 50 weeks per year

Sample One-Year TRCR Calculation

An establishment scheduled for inspection in October 1999 employed an average of 54 workers in 1998. Therefore, injury and illness cases and employment data for the preceding calendar year are used.

In this example:

- recordable injuries = 9
- recordable illnesses = 4
- employee hours worked in 1998 = 54 workers × 50 weeks = 108,000

$$TRCR = \frac{(9 + 4) \times 200,000}{108,000}$$

$$= \frac{2,600,000}{108,000} = 24.07 \text{ (rounded to 24.1)}$$

Sample Two-Year TRCR Calculation:

An establishment scheduled for inspection in October 2000 employed an average of 50 workers in 1999 and 54 workers in 1998. The injury and illness cases and employment data for the two preceding calendar years are used.

The two-year TRCR can be calculated using the following equation.

$$TRCR =$$

$$\frac{(\text{Yr 1 Recordable data} + \text{Yr 2 Recordable data}) \times 200,000}{\text{Yr 1 employee hrs worked} + \text{Yr 2 employee hrs worked}}$$

(5)

In calendar year 1998:

- recordable injuries = 9
- recordable illnesses = 4
- employee hours worked = 108,000

In calendar year 1999:

- recordable injuries = 14
- recordable illnesses = 7
- employee hours worked = 100,000

$$TRCR = \frac{(9 + 4) + (14 + 7) \times 200,000}{108,000 + 100,000}$$

$$= \frac{6,800,000}{208,000} = 32.69 \text{ (rounded to 32.7)}$$

When determining the rate for an employer who has been in SHARP for two or more years, calculate the TRCR in the same way as for the two-year rate, but include the third year's data.

TOOLS OF THE TRADE

Winning Over Top Management: Obtaining a Commitment to Safety

Obtaining management leadership is crucial to the success of an effective safety management system and positive safety culture (Anton 1989, Reese 2003, Manuele 2003, Petersen 2003). Many top CEOs understand the value and savings obtained from a sound safety program, while others just perceive safety as a compliance-driven expense (ASSE 2003, Colford 2005b). Saving and cost reductions obtained through an effective safety management system has been described as a return on investment so that these economic advantages gain the attention of top management. SHE professionals have many tools available to demonstrate that an investment in safety delivers a return on an investment in safety to a company's bottom line through cost savings. However, this positive message will not be effective within an organization unless the SHE professional can truly obtain the attention and gain the interest of top management (Della-Giustina 2000).

Safety competes for top-management attention with all other departments in an organization for time and resources. The SHE professional must use salesmanship combined with the language of business to deliver the benefits and values an investment in safety generates. Selling safety can be a challenge. This is further complicated by the fact that doing the right thing should not have to be sold to management. To ease this complication, SHE professionals should not see themselves as safety salesmen, but rather as SHE professionals who use salesmanship to obtain attention, generate interest, and deliver specific benefits of safety to each audience to whom they present (Carnegie 1981).

Gaining the interest of upper management can be done in a variety of ways. One method is to illustrate the regulatory benefits of a safety management program. Manuele (2008) believes that the ANSI Z10 standard for safety management systems "will become the benchmark against which the adequacy of occupational safety and health management systems will be measured." One selling point to management is that OSHA may use the ANSI Z10 as the basis of new safety management standards that they might promulgate in the future. The American Society of Safety Engineers (ASSE) published a legal perspective of the ANSI Z10 standard (see Appendix B) that makes strong legal arguments for establishing a safety management system. This legal perspective can be used to gain the attention of upper management.

Once attention is gained by upper management the value of safety can be better demonstrated. Asking for money may generate attention (albeit negative) but may not generate enough interest to deliver the benefits of the SHE proposal. However, making a proposal that management allocate funds for safety programs, which some say will return a savings of $3 to $6 for every $1 invested (LM 2005), not only generates attention, it also generates interest.

A proposed return on investment through overall cost reductions and/or savings may generate enough interest among management to ask, "How can safety pay?" This now requires proper communication coupled with salesmanship. These facts and associated benefits presented by the SHE professional now must be put in terms to which management can relate. Selling safety based solely on reduction in injury rates, compliance with OSHA requirements, or because it is the right thing to do, may not gain management's attention when competing with other departments that present production and profit issues. Nevertheless, demonstrating that the indirect costs of a $500 emergency room visit may very well exceed $15,000 can help illustrate an accident's effect on the organization's production. This $15,000 total expenditure

on an accident can be presented in terms of lost production to help gain motivation to abate the hazard. For instance, if the organization produces a product that generates a $15 net profit, it would take 1000 items to cover the cost of what appears on the surface to be a $500 injury due to the significant indirect costs associated with the incident. The SHE professional can now demonstrate that the investment in the safety management system will reduce injuries and thereby increase productivity and the company's bottom line.

Another example of how to demonstrate the savings generated by hazard-abatement activities is provided by the state of Oregon's Occupational Safety and Health (OR-OSHA) online safety training courses. OR-OSHA states, "Your supervisor may ask you what the Return on Investment (ROI) will be. If the investment to correct a hazard is $1,000, and it's likely the potential direct and indirect accident costs to the company may total $28,000 sometime in the foreseeable future (let's say five years), you can find the ROI by dividing the $28,000 by $1,000 to get 28. Now multiply that result by 100 to arrive at 2,800 percent (Total Incident Cost/Total Investment $\times$ 100 = ____% Return on Investment). Next, divide that total by 5 years to determine an annual ROI of over 500 percent. Now that's a return! Management may want to know how quickly the investment will be paid back: what the payback period is. Just divide $28,000 by 60 months

FIGURE 5. OSHA model for creating change (*Source:* OSHA 2001a)

and you come up with $467 per month in potential accident costs. Since the investment is $1,000, it will be paid back in a little over two months. After that, the corrective action is actually saving the company some big money" (OR-OSHA n.d.).

It is important to note that research (DeArmond and Chen 2007, Chen 2005) indicates that upper management often bases opinions of safety performance, programs, and personnel on statistics (for example, workers' compensation claims/costs and injury rates). The SHE professional should also be aware of the statistics to which top-level managers give the most attention, then either emphasize those statistics in negotiations or highlight alternative data that are more reflective/indicative of actual performance (DeArmond and Chen 2007).

The final aspect of salesmanship is painting a visual picture in management's mind of the future synergy generated by a sound safety management plan (see Figure 5). The vision presented should highlight the positive effects of a sound safety management system. The positive outcomes or benefits realized to present to upper management include a large percentage reduction in worker compensation costs and insurance rates, a resulting lowered accident/injury rate and related cost savings, and the subsequent leadership by management that involves employees and generates a healthier organizational (and safety) culture. On the other hand, do not present potential outcomes that are unrealistic or unachievable.

ANSI Z10 states that, "Organizations and the community may see additional benefits of implementing an OHSMS beyond the reduction of injury and illnesses. Some of these benefits may include: lowered workers' compensation costs, reduced turnover of personnel, reduced lost workdays, compliance with laws and regulations, increased productivity, improved employee health status, improved product quality, higher morale of employees, reduction or elimination of property damage due to incidents, reduced business interruption costs, and reduced impact on the environment due to incidents" (ANSI/AIHA 2005, 6).

The benefits discussed above are the positive visions of an effective safety management system that senior management can see. The job of the SHE pro-

fessional is to paint the picture of success and obtain a commitment from management while the vision is fresh. This is salesmanship. This is how to achieve commitment to safety from management.

A little salesmanship can integrate safety into the business model by illustrating incident and accident effects on production and profitability. Integrating the costs of safety into the business and demonstrating a return on investment has been identified as a major goal of the SHE professional (ASSE 2007b, ASSE/AIHA 2005). This puts safety into a language to which management, front-line supervisors, and even employees can relate. Doing the right thing is now right for many reasons.

Assessing the Culture of the Company

According to Manuele (2003), an organization's culture consists of its values, beliefs, legends, rituals, missions, goals, and performance measures, and its sense of responsibility to its employees, its customers, and its community, all of which are translated into a system of expected behavior. The culture of an organization dictates the effectiveness of a safety management system. Petersen (1996, 66) found that the culture of the organization sets the tone for everything in safety. "In a positive safety culture, it says that everything you do about safety is important." Consider this statement by OSHA: "The best Safety and Health Programs involve every level of the organization, instilling a safety culture that reduces accidents for workers and improves the bottom line for managers. When Safety and Health are part of the organization and a way of life, everyone wins" (OSHA 2002).

It is more important to understand what the culture is than to understand why it is that way (Petersen 1996). Perceptions of the safety culture of an organization can vary between management staff, various departments, front-line supervisors, and employees. The differences in perception can affect the levels of trust within an organization. A lack of trust can affect the overall performance of an organization, including production, profits, and safety attitudes. Strong management leadership combined with active employee involvement in the safety management system builds up trust and reinforces a positive safety culture. A

Safety Culture Profile Survey ©

MEMIC — Partners for Workplace Safety

Partnering with: **XYZ Company**

What is this sheet trying to measure and why is it important?

Culture is the sum total of values, beliefs and behaviors for a group of people in a society or workers within a given company. Culture can relate to art, science, community *and safety*.

This sheet presents 10 values that relate to *safety culture* within a company. Each value is followed by descriptions of six types of day-to-day experiences that employees encounter as they go about their jobs.

Based on your experiences, you are being asked to score the level at which your company operates for each of the 10 safety-related values.

First, select the Progress Level column that most nearly describes the value at your company.

Then, color in one of the dots from left to right to show how your company is progressing toward the next level.

The combined scores are averaged to determine which safety-related values are strongest at your company and which safety-related values have the greatest possibility for improvement.

Score	Safety Culture Value	Unaware 0	Beginner 1	Mediocre 2	Adequate 3	Excellent 4	Ideal 5.0
1	Continuity	Worker safety is not a factor at any time.	Safety is only applied after fines or accidents.	A safety program exists, but is not complete, and is often not applied.	A complete safety program exists, but is not always applied.	Safety is part of everything from new-hire orientations to all types of performance appraisals.	All workers at all levels understand and apply safety -- on and off the job.
2	Equality	Safety is always seen as the lowest priority.	Safety is mentioned to new hires and on workplace signs, but is rarely acted on.	Worker safety is said to be equal with production, but is not always practiced.	Safety is equal in importance to planning and budgeting, but is not always applied.	Worker safety is equally as important as planning, quality and production.	Worker safety shares an equal part in all production and performance reviews.
3	Individuality	Individual workers are not responsible for safety.	Each worker is told to be safe, but no follow-up method exists.	Sometimes individual workers take part in the safety process.	Individual workers are involved mainly through suggestion boxes or safety committees.	Individual workers are involved in all phases of the safety process.	Safety starts with each worker's personal commitment -- on and off the job.
4	Integrity	Efforts at worker safety don't exist or aren't credible.	Safety efforts come mainly from outside resources.	Safety program is administered part-time from within by workers with little training.	Some workers are assigned to safety duties full-time, but don't get regular training.	Regular training for all workers stresses that individuals apply safety to each aspect of their work.	Top management takes part in training and leads in applying the safety process.
5	Morality	Safety is done only to hold down the cost of insurance and fines.	Worker safety is talked about, but no one believes it.	Worker safety wins out over production, some of the time.	Safety training is provided to protect all workers, but is not always applied.	Worker safety is a major part of planning and production at all levels.	Well-being of the worker is considered 100% of the time, including off the job.
6	Profitability	Safety is always viewed as a cost or as overhead.	Worker safety is mainly to control costs of insurance and to prevent fines.	Worker safety is said to be a priority, but is most often seen as a major cost.	Worker safety is a priority but the cost of injuries is not subtracted from profits.	The cost benefits of worker safety and the cost of injuries subtracted from profits are publicized.	Safety is viewed as a key asset and profit center at all levels of the company.
7	Rationality	Worker safety is not part of any planning process.	Safety is only considered after fines or accidents.	Sometimes prevention of injuries is part of the planning process.	Preventing injuries is part of the planning process, but is not always acted on.	Worker safety is a main factor in all decision making and planning.	Top management expects and plans for worker safety at all levels within the company.
8	Responsibility	No one accepts responsibility for safety.	Issues related to safety are addressed mostly by the "safety person."	Workers some of the time are responsible for safety, but usually perform better with a "safety person" around.	Workers are responsible for safety, but some of the time productions wins out over safety.	Workers take action to ensure their own safety, and need limited support from a "safety person."	Every worker from top management down is responsible for safety.
9	Superiority	No efforts are made to improve any aspect of safety.	Excellence in safety is talked about, but is often not actually done.	Workers some of the time are responsible for safety, but usually perform better with a "safety person" around.	Excellence in safety is a stated goal, but steps to achieve this are not always taken.	Excellence in safety is achieved through budgeting for it, and by applying state-of-the-art equipment and training.	Ongoing improvement in safety is a stated goal and plans are in place to ensure this is attained.
10	Visibility	No method exists to report safety performance.	Signs or other methods report safety performance, but are not updated regularly.	Safety performance is tracked, but no goals or rewards are set.	Safety performance goals are set and made public, but are rarely attained.	Safety goals and rewards are set, and progress is published regularly companywide.	Safety performance is tracked and published at all levels equally with production and quality.

Are there any questions you would like to ask or suggestions you would like to make about this subject?

REQUIRED DATA:
○ Salaried
○ Hourly

○ Hourly   ○ Salaried   ○ Management
○ 1st Shift   ○ 2nd Shift   ○ 3rd Shift

FIGURE 6. MEMIC culture evaluation form (*Source:* MEMIC 2004)

well-written safety management program supported by management involvement sets the goals or vision of where the safety culture should be. However, it is important for the SHE professional to assess how close the current safety culture of an organization is to the desired culture. It is equally important for the SHE professional to assess the differences in the perception of the status of the safety culture between management, front-line supervisors, and employees. This perception survey can also extend among departments, facilities, regions, or any other combination of units within the organization.

Selecting the proper survey tool to assess safety culture perception is important. Reliable survey tools require careful design, implementation, and analysis. Options for conducting a perception survey include:

- What perceptions are being measured?
- Whose perceptions are being measuring?
- What survey methodology will be used?
- What questions will be asked?
- How does one test for bias or reliability of the survey?
- Who will analyze the data and how will it be reported?

Petersen (1996, 67) mentions a few considerations that determine an organization's culture:

- How decisions are made: Does the organization spend its available money on people? On safety? Or are these ignored for other things?
- How are people measured: Is safety measured as tightly as production? What is measured tightly is what is important to management.
- How people are rewarded: Is there a larger reward for productivity than for safety? This states management's real priorities.
- Is teamwork fostered? Or is it "them versus us?" In safety, is it "police vs. policed?"
- What is the history? What are the traditions?
- Who are the corporate heroes? And why?
- Is the safety system intended to save lives or to comply with regulations?
- Are supervisors required to do safety tasks daily? This says that safety is a big value.
- Do big bosses wander around? Talk to people?

- Is using the brain allowed on the work floor?
- Has the company downsized?
- Is the company profitable? Too much? Too little?

The use of an outside, independent professional can be an effective (but expensive) method for assessing the safety culture in an organization. SHE professionals who plan to conduct the culture assessment in-house should research the issue further to answer the questions posed above. Figure 6, the Safety Culture Profile Survey developed by the Maine Employers' Mutual Insurance Company (MEMIC 2004), is an example of a quick safety culture perception survey that can be used as-is or modified to fit individual organizational needs.

Culture surveys are also being researched as leading indicators of sound safety management performance. In Ontario, Canada, the Institute for Work and Health collaborated with labor and labor-based organizations to develop a set of consensus-based leading indicators that can be reliably linked to traditional lagging indicators, such as workers' compensation claims. The goal of this research is to provide leading, culture-based indicators for better managing the safety management system (Amick 2010).

The research indicated eight topic areas of an organization's culture that are considered leading indicators of safety management performance:

1. Formal safety audits at regular intervals are a normal part of our business.
2. Everyone at this organization values ongoing improvement in this organization.
3. This organization considers safety at least as important as production and quality in the way work is done.
4. Workers and supervisors have the information they need to work safely.
5. Employees are always involved in decisions affecting their health and safety.
6. Those in charge of safety have the authority to make the changes they have identified as necessary.
7. Those who act safely receive positive recognition.
8. Everyone has the tools and/or equipment they need to complete their work safely.

Once the safety culture is assessed and defined, the SHE professional can determine if the objectives of the safety management system work toward improving the culture. Metrics can be established to measure the effectiveness of the system. Areas where trust is lacking can be addressed. Poor communication and lack of participation or interest in the safety program can also be addressed. Training can be tailored to be more effective. These steps will close the perception gaps, improve trust and morale, and create a more positive safety culture within an organization.

Defining Roles for Effective Safety Management

Previous sections of this chapter established the importance of the leadership roles that must be taken by management, the involvement and active participation by employees, and oversight and program facilitation by the SHE professional. Nonetheless, a sound safety management system also assigns responsibilities, provides authority, and holds everyone accountable for the program's success. Each element of the organization's safety management system must be specifically assigned in writing to a specific job or position with coordination responsibilities and performance expectations delineated. Training should also be provided on the assigned responsibilities.

Management must grant written authority necessary to meet these assigned responsibilities (which is in the exclusive control of the individual). The employees must have confidence in their authority, understand how to exercise the authority, and then use their authority to meet assigned responsibilities in a timely manner. This authority also provides for adequate resources (personnel, methods, equipment, and funds) for the employee, along with the effective use of these resources to meet assigned responsibilities. All personnel are held accountable for meeting their safety and health responsibilities. Methods should also exist for monitoring personnel performance.

Management must have written policies for addressing situations when assigned responsibilities are not met. This can result in positive intervention, such as mentoring or coaching, or result in more negative consequences, such as verbal warnings, written warnings,

demotions, or termination. On the other hand, those employees who meet or exceed responsibilities should be recognized and receive positive reinforcement for their behavior. Tracking safety performance is necessary so all responsible parties are aware of performance status and what progress has been achieved. These metrics also are used by responsible parties to adjust objectives to meet assigned safety responsibilities and continuously improve the safety management plan.

It is important to emphasize that top management should not simply delegate implementation of the safety management system to other members of the management team. Top management should remain involved and committed to the safety management system by ensuring its visible inclusion as an element of the organization's business plan (ANSI/AIHA 2005). It is also important for supervisors to be involved with safety management. Petersen (1996) found that effective supervisors received top-level safety training upon initial assignment as well as through continuing education. Effective supervisors also walked the shop floor and engaged with at least one employee a day to discuss job safety performance. Finally, Petersen found that good supervisors "make good use of the shop safety plan and regularly review job safety requirements with each worker (Petersen 1996, 294).

Manuele (2003, 76) wrote that "Employees must believe that they are responsible for their safety, and they must be provided with training, tools, and necessary authority to act." Benefits of employee involvement include:

- substantial contributions in hazard identification
- proposing solutions to hazards or problems creating hazards
- participating in solutions that reduce or eliminate the hazards

Given the necessary training and opportunity, employees can make substantial contributions to the safety program (Manuele 2003).

The Evergreen Program—Continually Improving the Process

The safety management system must be periodically reviewed. ANSI Z10, *Standard for Occupational Health and Safety Management Systems,* addresses management's review of the safety management system in this excerpt from their standard:

> "The organization shall establish and implement a process for top management to review the OHSMS at least annually, and to recommend improvements to ensure its continued suitability, adequacy, and effectiveness. Management reviews are a critical part of the continual improvement of the OHSMS" (ANSI/AIHA 2005, 3).

Subjects recommended by ANSI Z10 for at least an annual review can include (ANSI/AIHS 2005):

- progress in the reduction of risk
- effectiveness of processes to identify, assess, and prioritize risk and system deficiencies
- effectiveness in addressing underlying causes of risks and system deficiencies

This management review should also occur as systems, operations, and processes change (Anton 1989, Petersen 2003, Reese 2003). This review can include one or more of the following components:

- Evaluate the impact of new regulations and national consensus standards on the program goals and objectives.
- Examine the status of goals and objectives of the program.
- Review accident and incidents including near-miss events.
- Evaluate the scope, findings, and follow up to inspections.
- Review any training provided.
- Gauge movements in the safety culture of the organization, including both management and labor.
- Evaluate observable employee safe work-practice behaviors.
- Evaluate the physical conditions of the workplace.

Manuele (2008) found several typical deficiencies or provisions of a safety management system where shortcomings exist. These include:

- risk assessment and prioritization
- application of a prescribed hierarchy of controls to achieve acceptable risk levels

- safety design reviews
- inclusion of safety requirements in procurement and contracting papers
- management of change systems

This review can be conducted by an individual (or team) determined competent in all applicable areas by virtue of education, experience, and/or examination. The results of the review are documented and drive appropriate changes or adjustments in the program.

Previously identified deficiencies do not appear on subsequent reviews as deficiencies.

A process should exist that allows deficiencies in the program to become immediately apparent and corrected, in addition to requiring a periodic, comprehensive review. There must be a demonstration that the safety management system results in the reduction or elimination of hazards, incidents, and accidents (Manuele 2003).

Defining the Professional Safety Practitioner

Robert DeSiervo offers this broad definition of a safety professional (DeSiervo 2004).

> Safety Professionals are individuals who are engaged in the prevention of events that harm people, property or the environment. Occupational safety professionals help organizations prevent injuries, illnesses and property damage. These professionals must acquire knowledge of safety sciences through education and experience so that others can rely on their judgment and recommendations. They use qualitative and quantitative analysis of simple and complex products, systems, operations, and other activities to identify hazards. They evaluate the hazards to identify what events can occur and the likelihood of occurrence, severity of results, risks (a combination of probability and severity), and cost. They identify what controls are appropriate and their cost and effectiveness. Safety Professionals make recommendations to managers, designers, employers, government agencies and others. Hazard controls may involve administrative controls (such as plans, policies, procedures, training, etc.) and/or engineering controls (such as safety features and systems, fail-safe features, barriers and other forms of protection). Safety Professionals may manage and provide help to implement controls.

Both conventional wisdom and a review of the literature reveal an ever-increasing need to produce

SHE educators and SHE practitioners in this country in order to meet the challenges confronting the SHE profession in the twenty-first century (DeLeo 2003).

The demand for competent and qualified SHE professionals continues to increase each year (ASSE 2007b). However, defining what makes a SHE professional qualified and competent often engenders a difficult and controversial discussion. Occupational safety and health management in the United States and throughout the world is, and always has been, dynamic. Therefore, those who work in the safety, health, and environmental professions must also be dynamic. One size does not fit all. There are some SHE competencies that stretch across most, if not all, professions, such as regulatory record keeping, ergonomics, hazard communications training, personal protective equipment, and job hazard-analysis concepts. Other professions require industry-specific SHE knowledge and skill sets. This includes industries in the healthcare, transportation, mining, construction, and environmental arenas. These industry-specific professions require the knowledge, competencies, and experience to address a much more defined set of regulatory compliance and job-specific occupational hazards and issues.

Safety is everyone's responsibility. But assigning safety responsibilities does not guarantee the success of a safety program. The importance of effective safety awareness and training as a component to developing a strong and effective safety culture in an organization is critical, as previously mentioned. At what point does an individual require higher levels of training, a more formal safety education or degree, on-the-job experience, and skill sets in safety to succeed? Job descriptions and responsibilities can identify the safety knowledge, education, and skills necessary to be competent in SHE-related duties. Entry-level positions may or may not require any formalized safety education or experience. Many employees find safety has been added to their current job descriptions as safety programs are implemented and expanded.

Consider the following positions that interface with an effective safety management system. What education, experience, and certifications make these individuals competent in their safety responsibilities?

- a part-time fire/safety officer (also employed as a local fire fighter) who checks fire extinguishers monthly, performs new employee fire safety training, and performs limited fire safety inspections throughout the facility
- an operations manager at a manufacturing plant who is responsible for employee safety
- a laboratory manager who is responsible for the chemical hygiene plan and OSHA compliance issues, in addition to chemical waste management, disposal, and emergency response
- a personnel manager who has the dual responsibility for the overall safety program
- a safety technician working within a larger safety department who conducts general safety awareness training and departmental safety inspections and issues PPE
- a union mechanic who is elected as the safety representative on the company safety committee
- a corporate safety director for a Fortune 500 company who is responsible for safety management for worldwide operations
- a CFO who understands how safety can reduce insurance costs and improve the bottom line
- a CEO who recognizes that good safety management improves morale and production of the workforce
- shareholders who benefit from improved productivity and reduced costs from a strong safety management program

Each of these job descriptions interfaces with the overall safety management system to different degrees. The uniqueness of SHE issues of a given industry and/or job description requires a variety of competencies and experience levels that must be adapted and molded for overall SHE management to be effective. So what makes a SHE professional competent? What experience, education, certifications, and skills are necessary for the competent safety practitioner to succeed?

Defining competencies can be a moving target. What competencies are needed for today's safety practitioner? What curricula or competencies may best prepare students to become the competent safety managers of tomorrow (Blair 2003)? What competencies are required of academia to provide curriculums that serve both of these groups? Competencies for the safety practitioner are defined by experience, skills, certifications, education, and an ever-changing body of knowledge.

Experience

Education and certification aside, there is no substitute for on-the-job experience in effective safety management. Years of on-the-job safety experience can develop skills that can be difficult to duplicate or measure through education or certification alone. Those who have witnessed near misses, accidents, injuries, and fatalities gain unique experiences that can change an individual forever. These first-hand experiences have been converted into learning tools to shock employees into learning the consequences of unsafe behavior. OSHA created a document called *Fatal Facts* (OSHA 2009) that captures unsafe behaviors and relates them to real-life occupational fatalities.

The experience that qualifies a competent safety practitioner is defined as *supervised experience*. Supervision by other experienced, competent safety professionals may be especially valuable to recent entrants into the field (DeSiervo 2004). Supervised experience can bring about anticipation of potential hazards by recognizing unsafe activities or conditions. However, workplace experience, such as experience shared by line workers, can also provide great knowledge and insight for the new safety practitioner. An experienced

line foreman might know more than a Certified Safety Professional (BCSP) about the safe operation of the equipment he operates, including lockout/tagout, machine guarding, and personal protection use.

Workplace experience can sometimes be a negative. Repetitive workplace experience can lull those who know better into complacency and carelessness when performing repetitive tasks. Workplace experience can also teach us tricks to bypass safety devices designed to protect employees and equipment. Safety practitioners should seek a balance between supervised experience and workplace experience.

Experience has its financial benefits, too. Safety practitioners with ten to twenty years' experience earn about $18,000 more per year than those with less than ten years' experience. Figure 7 breaks down average salary by years of experience:

Unfortunately, training and experience alone can be difficult to quantify. Many certifications and designations were designed to help measure an individual's competency in a given area. Finding a certification or educational opportunity that specifically fits the unique occupational requirements the safety practitioner needs to satisfy may prove to be difficult. It may be necessary for a safety practitioner to demonstrate or measure his or her competency in safety in order to advance and succeed. This can only be accomplished through the pursuit of academic degrees and/or professional certifications.

Education

"Safety is a relatively new academic discipline" (Adams et al. 2004, 1). Prior to the passage of the Occupational Safety and Health (OSH) Act of 1970 (OSHA 1970), there were few college or university safety courses or degree programs available for those entering the safety profession (ASSE 2003). Safety in academia emerged during the 1970s and has blossomed into a legitimate educational path at the associate, baccalaureate, masters, and doctorate levels of higher education. The American Society of Safety Engineers provides the following overview for higher education opportunities for the safety practitioner:

A number of community and junior colleges offer an associate degree in safety or a related field. People

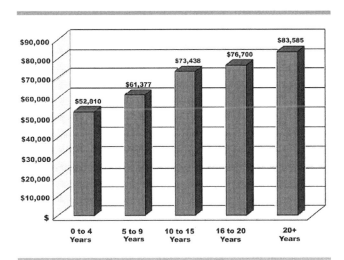

FIGURE 7. Average income for SHE professionals (*Source:* ASSE 2004)

graduating from these programs are hired for limited positions in safety. They may help manufacturers, construction companies or other industries meet OSHA's hazard control standards. A number of four-year colleges and universities offer undergraduate degrees in safety. Today, over 90% of those in the safety profession have earned at least a bachelor's degree. About 30% of those entering the field have a bachelor's degree in safety, while many move into safety from other disciplines (engineering, business, physical sciences, etc.) and later pursue safety studies. About 40% of today's safety professionals have advanced degrees. Some of those with an advanced degree in safety graduated with a bachelor's degree in a non-safety field. They may use a master's degree in safety to prepare for and enter the safety profession. Some who get their safety preparation at the bachelor's level also pursue graduate study in safety or a safety-related specialty, such as industrial hygiene, environmental science, public health or ergonomics. Some work toward advanced degrees in related fields, such as business and engineering that will enhance their career opportunities. (ASSE/BCSP 2007a)

As of May 2005, there were over 70 safety, health, and environmental-related programs offered by community colleges, colleges, and universities. Nearly 20 percent of these courses were Accreditation Board for Engineering and Technology (ABET)-accredited (ASSE 2007b). There are also many educational institutions offering SHE-related degrees, including environmental, industrial hygiene, engineering, and fire science programs. Many of these programs are available through distance learning programs that allow the SHE professional to obtain educational credentials over the Internet or through the mail. These emerging forms of distance learning provide a more convenient, self-paced opportunity for those who do not have accessible SHE programs available to meet individual needs.

An education provides a strong foundation for those entering the safety profession. It also can accelerate promotions and compensation. A study published by the American Society of Safety Engineers found that the average income for safety practitioners by education ranged from about $60,000/year for those with a high school education, to over $75,000/year for those with a bachelor's degree, to nearly $95,000/year for those with a Ph.D or Ed.D (ASSE 2004). Acquiring a formal degree in safety will also aid individuals in obtaining professional recognition, certifications, and credentials. Many safety certifications accept SHE academic achievements as prerequisite qualifications. Other professional safety organizations, including ASSE, BSCP, and AIHA, recognize and use academic qualifications to reduce experience prerequisites or to take the place of exams.

Accredited Education Program Criteria

According to *The Career Guide to the Safety Profession* (ASSE/BCSP 2007a, 19),

> To prepare for the safety professional courses, college students are normally required to take courses in mathematics through beginning calculus, statistics, chemistry with laboratory work, physics with laboratory work, human physiology or biology, and introductory courses in business management, engineering mechanics and processes, speech, composition, and psychology. Students in safety must also acquire good computer skills, including the ability to use the Internet and important business and safety software packages. Professional safety courses in higher education include safety and health system management, design of engineering hazard controls, industrial hygiene and toxicology, fire protection, ergonomics, environmental safety and health, system safety, accident/incident investigation, product safety, construction safety, educational and training methods, assessment of safety performance, and behavioral aspects of safety. Students may also elect to take specialty courses beyond the required courses.

In 1996, ABET embarked on an accreditation reform effort designed to foster an environment in which each graduate of engineering, technology, computing, and applied science, where the safety curricula reside, possesses the skills necessary for both lifelong learning and productive contributions to the profession, employers, economy, and society (ABET 2010). Accreditation criteria have changed from subject matter content to outcome-based activity (ASSE 2003). The major outcome criteria include a baseline understanding of math and science; analysis and interpretation of data; anticipating, identifying, and evaluating hazards; developing hazard control design, methods, procedures, and programs; the functioning of multidisciplinary teams and group activities; understanding SHE professional responsibilities; a knowledge of contemporary SHE issues in both global and societal contexts; communication skills; and training skills.

The ASSE Educational Standards Committee (ESC) developed revised safety curriculum guidelines in early 2005 to assist universities in the development of safety curricula and also to assist ASSE Program Evaluators participating in the accreditation process (ASSE 2005a). The revised criteria became effective during the 2006 evaluation cycle. The criteria that ABET Baccalaureate Safety Programs include must demonstrate that graduates are able to:

1. Anticipate, recognize, and evaluate hazardous conditions and practices affecting people, property, and the environment.
2. Develop and evaluate appropriate strategies designed to mitigate risk.
3. Apply principles of safety and health in a nonacademic setting through an internship, cooperative, or supervised experience.

"Topics for Safety Curriculum" identifies the appropriate topics to include in safety curricula (ASSE 2005a). Table 1 identifies both required topic areas as well as recommended areas. It is important to remember the topic areas are broad areas that were not intended to be all-inclusive. For example, within the Safety Management Topic, a program may choose to cover a variety of topics such as human behavior, cost-benefit analysis, organizational and management theory, safety management systems, safety program elements, record keeping, and so on. Where possible, all of these topic areas should be tied in with the three major program objectives discussed at the beginning of these guidelines that deal with recognition, evaluation, and control. Universities are encouraged to contact the ASSE Educational Standards Committee for further assistance in the development of safety curricula.

The American Society of Safety Engineers identified four purposes that institutional accreditation serves (ASSE 2005a):

1. It assures a level of quality.
2. It is required for student access to certain federal funds, such as student aid.

3. It eases transfer. Many regionally accredited colleges and universities will only accept transfer credit or admission to graduate school from students from regionally accredited colleges or universities.
4. It engenders employer confidence.

Current or future safety practitioners should evaluate educational opportunities carefully. Accredited programs offer a valuable third-party assurance of the curriculum of a given program.

Certifications

The question has been posed (Blair 2003), "Do safety, health, and environmental practitioners need to be Certified Safety Professionals?" What other certifications might benefit the safety practitioner? There are over 300 different certifications worldwide that one can achieve in the disciplines of safety, health, industrial hygiene, and hazardous wastes. Over 300 SHE designations, with only a handful meeting widely accepted accreditation requirements, create a confusing, even dangerous, practitioner landscape (ASSE 2005b). Many of these certifications are accredited by multiple third parties requiring rigorous qualifications, testing, and maintenance. Other certifications merely require an individual to fill out an application and pay an appropriate fee. Obtaining safety certification does not necessarily equate to safety competence. Therefore, what is a legitimate certification for the competent SHE professional? Gaining the right certification for one's industry can improve job qualifications, responsibilities, and compensation.

Certifications have demonstrated a positive impact on the average compensation paid to safety practitioners (ASSE 2007b, BCSP 2009, AIHA 2008). A compensation survey by the American Society of Safety Engineers (ASSE 2004) found that those who have some type of extra certification or credential earned on average $12,500 more than those who do not have any certification. One of the most recognized accredited safety credentials in the world is the Certified Safety Professional (CSP) designation administered by the Board of Certified Safety Professionals (BCSP). BSCP found that the average income for CSPs was

SIDEBAR 6

NEW JERSEY SAFETY PROFESSIONAL TRUTH IN ADVERTISING ACT
(State of New Jersey 2002)

New Jersey P.L.2002, c.050 (S894 1R) CHAPTER 50
An Act concerning safety professionals and
supplementing P.L.1960,
c.39 (C.56:8-1 et seq.).

Be It Enacted by the Senate and General Assembly of
the State of New Jersey:

C.56:8-113 Short title.

1. This act shall be known and may be cited as the
"Safety Professional Truth in Advertising Act."

C.56:8-114 Findings, declarations relative to
qualification of safety professionals.

2. The Legislature finds and declares that it is necessary
to provide assurance to the public that individuals
holding any safety certification have met certain
qualifications.

C.56:8-115 Definitions relative to qualifications of
safety professionals.

3. As used in this act:

"Safety profession" means the science and art concerned with the preservation of human and material
resources through the systematic application of principles drawn from such disciplines as engineering,
education, psychology, physiology, enforcement and
management for anticipating, identifying and evaluating hazardous conditions and practices; developing
hazard control designs, methods, procedures and programs; implementing, administering and advising
others on hazard controls and hazard control programs; and measuring, auditing and evaluating the
effectiveness of hazard controls and hazard control
programs.

A "Safety professional certification organization"
means a professional organization of safety professionals which has been in existence for at least
five years and which has been established to improve
the practice and educational standards of the safety
profession by certifying individuals who meet its
education, experience and examination requirements.
The organization shall be accredited by the National
Commission of Certifying Agencies (NCCA) or the
Council of Engineering and Scientific Specialty
Boards (CESB), or a nationally recognized accrediting

body which uses certification criteria equal to or
greater than that of the NCCA or CESB.

C.56:8-116 Certification by safety professional
certification organization required.

4. It shall be an unlawful practice for any person to
advertise or hold himself out as possessing a professional safety certification from a safety professional
certification organization unless that person is certified by the applicable safety professional certification
organization.

5. This act shall take effect on the first day of the 25th
month following enactment.

Approved August 3, 2002.

$99,448. Another highly recognized safety certification
is the Certified Industrial Hygienist (CIH) designation
administered by the American Industrial Hygiene
Association (AIHA). A 2008 AIHA salary survey also
confirmed the value of safety certifications to compensation (AIHA 2008). Their study found that safety
practitioners with a CIH received average compensation of $10,340. Compensation for both of those
certifications is well above the $79,809 average com-
pensation AIHA found for those with no certification
at all.

In today's economic and business climate, the
safety practitioner is not likely to work for the same
employer his or her whole career. Brauer and Murphy
(2005) found that third-party safety certifications can
also provide lateral mobility to safety practitioners
by providing those holding a quality, recognized certification with credentials to compete for positions
with other employers (Hintch 2005).

Certifications that have been accredited by a recognized third-party accreditation body are supported
by many professional safety organizations and government agencies. Because the work of safety professionals has a direct impact on public safety and health,
government organizations, employers, and those awarding contracts are concerned that safety professionals
be fully qualified and competent to do their jobs.
Safety professionals may therefore need other credentials in addition to their education degree. These
credentials might include licenses, registration, and

professional certification. To date, no state requires safety professionals to be licensed in order to practice (ASSE 2005b).

Third-party safety-accredited certifications have been incorporated into regulations, professional qualifications, and position statements for title protection of safety practitioners. One state has taken the lead in defining what constitutes a safety professional. New Jersey has enacted legislation to ensure those claiming the title of "safety professional" meet minimal standards. The "Safety Professional Truth in Advertising Act" is reproduced in part in Sidebar 6.

Many OSHA regulations cite accredited safety certifications for reviewing and/or modifying existing safe work practices at job sites. Safety associations, including the American Society of Safety Engineers, American Industrial Hygiene Association, National Safety Council, and the Institute of Hazardous Materials Managers, require third-party accredited certifications as the preferred way to achieve professional status in their respective organizations (see "Appendix A: Recommended Reading," for a list of organizations and their Web sites). Widely accepted organizations that provide highly reliable, quality mechanisms for accrediting certifications include:

1. The National Commission on Certifying Agencies (NCCA), established originally by the federal government to help ensure capabilities of federal allied health practitioners recognized under federal law
2. The Council of Engineering and Scientific Specialty Boards (CESB)
3. The Organization for International Standardization (ISO) under the American National Standards Institute

These are the only accreditation organizations that meet legal and psychometric standards closely similar to those followed by state licensing mechanisms (ASSE 2005a).

Many safety associations and certifying bodies have also pushed for title protection for the safety practitioners they represent. AIHA actively promotes and defends the CIH designation in a variety of legislative venues on local, state, federal, and international levels. These efforts are focused and effective since all of their professional members are CIHs. However, there are other, more diverse safety groups that have difficulty representing and satisfying a majority of their members with such diverse backgrounds. The American Society of Safety Engineers (ASSE) represents over 30,000 safety, health, and environmental professionals throughout the world. Only about 25 percent of its membership has achieved the status of CSP, CIH, or CHMM (ASSE 2005b). ASSE fully understands that there are uncertified members with experience, education, and training who perform as competently as those with these accredited certifications. However, to advance the profession as a whole through the regulatory and legislative process, ASSE has the responsibility to rely on the highest level of demonstrated competence to achieve that goal. The ASSE has developed a position paper for proposed safety regulations stating:

> When legislators and regulators insert a profession in a bill or regulation, they typically look to an accepted third party to provide some measure of the professional's qualifications. ASSE is not aware of a legislator or regulator who would be willing to write in an SHE practitioner simply because of their years of employment, education achievements, or unique experiences without those qualifications being validated by a widely accepted third party. States typically are not willing to provide such certification programs. Without such third-party validation of qualifications, every piece of regulation or legislation would be required to include a unique set of practitioner qualifications as well as a process to ensure the appropriateness or validity of those qualifications. (ASSE 2005b).

When selecting a certification, it is important to evaluate the many values it can provide, including (BCSP 2009):

- any third-party accreditation
- the incorporated body of knowledge
- prerequisites, qualifications, and necessary experience
- professional recognition
- professional growth and compensation
- regulatory recognition

The benefits of obtaining third-party accredited safety certification have demonstrated a positive impact on the professional development, advancement, and compensation of safety practitioners.

Competencies and Skills

Soule (1993, 6) found safety practitioners need to be more than just compliance technicians—"they must be good communicators who understand business language and possess good management skills." In his 2003 study, Dr. Earl Blair stated, "Knowledge of business, accounting, and marketing are topics that can meaningfully expand the safety, health and environmental practitioners should they be integrated into the safety curriculum. Safety professionals may lose credibility, if although otherwise highly competent in the technical aspects of safety, they appear ignorant in these important areas" (Blair 2003). Business skills are a must for the successful safety practitioner. They need to possess the total package in order to be successful (DeSiervo 2004).

According to the Blair study (2003), the business skills that have been identified as needing further definition include:

1. The particular areas of business expertise where safety managers need to be most knowledgeable.
2. The specific topics and curriculum most useful for promoting effective communication and interpersonal skills.
3. The most effective ways to measure safety performance that incorporate a broad spectrum of measures, such as trailing indicators, cost indicators, and leading indicators.

Additional competencies were identified and recommended for those seeking to develop doctoral-level safety programs for teaching future SHE professionals. William DeLeo conducted a study asking each member of the two groups, safety educators and practitioners/experts, to submit and rank safety competencies (DeLeo 2003). Those competencies that received a 100 percent ranking in the study's finding included:

1. Ability to effectively use the safety sciences literature.

2. Ability to critically evaluate existing research literature in occupational safety and health, and identify gaps in that literature.
3. Developing, implementing, managing, and evaluating safety and health programs.
4. Evaluating safety and health program performance and designing performance measures.
5. Ability to develop hazard control methods, procedures, and programs to include integration of safety performance into the goals, operations, and productivity of organizations and their management.
6. Ability to estimate the economic impact of safety issues and practices on a firm's economic performance (cost modeling).

Those competencies that received a 93 percent importance ranking in the study included:

1. Demonstrated in-depth knowledge of safety, health, and environmental issues.
2. Ability to stay current with the changing safety challenges in the workplace.
3. Ability to review, compile, analyze, and interpret data from accident and loss event reports and other sources regarding injuries, illnesses, property damage, environmental effects, or public impacts in order to identify causes, trends, and relationships.
4. Ability to understand and articulate what is an appropriate safety and health management system for an organization in an industry with a specific culture at a certain point on the life cycle of a business.

Recent safety literature, professional development conferences, and seminars have been inundated with multiple topics on safety business skills, including leadership, safety culture, business of safety, and management. These articles, books, research papers, and presentations provide the safety practitioner with an abundance of data to help fill in any gaps in the skills and knowledge necessary to succeed. These current competencies must be achieved to succeed in today's business climate. These competencies must be monitored and reevaluated to ensure our current safety students are prepared to succeed in the future as well.

The Safety Body of Knowledge (BoK)

The American Society of Safety Engineers defines the safety body of knowledge references of the SHE profession as ". . . a collection of commonly used general and specific information on the safety, health, and environmental theory, principles, and practice in the broad field of loss prevention and control" (ASSE 2003).

While the definition of the body of knowledge of the SHE profession has not yet been consolidated into one document, the ASSE has generally defined one as including the following elements:

- standards used to accredit SHE curriculum for colleges and universities
- ASSE-published documents and materials used to describe the scope and functions of the professional SHE position
- requirements for certification or licensure as an SHE professional, as currently stated by the Board of Certified Safety Professionals
- the ASSE Code of Professional Conduct
- SHE regulations, standards, and other legislation that define SHE compliance
- publications, books, and materials used by SHE professionals to implement effective SHE management programs

ASSE prepared a white paper defining a Safety Body of Knowledge in June 2003. One of the most significant findings published in the white paper was that safety practitioners use reference codes, standards, and regulations more than any text, and also use the Web extensively (ASSE 2003). However, there is strong consensus among safety leaders that significant portions of our body of knowledge continue to evolve. Therefore, the safety profession as a whole must continue to address the issue of an ever-changing body of knowledge reference for the safety,

health, and environmental profession that identifies those resources needed for the prevention of injury, illness, death, and the destruction of property and the environment.

Competencies for the Future Safety Practitioner

The American Industrial Hygiene Association also looks to the future of the safety practitioner in an expanding global arena by stating:

> . . . AIHA believes all parties (government, employers, and employees) should begin to discuss the changing workplace and expansion of the global economy and assume a lead role in offering recommendations to address occupational health and safety in the global economy of the 21st century. (AIHA 2004)

A study by DeLeo (2003) identified academic criteria necessary to meet this future need when it stated:

> New training programs and techniques must be designed to meet the needs and challenges of the 21st century workplace. One of the resultant competencies exiting the final round of this study was an ability to stay current with the changing safety challenges in the workplace.

Safety certification bodies are also looking to adjust to the future needs of safety practitioners. The BCSP has identified the need to study the flexibility in qualifications and examinations in its strategic plan. They are looking to expand the path to the safety profession for those who enter the profession with an adjunct role or as technicians and technologists (Brauer and Murphy 2005).

Competency requirements for the future safety practitioner will address a balance between supervised experience, higher education, and third-party certification. The competent safety practitioner will combine these competencies with character traits guided by professional ethics and a professional code of conduct to create a trustworthy safety practitioner. Both character and competency will be necessary for the safety practitioner to meet the challenges present in the twenty-first century.

REFERENCES

Abrams, A. 2005. Email communication to author (May 16).

_____. 2006. *Legal Perspectives of ANSI Z-10* (retrieved July 31, 2010). www.asse.org/membership/docs/92ArticleaboutZ10LegalPerspectives.pdf

Accreditation Board for Engineering and Technology (ABET). 2010. *History* (retrieved August 31, 2010). www.abet.org/history.shtml

Adams, P., R. Brauer, T. Bresnahan et al. 2004. "Professional Certification." *Professional Safety* 49(12): 26–31.

American Conference of Governmental Industrial Hygienists (ACGIH). 2007. *How to Develop a Simple, Cost-Effective Safety & Health Program: A Small Business Guide* (retrieved March 31, 2007). www.acgih.org/about/committees/SBguide.htm

American Industrial Hygiene Association (AIHA). 2008. "Compensation & Benefits Survey." Fairfax, VA: AIHA.

American National Standards Institute (ANSI) and American Industrial Hygiene Association (AIHA). 2005. *ANSI/AIHA Standard Z10-2005: Occupational Health and Safety Management Systems.* Fairfax, VA: AIHA.

American Society for Quality (ASQ). 2004. *Quality Tools: Fishbone Diagram* (retrieved March 24, 2007). www.asq.org/learn-about-quality/cause-analysis-tools/overview/fishbone.html

American Society of Safety Engineers (ASSE) and Board of Certified Safety Professionals (BCSP). 2002. *White Paper Addressing the Return on Investment for Safety, Health, and Environmental (SHE) Management Programs* (retrieved March 31, 2007). www.asse.org/bosc_articles_2.htm

_____. 2007a. *ABET/ASSE Accredited Safety Degree Programs* (retrieved December 11, 2007). www.asse.org/professionalaffairs/education/directory/directory_abet.htm

_____. 2007b. *Career Guide to the Safety Professional.* 3d ed. Des Plaines, IL: ASSE and BCSP.

American Society of Safety Engineers (ASSE). 2003. *White Paper of the Body of Knowledge Task Force of the American Society of Safety Engineers Council on Practices and Standards* (retrieved February 4, 2008). www.asse.org/practicespecialties/bok/docs/bok_wpapers6-03.pdf

_____. 2004. "ASSE Compensation Survey." *Professional Safety* (October) 49(10):26–27.

_____. 2005a. *Safety Curriculum Guidelines* (retrieved February 4, 2008). www.asse.org/professionalaffairs/govtaffairs/ngpost19.phpvarSearch=Safety+Curriculum+Guidelines

_____. 2005b. *ASSE Position Statement on ASSE Government Affairs Representation of SHE Professionals.* Des Plaines, IL: American Society of Safety Engineers.

Amick, B. C. 2010. "Managing Prevention with Leading and Lagging Indicators in the Workers' Compensation System" in *Use of Workers' Compensation Data for Occupational Injury & Illness Prevention* (pp. 83–87). Washington, D.C.: Department of Health and Human Services.

Anton, Thomas J. 1989. *Occupational Safety and Health Management.* New York: McGraw Hill.

Apollo Associated Services. 2007. *The Apollo Process* (retrieved December 13, 2007). www.apollorca.com/process/process.shtml

Barfield, G. 2004. "Safety in Business Terms." *Professional Safety* 49:8.

Blair, E. H. 1999. "Which Competencies Are Most Important for Safety Managers?" *Professional Safety* (October) pp. 28–32.

_____. 2003. "Culture and Leadership." *Professional Safety* (June) pp. 18–22.

Board of Certified Safety Professionals (BCSP). 2009. *CSP Facts* (retrieved July 31, 2011). www.bcsp.org/Salary_Survey

Brauer, R., and H. Murphy. 2005. "Workplace Safety Delivers ROI." *Human Capital Magazine* (June).

Bureau of Labor Statistics (BLS). 2006. *Industry Injury and Illness Data* (retrieved December 13, 2007). www.bls.gov/iif/oshsum.htm

Carnegie, Dale. 1981. *How to Win Friends and Influence People.* Rev. ed. New York: Simon and Schuster.

Chen, P. Y. 2005. How Can We Increase Safety Behaviors? Speech to the Chemistry Division at Los Alamos National Laboratory, Los Alamos, New Mexico.

Colford, J. 2005a. "CEOs Who Get It." *Safety and Health* (February) 171(2):25–33.

_____. 2005b. "The ROI of Safety: It Starts at the Top." *Business Week* (September).

Colvin, R. J. 1992. *The Guidebook to Successful Safety Programming.* Chelsea: Lewis Publishers.

DeArmond, S., and P. Y. Chen. 2007. Financial Executives' Perceptions of Safety Performance, Safety Programs, and Safety Personnel. Paper presented at the XIIIth European Congress of Work and Organizational Psychology, May 9–12, Stockholm, Sweden.

DeLeo, W. 2003. "Safety Educators and Practitioners Identify the Competencies of an Occupational Safety and Environmental Health Doctoral Degree: An On Line Application of the Delphi Technique." *Journal of SH&E Research* (Spring) 1(1).

Della-Giustina, D. E. 2000. *Developing a Safety and Health Program.* Boca Raton, FL: CRC Press.

DeSiervo, Robert. 2004. "The Education of a Safety Professional." *Journal of SHE Research* (Fall) 4(2).

Downs, D. E. 2003. "Management System Assessment." *Professional Safety* 48(11):31–38.

Easter, K., R. Hegney, and G. Taylor. 2004. *Enhancing Occupational Safety and Health.* Boston: Elservier.

Friend, M., and J. P. Kohn. 2006. *Fundamentals of Occupational Safety and Health.* New York: Government Institutes.

Hintch, B. 2005. "Interview with Roger Brauer." *Compliance Magazine* (May) pp. 3–6.

Indiana University of Pennsylvania. 2006. *Accident Investigation and Analysis* (retrieved December 13, 2007). www.coned.iup.edu/SafetyScience/OCCSafety/os2.htm

International Labour Office (ILO). 2001. *Guidelines on Occupational Safety and Health Management Systems.* Geneva, Switzerland: ILO.

International Occupational Hygiene Association (IOHA). 1998. *Occupational Health and Safety Management Systems.* Geneva, Switzerland: IOHA.

Ishikawa, Kaoru. 1968. *Guide to Quality Control.* Tokyo, Japan: Asian Productivity Organization.

Kepner-Tregoe, Inc. 2007. *The KT Way* (retrieved December 13, 2007). www.kepnertregoe.com/TheKTWay/OurProcesses.cfm

Liberty Mutual Research Institute for Safety (LM). 2005. *Liberty Mutual Workplace Safety Index.* Hopkinton, Massachusetts: Liberty Mutual Research Institute for Safety.

Maine Employers' Mutual Insurance Company. 2004. Safety Culture Profile Survey.

Manuele, F. A. 2003. *On the Practice of Safety.* 3d ed. Hoboken, NJ: John Wiley & Sons.

———. 2005. "Risk Assessment & Hierarchies of Control." *Professional Safety* 50(5):33–39.

———. 2008. *Advanced Safety Management.* Hoboken, NJ: John Wiley & Sons.

National Institute for Occupational Safety and Health (NIOSH). 2005. *Publication No 2005-112: A Compendium of NIOSH Economic Research 2002–2003* (retrieved February 11, 2008). www.cdc.gov/niosh/docs/2005-112/default.htm

Occupational Safety and Health Administration (OSHA). 1970. *OSH Act of 1970* (retrieved February 15, 2008). www.osha.gov/pls/oshaweb/owasrch.search_form?p_doc_type=OSHACT

———. 1989. *Safety and Health Program Management Guidelines; Issuance of Voluntary Guidelines; Notice.* Federal Register Vol. 54, No. 16, Jan. 26, 1989, pp. 3904–3916.

———. 1996. *Program Evaluation Profile (PEP)* (retrieved August 31, 2010). www.osha.gov/SLTC/safetyhealth/dsg/topics/safetyhealth/pep.html

———. 1998a. *Draft Proposed Safety and Health Program Rule. 29 CFR 1900.1. Docket S&H-0027* (retrieved February 4, 2008). www.osha.gov/dsg/topics/safety-health/nhsp.html

———. 1998b. *OSHA 2254, Training Requirements in OSHA Standards and Training Guidelines (revised).* Washington, D.C.: OSHA.

———. 1998c. *OSHA Software Expert Advisors, OSHA's $afety Pays E-tool* (retrieved August 31, 2010). www.osha.gov/dcsp/smallbusiness/safetypays.html

———. 2001a. *Safety and Health Management Systems E-tool* (retrieved August 31, 2010). www.osha.gov/SLTC/etools/safetyhealth/index.html

———. 2001b. *Directive 00-01 (CSP 02), TED 3.6, Consultation Policies and Procedures Manual, Chapter 1, Section IX: A Brief History of the OSHA Consultation Program* (August 6, 2001) (accessed February 28, 2008). www.osha.gov/pls/oshaweb/owadisp.show_document?p_table=DIRECTIVES&p_id=2584#8-I

———. 2002. *OSHA 3071, Job Hazard Analysis (revised).* www.osha.gov/Publications/osha2254.pdf

———. 2004. *Voluntary Protection Plans, Recognizing Excellence in Safety* (retrieved August 31, 2010). www.osha.gov/Publications/vpp/vpp_kit.pdf

———. 2005. *OSHA 2209-02R, Small Business Handbook.* www/osha.gov/Publications/smallbusiness/smallbusiness.pdf

———. 2006a. *Accident Investigation* (retrieved August 31, 2010). www.osha.gov/SLTC/accidentinvestigation/index.html

———. 2006b. *06-06 (CSP 02)—TED 3.6, Consultation Policies and Procedures Manual, Chapter 8: OSHA's Safety and Health Achievement Recognition Program (SHARP) and pre-SHARP* (retrieved March 17, 2007). www.osha.gov/pls/oshaweb/owadisp.show_document?p_table=DIRECTIVES&p_id=3489

———. 2007. *Fatal Facts Accident Reports* (retrieved March 10, 2007). www.osha.gov/OshDoc/toc_FatalFacts.html

———. 2009. *Fact Sheet, Voluntary Protection Programs.* www.osha.gov/OshDoc/data_General_Facts/fact-sheet-vpp.pdf

Oregon OSHA (OR-OSHA). 2006. *Online Course 100, Safety and Health Management Basics* (retrieved August 31, 2010). www.cbs.state.or.us/Esternal/osha/educate/training/pages/100outline.html

Paradies, M., and L. Unger. 2000. *TapRooT, The System for Root Cause Analysis, Problem Investigation, and Proactive Improvement.* Knoxville, TN: Systems Improvement, Inc.

Parker, J. G. 2005. "Stopping Injuries Means Getting Down to the Source." *Safety and Health* (May) pp. 6–8.

Petersen, Dan. 1996. *Human Error Reduction and Safety Management.* Hoboken, NJ: John Wiley and Sons.

———. 2003. *Techniques of Safety Management: A Systems Approach.* Des Plaines, IL: American Society of Safety Engineers.

———. 2004. "Leadership & Safety Excellence: A Positive Culture Drives Performance." *Professional Safety.* 49(10), 28–32.

Reese, C. D. 2003. *Occupational Health and Safety Management.* Boca Raton, FL: Lewis Publishers.

Schneid, T. 2000. *Modern Safety and Resource Control Management.* New York: John Wiley & Sons.

Shingo, S. 1981. *A Study of the Toyota Production System.* Tokyo, Japan: Productivity Press.

Soule, R. 1993. Perceptions of an Occupational Safety Curriculum by Graduates, Their Employers and Their Faculty. PhD diss, University of Pittsburgh.

State of New Jersey. 2002. *Safety Professional Truth in Advertising Act.* New Jersey P.L. 2002, c.050 (S894 1R) Chapter 50.

Walton, M. 1986. *The Deming Management Method.* New York: Perigree.

Workplace Safety and Insurance Board and Canadian Manufacturers and Exporters Ontario Division. 2001. *Business Results Through Health and Safety* (retrieved August 31, 2010). www.wsib.or.ca/wsib/wsibsite. nsf/LookupFiles/DownloadableFileBusinessResults ThroughHealth&Safety/$File/Biz.pdf

APPENDIX A: RECOMMENDED READING

Codes, Regulations, and Standards

American National Standards Institute (ANSI) standards.

Department of Transportation. 49 CFR. *Transportation.*

Environmental Protection Agency. 40 CFR. *Protection of the Environment.*

National Fire Protection Association (NFPA) codes and standards.

Occupational Health and Safety Administration. 1974. 29 CFR 1910. *Occupational Safety and Health Standards.* Washington, D.C.: U.S. Department of Labor

Occupational Health and Safety Administration. 1992. 29 CFR 1926. *Safety and Health Regulations for Construction.* Washington, D.C.: U.S. Department of Labor.

Texts, References, and Research Publications

Alli, B. O. 2001. *Fundamental Principles of Occupational Health and Safety.* Geneva, Switzerland: International Labour Office.

Deming, W. E. 1994. *The New Economics for Industry, Government, Education.* Cambridge, MA: MIT Center for Advanced Education Studies.

Downs, D. E. 2003. "Management System Assessment." *Professional Safety* 48(11):31–38.

Muller, S., and C. Braun. 1998. *Safety Culture—A Reflection on Risk Awareness.* Zurich, Switzerland: Swiss Reinsurance Company.

National Institute for Occupational Safety and Health (NIOSH). 2004. Publication #2004-135. *How to Evaluate Safety and Health Changes in the Workplace.* Cincinnati, OH: NIOSH.

National Safety Council (NSC). 2006. *Accident Prevention Manual.* Itasca, IL: NSC.

_____. 2006. *Supervisors Safety Manual.* Itasca, IL: NSC.

_____. 2007. *Injury Facts.* Itasca, IL: NSC.

Noncommercial Web Sites

American Industrial Hygiene Association (www.aiha.org)

American National Standards Institute (www.ansi.org)

American Society of Safety Engineers (www.asse.org)

Bureau of Labor Statistics (www.bls.gov)

Centers for Disease Control and Prevention (www.cdc.gov)

National Fire Protection Association (www.nfpa.org)

National Institute for Occupational Safety and Health (www.niosh.gov)

National Safety Council (www.nsc.org)

U.S. Department of Labor (www.dol.gov)

U.S. Department of Transportation (www.dot.gov)

U.S. Environmental Protection Agency (www.epa.gov)

U.S. Occupational Safety and Health Administration (www.osha.gov)

Journals and Periodicals

Industrial Safety and Hygiene News. BNP Media.

Journal of Occupational and Environmental Hygiene. American Industrial Hygiene Association. (www.aiha.org/Content/AccessInfo/joeh/)

NFPA Journal. National Fire Protection Association. (www.nfpa.org/journalPortal.asp?categoryID=187 &src=NFPAJournal)

Occupational Hazards Magazine. Penton Media. (www.occupationalhazards.com/)

Occupational Health and Safety Magazine. Stevens Publications. (www.ohsonline.com/)

Occupational Safety & Health Reporter. Bureau of National Affairs. (www.bna.com/products/ens/oshr.htm)

Professional Safety Journal. American Society of Safety Engineers. (www.asse.org/professionalsafety/)

Safety + Health Magazine. National Safety Council. (www.nsc.org/shnews/)

The Synergist. American Industrial Hygiene Association. (www.aiha.org/Content/AccessInfo/synergist/)

Workplace HR & Safety. Douglas Publications, LLC. (www.workplacemagazine.com/)

Classic Texts (initial publication date of 1974 or earlier)

Carson, Rachel. 1962. *Silent Spring.* Boston: Houghton Mifflin; Cambridge, MA: Riverside Press.

Clayton, George D., and Florence E. Clayton, eds. *Patty's Industrial Hygiene and Toxicology.* 1st ed. New York: Wiley.

Hammer, Willie. 1975. *Occupational Safety Management and Engineering.* Englewood Cliffs, NJ: Prentice-Hall.

Heinrich, H. W. 1931. *Industrial Accident Prevention, a Scientific Approach.* New York: McGraw Hill Book Company.

National Safety Council. 1946. *Accident Prevention Manual for Industrial Operations.* Chicago, IL: Wm. H. Pool Co.

_____. 1970. *Fundamentals of Industrial Hygiene.* Chicago, IL: National Safety Council.

Petersen, Dan. 1971. *Techniques of Safety Management.* New York: McGraw-Hill.

Simonds, Rollin, and John Grimaldi. 1956. *Safety Management. Accident Cost and Control.* Homewood, IL: R.D. Irwin.

APPENDIX B: ANSI Z15.1 STANDARD: A TOOL FOR PREVENTING MOTOR VEHICLE INJURIES AND MINIMIZING LEGAL LIABILITY

By Adele Abrams, Esq. (Copyright © by Adele Abrams LLC)

Motor vehicle crashes that occur on American roadways have historically been the leading cause of occupational fatalities in this country. In the decade between 1992 and 2001, more than 13,000 civilian workers died in such incidents—accounting for 22 percent of all injury-related deaths. According to the Occupational Safety and Health Administration (OSHA), every 12 minutes someone dies in a motor vehicle crash, every 10 seconds an injury occurs and every 5 seconds a crash occurs.[1] Moreover, despite overall decreases in the number and rates of occupational fatalities from all causes, the annual number of work-related roadway deaths has actually increased to a rate of 1.2 deaths per 100,000 full-time employees.[2] The majority of such crash victims are male (89 percent), and the toll is highest among 35–54 year old workers (47 percent).

Although, as expected, persons employed in the transportation industry make up the predominant occupational sector involved in motor vehicle crashes, other affected sectors include the service industry (14 percent), manufacturing (8 percent), and sales (7 percent). What is significant from a legal perspective is that 62 percent of the vehicles occupied by a fatally injured worker were registered to a business or to the government; 17 percent were driver-registered, and just 12 percent were registered to an entity or individual that was not connected to the driver.[3]

Employers whose workers are involved in such crashes have tremendous liability exposure, especially if the individuals injured or killed are third parties (non-employees), where no worker's compensation liability shield exists as an exclusive legal remedy. They bear not only the worker's compensation costs for their employees, and the potential damage awards from third-party tort claims, but also the costs of equipment replacement and the indirect costs of workforce disruption and lost productivity associated with such incidents.

Motor vehicle crashes cost employers $60 billion annually in medical care, legal expenses, property damage, and lost productivity. OSHA estimates that the average crash costs an employer $16,500. When a worker has an on-the-job crash that results in an injury, the cost to their employer is $74,000. Costs can exceed $500,000 when a fatality is involved.[4] If punitive damages are awarded, that figure can soar into the millions of dollars per incident.

The actions of drivers employed by a company, including their failure to inspect the motor vehicle for defects as well as any unsafe behaviors while driving a company vehicle, can be imputed to the employer

---

[1] See http://www.osha.gov/Publications/motor_vehicle_guide.html.

[2] Centers for Disease Control, *Roadway Crashes Are the Leading Cause of Occupational Fatalities in the U.S.,* DHHS (NIOSH) Publication No. 2004-137(March 2004).

[3] Census of Fatal Occupational Injuries (CFOI), 1992-2001, Bureau of Labor Statistics, and Fatality Analysis Reporting System (FARS), 1997-2002, National High Traffic Safety Administration (NHTSA).

[4] See NHTSA, *The economic burden of traffic crashes on employers: costs by state and industry and by alcohol and restraint use.* Publication DOT HS 809 682 (2003).

under the legal theory of *respondeat superior*.[5] Under this analysis, in the event of a work-related accident on a public roadway, all a tort attorney will need to demonstrate in order to name the employer as defendant in a personal injury or wrongful death lawsuit is that the company exercised some degree of control over the driver, and that the accident occurred while the driver was acting in the course of the employment relationship. Each state will apply its own twist to the vicarious liability doctrine.[6]

Other legal fault doctrines that can apply to employers arising from occupational motor vehicle incidents include:

- Negligent hiring/retention (failure to exercise due care when hiring workers who will drive in the course of their activities by checking driving records etc.)[7];
- Negligent supervision (failing to take corrective action where the employer becomes aware of prior incidents, tendencies toward aggressive or distracted driving);
- Negligent training (failure to provide appropriate documented training for the type of vehicle that the worker will operate); and
- Owner liability (failure to ensure that its agents inspect the vehicles appropriately to prevent operation with known defects, or negligent entrustment of the owner's vehicle to an unqualified or impaired individual).[8]

Even in those situations where the employer's own workers are the only victims of roadway incidents, there may be exclusions if the employer is found to be grossly negligent, as certain states permit tort actions to go forward in such circumstances or enhance the monetary awards available under worker's compensation programs.

Thus prevention through development of proactive initiatives is critical to preserve life, property and to avoid incurring the monetary costs associated with occupational motor vehicle incidents. The Liberty Mutual Insurance Company reported in 2001 that 61 percent of surveyed business executives believe their companies receive a Return on Investment of $3.00 or more for every $1.00 they spent on improving workplace safety.[9] In the case of occupational motor vehicle incidents, the underlying causes of these fatalities and injuries vary widely from mechanical failure to poor highway and vehicle design to driver error. Preventive measures also vary widely, including preventive vehicle maintenance, increased seat belt use, effective driver training, anti-lock brakes, road maintenance and safer vehicle design.

The causes and solutions are so varied that there is no single, simple strategy for prevention. There is, however, a new tool that can be utilized by employers, consultants, insurance industry experts, and other safety and health professionals to help reduce the occupational casualties, high costs, and legal liability associated with motor vehicle incidents. The American

---

[5]*Respondeat superior*, or "vicarious liability," is a key doctrine in the law of agency, which provides that a principal (employer) is responsible for the actions of his/her/its agent (employee) in the "course of employment. By definition, motor vehicle accidents that occur while a worker is in the course of his employer's business (whether or not operating an employer-owned vehicle) would fall within the scope of this legal theory, and the driver's negligence would be imputed to the employer for purposes of litigation.
[6]For example, under Maryland law, courts focus on whether the incident arose from employees' activities within the scope of the employment. To satisfy the legal test, the conduct must be of the kind the employee is employed to perform and must occur during a period not unreasonably disconnected from the authorized period of employment in a locality not unreasonably distant

from the authorized area, and actuated at least in part by a purpose to serve the employer. See *Jordan v. Western Distributing Company*, 135 Fed.Appx. 582 (4th Cir. 2005). The conduct must also be expectable or foreseeable. *Sawyer v. Humphries*, 587 A.2d 467, 471 (Md. 1991).
[7]This cause of action focuses on the employer's negligence in selecting the individual as an employee, rather than on the employee's wrongful act itself. See *Van Horne v. Muller*, 705 N.E.2d 898 (Ill. 1998). In a negligent selection claim, there normally is a rebuttable presumption that an employer uses due care in hiring an employee. See, e.g., *Evans v. Morsell*, 395 A.2d 480, 483 (Md. 1978).
[8]However, if the employer is a governmental entity, sovereign immunity may apply.
[9]See Liberty Mutual Insurance Company, *Liberty Mutual Executive Survey of Workplace Safety* (2001).

Society of Safety Engineers has released the ANSI Z15.1-2006 national consensus standard, *Safe Practices for Motor Vehicle Operations*.

The standard, approved by ANSI on February 15, 2006, took effect on April 28, 2006. It provides guidelines and establishes best practices for development of motor vehicle safety programs for all classes of employers—whether addressing a single vehicle or a fleet, whether the equipment is employer-owned, employee-owned, or leased from a third party.[10] It includes such key components as:

- Management, leadership and administration;
- Operational environment;
- Driver considerations;
- Vehicle considerations; and
- Incident reporting and analysis.

As noted in the ANSI Z.15.1, when developing a program to control risks associated with motor vehicle operation, it is critical to include both operator training and qualification criteria as well as a system for inspecting and maintaining the equipment. Although inspections are normally conducted in a systematic way by drivers who have commercial driver's licenses and operate large trucks that require CDL compliance, this step is too often ignored for passenger vehicles or for smaller trucks that may be used by sales and service personnel.

The Z15.1 standard includes these components, as well as methodologies for record keeping, reporting of motor vehicle-related incidents and data/trend analysis that can be used to prevent recurrences. This is a particularly significant component from a legal perspective, as employers who are found to have actual knowledge of program failures or unsafe actions/conditions and who fail to take appropriate remedial action are much more likely to be found grossly negligent in the event of a subsequent incident. This can, of course, lead to high dollar OSHA penalties,[11] as well as punitive damages in the tort law arena arising from personal injury or wrongful death suits. In particularly egregious circumstances, there could even be criminal prosecutions targeting management personnel who were aware of deficiencies and failed to take appropriate corrective action.

Among the critical features of the ANSI Z15.1 standard are attention to driver error and the risk factors arising from driver impairment and distraction as well as the high-profile issue of aggressive driving practices, which is being criminalized in some states. The standard also emphasizes safety considerations when purchasing or modifying motor vehicles.

The standard could be used as an affirmative defense during litigation. As a recognized national voluntary consensus standard (benchmark), an employer potentially could use the standard as an indicator that it implemented programs to enhance safety for its motor vehicle operations. Use of the standard, and the ability to document compliance with the standard, could also be used as an affirmative defense when contesting federal and state citations.

In the 1990s, motor vehicle safety was designated as one of the Occupational Safety and Health Administration's priority issue areas.[12] In July 1990, OSHA issued a Notice of Proposed Rulemaking for a standard, which would have required seat belt use and driver awareness programs.[13] Although this rulemaking effort was stalled, in part due to congressional

---

[10]The standard is not intended to apply to off-road equipment, agricultural equipment, recreational vehicles, haul trucks operated solely on industrial or mine sites, or unlicensed equipment.

[11]In addition to utilizing the ANSI Z-15.1 standard as a resource in program development, employers should also be aware of OSHA Guidelines for Employers to Reduce Motor Vehicle Crashes, which can be found at: http://www.osha.gov/Publications/motor_vehicle_guide.html.

[12]Today, OSHA continues to focus on this subject through its Alliances, including those with ASSE, the Independent Electrical Contractors, the Air Conditioning Contractors

of American, the Network of Employers for Traffic Safety and the National Safety Council.

[13]The Occupational Safety and Health Administration's proposed rule was published at 55 FR 28728 (July 12, 1990). That rule contained a mandatory safety belt requirement applicable to anyone driving or occupying any motor vehicle that is company owned, leased or rented or privately owned when used for official business on public highways and off highway. In addition, it included a driver training requirement for workers operate motor vehicles for official business on highway and off highway.

action that urged OSHA to further study the issue before proceeding, the agency can still regulate this recognized threat to safety through Section 5(a)(1) of the OSH Act, the "General Duty Clause."[14]

It should be noted that the standard does include this language in the Foreword section of the standard: *This standard is not intended to serve as a guide to governmental authorities having jurisdiction over subjects within the scope of the Z15 Accredited Standards Committee (ASC).* But even absent formal rulemaking, ANSI Z15 serves as a valuable reference. It also could have possible enforcement ramifications under the General Duty Clause (discussed above) by federal OSHA. It may be employed to satisfy regulatory requirements of certain state-plan OSHA programs. A number of States have enacted laws mandating such traffic management programs for employers,[15] so adoption of ANSI Z15 potentially at the state level may satisfy the compliance obligations for employers in those jurisdictions. Insurance companies encourage their client companies to implement safety and health management programs, and therefore utilization of Z15 potentially could generate monetary savings on insurance (both liability and worker's compensation).

The OSH Act covers every employer engaged in a business affecting interstate commerce who has one or more employees. By contrast, the Secretary of Transportation, acting through the Office of Motor Carrier Safety (OMCS), exercises statutory authority over the operation of motor vehicles engaged in interstate or foreign commerce.[16] However, the Department of Transportation still defers to OSHA to enforce safety related to motor vehicles where the Federal Motor Carrier Safety Administration standards in Title 49 of the Code of Federal Regulations do not address particular safety issues. Thus, reduction of work-related motor vehicle accidents is properly part of OSHA's 2003–2008 Strategic Management Plan. Of course, the U.S. Department of Transportation reserves the authority to regulate "commercial motor vehicles" which include, among others, vehicles with a gross vehicle weight rating of 10,001 pounds.[17]

Moreover, the National Advisory Committee on Occupational Safety and Health has recommended that OSHA promulgate a standard addressing motor vehicle safety, and that it involve other governmental agencies as well as safety organizations. Under OMB Circular A-119, which requires that any federal government agency rulemaking consider extant consensus standards and adopt those standards where feasible, the ANSI Z15.1 standard could eventually be incorporated by reference into a future OSHA rulemaking on this issue. OSHA also has a memorandum of understanding with ANSI (1/19/2001). The memorandum notes that: *ANSI and OSHA will maintain a mechanism for consultation in the planning of occupational safety and health standards development activities in the areas of mutual concern to the extent consistent with OSHA policy and section 6 of the OSH Act;*

---

[14]Section 5(a)(1) of the Occupational Safety and Health Act of 1970 (OSH Act) requires employers to "furnish to each of his employees employment and a place of employment which are free from recognized hazards that are causing or are likely to cause death or serious physical harm to his employees."

[15]See, e.g., Cal-OSHA's standard at http://www.dir.ca.gov/title8/8406.html.

[16]OMCS authority is found in title 49 of the United States Code in the following sections: 3101 et seq.; 2301 et seq. (known popularly as the Surface Transportation Assistance Act); 1801 et seq., dealing with the transportation of hazardous materials; and 2501 et seq. (known popularly as the Motor Carrier Safety Act of 1984).

[17]See, e.g., 49 USC §31132. Another distinguishing factor is that the term "employer" under the Motor Carriers Safety Act of 1984 means ". . . any person engaged in a business affecting commerce who owns or leases a commercial motor vehicle in connection with that business, or assigns employees to operate it," but such term does not include Federal, State, and local governments. Thus, in the case of the term "employer" under the Motor Vehicle Safety Act, there is a limitation on the OMCS jurisdiction. If, in any factual circumstances involving a section 4(b) (1) controversy between OSHA and the OMCS, where the employer does not come within the Motor Carrier Safety Act's definition of the term "employer," OSHA would have jurisdiction over the employer's working conditions and could enforce unsafe conditions or actions imputable to the employer under the General Duty Clause.

The OMB Circular (consistent with Section 12(d) of the National Technology Transfer Assistance Act (NTTAA)) directs agencies to use national consensus standards in lieu of developing government-unique standards, except when such use would be inconsistent with law or otherwise impractical. However, under the current OSH Act, only national consensus standards that have been adopted as, or incorporated by reference into, an OSHA standard pursuant to Section 6 of the OSH Act provide a means of compliance with Section 5(a)(2) of the Occupational Safety and Health Act, 29 U.S.C. § 651 et seq. ("the OSH Act").[18] Therefore, at some future time, Z15 could be adopted by OSHA as a mandatory safety and health standard through notice-and-comment rulemaking.

Another significant area of possibility would be development of consent orders with government agencies involving motor vehicle operations. There is the possibility of the standard being used as a benchmark for an employer to use in establishing such programs. The use of voluntary national consensus standards to settle such cases is a common practice and there is the possibility of Z15 being used in such a manner.

From a defensive strategy, employers who adhere to the recommendations in ANSI Z15.1 will not only see a reduction in the motor vehicle incidence rate but will also have appropriate documentation, such as written motor vehicle safety programs, safety policies, and maintenance programs and records, to reduce the likelihood litigation in the first instance because of the due diligence provided to elimination of motor vehicle risk factors. Application of ANSI Z15.1's recommendations concerning driver recruitment, selection and assessment, orientation and training, and impaired/distracted/aggressive driver prevention programs, can also be useful in defeating claims of negligent recruitment and retention of employees that might otherwise arise in third-party injury actions.

Finally, the attention to regulatory compliance and management program audits will help minimize the potential for enforcement actions brought by OSHA under the General Duty Clause, relevant DOT agencies, or even state and local governmental agencies under traffic and criminal laws.

Finally, ANSI Z15 has possible value in constructing settlement agreements or consent orders with federal OSHA, state-plan OSHA agencies or other state and federal transportation-related agencies. Often employers who have systemic safety problems will be encouraged or required, as a condition of abatement or settlement, to design and implement programs that will address management failures in a cohesive manner. The scope and function of Z15 would likely satisfy the enforcement goals of prevention of future safety issues while encouraging penalty reductions to offset the costs of program implementation. There is the strong potential of the standard being included in settlement proceedings for occupational safety and health citations involving motor vehicle operations.

SH&E professionals should be encouraged to take the following actions:

- Obtain a copy of this standard, review the standard and the background materials about it, and discuss it with senior management and legal counsel so that all parties are aware of what is expected. A legal opinion written by corporate counsel would also be a prudent action to take.
- Write and publish a policy addressing Z15 in regard to how it fits in with the organization's current program and the U.S. Occupational Safety and Health Act and the rules and regulations of the U.S. Department of Transportation. Write, implement, and document communication structures detailing how information is passed up the communication chain to senior management.
- Conduct through assessments to identify significant SH&E exposures and the means used

---

[18]Specific national consensus standards [e.g., American National Standards (ANSI) standards], which the Secretary of Labor adopted on May 29, 1971, were either used as a source standard and published in Part 1910 as an OSHA standard or explicitly incorporated by reference in an OSHA standard.

to communicate them to those in a position of authority.

- The Z15 Standard potentially could place accountability on senior management. There is some correlation with the requirements of Sarbanes Oxley Act of 2002 Public Law 107-204. It is important to ensure that SH&E audits are independent and that the results are reported and acted upon. Those ES&H practitioners who author/sign those audit reports and who fail to follow-up on the recommended actions may be subject to sanctions such as listed under the new law. The point has been made that they now have a duty that goes beyond just informing management.
- Follow the ASSE Code of Conduct.

In summary, ANSI Z15 provides safety and health professionals with a significant new tool to help enhance existing program design or to help smaller employers create a program that can protect workers while at the same time satisfying regulatory entities and insurers, effectuating cost savings and minimizing legal liability.

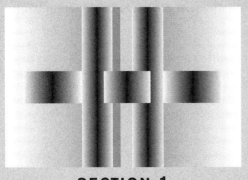

LEARNING OBJECTIVES

- ▌ Recognize and understand the relevant concepts of managing project work.

- ▌ Be able to analyze project status to ascertain budget.

- ▌ Establish a schedule for the overall performance elements of project work.

- ▌ Understand the relevant concepts of leadership, team building and interaction, and managing conflict.

- ▌ Be able to analyze one's own leadership abilities.

- ▌ Be able to analyze the interpersonal and managerial skills of others.

APPLIED SCIENCE AND ENGINEERING: MANAGING A SAFETY ENGINEERING PROJECT

Joel M. Haight

TO PROPERLY TREAT the subject of managing safety engineering work, some discussion should be provided about what safety engineering is. It is difficult to define since it is one specialty in the larger and more broadly defined safety and health discipline, and, as such, it is often loosely defined and discussed.

Paul Wright in his book *Introduction to Engineering* (1989) states that the ABET, Inc. (formerly known as the Accreditation Board of Engineering Technology) defines *engineering* as "A profession in which a knowledge of mathematical and natural sciences gained by study, experience and practice is applied with judgment to develop ways to utilize, economically, the materials and forces of nature for the benefit of mankind."

ABET defines an *engineer* as a person, who by reason of their special knowledge and use of mathematical, physical, and engineering sciences and the principles and methods of engineering analysis and design, acquired by education and experience, is qualified to practice engineering (Duderstadt, Knoll, and Springer 1982). Wright (1989) adds to this definition: "The engineer's knowledge must be tempered with judgment. Solutions to engineering problems must often satisfy conflicting objectives and the preferred optimum solution does not always result from a clean-cut application of principles or formulas." He also states that "Engineers are concerned with the creation of structures, devices and systems for human use."

In the foreword of James CoVan's book *Safety Engineering* (1995), Rodney D. Stewart writes: "Safety Engineering is an increasingly important and growing 'horizontal' dimension of engineering that cuts across all the traditional vertical dimensions (civil, mechanical, electrical, chemical and software)." CoVan writes: "Safety is a broad, multidisciplinary topic and this book addresses the engineering aspects of the subject." This indicates that there are engineering aspects of safety that must be managed.

Safety engineering is a diverse and often poorly understood subject. Many critics doubt that engineering is involved. "A weakness of the discipline that developed to serve the underlying need is that many of its practitioners were untrained and undisciplined in its application" (CoVan 1995). Roger Brauer writes in his book *Safety and Health for Engineers* (2005): "Safety engineering is devoted to application of scientific and engineering principles and methods to the elimination of hazards. Safety engineers need to know a lot about many different engineering fields." Gloss and Wardle (1984) write in their book *Introduction to Safety Engineering*: "Safety engineering is slowly maturing as a recognized profession. Safety engineering is a relatively new profession and reflects our mounting concerns for the environment, the consumer and the rights of workers." This lends importance to the need to apply established management practices to this new field.

Many aspects of the safety engineer's job fit the ABET definition for engineering. While safety engineers do not often create "structures" or "devices" as noted by Wright (1989), it can be strongly argued that the safety engineer does create "systems" for the benefit of humankind.

This chapter does not attempt to formally define safety engineering work, but proposes a working definition for the purposes of discussing specific management concepts, principles, and activities associated with projects and work in which safety engineering is inherent. These management concepts, principles, and activities include scheduling, manpower and other resource allocation, budgeting effectiveness, measurement systems, purchasing, work definition, and so on, associated with projects involving the design, construction, installation, operation, maintenance, and dismantling and/or disposal of equipment, systems, processes, or facilities in which safety engineering is an integral component. These types of projects may include excavation protection systems, fall-protection systems, energy-isolation systems, confined-space-entry systems, general construction, and general maintenance turnaround activities.

It is important to recognize that safety is no different than any other aspect of a project, or of work in general. It is often presented and discussed as a separate entity that must be accomplished and that must be treated individually. However, for the purposes of this chapter, *safety* is not a noun describing a specific activity; in most cases throughout the chapter, it will be used as an adjective describing the way all work gets done—*safely*. Even though it is not a separate entity, the safety-related aspects of the job have to be managed just like all other aspects of any project. For example, budgeting, developing specifications, ordering adequate quantities, and dispensing respiratory protective equipment must be done for a confined-space-entry job just as these functions must be done for the structural support members for a bridge, where fastening devices would be necessary equipment rather than respiratory protectors.

This chapter provides discussion on what a project is, as well as what a managed system is. It discusses where safety engineering fits into a project or system. It covers general management principles such as organizing, defining the work, scoping, scheduling, budgeting, and staffing. Workforce issues such as training and learning, motivating, team building, conflict, and leadership are covered, and the chapter also addresses work and workforce analysis concepts such as performance ratings, work sampling, allowances, time study, and resource allocation. Final products and deliverables are discussed, and many of the concepts are further illustrated in the form of examples and open-ended problems to work out.

INTRODUCTION TO MANAGING SAFETY ENGINEERING WORK

A *system* is defined throughout the literature in many ways, but for the purposes of this book, consider a system to be any process involving the interaction between humans and equipment in which raw materials (input) are converted to final products (output) (Eisner 2002). Managing the safety engineering aspects of work requires that one focus on the interaction between humans and equipment as well as on the conversion process of raw materials to final products.

This interaction involves such issues as workers responding, in the form of physical action, to signals from equipment in the process of its operation. The interaction could also involve workers being exposed to hazards associated with the raw materials or intermediate products or to hazards inherent in the equipment itself. The conversion process will likely involve moving parts, conveyor-belt operations, changing chemical states, heating or cooling, changing structural conditions, changing pressures, and so on. The manufacture of paper, pharmaceuticals, beer, or televisions, the refining of oil, the production of electricity, all involve work done by systems. The safety engineering aspects of these systems must be managed.

A *project* can be described as a formal gathering of people and equipment in an industrial setting, working toward satisfying a set of goals, objectives, and requirements. A project usually has a defined time period, a limited scope, and an established budget, and is managed by a project manager. In many cases, a project deals only with one aspect of a system's life cycle, such as design, construction, installation, or maintenance. Projects have a safety engineering aspect just as a system does, and many times this aspect is related to exposure to hazards, time pressure to complete the work, or implementation with people who may not yet be trained or experienced (Eisner 2002). The safety engineering aspects of a project must therefore also be managed.

What does it mean to manage safety engineering work associated with projects or systems? To answer this question, one must go back to the traditional key elements of managing any type of work. The classic definition of management usually includes a discussion of planning, organizing, leading, and controlling the operation for the purpose of productivity (Schermerhorn 1993).

Managers rely on a number of different management approaches to control their operations. A *classical approach* to management includes scientific management, administrative principles, and bureaucratic organizations. It assumes all people are rational. The *scientific approach* to management is one that Fredrick Taylor helped to develop in 1911. His principles involve developing a "science" for every job that would include the rules of motion, standardized work tools and proper working conditions, carefully selecting the right person for each job, properly training each worker for the job, giving them the right incentives, and supporting the workers by planning their work (Freivalds and Niebel 2008). The *behavioral approach* to management assumes that people are social and self-actualizing. It assumes people act on the basis of desires for satisfying social relationships, responsiveness to group pressures, and the search for professional fulfillment. In the *quantitative approach* to management, managers focus on the use of mathematical techniques for managing the problem solving of the operation. *Modern approaches* to management focus on the total system and look at the business as one interrelated big picture, utilizing contingency thinking and an awareness of a more global picture. Each approach has its own merits, advantages, and disadvantages, and one should understand the system under which he or she is operating to allow for a smooth integration.

PROJECT PLAN
Objectives

Objectives are usually statements that express the desires and expectations of the organization managing an overall operation. Objectives for the safety engineering aspects of the project often are developed as a result of a safety, health, fire, or compliance problem and are identified through the various analytical and evaluation methods used in the safety engineering community. Once a safety-related problem is identified, objectives for its resolution must be developed. These objectives describe expected accomplishments that will help to resolve or correct the safety-related problem and ensure the success of the organization. Usually, when safety engineering work results from a problem, the scope is bigger than just managing the implementation of corrective actions. Correcting the problem may require implementing a large-scale, resource-demanding effort. Such an effort must be cost effectively and efficiently managed. Examples of project-level objectives might include: ensure all operations personnel learn to operate the waste water plant to ensure human-error-induced catastrophic incidents do not occur, reduce exposure to noise in the compressor operation area to a level that does not exceed 50 percent of the allowable daily dose (ADD), or reduce the risk of a catastrophic release of chlorine from the five one-ton storage cylinders in the cooling water operation to a value of lower or tolerable risk. To achieve these objectives will likely require the implementation of a large-scale, project-driven course of action.

PROJECT REQUIREMENTS

Once the objectives are defined, it is the project coordinator who must determine the next course of action. This cannot take place without first identifying all of the *requirements* that must be met to safely and efficiently achieve the stated objectives. This will have a large bearing on nearly all aspects of the project, namely, schedule, cost, satisfaction of objectives, satisfaction of regulatory demands, resource allocation, and so on. While each project will have its own specific requirements, objectives, audience, and scope, there are some standard areas that must be addressed by the project safety engineer that can be generalized across all projects. Considering project requirements from a generalized approach will help analysts be sure they have addressed every necessary requirement and worked them into the project plan (Eisner 2002).

CUSTOMER OBJECTIVES: TECHNICAL AND FUNCTIONAL

One must start with the requirements of the customer. What objective must be achieved to satisfy the person or organization requesting the accomplishment? In the field of safety engineering, the customer is often an operation's management team, and, to a large extent, the workforce. The customer's objective is likely to be a safer operation, a product made with less risk of incident, fewer injuries, fewer failures, less damage, and so on. These objectives are general in nature, so the safety engineer in charge of managing the project must be sure that agreement is reached or approval given for the means by which the objective will be achieved. For example, if the objective is to reduce benzene exposures plantwide, a project team must assemble to determine and agree on what achieving the objective will entail. Will it be achieved through the use of personal protective equipment and training? Or will engineering controls and hardware installation be required, such as zero-leak valves, enclosed and ventilated sample stations, and activated-carbon filtration systems on building air intakes?

The customer's requirements will usually be technical and have functional requirements such as fire resistance, structural integrity, spacing and layout, level of system automation and control-system logic, warmth, adequate illumination, vessels that meet appropriate pressure ratings (see the Pressure Vessel chapter in the Risk Assessment and Hazard Control section of this handbook), accessibility (foot, reach, and traffic), ease of maintenance, or personal protective equipment (PPE) comfort and aesthetics.

An additional factor that must be considered by the project manager and discussed among the project team is the potential for future expansion and growth. This must be considered from a space and real-estate point of view as well as from the standpoint of interface and integration of old and new systems. In other words, it is important to leave a system owner with the ability to tie old and new together without having to worry about complete replacement due to obsolescence of interfaces, fittings, power requirements, control-system logic, and so on.

REGULATORY OBJECTIVES

Once the customer's requirements are determined, the project manager (or, in the case of a safety-related project, the safety engineer) must determine the requirements of government agencies, local municipalities, and consensus organizations. Regulatory requirements that must be considered include those involving proximity to local businesses and residences, process and storm water runoff (during construction and normal operations), odors, airborne concentrations, noise levels (during construction and normal operations), local building and fire codes, evacuation and emergency vehicle access/egress, rail or trucking access, pressure vessel or boiler codes, and Americans with Disabilities Act (ADA) access requirements. A project manager will meet and work with agency representatives (or internal compliance representatives) to identify all of the applicable regulatory requirements that must be satisfied and then estimate the time needed to satisfy the demands of all the agencies so that the project schedule includes this time. Sometimes project managers consider only the technical and functional requirements of the project and then become frustrated when agency needs hold up the schedule after the fact, or after the regulatory need has been defined. They must realize that it takes time to perform all the necessary analysis and design reviews and get the necessary permits processed and that this time must be incorporated into the schedule.

HUMAN RESOURCE AND EXPERTISE OBJECTIVES

Technical, functional, and regulatory requirements are critical to any project's success but no more important than the human requirements for the project. The expertise of the personnel who will help develop, design, and install the project is likely to be varied and wide ranging. The existing expertise and experience of the project team is one requirement, but the project manager may also need to consider the availability of outside expertise. He or she may also need to consider on-site training requirements necessary to bring a fully functioning project team up to speed on site. Once the necessary expertise categories are defined, they must be quantified—how many crews or individuals are needed for the project? For example, if three welding crews are needed and only one is available at a given time, the schedule will be affected, and the effect may not necessarily be linear, because other types of crews will also be held up waiting for the welding to be completed.

The project manager must consider the types of engineers (e.g., industrial, chemical, mechanical, electrical) and analysts that are needed for their expertise during the design phase of the project's life cycle. He or she needs to obtain the input of regulatory experts; industrial hygienists; operations and maintenance experts; instrumentation experts; and human factors experts, or ergonomists, among others. One expert in

each discipline is usually considered adequate; however, this is dependent upon the size and complexity of the project. It is critical to avoid delays in project implementation due to the lack of input from any of the team's members. Regular project meetings must include the presence and input of each discipline on the team, and it is the project manager's responsibility to ensure that all team members attend project meetings. It is not the objective of this chapter to provide a formula for determining the correct number of personnel for each discipline; the objective is to provide information to consider in determining the makeup of the project team (Shermerhorn 1993).

STATEMENTS OF WORK, TASK STATEMENTS, AND WORK BREAKDOWN STRUCTURE

When objectives, goals, and project requirements are defined and agreed upon, descriptions of the work to be done can then be developed. This is started through the development of a statement of work, task statements, and a work-breakdown structure. The *statement of work*, although often used interchangeably with a task statement, could be viewed more as a description of the overall work to be completed. It can also contain a complete list of task statements (or individual tasks within the overall project). Examples of statements of work are:

1. Excavation and earthwork
2. Driving piles
3. Laying concrete foundations
4. Running electricity to the site
5. Running water and steam to the site
6. Installing structural steel
7. Setting the vessels
8. Installing the pumps, exchangers, valves, etc.
9. Installing the piping, valves, etc.
10. Installing control-system wiring and computers

Each of these statements of work will include a description of any work that requires the input and coordination of the safety engineer/project manager.

Task statements are more defined, specific task descriptions within each statement of work, and they lend themselves to integration into a work breakdown structure (which will be discussed in upcoming paragraphs). Task statements associated with the excavation work of a project might be: perform a soil analysis, complete a nearby exposure and structures analysis, perform a water-content analysis, perform water influx and drainage analysis, complete a shoring or sidewall angling design, implement a spoil pile management plan, and design a confined-space-entry plan. Task statements for a "Complete Pile Driving" statement of work may require the safety engineer to evaluate the vibration impact on nearby structures and perform an evaluation of noise exposure for crews working in the area. Setting vessels, installing piping, and bringing utilities to the site may require the safety engineering project manager to evaluate layout and placement as well as accessibility and adherence to material specification and welding requirements. These are a few examples of possible task statements that may be developed in a project that has a particularly significant amount of safety engineering issues associated with it. Each task statement list is specific to the type of project being undertaken (Eisner 2002).

A *work breakdown structure* is a formal categorization of the work to be performed as part of a project. Task statements are developed under each work categorization. Organizing the project work into categories can help in establishing the project schedule and in allocating human resources—in terms of both crafts and expertise and pure worker numbers (Eisner 2002). In a safety engineering project, a work breakdown structure and associated task statements may look like the following example, which could describe the elevated-work aspects associated with the "installing the piping and valves" statement of work noted in the list above.

Work Breakdown Structure Example

1. Pre-project analyses
   1.1. Support structure analysis of integrity of members intended for use in fall-protection systems
   1.2. Determination of attachment points and weight limitations
   1.3. Determination of scaffold vs. harness and lanyard
   1.4. Support structure analysis of scaffold base if scaffolding is required
   1.5. Analysis of fall-protection equipment status and condition
2. Fall-protection system design (based on pre-project analyses)
   2.1. Scaffold design (and approval if large enough to require design oversight by a professional engineer)
   2.2. Lanyard and harness system design (allowing for adequate mobility and fall-distance limitation)
   2.3. Access system design
   2.4. Specification development for harnesses, lanyards and connections
3. Fall-protection system construction and installation
   3.1. Oversight of contractors or employee construction crews
   3.2. Inspection and testing of system upon installation completion
   3.3. Approval of necessary scaffolding permits
4. Site inspections during elevated work to determine continued compliance and condition integrity
5. Updating of fall-protection permits as needed throughout project

Most safety engineers would not be assigned as a project manager for a construction project. However, a safety engineer might be assigned to manage the safety-related aspects of an overall construction project, and all the same principles apply to the tasks and organization of the safety-engineering-related work (such as for the fall-protection example noted above). It is also important for a safety engineer to understand how a construction project is described, organized, arranged, and managed so that he or she will be able to participate in, integrate with, and contribute to its development and implementation (Eisner 2002).

SCHEDULING
PERT Charting

PERT is an acronym for *Program Evaluation and Review Technique*. This technique is often used to create the project network layout and is also referred to as a network diagram. PERT is described as a critical path analysis tool since it can help an engineer to determine which pathway through a network is critical to the project's on-schedule completion.

A safety engineer can use a PERT chart as a planning tool to lay out the steps of a project and determine a sequential relationship between activities. It allows the project safety engineer to find the optimum route through the project to achieve its objective. It can be used in assessing the risk of not completing a project on time (or to the project team's satisfaction) through a time-estimating process that assigns three levels of estimated implementation time to each activity—an optimistic time, a pessimistic time, and a most likely time. From these estimates, it is possible for the safety engineer to develop probability distributions around the completion time for each activity. From that, a risk value can be assigned to the completion of the project. From a practical standpoint, most practicing engineers use only two time-estimate levels (earliest and latest) for completion and often do not carry out probability distribution determinations. This type of time estimating is most often used to determine a project's critical path or to identify possible bottlenecks.

On a PERT chart, activity milestones are represented by *nodes* (see Figure 1) that are generally shown as positions in time using either the beginning or the end of an operation. The nodes are connected by lines called *arcs*. Each arc represents the time needed to complete the activity within the project's scope. Activities that are needed to ensure a correct sequence in a project but have zero time or no cost are referred to as *dummy activities* or *dummy nodes* (Freivalds and Niebel 2008).

A PERT network is devised and analyzed using its principles and methods as follows (as shown in Figure 1 and Table 1):

1. Determine and define known end events and milestones; ask what needs to be accomplished to achieve each objective (or milestone).
2. Work backward from each milestone (node) until reaching the project start. This will help to define the steps in the project.
3. While determining the steps in the project, this backward approach will help to define the sequential relationship of each node to each other (i.e., node A must be done before node B, node C can be done concurrently with node D). This sequence can be serial and/or parallel. Each node should be labeled—in this case, they are given letters.
4. These first three steps allow the analyst to draw a network, as shown in Figure 1. At this point he or she must estimate the amount of time, given available resources, that it will take to achieve each milestone and assign that number of hours, days, or weeks to the arc between the

TABLE 1

PERT Chart Analysis Data

Activity	Description	Task Duration	Early Start (Day)	Late Start (Day)	Slack Time
AB	Analyze excavation incidents	8 days	0	$10 - 8 = 2$	2 days
AD	Analyze lockout/tagout incidents	11 days	0	$11 - 11 = 0$	0 days
AF	Analyze confined-space incidents	3 days	0	$13 - 3 = 10$	10 days
BC	Create soil analysis survey and map	7 days	8	$17 - 7 = 10$	2 days
BD	Include excavation findings in LO	1 day	8	$11 - 1 = 10$	2 days
BE	Develop excavation procedures	7 days	8	$18 - 7 = 11$	3 days
DC	Identify and diagram energy sources	6 days	11	$17 - 6 = 11$	0 days
DE	Develop LO/TO procedures	5 days	11	$18 - 5 = 13$	2 days
DF	Dummy node	0 days	11	--	--
FE	Develop confined-space-entry procedure	5 days	11	$18 - 5 = 13$	2 days
FG	Develop confined-space-entry-training program	7 days	11	$27 - 7 = 20$	9 days
CG	Develop excavation training program	10 days	17	$27 - 10 = 17$	0 days
EG	Develop LO/TO training program	9 days	16	$27 - 9 = 18$	2 days
GH	Present complete training program to workers	5 days	27	$32 - 5 = 27$	0 days

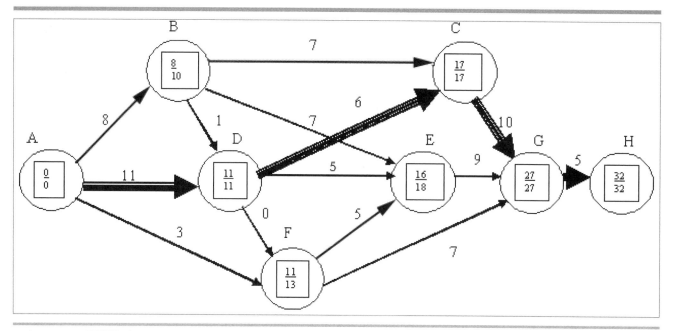

FIGURE 1. PERT chart representing a project to develop a training program based on injury-type history (critical path is highlighted with bolder arrows)

starting milestone node and its related end node. For example, in the Figure 1 network, start at node A (day 0). Achieving node B (arc AB—Analyze excavation accidents, Table 1)—is expected to take 8 days with available resources.

5. Once all the time estimates are assigned, begin at node A, and using the 8-day estimate for arc AB, the 11-day estimate for arc AD, and the 3-day estimate to achieve node F, determine the earliest possible time to achieve each milestone. This will define the earliest possible time in which each of the following nodes can be achieved. Input that number (day) inside the node above the line. Work your way through the network, being sure to respect the sequential relationship you built for the project. [Suppose you have only one welding crew and they have two steps in the project (arc-node combinations). One crew can work on only one step at time, so one step must be completed before the next can be started.]

6. When you reach the node indicating project completion, you will have defined the earliest completion time (the smallest number of days to complete the project). In the Figure 1 example, it will take 32 days to complete the project.

7. From the final node, work backward through the network, again using the completion-time estimates to determine the latest possible completion time for each node. This number is recorded below the line inside the circle of each node. In the example, the project completion (node H) is at day 32 and with only one node immediately preceding it (node G), the analyst must address only the 5 days needed to accomplish task GH and record 32 – 5 = day 27 below the line at node G. From node G, the analyst travels backward, subtracting the 10 days it will take to complete task CG from day 27 and determines that the latest completion of node C is achieved at day 17. This number is recorded below the line inside the node C circle. At this point, care must be exercised when a node has more than one arc coming from it. The analyst must record the value defined by the arc yielding the lowest value. For example, from node G, the analyst travels backward, subtracting the 7 days needed to complete task FG from day 27 and records the latest completion of node F. This is 20; however, the lowest value is achieved for node F when subtracting the 5 days it takes to complete

task FE from node E's latest value of 18, so the latest start for node F is at day 13. This number is recorded below the line inside the circle of node F. The analyst works back through the entire network in this manner until reaching day zero at the project's first task.

8. Once the earliest and latest start times are determined, the analyst can set up a table, such as Table 1, and determine slack time for each task where it applies, and most importantly, can determine the project's critical path. This is the path through the network along which the project can afford no slack time; a delay in the tasks along it will result in a delay in the project.

9. Complete the first three columns of the table (Table 1) from the information already developed as shown on the network. The earliest start day for each node is the number above the line inside the node circle—enter that in the fourth column of the table.

10. For the fifth column, labeled "Late start (day)," some additional considerations must be integrated into the entries. First, use the day value below the line in the final node and subtract the task duration leading to it. Then subtract the earliest start value for that task (the number below the line inside the project's final milestone or node). This result is the slack time or the amount of delay time the project can stand without suffering a delay in the overall project. For example, if slack time is established at 2 days and a task requires an order of materials to be received on day 22, the project will not be delayed as long as the material arrives and the task can be completed by day 24.

11. As the analyst looks down the last column, it is easy to determine the critical path from the arcs or tasks that have zero (0) slack time. In this example, the critical path shows that the tasks AD (Analyze the lockout/tagout incidents), DC (Identify and diagram energy sources), CG (Develop excavation training program) and GH (Present complete training program to workers) cannot experience any

delays or the whole project will take longer than the 32 days expected.

For projects of critical time or financial demand, the most resources or most attention should be focused on the critical path tasks to ensure that they are not delayed. In giving information to the operation's decision makers, the analyst can provide these same data at three levels: optimistic estimate, expected estimate, and pessimistic estimate. The analyst can also draw confidence bands around each duration estimate. The PERT chart provides much information for decision makers to use in determining time estimates, human resource allocation, costs, and so on for achieving a project's objective (Eisner 2002; Freivalds and Niebel 2008). There are many project management software tools available on the market that provide these scheduling tools, such as *Microsoft Project*, *Tenrox Project Management*, *Matchware Mindview*, *Genius Project* for Domino, *Seavus Project Planner*, *Method 123 Project Plan*, and AEC Software's *Fast Track Schedule*. A comparison can be found at www.project-management-software-review.toptenreviews.com.

Gantt Charting

A Gantt chart is a valuable tool that is used extensively throughout industry today even though it was developed in the 1940s. It is often used in safety engineering applications as well as in many other types of project-based applications. It is a project planning and control technique that is designed to show the expected completion times for each step in a project. It makes use of a horizontal timeline. Bars are plotted against this timeline to represent first the expected and then the actual completion times for each project activity. The benefits of its use are many. First, it forces a safety engineer to plan and lay out a project before starting the work. Second, the engineer can tell from the layout whether there is activity overlap, and where this is the case, determine whether resources are available to support the overlap. Third, from this graphical representation of project status, the engineer can easily tell whether the project is ahead of or behind schedule.

Gantt charts have some disadvantages in that they don't always give the project engineer the ability to see the interactions between two or more activities—if the same group of workers for a specific craft is scheduled to do three things at once, the Gantt chart alone would not show this. For example, suppose that the same group of pipe fitters is expected to install energy-isolating blinds or blanks in three separate toxic liquid lines in three separate locations in the plant during a maintenance turnaround all at the same time. The Gantt chart would not show this. It does not point out specific manpower allocation problems, but it does at least help to provide the impetus for a project engineer to think about the problem when an overlap occurs. See Figure 2 for an example of a Gantt chart.

Bars are used to show the expected time to complete each activity in terms of start and finish dates as well as expected duration. The bars are also darkened to indicate activity completion status. In the Figure 2 project, the darkened bars indicate completion; the bar colored on the left and uncolored on the right indicates an activity that is in progress. One can see that everything is completed through September. The activities corresponding to the uncolored bars have not yet been started. From this Gantt chart, one can tell that the

first five activities were completed as scheduled, as were the seventh and eighth. Completing the PHAs is in progress and still on schedule, but training, writing, and implementing the contractor safety program are not started yet. If the current date is 30 September, all is on schedule, but if it is 20 November, these four activities would be behind schedule.

One powerful benefit of a Gantt chart is that it allows a project safety engineer to determine whether there are enough resources (humans, computers, etc.) to work on overlapping activities. This is illustrated in the following example:

The safety engineer may ask if there are enough hourly employee time resources available in February to "implement employee participation" at the same time as they provide input to "writing the process safety information (PSI) document." If so, the project schedule is acceptable as is, but if a maximum-production test happens to be scheduled, which demands people time, and enough people are no longer available at the same time, the schedule will have to be adjusted. The PSI activity may have to be moved to March, but then that will impact the rest of the schedule.

This short example illustrates one of the benefits of Gantt-charting a project, but there are many. This

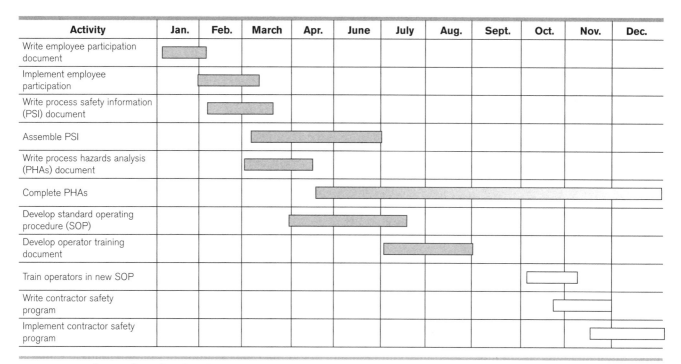

FIGURE 2. Gantt chart for developing a written process safety management program (not a complete project) Figure key: darkened color completed, fading color in progress, white is not started.

TABLE 2

	Welders		Pipe Fitters		Inspectors		Instrument Engineers		
	No. people in crew	Person-weeks	No. people in crew	Person-weeks	No. people in crew	Person-weeks	No. people in crew	Person-weeks	Total Person-Weeks
Task A	4	4	5	5	2	2	2	2	13
Task B							1	1	1
Task C	4	4	5	5	2	2			11
Task D	4	2	7	3.5	2	1			6.5
Task E	4	8	7	14	2	4	2	2	28
Task F							2	1	1
Task G							2	1	1
Task H	4	4	7	7	2	2	2	2	15
Totals		22		34.5		11		9	76.5

Table title: Task Responsibility Matrix: Vessel and Piping Installation Tasks

(Adapted from Eisner 2002)

type of schedule/chart is regularly used as a reference whenever project schedule and resource estimates are discussed.

FINANCIAL CONSIDERATIONS AND COST MONITORING
Project Budget

Once the project manager has a solid project plan in place and the work is defined, he or she must determine a budget for the project and a means to determine the financial performance and budget status throughout the life of the project. This process includes developing a task responsibility matrix, developing a direct labor and materials budget from the matrix, and then determining a cost budget per week. An example is the best way to illustrate the process. The sour gas processing plant project described above will be used to show the budget development steps. The example will not provide specific costs for each budget element, as this responsibility will reside with individual project managers and their staff analysts. The cost (in dollar amounts) used in this example are for illustration purposes only.

From Table 2 we determine that the project will require 22 person-weeks of work for the welding crew, 34.5 for the pipe fitters, 11 for the inspectors, and 9 for the instrument engineers. The total human-resource demand for the project is 76.5 person-weeks. The chart shows the person-weeks by task as well.

The process of establishing a project budget and analyzing the project's financial performance on a weekly basis (or other appropriate frequency), allows the project manager to maintain fiscal control early enough in the project so that available funds do not run out before the project is complete. There are several means for assessing budget performance; however, this tabular method is a relatively straightforward means that does not require extensive financial training (see Tables 3 and 4). It should be noted that the examples used in this chapter propose cost percentages

TABLE 3

Project Budget: Vessel and Piping Installation Tasks

Direct Labor	Rate/Week (in $)	Person-Weeks Required	Cost (in $)
Welders	1400	22	30,800
Pipe fitters	1120	34.5	38,640
Inspectors	1200	11	13,200
Instrumentation engineers	1500	9	13,500
Subtotal 1			96,140
Fringe rate @ 30%			28,842
Subtotal 2			124,982
Overhead rate @ 68%			84,988
Direct costs (materials, supplies, delivery, etc.)	vessels, piping, welding supplies		526,700
Subtotal 3			736,670
General and administrative @ 12%			88,400
Total cost			825,070

(Adapted from Eisner 2002)

TABLE 4

Cost category	Week 1		Week 2		Week 3		Week 4		Week 5		Week 6		Week 7	
	Person-weeks	Cost ($)	Person-weeks	Cost ($)	Person-weeks	Cost ($)	Person-weeks	Cost ($)	Person-weeks	Cost ($)	Person-weeks	Cost ($)	Person-weeks	Cost ($)
Welders	4	5.6	--	--	4	5.6	2	2.8	8	11.2	--	--	4	5.6
Pipe fitters	5	5.6	--	--	5	5.6	3.5	3.92	14	15.7	--	--	7	7.84
Inspectors	2	2.4	--	--	2	2.4	1	1.2	4	4.8	--	--	2	2.4
Instrumentation engineers	2	3.0	1	1.5	--	--	2	3.0	1	1.5	1	1.5	2	3.0
Fringe @ 30%	--	4.98	--	0.45	--	4.08	--	3.3	--	9.95	--	0.45	--	5.65
Subtotal 1	--	21.58	--	1.95	--	17.68	--	14.2	--	43.15	--	1.95	--	24.5
Overhead @ 68%	--	14.7	--	1.33	--	12.0	--	9.7	--	29.4	--	1.33	--	16.65
Subtotal 2	--	36.3	--	3.28	--	29.7	--	23.9	--	72.6	--	3.28	--	41.15
Materials and supplies	--	95.14	--	10	--	95.14	--	105	--	96	--	10	--	115.42
Subtotal 3	--	131.5	--	13.3	--	124.8	--	128.9	--	168.6	--	13.3	--	156.6
General and administrative @ 12%	--	15.8	--	1.6	--	14.9	--	15.5	--	20.2	--	1.6	--	18.8
Total cost	--	147.3	--	14.9	--	139.7	--	144.4	--	188.8	--	14.9	--	175.4
Cumulative cost	--	147.3	--	162.2	--	301.8	--	446.2	--	635.1	--	650.0	--	825.2

Cost Budget by Week (in thousands of dollars)

(Adapted from Eisner 2002)

that are only for example purposes. Anyone using these types of tables should use only their company's internal cost data.

Engineering Economics

Engineering economics is an area used by most engineers and project managers to determine specific project options and to monitor the progress of the project performance. For more information on this subject, as well as general economic analysis, refer to the opening chapter in this handbook as well as several of the cost analysis and budgeting chapters in each topic area. Engineering economics will be treated here briefly in the context of managing safety engineering projects. Some of the concepts considered include:

- engineering economic decisions
- equivalence and interest formulas
- loan transactions
- annual equivalent worth analysis
- internal rate of return
- depreciation
- minimum acceptable rates of return
- lease versus buy decisions
- inflation analysis
- capital budgeting
- bond investments
- interest rates
- present and future worth analysis
- rate of return analysis
- return on investment (ROI)
- taxes
- developing project cash flows
- replacement decisions
- project risk and uncertainty
- economic equivalence

These tools allow project managers to make informed decisions about projects from a financial, risk, and uncertainty point of view. While each of these concepts, principles, and analytical techniques is used in managing a project, this chapter will address only a few of them to avoid overlap with other chapters in this handbook.

The Time Value of Money

The *time value of money* is an important concept in engineering economics and bears discussion and a review of the equations that are used to determine it.

Some of the following equations will be used in a subsequent example:

Single Flow

Convert present value to future value:

$$F = P(1 + i)^N \qquad (1)$$

Convert future value to present value:

$$P = F(1 + i)^{-N} \qquad (2)$$

Equal Payments

Convert periodic annuities (monthly or annual payments) for a given period to a future value:

$$F = A[(1 + i)^N - 1/i] \qquad (3)$$

Convert a future value to annuities (monthly or annual values) for a given period:

$$A = F[i/(1 + i)^N - 1] \qquad (4)$$

Convert periodic annuities (monthly or annual payments) for a given period to a present value:

$$P = A[(1+ i)^N - 1/i(1 + i)^N] \qquad (5)$$

Convert a present value to annuities (monthly or annual values) for a given period:

$$A = P[i(1 + i)^N/(1+ i)^N - 1] \qquad (6)$$

where:

P = present value
F = future value
A = annuity
i = interest rate
N = number of compounding periods

The example will be the determination of the cash flow for each of two projects in which a decision will be made either to develop a new project or to invest in the upgrade or improvement of an existing facility. A comparison will be made by converting cash flows for each project to a *net present value* (also referred to as *net present worth*) (Park 1997).

The decision to upgrade an existing methanol (MeOH) storage facility (Defender) or to design and install a new methanol storage facility (Challenger) is both a safety and an economic decision. One method for making this decision is shown in the "Question for Study" sidebar.

QUESTION FOR STUDY

Applying Engineering Economics

Some crude oils are difficult to keep flowing in temperatures below zero. Hydrate salts can precipitate out of the liquid phase as the oil gets further from the well and cools. These salts create a dangerous condition as they form plugs in the line. This traps high pressure and creates a condition that results in a projectile being rocketed down the pipeline as one of the hydrate plugs dislodges and releases the trapped pressure behind it. There is a risk of pipeline damage, potential physical injury, exposure to hydrocarbon, and environmental damage.

A method for preventing this trapped pressure condition is to inject methanol (MeOH) into the oil stream. This keeps the hydrate salts from precipitating out and thus keeps the line from plugging. The present methanol storage and loading facility is manually controlled, with no fire protection and deteriorating tanks. Methanol leaks occur frequently. The scope of repairs and upgrades to this system is extensive. The storage tanks are rusting and leaking at the riveted joints. The manual-level control system allows frequent overfills. There is no fire water available at this site and MeOH is flammable. The present system has been in service for 5 years. Due to permit requirements, upgrades are required to achieve minimum acceptable environmental and safety standards. Upgrades costing $134,000 will extend the system's life for five more years. However, upgrades will not completely stop the leaks. The expected leak losses will amount to $5000/year and the clean-up costs will be another $5000/year. The annual operating costs for this upgraded facility are expected to be $36,000 and maintenance costs are expected to be $24,000/year. Revenues generated would be realized from operational efficiency improvements. Savings are due to reduced risk and reduced compliance costs. The amounts would be:

Year 1 = $158,000
Year 2 = $160,000
Year 3 = $140,000
Year 4 = $137,000
Year 5 = $126,000.

A project design team has proposed an entirely new facility design with input from a safety analysis team. The design meets all acceptable environmental and industry standards and practices, including appropriate fire protection and level control system. The new facility, which requires an investment of $325,000, would last 5 years before a major upgrade would be required. However, it is believed that in five years oil transfer technology will be developed to the point that methanol will become obsolete (pipeline heating systems and insulation material). Management does not expect any spill clean-up costs; however, they would like a $5000 per year contingency set aside for education of the community (on MeOH safety), possible clean up, possible evacuation, etc., just in case. The annual operating and maintenance costs would be $12,000 and $6000 respectively. For this new system, revenues generated would be realized from operational efficiency improvements. The savings are due to reduced risk and reduced compliance costs. The amounts would be:

Year 1 = $180,000
Year 2 = $170,000
Year 3 = $160,000
Year 4 = $150,000
Year 5 = $140,000.

Even though a methanol system is expected to become obsolete, some of the parts in this system could be salvaged at the end of five years. The equipment should be worth $10,000. If this company's minimum acceptable rate of return is 15 percent, its tax rate is 40 percent, and the depreciation class for each system is 5-year class Modified Accelerated Cost Recovery System (MACRS), should this company upgrade the old facility or build a new one?

Net Present-Worth Analysis—Cash Flow Statement—Defender (Existing System)

		5-Year MACRS Depreciation				
Income Statement	0	1 (20%)	2 (32%)	3 (19.2%)	4 (11.52%)	5 (11.52%)
Revenue						
Savings, reduced risk		$158,000	$160,000	$140,000	$137,000	$126,000
Expenses						
• Operating costs		$36,000	$36,000	$36,000	$36,000	$36,000
• Maintenance costs		$24,000	$24,000	$24,000	$24,000	$24,000
• Materials (losses)		$5000	$5000	$5000	$5000	$5000
• Spill clean-up		$5000	$5000	$5000	$5000	$5000
• Depreciation		$26,800	$42,880	$25,728	$15,436	$15,436
Taxable Income		$61,200	$47,120	$44,272	$51,564	$40,564
• Income tax (40%)		$24,480	$18,848	$17,709	$20,625	$16,225
• Net income		$36,720	$28,272	$26,563	$30,938	$24,339
Cash Flow Statement	0	1	2	3	4	5
Operating Activities						
• Net income (A)		$36,720	$28,272	$26,563	$30,938	$24,339
• Depreciation (B)		$26,800	$42,880	$25,728	$15,436	$15,436
Investment Activity						
• Investment (I)	($134,000)					
• Salvage (S)						$0
Net Cash Flow (A + B + S)		$63,520	$71,152	$52,292	$46,374	$39,775

$$NPW = I + F_1(1 + i)^{-N} + F_2(1 + i)^{-N} + F_3(1 + i)^{-N} + F_4(1 + i)^{-N} + F_5(1 + i)^{-N}$$

$$NPW = \$134,000 + \$63,520(1 + 0.15)^1 + \$71,152(1 + 0.15)^2 + \$52,292(1 + 0.15)^3 + \$46,374(1 + 0.15)^4 + \$39,775(1 + 0.15)^5$$

$$NPW = -\$134,000 + \$63,520(0.8696) + \$71,152(0.7514) + \$52,292(0.6575) + \$46,374(0.5717) + \$39,775(0.4971)$$

$$NPW = -\$134,000 + \$55,236 + \$53,463 + \$34,381 + \$26,512 + \$19,772$$

NPW = $55,364

Net Present-Worth Analysis—Cash Flow Statement—Challenger (New System)

Income Statement	0	1 (20%)	2 (32%)	3 (19.2%)	4 (11.52%)	5 (11.52%)
Revenue						
Savings, reduced risk		$180,000	$170,000	$160,000	$150,000	$140,000
Expenses						
• Operating costs		$12,000	$12,000	$12,000	$12,000	$12,000
• Maintenance costs		$24,000	$24,000	$24,000	$24,000	$24,000
• Materials (losses)		$0	$0	$0	$0	$0
• Spill clean-up (contingency)		$5000	$5000	$5000	$5000	$5000
• Depreciation		$65,000	$104,000	$62,400	$37,440	$37,440
Taxable Income		$92,000	$43,000	$74,600	$89,560	$79,560
• Income tax (40%)		$36,800	$17,200	$29,840	$35,824	$31,824
• Net income		$55,200	$25,800	$44,760	$53,736	$47,736

Cash Flow Statement	0	1	2	3	4	5
Operating Activities						
• Net income (A)		$55,200	$25,800	$44,760	$53,736	$47,736
• Depreciation (B)		$65,000	$104,000	$62,400	$37,440	$37,440
Investment Activity						
• Investment (I)	($325,000)					
• Salvage (S)						$0
Net Cash Flow ($A + B + S$)		$120,200	$129,800	$107,160	$91,296	$95,176

$$NPW = I + F_1(1 + i)^{-N} + F_2(1 + i)^{-N} + F_3(1 + i)^{-N} + F_4(1 + i)^{-N} + F_5(1 + i)^{-N}$$

$$NPW = -\$325,000 + \$120,200(1 + 0.15)^1 + \$129,800(1 + 0.15)^2 + \$107,160(1 + 0.15)^3 + \$91,296(1 + 0.15)^4 + \$95,176(1 + 0.15)^5$$

$$NPW = -\$325,000 + \$120,200(0.8696) + \$129,800(0.7514) + \$107,160(0.6575) + \$91,296(0.5717) + \$95,176(0.4971)$$

$$NPW = -\$325,000 + \$104,525 + \$98,146 + \$70,457 + \$52,193 + \$47,311$$

NPW = $47,636

Final Result and Decision:

The company should choose the Defender. Its net present worth is $55,364 versus the Challenger's net present worth of $47,636.

LEADERSHIP AND PROJECT MANAGEMENT

Attributes of Leaders and Project Managers

It has been said that people usually do not get fired for a lack of technical skills; they lose their jobs more often because of their lack of interpersonal skills. A person can be a project manager by title but may not be an effective leader. An effective leader without sound technical skills may still succeed; but to do so, he or she must be strong on interpersonal skills. A manager may be strong at handling the details of day-to-day project management but unable to achieve success due to a lack of execution when team support is missing. Schermerhorn (1993) highlights some important points from a speech by management consultant Abraham Zaleznick to a group of business executives about the differences between leaders and managers. Zaleznick said, "Leaders . . . can be dramatic and unpredictable in style. They are often obsessed by their ideas, which appear visionary and consequently excite, stimulate, and drive other people to work hard and create reality out of fantasy. They often create an atmosphere of change." About managers, Zaleznick said, "Managers . . . are usually hardworking, analytical, and fair. They often have a strong sense of belonging to the organization and take pride in maintaining and improving the status quo. They tend to focus on the process, while leaders focus on substance." Leaders are not managers, and managers are not necessarily leaders, but for a project to succeed they should be (Schermerhorn 1993).

Project managers are expected to accomplish project objectives through effective planning, organizing, directing, and monitoring. The planning and organizing can be done in the office with the door closed, but when it becomes necessary to move on to directing and monitoring, interacting with people is inevitable (Eisner 2002). Schermerhorn (1993) explains, "Great leaders . . . get extraordinary things done in organizations by inspiring and motivating others toward a common purpose." In order for project managers who are good leaders to succeed in the directing and monitoring, they must be effective motivators, communicators, and team players, as well as strong in interpersonal relations. They must also be strong in managing the dynamics of a group with all of its interactions, friction, conflict, synergism, and antagonism.

Eisner (2002) suggests twenty attributes that a project manager should have to succeed. While it would be difficult for any one person to have all twenty, a project manager should make a strong effort to develop these attributes:

- communicates well and shares information
- delegates appropriately
- is well-organized
- supports and motivates people
- is a good listener
- is open-minded and flexible
- gives constructive criticism
- has a positive attitude
- is technically competent
- is disciplined

- is a team builder and player
- is able to evaluate and select people
- is dedicated to accomplishing goals
- has the courage and skill to resolve conflicts
- is balanced
- is a problem solver
- takes initiative
- is creative
- is an integrator
- makes decisions

These attributes are likely to be desirable in anyone; however, a manager who has a high percentage of them is likely to be a successful project manager. Although Eisner (2002) defines each attribute further, they are not defined here so that readers can consider the attributes from their own perspective and consider how and how much they might improve their own project management performance.

Leadership Self-Evaluation

While it is left up to readers to assess themselves as to adherence to behaviors supportive of these attributes, Eisner (2002) proposes a method to assess one's own leadership and managerial scores. He suggests using the twenty attributes listed in the preceding section and ranking oneself for each attribute using a scale of 0 to 5, with 5 being "almost always," 4 being "most of the time," 3 being "often," 2 being "sometimes," 1 being "rarely" and 0 being "never." With a score of 80 to 100, you are likely to be a good project manager. With a score between 60 and 79, you are doing well but should seek ways to improve in the areas where you scored lower. If you scored in the 40-to-59 range, you may still be considered for a project manager position, but you may need more training and/or experience. A score below 40 indicates that you may need extensive work before becoming a project manager.

Eisner (2002) also provides the attributes of a leader, which come from his survey results. They are broken down into *critical*, *extremely important*, and *significant* attributes:

Critical

1. Empowering, supporting, motivating, trusting
2. Having a vision—a long-term viewpoint
3. Cooperating, sharing, team playing, and team building
4. Renewing, learning, growing, educating

Extremely Important

1. Being communicative
2. Having culture and values, serving as a role model
3. Being productive, efficient, determined

Significant

1. Demonstrating time management
2. Being action-oriented
3. Making a contribution, commitment, legacy
4. Being innovative, imaginative
5. Having integrity, morality, humanity
6. Demonstrating skill, knowledge, substance

One may want to consider using the same scoring mechanism for these leadership attributes as suggested for the managerial attributes. With thirteen attributes, the maximum score is 65; someone with aspirations of becoming a good leader and good manager should seek to score in the 50-to-65 range.

Situational Leadership

Hersey and Blanchard (1977) introduced the concept of *situational leadership*—leaders changing and adjusting their style to fit the situation and the people involved. Situational leadership is a well-established model built around the concept that each situation requires the application of a combination of two possible behavior dimensions—task or directive behavior and relationship or supportive behavior (Hersey and Blanchard 1977). In each case, a leader has to determine which combination is required by the situation and then correctly apply the appropriate behavior to properly manage the situation. They use four situations to describe the fundamentals of their model:

Situation 1 (S1): High task, low relationship—leader assumes *telling* role
Situation 2 (S2): High task, high relationship—leader assumes *selling* role
Situation 3 (S3): High relationship, low task—leader assumes *participating* role
Situation 4 (S4): Low relationship, low task—leader assumes *delegating* role

In an S1 situation, subordinates are usually new to a task and do not know how to do it. At this stage they don't know what they don't know. They need to be *told* what the task is and how to do it. They don't necessarily need a close relationship with the leader. In an S2 situation, workers are thought to be developing some competence, and now at least they know what they don't know. Because of this, they begin to develop more of an interest but still have to rely on the leader for guidance, so the need for a closer relationship is there. Developing workers want to know what the leader knows. In an S3 situation, workers have developed confidence and competence. They can handle the situation or task without input (task direction is not necessary); however, it is, figuratively speaking, the first time on their own, so they would like input and feedback about their performance and need a close (or *high*) relationship with the leader. In S4 situations, workers are fully developed and know how to handle the situation or perform the task without input and do not need feedback. Task-direction need and relationship with the leader are both low (Hersey and Blanchard 1977).

A leader must be able to constantly assess this very dynamic process and correctly determine in which of these four categories workers or situations are. Leadership behavior must be applied accordingly. In an S4 situation, a leader can delegate a task and stand back without involvement, but if a leader gives S4 workers detailed instructions on how to do a task, they will become frustrated. If the leader delegates a task to S1-level people and walks away without instruction or direction, there will also be frustration and task performance problems. Correct application of the appropriate leadership behavior is critical and constantly changing. People who subscribe to this leadership model cannot stay with one leadership style and apply it in all cases. If they do, team or project performance will likely be low (Hersey and Blanchard 1977).

Team Building and Interaction

One who manages a project knows the value of a contributing project team that works effectively together. Before teamwork is discussed, it will be of value to define some of the basic aspects of teams. A team is generally considered to be a group of people (more than two) gathered together to accomplish an established objective through regular interaction and input. *Interaction* is the critical word in this definition, as this is where we apply the word *teamwork*. Teamwork might be defined as the process of coming together in this interaction. It is this interaction that can produce significant accomplishment, but it can also be the greatest contribution to project failure if the interaction is not managed properly. It is generally recognized that a team, through synergy of ideas and talents, can produce products of much greater value than if each individual on the team worked alone toward the same goal. Unfortunately, many things get in the way of this positive synergy, and the project manager is challenged to keep it functioning (Eisner 2002, Nahmias 1993).

There are many safety engineering examples in which multidisciplinary teams working together are absolutely essential to preventing incidents. Any type of complex hazard analysis requires the input of many disciplines and many types of expertise. When a hot work project or a confined-space-entry or excavation project is proposed, a multidisciplinary team is necessary to plan the work as well as to implement it. Before we look at a specific safety engineering project, we will illustrate teamwork with a sports example. Lack of teamwork on the basketball court can create problems; the most evident problem is losing the game. Suppose a playground basketball star playing on a formal basketball team hogs the ball, takes all the shots without passing to teammates, and does not try to get others in a position to take shots or get the ball. He cannot beat a team of five on the basketball court, but

because of selfish play, he becomes alienated from his other four team members. They then either take steps to isolate the selfish player or stop contributing. Both courses of action are a detriment to the performance of the team. A coach (leader) must recognize selfish play and do what is necessary to get everyone playing together, or the team will lose games.

In a safety engineering example, a process hazards analysis team (such as a hazard and operability study team—HAZOP) must work together, because the expertise of a team of many disciplines is necessary to thoroughly study a complex system to identify its hazards. As discussion takes place during the study, ideas develop through discussion among team members, each relying on the expertise and experience of other members. Team members confirm their opinions with teammates, the final conclusions are usually well thought out, and the thoroughness and accuracy of the study is high. If one team member thinks he or she knows everything and monopolizes the conversation, other team members either discount what that person says or they themselves keep quiet and do not contribute. Both courses of action are a detriment to the performance of the team. The study facilitator (leader) must recognize that this is happening and redirect the energies of the know-it-all toward the objectives of the team.

Teams provide great benefit to an organization. According to Schermerhorn (1993), teams can provide this benefit through:

- increasing resources for problem solving
- fostering creativity and innovation
- improving quality of decision making
- enhancing members' commitment to tasks
- raising motivation through collective action
- helping control and discipline members
- satisfying individual needs as organizations grow

Teams can be ineffective when individual differences are not embraced, when tasks are poorly designed, when team members are not prepared to work or are not committed to accomplishing the objective, or when the team process is not strong—either communication is poor, the decision-making process is not well defined or established, or there is no conflict resolution mechanism (Schermerhorn 1993). According to Eisner (2002), there also may be team members who are referred to as *team busters*. These people exhibit any of these behaviors:

- question the authority of the project manager on every issue
- challenge the technical approach of the project manager
- do not follow agreed-upon decisions
- consistently go over the boss's head
- try to monopolize meeting agendas
- attempt to embarrass or challenge the project manager in front of others
- try to create a "we and they" mentality

Teams are also subject to a phenomenon called *groupthink*. According to Schermerhorn (1993), this phenomenon can be characterized by:

- having illusions of group invulnerability—the team is above criticism
- rationalizing unpleasant and disconfirming data—refusal to accept contradicting data
- believing in inherent group morality—the team is above the reproach of others
- stereotyping competing teams as weak or stupid
- applying direct pressure to those with different points of view to conform to team wishes
- self-censoring by members—they won't accept that the team may be wrong
- having illusions of unanimity—accepting consensus prematurely
- mind guarding—protecting the group from hearing disturbing or competing ideas from those not on the team

Project managers must ensure that, given the problems of team interactions, they manage the personality differences and friction effectively to achieve and maintain a high performance. They must listen to what team members are saying, should work with and spend time with team members as much as possible and feasible, and should encourage all participants to work together and contribute. Project managers should meet with key team members regularly and frequently,

integrate the input of team members into the flow of the project work, and talk with the project "customer" as well as other project support people regularly and often. As the leader, the project manager should maintain a positive attitude, be supportive of all team members, and offer to help team members communicate with each other when and where necessary (Eisner 2002).

According to Schermerhorn (1993), characteristics of a high-performing project team that project managers should seek to build and achieve through their effective leadership are:

- working toward a clear and team-elevation goal
- a task-driven, results-oriented team structure
- competent, competitive team members who are willing to work hard
- a collaborative climate where people like and expect to work together
- high standards of excellence
- external support and recognition from the rest of the organization
- strong principled and ethical leadership

Eisner (2002) suggests several activities for leaders that support many of Schermerhorn's characteristics of a high-performing project team. They include:

- Develop and maintain a personal plan for team building and for operation.
- Hold periodic as well as special team meetings.
- Clarify missions, goals, and roles.
- Run the team in a participative and, where possible, consensual manner (consensus can mean that everyone does not necessarily agree with a decision, but can live with it).
- Involve the team in situation analysis and problem solving.
- Give credit to active, positive team members and their contributions.
- Assure team efficiency and productivity.
- Obtain feedback from team members.
- Integrate, coordinate, facilitate, and assure active information flow up and down, as well as sideways.
- Maintain effective communication.

Since in all cases we are talking about humans, the information presented here is for project managers and readers to think about, refer to, try to apply, and try to live by, but not to take as a guarantee for one hundred percent maximum project team performance all of the time. Managing a project and a project team is a dynamic process, and it is affected by emotions, motivations, conflict, and the general pressures of daily life. These factors contribute to making project management a challenging and sometimes frustrating experience.

Managing Conflict

No matter how project managers try to keep a team focused and working effectively toward achieving an objective on time and within budget limitations, there will be conflict between team members that can impact the team's performance. Conflict on a team is natural and can be directed toward the positive benefit of the team. When conflict arises, the project manager must resolve it by eliminating it or directing it positively.

Conflict arises in a number of areas, some of which are impersonal, such as those involving scheduling, budgets, or procedures. These are usually easier to resolve than those involving emotional attachment to a conflict position. Conflict areas such as priorities, personalities, or technical opinions are personal, and since team members may be emotionally attached to their positions, especially when personalities and opinions are involved, these types of conflicts may be more difficult to resolve. There is no one formula leaders should use to resolve conflict on the project team in all situations. In fact, the same method used to resolve one type of conflict between two team members may make the conflict worse if the same method is used for two different people. Leaders are in the difficult position of having to recognize the type of conflict as well as how each participant responds to managerial resolution action before determining the right conflict-resolution method (Eisner 2002).

There are a number of approaches to conflict resolution, and some of them are an indication of the personality of the leader trying to help resolve the conflict. If there is a conflict between two (or more) team members, project managers can choose (or will naturally resort to) the *forcing approach*, where they use their position to order the immediate resolution of the conflict. This will probably resolve the conflict temporarily, but participants are likely to remain frustrated and avoid the issue. Parents sometimes use this method when they force their fighting children to "shake hands and make up." Sometimes the conflicting parties remain angry and can respond with greater force at a later date.

A *compromising* or *sharing* resolution style means working with participants to find a mutually agreeable position that both parties can live with. This is traditional negotiating; many times both parties must give up something, and the losses may cost the project in the long run. Care should be used with this approach to ensure that the compromise solution is also optimized for the sake of the project.

An approach used by weak project managers is the *avoidance* or *withdrawal* style. This is not really considered a conflict-resolution approach; it is considered a management style, but involves simply pretending the conflict doesn't exist. Great care should be taken by upper-level management to keep this from happening, especially when project managers are new to a leadership position.

Another resolution approach is the *accommodation* or *smoothing* approach, in which the resolution is acknowledged, but its seriousness is deemphasized. This should be considered only a temporary measure to reduce the impact of the conflict at the particular moment that it surfaces, in case there is anger or too much emotion involved to deal with it in the heat of battle. It is a perfectly legitimate means to temporarily resolve a conflict (with emphasis on *temporarily*) during the process of permanent resolution when that can be accomplished professionally and when clearer heads prevail.

Probably the most effective approach to resolving conflicts is the *collaborating* or *problem-solving* approach. Team members in conflict are brought together in an analytical and problem-solving environment and collaboration becomes necessary to resolve the issue. For this approach to work, leaders (in this case, they are often facilitators) must listen closely to both sides and encourage the participants to listen to each other's position. When each position is clearly understood by both sides, misunderstandings are often highlighted and become much easier to address. If the conflict is approached as a problem, it can be made less personal and can more easily be dealt with analytically, with less emotion, and in a collaborative way. This is the recommended approach to resolving conflict on a project (Eisner 2002).

Each conflict will bring with it its own set of complexities and personalities, and there is no one right answer or tool that will be successful in resolving conflicts every time. However, if the conflict's resolution is approached through collaboration, analysis, and conversation between team members, it is likely to be more effective and will probably result not only in resolution of that conflict, but also in better project performance.

Motivation and Incentives

Many safety engineers find themselves involved in some way with motivation and incentive programs. While it is not the objective of this chapter to argue the merits of these types of programs, it is still important to discuss the role that motivation and incentives play in managing safety engineering work. This chapter will not address motivation or incentives for the purpose of working safely; it will address them from the vantage point of motivating workers and providing incentives to ensure overall project performance. Safety performance is one component in that overall measure, but safety incentive programs will not be specifically addressed.

Motivation, according to Schermerhorn (1993), is a term that refers to forces within people that drive them toward a specific goal, and it explains a level of "direction and persistence of effort expended" that people have inside for the accomplishment of a goal (in this case, work-related objectives). The impression most people would agree with is that motivated people work harder to achieve their goals than unmotivated people (Schermerhorn 1993). *Incentives* are

thought to increase the level of motivation present in people.

Abraham Maslow helped the world understand the idea of motivation with his Hierarchy of Needs theory. He introduced the concept of higher- and lower-order needs and suggested that people's lower-order needs must be satisfied before someone can try to motivate them by addressing higher-order needs. Maslow tells us that physiological needs, such as rest (adequate breaks), physical comfort on the job, and reasonable work hours must be satisfied before safety needs such as safe working conditions. Both need to be satisfied before social relationships, such as friendly coworkers, interaction with customers, and a pleasant supervisor, can be satisfied. Physiological needs are considered lower-order needs, and once they are all satisfied, we should be able to motivate people by appealing to their higher-order needs, such as esteem and self-actualization (Schermerhorn 1993).

Schermerhorn saw this phenomenon firsthand during a six-year job assignment in one of the former Soviet republics. Team meetings always started out with discussions of project status and upcoming work needs, but they would often deteriorate into discussions about the problems team members were having with their living quarters, their food, lack of heat in the buildings in the winter, and so on. After much frustration on the part of management, it became apparent that it was important to listen intently to and help solve the lower-order needs of the workforce. It was an important revelation to understand that in order to get the project team focused on the work, it was necessary to first ensure that their living quarters, food, and heat were adequate. It was a classic Maslow example in real life.

Provided the project team is adequately compensated for their normal positions and their lower-order needs have been met, some of Maslow's higher-order needs could be addressed by motivation efforts. Important issues should be considered when determining the level of motivation of the team or when determining whether more motivation is needed and, if so, how much more. Almost everyone wants interesting work, and they would like it to challenge their ability to think. If a position can keep a person in the active thinking mode for most of the day, some motivation is already built into the job. If the position causes a person to switch to a mode referred to as *habits of mind* (Louis and Sutton 1991), the chances are greater that performance will be low and additional motivation will be needed (Eisner 2002).

The project team members must be treated fairly and equitably. Many people want to be recognized as being part of a team, and they show their affiliation proudly. One only needs to take a walk through a busy airport on a heavy business travel day to see all the company logos on bags and bag tags, shirts, hats, and coats to realize that team affiliation is important to people. They are proud of their employer. In addition to treating team members fairly and equitably, it is important that the leader or project manager show appreciation for what the team is accomplishing and publicly recognize its accomplishments. When there is an opportunity, the leader should also celebrate the team's successes somehow, such as by hosting a dinner or a trip to a conference or training seminar or with physical rewards (Eisner 2002).

Incentives can serve to motivate workers, and although many incentives are associated with pay for production, the space constraints of one chapter in a large reference manual limit discussion to basic principles of incentives with detailed discussion of a few. Some key principles of incentive programs that should be considered, according to Niebel and Freivalds (1999) are that the incentive program be simple, fair, and based on proven standards. They also suggest that it provide individual incentives above base pay rates and tie the incentives directly to increased production, improved safety performance, and better product quality.

The incentive can be psychological, financial, or both, but it must be meaningful to the worker (Niebel and Freivalds 1999). Care should be taken to understand individual workers in this area, because what is considered meaningful to one worker may not be meaningful to another. This author was very strongly given this message early in his career by approximately 80 percent of the women in his workforce as he passed out the 1982 safety incentive award. The award was a very large cowboy-style belt buckle that, in hindsight, was not considered meaningful by these women. Population stereotypes are important considerations when developing incentive programs. Another important consideration with incentive programs is the fact that their effect is thought to deteriorate over time—interest in any program tends to wane after the newness wears off. Also, receipt of any incentive reward long after the *rewardable* performance may make the incentive less meaningful.

According to Niebel and Freivalds (1999), a motivational climate must be present for a sound incentive program to work. This is one that supports the notion that workers want to work, want to contribute to achieving the project's stated objectives, and want to be properly and adequately rewarded for what they contribute. This type of climate is supported when the project objectives are clearly stated, supported, and realistic and when they emphasize both measurable quantity and measurable quality of output. Workers must feel like the work is their responsibility, that their supervisor is there to support their effort, and that he or she provides frequent feedback.

Some types of incentive plans are those based on piecework, measured daywork, gain-sharing, profit-sharing, and employee stock ownership (Niebel and Freivalds 1999). For more detailed discussion on pay-related incentive programs, please refer to *Methods Standards and Work Design* by Niebel and Freivalds (see reference section). According to Lack (1996), incentive programs can be established to address and recognize outstanding safety results and performance (which can be extrapolated to include production or project performance) or to address and recognize specific significant acts of good performance.

Motivating people through incentives and the work itself is a complex process and should not be taken lightly. If a program is not developed or implemented correctly, it can be worse than no program at all. If it is properly developed, actively implemented, well supported by management, and dynamic, the results can be dramatic and positive. Haight et al. (2001b), Haight and Thomas (2003), Iyer et al. (2004), and Iyer et al. (2005) show that an awareness, incentive, and motivational program had a significant effect on the rate at which loss incidents occurred in an oil production operation and the forestry division of a power company.

Much has been written on the subjects of motivation and incentives. Anyone wishing to develop a motivational or incentive plan should read the available literature and plan the program well ahead of its implementation.

Work and Workforce Analysis

Managers are often concerned about the level of performance their employees are achieving. Many standards have been established and techniques used to determine whether performance is acceptable. One aspect of performance that managers seem to pay significant attention to is the length of time it takes to complete a task or to finish a project. It is important to know how long each task will take to complete because human time costs money, and task duration will have a bearing on the total cost of the project. For this reason, it is critical that criteria be established for each task that is part of a safety engineering project. There is discussion of performance ratings in this chapter, and one of the challenges in this area is to define what is considered *normal* performance.

Allocation of Human Resources

Almost every project involves crews of people working throughout the project area during several days and under varying conditions. Except for the smallest of projects, it would be difficult for a project manager to keep up with what everyone on the project is doing. Since in many cases labor is one of the most expensive resources associated with a project, it is important for a project manager to understand how to quantify and manage the project's human resources. It is also critical that the project manager ensure that workforce crews are efficiently allocated in sufficient numbers to the most appropriate tasks for efficient execution of the project work.

Many construction and maintenance turnaround activities are defined by a particular design or repair task. Often these are well known and frequently used, so an established procedure has already been developed and manpower requirements established. Determining the manpower allocation for these tasks, takes only the

knowledge and experience of a person well versed in the type of construction or maintenance being performed. Manpower requirements for many of these tasks have been defined through several years of observation and analysis of time-study and time-accounting data. Time standards have been established with efficiency and cost in mind. Because of this, many project tasks seem to push the limits of human capacity if allowances are not built in. Time studies and allowances will be discussed later in the chapter. In any case, adherence to time and performance standards will, for cost estimating, allocating resources, and implementing tasks, likely result in lower costs.

For projects and tasks that are not so stable and well established (such as safety-related program activity), one has to rely on the concept of an input-output model to measure the process and analyze the data. This should result in understanding the relationship between the quantified task activities as the input and the performance dimension variation as the output. Once the mathematical relationship is understood, one can use it to change task activities in terms of the extent of the use of available manpower to achieve task performance outcomes. Usually, higher output is desired, but the best approach to achieve that is not necessarily to bring in more people. The choice of activities can be determined through this approach as well.

Haight et al. (2001a, 2001b) and Iyer et al. (2004) determined that manpower allocation to implement a safety and health program can be designed just as any other engineered human–task-based system can. The model shown in Figure 3 depicts a safety and health

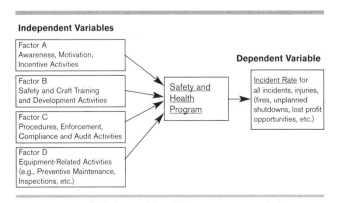

FIGURE 3. Safety and health program model
(adapted from Haight et al. 2001a)

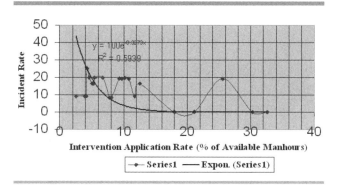

FIGURE 4. Intervention application rate vs. incident-rate relationship (adapted from Haight et al. 2001b)

program set up as an input-output model. This graphic representation shows how one might consider that the program has some quantifiable input and output variables that would allow program effectiveness to be measured and designed to achieve predictable results.

Each of the input variables represents an activity implemented as part of a safety and health program, and each requires the allocation of human resources. How much manpower to allocate and to what extent is not known. The objective is to collect program input and performance data that can be analyzed to develop the mathematical relationship between input and output. Data were collected in the Haight et al. (2001a) study and in the Iyer et al. (2004) study, and a typical mathematical relationship is shown in Figure 4.

The resulting complete mathematical relationship from the Iyer et al. (2004) study is:

$\rho = \mathrm{Ln}\,[\mathrm{Ln}\,(\hat{y})]$
$\quad = x(1) \times x(2) \times x(3) \times x(4) - 3.13 \times x(2) \times x(3) \times$
$\quad\quad x(4) - 1.42 \times x(1) \times x(3) \times x(4) + 0.07 \times x(1) \times$
$\quad\quad x(2) \times x(4) - 2.34 \times x(1) \times x(2) \times x(3) + 4.79 \times$
$\quad\quad x(3) \times x(4) - 0.26 \times x(2) \times x(4) + 8.10 \times x(2) \times$
$\quad\quad x(3) - 0.23 \times x(1) \times x(4) + 2.15 \times x(1) \times x(3) -$
$\quad\quad 0.096 \times x(1) \times x(2) + 0.76 \times x(4) - 6.94 \times x(3) +$
$\quad\quad 0.25 \times x(2) + 0.41 \times x(1) - 0.14$

This is the best-fit equation representing the mathematical relationship between manpower allocation to specific safety and health program tasks where ρ represents the incident rate, x is the intervention application rate for each specific intervention activity, and the numerical value is the fit factor.

This equation is an example from a specific operation and can be used only for that operation, as the operation is where the equation's data came from. Each operation's equation would look a little different; this one is presented for illustration purposes. One can take each activity in a safety and health program, allocate the indicated percentage of available manpower to each, and predict relatively accurately what the resulting incident rate will be with that allocation of resources (Iyer et al. 2004). This model is still emerging, but the five publications currently in existence on the subject indicate that it is useful, viable, and accurate in choosing which intervention activities should be implemented to prevent injuries and loss incidents and to determine the appropriate level of the activities.

New research has been developed to further the work of Haight et al. 2001 and 2003 and Iyer et al. 2004 and 2005. It provides an advanced analytical method for the development of an effective safety intervention program with the aim of minimizing incident rates (Shakioye and Haight 2010, Oyewole et al. 2010). Over a two-year period, incident-prevention-directed intervention activity data and incident rate data were collected from an American-owned oil company in Nigeria. From these data, an analysis was completed and a mathematical model was developed to allow measurement and optimization of the effectiveness of a suite of interacting intervention activities that minimize incident rates while concurrently allowing for the development of an improved resource allocation plan and strategy. In this work, Oyewole et al. (2010) investigated five main intervention program factors (Factor A: Leadership and Accountability; Factor B: Qualification Selection and Pre-Job; Factor C: Employee Engagement and Planning; Factor D: Work in Progress; Factor E: Evaluation, Measurement and Verification). As in previous work (Haight et al. 2001 and 2003 and Iyer et al. 2004 and 2005), this was done to define the mathematical relationship between model input and output and to show the effects of each factor and their interactions on the incident rate. Oyewole et al. (2010) completed an analysis of variance, which showed that four safety factors (A, C, D, and E) had a significant effect. The innovation that Oyewole et al. (2010) brings to this line of research is the use of response surface design plots to determine the resource allocation method. This particular incident prevention intervention model indicates that the incident rate can be minimized at an optimum allocation of 16.66 percent of the available human resource time. From this, one can determine the significant safety intervention activities that have the most certainty for achieving the desired incident rate.

In order to reap the benefits of this research, it will be important to concentrate more effort and resources on model-indicated significant incident prevention intervention activities that contribute significantly to minimizing incident rates. Using surface response methodology, a point on the model-generated surface can be selected as the point at which the incident rate is at its minimum point. One then finds the human resource time allocation for each intervention activity shown on the graph to use in designing the incident prevention program. One chooses the activities indicated on the graph (the model indicates that they significantly contribute to incident prevention) to determine how much available resource time should be allocated to the indicated incident prevention activities. An example of these results are shown in Figures 5 and 6. From these figures, one can determine the optimum values for each interactive factor from the *minimum* or *lowest* point on the three-dimensional plot (Shakioye and Haight 2010, Oyewole et al. 2010).

This information includes the development of the previous Haight and Iyer work and now provides a more direct solution to the model. These results allow an optimized solution to be chosen from the factors that have been analyzed and presented on the three-dimensional graph. In this case, the results allow a manager to allocate a specific amount of available human resource hours to specific intervention activities from each of the two factors shown. Of course, all models are just mathematical representations of real life, so it is expected that those responsible for allocating resources use the results from these types of models in their own decision making while also incorporating their experience, intuition, and expectations.

Oyewole et al. (2010) further proves that, in order to thoroughly measure the effectiveness of an incident

prevention program, one must understand all leading indicators and all lagging indicators (or performance-driving factors) within a loss prevention system and then must define and develop the mathematical relationship between the leading and lagging indicators. It further appears from this work, that it is not enough to measure leading indicators alone or to base resource allocation decisions purely on lagging indicators either. One must determine all performance-influencing factors and build an input-output model around those factors in order to truly understand how to design a loss prevention program and truly drive an incident rate lower. If a suite of intervention activities that make up a loss prevention program are not designed using this methodology, one is leaving this

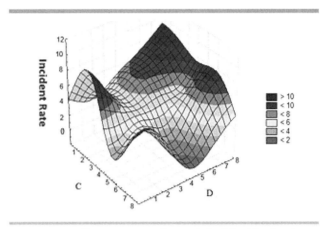

FIGURE 5. Response surface plot of incident rate vs. factors **C** and **D** (Oyewole et al. 2010)

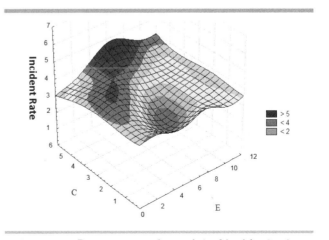

FIGURE 6. Response surface plot of incident rate vs. factors **C** and **D** (Oyewole et al. 2010)

important function up to chance. It is suggested that the reader refer to these studies in the reference list to learn more about the process.

Training and Learning Curves

A workforce is one of any company's most valuable and important resources. It is critical that this workforce be skilled and capable of performing its functions in the most efficient, correct, and safe way. To achieve this skilled performance, a management team must provide a mechanism to ensure that the workforce is adequately and appropriately trained. A project manager overseeing a safety-engineering-related project or any type of project involving safety-engineering-related work must incorporate compliance issues as well as skill issues into training programs.

While many training courses are compliance-driven, especially in the safety engineering area, some training and learning needs are not so well established. To effectively address the important training needs of the workforce, one of the first things a project manager or management team should do is to conduct a *training needs assessment* to determine the subject matter that should be addressed in the training program. This needs assessment should center around the specific hazards to which the workers could be exposed, the specific work or tasks they are expected to perform, and specific improvements that need to be made in the operation. The assessment specialist must consider who does what jobs as well as what they do and where, when, and why they do them. This helps the organization to make a distinction between training and nontraining solutions; it helps them to understand problems thoroughly instead of jumping to a training solution before the problem is fully or adequately understood; and it helps to ensure that money and time are not wasted by providing training courses that do not solve the problems of the organization (Hagan, Montgomery, and O'Reilly 2001). Once the training needs are defined, training experts can take over and develop learning objectives, the course content, the lesson plans, and training-frequency requirement schedules for the target audience.

When implementing a training program, care must be taken to ensure that it addresses not only the overall needs of the group of workers but also that it is directed in such a way as to provide for the individual needs of each trainee. Everyone does not learn at the same rate, so project managers must ensure that the training staff properly evaluates the learning curves of a group of trainees for the specific material in which they are being trained. Trainers must first recognize that learning is a time-dependent phenomenon and then address the progress people are making along their particular curve using a process in which the time it takes someone to master a particular skill or task is measured. Depending upon a task's complexity, it could take days or even weeks for people to master a skill to the point where they possess the necessary mental and physical capabilities and coordination to successfully and efficiently transition from one task element to the next without hesitating.

A learning curve is typically exponential and usually indicates that the more people practice a skill, the more often they can perform it quickly, efficiently, or with higher-quality results. If, for example, a person is required to don a self-contained breathing apparatus (SCBA), it usually has to be done very quickly due to the emergency nature of such an action. Once people are taught how to don this equipment, their first attempt at doing it will probably take much longer than their hundredth attempt. The learning curve in Figure 7 shows that the more times people donned breathing apparatus, the better they got at doing it and the faster they did it.

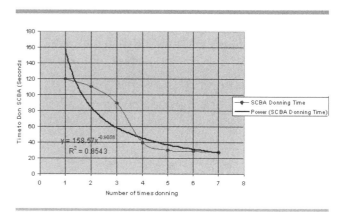

FIGURE 7. Example of a learning curve plot

The learning curve, in this case, is a power curve of the form:

$$y = kx^n \qquad (7)$$

where

y = time to achieve task

x = number of task performances

n = exponent representing the slope of the curve

k = value of the first task attempt

To determine how many times one must don self-contained breathing apparatus before achieving the expected time of 25 seconds, substitute 25 seconds into the equation, take the log of both sides and solve for x:

$$y = kx^n$$
$$25 = 158.57x^{-0.9058}$$
$$\log_{10}(25/158.57) = -0.9058 \log_{10}x$$
$$\log_{10}x = -0.8023/-0.9058$$
$$x = 10^{0.8857}$$
$$x = 7.69 \text{ or } 8$$

The results of this learning-curve analysis indicate that one must practice putting on the SCBA at least eight times to achieve 25 seconds donning time. If the training course does not have a provision to allow for at least eight practice attempts, its objectives must be reevaluated. Whatever the acceptance criteria, one can determine the learning curve in the same fashion. For example, if the task were learning to set up and wear a fall-protection harness system, the trainer could collect data to determine how many practice sessions are needed before the fall-protection system is set up and donned without errors (Niebel and Freivalds 1999).

When developing and managing a training program, it is critical to ensure that if training is being proposed in response to a safety-engineering-related problem, a significant effort is expended to be sure that training is the correct solution to the problem. Training is generally the correct approach if the desired goal is to provide "how-to-do" information to workers. Training is done for the purpose of changing behavior or increasing knowledge, improving performance, reinforcing operational goals, reducing incidents, improving efficiency, or reducing costs. It

is not necessarily the solution to a problem in which workers do not do what they are supposed to do. Many times workers take incorrect actions even when they know the correct actions and how to carry them out. Much money is lost each year in training costs because organizations make a decision to train their workforce when a nontraining solution is more appropriate. For example, if workers won't wear their protective equipment because it is heavy or bulky, fogs up, or is otherwise uncomfortable to wear, putting everyone through a 4-hour training session on the importance of wearing protective equipment just to get them to wear it is a waste of time and money. During the needs-assessment stage in the process, a project manager should ensure that all possible training and nontraining solutions are explored (Hagan, Montgomery, and O'Reilly 2001).

Training programs are of many shapes and sizes—they have to be in order to address the many possible subject areas that must be covered. They must also be flexible enough to work around day-to-day production operations and the possibility of high turnover (especially in construction and maintenance turnaround projects, and project work in general). They have to account for individual differences in the workforce, such as differences in experience levels, physical and cognitive capacity, trade-based knowledge, health, age, dexterity, and the types of tasks each worker performs. Training programs must include a provision for ensuring that individual workers understand the training they receive. This can be in the form of a written or oral examination, a hands-on demonstration (for example, an employee shows how to make a safe lift after taking an ergonomics training class), or an assignment for the trainee to now train others (Niebel and Freivalds 1999).

Training can take these many forms and still be effective. It does not have to involve workers sitting in a classroom. It can be as simple as asking employees to read a new procedure or watch a videotape, or it may be all on-the-job training in which employees spend their early years with an experienced mentor. Workers can use simulators that put them in a very real, joblike situation but without the consequences of wrong actions (such as pilots being trained in a flight simulator—there is no crash after an error). Training can involve physical activity such as learning to take flammable gas concentration measurements inside a confined space by actually testing air in a confined space under the guidance of a qualified gas tester (Freivalds and Niebel 2008). Training techniques can involve case studies, facilitated discussions, role playing, lectures, drills, brainstorming, independent study, videos/DVDs, or even computer-aided or online training (Hagan, Montgomery, and O'Reilly 2001).

It addition to the content area of a training program, project managers must consider logistical and administrative issues. Issues such as instructors, location, schedule, frequency, student availability, testing, and record keeping require resolution before beginning any safety engineering training. For more detailed information on training, please refer to the "Safety and Health Training" section in this handbook.

Work Sampling

More traditional allocation methods can be relied on when tasks are well defined. *Work sampling* is a method of observing a task while it is being performed to determine whether a specific outcome will occur. It is described somewhat by the laws of probability. The probability that event x will occur in n observations is

$$(p + q)^n = 1 \tag{8}$$

where

p = the probability of a single occurrence
$q = (1 - p)$ (the probability of an absence of the occurrence)
n = the number of observations

The distribution of many of these probabilities follows binomial distribution laws. It is known that as n becomes larger, the binomial distribution begins to approach a normal distribution. Therefore, with large enough numbers of observations, one can use the normal distribution laws to approximate the results of a task. Since this is the case, p can represent the mean of the distribution and the standard deviation of $\sqrt{pq/n}$ is approximately a normally distributed

random variable. Using the laws of normal distribution, we can estimate that 95 percent of the expected outcomes of our observations will fall within two standard deviations of the mean. For a binomial distribution, the function is as follows (Niebel and Freivalds 1999):

$$F_x = (x; p, n) = P(x) = \binom{n}{x} p^x q^{n-2} \tag{9}$$

where

n = the number of samples
x = the number of successful samples
p = the probability of success
q = the probability of failure

QUESTION FOR STUDY

You are managing a job involving a confined-space entry and are worried about possible delays caused by problems with the availability of supplied air. You can get an idea of both the probability of the unavailability occurrence and the approximate delay time by using this equation. Observations over the previous year indicate that supplied breathing air was unavailable 8 percent of the time, and 25 confined-space-entry jobs were performed. This caused delays to the projects totaling 10 days (no entry work can be done without breathing air). Twenty-five more confined-space-entry jobs are planned for 2012, and all require the use of supplied breathing air. What is the probability that two jobs will be delayed due to unavailability of supplied breathing air?

$n = 25$
$p = 0.08$
$q = 0.92$
$x = 2$

$P(x = 2) = \binom{25}{2} p^x q^{n-2}$
$P(x = 2) = (300)(0.08)^2 (0.92)^{23}$
$P(x = 2) = 0.282$

With a probability this high, you might consider adding back-up respiratory equipment or more people.

Another example of work sampling with a quantitative sampling analysis method uses a Poisson distribution. The Poisson distribution determines discrete probabilities of a specific number of events occurring in a known amount of time if there are adequate observation data and those data follow a Poisson distribution (Eisner 2002):

$$P(k) = (\lambda t)^k e^{(-\lambda t)}/k! \qquad (10)$$

QUESTION FOR STUDY

Equation 10 could be used to analyze a situation in which you want to know how many hot-work and confined-space permits you will be able to process in one hour given the current manpower availability.

In the process of planning a major maintenance turnaround, you are concerned that the necessary day-to-day work permits required to keep the turnaround on schedule will be too high, given the number of employees assigned, to evaluate and approve safety-related permits. Bid estimates require that at least ten permits be processed in an hour. This appears to be a potential bottleneck for the project, so past work-sampling data are evaluated and a Poisson calculation is undertaken to determine the probability that five permits can be processed every 30 minutes (given the current staffing and availability of analysis equipment). Over the last four maintenance turnarounds in this unit, permits have been processed at an overall rate of eight permits per hour. The probability that five permits can be processed in 30 minutes (or $t = 0.5$ hours) is:

$$P(5) = [(8)(0.5)]^5 e^{[-(8)(0.5)]}/5!$$
$$P(5) = (1024)(0.0183)/120$$
$$P(5) = 0.156$$

This probability is low and indicates that a project slowdown is likely to occur. If this is a critical turnaround and the unit has to be back up and running by exactly the originally scheduled turnaround completion date, this probability—15.6 percent that the project team can process permits at the rate needed to stay on schedule—means that staffing allocations will have to be reevaluated.

where

$P(k)$ = the probability of exactly k events of interest occurring

λ = the rate at which the events occur

t = the time over which the events occur

When observing and sampling any type of work for the purpose of making risk decisions, or even just likelihood decisions, the appropriate number of observations or data points needed to make statistically supported decisions must be determined. To accomplish this, the desired accuracy requirements must be identified. The basis for this consideration is that the more observations made, the more valid the final answer will be from the standpoint of predicting an actual outcome. To do this, the following formula can be used:

$$n = 4p(1 - p)/l^2 \qquad (11)$$

where

n = the number of observations

p = the probability of occurrence of the event you are trying to prevent

l = the error limit or desired accuracy

QUESTION FOR STUDY

You want to determine the likelihood that employees are not wearing proper protective equipment. It has been reported that 10 percent of the employees are not wearing their protective equipment, but you claim that the violators make up only 5 percent of the employees (Niebel and Freivalds 1999). To confirm this, you want your accuracy to be plus or minus 2 percent. The number of observations needed is

$$n = 4(0.05)(1 - 0.05)/(0.02)^2$$
$$n = 475 \text{ observations}$$

If you can afford the time to make only 250 observations, you can solve for the expected accuracy by:

$$l = \sqrt{4(p)(1 - p)/n} \qquad (12)$$
$$l = \sqrt{4(0.05)(0.95)/250} = 0.0275$$

or ±2.75% accurate

In general, many types of analyses can be done to understand the work going on in an operation. Safety engineering project managers must first understand the performance output they are most interested in and then determine whether successful performance is related to time (on schedule), number of occurrences (number of permits processed), or number of people required to safely complete a job. Once the desired output and its expected quality are known, they need to determine and quantify the variables that affect the output performance. The rest of the work-sampling approach involves data collection (performance variables) and analysis (the appropriate analysis for the resulting distributions). This sampling and analytical process will aid decision making and help project managers to ensure an efficient operation that completes work on schedule and within budgetary constraints, while still allowing for safe completion.

Performance Ratings

There is no universal method to rate worker performance in terms of productivity, efficiency, safety, or accuracy. There is no universal measure of what represents normal performance. For each task in a safety engineering project, acceptable performance must be defined. Consideration must be given to what task completion comprises, how much time it should take to carry out each task, and how acceptable quality is determined.

Benchmarking is often used to help determine these characteristics of a task. Standards and acceptance criteria are established for each step in a task from benchmarking observations of the same task being completed at another company location or at a different company's operation. From the acceptance criteria, a performance rater can be trained to do the observation (he or she will know what to look for) and an actual performance rating can be carried out.

When benchmarking, determine whether all necessary steps (as defined by initial internal task design) are included. If not, the benchmarking analyst should ascertain the reasons the steps are missing and resolve the situation by redesigning the task or deciding that the missing steps are not necessary. The analyst should determine what equipment is being used for the job

and decide whether it is appropriate. He or she should determine how long each step in the task takes to complete and how to determine when it is complete. Each of these criteria should be documented in a form that is easy to follow for a performance rating analyst observing the same task in the future.

The acceptance criteria must take into account the fact that there are individual differences in the people carrying out the task. Differences in general fitness, experience, dexterity, strength, age, level of training, and so on may affect any or all aspects of task performance. The analyst who develops the performance rating criteria must define acceptance in terms of a range that takes into account the fact that workers should be well adapted to the task, adequately trained and experienced to perform the task, in adequate physical shape, and coordinated both physically and mentally to a level that allows efficient movement from one step in the task to the next, while obeying the principles of motion economy (Niebel and Freivalds 1999, Freivalds and Niebel 2008). The analyst may consider recording time-and-motion data for all steps and developing performance ranges and frequency distributions that allow the establishment of a statistically supported acceptance range.

For example, this performance rating may be applied to an excavation job because each of the preparation, permitting, and implementation steps can be observed and rated against a known acceptance standard. The project person responsible gathers all relevant subsurface soil data, identifies the location of the excavation, seeks appropriate concurrence and approvals for the job, seeks appropriate approval signatures on the permit, arranges for appropriate equipment and manpower, ensures appropriate excavation design (e.g., step-back method or shoring), ensures appropriate dewatering of excavation and deposition of the spoil pile, and so on. Each of these steps receives a score based on whether the steps taken match established excavation and permitting protocol. A performance rating analyst scores each task as present or absent—and if present, to what quality is it being applied—and overall time it takes to complete the job. An indexing score can be used to allow consistent relative ranking on quality.

This process is the same as ones used by many organizations implementing behavior-based safety observation programs. These programs are, in essence, performance-rating processes. In the case of behavior-based safety programs, the ratings are based on an observer-developed, critical, acceptable behaviors library. All observations are done by comparing actual performance to the critical behaviors definition. Task performance is rated either *safe* or *at risk*. At risk, or unacceptable task performance is addressed and changed so that a *safe* score can be achieved.

Even though there is no universally accepted standard, after a task or a project is observed long enough, a picture emerges of what it should look like. The challenge then becomes to capture that acceptable performance on an observer-used data-gathering tool, such as a checklist, a rating sheet, or a scoresheet. These ratings can then be used to address individuals or contract companies whose performance does not meet expected, accepted levels.

Time Study and Allowances

The concept of *time study* has been a part of industrial engineering for many years. It is a process by which an observer watches a particular task being performed many times by many people; from the observation data, time standards are developed for each target task. Its main purpose is to see that a task is carried out efficiently and with minimal wasted effort, motion, or time. The method is based on the measurement of the content of a task based on a specific and defined method for carrying out the task, given that there are adequate allowances for fatigue and for certain unavoidable delays. Adequate data should be collected to ensure that the time standards established for a particular task are in fact accurate and are also based on sound statistical significance.

The first step in this process is to divide a job into its component elements. Once this is done and the task steps for each job are established, the dispatch of each component task is timed and recorded. Once a statistically significant number of observations has been obtained and appropriate allowances have been considered, a suitable time standard is established and used for all future time-study observations. Allowances that must be considered in establishing time standards are fatigue, abnormal posture requirements, muscular force application requirements, illumination levels, atmospheric conditions (e.g., too hot, too cold, damp, icy, slippery), noise levels, visual strain, mental strain, monotony and tediousness, as well as a constant allowance for personal needs (work stoppage related to maintaining personal well-being).

These allowances were quantified by the International Labor Office in 1957 and are still used today for the most part (Niebel and Freivalds 1999, Freivalds and Niebel 2008). Allowances are considered after normal time (NT) has been determined by the formula NT = OT (observed time) $\times R/100$, where R is a rating based on a percentage of efficiency compared to 100 percent—a level applied by a qualified, experienced operator working under normal conditions at the workstation with no undue time burden or pressure. Knowing normal time and allowances, standard time for each task can be determined. The formula for determining the standard time (ST) for completing a job is:

$$ST = NT + NT \times allowance \qquad (13)$$
$$ST = NT \times (1 + allowance)$$

For example, if a task step in a job has a normal time of 0.145 minutes and a particularly high level of mental strain is associated with it, requiring an allowance of 0.08 (considered "very complex" in the International Labor Office, 1957 recommendations), the standard time would be:

$$ST = 0.145 \text{ min} \times (1 + 0.08)$$

An ST of 0.156 minutes should be allowed to complete this task.

Time-study and allowances consideration is quite involved and often for safety-engineering-related work is not necessary; however, someone charged with managing safety-engineering-related work should be familiar with time study and should understand thoroughly the concept of allowances. Many allowances are necessary to preserve the health and safety of workers. Therefore, safety engineering managers are encouraged to do additional reading on the subject of time study and allowances, as can be found in Niebel and Freivalds (1999).

PROJECT COMPLETION

What does completion mean?

In day-to-day operations, it is often the case that safety engineering work is never complete. Everyday operations require the input of the safety engineer, and, in fact, the safety engineer often assists line management personnel in managing their safety-related responsibilities. *Completion* as discussed here refers to finite project work in which projects such as construction, installation, and maintenance are undertaken, managed throughout their course, and then closed out as the effort is completed and the workers are reassigned. When the building construction is completed, the pipeline is laid, or the paper machine repair work is completed, the project is finished and it is time to assess performance. This closeout work may mean that scaffolding is taken down, excavations are covered, open vessels are resealed, and the workers depart. Project records must be addressed and information worked into the plans for the next time the project is undertaken. Lessons learned from incidents, injuries, or other problems must be sorted out and communicated. There is much to be done as and after a project is completed.

For this effort, one should rely on an element from the field of controlling referred to as *post-action* or *feedback controls*. While active pre-action (feedforward) and concurrent (steering) controls have been in place throughout the project to help manage the project itself, the concept and tools of feedback or post-action controls are needed in order to learn from project results and improve them the next time such a project is implemented (Schermerhorn 1993).

One example of a post-action control is the final project budget summary. It will not help project managers to get the budget under control, but it will help to determine where they should place emphasis next time if there is a budget overrun. Another example is a final site inspection. This post-action control may tell a project manager that the project is not really finished. If a state regulatory agency does a post-clean-up inspection after an asbestos removal job

and finds high concentrations of asbestos in the air, the project team will likely have to come back and continue the removal and clean up. Post-action controls such as these are intended to help project managers (especially those managing the safety engineering aspects of a project) in the planning process and to improve project performance the next time the work is done. They can also be used to document and recognize good performance during the current project (Schermerhorn 1993).

Project Closeout

When project work is completed, proper closeout is critical for many reasons, including financial concerns, but most importantly from a safety engineering point of view. In many cases, the project management system includes a provision requiring a closeout inspection of the work. One Occupational Safety and Health regulation (29 CFR 1910.119, *Process Safety Management of Highly Hazardous Chemicals*) calls this step the "pre-startup safety review." It is critical that buildings are not occupied, vessels are not pressured, conveyor belts are not started, flammable liquids are not introduced, and earth is not tread upon until there has been some type of inspection to determine that all is structurally sound, all codes have been met, all affected workers have been trained, and all facility documentation (e.g., maps, plot plans, piping and instrument diagrams, procedures) have been revised and updated. A number of projects over the years illustrate the importance of such a closeout phase in a project—for example, wrenches and hard hats (left in a vessel) clogged flowing liquid systems and parking decks collapsed. There was even a situation in which someone wanting to do a final inspection inside a vessel didn't follow the confined-space-entry rules and was nearly closed up in the vessel, which was about to have raw materials, heat, and pressure reintroduced (this last example is from the author's own history).

Many disciplines should be involved in the closeout process. Project managers must make arrangements to include representatives from all of the required disciplines, including regulatory agency representatives who may be required to issue such documents as certificates of occupancy.

Operating experts are required to ensure that the system and equipment can be operated by the people who will need to operate it.

Accountants and cost analysts are required to track the budget performance.

Planning (time and resource allocation) analysts may be required to determine schedules and inventory performance.

Structural engineers and safety engineers may be required to determine whether the buildings, ladders, stairwells, decks, flooring, earthen dikes, accessways, support structures, and so on were built as designed and are adequate for their intended purpose.

Electrical and instrument engineers may be required to determine whether the wiring, power generating and supply, and control systems are built to code, as designed, and are adequate for the intended service.

Fire protection engineers may be required to determine whether exits, exit accessways, fire suppression systems, detection and alarm systems, fire department access, and water supplies are adequate and meet required codes and that emergency response provisions have been met.

Environmental engineers may be required to ensure that pollution prevention systems have been installed properly and will perform as intended.

Safety engineers may be required to determine whether the site has been adequately cleared of all equipment, parts, and supplies that could make access to and travel through the site unsafe. They may also be required to determine and ensure that documentation has been adequately and thoroughly revised to reflect the new facility or system.

Regulatory agency experts or officers may be required to do an overall project or site inspection to ensure adequate clean up (asbestos), sizing of storm water drainage (water pollution), adequate incinerator stack height (air pollution), and so on.

The records of these inspection results must be maintained and an approval signature must be received for each. Project managers should not allow start-up and use of the new facility until they have been adequately assured by each expert that it is safe and approved to do so. While experts in each discipline may have their own systems, checklists, or similar means to determine whether the facility is safe to start up will help to ensure consistency. Safety engineers may assist in the project by developing, in collaboration with a representative of each discipline, these inspection checklists. The checklists not only facilitate the inspection, but they can also form the record of the inspection. If a provision is made for an approval signature on the checklist, everything is in one package (Hagan, Montgomery, and O'Reilly 2001). It stands to reason that after all representatives with a vested interest in the project and the expertise to evaluate it have given their approval, it is safe to initiate occupancy and/or operation.

Presentation of Results

While project work is going on, presentations of ongoing status information are likely to be given on a regular and frequent basis. Usually these presentations are less formal and contain less information as well as less-detailed information than a final presentation of all the project results. These presentations serve a somewhat different purpose than the presentation of the final project results in that their objective is usually to help people to know where they need to steer things back on track. Since they are usually less formal, they may take many formats, so they will not be treated here. This section addresses the larger, more formal, final presentation of project completion results.

The purpose of presenting final project results is similar to the objectives discussed above for feedback or post-action controls. It is desirable to know how the methods employed during the project worked so that the results can be used in planning for the next project. It is also desirable to use this forum to recognize and document positive accomplishment (Schermerhorn 1993). If outside contractors are involved in a project and performance incentive clauses are built into the contract, this presentation also recognizes the achievement of performance awards.

Some issues that can or should be addressed in a final project presentation are budget and costing performance; completion schedule performance; safety performance; equipment condition reports (for maintenance turnarounds); new building, facility, or system uses; output improvements (production capacity increases); and new products to be manufactured or new markets to be entered. It may be appropriate for this presentation to include some discussion of the ongoing needs or responsibilities of the new or newly renovated facility.

This presentation should be developed, managed, and given like any other presentation in that it should be guided by the same established rules of effective presentations that guide other presentations. Presenters should know the audience and what it will be most interested to hear. They should tell the audience what they are *going* to tell them, what they *are* telling them, and then what they *told* them. They should present material visually (e.g., PowerPoint-type slide) and explain what the visual material means, but not read from the visual material. They should make sure that the visual material is not too busy; the information can be seen or read by everyone in the room (considering lighting, clarity, contrast, and so on); the information is not condescending to an audience that already knows the subject matter; and the slides are not too flashy, colorful, or otherwise distracting. During the presentation itself, presenters should make eye contact with everyone and ensure that the pace allows people some time to think about each point being made. They should decide how to handle questions (during or after the presentation) and provide hard copies of the presentation material after it (Eisner 2002).

Presenters also must make some decisions about the presentation format and logistics. Considerations include whether the content will be lecture-based or activity-based, the number of speakers and the logistics associated with changing speakers, the topics and information that will be covered (just a bottom-line status report of costs, duration, and incidents, or a discussion of lessons learned), and whether there will be roundtable open discussion or a closed presentation of the facts. They must consider lighting (e.g., no bright lights over the projection screen, adequate lighting for attendees to take notes), break schedules (attendees may need a break shortly after lunch as well as at every hour)

and getting attendees to return from breaks on time, comfortable seating (but not so comfortable as to induce sleep), room temperature (public spaces are often kept so cold that participants cannot focus on presentations, so presenters should ensure that the room is not too cold), refreshments, cell phone use, and laptop use (and availability of power for them). Even though there is no correct combination of decisions and conditions (this is very site- and situation-specific), a good presentation given under the right conditions will often be a successful presentation (Eisner 2002).

Ongoing Implementation, Record Keeping, and Communication of Lessons Learned

When the final presentations are completed, an organization will be best served by an effort in the routine management plan to capture and make use of all that was learned during the implementation of the project. The objective is to ensure a successful implementation the next time a similar project is undertaken. Since people change jobs and move on to other issues, a mechanism and a system must be in place to record, retrieve, and communicate the valuable lessons learned and the important records from the project.

The information is the same as that discussed in the final presentation of project results. The cost and budget information will be useful for future estimating purposes. The schedule performance information, broken down by task or job segment, will also contribute to manpower and time estimation for the next time. Materials of construction, repair details, spare-part usage rates, equipment condition inspection records, protective equipment availability and usage rates will all help in putting the right people and equipment on the job in adequate levels and quantities. Training topic and attendance records, meeting topic and attendance records, contractor turnover records, injury rates, and industrial hygiene monitoring program and results will help to determine what the safety and health program should look like for the next project. Information on traffic patterns, laydown areas, delivery locations, and equipment storage issues will help to relieve congestion and ensure that adequate space is allotted for implementation of similar projects in the future.

In general, all of these records, lessons, and information should be maintained and used in the planning process of a new project. They should be communicated to the planning team set up to implement the next project to ensure that old lessons are not forgotten and new people on the project do not waste time solving problems long since solved.

CONCLUSION

In managing any project, in the safety engineering area or any other area, one must consider the budget, the schedule, protection of the workforce, and the objectives of the customer, as well as learning something from the mistakes made. While managerial skills are critical, people manage this type of work through effective leadership. They have to rely on strong interpersonal skills, all of which may not be teachable but are acquired over time through living and experience. All the analysis in the world may not guarantee the successful completion of a project. We all have to remember that managing work means managing people, and managing people means relying a lot on what we learned in kindergarten and the first grade.

REFERENCES

Accreditation Board of Engineering and Technology (ABET), Inc. *Criteria for Accrediting Applied Science Programs, 2002–2003 Accreditation Cycle*. Baltimore, MD: ABET.

Brauer, R. L. 2005. *Safety and Health for Engineers*. New York: Van Nostrand Reinhold.

CoVan, J. 1995. *Safety Engineering*. New York: John Wiley & Sons, Inc.

Duderstadt, J. J., G. F. Knoll, and G. S. Springer. 1982. *Principles of Engineering*. New York: John Wiley & Sons, Inc.

Eisner, H. 2002. *Essentials of Project and Systems Engineering Management*. 2d ed. New York: Wiley Interscience, John Wiley and Sons, Inc.

Freivalds, A., and B. Niebel. 2008. *Methods, Standards and Work Design*. 11th ed. Boston: WCB McGraw Hill.

Gloss, D. S., and M. G. Wardle. 1984. *Introduction to Safety Engineering*. New York: John Wiley & Sons.

Iyer, P. S., J. M. Haight, E. del Castillo, B. W. Tink, and P. W. Hawkins. 2004. "Intervention Effectiveness Research: Understanding and Optimizing Industrial Safety Programs Using Leading Indicators." *Chemical Health and Safety American Chemical Society Division of Chemical Health and Safety* 11(2):9–19.

_____. 2005. "A Research Model—Forecasting Incident Rates from Optimized Safety Program Intervention Strategies." *Journal of Safety Research* 36(4):341–351.

Hagan, P. E., J. F. Montgomery, and J. T. O'Reilly. 2001. *Accident Prevention Manual for Business and Industry – Administration and Programs*. 12th ed. Itasca, IL: National Safety Council.

Haight, J. M., and R. E. Thomas. 2003. "Intervention Effectiveness Research—A Review of the Literature on 'Leading Indicators.'" *Chemical Health and Safety—American Chemical Society—Division of Chemical Health and Safety* 10(2):21–25.

Haight, J. M., R. E. Thomas, Leo A. Smith, R. L. Bulfin, and B. L. Hopkins. 2001a. "Evaluating the Effectiveness of Loss Prevention Interventions: Developing the Mathematical Relationship Between Interventions and Incident Rates for the Design of a Loss Prevention System (Phase 1)." *Professional Safety— The Journal of the American Society of Safety Engineers* 46(5):38–44.

_____. 2001b. "An Analysis of the Effectiveness of Loss Prevention Interventions: Design, Optimization, and Verification of the Loss Prevention System and Analysis Model (Phase 2)." *Professional Safety—The Journal of the American Society of Safety Engineers* 46(6):33–37.

Hersey, P., and K. Blanchard. 1977. *Management of Organizational Behavior Utilizing Group Resources*. 3d ed. Englewood Cliffs, NJ: Prentice Hall.

Lack, R. W. 1996. *Essentials of Safety and Health Management*. Boca Raton, FL: Lewis Publishers, CRC Press LLC.

Louis, M. R., and R. Sutton. 1991. "Switching Cognitive Gears: From Habits of Mind to Active Thinking." *Human Relations* 44(1):55–76.

Nahmias, S. 1993. *Production and Operations Analysis*. 2d ed. Homewood, IL and Boston, MA: Richard D. Irwin, Inc.

Niebel, B., and A. Frievalds. 1999. *Methods, Standards and Work Design*. 10th ed. Boston: WCB McGraw Hill.

Occupational Safety and Health Administration (OSHA). 29 CFR 1910.119. (accessed 15 January 2005). www.osha.gov

Oyewole, S. A., J. M. Haight, A. Freivalds, D. J. Cannon, and L. Rothrock. 2010. "Statistical Evaluation of Safety Intervention Effectiveness and Optimization of Resource Allocation." *Journal of Loss Prevention in the Process Industries* 23(5):585–593.

Park, C. S., 1997. *Contemporary Engineering Economics*. 2nd ed. Menlo Park, CA: Addison-Wesley Longman, Inc.

Schermerhorn, J. R. 1993. *Management for Productivity*. 4th ed. New York: John Wiley and Sons, Inc.

Shakioye, S., and J. M. Haight. 2009. "Modeling Using Dynamic Variables—An Approach for the Design of Loss Prevention Programs." *Safety Sciences* 48(1):46–53.

Wright, P. H., A. Koblasz, and W. E. Sayle II. 1989. *Introduction to Engineering*. New York: John Wiley & Sons.

SECTION 1

MANAGEMENT OF SAFETY ENGINEERING WORK

LEARNING OBJECTIVES

▌ Be able to demonstrate through examples how worker safety and health risk impact the economic and operational integrity of a global company.

▌ Identify and understand the challenges a multinational company faces when managing global workplace safety and health risks.

▌ Develop global strategies to manage global workplace safety and health risks.

▌ Understand how country and business cultures impact global worker safety and health implementation and performance.

▌ Identify and assess personal workplace risk when working and traveling globally.

APPLIED SCIENCE AND ENGINEERING: GLOBAL ISSUES

Kathy A. Seabrook

THIS CHAPTER provides a business perspective on managing worker safety and health risks as they relate to global companies. Global companies are changing rapidly, whether through joint ventures, organic expansion, acquisitions, or divestiture. These changes, tied to the increased interdependency of global manufacturing and distribution systems, combined with the interconnectivity of global communication, media, and information systems, are significantly impacting global trade and presenting a myriad of new challenges for business (Friedman 2005). One of these challenges is managing worker safety and health risks throughout a global organization.

Using a business-perspective and model-centric approach, rather than strictly a safety and health regulatory-driven perspective, this chapter examines worker safety and health issues as a critical part of the overall strategic planning process companies engage in when running a global organization. It will demonstrate how managing worker safety and health as a business risk can either positively or negatively impact profit, market share, brand, and manufacturing and distribution within international organizations. Whether mitigating reputational risk, complying with safety and health laws, or handling risk litigation, managing worker safety and health is a good strategy for global companies. This strategy ensures that global companies are not prohibited or inhibited from operating in any market, including new or emerging markets.

The role of a safety and health professional within a global company is to provide senior management with both the short- and long-term perspective on how worker safety and health risk impacts the functional, financial, and operational future of the organization. It is therefore critical that the management of worker safety and health risk is embedded in the fabric of global companies as they continue to seek business opportunities in new, emerging, and existing markets.

A GLOBAL BUSINESS PERSPECTIVE

The global business community continues to expand into new and emerging markets in an effort to grow their global market share, enhance their profits, and expand their customer base. This, along with the rise in global interconnectivity (instantaneous communication, information sharing, and media access), has changed how global and international companies operate over the past twenty years. For example, access to portals of information, official and unofficial, has changed many global companies' perspectives on what constitutes a risk to their business operations. They are now recognizing that worker safety and health risks can pose as great a reputational risk as the traditionally recognized reputational risks associated with branding, manufacturing operations, marketing, sales, and the financial areas of an organization (BP 2005, Knight 2004).

This globalization trend continues with more competition from private local companies in developing markets. China is an example. According to the National Bureau of Statistics of China, Chinese companies have increased their market share from 3 to 23 percent, while foreign multinationals have only grown their market share from 25 to 31 percent (1999–2009). This domestic growth provides Chinese companies the financial ability, in industries such as mining, to be more aggressive in penetrating markets internationally (Moody 2009).

Integral to globalization is the expansion of manufacturing and distribution systems to meet the organizational growth targets of emerging markets such as China, Brazil, and India. This increases the interdependence of manufacturing and distribution systems in regional and local markets to deliver goods and services. As an example, China has developed export processing zones (EPZs), where multinational companies and joint ventures are finding incentives to locate manufacturing and distribution facilities, enabling them to expand their market share by bringing their products and services to the region (China Association of Development Zones 2002). The State Council in China has developed enclosed management schemes over these EPZs to further open its market to the outside world and attract international business. EPZs are special enclosed areas supervised by the customs authority, and include the cities of Guangzhou, Beijing, and Dalian (China Association of Development Zones 2002).

With the expansion of manufacturing and distribution systems comes the need for a skilled indigenous workforce to manage and operate those systems. In most cases, the cost for educating the workforce is borne by the global company, and competition for these educated, skilled workers is fierce. This is especially true in China. Globalization has both risks and rewards. From a regulatory standpoint, compliance with a country's local safety and health regulations, as well as being a good corporate citizen, is an organization's license to do business in that country, and may very well be a measure of the business' survival.

The remainder of this section demonstrates, through real-world business cases, that worker safety and health risks can and do impact the financial health and future of a global company. These real-world examples clearly demonstrate the need for companies to manage worker safety and health risks as a strategic imperative rather than a simple regulatory compliance exercise.

REPUTATIONAL RISK

In the following case studies, the significance of reputational risk is demonstrated. Global companies such as British Petroleum p.l.c. (BP) and Nike, Inc. recognize that worker safety and health risks are a leadership issue and have experienced the direct impact of worker safety and health-related incidents on their company's reputation (Nike 2003, BP 2005).

The case studies of BP and Nike, Inc. demonstrate how important it is for global companies to recognize and manage their worker safety and health risks as a strategic business risk that has an impact on the reputational, financial, and operational integrity of their businesses. Figure 1 depicts the interrelationship of these risks.

The BP, Nike, and Union Carbide examples are good reminders that worker safety and health risks must be identified and then managed through an organization's strategic planning process.

CASE STUDY

British Petroleum

British Petroleum (BP) is one of the world's largest global energy companies. An incident on March 23, 2005 at BP Products North America, Inc., in Texas City, Texas, demonstrated to BP's senior management the direct financial and reputational impact of a worker safety and health incident on their company. According to a May 2005 press release issued by BP Products North America, Inc., an explosion in the Texas City facility's isomerization process unit killed fifteen and seriously injured 170 workers at the facility (British Petroleum p.l.c. 2005a).

Immediately following the reports of the incident, BP's senior leadership recognized the reputational risk implications that media coverage of the incident was having on the company. The company, led by John Browne, Group Chief Executive, set out to address the situation and manage all information associated with the incident. According to a communiqué from Browne that was posted on their Web site in May 2005, BP wanted transparency and access to factual information by all stakeholders, including the injured workers and their families (British Petroleum p.l.c. 2005).

BP initiated an immediate investigation of the incident with subsequent implementation of recommendations, along with claiming responsibility for the incident. In a press release, Ross Pillari, who was then President of BP Products North America, Inc., publicly apologized for BP's mistakes. He also disclosed the failure of BP's isomerization unit process managers to provide leadership, by not always being on site during critical periods or verifying that the unit operators were using correct procedures (BP Products North America, Inc. 2005). Subsequently, BP entered into a settlement agreement with OSHA in March 2005 and paid $21,361,500 in fines for violations relating to the incident (U.S. Department of Labor 2009a, 2009b).

March 2005, BP appointed former U.S. Secretary James Baker III, to head a U.S. Refineries Independent Safety Review Panel. The panel was charged with conducting an independent assessment of the company's U.S. refineries and of the company's corporate safety culture (Allars 2007). The resulting report, known as the "Baker Report," was published on January 16, 2007, and found process safety performance problems within BP's U.S. refineries (Allars 2007). In March 2007, the U.S. Chemical Safety and Haz-

ard Investigation Board (CSB) released a report of their investigation, which also found "systemic process safety issues at the BP refineries in the United States" (U.S. Department of Labor 2009b).

According to the OSHA fact sheet on the BP Monitoring Inspection, the September 22, 2009 BP deadline for abatement outlined in the 2005 Settlement Agreement was not met and OSHA issued a "Notification of Failure to Abate" and additional willful citations. The proposed penalties were a record-breaking $87,430,000 (U.S. Department of Labor 2009b and 2009c). BP has contested the fines before the Occupational Safety and Health Review Commission; the Occupational Safety and Health Administration and BP were in settlement discussions as this book went to press.

The events of the Deepwater Horizon drill rig incident were unfolding as this book went to press. According to U.S. President Barack Obama in his weekly address, ". . . BP's Deepwater Horizon drilling rig exploded off Louisiana's coast, killing 11 people and rupturing an underwater pipe. The resulting oil spill has not only dealt an economic blow to Americans across the Gulf Coast, it also represents an environmental disaster" (The White House 2010).

CASE STUDY

Union Carbide

All risks to business are interdependent, whether worker safety and health, operational, financial, personal (senior management), or reputational. Union Carbide experienced this fact in a December 3, 1984 incident at their facility in Bhopal, India. According to the Indian state government of Madhya Pradesh and Union Carbide, the cause of the incident was the introduction of a large volume of water into a methyl isocyanate (MIC)

tank, triggering a reaction that led to a gas release. The incident resulted in the loss of approximately 3800 lives, with another 40 individuals experiencing permanent total disability, and 2680 experiencing permanent partial disability, according to the state government for Madhya Pradesh (Union Carbide Corp. 2004) .

This worker safety and health incident impacted the company's operations, financials, and reputation, along with raising the question of the personal

and criminal liability of the chairman at that time, Mr. Warren Anderson. The incident resulted in litigation, financial settlements, and legal costs. In the end, Union Carbide sold their Indian operations, and today Union Carbide Corporation is a wholly owned subsidiary of The Dow Chemical Company (Union Carbide Corp. 2004).

A more detailed recap of the Union Carbide Bhopal incident and its impact on the company is found in Appendix B of this chapter.

CASE STUDY

Nike, Inc.

Nike, Inc. is the most dominant global athletic shoe and apparel company in the world today (Locke 2005). This place in the global market has come by way of a bumpy road through the hazards of globalization.

In the mid-nineties, Nike faced a series of allegations involving their use of underpaid workers in Indonesia, child labor in Cambodia and Pakistan, and poor (health and safety) working conditions in Vietnam. These workers were not Nike employees, but employees of independent contractors and vendors working within Nike's global sourcing network (Locke 2005). Although these manufacturing sites were not owned or operated by Nike, the company's stakeholders were holding them accountable for their supply chain. This, coupled with the negative media coverage, significantly impacted Nike's reputation and financial performance. At the time, Nike did not recognize the full implications of the reputational risk of this incident. Lacking proactive media management and a coherent response to these allegations, Nike's global reputation and future sales were significantly impacted (Locke 2005).

Nike senior management recognized the growing threat to its brand, its most important asset, and went on the offensive (Gordon 2001). By demonstrating their ability to proactively manage media allegations, and taking responsibility for the actions of their supply-chain network, Nike was once again considered a good global corporate citizen.

With the Nike brand intact, the company launched several socially responsible initiatives, such as the Management of Environment, Safety, and Health (MESH) program and the Global Alliance for Workers and Communities (Nike 2003). MESH was launched to assist Nike's Asian business partners (supply-chain companies) with developing goals, targets, objectives, monitoring systems, and self-assessments for environmental safety and health (ES&H) risks. In addition to supply-chain ES&H management, the program incorporated better manufacturing practices, along with community affairs and health and nutrition programs. Nike also provided educational forums for their contract footwear manufacturers in the development, implementation, and monitoring of their MESH programs (Nike 2003).

Nike also became a partner of the Fair Labor Association (FLA). FLA provides independent assessments of the working conditions of apparel and footwear facilities throughout the world. They publish an annual public report of organizations that have been independently assessed by FLA (Nike 2005a). Nike's involvement directly reflects an understanding of reputational risk and the need to manage workplace risk, including safety and health issues (Nike 2003).

Did Nike, Inc.'s ES&H strategy work to mitigate negative publicity and rebuild their stakeholders confidence? The answer appears to be yes. According to their 2004 annual report, Nike, Inc.'s revenues were just over $12 billion for the fiscal year ending May 31, 2004, a 15 percent increase over revenues for the previous year (Knight 2004). They also capitalized on their international presence, launching Nike-Russia alongside already existing Nike-Brazil, Nike-India, and Nike-China, three of the largest and fastest-growing consumer markets in the world, according to founder and first Nike CEO, Philip Knight (Knight 2004). Nike's disclosures in their subsequent annual reports still raise issues, but the transparency in reporting the management of those issues has had a positive impact on their stakeholders.

The remainder of the sections in this chapter provides an overview of tactical challenges and strategies for managing worker safety and health risks in the global arena. In the author's opinion, strategies are typically considered best practice and are used by global companies to successfully manage their organization's worker safety and health risks on a global level.

CHALLENGES AND STRATEGIES OF GLOBAL WORKPLACE SAFETY AND HEALTH MANAGEMENT

There are significant challenges to managing the worker safety and health risks of a global and international organization. They include leadership commitment, identifying and prioritizing risks on a global level, resource allocation, developing a global management system or process, conformity assessment, developing key global performance indicators, and competent global safety and health resource networks. In addition, one cannot ignore the important challenge of managing the safety professional's own workplace risk while traveling and working outside the home country.

Without a well-thought-out strategy, leadership commitment, and allocated resources, this can sound daunting. What is needed is an understanding of the challenges to expect and the strategies that have proven successful in managing worker safety and health risk throughout an organization's global operations.

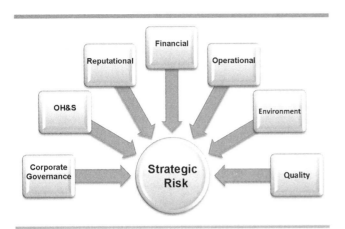

FIGURE 1. Interrelationship of strategic (business) risk and occupational safety and health risk (Global Solutions, Inc. 2011)

Leadership Commitment

Transparency and Outside Influences

Business risk management is influenced by the advent of government-led legislation and industry-led guidance, along with stakeholder social and environmental expectations, to improve financial transparency within domestic and multinational organizations. In the United States, the Sarbanes-Oxley Act of 2002 requires an organization to identify, control, and report financial risk to shareholders (U.S. Congress 2002). As a result, some U.S. multinational companies that are implementing a formal business risk assessment process are identifying and assessing health and safety risks that could significantly impact the financial integrity of the organization (Seabrook 2006b, Nash 2005). This business risk-assessment process expands all operations around the world, placing a company's brand integrity and business continuity implications at the forefront of risk identification and assessment (Nash 2005, ASSE 1996).

There are other Sarbanes-Oxley-type requirements in other countries around the world, such as the United Kingdom and Australia. In the United Kingdom, for example, the Turnbull Report, the Institute of Chartered Accountants' guidance document, *Internal Control: Guidance for Directors on the Combined Code*, was published in 1999. It proposed a risk-based approach, including internal control mechanisms, for the reporting of company risk to shareholders. The identification and reporting of significant health and safety risks is referenced in the guidance document. This guidance document applies to companies listed on the London Stock Exchange (Institute of Chartered Accountants 1999). There are similar requirements for trading on the Australian Stock Exchange (Australian Stock Exchange Corporate Governance Council 2003, Australian Securities and Investments Commission 2004).

In the financial markets, stakeholders are expecting a greater degree of socially responsible performance from the companies in which they invest. This includes social, environmental, and worker safety and health performance. Investors are looking to companies to be good corporate citizens, going beyond the legal requirements of safety, labor, or environmental regulations (European Agency for Safety and Health at Work 2004). Stakeholder expectation is beginning to emerge as a driver for greater health and safety risk transparency in multinational companies (Greenbiz 2005).

The number of companies publishing annual sustainability and corporate responsibility reports to stakeholders (which include health and safety performance) continues to grow. Sustainability—corporate social responsibility (CSR) and environmental, social, and governance awareness (as CSR is known in Europe) (Kaye 2010)—is beginning to impact business initiatives in European and U.S. companies. The number of companies identifying metrics and reporting their sustainability and corporate social responsibility performance has increased in the last 5 years. This increase is being influenced by several factors, including the investment community; customer requirements; "green" consumers; European Union, Chinese, and U.S. environmental regulations; supply-chain accountability; and the rise of regulatory and volunteer carbon emissions trading markets. Some companies see it as a competitive advantage (Seabrook 2010 and United Nations Environment Programme, KPMG Advisory N.V. 2010). Another incentive is the direct return on investment and operational efficiencies resulting from implementing environmental initiatives such as reduced packaging and transportation costs.

The Global Reporting Initiative™ (GRI) a European-based organization (Secretariat office: Amsterdam, The Netherlands) has developed a sustainability reporting framework, which is widely recognized, referenced, and used as a guidance framework for disclosing sustainability performance. The framework sets out performance indicators for disclosure as well as disclosure requirements to assure the quality and accuracy of the information disclosed in a performance report (Global Reporting Initiative™ 2006).

On the workplace safety and health side of sustainability performance reporting, the GRI framework lays out social performance indicators under "Labor Practices and Decent Work Aspect: Occupational Health and Safety" (Global Reporting Initiative™ 2006). Currently there are two core performance indicators associated with workplace safety and health sustainability. The first is injury, occupational diseases, fatalities, lost work days, and absenteeism rates. The second is risk control measures, including training and education, counseling, and prevention for serious diseases (Global Reporting Initiative™ 2006). While these are not optimal safety and health metrics in and of themselves, and occupational safety and health management systems would be better, these GRI metrics open the window of opportunity for safety professionals to engage in sustainability initiatives within their organizations. Some multinational companies such as Henkel (German-based) and Hewlett Packard (HP) (American-based) have gone beyond these core performance indicators to include areas such as risk management in the area of occupationally related motor-vehicle injuries and illnesses (Henkel 2009) and EHS management system performance (HP 2009).

For the safety professional, the environmental aspect of sustainability also has a direct impact on worker health and safety. Reducing or eliminating hazardous substances used in manufacturing processes reduces hazardous waste generated. Identifying and managing health and safety risks prior to implementing alternative energy solutions has a direct impact on a potential worker, as well as on the safety and health of the community, customer, and general consumer. The basic tools of risk and hazard identification, assessment, and control should be incorporated into the corporate (global) safety and health standards, as well as into the standard operating procedures at site locations around the world. For example, proac-

tively assessing and managing the risks to workers involved in the routine maintenance of roof-mounted solar panels would reduce the potential for falls, burns, and muscular or skeletal injuries.

Another influence on transparency and identification and management of health and safety risk is the International Standards Organization (ISO) guideline *ISO 26000 Standard on Social Responsibility*. The joint secretariat for the proposed ISO 26000 standard is the Swedish Standards Institute and the Brazilian Association of Technical Standards (ISO 2010).

Integration

In order to effectively manage workplace safety and health risk, an organization's leadership must be committed to developing and implementing a system to manage this risk throughout their global organization (BSI 1999, Seabrook 1999a). By definition, an occupational safety and health management system (AIHA 2005, BSI 1999, ILO 2001) provides an internal control mechanism for workplace safety and health risk, a requirement under Section 404 of the Sarbanes-Oxley Act of 2002 (U.S. Congress 2002).

Workplace safety and health risk is one of many business risks an organization must manage. The author worked with a U.S.-based multinational company that had purchased a Swedish-based European multinational company, which manufactured and distributed components for the automotive industry throughout Europe and Scandinavia. The Swedish company's business model was based on a philosophy of one management system for all business risk. This meant that all functional areas of the business reported to one manager of management systems, who oversaw the planning, implementation, monitoring, control, and continual improvement processes for all of the company's business risk. Some examples of functional areas that this included were finance, human resources, research and development, marketing, sales, technical services, the environment, worker health and safety, quality, production, and distribution.

This demonstrates a truly integrated systems approach to business risk management. It also demonstrates that various safety and health risk management models work as long as the model and approach are aligned with the company's organizational structure, business model, and culture. The ANSI Z10, *Occupational Health and Safety Management* standard's guidance section suggests that health and safety risks associated with all functional areas of an organization are included in the risk management (identification and assessment) process (ANSI/AIHA 2005).

In order to successfully manage safety and health risk within a global company, the safety and health professional should understand the interconnectivity of local country cultural norms and their company's core business strategies, operational structure, and type of products and services, as well as the extent of worker safety and health risks. Understanding integration at this level will position the safety and health professional to successfully contribute to the financial, operational, and health and safety performance of their company.

Figure 2 depicts a global business model where worker safety and health risk-reduction strategies are integral to the business strategies, models, ethics, values, and organizational structure of an organization. The impact of local cultural norms is reviewed in the section, "Global Strategy–Local Implementation."

On a global basis, there is no typical U.S. business model for corporate workplace safety and health. Depending upon a company's organizational structure, the safety and health function may report to either the chief executive officer, chief financial officer,

chief risk officer, global operations executive, legal department, or human resources. In many companies, the safety and health function is integrated with the environmental management function to form the corporate environment, health, and safety (EHS); health, safety, and environment (HSE); or safety, health, and environment (SHE) services. In recent years, some U.S. organizations have moved toward integration of worker-focused staff functions, such as employee well-being service centers.

While the name of the department may differ from company to company, it typically incorporates workplace safety and health, environmental issues, medical services, security, workers' compensation claim management, and sometimes overall risk management/insurance services. With the emphasis on security, antiterrorism, and emergency preparedness following the 2001 World Trade Center attacks in New York and the potential for global flu and other health-related pandemics, U.S. multinationals have focused on security and preparedness (emergencies resulting from natural disasters, fire, business contingencies, war, terrorism, and health issues) within the workplace safety and health function (Global Solutions, Inc. 2011).

The organizational structure, defined functionally with clearly delineated responsibility, accountability, and authority for workplace safety and health, is the key to effectively managing global workplace safety and health risks (Seabrook 1999). These areas of functionality, responsibility, accountability, and authority must be clearly communicated by the CEO throughout the business units and throughout the world. The communications should be written and include a corporatewide policy statement, backed by annual goals, objectives, and targets that are integrated into the global business plan and reported to stakeholders in the annual report. Global business units live and die by their projected goals, objectives, and targets. If managing global workplace safety and health risk is the CEO's expectation, and goals and targets are set, these risks will be controlled by the management team throughout every business unit and facility in the global organization (BSI 1999; ILO 2001; AIHA 2005; and Global Solutions, Inc. 2011).

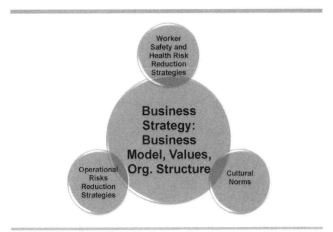

FIGURE 2. Worker safety and health aligned with business strategies (Global Solutions, Inc. 2011)

- Protecting the worker from work-related injuries, illnesses, disease, and death
- Integrating occupational safety and health management systems as part of the overall management of the organization
- Providing human, financial, and technological resources for safety and health management
- Complying with country-specific regulations
- Providing transparency and the communication of workplace safety and health risk information to all employees and stakeholders
- Including worker participation
- Improving safety and health performance

FIGURE 3. Leadership commitment (AIHA 2005, BSI 2008, Seabrook 2011)

Figure 3 outlines the areas of leadership commitment in managing global worker safety and health risks. At a minimum, these should be included in the organization's safety and health policy statement.

In order to clearly communicate the organization's worker safety and health expectations, the CEO and the leadership team must complete the following tasks (AIHA 2005; BSI 2007; ILO 2001; Global Solutions, Inc. 2011):

- Develop a written statement of policy, signed by the CEO, demonstrating leadership commitment to managing the organization's global safety and health risks (see Figure 3).
- Communicate expectations for managing workplace safety and health risks for both management and the workers throughout the global organization, using all communication media available (for example, the annual report to shareholders, the corporate intranet, and training and development documents).
- Commit resources to manage worker safety and health risks within the organization.
- At the corporate level, develop, communicate, implement, track, update, and report strategic goals, objectives, targets, and results of workplace safety and health risk-management processes.
- Integrate corporate goals, objectives, and targets into the organization's strategic business plan.

- Develop, communicate, implement, track, update, and report on annual goals, objectives, and targets at the global business unit level to manage workplace safety and health risks.
- Integrate each business unit's goals, objectives, and targets into its business plan.
- Develop performance-measured individual and group reward systems based on the results of goals, objectives, and targets, beginning with executive leadership at the corporate level, and moving down through the organization to the line management and workers within global business units.
- Integrate worker safety and health expectations into job descriptions and job procedures.
- Audit performance and have senior management review results at least annually.

Corporate safety and health policy globally is dependent upon the leadership's commitment and ability to translate the policy locally, tying worker safety and health performance to the business unit and local facility results (AIHA 2005; Global Solutions, Inc. 2011).

These business leaders must agree on worker safety and health goals, objectives, targets, and the organizations' values and key performance indicators in order for the worker safety and health process to move forward. Once this is accomplished, the corporate, business unit, regional, and facility-level safety and health managers, coordinators, and outside resources can develop business plans and allocate resources to carry out those plans.

Following the leadership commitment, organizational resource allocation is the next key factor in effective global worker safety and health management. In order to implement business plans, leadership throughout the organization must allocate resources to implement the worker safety and health aspects of the plans. This includes human, technological, informational, and financial resources. If resources are not committed at the highest levels, worker safety and health risks will not be managed (BSI 2007, AIHA 2005, ILO 2001).

Organizationally, having an effective corporate/business unit/regional/facility safety and health professional is a technical and managerial resource to leadership. The professional's expertise in assessing worker risk and providing fact-based information and solutions enables leadership to make informed decisions based on understanding all business risks.

Without senior leadership direction, worker safety and health is generally not integrated into the business plans for each business unit and facility. This is typically due to societal and business cultural norms in Asia, Latin America, Africa, and the Middle East, where worker safety and health strategies for an organization's facilities are not advanced at the grass roots level. This is also true in countries with a high level of poverty, where workers do not have a stable source of food, water, shelter, and personal safety available to them. In these countries, workers may willingly suffer poor working conditions because the alternative is extreme poverty (Global Solutions, Inc. 2011).

For example, in Hong Kong, the perception of risk acceptance in regard to construction scaffolding is different than in countries such as the United Kingdom, Australia, Germany, France, and Canada. In Hong Kong, the use of multistory bamboo scaffolding is a standard industry practice and meets regulatory standards under the Factories and Industrial Undertakings Ordinance and Construction Sites (Safety) Regulations (Hong Kong Labour Department 2001). Country-to-country, the perception of risk and risk acceptance may differ. It is hard to imagine contractors in the United States working on six-story bamboo scaffolds.

Therefore, without leadership at the business unit and facility level and organizational time and resource commitment, the safety and health professional will be wasting time, as well as the organization's resources, when attempting to conduct an audit at the organization's local facility without a proper introduction at the leadership level. For example, in India and Japan it is essential to be properly introduced to local management by company senior management before scheduling visits or audits.

The role of the corporate safety and health function is to assist leadership in developing and implementing a global safety and health management system, along with corporate standards, programs, internal report-

ing, and document control processes. Once developed, leadership must communicate these expectations throughout the global business units.

A GLOBAL SAFETY AND HEALTH RISK PROFILE/SCORECARD

A global safety and health risk profile (GRP) or a safety and health scorecard provides an organization's leadership with a current status of significant global safety and health issues. This tracking tool also assists leaders and safety professionals with managing workplace safety and health risk through an organization's strategic planning process. It enables the safety and health professional to actively engage senior management by integrating global workplace safety and health issues into a company's strategic risk-management framework. The GRP is comprised of an Executive Summary with supporting documentation, and identifies and assesses significant workplace safety and health risks throughout an organization's global operations. These significant worker safety and health risks pose a threat to human life and the economic and operational health of the company (Global Solutions, Inc. 2011).

The GRP is a dynamic document. It changes as the nature of the operations, risks, scope, and size of an organization change. Ideally, the GRP should be updated and communicated to senior leaders and management, including the Board of Directors, on a regular basis (Global Solutions, Inc. 2011).

The GRP incorporates a country-by-country, site-by-site analysis of significant safety and health risks. The company should use their global safety and health management process to identify and assess the management of significant safety and health risks throughout all global operations, including manufacturing, distribution, warehousing, offices, home offices, and fleets. The Executive Summary in the GRP provides a high-level economic and operational assessment of these significant safety and health risks and the potential economic impact they could have on the company.

For example, the improper handling or storage of hazardous materials at a multinational company's Chinese manufacturing operations could have a significant impact on the financial integrity of that company.

Without a hazardous materials management process in place, the storage of these materials presents a significant fire and explosion risk to adjacent manufacturing operations. If an explosion occurred in the storage area, it would cripple the main manufacturing and storage areas. Loss of the plant, people (workers and the public), or damage to the environment would affect public confidence and the company's reputation with the government and public officials. This could result in governmental intervention and work stoppage, fines, and litigation. It could also impact the timeframe to rebuild the facility due to permits and the ability to retain a contractor. If this manufacturing site is the sole supplier for the company's largest U.S. customer, loss of customer confidence could also impact current and future orders and revenue from that customer.

Another example of a significant worker safety and health risk that could impact the financial health of a business is asbestos liability. The scenario: during the initial safety and health audit of a recently acquired Mexican manufacturing company, the audit team discovers that along with the purchase of a manufacturing operation, the Mexican operations include a medium-sized asbestos removal contractor. This fact was not disclosed during the preacquisition due-diligence process. The asbestos health risk to past and present workers and the resulting financial implications for asbestos liability could be significant. This asbestos health risk is an example of the type of significant safety and health risk that should be assessed and monitored through the global safety and health risk profiling process.

From a regulatory standpoint, the United Kingdom's Financial Services Authority (a governmental oversight agency similar to the U.S. Securities and Exchange Commission) requires all financial services companies operating in the United Kingdom to develop a risk register. The risk register incorporates all risks that could negatively impact a company's financials and financial reporting, including environmental, health, and safety issues. United Kingdom financial services companies should incorporate the global safety and health risk profile into the risk register.

From an investor's perspective, nonfinancial reports provide an annual overview of a company's environmental, health, and safety risks. As early as 2005, the European Agency for Safety and Health at Work within the European Union stated, "corporate social responsibility (CSR) is becoming an increasingly important priority for companies of all sizes and types in 2005. Occupational safety and health is an essential component of CSR. . . ." (European Agency for Safety and Health at Work 2004, 2005). Although CSR is not regulatory-driven, stakeholder awareness of corporate social responsibility (sustainability) issues continues to grow as an economic driver for nonfinancial reporting to stakeholders. Companies such as BP, HP, Unilever, Ford Motor Company, Intel, Gap Inc., Johnson & Johnson, Henkel, General Mills, Royal Dutch/Shell, and Novo Nordisk recognize and report their environmental and social impacts in an annual or biannual nonfinancial report. As early as 2004, the United Nations Environment Program, along with the consulting firm, SustainAbility, who partnered with the credit rating agency Standard & Poor's, began to rank participating companies based on their nonfinancial environmental and social impact and performance. Standard & Poor's uses these reports to assess a company's risk profile (The Economist 2004). Therefore, there is an economic incentive for companies with good CSR/sustainiblity performance in nonfinancial risk areas such as health and safety to disclose this information. Some companies see this as a competitive advantage and manage safety and heath risks accordingly. The Nike supply-chain management case study at the beginning of this chapter is an example of a significant safety and heath risk that would be identified and tracked by senior management as a significant business risk in a global safety and heath risk profile.

GLOBAL STRATEGY–LOCAL IMPLEMENTATION

Global Strategy

One of the greatest challenges a multinational organization may face is balancing global corporate goals, objectives, and targets with local, in-country infrastructure, facilities, knowledge, regulatory environment, culture, healthcare systems (government-run versus third-party insurance), capability, and competence.

Many multinational companies implement a corporate-driven global worker safety and health management system strategy throughout their facilities. This provides consistent set of standards, process, approach, and means for communication across the globe. This global safety and health management strategy is coupled with knowledge that there may be more than one way to manage a risk at a local facility, while being in compliance with corporate standards and guidance. The size of the organization does not matter, this strategy can be implemented within a global organization that has 5 or 115 sites around the world (Nash 2005; Global Solutions, Inc. 2011).

What does a centralized corporate management system look like? It will differ from one company to another, based upon the company's leadership commitment to workplace safety and health, corporate culture, size, type of operations, level of risk, and resource allocation. The management system may differ in organizational structure, terminology, methodology, and implementation. A management systems approach is discussed more thoroughly in the section, "Global Safety and Health Management Systems." From a strategic perspective, the occupational safety and health management system implementation should embrace the local culture and local regulatory environment.

Local Implementation: Cultural Impact

An example of thinking globally and implementing locally is seen in differing risk-control methodologies. For example, in operations in developing countries, where the cost of labor is inexpensive and equipment and facility costs are high, one is likely to see a very different way of doing work. In Indonesia, moving raw materials from storage to processing may mean employing several workers to do the manual material handling as opposed to automating the raw materials transfer or using manual handling equipment. Culturally, this is perceived to increase jobs, reduce expenses on the organization, and provide a safe methodology to do the work. Upon closer observation and questioning, it may be determined that the loads lifted are within the corporate safety and health lifting/manual handling standards and guidelines. Due to local culture

and business practices, automating the raw materials transfer process may not be the best option for local leadership.

In another example, a multinational organization found that their operations in India used a state-of-the-art, continuous chlorine gas-monitoring system in their chlorine water treatment operations for the facility. Upon closer inspection and questioning, it was discovered that this monitoring equipment (an American model) had not been serviced or tested since its installation, and the technology and knowledge to test the system, calibrate the test equipment, and do preventive maintenance on the equipment was not available locally. The multinational organization replaced the American system with one that could be properly maintained and tested locally.

It is important to incorporate cultural elements into the management system.

A successful strategy for assessing the management of risk at local in-country facilities is to:

- Focus on outcomes: What is the risk? How is it managed? Is the risk adequately controlled?
- Allow for cultural, technological, legal, regulatory, healthcare, social system, and other differences in developing solutions to risk-control challenges, findings, and other implementation strategies. The best advice: Ask a lot of questions before mandating risk-control solutions for your global facilities (Global Solutions, Inc. 2011).

Local Implementation: Regulatory Environment

An important lesson in global safety and health management is to understand that the United States Occupational Safety and Health Administration (OSHA) does not have jurisdiction outside the United States; therefore, its regulations are also not recognized or, in some cases, known outside of the United States. Most developed countries in the world have their own set of regulatory requirements for worker safety and health. Just as the United States does not recognize the Korean Ministry of Labour as having jurisdiction

TABLE 1

Some Government Worker Safety and Health Regulatory Agencies

Country	Agency
Australia -New South Wales	Minister for Commerce - WorkCover New South Wales
Australia - Victoria	Victorian WorkCover Authority
Canada - Federal	Labour Program Human Resources and Skills Development
Canada - Ontario	Ministry of Labour - Occupational Health and Safety Branch
Mexico	Federal Secretary of Labor and Social Welfare (Secretaría del Trabajo y Previsión Social - STPS)
China	The Ministry of Labour and Social Security
India	Directorate General, Factory Advice Service and Labour Institutes, Ministry of Labour
Japan	Ministry of Health, Labour and Welfare - Industrial Safety and Health Department
Korea	Ministry of Labour
European Union	Directorate-General for Employment, Social Affairs and Equal Opportunities
United Kingdom	Health and Safety Executive
Germany	Bundesministerium für Wirtschaft und Arbeit
France	Ministère de l'emploi, du travail et de la Cohésion Sociale DRT

(*Source*: Global Solutions, Inc. 2011)

in the United States, so Korea does not recognize OSHA as having jurisdiction in Korea. Table 1 references some country-specific government regulatory agencies that oversee worker safety and health (Global Solutions, Inc. 2011).

The safety and health regulatory environment is different from country to country. In Germany, Singapore, the United Kingdom, and the European Union, some worker safety and health regulations are more stringent than in the United States. In other countries, such as Mexico, there are good regulations with limited resources for enforcement. There are other countries with limited or no regulations, such as Vietnam and Cambodia. In the European Union, for example, it is an organization's statutory duty to implement a system to manage worker safety and health risk. In Singapore, organizations are required to conduct self-audits and report findings to the regulatory agency. Safety committees are required in organizations with nineteen or more workers in Brazil (Secretaria de Segurança e Medicina do Trabalho 2004), and in the United Kingdom, eye testing is required of all significant display screen equipment users (HSE 1998).

In Canada, Part II (Occupational Health and Safety) of the Canada Labour Code imposes a legal duty on employers and "those who direct work" to take reasonable measures to protect worker and public safety. This legal duty has been codified in the Canadian Criminal Code, Bill C-45, which indicates that charges of criminal negligence can be made against an organization if death or bodily harm results due to "wanton or reckless" disregard of this legal duty. How this will impact individuals such as CEOs, managing directors, or executive leadership will be determined as cases go through the Canadian court system (Human Resources and Skills Development Canada 2005 and CCOHS 2010).

GLOBAL SAFETY AND HEALTH MANAGEMENT SYSTEMS

The challenge faced by all multinationals is to develop a management system or process that is valued and used by leadership to identify, communicate, implement, and monitor country-specific worker safety and health regulatory obligations, as well as global, internal corporate requirements for worker safety and health.

An organization must develop a system to manage its safety and health risks that is aligned with the business strategies of the organization. As described in the section, "Leadership Commitment," and illustrated in Figure 2, business strategies include business focus, culture and models, organizational structure, and philosophy. Within the U.S. pharmaceutical industry, for example, the U.S. Food and Drug Administration (FDA) approves all prescription drugs for the U.S. market, thus providing the key to the sustainability of a U.S. pharmaceutical company. Because of this, a pharmaceutical company's focus, culture, and organizational structure, from the research and development team to the operational aspects of the organization, are typically based on FDA approvals and standards of practice. Operationally, this translates into a corporate value and ethos of high standards for quality and hygienic production at their facilities. From the author's experience, those U.S. workplace safety and health professionals who understand this business culture and motivation, and who work to communicate

Worker Safety, Health, and Environmental Management System Standards

Australia/New Zealand (AS/NZS) 4801: 2001 *Occupational Health and Safety Management Systems-Specification with Guidance for Use.* Standards Australia.

American National Standards Institute (ANSI) *ASC Z10: 2005 Occupational Health and Safety Systems* (in development at the time of writing). American National Standards Institute.

Occupational Health and Safety Assessment (OHSAS), Series 18001: 2007. British Standards Institute.

International Labor Organization ILO-OSH 2001 *Guidelines on Occupational Safety and Health Management Systems.* International Labour Organization.

International Standards Organization (ISO) 14000: 2004 *Environmental Management Systems, Specification with Guidance for Use.* International Standards Organization.

Management of Health and Safety at Work Regulations, 1999 – Approved Code of Practice. United Kingdom implementation guidance on European Union Directive.

United States Occupational Safety and Health Administration. *Voluntary Protection Program.* OSHA.

FIGURE 4. Occupational safety, health, and environment workplace management systems standards, regulations, and models (*Source:* Global Solutions, Inc. 2011)

with leadership and integrate the management of worker safety and health risks with the management of product quality, are more successful.

Alternatively, the automotive industry is driven by lean manufacturing and efficiencies, and waste minimization is gained through product design and quality. Therefore, aligning and integrating worker safety and health management systems with operational, engineering, design, and quality systems proves more successful in this business environment.

It is not within the scope of this chapter to provide an in-depth review of Occupational Health and Safety Management Systems (OHSMS). However, Figure 4 is included to provide a quick reference for recognized, published OHSMS standards available to the safety and health professional. These OHSMS standards provide a template to develop and implement an OHSMS that is aligned with an organization's business strategy. Figure 5 provides the basic components of a graphic illustration of a global management system.

CONFORMITY ASSESSMENT: MANAGING CORPORATE AND EXTERNAL COMPLIANCE ASSURANCE

An organization's conformity-assessment and local regulatory compliance process applies to the corporate headquarters, all business units, and facilities throughout the world. The goal of conformity assessment is to ensure that the organization meets its external country-specific regulatory obligations and internal corporate requirements for managing worker safety and health throughout its global operations. The challenge is to develop an assessment process that will be used by leadership to assess and monitor conformance with predetermined local and corporate worker health and safety obligations and requirements.

There are three forms of conformity assessment that an organization should consider when developing its conformity assessment process:

- self-declaration, based upon the organization's execution, audit, and review of performance
- second party, where companies may audit their suppliers
- third-party certification by an accredited body (often done for ISO 9000 and 14000)

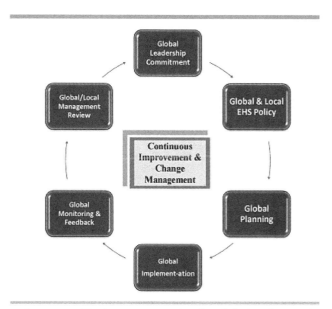

FIGURE 5. Basic components of a global safety and health management system (*Source:* AIHA 2005; BSI 2007; and Global Solutions, Inc. 2011)

In the experience of Stuart Wood, the head of the American Society of Safety Engineers' International Practice Specialty, companies that develop and implement good global safety and health standards, and apply these standards to all business units throughout the world, will be in compliance with approximately 90 percent of the local safety and health regulations under which a multinational operates around the world (Wood 2006). According to Wood, the most important strategy for an organization is "to assure the right safety and health people are in place" within a company's business structure, and throughout the company's global organizational structure. He emphasized that the safety and health organizational structure should be aligned with the company's business structure to be successful (Wood 2006). For example, does the business operate regionally using an American, Asian Pacific, European, African, or Middle Eastern regional model, or is it organized by other geographical parameters or by type of business? An example of safety and health organizational structure by type of business is seen in the petrochemical industry, where there may be separate safety and health management structures deployed for global exploration, production, drilling, and manufacturing business units.

With the right people in place, a good regional or countrywide safety and health management team will assess safety and health regulatory compliance by identifying gaps in the corporate global safety and health standards, and ensuring that the local business unit is in compliance with both the corporate global safety and health standards and local regulatory safety and health requirements. Having corporate safety and health standards essentially levels the playing field for safety and health expectations around the world (Wood 2006).

Strategies for Developing a Conformity Assessment Process

Conformity assessment strategies focus on developing and implementing a global corporate conformity assessment process that involves understanding local safety and health regulations and reporting requirements while allowing for how a culture may impact the implementation of corporate safety and health management systems and programs.

Trained corporate assessment teams conduct the review, and results are reported to the leadership of the organization and business units. For larger organizations, this is often part of the overall governance process of an organization. Assessment teams will benefit from an educational program on working internationally, specifically on how a country's local culture can impact how business is done in facilities outside their home country. There are many cross-cultural resources available. An organization's human resources department usually has access to this information.

The assessment results are a scorecard on how well a facility or business unit is doing relative to managing their worker safety and health risks. There is no one *best* assessment tool. Some companies use a numerical scorecard system to identify the level of compliance with corporate requirements, while others us a color-coding system. Both have become accepted practices over time. What is essential is that the system used has value to company leadership in managing their global safety and health risks. Figure 6 is an example of a color-coded scorecard system. Many safety and health consultants and multinational companies use these universal colors to indicate action in their conformity assessment process. The premise is analogous to a stop light. Green depicts safety and health risks are controlled and that no immediate action is needed. Yellow means caution, that safety and health risks may not be completely controlled,

RED ⊕
Significant (imminent danger, loss of life, property or damage to the environment) Safety and Health (S&H) risks exist and are not controlled; no S&H systems are in place.

YELLOW ◑
Significant S&H risks exist but are controlled; some non significant, uncontrolled S&H risks exist; most S&H systems are in place.

GREEN ⊖
No significant S&H risks exist; all S&H systems are in place.

FIGURE 6. Sample score card (*Source:* Global Solutions, Inc. 2011)

but they are not so significant as to require immediate action. Finally, red means that safety and health risks are significant and that action is required immediately (Global Solutions, Inc. 2011).

Assessments often focus on the evaluation of the company's occupational safety and health standards and processes in addition to an audit of the workplace. Assessment frequency will be different for each facility, based on its size, nature of operations, number of workers, and the level of risk to workers, the public, the environment, and the business.

The assessment tool itself determines whether an organization is meeting its worker safety and health regulatory obligations and internal requirements. The following provides examples of these requirements.

Country-Specific Worker Safety and Health Regulations

Country-specific worker safety and health regulatory requirements may be stricter than the corporate standards in areas such as electrical safety, forklift driver certification, safety committees, medical monitoring, and hazard communication. In addition, regulatory reporting requirements may apply, such as worker safety and health-related incidents and accidents, self-audit results, use of specified hazardous materials, dangerous occurrences, spills or other releases of hazardous materials. An example of a country-specific regulatory requirement is the Canadian Workplace Hazardous Materials Information System (WHMIS). This legislation applies to all manufacturers, distributors, and users of specified hazardous materials, and incorporates labeling, material safety data sheets, and training requirements for workers using or being exposed to hazardous materials identified in the WHMIS regulations (Health Canada 2010). In the United Kingdom, the Reporting of Injuries, Diseases and Dangerous Occurrences Regulations, 1995 (RIDDOR) require dangerous occurrences to be reported to the regulatory authority when they occur. Dangerous occurrences include the malfunction of a breathing apparatus, collapse of scaffolding or an overhead crane, or turning over a forklift truck (HSE 2008). In Korea, it is an employer's duty under the Industrial Health and Safety Act (amended September 22, 2006) to assign a

facility safety and health management officer to oversee implementation of the worker safety and health management system (OSHA 2009).

CORPORATE SAFETY AND HEALTH MANAGEMENT SYSTEMS

Corporate safety and health management system requirements include, but may not be limited to, management system components such as safety policies, communications systems, safety and health performance requirements in all worker job descriptions and annual performance goals, a risk assessment process, annual management reviews, self-assessment processes, document control processes, and change management.

Corporate Safety and Health Standards and Country-Specific Safety and Health Regulations

Corporate worker safety and health standards include facility and equipment self-inspections, lockout-tagout processes, forklift driver certification and licensing, incident investigation, safety committees, confined-space-entry permitting, medical monitoring, preventive maintenance action item tracking, safety and health training and retraining, and contractor safety and health management control and monitoring systems. These corporate safety and health standards may be in compliance with country regulations. In many cases, implementing the corporate safety and health standards will ensure "90% compliance with most country specific regulations" (Wood 2006). If a country does not have a developed worker safety and health regulatory environment, the corporate safety and health standards provide the framework for governing safety and health practice for the company in those countries. If a country does have a mature worker safety and health regulatory environment, where these regulations are stricter than the corporate safety and health standards, local personnel must be responsible and accountable for identifying and implementing these additional measures to assure compliance (Avon 2011).

According to L'Oreal's 2008 sustainability report, it is a consumer products manufacturer with 64,600 employees operating in 130 countries around the world. The company has implemented a corporate safety and health management system. All U.S. sites are part of the OSHA VPP program; other sites (with the exception of two) are Occupational Health and Safety Assessment Series (OHSAS) 18001 accredited. L'Oreal also piloted a joint safety management program with senior managers instead of graduate school for business in France (L'Oreal SA 2008).

RESOURCES

Whether a large, medium, or small organization, local external safety and health resources can provide the assessment team with important in-country expertise on the implementation expectations of local regulatory agencies. The best source for good safety and health resources is from other global organizations, as well as through industry-specific associations, professional societies, and personal networking. The Web is another good means for identifying resources; however, a word of caution—always get good references and follow up on them. For example, when a multinational, service-based industry, operating 300 facilities in 23 countries around the world, needed to find a vendor to do thermal imaging for their electrical panels at their India facility. The global safety and health director eventually found an India-based vendor from the Internet, and the thermal imaging task was successfully completed. The key to success was having the local facility management vet the potential vendor. They knew the local market, could speak the local language, and reviewed and contacted the vendor's references to assure its credibility.

Appendix A highlights a number of online resources that may be useful in identifying in-country worker safety and health regulations and requirements.

IDENTIFY KEY GLOBAL SAFETY AND HEALTH PERFORMANCE INDICATORS

Another challenge that a multinational organization experiences is developing meaningful safety and health performance criteria that are applicable to all of their global business units. These indicators must be recog-

nized by leadership and reflect an accurate measurement of a facility or a business unit's worker safety and health performance.

When managing safety and health globally, it is important to use both proactive (leading) and reactive (lagging) performance indicators. Using country-specific accident/incident statistics (a lagging indicator) will not always provide an organization with accurate, comparable performance data. Therefore, it is important to use proactive performance indicators as well. Some examples of performance indicators used in business include the percentage of audit findings closed based on a site action plan, the number of workers trained in confined space entry against the target in the annual worker training plan, and the percentage of risk assessments completed against the targets set in the annual plan. It is important to normalize raw numbers. For example, the number of injury, illness, or driving incidents should be normalized against the number of employee hours worked, the number of finished products, or the total number of miles traveled. This provides consistency and value to statistical data.

Statistical data variables and calculations for injuries and illnesses vary from country to country. For U.S. domestic operations, OSHA recordable incident definitions apply as well as OSHA's lost-workday injury calculations. Once outside the United States, lost-time case rate definitions and calculations may vary from country to country. In most cases, U.S. facilities would typically have a higher lost-time case rate than, for example, their Japanese and EU counterparts, due to a more conservative definition of a lost-time case.

Specifically, discrepancies in lost-time case rates (LTCRs) country-to-country are due to differences in how they are defined, calculated, and reported to the local regulatory agencies. In an organization's Japanese facility, for example, the LTCR could be artificially lower than that in their similar UK, EU, or U.S. facilities. Figure 7 illustrates the number of days a worker must be away from work (due to a workplace injury) for the injury to be classified as a lost-time case. In Japan, a lost-time case is reported to the regulatory agency after a worker has been away from work seven days following a workplace injury or illness. In the EU, it is after three days, and in the United States, it is after one full day away from work. Therefore, a company using a consistent LTCR calculation globally (for example, the number of lost-time cases per 200,000 hours worked) will not find an accurate comparison of performance because each of the above countries defines a lost-time case differently.

Another issue that can influence the LTCR is the healthcare system practiced in a country. In countries where a government-run socialized health system is in place (e.g., Spain, Italy, and France), it is more difficult, or not legally possible, to implement a return-to-work program. Again, an accurate comparison of performance site-to-site or country-to-country is impacted.

To overcome discrepancies in incident reporting, and to develop meaningful data, multinational organizations require their facilities to report two sets of accident data and statistics. One set is developed to comply with the local regulatory agency's reporting requirements, and the other for corporate reporting to track internal safety and health performance for global comparison.

Accurate local incident data and reporting can impact government oversight and action as well. In the United Kingdom, the Reporting of Injuries, Diseases and Dangerous Occurrences Regulations, 1995 require specific incidents to be reported to the Health and Safety Executive (the United Kingdom Health and Safety regulatory body) within 24 hours following the incident. The type and nature of the incident determines whether a visit from the Health and Safety Executive ensues (HSE 1998).

Examples of Safety and Health Performance Indicators

- Improvement of corporate worker safety and health audit/assessment scores (quarter to quarter/ year to year)
- Percentage of corporate audit findings closed, by quarter
- Percentage of self-inspections completed on time, by a competent inspector
- Percentage of regulatory inspection findings closed one month following the date of inspection
- Percentage of retraining conducted on schedule
- Percentage of incidents investigated
- Percentage of risk assessments completed
- Percentage of risk assessment action items completed
- Percentage of safety and health goals, objectives, targets, and milestones completed

FIGURE 8. Safety and health performance indicators

To increase the likelihood of receiving accurate, meaningful incident rate performance data, an organization should develop and communicate written corporate reporting requirements, including:

- defined terminology: reportable (if used), lost time, incident
- defined timeframes for a lost-time case (e.g., worker away from work following an injury or illness after one full day, two full days, and so on)
- the accident rate calculation method (for example, based on 200,000 or 1,000,000 man-hours worked)
- written reporting procedures (local and corporate)
- developing and disseminating incident reporting forms
- other requirements based on individual organizational needs

Figure 7 illustrates lost-workday cases by country. Performance metrics define the expectations of an organization and allow the organization to measure its performance against set worker safety and health goals, objectives, and targets at the facility, regional, business unit, and corporate levels. Figure 8 provides some examples of proactive measurement criteria. They

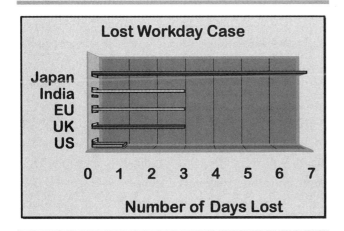

FIGURE 7. Defining lost-workday cases by country (*Source:* Global Solutions, Inc. 2011)

are proactive because they provide leadership with a measure of worker safety and health performance before an incident occurs. The intent of proactive measurement criteria is to identify management system deficiencies, provide corrective measures, and prevent an incident from occurring. Proactive indicators should include quantitative as well as qualitative measurement of performance.

SAFETY AND HEALTH RESOURCES: COMPETENCY AND EXPERTISE

Sourcing competent local safety and health resources is essential. Local safety and health resources (ASSE 1996; Global Solutions, Inc. 2011):

- provide local regulatory and enforcement expertise
- understand the company's organizational structure
- know how to effectively implement systems, policies, and programs locally
- can assist corporate safety and health in translating local safety and health issues (such as why audit findings are not being closed)
- mitigate local language barriers
- understand local cultural norms, which influence effective implementation of safety and health systems, policies, and programs

Identifying and deploying these resources is crucial to effectively implementing a global safety and health process.

Needs Assessment

A needs assessment assists in identifying safety and health resource requirements for the facility or global region. The needs assessment should be based on an evaluation of facility locations, both regionally and locally, individual facility size, financial resources, nature of operations, and level of safety and health risk for the facility.

The following provides examples of how some multinational companies have deployed safety and health resources, including internal dedicated em-

ployees, internal shared (part-time) employees, and external consultants (Global Solutions, Inc. 2011):

- Regional—full-time/facility-shared resource: three light assembly facilities located in China, where the level of worker safety and health risk is low to medium at each facility. The organization employs a regional safety and health manager who oversees safety and health activities using internal, shared, local safety and health employees at each facility within the region.
- Facility—full-time resource: a 300-employee, high-risk ammonia processing facility. The organization employs two full-time safety and health employees.
- Facility-shared resource/external resources: an office with 50 employees. The organization employs one internal shared safety and health coordinator and uses external resources to manage specific safety and health issues, such as ergonomics, home office workers, electrical safety, fire, life safety, and fleet. The safety and health coordinator is a shared resource with human resources.

Regardless of how an organization assesses staffing needs, all safety and health resources must have the competency to fulfill their safety and health role within the organization.

Competence

A needs assessment identifies safety and health competency levels required at the facility and regional levels. Competence is broken down into the specific skills and knowledge required to do the job. Skills and knowledge include risk identification and assessment; accident investigation; integrated management systems; and specific risk-control processes such as confined space entry, contractor safety, ionizing radiation, lockout/tagout programs, forklift truck safety, asbestos abatement, hazardous chemicals, hazard communication, and transport (ASSE 1996).

Competence can also be demonstrated through third-party certification or registration, examination, university or college matriculation, on-the-job training, and/or experience.

Tips for Identifying Competent Safety and Health Resources (Internal and External)

- Certification bodies have a registry of verified (certified/registered) third-party safety and health professionals, by country .
- Contact your industry trade groups for recommendations.
- Consult international safety and health professional networks, such as the American Society of Safety Engineers (ASSE) International Practice Specialty or the Institution of Occupational Safety and Health (IOSH) International Specialist Group.
- Professional safety and health organizations such as ASSE, IOSH, the Singapore Institution of Safety Officers, the Safety Institute of Australia, the Canadian Society of Safety Engineers, and the International Network of Safety Practitioner Organizations.
- Contact other multinational companies working in the region or country where resources are needed.

FIGURE 9. Finding global health and safety resources (*Source:* Global Solutions, Inc. 2011)

Recognized third-party competence designations include (Global Solutions, Inc. 2011):

- Certified Safety Professional (CSP) - American Board of Certified Safety Professionals
- Certified Industrial Hygienist (CIH) – American Board of Industrial Hygiene
- Charter Member of the Institution of Occupational Safety and Health (previously Registered Safety Practitioner, RSP) (UK)
- Canadian Registered Safety Professional (CRSP) - Board of Canadian Registered Safety Professionals
- Registered Safety Professional [RSP (Aust)] - Safety Institute of Australia

Some government legislation dictates competency requirements for operations and supervisory- and managerial-level staff within an organization. This is true for Singapore, where the Ministry of Manpower, in conjunction with the Singapore Workforce Development Agency, published formal occupational health and safety competency standards (Singapore Ministry of Manpower and Workforce Development Agency 2006).

Figure 9 provides some common tips used by global safety and health professionals to identify competent internal and external safety and health resources.

Once safety and health resources are identified, it is imperative to review their resumes/curriculum vitae and to check references thoroughly. Outside the United States, references are generally more readily provided. Language capability is also important. The resource should be fluent in English as well as the local dialect of the facility's management and employees. Dialects can pose a language barrier. One final area to consider is the nationality and religious compatibility of the safety and health resource and the country in which the individual will work. This can be a significant barrier in accomplishing the safety and health objectives intended by the safety and health resource when hired. To mitigate this potential issue, assure that local national management interviews the potential candidate before hiring, and, as a corporate safety and health leader, listen and work with the local facility if you are told the candidate is not suitable.

GLOBAL COMMUNICATION: THE KEY TO EFFECTIVE IMPLEMENTATION

Communicating corporate values and setting expectations for workplace safety and health are all part of good global safety and health management. Operationally, this includes communicating processes, procedures, executive-level safety and health tracking reports (e.g., the global profile), best practices, and loss-trending and prevention information.

Today, global communication is 24/7, 365 days a year via new and evolving technology capabilities. Use of Web-based platforms for information sharing, video conferencing, and access to sophisticated incident and risk-trending software promotes teamwork and a focused approach to data and people-driven management of safety and health risk. It is worthwhile to mention there are instances where face-to-face meetings are the most effective communication tool. Some examples may include one-on-one transfer of critical information or skills—a relationship needs to be developed before process/procedure/system implementation can occur—or when the senior leader requests your presence.

The safety professional should look to identify the most effective communication tools available within the organization, choosing the best tool based on the nature and purpose of the communication.

INTERNATIONAL TRAVEL: A PERSONAL RISK ASSESSMENT

This chapter would not be complete without a discussion on global business travel risks. Key factors employees should assess for work-related international travel risks include the destination of travel, political climate, work activities, climate and weather conditions, access to medical services, and length of stay in the destination country. The following outlines considerations for all company employees who travel outside their home country—including the safety professional—to ensure safe arrival and return from an international destination (Institution of Occupational Safety and Health (IOSH) 2007; Global Solutions, Inc. 2011). Table 2 presents an example of an international pretravel checklist. Employee travel risk should be part of the overall company safety and health risk assessment process. In many companies this is managed by human resources and the corporate or local travel departments. Employee training on global travel risks should be incorporated into the onboarding process, and guidance should be provided in the employee handbook.

Personal Security/Terrorism

Know where and when you will be traveling and the time of year. To assess your personal security and determine whether you should travel to a country, do your homework. Are you traveling to a destination where you may be impacted by civil unrest, be subject to a natural disaster (such as a tsunami, hurricane, or cyclone), or become a target of terrorism due to your nationality? The final decision to travel internationally rests on your shoulders. The deciding questions to ask are whether the international travel risk is too great and whether there is a high probability of injury, illness, or death? If the answers are yes, do not travel.

Personal security should be considered when dressing. Leave expensive jewelry, watches, and so on at home, as it makes you a greater target for theft.

TABLE 2

International Pretravel Checklist

1. Do you know the countries to which you are traveling? Does the time of year coincide with that of natural disasters (tsunami, cyclones, hurricanes, tornadoes)?	YES	NO
2. Do you have a valid passport?	YES	NO
3. If a visa is required to enter the destination country, do you have a valid visa?	YES	NO
4. Do you keep copies of your passport with visas with you while traveling? At a secondary location (for example, at home and office)?	YES	NO
5. Has your physician assessed your medical capability for international travel?	YES	NO
6. Are your immunizations up to date? Are they adequate for the destination country to which you are traveling?	YES	NO
7. Do you have Certificates of Immunization where required for destination countries?	YES	NO
8. Do you have a copy of emergency contact numbers for your destination country and country of origin?	YES	NO
9. Do you know how to access medical facilities in your destination country?	YES	NO
10. Does your company subscribe to an emergency service? Do you have an ID card for the service?	YES	NO
11. Has ground transportation been arranged prior to travel?	YES	NO
12. If you require prescription drugs, do you have enough for the duration of your trip? Are they in their original containers?	YES	NO
13. If recommended by your doctor or company travel service, do you have a medical kit with antibiotics, clean syringes, and needles, if required?	YES	NO
14. Are your clothes appropriate for the anticipated climate (for example, cold or tropical), including sunglasses with ultraviolet protection from the sun?	YES	NO
15. Do you have a valid drivers license to operate a vehicle in the country where you are traveling?	YES	NO

(*Source*: Institution of Occupational Safety and Health 2008; Global Solutions, Inc. 2011)

There are many government and private consultancies that provide timely security information on go and no-go zones around the world. Your own company may have access to or contractual arrangements with some of these consultancies. See the list of resources at the end of this section.

Emergency Contacts

Keep an itinerary with contact numbers for each country and facility you are visiting on your trip. Also keep emergency contact information for your corporate headquarters, and family members who should be contacted in the event of a medical or other emergency. Make sure you have 24-hour emergency contact information, as the time zone differences may mean you need to contact corporate headquarters outside of business hours. Also, keep a list with contact information for the embassies or consulates in the countries and areas in which you are traveling. The U.S. State Department Web site has contact information for U.S. embassies around the world. See the Web site Resources section at the end of this chapter for more information on the U.S. State Department.

Transportation

Make arrangements for ground transportation prior to arrival in the destination country, and have local company staff arrange for your transportation from the airport to your hotel and the office. If your company permits employees to drive in the destination country, the following considerations should be incorporated into the employee travel policy:

- Make sure you hold a valid driver's license to drive in the country.
- Know the local automobile insurance requirements.
- Know your legal rights if in an accident.
- Know who to contact within the company in an emergency.
- Consider how to deal with communication and language barriers.
- Understand the meaning of road signs.
- Understand local traffic regulations.
- Preplan your route, avoiding dangerous travel areas.
- Have local currency ready for tolls.

A local driver vetted by your company knows the language, roads, customs, tolls, or gratuities needed to safely get you to where you need to go. Unless you are fluent in the language, customs, and laws, leave the driving to a local national. A high-risk situation once occurred when a safety professional from a large multinational consumer goods manufacturing

organization was traveling to his facility in Central Mexico. The security risk was considered high, and the company provided him transportation by armed guards. While traveling from the company facility to the airport, their security vehicle was stopped by armed bandits. In this case, the bandits only wanted money, so the driver paid the "toll," and they were allowed to leave unharmed.

Automatic Teller Machines (ATMs)

The American Bankers Association (ABA) recommends that ATM users ensure they are in a well-lighted, secure area before using an ATM. This applies no matter where you are in the world (from New York City, U.S., or Bangkok, Thailand). In the past, kidnapping was a risk limited to a company's executives. In Latin America, more junior-level individuals have been detained and forced to withdraw the daily maximum amount from their ATM account until it reached a zero balance. Always be aware of your surroundings and travel in groups (ABA 2006).

An Exit Strategy

If you are going to places where there may be civil unrest, a political crisis, terrorism, other security warnings, or the threat of a natural disaster, you should contact your local embassy upon entering your destination country and provide them with local contact information. The embassy will keep you up to date in the event of a natural disaster or security issue that requires evacuation or additional security measures.

Do you have an exit strategy from your destination country? Always know the best means to leave the country in the event of an emergency. What are your air, land, and sea options? How will you get to the airport, port of call, or car rental center?

The United States government provides a pretrip registration service for U.S. citizens who would like to register with the nearest U.S. embassy or consulate in the destination country. This enables the government to contact the traveler in the event of an emergency that may significantly impact their life or travel.

The State Department Web site provides tips for travel outside the United States, document requirements, and passport and visa information to U.S. citizens (www.travel.state.gov).

Medical Concerns

Take your health seriously prior to and during international travel. Many travelers have died or become seriously ill from traveling internationally due to inadequate immunizations, lack of local medical knowledge, facilities, prescription drugs, clean hypodermic needles, medical evacuation availability, and procedures carried out in the event of a medical emergency. In addition, poor food hygiene can be the cause of dehydration and serious illness.

International travelers should have a physical examination and make sure that immunizations are up to date prior to commencing international travel. If you have a medical condition, have your physician assess travel requirements relative to the medical condition. Keep a letter with you at all times describing your medical condition and signed by your doctor.

Have your corporate medical team or a local international travel medical center do an immunization profile based on your anticipated travel. This will compare your current immunization status with required immunizations for prevalent diseases in the countries to which you are traveling. Common diseases include typhoid, hepatitis A and B, tetanus, malaria, diphtheria, yellow fever, and meningococcal meningitis.

Some countries require certification of immunization prior to gaining entry. Know what countries require these, and keep them with your travel documents.

Prior to departing from your home country, find out what medical services will be available to you at your destination, and what payment method your company has in place for medical services rendered? Most companies arrange this for you, but it is always best to confirm this information in writing before departure.

The U.S. Centers for Disease Control or your own company travel department will provide immunization requirements for pretravel. Make sure you have enough time to take all the courses of immunization before your trip. In some cases, the immunization process can take three months.

Work Travel

Passports should be up to date. Some countries now require the traveler to have held the passport six months in advance of travel. Know where you are traveling, and make sure your travel itinerary allows transit from one country to another. For example, if one has recently visited Israel, some Arab countries may not grant entry; the same may hold true in the reverse situation.

Plan your travel well in advance and know where visas are required for entry to a country. Visa requirements to enter a country are based on the country from which the traveler (traveler's passport) originates. Your company's corporate travel department or external travel resource should be able to secure a visa for travel well ahead of the date of planned travel. This will allow for any unplanned delays in the visa procurement process, such as the embassy requiring additional documents prior to issuing a visa. If you do not possess the required visa for entry into a country, you may be denied entry onto the plane or worse, denied entry to the country to which you have just traveled 22 hours by airplane.

Travel Resources

- Institution of Occupational Safety and Health Safety: *Safety in the Global Village. International travel safety assessment and guidance.* (www.iosh.co.uk/information_and_resources/guidance_and_tools.aspx)
- United States Department of State (www.travel.state.gov)
- American Society of Safety Engineers' global seminars (www.asse.org)
- The Centers for Disease Control and Prevention (CDC) Web site (www.cdc.gov) provides up-to-date medical advice for travelers around the globe. Includes information on countries with epidemics.

CONCLUSION

Managing worker safety and health risks is good business. In some cases it is a license to do business in a country; in others, it is the survival of a company when a safety and health incident occurs. Managing worker safety and health risks is a critical part of the overall strategic planning process companies engage in when running a global organization. The effective management of worker safety and health as a business risk has a positive impact on profit, market share, brand, and manufacturing and distribution within multinational organizations.

REFERENCES

Adidas Group. 2005. *Connected by Football: Social and Environmental Report 2005*. Germany: Adidas Group.

Allars, Kevin. "BP Texas City Incident: Baker Review." *Health and Safety Executive*. December 2007 (retrieved May 29, 2010). www.hse.gov.uk/leadership/baker report.pdf

American Bankers Association (ABA). 2006. *ATM Safety Tips* (retrieved August 9, 2006). www.aba.com/Consumer Connection/CNC_contips_atm.html

American National Standards Institute and American Industrial Hygiene Association (ANSI/AIHA). 2005. ANSI/AIHA Z10-2005, *Occupational Health and Safety Management Systems*. Fairfax, Virginia: AIHA.

American Society of Safety Engineers (ASSE). 1996. *Scope and Functions of a Safety Professional* (retrieved June 3, 2010). www.asse.org/hscopa.html

Australian Securities and Investments Commission. 2004. *The Corporate Law Economic Reform Program* (Audit Reform and Corporate Disclosure) Act 2004 (CLERP 9). Australian Securities and Investments Commission.

Australian Stock Exchange Corporate Governance Council. 2003. *Principles of Good Corporate Governance and Best Practice Recommendations* (retrieved March 2003). www.asx.com.au/supervision/governance/index.html

Avon. 2011. *Global Safety Strategy, #6* (retrieved June 30, 2011). www.avoncompany.com/corporatecitizenship/corporateresponsibility/whatwecareabout/workplace safetyandhealth/safetystrategy.html

British Petroleum p.l.c. 2005a. *A Message from BP's Group Chief Executive* (retrieved May 31, 2005). www.bp.com

_____. 2005b. *Health and Safety* (retrieved January 25, 2005). www.bp.com/liveassets/bp_internet/globalbp/STAGING/global_assets/downloads/E/ES_new2005_safety.pdf

_____. 2005c. *Making More Energy: Sustainability Report 2005*. United Kingdom: BP p.l.c..

_____. 2005d. Press Release: *BP Products North America Accepts Responsibility for Texas City Explosion* (retrieved May 31, 2005). www.bp.com/genericarticle.do?categoryId=2012968&contentId=7006066

British Standards Institute (BSI). 2007. *Occupational Health and Safety Assessment Series 18001-2007: Occupational Health and Safety Management Systems-Specification*. London, England: British Standards Institute.

_____. 2008. Occupational Health and Safety Assessment Series 18002: 2008, *Occupational health and safety management systems – Guidelines for the implementation of OHSAS 18001:2007*. London, England: British Standards Institute.

Brown, Garett. 2004. "Vulnerable Workers in the Global Economy." *Occupational Hazards* (April) pp. 29–30.

Browning, Jackson B. 1993. "Union Carbide: Disaster at Bhopal." Gottschalk, Jack A., ed. *Crisis Response: Inside Stories on Managing Under Siege*. Detroit, Michigan: Visible Ink Press.

Burgess, Kate, and Rebecca Bream. 2006. *Investors Seek BP Safety Assurances* (retrieved September 14, 2006). www.ft.com/cms/s/0/ee78d5ce-4455-11db-8965-0000779e2340.html

Canadian Centre for Occupational Health and Safety (CCOHS). 2010. "Bill C45-Overview" (retrieved June 1, 2010). www.ccohs.ca/oshanswers/legisl/bill c45.html

China Association of Development Zones. 2002. *National Export Processing Zone* (retrieved January 14, 2005). www.cadz.org.cn/en/kfq/jj.asp?name=EPZ

Corporate Responsibility Magazine. 2010. "Corporate Responsibility Magazine: 100 Best Corporate Citizens for 2010" (retrieved March 3, 2010). www.thecro.com/files/CR100Best3.pdf

European Agency for Safety and Health at Work. 2004. *Issue 54: Corporate Social Responsibility and Occupational Safety and Health* (retrieved May 6, 2006). www.osha.europa.eu/publications/factsheets/54/index.htm/view?searchterm=issue%2054

European Agency on Health and Safety at Work. 2005. *Introduction: Corporate Social Responsibility and Safety and Health at Work: Volkswagen, Automobiles (Germany)* (retrieved August 4, 2006). www.osha.eu.int/publications/reports/210/index_24.html

Friedman, Thomas L. 2005. *The World Is Flat*. New York: Farrar, Straus and Giroux.

Global Reporting Initiative™. 2006. "G3 Sustainability Reporting Guidelines" (retrieved March 3, 2010). www.globalreporting.org/ReportingFramework/G3 Guidelines

Global Solutions, Inc. 2011. *Global Environmental, Health and Safety Management Seminar Workbook*. Mendham, New Jersey: Global Solutions, Inc.

Gordon, Margery. 2001. *Advantage Reebok* (retrieved October 10. 2006). www.calbaptist.edu/dskubik/rebok_nike.html

Greenbiz. 2005. *UN Global Compact Participants Report Progress So Far* (retrieved July 19, 2005). www.global policy.org/reform/business/2005/0719gcreport.html

Health and Safety Executive (HSE). 2008. *A Guide to the Reporting of Injuries, Diseases and Dangerous Occurrences Regulations (RIDDOR) 1995, L73a*. Sudbury, England: HSE Books.

Health Canada. 2010. *Workplace Hazardous Materials Information System* (retrieved May 31 2010). www.hc-sc.gc.ca/ewh-semt/occup-travail/whmis-simdut/index-eng.php

Hewlett Packard (HP). 2006. *2006 Global Citizenship Report*. California, USA: HP.

_____. 2008. "Working Safety, Staying Healthy." *2008 HP Corporate Social Responsibility Report* (retrieved March 3, 2010). www.hp.com/hpinfo/globalcitizenship/gcreport/employees/health.html

_____. 2009. *HP Global Citizenship Report 2009*. California, USA: HP (retrieved June 1, 2010). www.hp.com/hpinfo/globalcitizenship/index.html

Hong Kong Labour Department. 2001a. *Construction Sites (Safety) Regulations*. Hong Kong: Hong Kong Labour Department.

_____. 2001b. *Factories and Industrial Undertakings Ordinance*. Hong Kong: Hong Kong Labour Department.

Howell, Karen. 2004. "Working Abroad: Foreign Offices." *Safety and Health Practitioner* (August), pp. 27–30.

Human Resources and Skills Development Canada. 2005. *Occupational Health and Safety in Canada – Legislative Changes from September 1, 2003 to August 12, 2004* (retrieved May 28, 2005). www.hrsdc.gc.ca/en/lp/spila/clli/dllc/15_2003_2004.shtml#iii_a

Institute of Chartered Accountants. 1999. *Internal Control—Guidance for Directors on the Combined Code for Corporate Governance*. England: Institute of Chartered Accountants.

Institution of Occupational Safety and Health (IOSH). 2008. *Safety in the Global Village* (retrieved May 20, 2010). www.iosh.co.uk/information_and_resources/guidance_and_tools.aspx

International Labour Office (ILO). 2001. *ILO-OSH 2001 Guidelines on Occupational Safety and Health Management Systems*. Geneva, Switzerland: ILO.

International Standards Organization (ISO). 2006. *Guidance on Social Responsibility* (retrieved December 10, 2006). www.iso.org/iso/en/CatalogueDetailPage.CatalogueDetail?CSNUMBER=42546&scopelist=PROGRAMME

_____. 2010. *ISO 26000 on Social Responsibility approved for release as Final Draft International Standard* (retrieved June 1, 2010). www.iso.org/iso/pressrelease.htm?refid=Ref1321

Johnson & Johnson. 2005. *2005 Sustainability Report*. www.jnj.com/community/environment/publications/2005_environ.pdf

Kaye, Leon. 2010. "Report from GRI Amsterdam: The Future of Transparent Sustainability Reporting." *Triplepundit*. June 1st, 2010 (retrieved June 2, 2010). www.triplepundit.com/2010/06/report-from-gri-amsterdam-the-future-of-transparent-sustainability-reporting/

Knight, Philip H. 2004. "Chairman's Letter to Shareholders: We're Faster Than Ever." *2004 Annual Report*. Oregon: Nike Inc.

Korean Occupational Safety and Health Agency. 2010. Enforcement *Decree of the Industrial Safety and Health Act* (retrieved June 1 2010). www.english.kosha.or.kr/main?act=VIEW&boardId=16&urlCode=T1││1240│1197│1197│1240│││/cms/board/board/Board.jsp&communityKey=B0488

L'Oreal SA. 2005. *2005 Sustainability Report* (retrieved August 10, 2006). www.loreal.com/_en/_ww/group/Img/LOREAL_RDD_GB.pdf

Locke, Richard M. 2005. *The Promise and Perils of Globalization: The Case of Nike* (retrieved January 15, 2005). www.mitsloan.mit.edu/50th/pdf/nikepaper.pdf

Moody, Andrew. 2009. "Multinationals Battling Locals for Market Share." *China Daily* (retrieved June 30, 2011). www.chinadaily.com.cn/business/2009-03/30/content_7628472.html

Mooney, Joseph W. 2004. "Investigate – Partner – then Export." *Northeast Export* (December), pp. 27–28.

Nash, James L. 2005. "Managing Global Safety: The Power of One." *Occupational Hazards* 67(9):28–32.

Nike Inc. 2003. *M.E.S.H.* (retrieved July 30, 2003). www.nike.com/nikebiz/nikebiz.html

_____. 2005a. *FY 04 Corporate Responsibility Report*. www.nike.com/nikebiz/nikebiz.jhtml?page=29&item=fy04

_____. 2005b. *Independent Monitoring & Assessment* (retrieved January 25, 2005). www.nike.com/nikebiz/nikebiz.jhtml?page=25&cat=monitoring&subcat=fla

Novartis AG. 2005. *Novartis Global Reporting Initiative 2005*. Basel, Switzerland: Novartis AG.

Seabrook, Kathy A. 1999a. "10 Strategies for Global Safety Management." *Occupational Hazards* 61(6):41–45.

_____. 1999b. "Multinational Organizations." *Safety and Health Management Planning for the 21st Century*. James P. Kohn and Theodore S. Ferry, eds. Rockville, MD: Government Institutes.

_____. 2006a. "A Briefing: Global Issues in Workplace Safety and Health." *World Focus. American Society of Safety Engineers International Practice Specialty*. 6(1):7–9.

_____. 2006b. *An Interview with Stuart Wood, Administrator, International Practice Specialty, American Society of Safety Engineers*. Mendham, New Jersey: Global Solutions, Inc.

_____. 2010. *2010 Global Safety and Health Briefing*. 2010 ASSE Professional Development Conference Proceedings, Session 534. Des Plaines, Il: American Society of Safety Engineers.

_____. 2011. Global Environmental, Health and Safety Managemental Seminar. Presented at Seminarfest 2011, January 21–29, 2011. American Society of Safety Engineers, Las Vegas.

Secretaria de Segurança e Medicina do Trabalho. 2004. *Federal Law 6514/77 and Normas Regulamentadoras -5*. Sao Paulo, Brazil: Secretaria de Segurança e Medicina do Trabalho.

Singapore Ministry of Manpower and Workforce Development Agency. 2006. *Generic Occupational Safety and Health Competency Standards*. Singapore: Ministry of

Manpower and Singapore Workforce Development Agency.

The Economist. 2004. *Wood for the Trees* (retrieved May 29, 2005). www.economist.com

The White House. 2010. Office of the Press Secretary. May 22, 2010. "Press Release: Weekly Address: President Obama Establishes Bipartisan National Commission on the BP Deepwater Horizon Oil Spill and Offshore Drilling." (May 29 2010).

U.S. Census Bureau. 2005. *U.S. International Trade in Goods and Services Highlights* (retrieved May 29, 2005). www.census.gov/indicator/www/ustrade.html

Union Carbide Corporation. 2004a. *Chronology of Key Events Related to the Bhopal Incident* (retrieved November 18, 2004). www.bhopal.com/chrono.html

_____. 2004b. *Incident Review* (retrieved November 18, 2004). www.bhopal.com/review.html

_____. 2004c. *Opinion of the Attorney-General: Extradition of Warren Anderson* (retrieved November 18, 2004). www.bhopla.com/opinion.html

United Nations. 2006. *The Global Compact* (retrieved June 29, 2006). www.un.org/Depts/ptd/global.html

_____. 2010. KPMG Advisory N.V., United Nations Environment Programme, Global Reporting Initiative, Unit for Corporate Governance in Africa. "Carrots and Sticks—Promoting Transparency and Sustainability: An update on trends in Voluntary and Mandatory Approaches to Sustainability Reporting" (retrieved June 1, 2010). www.globalreporting.org/ NR/rdonlyres/20F03459-4104-4B6D-AC3C-3C100F 307EA2/4198/Carrots2010final.pdf

United Technologies Corporation. 2004. *2004 Corporate Responsibility Data Index* (retrieved August 10, 2006). www.utc.com/responsibility_reports/2004/html/ contents/page26.html

U.S. Congress. 2002. Sarbanes-Oxley Act of 2002, Public Law 107-204. 107th Cong., 2002.

U.S. Department of Labor. 2009a. *Top 10 Enforcement Citations*, January 30, 2009 (retrieved May 28 2010). www.osha.gov/dep/bp/Top_Ten_Enforcement.html

_____. 2009b. Occupational Safety and Health Administration. *Fact Sheet on BP 2009 Monitoring Inspection* (retrieved May 29, 2010). www.osha.gov/dep/bp/ Fact_Sheet-BP_2009_Monitoring_Inspection.html

_____. 2009c. Occupational Safety and Health Administration. Press Release: October 30, 2009. "US Department of Labor's OSHA issues record-breaking fines to BP" (accessed May 31, 2010). www.osha.gov/pls/ oshaweb/owadisp.show_document?p_table=NEWS_ RELEASES&p_id=16674 09-1311-NAT

_____. 2010. Occupational Safety and Health Administration. "A Guide to Globally Harmonized System of Classification and Labelling of Chemicals" (retrieved February 23, 2010). www.osha.gov/dsg/hazcom/ghs

Vodafone Group Plc. 2006. *Group Corporate Responsibility Report for Financial Year 2005/06*. United Kingdom: Vodafone Group Plc.

APPENDIX A: ONLINE RESOURCES

Health and Safety Guidance and Regulations

General Resources

Global Solutions, Inc. Links to global websites sites with access to EHS regulations. www.globalEHS.com

International Network of Safety and Health Practitioner Organisations (INSHPO). Network of safety and health professional organizations founded in 2001. www.inshpo.org

Asia Pacific

Asia Pacific Occupational Safety and Health Organization(APOSHO) www.aposho.org

Australia

Australia National Occupational Health and Safety Commission. www.nohsc.gov.au/OHSLegal Obligations

Safety Institute of Australia. Australian association for safety and health professionals. www.sia.org.au

Baltic Region

Baltic Sea Network on Occupational Health and Safety. Provides regulations for Denmark, Estonia, Finland, Latvia, Lithuania Poland and Russia. www.balticseaosh.net

Canada

Canadian Center for Occupation Health and Safety. www.ccohs.ca

Canadian Society of Safety Engineers. Canadian association for safety and health professionals. www.csse.org

Health Canada. Information on the Workplace Hazardous Materials Information System (WHMIS)— Hazard Communication Requirements. www.hc-sc. gc.ca

European Union Countries

European Agency for Safety and Health at Work. www.agency.osha.eu.int

European Network of Safety and Health Professional Organizations (ENSHPO). www.enshpo.org

International Labour Organization (ILO). Provides United Nations conventions for worker safety and health. These conventions have been adopted by most countries in the World Trade Organization (WTO). www.ilo.org

India

Indoshnet. www.dgfasli.nic.in

Japan

Japan International Center for Occupational Safety and Health. Provides links to Web sites for regulations of other countries as well. www.jicosh.gr.jp/english/osh/list-of-laws.html

Malaysia

Laws of Malaysia - Act 514 and Occupational Safety and Health Act 1994. www.niosh.com.my/osha.htm

Korea

Korea Occupational Safety and Health Agency. www.kosha.or.kr/english/english.htm

Russia

Department of Occupational Health, Saint Petersburg Medical Academy of Postgraduate Studies. www.leivo.ru/mapo/model.html

Singapore

Ministry of Manpower. www.mom.gov.sg/MOM

United Kingdom

Health and Safety Executive. UK regulatory agency for worker health and safety. www.hse.gov.uk/pubns/hsc13.htm#2

Institution of Occupational Safety and Health (IOSH). British association for safety and health professionals. www.iosh.co.uk

United States

Board of Certified Safety Professionals. Registry of board-certified safety and health professionals. www.bcsp.org

Center for Disease Control and Prevention (CDC). Provides up-to-date medical advice for travelers around the globe. www.cdc.gov

Occupational Safety and Health Administration. Regulatory agency for worker health and safety. www.osha.org

United States State Department. Travel and visa information. www.travel.state.gov

Sustainability and Corporate Social Responsibility

Business for Social Responsibility. www.bsr.org
CERES HYPERLINK. www.ceres.org

Corporate Governance. www.corpgov.net/wordpress
CSR Wire. www.csrwire.com
Future 500. www.future500.org
Global Reporting Initiative. www.globalreporting.org/Home
International Organization for Standardization. *ISO 26000 Social Responsibility*. www.iso.org/iso/socialresponsibility.pdf
International Organization for Sustainable Development. www.iosd.org
SAM. www.sustainability-index.com/07_htmle/assessment/infosources.html

Supply-Chain Management Resources

Nike Sample Supply Chain Assessment Tools. www.nikebiz.com/responsibility/workers_and_factories.html

Avian Flu/Global Health Preparedness Resources

General

World Health Organization for Influenza Pandemic Preparedness Planning. www.who.int/entity/csr/disease/influenza/pandemic/en/index.html

Australia

"Fact Sheet – Pandemic Influenza Levels of Alert." www.health.gov.au/internet/wcms/publishing.nsf/Content/phd-health-emergency-threat-level.htm

General Information

www.health.gov.au/internet/wcms/publishing.nsf/Content/Pandemic+Influenza-1

European Union

Assessment Tool. National Pandemic Influenza Preparedness: Unit for Preparedness and Response at the European Centre for Disease Prevention and Control (ECDC) in Stockholm, in collaboration with the European Commission and the World Health Organisation Regional Office for Europe. www.ecdc.eu.int/Influenza/Assessment_Tool.php

United States

Checklist: Business Pandemic Influenza Planning. Department of Health and Human Services. www.pandemicflu.gov/plan/pdf/businesschecklist.pdf
United States Centers for Disease Control. www.cdc.gov/business

APPENDIX B: CASE STUDY: THE UNION CARBIDE BHOPAL INDIA INCIDENT

The following case study demonstrates the financial impact a U.S. multinational company can face when an incident that affects the safety and health of its employees and the surrounding community occurs at a non-U.S. site.

Background: The Incident

The following gives an overview as provided by Union Carbide Corporation. The purpose is to recognize how safety and health, operational, financial, and reputational risks can impact the survival of a business domestically and internationally.

On December 3, 1984, gas leaked from a tank of methyl isocyanate (MIC), resulting in a gas release at the Union Carbide plant in Bhopal, India. According to the state government of Madhya Pradesh, approximately 3800 people died and 11,000 people were left with disabilities (Browning 1993). Workers and their families living in close proximity to the plant site where they worked, which is the cultural norm in India, exacerbated the loss of life.

The Cause

The Indian government and Union Carbide confirmed the cause of the incident was the introduction of a large volume of water into an MIC tank, triggering a reaction that resulted in a gas release (Union Carbide Corporation 2004).

Reputational Risk and Financial Impact

Who were some of the first outside entities at the scene of the incident? The news media provided the world with a window to view the death and destruction caused by the incident. This event changed the future of Union Carbide in India. The reputation of Union Carbide was on the line; many questions, investigations, and litigation would befall the company for years following the explosion, and Union Carbide would sell its worldwide battery business in 1986 (Union Carbide Corporation 2004).

In February 1989, the Supreme Court of India directed Union Carbide Corporation (UCC) and Union Carbide India Limited (UCIL) to pay a total of $470 million in full settlement of all claims arising from the tragedy. In 1991, the Supreme Court of India also requested UCC and UCIL to voluntarily fund capital and operating costs of a hospital in Bhopal for eight years, estimated at approximately $17 million, to be built on land donated by the state government (Union Carbide Corporation 2004).

In November 1994, UCC completed the sale of its 50.9 percent interest in Union Carbide India Limited, a profitable operation for Union Carbide Corporation (Union Carbide Corporation 2004).

CEO Accountability

Another important factor in the Union Carbide incident is the implication of a CEO's criminal accountability for its global facilities when they are outside of where the global headquarters are domiciled. In the case of Union Carbide–Bhopal, the Attorney General of India, Soli Sorabjee, was asked to provide an opinion on whether extradition proceedings against Warren Anderson, Chairman of Union Carbide Corporation at the time of the gas tragedy, were legally sustainable (Union Carbide Corporation 2004). In the end, Mr. Anderson was not extradited. The premise for this verdict did not set a legal precedent for the criminal acts of a CEO, therefore, it leaves open the question of both criminal and civil legal liability of a CEO for the health and safety of workers and the public in India.

Mr. Sorabjee determined there must be the following "missing evidentiary links" (Union Carbide Corporation 2004):

1. the actual cause of the gas leak
2. Mr. Anderson's knowledge of the cause of the gas leak prior to its occurrence
3. the extent to which Mr. Anderson had decision-making control over UCIL's safety and design issues
4. whether Mr. Anderson refused to correct the hazard

Although the Attorney General of India determined that these missing evidentiary links (Union Carbide Corporation 2004) could be established, the Indian government never made a formal request for Mr. Anderson's extradition. According to the Union Carbide Website article, "Bhopal," general opinion by the United States' legal community was that, for humanitarian reasons, Mr. Anderson would probably not be extradited. He was 81 years old and in poor health, and there was a 17-year gap between the request for extradition and the Bhopal incident. Perhaps if Mr. Anderson had been younger and in better health, the Indian Attorney General, Soli Sorabjee, may have decided to pursue extradition (Union Carbide Corporation 2004).

The Bhopal facility incident impacted Union Carbide's reputation, along with its financial and legal standing in India. It also implicated the CEO, who could have been held legally responsible and accountable for operational incidents at Union Carbide sites throughout the world. That legal precedent was not tested. Today, with newer technology, news travels faster, images are more vivid, and information is transmitted without interruption. Organizations employ media management consultants who manage both positive and negative media events with a goal of making sure that the organization's reputation remains intact.

MANAGEMENT OF SAFETY ENGINEERING WORK

LEARNING OBJECTIVES

▌ Be able to identify direct, indirect, and intangible costs and benefits that should be considered when evaluating safety investments.

▌ Be able to summarize and apply fundamental engineering economic concepts such as cash flows, time value of money, and discount rate.

▌ Be able to use common engineering economic methods, such as net present worth, annual cost, payback period, benefit-cost ratio, and internal rate of return.

COST ANALYSIS AND BUDGETING

T. Michael Toole

ALL ORGANIZATIONS have goals. Most for-profit companies have corporate financial goals concerned with providing their shareholders with a certain rate of return on investment, which requires such companies to earn a certain level of profits, or net income. Within companies, resources such as people, equipment, physical plant, materials, and cash are *deployed* in ways thought to provide the best chances of meeting or exceeding corporate goals. Whether developing a new product, expanding into a new geographic area, or implementing a new information technology system to streamline operations, all projects require resources in order to bring the project to fruition, thereby eventually contributing to the achievement of corporate goals. One of management's key duties is to decide which projects—out of hundreds of possible projects—should be pursued. Managers must choose projects that they believe will deliver an acceptable *payoff* for the resources expended in pursuing them.

Profit is the difference between revenue and costs. Profit can be increased by increasing revenue, decreasing costs, or increasing revenues more than costs. Every safety professional knows that providing a safe and healthy work environment is a critical component in managing costs (ASSE 2002, Veltri et al. 2007). Although safety programs are rarely viewed as increasing revenues, they are typically recognized as essential to reducing costs, or to ensuring that costs do not increase faster than revenues do. Effective safety programs, therefore, can contribute to achieving corporate goals involving profitability just as much as more visible initiatives that involve new products, services, and so on.

In short, managers know that effective safety management is a good corporate investment. Like all investments, safety programs need dedicated resources. These resources usually include people, such as reassigned employees or newly hired employees, who must perform new safety functions. Resources needed for safety programs also routinely include infrastructure-related items such as office space, utilities, clerical support, and other administrative expenses. Specialized materials or equipment are also common safety-related resources.

Nearly all these resources require managers to spend money at the time the resources are received. In other words, the costs of resources are short-term costs. Yet, as is true of most strategic programs, the benefits or payoffs resulting from spending money now may not be felt until months, or even years, later. Moreover, because benefits occur in the future, they cannot be predicted with absolute certainty. Thus, managers who keep close watch over their organization's expenditures and profitability will be understandably reluctant to invest in any programs that may not deliver enough "bang for their buck." This may be especially true for safety programs, which have traditionally not been viewed as critical to company operations.

All managers—whether champions of safety or those with less progressive attitudes—need to be provided with thorough and objective analyses demonstrating that proposed safety expenditures represent solid investments deserving of their approval and unwavering support. Safety professionals know that the cost of preventing or reducing accidents is considerably less than the cost of actual accidents. But they need tools that can be applied to demonstrate that safety programs are cost-effective, worthwhile investments.

Several recent books and articles deal explicitly with this issue. In a book entitled *Safety and the Bottom Line*, Bird (1996) quoted the axiom of economic association: A manager will usually pay more attention to information when expressed or associated with cost terminology. Adams (2002) reported the results of a survey indicating that the need for "SH&E professionals to show management how safety can positively impact the bottom line" was widely recognized. Behm, Veltri, and Kleinsorge (2004) affirmed the need for making an economic case for safety, suggesting that framing safety investments using a cost-of-quality perspective might prove effective. In the book *Increasing Productivity and Profit through Health and Safety*, Oxenbaugh, Marlow, and Oxenbaugh (2004) also discuss the application of

quantitative economic analysis to safety and health programs. Linhard (2005) discusses the development of a software called the "Return on Health, Safety and Environmental Investments" that analyzes the potential financial impacts of safety investments. Veltri et al. (2007) found statistically significant relationships between safety programs and operating performance in manufacturing firms. Specifically, the wider the gap between management and employee perceptions about safety programs, the higher the scrap and rework costs and the higher the production costs relative to competitors. Veltri and Ramsey (2009) provide a valuable review of the literature to identify the challenges of performing economic analysis and propose a detailed three-stage SH&E economic analysis model.

This chapter will provide the reader with tools that can objectively evaluate whether a project should be pursued. While the tools are often referred to as being associated with *engineering economics*, they are really financial analysis tools that are applied every day to projects having nothing to do with either engineering or safety. For example, the tools summarized in this chapter can help one decide whether to invest in real estate, launch a new product, or buy an extended warranty on a consumer purchase. Similarly, the fundamental concepts from engineering economics that will be introduced at the beginning of this chapter apply to all financial analysis situations, not just to those involving safety or engineering.

FUNDAMENTAL CONCEPTS UNDERLYING COST ANALYSIS

Before introducing the powerful analytic methods that can be used to demonstrate that safety programs are good investments, it will be helpful to introduce several basic financial concepts and assumptions underlying these tools. This section will deal with life-cycle costing, direct and indirect costs and benefits, cash flow diagrams, time value of money, and the uncertainty of future costs and benefits.

Life-Cycle Costs

An important principle of engineering economic analysis is that all cash flows relevant to the decision must be included in the analysis. A cradle-to-grave approach should be taken, including all costs from the conception of a project (including engineering and design costs) through acquisition, startup, the end of its useful life, and disposal or salvage. The full life cycle of a project must be considered. Many consumers focus only on initial costs and ignore important future costs, such as in the purchase of computer printers, an instance in which many buyers are penny-wise but pound foolish, buying discount printers but paying many times their initial savings for expensive ink cartridges over the printer's life. The purchase of a car is another example of an instance in which some consumers do not consider costs accrued throughout the life cycle. Some buyers decide they can afford the higher initial cost of an expensive car but ignore the continuing need to purchase high-octane gasoline and pay more in insurance premiums and maintenance costs.

Life-cycle costing is also important for safety investments. Managers must think beyond the immediate and obvious costs and include in their analysis all annual maintenance costs and any end-of-life costs. Consider, for example, the hiring of a safety manager or other safety employee. The immediate and obvious cost is the employee's salary. Less obvious are the direct costs associated with payroll taxes, fringe benefits, new computer, and cell phone. Furthermore, annual increases in salary and overhead costs, the cost of periodic training, and similar costs should also be included. The analysis should also include any costs associated with the employee's termination (such as severance pay or unemployment) or retirement.

Safety-related equipment purchases also typically have obvious initial costs and less than obvious future costs. The large initial cash outlay in year 0 is followed by a series of annual benefits and costs. Annual benefits may include the operational cost savings per year resulting from the equipment and depreciation "charges." Annual costs often include maintenance or testing costs. At the end of the useful life of the equipment there may be a salvage benefit (as when used equipment is bought from the company). Alternatively, some equipment carries with it a required end-of-life disposal cost.

Indirect Costs and Benefits for Investment Decisions

A fundamental concept that applies to both short- and long-term projects is the concept of indirect costs and benefits. Most people would define a good project as one that results in more benefits than costs—a project that gives back more than is put into it. If asked to actually add up the benefits and costs, however, most only include direct benefits and costs, cash flows they consider to be directly associated with or directly resulting from a project that have obvious values. For example, OSHA's *Success Stories and Case Studies* Web page (2010) includes a link to success stories that summarize direct benefits.

It is important that financial analysis also include indirect costs and benefits and intangible costs and benefits (Labelle 2002). Some people use the terms tangible and intangible as synonymous with direct and indirect, but they are not. *Indirect costs and benefits* are tangible amounts that should be included in financial analysis but are not readily visible as being associated with an investment because one does not write a check for an indirect cost or cash a check for an indirect benefit. Indirect costs and benefits can be objectively quantified by people with expertise in cost accounting. Intangible costs and benefits are cash flows associated with an investment that are difficult to exactly apportion to the investment. They represent dollars that are real but are very difficult to quantify objectively, yet are still needed to perform the quantitative analysis discussed in this chapter. This subsection deals with indirect costs and benefits, and the next subsection addresses intangible costs and benefits.

Income Tax Benefits

Three specific types of indirect cash flows are summarized here. A full discussion of each of these cash flow types would require a book chapter alone, but they should at least be mentioned. One type of indirect cash flow is the effect of income tax. Investments are undertaken to generate profits, but these profits are subject to business income tax. Thus, proper cash flow diagrams for an income-producing investment should reflect the net income produced by the investment after tax. Because corporate tax rates are typically above 30 percent, income taxes can significantly reduce a potential project's apparent net income. Companies in special circumstances, allowing them to pay little or no corporate taxes, may not need to incorporate corporate taxes in their analyses.

Depreciation

A second important indirect cash flow that is easy to incorrectly omit is depreciation. Depreciation is an accounting concept, not an operational concept, but it carries with it implications for investment decisions. When certain types of major assets are purchased, their acquisition costs cannot be fully expensed (i.e., entered into the accounting books under cost of goods, thereby reducing net income) in the year they are purchased. Instead, the costs are amortized over the number of years set forth in tax law. In other words, although a firm may have paid a vendor the entire cost of a new piece of capital equipment, the income statement for that year can only include a portion of the costs. In each of the remaining years of the asset's service life, the income statement includes an entry for depreciation in the book value of the capital asset. This entry acts on paper like a current expense, thereby reducing net income and income tax owed. The U.S. government allows multiple methods of depreciation. Straight-line depreciation—in which the cost, less salvage value, of a purchase is simply divided by its useful life—is not commonly used, which is why depreciation is an indirect cash flow that frequently requires professional expertise to calculate.

Allocated Overhead Charges

The third type of indirect cash flow that should be mentioned is *allocated overhead* charges. Overhead costs may include portions of managers' salaries and fringe benefits, office space, utilities, and other costs that may be necessary infrastructure for a new investment. Adding overhead charges to cash flow diagrams typically reduces the attractiveness of a project because it reduces the positive cash flow associated with the investment. The amount of overhead to include in the analysis can be a difficult decision. Some companies establish

a fixed rate and apply it to all direct costs. Other companies establish a fixed rate but often reduce or waive it during the early years of a new investment.

One reason it is sometimes difficult to determine whether overhead should be included in financial analysis is that overhead is typically associated with *fixed costs* (costs the company must pay regardless of the number of units produced, the number of hours worked, and so on) that may be independent of the investment under consideration. Existing management salaries and office rent and utilities usually are paid regardless of a new investment, so why should these costs be allocated to the investment under consideration? (The common-sense answer is that managers whose projects had to continue contributing toward corporate overhead would reasonably complain about other managers' projects that looked better because they did not have to contribute to overhead.) But to the extent that an investment ends up increasing fixed costs, the increases should clearly be assigned to the investment's project cash flow. *Variable costs* (costs incurred when additional hours are worked, etc.) should clearly be included in an investment's cash flow.

Intangible Costs and Benefits

Direct and indirect cash flows are those that are clearly associated with a project or investment and can be unequivocally measured. Intangible cash flows are those that are *real* but are nebulous and harder to quantify. ASSE's white paper on the return on investment for safety and health programs (ASSE 2002) refers to these costs as *hidden costs*.

Although there are always tangible costs associated with any safety program, there are rarely tangible benefits. Consider a company deciding whether to hire a full-time safety manager. One obvious set of costs would be the new manager's salary and fringe benefits. These are tangible costs because there are clearly future expenditures associated with hiring the new safety manager. However, if having a full-time safety manager was determined through appropriate analysis to automatically result in a 10 percent discount in workers' compensation or general liability insurance premiums, this would be reckoned a tangible benefit, because the savings would be easily quantifiable and would be directly associated with the new hire.

But such explicit benefits are often not present. Rather, the benefits associated with safety expenditures are usually intangible. For example, having a safety manager will eventually result in reductions in accidents, which will increase productivity and make the firm more attractive to clients who understand the importance of safety. Although these effects are important and may significantly improve the company's profits, they are hard to quantify, and it is difficult to *prove* as having resulted from the investment. If productivity increases, for example, line managers may attribute the increase solely to management initiatives wholly unrelated to safety. If other factors result in no increase in productivity, or even a decrease, line managers may fail to understand that productivity would have been even lower had the safety investment not been made.

It is important to note, however, that although intangible cash flows may be difficult to quantify and estimate, it is still usually appropriate to include them in economic analysis. After all, nearly all investment decisions are based on *estimates* of future returns on investments, not on locked-in cash flows. (This point is discussed more fully in the section entitled "Future Cash Flows Are Uncertain.") For example, Americans routinely buy equity stocks based on estimates of the future dividends and appreciation in the stock values. Product managers routinely decide to pay product development and marketing costs based on estimates of future sales and prices. Safety professionals should not hesitate to identify the specific intangible benefits associated with a safety investment, estimate their magnitudes, and let operational managers decide if these magnitudes should be adjusted or subjected to sensitivity analysis (a term that is discussed further in a section titled "Future Cash Flows Are Uncertain"). For example, many safety managers have historical data on the frequency of occurrence of specific types of injuries and the average direct cost associated with each type of injury. It is rational to estimate the savings resulting from an investment that will result in reduction in injuries by multiplying the number of

fewer injuries expected by the average costs of each such injury.

Literature on Direct and Indirect Safety Costs

A number of authors have written about direct and indirect safety-related costs—especially on the indirect costs of accidents, which though often difficult to measure are nonetheless very significant. Leigh et al. (2000) reported that indirect costs comprise 71 percent of the total costs of an injury in the United States. It is important to point out, however, that this figure reflected all costs, including those borne by the injured employee and by government programs. An organization analyzing a safety investment, on the other hand, should only include costs borne by the organization, as explained below.

In an article titled "Hitting the Injury Iceberg," Brandt (1999) stated that "most insurance loss control experts agree the indirect costs of workplace injuries (costs usually not covered by insurance) can range anywhere from two to ten times the cost of the face value of the claim." Kinn et al. (2000) reported that indirect costs may range from two to twenty times the direct costs in the cases of plumbers and pipefitters. The introduction to OSHA's Safety & Health Management Systems eTool states that "studies show that the ratio of indirect costs to direct costs varies widely, from a high of 20:1 to a low of 1:1" (OSHA 2010).

Brody, Letourneau, and Poirer (1990) identified indirect accident costs for general industry, including wages paid to employees at the accident site immediately after an accident (which are not covered by insurance), damaged materials, occupation of administrators' time, production losses, tarnished public image, deteriorated labor relations and morale, and higher wages (due to perceived risk). This same article also identified prevention costs, including fixed prevention costs (those that occur before production occurs and do not vary with accident rate), variable prevention costs (those that occur as a result of accidents in an effort to prevent recurrences, such as accident investigations), and unexpected prevention costs (those associated with reducing the risk of injury but not foreseen at the time a piece of equipment was purchased).

Brady et al. (1997) identified (1) the direct costs associated with a specific injury, (2) the indirect costs associated with a specific injury, and (3) the indirect costs associated with other health and safety requirements (such as prevention programs) instead of with a specific injury (see the lists set out below). Lanoie and Tavenas (1996) reported on a detailed study of the direct and indirect costs and benefits of a participatory ergonomics program.

Direct Costs Related to Specific Illness or Injury

Direct costs related to a specific illness or injury include the following:

- medical care
- physician, other provider services
  - inpatient
  - outpatient
- clinic, hospital services
  - inpatient
  - outpatient
- ancillary diagnostic services
  - laboratory
  - radiology
  - electrocardiography
  - electromyography
  - other
- patient-specific medical supplies, equipment
- medications, pharmacy services
- rehabilitation, occupational/physical therapy
- employee assistance counseling
- other injury- or illness-specific requirements
- workers' compensation payments (as applicable)
- sick pay (as applicable)
- other benefits (as applicable)
- compliance with Occupational Safety and Health Administration reporting required for the illness or injury
- costs for temporary employee to accomplish tasks of ill or injured worker
- case-management costs
- vocational rehabilitation counseling
- case-specific litigation costs
- case-specific human resources or personnel costs
- specific accommodations required by the Americans with Disabilities Act

Indirect Costs Related to Specific Illness or Injury

Indirect costs related to a specific illness or injury include the following:

- reduced productivity
  - absence of injured or ill employee
  - shift in activities of co-worker to accomplish absent employee's work
  - increased supervisor effort to cope with absence of employee
  - temporary or long-term absence of corporate memory possessed by the ill or injured employee
  - start-up and training time for replacement employee
  - start-up and training time for the returned ill or injured employee
  - development of limited work position for ill or injured worker, as appropriate
  - reduced effectiveness of "nearby" co-workers
  - overtime pay
- impacts on competitiveness
  - potential for reduced customer satisfaction because of absent employee and effects of employee's absence
  - effect of greater-than-projected medical costs
  - increased risk of illness or injury by temporary or replacement employee because of limited time for hazard or safety training, or other factors
  - increased insurance premiums
  - increased overtime costs
  - increased training and retraining costs
  - increased legal costs, including class-action defense, coordination of new policies to respond to event or prevent recurrence, and other such costs
  - loss of senior management time in responding to event
  - reduced performance and effectiveness of ill or injured person once returned
  - effects on labor relations, including potential strikes as well as requests for hazard

pay and new safety programs or protective
equipment

– potential for adverse media coverage

– effect on worker morale (which also impacts
productivity)

– requirements for increased quality-control
efforts, as required, for replacement or
returning employee

– increased human resources and personnel
department costs incurred in efforts to
replace ill or injured worker

– medical, industrial hygiene, and safety costs
involved in investigation of accident or
exposure site

– risk-management activities involved in
investigation of accident or exposure site,
or other activities

Indirect Costs Related to Other Health and Safety Requirements, Not to a Specific Illness or Injury

Indirect costs related to other organizational health
and safety requirements include the following:

- the health and safety program (in-house,
  consultant, contract) costs
  – staffing to provide care for ill and injured
    employee on site (or costs to arrange such
    capability off site)
  – regulatory compliance, including medical/
    industrial hygiene monitoring, surveillance
    programs
  – development and maintenance of capabilities
    for case management
  – employee assistance program other than
    costs for specific illnesses or injuries
  – development of health and safety policies
  – data-processing and data-management costs
  – research expenditures, as appropriate
  – wellness, health promotion, immunizations
  – health and safety committees
  – evaluation of options for provision of
    services
  – program evaluations
  – interactions with other organizations,
    departments, and managers, including risk
    managers

– drug and alcohol testing programs

– preplacement and periodic examinations
and evaluations

– other organization-specific costs

- other costs of health and safety activities—
  other than those involving a specific illness or
  injury
  – human resources and personnel
  – benefits
  – legal
  – labor relations and unions
  – management (other than health and safety)
  – other organization-specific costs

Hinze (2000) investigated typical indirect costs
associated with construction injuries and reported that
indirect costs are typically four times direct costs. He
identified the following typical indirect costs associated
with medical case injuries in construction:

- 15.7 hours lost time by the worker
- 3 hours transporting the worker from the job
  site
- 12 hours lost by the injured worker's crew
- 4 hours to repair damaged equipment and
  material
- 5.5 hours lost by the supervisor responding to
  and reporting the accident

Hinze also identified typical direct costs associated with the following common safety investments
for construction firms:

- substance abuse testing
- safety inspectors and managers
- safety training
- personal protective equipment (PPE)
- safety committees
- accident investigations
- safety incentives

Behm, Veltri, and Kleinsorge (2004) provided a
helpful framework for analyzing direct and indirect
costs. Specifically, they discussed how a cost-of-safety
analysis should include four classes of costs and
benefits: prevention, detection, internal failure, and
external failure. They suggest that the appropriate
level of spending on a safety project or total safety

FIGURE 1. Indirect benefits of a safety and health program (OSHA et al 2005)

program is the point where the sum of prevention and detection costs equals the sum of internal and external failure costs. Their article also articulates the practical challenges of collecting the necessary data.

OSHA has made available an eTool called "$afety Pays" (OSHA 2010), which calculates both direct and indirect cost savings, and the resulting increase in profit margins, from estimated reductions in specific types of injuries. OSHA has also made available a powerpoint file (OSHA et al. 2005) that includes slides relating to indirect benefits (see Figure 1) and indirect costs. NIOSH (2004) has made available a practical guide for collecting and evaluating direct, indirect, and intangible costs and benefits associated with safety investments under consideration. The process recommendations are summarized in the opening chapter of this handbook.

Cash Flow Diagrams

One of the first steps in performing an effective evaluation of any investment should be creating a cash flow diagram (CFD) of the proposed investment. As the name implies, CFDs are diagrams that indicate all of the incoming and outgoing monies associated with an investment. CFDs are two-dimensional and have an invisible x–y grid underlying them. The x-axis represents time and typically shows units of months

or years. The y-axis is the amount (that is, magnitude) of the cash flow and typically shows units in dollars or thousands of dollars.

The first step in creating a CFD is to identify the length of time associated with the investment decision. The length of time is typically the life cycle of the item or project being considered. For example, a piece of capital equipment might have an expected service life of 25 years, but PPE might have an expected service life of only five years. At the end of the investment's service life the item must be replaced, or the project repeated, with the same cash flow assumed during the first life cycle. Because the cash flows associated with the subsequent items or projects is assumed to be identical to those of the first item or project, there is no need to repeat them again. The evaluation can be made solely on the cash flows expected during the first service life. Once the length of analysis is determined, a scaled horizontal line 2 to 4 inches long is drawn with tick marks for each month or year, as shown by the horizontal line in Figure 2, which is a CFD for typical capital equipment. Each tick mark represents the end of that period. For example, the tick mark labeled "2" represents the end of year 2.

The next step is to draw vertical arrows corresponding to each cash inflow (benefit) or outflow expected each year. Note that a cash flow diagram is always created for the perspective of one individual or organization. Different entities associated with a transaction may have very different cash flow diagrams for the same transaction. Cash outflow lines are drawn with the arrows pointing down, and inflows

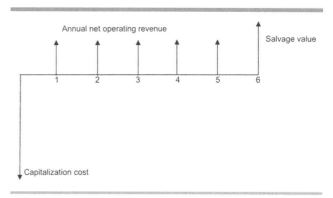

FIGURE 2. Typical cash flow diagram for capital equipment

up. The length of each arrow is scaled to provide a graphical indication of the magnitude of the cash flow it represents. Thus, a $2000 outflow should be twice as long as a $1000 outflow. The amount associated with each arrow is usually shown near the arrowhead. It is traditional to show the total amount of inflows or outflows in a given period at the end of that period. Thus, all cash flows expected during the second year of the investment would be shown by an arrow located at the tick mark labeled "2."

Time Value of Money

One of the assumptions underlying investment decisions, the Western banking system, the stock and bond markets, and essentially all economic systems, is that there is a time value of money. The time value of money refers to the idea that having a certain amount of money now is not the same as having an identical amount of money a few months or years from now. Everyone recognizes this time value of money even without using the term. Someone offered $100 would be happy. If asked whether he wanted it now or a year from now, he would be forced to consider the various pros and cons of having $100 now versus having it a year from now.

Part of the preference reflects the old saying that "a bird in the hand is worth two in the bush." If not given the money now, there is a chance that he will never receive it. But an even more quantifiable reason why one might prefer the $100 now is that he could spend it right away or put it in a savings account at a bank and know that one year from now the money would have accrued interest (money paid by a borrower, such as a bank, for the use of others' money). So if one receives $100 now, he could have more than $100 a year from now. On the other hand, if one does not receive $100 until a year from now, he would clearly only have $100 then.

Opportunity Costs

The simple example above illustrates an important concept related to the time value of money: *opportunity cost*. Money (and any other resource) can be invested today to possibly secure even more tomorrow. The notion of opportunity cost is important whether one is the lender or the receiver. If a person loans someone $100, he can-

not earn bank interest on that money until he is paid back, so he might likely charge the borrower interest to compensate for the bank interest he would otherwise have earned. As a borrower, he recognizes that the lender could have used the money loaned out for other things, so he is willing to return interest for the privilege of having the money. However, the return the lender hopes to receive from the money must outweigh the interest willing to be paid. It would not make sense to borrow money at 10 percent interest so that one could put it in a bank account where it would earn 5 percent interest.

The concept of opportunity costs applies to companies just as much as—if not more than—to individuals. For-profit companies exist for the explicit purpose of earning profits that allow those companies to provide satisfactory returns on investments to their shareholders. Companies may establish many company goals each year, but goals expected to increase net income always top the list. Large and established companies typically have formal, explicit procedures for evaluating new expenditures to increase the chances that all monies spent will increase profit margins. Established companies do this by establishing minimum rates of return or discount rates. The term *discount rate* reflects the fact that all future expenditures or benefits are discounted (or systematically reduced) by an interest rate to be used in project evaluations. The choice of discount rate is discussed later in the chapter.

Equivalency

The concept of a discount rate can be better understood by introducing another new term, *equivalency*. As a simple example, assume that one is offered either $1000 now or $1060 one year from now; and assume that the money is received now and left untouched in a bank account earning 6 percent interest. Either way, one ends up with $1060 one year from now. The two cash flows are considered equivalent. Although they seem to involve different amounts of money ($1000 versus $1060), once the time value of money is considered they are recognized as equivalent.

The formula underlying the time value of money and equivalency is provided in Equation 1.

$$F = P(1 + i)^n \qquad\qquad (1)$$

TABLE 1

Compound Interest Formulas								
Present Worth Factors $(1+i)^n$								

Number of Periods	Interest rate 1%	2%	3%	4%	5%	6%	7%	8%	9%
1	0.990	0.980	0.971	0.962	0.952	0.943	0.935	0.926	0.917
2	0.980	0.961	0.943	0.925	0.907	0.890	0.873	0.857	0.842
3	0.971	0.942	0.915	0.889	0.864	0.840	0.816	0.794	0.772
4	0.961	0.924	0.888	0.855	0.823	0.792	0.763	0.735	0.708
5	0.951	0.906	0.863	0.822	0.784	0.747	0.713	0.681	0.650
6	0.942	0.888	0.837	0.790	0.746	0.705	0.666	0.630	0.596
7	0.933	0.871	0.813	0.760	0.711	0.665	0.623	0.583	0.547
8	0.923	0.853	0.789	0.731	0.677	0.627	0.582	0.540	0.502
9	0.914	0.837	0.766	0.703	0.645	0.592	0.544	0.500	0.460
10	0.905	0.820	0.744	0.676	0.614	0.558	0.508	0.463	0.422
11	0.896	0.804	0.722	0.650	0.585	0.527	0.475	0.429	0.388
12	0.887	0.788	0.701	0.625	0.557	0.497	0.444	0.397	0.356
13	0.879	0.773	0.681	0.601	0.530	0.469	0.415	0.368	0.326
14	0.870	0.758	0.661	0.577	0.505	0.442	0.388	0.340	0.299
15	0.861	0.743	0.642	0.555	0.481	0.417	0.362	0.315	0.275
16	0.853	0.728	0.623	0.534	0.458	0.394	0.339	0.292	0.252
17	0.844	0.714	0.605	0.513	0.436	0.371	0.317	0.270	0.231
18	0.836	0.700	0.587	0.494	0.416	0.350	0.296	0.250	0.212
19	0.828	0.686	0.570	0.475	0.396	0.331	0.277	0.232	0.194
20	0.820	0.673	0.554	0.456	0.377	0.312	0.258	0.215	0.178
21	0.811	0.660	0.538	0.439	0.359	0.294	0.242	0.199	0.164
22	0.803	0.647	0.522	0.422	0.342	0.278	0.226	0.184	0.150
23	0.795	0.634	0.507	0.406	0.326	0.262	0.211	0.170	0.138
24	0.788	0.622	0.492	0.390	0.310	0.247	0.197	0.158	0.126
25	0.780	0.610	0.478	0.375	0.295	0.233	0.184	0.146	0.116

In this equation, F is the amount one will end up with after n years if earning i percent interest on an initial amount P. This equation may initially seem a bit intimidating, but it is very intuitive. If one starts with $1000 and can earn 6 percent interest yearly, he will have $1060 after one year: the original $1000 plus $60 in interest [$1000 + (1000 \times 0.06) = 1060] during the year. Thus the equation for the amount after one year is simply $P(1 + i)$. During the second year, because interest is earned on the amount one started with at the beginning of the year [$P(1 + i)$], one ends up with $P(1 + i)(1 + i)$, which can be written more simply as $P(1 + i)^2$. If this logic is continued, it is not hard to see that the amount accrued after n years is $P(1 + i)^n$. (*Simple interest* arrangements, in which interest is not earned on previously earned interest, will be discussed shortly.)

This equation can also be used in reverse to calculate how much should be invested now (P) in order to end up with F after n years if the interest rate is i percent. This equation defines equivalent cash flows. That is, if the interest rate of i percent is assumed, having P now or F in n years from now are equivalent.

The term $(1 + i)^n$ is referred to as the *single payment discount factor*—written as $(F/P, i, n)$ and read as "Find F given P, i, and n." Because not every calculator has a y^x button, most engineering economics textbooks include the single payment discount factors for different combinations of interest rates (i) and number of time periods (n). Table 1, which was created using a spreadsheet, provides an example. Such tables make it easy to multiply P by the discount factor to calculate F or to divide F by the discount factor to calculate P.

It is important to note that individual cash flows are additive. To calculate how much money one would need to have now if he were going to pay out $2000 at the end of year 3 and $3000 at the end of year 5, simply multiply the amount of each payment by the appropriate discount factor and add the products together. $P = (2000)(0.840) + (3000)(0.748) = \$3921$ for $i = 0.06$ (see Table 1).

Calculating F or P if the cash flow diagram includes a series of uniform cash flows can be accomplished through two methods. One is to follow the procedure in the previous paragraph and add up the products of each cash flow and the appropriate discount factor. An easier way is to use Equation 2:

$$P = A \frac{(1 + i)^n - 1}{i(1 + i)^n} \tag{2}$$

The A in Equation 2 is the amount of the uniform payments (or cash outflows), which are assumed to start in the first year and occur each year through year n. The portion of the equation to the right of the A is the uniform series discount factor, which is abbreviated as $(P/A, i, n)$ and is often tabulated for various combinations of interest rates and number of time periods. Such tables make it relatively easy to calculate how much one would need now to be able to make uniform payments over a specified number of time periods. For example, because the discount factor for a uniform payment over five time periods at an interest rate of 6 percent per time period is 4.212, one would need \$4212 now to make these payments of \$1000 each year.

Arithmetic and Geometric Gradients

There are two additional sets of discount factors that are less common than the single payment or uniform series factors discussed above: *arithmetic gradient* and *geometric gradient*. As the names suggest, both factors reflect gradients, or increasing patterns. Arithmetic gradients increase linearly, such as by 10 percent each time period. (For example, an analysis could include health-insurance costs, which have historically increased by ranges of percentages above inflation.) The equation for calculating the present worth of a cash flow with an arithmetic gradient is provided in Equation 3. Note that these equations assume there is no cash flow during the first year and that the cash flow is G in year 2, $2G$ in year 3, and so on, and $(n - 1)G$ in year n. Geometric gradients increase nonlinearly. The equation

for calculating the present worth of a cash flow with a geometric gradient is provided in Equation 4. Readers who need the equations for gradient series discount factors should refer to Blank and Tarquin (2005), to Newnan, Eschenbach, and Lavelle (2004), or to other engineering economic textbooks.

$$P = G \frac{(1 + i)^n - in - 1}{i^2(1 + i)^n} \tag{3}$$

$$P = A_1 \frac{1 - (1 + g)^n(1 + i)^{-n}}{1 - g} \tag{4}$$

Instead of looking up the appropriate discount factor in a published table or punching the formula into a calculator, one can use financial analysis functions built into most spreadsheets. In *Microsoft Excel*, for example, financial functions include *PV* (present value), *FV* (future value), *PMT* (uniform payment), *NPV* (net present value), and others.

Effective Interest Rate versus Nominal Rate

It is important to note that economic analysis should be based on the *effective interest rate*, not on the *nominal rate*. The nominal rate is typically given in years (as for bank accounts) or months (as for credit cards). The effective rate reflects how often during the nominal time period interest is actually calculated. For example, bank savings accounts are often quoted as "x percent annual interest, compounded quarterly." This means that each quarter, the appropriate prorated interest rate is applied to the account's balance at that time. The principal that earns interest during the second quarter is therefore greater than if interest had not been calculated until the end of the year.

As an example, compare the balance in an account if \$1000 is deposited for three years in a savings account earning 6 percent interest compounded annually instead of quarterly. The single payment discount factors found in tables in the back of engineering economic textbooks make this comparison simple. The discount factor for the account compounded annually is $(F/P, 6\%, n = 3) = 1.191$. The discount factor for the account compounded quarterly is $(F/P, 1.5\%, n = 12) = 1.196$. In this case, the account compounded quarterly would earn \$5.00 during three years, illustrating that when the compounding period is less than a year, it is necessary to divide the nominal rate by the number of compounding periods per year and multiply the number of years by the number of compounding periods per year when using compound interest tables.

The differences between nominal and effective interest rates are related to the differences between simple and compound interest. *Simple interest* is the amount of interest earned with no intermediate compounding. If one borrows $1000 at a 6 percent interest rate for three years, the interest payment at the end of three years is $180 (1000 × 0.06 × 3) under a simple interest arrangement. *Compound interest*, on the other hand, adds interest to the principal at the end of each compounding period. If one borrows $1000 at 6 percent interest for three years, the interest payment at the end of three years is $191 under a quarterly compounded interest arrangement. (The previous paragraph shows that the future value factor was 1.191 for this combination of interest rate and number of time periods).

Future Cash Flows Are Uncertain

The examples used thus far have been simple because they involved interest charged for loans or earned in bank accounts. Interest rates are usually fixed, which means that the cash flows associated with interest payments are precisely known ahead of time. When taking out a car loan, the purchaser knows he will have to pay back a certain amount of money each month (a sum including both a portion of the principal and interest on that portion). Cash flows associated with most investment decisions, however, are not nearly so predictable. The exact amount of cash flows occurring right away are known, but the exact amounts of cash flows in future periods are unknown.

Immediate and Future Cash Flows

But even buying a new car is not as predictable as one might think. When attempting to draw a cash flow diagram for this decision, all immediate and future cash flows should be included. The purchaser should know exactly how large the initial downpayment will be as well as the exact amount of the monthly car-loan

payment. But the cash flow diagram should also include the amounts needed for car insurance, maintenance, gasoline, and similar considerations. Gasoline costs can be predicted with a high degree of certainty during the first year, but costs in future years are less certain: one's travel habits could change, the price of gas may escalate, and so on. Similarly, future maintenance or insurance costs cannot be reliably predicted.

The simple example above illustrates that specific amounts of future cash flows cannot be predicted with certainty unless they are associated with a fixed interest rate or with some type of business contract. Insurance premiums are a form of contract. In the case of health insurance, for example, a firm agrees to pay a specified premium each month, and the health insurance company agrees to pay for the actual costs of providing the firm's employees with major medical healthcare, whether costs are below or above the total premiums. (Employee co-pays and major medical caps are ignored here for simplicity's sake.) But a company's contract with a health insurer typically lasts a year, or less. At the end of that year, the company will have the choice of signing a new contract that will likely include higher premiums. In other words, businesses have no control over price escalation.

Most cash flows associated with investment decisions cannot be fixed through a contract. Going back to the example of hiring a safety manager, even the tangible costs associated with this decision are subject to a high degree of uncertainty. The employer could know with confidence the amounts of salary, fringe benefits, and training costs this person would receive the first year she worked for the company, but the exact amounts for these cost categories are less certain for the second year and even more uncertain for later years. Similarly, even if the employer felt he could quantify the intangible benefits of hiring this person during the first year (reduced accident costs, increased productivity, and other such things), the estimated benefits in future years would be considerably less certain.

Threat of Inflation

Even were it possible to know the benefits of an investment for several years into the future, the threat of *inflation* would still cause the real value of one's future cash flows to be uncertain. Inflation is the economic phenomenon by which labor wages and the prices of most goods rise—which means that a given sum of money will buy less a year from now than it does today. If $50,000 today purchases 50 sets of PPE, $50,000 might only purchase 40 sets of PPE a year from now, if inflation is excessive. Thus, even if it were somehow possible to calculate the amount of cash one will, without question, receive from an investment each year, controlling the actual worth of those dollars' purchasing power is impossible. Thus, inflation will always decrease the actual rate of return for investments involving a sizable initial expense followed by a stream of positive cash flows (such as benefits), because the future positive cash flows will be worth less in terms of real dollars because of inflation. Inflation can also pose an investment risk if benefits inflate at a different rate than costs do. For example, if the benefits of a safety investment included reduced workers' compensation insurance premiums and the costs included a safety manager's salary, the payback in real dollars would be less than the payback in actual dollars if the salary inflated at a greater rate than the insurance premiums did.

Because future cash flows cannot be predicted with certainty, two things should be done when making investment decisions. First, all future cash flows should be discounted, or multiplied by a factor that makes their present worth well below their future nominal amounts. The interest rate or discount rate used in the analysis reflects both the uncertainty of the future cash flows and the opportunity cost. The higher the uncertainty of the future cash flows, the higher the discount rate.

Sensitivity Analysis

Next, sensitivity analysis should be performed. This involves identifying the assumptions underlying the analysis, changing those assumptions, and rerunning the analysis—analyzing how sensitive the outcome is to variation in the assumed cash flows. An investment that looks worthwhile under one set of assumptions may be very unattractive under another set of assumptions. If the likelihood that the second set of

assumptions will turn out to be true is considerable, it should not be ignored. Proper risk-management principles require a manager to at least consider other possible scenarios, and sensitivity analysis is a tool that does this thoroughly and systematically.

For example, when analyzing whether to hire a safety manager, one might run a series of analyses with different rates of escalations in healthcare insurance, with different amounts of productivity increases, and with different discount rates (because the time value of money for the company may change if the prime rate changes). Because sensitivity analysis typically involves a lot of number crunching, it is easiest to enter the estimated cash flows into a spreadsheet, then methodically vary each assumed value individually, noting how each change affects the final value. Table 2 provides an example in which the net result on internal rate of return (discussed shortly) of an investment ranges between 4 and 12 percent, depending

TABLE 2

Sensitivity Analysis			
Health Insurance Increase	Productivity Increase	Discount Rate	Internal Rate of Return
8	1	5	5.2%
10	1	5	5.5%
12	1	5	5.7%
8	2	5	7.8%
10	2	5	8.3%
12	2	5	8.8%
8	3	5	10.4%
10	3	5	11.2%
12	3	5	12.0%
8	1	7	4.6%
10	1	7	4.8%
12	1	7	5.1%
8	2	7	6.9%
10	2	7	7.4%
12	2	7	7.8%
8	3	7	9.2%
10	3	7	9.9%
12	3	7	10.6%
8	1	9	4.0%
10	1	9	4.2%
12	1	9	4.4%
8	2	9	6.0%
10	2	9	6.4%
12	2	9	6.8%
8	3	9	8.0%
10	3	9	8.6%
12	3	9	9.2%

on whether healthcare insurance is assumed to increase by 8, 10, or 12 percent, productivity is assumed to increase by 1, 2, or 3 percent, and the discount rate is assumed to be 5, 7, or 9 percent. By estimating the likelihood of each possible situation (for example, that there is a 20 percent chance that healthcare will increase 12 percent per year), one can determine the risk that the actual return on investment will turn out considerably less than expected. If performing a manual sensitivity analysis such as the one in Table 2 seems somewhat tedious, one may wish to consider using the Scenarios tool in *Microsoft Excel*.

Expected Value

The previous paragraphs have indicated that most cash flows and other outcomes associated with safety investments cannot be predicted with certainty and that effective managers will consider the possible outcomes of their decisions. This discussion emphasizes the risk that underlies all management decisions. Managers make decisions based on the predicted outcomes of their chosen courses of action. The fact that the actual outcomes may vary significantly from those predicted means that the decision may appear, in hindsight, to have been the wrong choice. The final fundamental concept is *expected value*, a rational method for making risky decisions.

The expected value of a choice is the value of the sum of each possible outcome multiplied by the probability associated with each outcome. For example, if a friend offers to flip a coin and the winner pays the other $1, the expected outcome would be the probability of a head (0.5, or 50 percent) multiplied by the outcome of a head (winning $1) plus the probability of a tail (50 percent) multiplied by the outcome of a tail (losing $1). The expected value of this bet therefore equals $(0.5)(+1) + (0.5)(–1)$, which equals zero, meaning that one should not really care if he takes the bet or not. One might be ahead or behind if he took this bet several times, but over the long run, the heads and tails would balance out and one would end up even.

The next calculation is for the expected value of a slightly more complicated choice: whether to hire a safety inspector. (Note that this analysis will be grossly

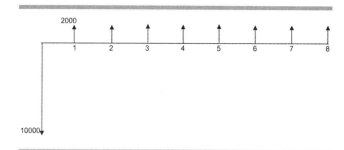

FIGURE 3. Payback-period example

oversimplified for this example.) Assuming that the company will definitely incur total costs of $100,000 per year for salary, fringe benefits, office space, and other such expenses, an employer estimates there is a 25 percent probability that this person will be totally ineffective and result in no benefit at all to the company; a 50 percent probability that this person will result in productivity savings of $100,000; and a 25 percent probability that the inspector will make a bigger difference, resulting in a total savings of $250,000. Should the inspector be hired? A risk-averse manager might focus on the admittedly significant chance (25 percent) that the person may be a complete loss, costing the company $100,000, but a smart manager will recognize that the expected value of this inspector is positive: $(1)(–100,000) + (0.25)(0) + (0.5)(100,000) + (0.25)(250,000) = \$12,500$. Because this number is significantly positive, the inspector should be hired.

Real-world decisions are much more complicated than the oversimplified example above, but expected value still represents a tool that managers can use to make rational decisions. Managers often make irrational choices because they focus excessively on one aspect of a decision, such as the risk that the worst possible outcome may occur. Expected value can be a helpful tool for forcing managers to methodically consider *all* outcomes—not just the ones that may make managers look particularly good or exceptionally bad.

INVESTMENT ANALYSIS METHODS

Now that the fundamental concepts underlying engineering economics and financial analysis have been presented, it is time to introduce the specific analytical techniques that can be applied to make effective decisions about safety investments. As stated at the beginning of this chapter, these concepts and techniques can be appropriately applied to nearly all investment decisions, whether safety management is involved or not.

Payback Period

The simplest but least-effective analytical technique is *payback period*. The payback-period procedure involves simply determining the earliest point in time when cash outflows are exceeded by cash inflows. Assume, for example, a safety project that cost $10,000 to implement in year 0 and provided benefits of $2000 each year indefinitely. The cash flow diagram for this project is shown in Figure 3. The payback period for this investment would be five years because, by the end of the fifth year, the initial outlay would have been offset by the cumulative annual savings.

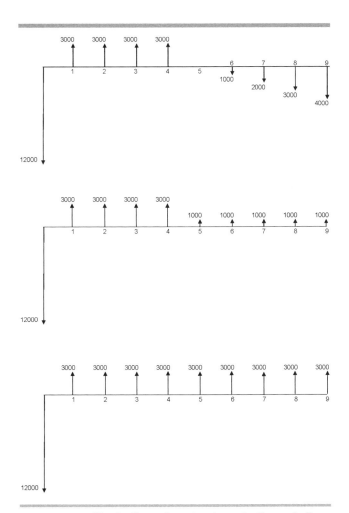

FIGURE 4. Illustration of payback period's cash flow projection shortcomings

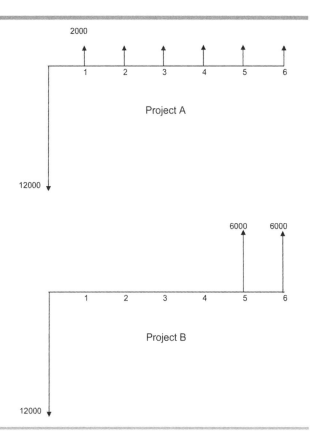

FIGURE 5. Illustration of payback period's benefit-cost shortcomings

The primary strength of the payback-period method is its simplicity. One hardly even needs a calculator to do the math. Another strength is that it captures the question that some managers first ask about a candidate investment: "How soon before I get my money back?"

The weaknesses of the payback period are severe. Most fundamentally, it ignores all cash flows after the time when total cash inflows equal total cash outflows. Consider the three cash flow diagrams shown in Figure 4, all of which are from the perspective of the same firm. All three projects have a payback period of four years, but the cash flows that occur after year 4 are clearly very different. Project A has a very negative cash flow after year 4, Project B has a decent cash flow after year 4, and Project C has a very attractive net cash flow after year 4. Yet the payback-period approach would rate all three projects as being equally attractive.

Another major weakness of the payback period is that it ignores the time value of money. Consider, for example, the two cash flow diagrams in Figure 5.

Both projects have a payback period of 6 years, but Project A's cash inflows start immediately while Project B's cash inflows do not occur until year 5. Clearly, the early cash inflows from Project A could be invested right away to earn interest or other types of earnings, making it more attractive than Project B.

A third weakness of the payback period is that it does not indicate how attractive a project is. Projects A and B in Figure 6 both have the same payback period, but Project B is clearly more attractive than Project A because the amount of cash inflow in the fifth year is twice that of Project A.

Break-Even Analysis

Break-even analysis is in some ways similar to payback period and in other ways is quite dissimilar. It resembles payback period because both methods involve determining a point where the incremental benefits (periodic cash inflows) first offset the initial costs (cash outflows). However, when reckoning with payback period in mind, the initial costs are the capitalization costs, and the cash inflows are associated with each time period. When reckoning with break-even analysis, the initial costs tend to be fixed costs, and the incremental benefits are variable cash inflows associated with each unit sold, or are otherwise associated with the initial costs.

The decision about whether to hire a full-time safety inspector could serve as an example. The new hire's salary and fringe benefits are clearly fixed costs associated with the decision. To the extent that the mere circumstance of having a full-time safety inspector resulted in a certain number of additional sales to clients who value safety, one set of benefits accruing from this hire would be fixed. On the other hand, another set of benefits accruing from having this employee would likely be variable, because each labor hour worked by the company should have a lower chance of an accident and, therefore, eventually result in a lower workers' compensation insurance premium. An appropriate break-even analysis should calculate the direct labor payroll the company needed to offset the safety inspectors' fixed costs, less fixed benefits.

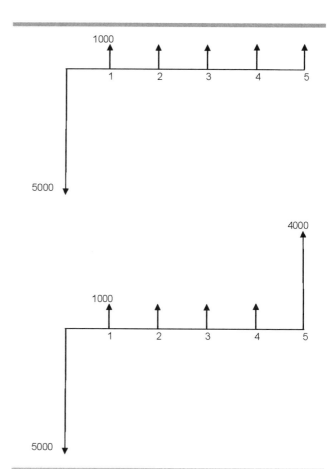

FIGURE 6. Illustration of the payback period's shortcomings when measuring project attractiveness

Assume that the total fixed costs associated with having a safety inspector are $100,000; that simply having an inspector results in $40,000 of additional profit; and that the workers' compensation reduction, per $100 of payroll, is $25. The break-even analysis would therefore be $0 = -\$100,000 + \$40,000 + (0.25 \times \text{payroll})$. Solving for payroll in this equation indicates that the break-even payroll is $240,000 per year. Therefore, if the company's total labor payroll is less than $240,000 annually, the company did not break even by hiring the inspector. On the other hand, every $100 of payroll over $240,000 yearly means that the hire was even more beneficial.

Benefit-Cost Ratio

Another common analytical method is the *benefit-cost* ratio (B/C), the method, which has historically been required for all large projects involving federal funds. The best aspect of this method is its simplicity:

dividing the sum of all of the benefits associated with an investment by the sum of all of its costs. Projects with a benefit-cost ratio greater than 1 are typically acceptable. But this simple application of BCR analysis shares a common critical flaw with the payback period: the time value of money is ignored. Consider the two projects in Figure 6. Both projects have a benefit-cost ratio of 1.0, but Project A is clearly more attractive than Project B because the benefits accrue shortly after the outlays. If the cash inflows from project A were put into a savings account as soon as they were received, one would end up with a higher amount at year 5 than if project B had been chosen.

The flaw in the simplest benefit-cost analysis technique discussed above can be resolved by including discounted cash flows—in other words, by including benefits and costs that have been multiplied by appropriate factors of present–future worth.

Internal Rate of Return

The analysis of the *internal rate of return* (IRR) is a powerful, precise tool for evaluating candidate investments. The process identifies the timing and amounts of all cash flows, then uses a spreadsheet, a programmable calculator, or specialized software to calculate the interest rate that would make the outgoing cash flows equivalent to the incoming cash flows. Many companies establish a minimum acceptable rate of return and reject any projects that have a projected IRR lower than their minimum acceptable rate of return.

The main advantage of the IRR method over the payback-period and benefit-cost-ratio methods is that it reflects the time value of money. Another strength of the IRR method is that it provides an objective way to compare one acceptable project against another. For example, all other things being equal, a project with an IRR of 10 percent is clearly superior to a project with an IRR of 8 percent.

The main disadvantage of the IRR method is that it is somewhat difficult to explain to individuals lacking backgrounds in financial analysis, and it is very difficult to calculate without a specialized computational tool such as the IRR function in *Excel*. A lesser-known weakness of IRR is that a series of cash flows may have

TABLE 3

Spreadsheet Internal Rate of Return Analysis of Figure 6			
Year	Cash Flow	Year	Cash Flow
0	−5000	0	-5000
1	1000	1	1000
2	1000	2	1000
3	1000	3	1000
4	1000	4	1000
5	1000	5	1000
IRR	0% = IRR (B6:B11)		14% = IRR (E6:E11)

more than one IRR (although this is rarely a problem, because few cash flows have U-shaped patterns).

Table 3 shows the contents of a spreadsheet used to calculate the IRR of the cash flow diagrams in Figure 6. The contents of the IRR cell have been pasted to show that the IRR function has been applied to cells B6 through B11 and E6 through E11, resulting in IRR values of 0 and 14 percent, respectively.

Net Present Worth

The financial analysis method most widely accepted today is *net present worth*, which is sometimes referred to simply as *present value*. It involves summing the discounted cash flows—that is, adding the product of each future cash flow and the appropriate discount factor. Outgoing cash flows are negative, and incoming cash flows are positive. Projects with net present worth greater than 0 are considered worthwhile.

One advantage of this method over the payback-period and benefit-cost-ratio methods is that it reflects the time value of money. Indeed, the choice of the exact value of money over time (the discount rate or interest rate) is the most important decision that must be made in the analysis. The higher the discount rate chosen, the higher the discount factors associated with each cash flow. (Note how the discount factors in Table 1 decrease as the interest rate increases.) In other words, the higher the assumed interest rate, the less future cash flows affect the net present worth. The discount factor for a single payment five years in the future is 0.822 if a 4 percent interest rate is assumed and 0.621 if a 10 percent interest rate is assumed.

Given that the discount rate chosen has such a significant effect on the results of a net present worth analysis, it is important to choose wisely. As stated earlier, most companies establish a minimum rate of return and dictate that this number be used as the discount rate in all financial analysis. Some companies choose a discount rate that reflects the interest rate at which they can borrow money. (If a project cannot even generate enough cash inflows to cover the cost of borrowing the money used to fund it, it is certainly not worthwhile.) Most companies establish a discount rate equal to what they see as their true opportunity costs, or the highest rate of return that the company could obtain by investing it in other projects, or even in other companies. Sophisticated financial analysts use a method called the capital assets pricing model (CAPM) to establish their discount rate. CAPM is powerful and logical, reflecting the special risk that a project represents relative to the risk inherent in the company's existing portfolio; but it is more complicated than is necessary for most safety-investment decisions.

Annual Cost Analysis

Like present worth analysis, this method uses discount factors to adjust each future cash flow based on the assumed time value of money. Unlike NPW, which brings all of the cash flows back to year 0, this method calculates the equivalent net costs or benefits on an annual basis. It is a preferred method for managers, who evaluate projects by asking, "How much will this cost me (or benefit me) each year?"

Rather than using the discount factors that apply to present or future worth, this method uses discount factors that apply to uniform series. Another name for this analysis is the equivalent annual benefit and cost analysis, because all cash flows are converted to their equivalent in terms of an annually recurring amount. The formula for calculating the discount factor associated with converting a future cash flow (F) to an equivalent annual amount is given in Equation 5. Note that this equation assumes the annual cash flows begin in year 1 and continue through year n. As such, there will be two cash flows in year n, A and F. Most

engineering economic textbooks include these factors in their compound interest tables.

$$(A/F, i, n) = \frac{1}{(1 + i)^n - 1} \quad (5)$$

As an example, compare the Equivalent Annual Costs of the two cash flow diagrams seen in Figure 5. $EUAC_A = (-12,000 \times 0.2034) + 2000 = -440.80$. $EUAC_B = (-12,000 \times 0.2034) + (6000 \times 0.1774) + (6000 \times 0.1434) = -516.00$. Because project A has a lower negative annual cost, it is more attractive than project B.

INTRODUCTION TO BUDGETING

The chapter thus far has discussed fundamental economic analysis assumptions and tools for analyzing whether to pursue specific safety investments. Once the decision has been made to pursue a project, the budgeting process should occur. A budget is a financial plan that establishes specific amounts of cash (and sometimes employee hours) that are expected to be spent on specific activities. Budgeting accomplishes a number of related purposes discussed very briefly below.

Budgeting is a form of *prioritization*. By establishing a budget for a safety-related expenditure, one is securing management approval for this expenditure and is decreasing the chance that unexpected cash flow problems, or a manager's bad day, will prevent a planned safety expenditure from taking place.

Budgeting is an important part of *cost control*. Expenditures should be tracked and compared against expected expenditures for each point in time. Significant differences between actual and expected expenditures indicate either poor tracking (in that actual expenditures are not being assigned to the correct budget item), unexpected circumstances, or poor initial estimation and budgeting. This indicates that budgeting is part of the Plan–Do–Check–Act (PDCA) cycle of process improvement. Budgets are part of the short-term operational *plan*. This plan is then executed as the *do* step. During operational execution, management should *check* by comparing actual expenditures to planned expenditures. If a significant difference exists between the two, managers *act*, resolving any unforeseen problems and, if necessary, adjusting future budgets to prevent future deviations from plans.

Budgeting is an important part of decision making. A manager must estimate the costs to include in an economic analysis. This estimate usually forms the basis for one's budget. But decision making does not end once the budget is established. If actual expenditures significantly exceed planned expenditures at any time, it may be appropriate to reevaluate the entire project. Many managers forget that *sunk costs* should be disregarded in decision making. They subconsciously think that if they have invested money in a project, the project must be pursued at all costs, feeling that abandoning the project indicates that their initial decision to pursue the project was flawed. In some cases, the initial decision *was* flawed—and continuing to pursue the project will only compound the problem. Heed the maxim and "don't throw good money after bad." Managers should ignore what has been spent in the past (sunk costs) and only continue to pursue a project if the revised estimate of *future* costs is outweighed by revised estimates of future benefits.

The Budgeting Process

Safety engineering expenditures are typically associated with one-time projects, not with recurring expenditures. Nevertheless, project expenses must always be included in a company's annual budget. Company budgets are typically established for the company's fiscal year, which may end on December 31, June 30, or September 30. The process of establishing the company budget typically is begun approximately midway through a fiscal year and is completed several months before its end.

The overall expenditure associated with a safety engineering project is typically broken down into a number of specific items to facilitate cost control and project management. For example, a project may be broken down into discrete tasks, each with an obvious beginning and end. The budget for each task is often further broken down into labor, materials, equipment, and, sometimes, overhead. Actual expenses for similar items on past projects may be used to help establish the budget for each item. Because budgets

are often managed by sophisticated cost-accounting software, each cost item is typically assigned a unique cost code or number used both for entering and reporting purposes. Such account codes eliminate the need for entering awkwardly long word descriptions. In construction and other industries, this numbering system is often referred to as the *work breakdown system*.

Depending on the industry, the company, and the cost-accounting software used, overhead costs associated with a task may be budgeted and tracked as individual cost items or as part of an overall overhead mark up. For example, the salary of a safety project manager may be budgeted as a specific cost item or simply included in an overall overhead percentage that is applied to the budgeted direct costs.

It was mentioned earlier that an important step in cost control is the comparison of actual costs with expected costs at various points during a project's execution. It should be noted that it is often appropriate to identify the pattern over time associated with each cost item. Many project costs are not incurred over time in linear fashion. For example, project labor costs typically exhibit an S shape as costs are initially incurred slowly, then rapidly increase as the crew becomes productive, and then decrease as the project nears completion. Other project costs may occur at discrete intervals, such as the ends of fiscal-year quarters. Managers who assume that cost items will be incurred uniformly over a time period in cases when actual costs occur nonlinearly may make unnecessary and inappropriate cost-control decisions.

The Dark Side of Budgeting

Although budgeting is an important administrative process in all organizations, organizational budgeting also has its "dark side." How future cash flows almost always hold some degree of uncertainty, as discussed earlier, means there is always a risk that the best estimates of future costs may be low. Most managers understandably want to reduce that risk by proposing a budget that includes a contingency amount; but two problems arise when including such buffers in budgets. One problem is that allocating contingency resources to a budget prevents those resources from being used for other good projects. A second and even worse problem is that many managers will attempt to hide their overbudgeting by inefficiently spending any remaining funds as the end of the fiscal year approaches.

It should be obvious from this chapter that decisions about budget allocation should be based on which projects will provide the greatest return on investment to the company as a whole. Another dark side of budgeting is that some managers propose excessively large budgets, because the larger the budgets they manage, the more status, power, security, and salary they personally can enjoy. Because managers enjoying power and status typically are loathe to brook any reduction, it is not uncommon for managers to submit budgets for the next year that are based mostly on similar budgets in years past. In recent decades, a process called zero-based budgeting has emerged to combat such budget inertia. Instead of assuming that each project or manager will receive approximately the budget they had previously, managers and projects are assumed to have no budget until they justify in detail why they should receive any funds at all.

CONCLUSION

Successful safety professionals should be able to identify which safety-related initiatives represent good investments for their organizations. This chapter has provided fundamental financial analysis concepts—such as the time value of money, direct and indirect costs and benefits, and the uncertainty of future cash flows—that safety managers should integrate into their decisions and their communications with superiors. This chapter has summarized five objective methods of economic analysis commonly used to evaluate investments: payback period, benefit-cost ratio, rate of return, net present worth, and annual cost analyses. Payback period and benefit-cost-ratio analyses were identified as inferior methods because they fail to consider the time value of money. Sensitivity analysis was identified as an important step in the decision process because it requires a methodical consideration of the possible variations in cash flows and of whether such variations dramatically change the outcome of the analysis.

Acknowledgments

The help of Dr. Tim Bushnell at NIOSH in identifying relevant literature, as well as comments of three anonymous reviewers, were much appreciated for the first edition.

REFERENCES

Adams, S. "Financial Management Concepts: Making the Bottom-Line Case for Safety." *Professional Safety* (August 2002), pp. 23–26.

American Society of Safety Engineers (ASSE). 2002. *The Return on Investment for Safety, Health, and Environmental (SH&E) Management Programs* (accessed June 11, 2010). www.asse.org/practicespecialties/bosc/bosc_article_6.php

Behm, M., A. Veltri, and I. Kleinsorge. "The Cost of Safety." *Professional Safety* (April 2004), pp. 22–29.

Bird, F. E. 1996. *Safety and the Bottom Line*. Loganville, GA: Institute Publishing.

Blank, L., and A. Tarquin. 2005. *Engineering Economy*. 6th ed. New York: McGraw-Hill.

Brady, W., J. Bass, R. Moser, Jr., G. W. Anstadt, R. R. Loeppke, and R. Leopold. 1997. "Defining Total Corporate Health and Safety Costs—Significance and Impact." *Journal of Occupational and Environmental Medicine* 39(3):224–231.

Brandt, J. 1999. "Hitting the Injury Iceberg." *Ergonomics Supplement*, pp. 160–165.

Brody, B., Y. Letorneau, and A. Poirer. 1990. "An Indirect Cost Theory of Work Accident Prevention." *Journal of Occupational Accidents* 13(4):255–270.

Hinze, J. 2000. "Incurring the Costs of Injuries Versus Investing in Safety." In *Construction Safety and Health Management*. Edited by R. J. Coble et al. New York: Prentice-Hall.

Kinn, S., S. A. Khuder, M. S. Besesi, and S. Woolley. 2000. "Evaluation of Safety Orientation and Training Programs for Reducing Injuries in the Plumbing and Pipefitting Industries." *Journal of Occupational and Environmental Medicine* 42:1142–1147.

Labelle, J. A. "What do Accidents Truly Cost?" *Professional Safety* (April 2002), pp. 38–42.

Lanoie, P., and S. Tavenas. 1996. "Costs and Benefits of Preventing Workplace Accidents: The Case of Participatory Ergonomics." *Safety Science* 24(3):181–196.

Leigh, J. P., S. Markowitz, M. Fahs, and P. Landrigan. 2000. *Costs of Occupational Injuries and Illnesses*. University of Michigan Press.

Linhard, J. B. 2005. "Understanding the return on health, safety and environmental investments." *Journal of Safety Research*, ECON proceedings 36:257–260.

National Institute for Occupational Safety and Health. 2004. *Does It Really Work? How to Evaluate Safety and Health Changes in the Workplace* (last accessed June 13, 2010). U.S. Department of Health and Human Services (DHHS), NIOSH Pub. No. 2004-135. Available for download at www.cdc.gov/niosh/docs/2004-135/

Newnan, D. G., T. G. Eschenbach, and J. P. Lavelle. 2004. *Engineering Economic Analysis*, 9th ed. New York: Oxford University Press USA.

Occupational Safety and Health Administration. 2010. *Making the Business Case for Safety and Health* (accessed June 11, 2010). www.osha.gov/dcsp/products/topics/businesscase/index.html

_____. 2010. OSHA's "$AFETY PAYS" Program (accessed June 11, 2010). www.osha.gov/dcsp/smallbusiness/safetypays/index.html

_____. 2010. "Safety & Health Management Systems eTool" (accessed June 11, 2010). www.osha.gov/SLTC/etools/safetyhealth/mod1_costs.html

_____. 2010. *Safety Success Stories* (accessed June 11, 2010). www.osha.gov/dcsp/compliance_assistance/success_stories.html

Occupational Safety and Health Administration, Abbott Laboratories and Georgetown University Center for Business and Public Policy. 2005. "The Business Case for Safety: Adding Value and Competitive Advantage" (powerpoint file) (accessed June 12, 2010). www.osha.gov/dcsp/success_stories/compliance_assistance/abbott/abbott_casestudies/index.html

Oxenbaugh, M., P. Marlow, and A. Oxenbaugh. 2004. *Increasing Productivity and Profit through Health & Safety*. London: CRC Press.

Veltri, A., and J. Ramsay. 2009. "Economic Analysis: Make the Business Case for SH&E." *Professional Safety* 54(9):22–30.

Veltri, A, M. Pagell, M. Behm, and A. Das. 2007. "A Data-Based Evaluation of the Relationship between Occupational Safety and Operating Performance." *Professional Safety* 49(1):1–21.

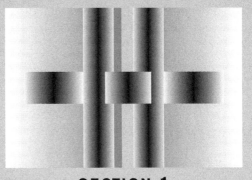

SECTION 1

**MANAGEMENT
OF SAFETY
ENGINEERING WORK**

LEARNING OBJECTIVES

- Develop various leading, trailing, and current indicators that can be used to assess a safety program activity.

- Develop an effective safety performance measurement program designed to address a safety issue in the workplace.

- Evaluate the performance of a safety program activity using a variety of measurement techniques.

- Incorporate a continual improvement process into safety performance activities in the workplace.

BENCHMARKING AND PERFORMANCE CRITERIA

Christopher Janicak

A QUESTION OFTEN POSED by a safety manager is "Are my safety activities working?" Safety performance should be evaluated in an organization in the same manner as productivity and other aspects of the business. Areas to evaluate include determining the overall effectiveness of a particular intervention, where a company's safety performance stands with regard to other companies, identifying potential impediments to safety success, and determining the trends in accidents and losses over time.

An integral part of any safety activity should include techniques for developing goals and objectives, collecting data to measure the success of the safety interventions, evaluating the results, and implementing the appropriate corrective action. The manner in which safety performance is measured can range from developing safety performance measures unique to a particular organization to using existing performance measures and standards to benchmarks derived from similar industries and organizations.

Regardless of the approach, the measurement and evaluation of safety performance requires a carefully structured program of planning, establishing goals and objectives, identifying valid measures, conducting proper data analysis, and implementing appropriate follow-up measures.

INTERVENTION EFFECTIVENESS

The overall effectiveness of the safety program in reducing accidents, controlling losses, and improving the overall working conditions in an organization is contingent upon a number of aspects, all of which are interrelated. These aspects can be broken down into seven main categories (Swartz 2000, 42):

1. Management commitment and support
2. Employee participation

199

3. Control or elimination of hazards
4. Integration of safety and health throughout the organization
5. Job safety analyses (JSAs)
6. Employees who are selected and trained for their positions
7. Safety and health professionals who are up to date on scientific, technical and regulatory, and legislative knowledge.

Incorporating these strategies into a safety intervention program can increase overall effectiveness and lead to measurable outcomes. Management commitment and support includes having adequate financial resources and staffing for safety. To gain acceptance of safety activities and to provide input into solutions, employee participation is vital for any successful safety intervention. Employee participation in a safety metrics program can involve defining safety performance measures, collecting data, and developing countermeasures to help the organization improve.. The key to the success of a safety intervention is the organization's ability to identify and correct hazards through the use of a well-structured hazard recognition, evaluation, and elimination program. Finally, a safety program cannot function adequately if it is disassociated from the rest of the activities in the organization. Safety should be integrated into all aspects of the company's activities, assigning responsibilities for meeting the safety goals and objectives to all employees.

Along with the identification and control of physical hazards in the workplace, the identification and control of unsafe job procedures is equally important. Job hazard analyses (JHAs) involve the identification and elimination of hazards associated with the job tasks in the workplace. JHAs are also useful in developing safe job procedures used in training new employees. Performing safe job procedures requires training across all aspects of safety in the workplace, from the safety procedures for performing a job task to the procedures necessary to implement various interventions, such as hazard recognition programs and emergency response procedures.

Finally, managing safety in the workplace requires specialized managerial and technical skills. The overall administration of safety requires someone who is knowledgeable in the technical, managerial, and legal aspects of safety.

SAFETY MANAGEMENT SYSTEM

The effectiveness of any safety intervention can be tied to two main aspects of the overall safety program: the existence of a safety management system and an organizational culture that is supportive of the safety efforts. The Occupational Safety and Health Administration (OSHA) defines a safety management system as being comprised of four areas, all of which are necessary for a safety and health program to be effective in meeting its goals and objectives. The components of the safety and health management system include management leadership, employee involvement, work-site analysis, hazard prevention and control activities, and safety and health training (OSHA 2004a).

Management Leadership and Employee Involvement

Without management leadership for safety, a safety program can be almost guaranteed to be ineffective. Through their actions, members of senior management display the importance that safety plays in an organization. Including safety performance as part of the overall organizational goals is one way management conveys this importance. If safety is not perceived by the employees to be important to management, then it will almost certainly not be seen as being important by the workers. Where management has placed safety on a par with other functions, they must be genuinely committed to following through or employees will not abide by company policies (Swartz 2000, 42). Getting employees involved in the development and implementation of safety program tasks increases the chances that their programs will be accepted and followed by the employees.

Work-Site Analysis

Work-site analysis involves the identification of hazards with the goal of correcting hazardous conditions before an accident occurs. Tools to consider as part of the work-site analysis include conducting property hazard assessments, environmental audits, accident investigations, and job hazard analyses, and analyzing accident data. Proactive safety programs are implemented with the goal of preventing potential accidents and the losses from those accidents before they occur. Reactive safety programs, on the other hand, focus their attention on activities aimed specifically at the causal factors attributed to accidents and losses that have already occurred.

Hazard Prevention and Control

Hazard prevention and control includes those program components designed to prevent accidents from occurring, and the components intended to minimize their severity should an accident occur. Examples of programs aimed at hazard prevention and control include preventive maintenance programs and emergency preparedness. A recognized hierarchy for hazard control is elimination, substitution, engineering, warning, administrative action, and the use of personal protective equipment (PPE) (ANSI 2005).

Safety and Health Training

The fourth component of a safety management system is safety and health training. The training should ensure that employees at all levels of the organization are aware of safety and health policies and procedures that may impact them. Additionally, task-specific safety and health training should be provided to employees with unique exposures to hazards on the job.

To evaluate the safety and health management system, OSHA has developed, as part of their outreach programs, an evaluation tool referred to as the Safety and Health Program Assessment Worksheet (OSHA Form 33). As part of the assessment, consultants review an employer's existing safety and health management program to identify elements considered adequate and elements that need development or improvement. To assist employers in meeting their training obligations, OSHA published the training requirements in *OSHA Standards and Training Guidelines* (OSHA 1998). This document provides employers with

guidance on how to identify training needs, develop a training program, and evaluate the effectiveness of the program.

Components of a Comprehensive Safety and Health Program

The components identified as necessary for a comprehensive safety and health program include the following (OSHA 2008b):

1. Hazard anticipation and detection programs, including hazard surveys, self-inspections, and accident investigations
2. Hazard prevention and control measures, including the use of engineering controls, personal protective equipment, emergency response plans, and adequate medical care for employees
3. Planning and evaluation programs, including data collection and analysis methods, development of safety goals and objectives, and a review of the overall safety and health management system
4. Administration and supervision activities, including coordination of safety and health program activities, accountability mechanisms, and safety responsibilities communicated to those who must perform the duties
5. Safety and health training, encompassing new employee orientations, supervisor safety training, and management safety training
6. Management leadership and commitment is vital to the success of any safety program. Performance measures include adequate resource allocation for safety and top management involvement in the planning and evaluation of safety performance.
7. Effective safety performance requires employee participation in all areas of the planning, evaluation, and implementation of safety program tasks. Employee involvement can take on many forms, including employees involved in the decision-making process for safety, and participation in the detection and control of hazards.

Occupational Safety and Health Management System Cycle

The *American National Standard for Occupational Health and Safety Management Systems* (ANSI/AIHA A10) defines an occupational health and safety management-system cycle as an initial planning process and the implementation of the management system, followed by a process for checking the performance of these activities and taking appropriate corrective actions (AIHA 2005). This is then followed by a management review of the system for suitability, adequacy, and effectiveness against its policy and the ANSI standard (AIHA 2005).

Components of this cycle include the plan-do-check-act cycle along with management leadership and employee participation, management planning activities, implementation, checking and corrective action, and management review (AIHA 2005).

The purpose of this cycle is to ensure that continuous improvement activities are systematically incorporated into the organization's management functions, resulting in a coordinated effort to continually improve safety performance.

SAFETY CULTURE

An organization's culture consists of its values, beliefs, legends, rituals, mission, goals, performance measures, and sense of responsibility to its employees, customers, and community, all of which are translated into a system of expected behavior (Swartz 2000, 18). The safety culture of an organization defines how the organization values and perceives safety in the workplace. This safety culture plays an important role in determining the success of safety and health activities. If management promotes a culture in which safety is perceived as not being important to the organization, then the employees will perceive safety as something that is not important. It is the organization's culture that determines whether the safety program as a whole will be effective. An assessment of the safety culture should include asking questions such as the following (Weinstein 1997, 24):

- Is there a strong safety culture established with no tolerance for unsafe practices?
- Is the cultural goal zero injuries?
- Are health and safety procedures followed all the time?
- Is there a vision of a safe work environment, and do all employees share in it?
- Do employees value safe behavior, themselves, and their continued well-being?
- Is the management style and culture nonautocratic with a win-win atmosphere?
- Is there a trusting relationship between management and employees?
- Do employees believe that safety is a company priority?

In organizations with a strong safety culture, the following characteristics exist (Weinstein 1997, 24):

- Executives and managers visibly support safety with no contradictory decisions, and they accept full accountability.
- Employees are involved with safety and their views are sought and acted upon.
- Supervisors' actions support safety, including recognizing and appreciating safe work practices and behaviors.

It is accepted in the safety profession that there is a relationship between an organization's culture and safety performance and that the organization's culture can be measured and managed (Swartz 2000, 82–83; Mohamed 2000, 384). Methods used to measure the safety culture in an organization include employee surveys directed at their perceptions about management leadership for safety, reinforcement by management to report hazards, employee attitudes and perceptions about safety, how employees view the management and supervision of safety, and whether they feel there is a real and genuine commitment for safety.

MEASURING SAFETY EFFECTIVENESS

In occupational safety and health, the need for a particular intervention can be determined by legislation in which a regulation stipulates that a particular safety and health activity be provided in addition to other areas not regulated by standards, such as ergonomics. It can also be determined by analysis and investigation. For example, an analysis of the work site and loss data may indicate the need to prevent back injuries. Once the intervention is in place, many times a more difficult question presents itself: "Is the safety intervention working?"

The methods safety professionals use to answer this question vary widely. Some companies count the number of people injured at the end of the year, and others may use a continuous improvement process. As with any intervention in the workplace, an organization must determine if the activities implemented are effective in meeting the organization's goals and objectives. Safety activities are no different than any other business activities. Over the years, it has become more commonplace for the safety professional to tie safety activities to results in an effort to show how improving safety activities equates to improving business operations.

Historically, the effectiveness of a safety activity has been measured in terms of the number of accidents incurred, the organization's OSHA recordable incidence rates, the dollars spent on accidents, and the costs for insurance coverage. There is no one way to measure safety and health program effectiveness; rather, a systems approach is necessary (Swartz 2000, 98). These multiple methods for measuring safety performance include an approach in which leading, trailing, and current indicators are used.

As methods for continual improvement evolved in the workplace along with statistical process control, the safety profession has slowly moved toward some of these methods now routinely used in other aspects of the organization's management structure. Safety managers are increasingly held accountable for their activities and must show management how their activities positively impact the organization.

With an ever-increasingly global economy, and international standards becoming the framework by which management practices are designed and monitored, safety practices have evolved to systems approaches for continual improvement. An organization must accurately and validly assess where they are in terms of their safety performance, how they decide where they would like to be, and what needs to be done to get there (Petersen 1996, 3).

In recent years, much research has been conducted to evaluate the effectiveness of interventions designed to improve safety performance (Al-Mutairi and Haight 2009, Iyer et al. 2004). Through modeling techniques and statistical analysis, it is possible to optimize the effects of the the safety and health interventions by decreasing injury rates and property damage with less costly programs.

Valid Measurements

Measuring safety performance is a critical step in the safety performance improvement process. The purpose of safety performance measurement is to determine if the goals and objectives have been met. The measures selected to monitor and evaluate safety performance must be valid and reliable. Valid performance measures are measures that are true indicators of performance. There must be a relationship between what is being measured and safety performance.

Because follow-up action is planned and implemented based on the outcomes of the performance measures, it is only logical that the corrective actions are also valid means for improving performance. For example, a safety manager determined that an indicator of the number of cumulative trauma disorder (CTD) injuries reported was the number of employees that successfully completed CTD injury prevention training. Using this measure, the safety manager tracked the number of employees trained each month and the number of CTD injuries reported. The safety manager found that as the number of employees in the facility trained on CTD injuries increased, so did the number of CTDs reported, indicating that the training was unsuccessful in reducing the number of injuries.

What the safety manager failed to take into account was the fact that the training also included early symptom reporting procedures and information about the early symptoms of CTD injuries. Thus, using the completion of CTD training as an indicator of CTD injury prevention may not be considered a valid measure because the training introduced a confounding factor—the early reporting of CTD symptoms. Variables confounding in data research are variables whose individual effects upon an outcome cannot be readily measured. In some cases, statistical procedures may be used to control for this confounding.

Another important trait of any measure used to evaluate safety performance is *reliability*. The reliability of a performance measure is the consistency of results obtained through the measurement. This consistency means that the same results are obtained when the measurement is taken multiple times. A measurement used to describe the number of CTD injuries suffered must be well-defined to ensure the reliability of the data collected. An unreliable measure can yield different numbers when measured by different people. Data must first be proven to be reliable before it can be evaluated for validity. Otherwise stated, unreliable data is always considered invalid. Reliable data may or may not be valid.

Reliability of data can be statistically evaluated using a variety of techniques. Two examples of these methods include the test-retest method and the split-half method. In the test-retest method, a performance indicator is measured multiple times. If the measurements are highly correlated, meaning the same results are obtained over the multiple trials, the measurement technique and data can be shown to be reliable.

The split-half method is commonly used with tests and survey instruments. With the split-half method, the items are randomly distributed throughout the instrument. If the items are consistently measuring the same outcome, one would expect to find a strong correlation when comparing the first half of the responses to the second half.

Leading Indicators, Trailing Indicators, and Current Indicators

The effectiveness of a safety activity should be measured via three indicators: leading indicators, current indicators, and trailing indicators. Trailing indicators are the most common measures used by safety professionals. *Trailing indicators* are those measures that indicate the results of an intervention strategy after the fact. Examples of trailing indicators include lost-workday rates, the number of injuries over a period of time, and the losses incurred by the organization. Some reasons why trailing indicators are so widely used to measure

safety performance include the availability of data to make such measurements, the influence of OSHA's record-keeping guidelines, and use of various OSHA rates and measures of safety performance in the United States. One major downside of using trailing indicators is that they are measuring unwanted events after the fact, thus providing no means for implementing improvement strategies to impact their outcomes.

Current indicators measure the current status of the organization's safety performance. An example of a current indicator is the number of safety audits conducted up to a particular point in time. A positive outcome from using current indicators is that as soon as the measure is obtained, action can be taken immediately to improve the measure and thus improve safety performance.

Leading indicators are those measures that are correlated to future safety performance. For example, participation in safety training may be an indicator as to whether employees suffer back injuries on the job. Measuring the number of workers trained at a point in time may be indicative of the number of back injuries expected in the future. As with current indicators, leading indicators provide the safety manager with information that can be acted upon today with positive results on the safety performance in the future. A key to using current and leading indicators is that these measures must be directly correlated to safety performance. Without this relationship, a safety manager may find that activities taken to improve safety performance based on uncorrelated measures will have no effect on safety performance.

Safety performance should *not* be measured using only one or two performance measures. Instead, it should be measured with a variety of leading, current, and trailing indicators that have been shown to be correlated to safety performance in the workplace. When selecting these performance measures, keep in mind that the data needed for the performance measure should be valid, reliable, and readily available.

When using multiple measures, the data's main effects and interactive effects become important when interpreting the results. Main effects are the variables examined separately in order to determine their role in influencing the outcome measure. For example, a safety manager wishes to determine the influence the age of the worker and the number of training sessions attended have on the number of injuries reported over a given period. The age of the worker and the number of training sessions attended can be considered the main effects. Next, the safety manager wishes to determine the influence that both age and number of training sessions attended together have on the number of injuries reported. When examining the two variables simultaneously, the safety manager is assessing the interactive effects of the two variables.

BENCHMARKING

Benchmarking, measurement, and evaluation are all essential for program success (Lack 2002, 684). The benchmarking process establishes a standard that the company has determined signifies successful performance. *Benchmarking* is a technique for measuring an organization's products, services, and operations against those of its competitors, resulting in a search for best practices that will lead to superior performance (Hoyle 2003, 15). Benchmarking safety performance entails identifying similar organizations with outstanding safety performance and identifying the key aspects of their activities that make them stand out.

Benchmarking is more than taking another organization's safety programs and copying them. Much research is necessary to be able to identify those aspects of safety activities that result in superior performance, and much work is required to tailor them so similar outcomes can be duplicated in another organization. Meaningful benchmarks are typically set using successful performance results from similar industries and other facilities. The benchmarking process can be completed in six steps (Pierce 1995, 177–178): survey programs, identify solutions, prioritize, develop a plan, implement the plan, and then follow up.

Surveying

The first part of benchmarking is surveying front-running programs or organizations. This step is the most crucial in the entire process. Identifying who the best organizations are and what they are doing

to generate exemplary safety performance is critical in establishing benchmarks and program priorities.

Identifying Solutions

The second part of benchmarking is identifying the complementary solutions used by the target organization or program. As stated previously, the benchmarking process is not merely copying what other successful organizations are doing, but incorporating their programs into your organization in a manner that fits the organization structure and goals.

Prioritizing

Part three of benchmarking is prioritizing growth opportunities from the list of complementary solutions. The purpose of prioritization is to determine which program changes will provide the organization with the largest improvement in business and safety performance.

Planning

The next part of the process involves developing a plan to achieve the goals. Incorporating changes in an organization will take time and careful planning. The programs identified as being crucial for success must be tailored to the organization.

Implementing

Implement the plan. Adequate personnel and resources must be made available to ensure the benchmarking plan is carried out. Inadequate resources in the implementation phase, a lack of commitment, and a lack of motivation to continue implementing the benchmarking plan will result in poor results.

Following Up

Benchmarking is a dynamic process. Follow-up activities include monitoring to ensure the changes are meeting the needs of the organization. Just because they were found to be successful in one organization

CASE STUDY

Benchmarking a Safety Measure

An organization was experiencing ever-increasing workers' compensation costs due to employee back injuries. To control these costs, the safety director decided to apply a benchmarking approach. First, companies that had been recognized by the industry as leaders in safety were identified and invited to participate in benchmarking focus groups. In these focus group meetings, the activities that were being used to control workers' compensation costs were identified and prioritized in terms of their effectiveness. Following the focus group meetings, the safety director developed a plan to tailor the activities to best meet the needs of his facility and implement them. Using a continuous improvement approach, results from the cost-control activities were measured and further interventions implemented based on the measurable results.

does not necessarily mean they will achieve the same results in another. Follow-up may involve modifying the activities or identifying new ones to achieve the desired safety performance.

QUALITY CONTROL

Quality control is a universal management process for conducting operations in order to provide stability, for preventing adverse change, and for maintaining the status quo (Juran and Godfrey 1999, 4.2). *Process control* is about maintaining variation in a process at a level where the only variation present is random and the process is stable and, therefore, predictable (Hoyle 2003, 28). The major distinction between the two is that quality control focuses on outputs and process control focuses on inputs.

Continuous improvement is about improving the efficiency and effectiveness of products, processes, and systems that are under control (Hoyle 2003, 28). Continuous improvement efforts are directed toward both inputs and outputs.

Safety performance, like other aspects of business, can be managed using the tools and techniques found in quality control. Quality safety performance begins with proper planning and the development of performance goals and objectives. Methods for measuring this performance, commonly referred to as safety metrics, are then developed to define measures that

are indicative of acceptable performance. Data are collected and analyzed, making comparisons against the established levels of acceptable performance. When gaps are identified between acceptable performance levels and actual performance levels, action is warranted. This quality control process is known as a *continuous improvement process*.

Continuous Improvement

During the 1990s the use of continuous improvement processes increased dramatically in the business world. In the context of ISO 9000, there is no difference between continuous improvement and continual improvement. Improvement that is continuous has no periods of stability; it is attainable all the time. Although the rate of change may vary, improvement does not stop. In reality, there are periods of stability between periods of change, and therefore, continual improvement is a better term to describe the phenomenon (Hoyle 2003, 29).

Continuous improvement is the process of establishing performance measures with a desired goal, implementing an intervention designed to meet that goal, measuring the performance, and implementing change in the intervention until the desired goal is met.

Juran and Deming say that putting out fires is not improvement of the process, and neither is the discovery and removal of a special cause detected by a point out of control (Hoyle 2003, 28). This only puts the process back to where it should have been in the first place. If there is no status quo (no normal level), action needs to be taken to establish a normal level, that is, bring operations under control. When a process is in control, data measurements are consistent without wild fluctuations and wide ranges. You can only improve what is already under control. Bringing operations under control is not improvement.

Plan-Do-Check-Act

The Plan-Do-Check-Act (PDCA) cycle has been adopted by a variety of industries in their quest for safety performance improvement. This cycle has also been incorporated into standards such as ISO 9001:2008, the ISO 14000 family of standards, and ANSI/AIHA A10:

2005. Various people in the United States and Japan have been associated with the early evolution of the PDCA cycle, including Deming, Shewhart, and Mizuno (Juran and Godfrey 1999, 11.16). This continuous improvement approach has been the cornerstone of a variety of approaches to both safety and process control.

First, safety activities and performance goals are defined and prioritized in the Plan phase. Next, the safety activities are implemented in the Do phase, followed by measurement of the results of the activities and comparisons of the results with the planned or desired outcomes in the Check phase. In the Act phase, if the desired performance levels are not achieved, then changes in the activities may be warranted to achieve the desired outcomes. If the performance goals are successfully met, then modifications to the planned outcomes can be made so that further improvements in performance can be planned. By repeating this cycle and planning for better safety performance with each successive time through the process, continuous improvement can be successfully planned, implemented, measured, and achieved.

The first edition of the ISO 9000 standards sees PDCA management as compatible with the contemporary concept that all work is accomplished by a process (Juran and Godfrey 1999, 11.16). Safety management practices also lend themselves well to a PDCA process in which safety activities are planned and implemented, outcomes are evaluated, and interventions are acted upon to close the gaps between desired performance and actual performance.

STATISTICAL PROCESS CONTROL

Process control means that processes are planned, executed, and controlled such that the equipment, environment, personnel, documentation, and materials employed constantly result in meeting quality or safety requirements (Weinstein 1997, 85). *Statistical process control* involves setting quantifiable performance goals, measuring performance against those goals, and determining with a degree of statistical certainty that the performance goals have been met. If there is a difference between the desired level of performance and actual performance, then appropriate measures are taken to close the gap between the two.

An underlying assumption of statistical process control is that the data collected on performance measures is assumed to follow a normal distribution. On a control chart that is recording data compared to an average measure, for example, the center line on the chart represents the sample average, and the control limits represent the upper and lower boundaries for which any data point lying above or below the control limits have a 5 percent chance of falling there. Points falling between the control limits have a 95 percent chance of falling there. Much the same way a bell-shaped curve is interpreted, those points lying at the extremes may be considered to be significant.

Some fluctuations in performance can always be expected. This is taken into account in statistical process control. Action is taken when the performance is statistically significantly different from what is acceptable.

The key to being able to use statistical process control techniques to monitor a process is that the process must be in control. A process is considered in control when the performance measures are stable, falling within a narrow range. Large fluctuations in measures indicate that the process is not in control, and any resulting controls established for a process that is not in control may not be meaningful. With a process that is in control, performance measures can be taken and compared against established control limits. When data points fall outside of the control limits, it is an indication that some action may be necessary to bring the process back into control.

There are a number of criteria that have been developed to determine if a process is in control. Data trends that indicate an out-of-control process include one or more points outside the limits on a control chart, two or three points outside two standard deviations from the average, and four or five points outside one standard deviation from the average.

With the data indicating a process that is in control, interventions are then implemented with a goal of creating a trend in the data. For example, a safety manager wishes to decrease the number of hand injuries reported in a facility. Data is collected to determine the current extent of hand injuries reported each month, and this is used as a baseline. A control chart is created using this past data. A variety of activities designed to decrease these injuries is implemented and the performance is measured. Over the months, a downward trend in reported hand injuries is observed. The criteria for indicating a trend, either upward or downward, can include points that are lying outside of the control limit but are doing so in a pattern that is either increasing or decreasing.

When the data points consistently fall below the lower control limit when a downward trend is desired, or above the upper control limit when an upward trend in data is desired, a performance shift has occurred. It is necessary to recalculate the control chart limits using the new data. This will, in effect, further improve the performance goal and require continuous improvement.

Finally, from a practical standpoint, if statistical process control methods are to be used successfully in an organization to monitor safety performance, the data required to measure the performance must be readily accessible to the users, valid, and reliable. To aid in the data collection process, data should be designed carefully to make the data readily available.

Control Charts

Control charts are widely used in industry as the principal tools of statistical process control (SPC). In 1931, Shewhart published his classic book, *Economic Control of Quality of Manufactured Product*. The first applications of the control chart by Shewhart were on fuses, heat controls, and station apparatus at the Hawthorne Works of the Western Electric Company (Juran and Godfrey 1999, 45.3). Today, control charts can be a very useful tool for the safety professional to determine if performance is within acceptable ranges.

Control charts can be broadly classified into two distinct types. The first type is control charts in which no standard is given. These are used to determine if the data points collected vary among themselves by an amount greater than is attributed due to chance. The second type is control charts developed against a standard. These charts use a standard value based on prior experience or an established acceptable level of performance. Data are collected and comparisons

are made to the acceptable standard. Control charts based on a standard are particularly used to control processes and maintain quality uniformly at the desired level (ASTM 1995, 52).

Control charts use the normal distribution, or bell-shaped, curve as the basis for their use and construction. If the safety performance measurements are truly random, then they can be assumed to follow a normal distribution. It is this assumption of normally distributed data that must be met in order to use control charts with safety performance data.

Formats of Control Charts and Their Uses

There are a variety of different types of control charts that can be developed and used to monitor safety performance. The selection of the type of control chart to be used is based on the format of the data being measured. The following guidelines should be followed when constructing control charts when a standard is given. When using a given standard, only the information regarding sample size is required in order to compute central lines and control limits. These standard values are set up before the detailed analysis of the data at hand is undertaken, and frequently before the data to be analyzed are collected. The data must exhibit not only control, but also control at the standard level and with no more than standard variability. Extending control limits obtained from a set of existing data into the future, and using these limits as a basis for purposive control of quality during production, is equivalent to adopting the values obtained from the existing data as standard (ASTM 1995, 61).

X Control Charts

The X chart (see Figure 1) is one of the most commonly used statistical process control procedures. It is used whenever there is a particular quality characteristic that one wishes to control, since the chart can use one characteristic at a time. In addition, the data must be of a measurement or variables type. Most users of process control are interested in individual

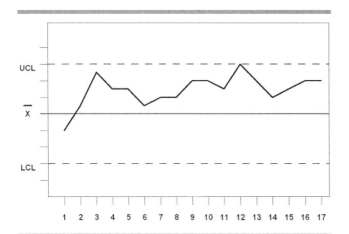

FIGURE 1. Sample X control chart

items of product and the values of a few quality characteristics on these items. Averages and ranges computed from small samples or subgroups of individual items provide very good measures of the nature of the underlying universe. They permit control and decision making about the process from which the items came. The chart for averages is used to control the mean or central tendency of the process, whereas the chart for ranges is used to control the variability. In place of the range, the sample standard deviation is sometimes used, but the range (the largest minus the smallest values in the sample) is easier to calculate and is more easily understood by the operators (Juran and Godfrey 1999, 45.5).

For averages, the central line is the established mean set for the acceptable level. The upper and lower control limits are then calculated using the formula for small samples and equal sample sizes:

Equation 1: Central Line and Control Limits for X Control Charts

Central line is a predetermined set standard: μ

$$\text{Upper Control Limit} = \mu + 3\frac{\sigma}{\sqrt{n}}$$

$$\text{Lower Control Limit} = \mu - 3\frac{\sigma}{\sqrt{n}}$$

where

μ = average number of nonconformities

n = number of cases

σ = standard deviation

CASE STUDY

Example X Control Chart

Data was collected so that ten safety audits were performed each day throughout the plant over a 10-day period. The average number of hazards identified each day was calculated. Using past data, an average of 1.1 hazards each day was to be expected with a standard deviation of 0.94. The raw data for Day 1 was as follows:

Audit Number	Number of Hazards Identified
1	0
2	1
3	0
4	2
5	2
6	0
7	1
8	2
9	0
10	2

The average number of hazards for Day 1 was calculated as follows:

$$(0 + 1 + 0 + 2 + 2 + 0 + 1 + 2 + 0 + 2) \div 10 = 1.0$$

The standard deviation for the sample was determined to be 0.94

The average and standard deviation are then calculated for the remaining days. The following table displays the data from which a control chart was constructed:

Day	Number of Audits Conducted	Average Number of Hazards Identified	Standard Deviation
1	10	1.0	0.94
2	10	1.5	1.1
3	10	1.2	0.89
4	10	1.1	0.93
5	10	0.98	0.99
6	10	1.3	0.96
7	10	0.99	0.99
8	10	1.0	0.93
9	10	1.2	0.95
10	10	0.93	0.98

Central line is a predetermined set standard: $\mu = 1.10$

$$\text{Upper Control Limit} = 1.10 + 3\frac{0.98}{\sqrt{10}} = 2.03$$

$$\text{Lower Control Limit} = 1.10 - 3\frac{0.98}{\sqrt{10}} = 0.17$$

The data in the table is then plotted on the control chart using the central line and control limits calculated above.

CASE STUDY

Example P Control Chart

In a p chart, the fraction of nonconforming items is determined for each sample. In this example, the samples are equal in size. A systems safety engineer collected data to determine the fraction of defective bolts making their way to the production floor from their suppliers. A random sample of 500 bolts was examined on a daily basis, and the fraction of defective bolts calculated. An acceptable p was established by the company to be 0.002. The following data table was developed:

Day	Sample Size	Number of Defective Bolts	Fraction Nonconforming (p)
1	500	1	0.002
2	500	2	0.004
3	500	1	0.002
4	500	2	0.004
5	500	4	0.008
6	500	2	0.004
7	500	1	0.002
8	500	3	0.006
9	500	4	0.008
10	500	2	0.004

Central line is a predetermined set standard: $p = 0.002$

$$\text{Upper Control Limit} = 0.002 + 3\sqrt{\frac{0.002(1 - 0.002)}{500}}$$
$$= 0.008$$

$$\text{Lower Control Limit} = 0.002 - 3\sqrt{\frac{0.002(1 - 0.002)}{500}}$$
$$= -0.004$$

Note: Because the lower control limit (LCL) is negative, the LCL is set to 0.

The data in the table is then plotted on the control chart using the central line and control limits calculated above.

P Control Charts

A p control chart is used to represent the fraction of nonconforming parts in a sample. Ordinarily, the control chart for p is most useful when the sample sizes are large—when n is 50 or more and when the expected number of nonconforming units (np) is 4 or more. When n is less than 25 or the expected np is less than 1, then the control chart for p may be more reliable (ASTM 1995, 64).

Equation 2: Central Line and Control Limits for P Control Charts

Central line is a predetermined set standard: p

$$\text{Upper Control Limit} = p + 3\sqrt{\frac{p(1 - p)}{N}}$$

$$\text{Lower Control Limit} = p - 3\sqrt{\frac{p(1 - p)}{N}}$$

where
   p = set standard proportion of cases
   N = number of cases

Np Control Charts

An np chart is used to chart the number of nonconforming parts in a sample. It is equivalent to the control charts for the fraction of nonconforming parts,

CASE STUDY

Example Np Control Chart

Using the data in the p chart example, an np chart can be developed. In this example, np represents the number of defective bolts.

Day	Sample Size (n)	Number of Defective Bolts (np)	Fraction Nonconforming (p)
1	500	1	0.002
2	500	2	0.004
3	500	1	0.002
4	500	2	0.004
5	500	4	0.008
6	500	2	0.004
7	500	1	0.002
8	500	3	0.006
9	500	4	0.008
10	500	2	0.004

Central line is a predetermined set standard: $np = 1.00$

$$\text{Upper Control Limit} = 1.00 + 3\sqrt{1.00} = 4.00$$
$$\text{Lower Control Limit} = 1.00 - 3\sqrt{1.00} = -2.00$$

Note: Because the lower control limit is negative, the LCL is set to 0.

CASE STUDY

Example *U* Control Chart

In this example, a safety manager collects data from supervisors who have conducted job observations of workers packing boxes on the production lines. The supervisors sampled 10 workers over 10 work shifts and counted the number of unsafe material-handling events. The predetermined standard was set at 0.75.

Work Shift	Number of Unsafe Events	Unsafe Events Per Worker (u)
1	4	0.4
2	6	0.6
3	3	0.3
4	6	0.6
5	8	0.8
6	6	0.6
7	5	0.5
8	4	0.4
9	3	0.3
10	3	0.3

Central line is a predetermined set standard: $u = 0.75$

$$\text{Upper Control Limit} = 0.75 + 3\sqrt{\frac{0.75}{10}} = 1.57$$

$$\text{Lower Control Limit} = 0.75 - 3\sqrt{\frac{0.75}{10}} = -0.07$$

Note: Because the lower control limit is negative, the LCL is set to 0.

particularly when all samples have the same n (ASTM 1995, 64).

Equation 3: Central Line and Control Limits for *Np* Control Charts

Central line is a predetermined set standard: np

$$\text{Upper Control Limit} = np + 3\sqrt{np}$$

$$\text{Lower Control Limit} = np - 3\sqrt{np}$$

where

p = fraction of cases
n = number of cases in the sample

U Control Charts

The control chart for nonconformities per unit (u chart) is calculated using the total number of nonconformities in all of the units divided by the number of units in the sample (ASTM 1995, 65). The u chart is desirable when inspections look at multiple characteristics of a unit. It is assumed that for each characteristic under consideration, the ratio of the expected to the possible number of nonconformities is small—less than 0.10.

Equation 4: Central Line and Control Limits for *U* Control Charts

Central line is a predetermined set standard: u

$$\text{Upper Control Limit} = u + 3\sqrt{\frac{u}{N}}$$

$$\text{Lower Control Limit} = u - 3\sqrt{\frac{u}{N}}$$

where

u = number of nonconformities per unit
N = number of cases in the sample

C Control Charts

C charts are used to chart the number of nonconformities in a sample. The c chart is equivalent to the control chart when all sample sizes have the same n. The u chart is recommended as preferable when the sample sizes vary from sample to sample (ASTM 1995, 61).

Equation 5: Central Line and Control Limits for *C* Control Charts

Central line is a predetermined set standard: c

$$\text{Upper Control Limit} = c + 3\sqrt{c}$$

$$\text{Lower Control Limit} = c - 3\sqrt{c}$$

where

c = number of nonconformities

CASE STUDY

Example *C* Control Chart

Using the data set in the *u* chart example, a *c* chart can be constructed. A standard of 3.0 was established as the *c*-chart control line by the safety manager.

Work Shift	Number of Unsafe Events (*c*)	Unsafe Events Per Worker (*u*)
1	4	0.4
2	6	0.6
3	3	0.3
4	6	0.6
5	8	0.8
6	6	0.6
7	5	0.5
8	4	0.4
9	3	0.3
10	3	0.3

Central line is a predetermined set standard: $c = 3.00$

$$\text{Upper Control Limit} = 3.00 + 3\sqrt{3.00} = 8.20$$

$$\text{Lower Control Limit} = 3.00 - 3\sqrt{3.00} = -2.20$$

Note: Because the lower control limit is negative, the LCL is set to 0.

Constructing a Control Chart When No Standard Is Given

When no standard is given as the acceptable level of performance, it must be determined using data collected from the process itself. The average and the control limits are determined using data collected from the process, and the appropriate standard is derived. The procedure for constructing all types of charts previously described when no standard is given is as follows (Juran and Godfrey 1999, 45.5):

1. Take a series of 20 to 30 samples from the process.
2. During the taking of these samples, keep accurate records of any changes in the process, such as a change in operators, machines, or materials.
3. Compute trial control limits from these data.
4. Plot the data on a chart with the trial limits to determine if any of the samples are out of

control, that is, if any plotted points are outside the control limits.

If none of the plotted points are outside the trial control limits, one can say the process is in control and these limits can be used for maintaining control. If, on the other hand, some of the plotted points are outside the trial control limits, then the process is not in control. That is, there are assignable causes of variation present. In such a case, one must determine from the records in Step 2 above, if possible, the cause of each out-of-control point. Then eliminate these samples from the data and recalculate the trial control limits. If some points are outside these new limits, this step must be repeated until no points are outside the trial control limits. These final limits can then be used for future control.

Formulas for Central Lines and Control Limits for Control Charts When No Standard Is Given

Equation 6: X Charts

Control Charts for Averages (large sample more than 25 observations) (ASTM 1995, 54).

Central line = $\bar{x}$

$$\text{Upper Control Limit} = \bar{x} + 3\,\frac{\bar{s}}{\sqrt{n - 0.05}}$$

$$\text{Lower Control Limit} = \bar{x} - 3\,\frac{\bar{s}}{\sqrt{n - 0.05}}$$

where

$\bar{x}$ = average number of nonconformities

n = number of cases in the sample

$\bar{s}$ = average standard deviation

Equation 7: *P* Charts

Fraction of Nonconforming Parts (ASTM 1995, 58).

Central line = $\bar{p}$

$$\text{Upper Control Limit} = \bar{p} + 3\,\sqrt{\frac{\bar{p}(1 - \bar{p})}{N}}$$

$$\text{Lower Control Limit} = \bar{p} - 3\,\sqrt{\frac{\bar{p}(1 - \bar{p})}{N}}$$

where

$\bar{p}$ = average proportion of cases

N = number of cases

Equation 8: *Np* Charts

Number of Nonconforming Units (ASTM 1995, 58).

Central line = $n\bar{p}$

Upper Control Limit = $n\bar{p} + 3\sqrt{n\bar{p}}$

Lower Control Limit = $n\bar{p} - 3\sqrt{n\bar{p}}$

where

p = average fraction of cases

n = number of cases in the sample

Equation 9: *U* Charts

Nonconforming Per Unit (ASTM 1995, 59).

Central line = $\bar{u}$

Upper Control Limit = $\bar{u} + 3\sqrt{\dfrac{\bar{u}}{N}}$

Lower Control Limit = $\bar{u} - 3\sqrt{\dfrac{\bar{u}}{N}}$

where

$\bar{u}$ = number of nonconformities per unit

N = number of cases in the sample

Equation 10: *C* Charts

Number of Nonconformities (ASTM 1995, 61).

Central line = $\bar{c}$

Upper Control Limit = $\bar{c} + 3\sqrt{\bar{c}}$

Lower Control Limit = $\bar{c} - 3\sqrt{\bar{c}}$

where

$\bar{c}$ = average number of nonconformities

There are a variety of other charts and graphs that can be used to monitor safety performance in addition to the control charts used in statistical process control. Some of the more common types include cumulative frequency distributions and Pareto charts.

CUMULATIVE FREQUENCY DISTRIBUTIONS

Cumulative frequency distributions are used to display the frequency of observations having a value greater than or less than a particular scale value (ASTM 1995, 10). Cumulative frequency distributions can be displayed in

TABLE 1

Cumulative Frequency Distribution Table

Number of Reported CTD Symptoms	Number of Subjects Reporting CTD Symptoms Less than the Given Values	Percentage of Subjects Reporting CTD Symptoms Less than the Given Values
1	10	45.5%
2	15	68.2%
3	17	77.3%
4	19	86.4%
5	22	100.0%

a table format or graphically. Table 1 represents a cumulative frequency distribution in tabular format. Using this table, it is possible to determine the number of cases above or below a particular category. To interpret this table, 10 subjects reported the presence of one CTD symptom, 15 subjects reported two or fewer CTD symptoms, 17 subjects reported 3 or fewer CTD symptoms, and so on. The entire sample consisted of 22 subjects reporting 5 or fewer CTD symptoms. By using the cumulative frequency distribution table, you can readily see that approximately 77.3 percent of the subjects reported 3 or fewer CTD symptoms.

Thus far, the control charts presented assume a normal distribution, meaning that the data can be expected to follow a bell-shaped curve. This may not always be the case. Two other common distributions that data can also follow are the Poisson distribution and the binomial distribution. If the data collected for the performance measure are assumed to follow either of these distributions, then the appropriate control should be used.

POISSON DISTRIBUTIONS

Poisson distributions can be expected when the sample size is very large and the probability of the occurrence of an event of interest is very small. A good approximation to use in determining if the Poisson distribution is appropriate is when the sample size is greater than 50 and the probability of the occurrence of an event is less than 0.20 (Hays 1988, 145). In safety, many accident measures assume a Poisson distribution. For example, the probability of an accident

CASE STUDY

Example Poisson Distribution

A safety manager collected data on the number of damaged fire extinguishers throughout the entire company. He found that the overall probability of finding a damaged extinguisher is 0.003. However, at one facility, which has 500 extinguishers, he found 4 damaged extinguishers. What is the probability of finding this many damaged extinguishers in one facility?

$$p(x,m) = \frac{2.718^{-1.5}1.5^4}{4!} = 0.05$$

where

$e = 2.718$
$m = 500 \times 0.003 = 1.5$
$x = 4$.

Therefore, based on prior experience with damaged fire extinguishers, the probability of finding 4 damaged extinguishers out of the 500 is 0.05, or a 5 percent chance.

can assume to follow a Poisson distribution when the frequency of accidents is small and the total exposure is large. The formula for calculating a Poisson probability is:

$$p(x,m) = \frac{e^{-m}m^x}{x!}$$

where

$e = 2.718$
m = expected number of events (number in sample $\times$ probability of one event)
x = number of events.

BINOMIAL DISTRIBUTIONS

A variable follows a *binomial distribution* when there are two possible outcomes. As with the Poisson and normal distributions, when collecting data for a performance measure that has two possible outcomes, the appropriate control chart based upon the binomial distribution must be used. The formula for calculating a binomial probability is:

$$p(x = r, n, p) = \frac{n!}{r!(n-r)!}p^r(1-p)^{n-r}$$

where

n = number of cases in sample
r = number of cases of interest
p = probability of one event.

PARETO CHARTS

The *Pareto Principle* states that in any population that contributes to a common effect, a relatively few of the contributors—the vital few—account for the bulk of the effect (Juran and Godfrey 1999, 5.20). The principle applies widely in human affairs. Like their tabular counterparts, each of these Pareto charts contains three elements (Juran and Godfrey 1999, 5.20):

1. The contributors to the total effect, ranked by the magnitude of their contribution
2. The magnitude of the contribution of each, expressed numerically and as a percentage of the total
3. The cumulative percentage of total contribution of the ranked contributors.

CASE STUDY

Example Binomial Distribution

It was determined that the probability of a worker from a particular construction company being trained on fall protection was 94 percent (6 percent are untrained). During an audit at one of the construction sites, a safety technician found that, out of 400 laborers interviewed, 10 stated they had not been trained in fall protection. What is the probability of finding this many untrained laborers?

$$p(x = r, n, p) = \frac{400!}{10!(400 - 10)!}0.06^{10}(1 - 0.06)^{400-10}$$
$$= 0.0005$$

where

$n = 400$
$r = 10$
$p = 0.06$.

When selected at random, 6 percent of the workers could be expected to be untrained. With a workforce of 400 laborers, one could expect to find 24 untrained laborers. However, only 10 were identified which is considerably less than expected. The probability of this occurring is 0.0005. Based on these results, the safety technician can conclude that there are significantly fewer untrained workers on this job site than can be expected due to chance.

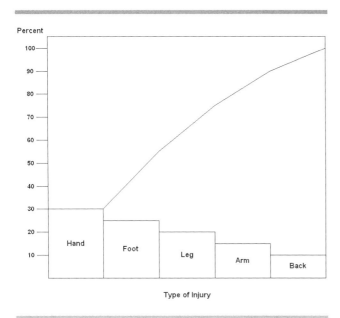

FIGURE 2. Sample Pareto chart

In the displayed Pareto chart (see Figure 2), the frequencies of injuries reported by body part were collected. The injury categories are arranged in order from highest to lowest percentage of cases. The bars represent the percentage of reported cases by category, while the line represents the cumulative percentage of reported cases. As can be inferred from Figure 2, hand injuries account for 30 percent of the reported cases, hand and foot injuries account for 55 percent, and so on. The Pareto analysis indicates that, in this example, hand injuries account for the greatest percentage of reported cases.

USING EXISTING CRITERIA TO DEVELOP PERFORMANCE MEASURES

Rather than develop unique performance measures, it is common for safety professionals to use existing performance measures developed by other entities. Examples of sources of safety performance measures used in industry include OSHA's Voluntary Protection Program Criteria, OSHA's Safety and Health Program Assessment Worksheet (Revised OSHA Form 33) (which was discussed previously in this chapter), ISO 9000:2000 Standards, ISO 14000 Standards, and Six Sigma methodologies. Each of these criteria have been used in industry as a means to measure and improve safety performance in the workplace.

VOLUNTARY PROTECTION PROGRAM CRITERIA

On July 2, 1982, OSHA announced the establishment of the Voluntary Protection Programs (VPP) to recognize and promote effective work-site-based safety and health management systems (OSHA 2008a). VPP is OSHA's official recognition of the outstanding efforts of employers and employees who have created exemplary work-site safety and health management systems. The following principles are embodied in the Voluntary Protection Programs (OSHA 2008a):

- **Voluntarism.** Participation in VPP is strictly voluntary. The applicant who wishes to participate freely submits information to OSHA on its safety and health management system and opens itself to agency review.
- **Cooperation.** OSHA has long recognized that a balanced, multifaceted approach is the best way to accomplish the goals of the OSH Act. VPP's emphasis on trust and cooperation between OSHA, the employer, employees, and employees' representatives complements the agency's enforcement activity, but does not take its place. VPP staff and participating sites work together to resolve any safety and health problems that may arise. This partnership enables the agency to remove participating sites from programmed inspection lists, allowing OSHA to focus its inspection resources on establishments in greater need of agency oversight and intervention. However, OSHA continues to investigate valid employee safety and health complaints, fatalities, catastrophes, and other significant events at VPP participant sites.
- **A Systems Approach.** Compliance with the OSH Act and all applicable OSHA requirements is only the starting point for VPP sites. VPP participants develop and implement systems to effectively identify, evaluate, prevent, and control occupational hazards so that injuries and illnesses to employees are prevented. Star sites, in particular, are often on the leading edge of hazard prevention methods and technology. As a result, VPP work sites serve as models of

safety and health excellence, demonstrating the benefits of a systems approach to worker protection. NOTE: Federal agencies participating in VPP also must comply with Executive Order 12196 and 29 CFR 1960, in addition to Section 19 of the OSH Act.

- **Model Work Sites for Safety and Health.** OSHA selects VPP participants based on their written safety and health management system, the effective implementation of this system over time, and their performance in meeting VPP requirements. Not all work sites are appropriate candidates for VPP. At qualifying sites, all personnel are involved in the effort to maintain rigorous, detailed attention to safety and health. VPP participants often mentor other work sites interested in improving safety and health, participate in safety and health outreach and training initiatives, and provide OSHA with input on proposed policies and standards. They also share best practices and promote excellence in safety and health in their industries and communities.
- **Continuous Improvement.** VPP participants must demonstrate continuous improvement in the operation and impact of their safety and health management systems. Annual VPP self-evaluations help participants measure success, identify areas needing improvement, and determine needed changes. OSHA on-site evaluation teams verify this improvement.
- **Employee and Employer Rights.** Participation in VPP does not diminish employee and employer rights and responsibilities under the OSH Act and, for Federal agencies, under 29 CFR 1960 as well.

The categories of VPP participation consist of (OSHA 2008a):

- **Star Program.** The Star Program recognizes the safety and health excellence of work sites where workers are successfully protected from fatality, injury, and illness by the implementation of comprehensive and effective workplace safety and health management systems. These work sites are self-sufficient in identifying and controlling workplace hazards.
- **Merit Program.** The Merit Program recognizes work sites that have good safety and health management systems and that show the willingness, commitment, and ability to achieve site-specific goals that will qualify them for Star participation.
- **Star Demonstration Program.** The Star Demonstration Program recognizes work sites that have Star quality safety and health management systems that differ in some significant fashion from the VPP model and thus do not meet current Star requirements. A Star Demonstration Program tests this alternative approach to protecting workers to determine if it is as protective as current Star requirements.

OHSAS 18001:2007

OHSAS 18001:2007 is an international standard for safety management systems. The standard was developed by a selection of leading trade bodies and international standards and certification bodies to address a gap where no third-party certifiable international standard exists (BSI 2010).

While OHSAS 18001:2007 is not recognized by the International Organization for Standardization (ISO), it is compatible with ISO 9001 and ISO 14001 (BSI 2010).

The following key areas are addressed by this international standard:

- planning for hazard identification, risk assessment, and risk control
- OHSAS management program
- structure and responsibility
- training, awareness, and competence
- consultation and communication

- operational control
- emergency preparedness and response
- performance measuring, monitoring, and improvement

OHSAS 18002 provides the guidelines for the implementation of OHSAS 18001.

ISO STANDARDS

The International Organization for Standardization, commonly referred to as ISO, is a nongovernmental organization founded in 1947 with its headquarters in Geneva, Switzerland (ISO 2004a). Its mission is to promote the development of standardization and related activities in the world. While the organization develops hundreds of standards, two families of standards—ISO 9001:2008 and ISO 14000 in particular—have had a dramatic impact on how safety programs are implemented and how performance is measured in the workplace.

ISO 9001:2008

The ISO 9001:2008 standard represents an international consensus on good quality management practices (ISO 2010a). Revisions to the ISO 9000 family of standards in 2008 resulted in a consolidation of ISO 9001, 9002, and 9003 into the ISO 9001:2008.

The ISO 9001:2008 standard provides guidance on the development of a quality management system, management responsibilities, resource management, product realization, and measurement and improvement processes.

Safety professionals have found it advantageous for organizations that have adopted the ISO standards as their quality improvement process to incorporate safety into the ISO management processes.

ISO 9004:2009

In addition to ISO 9001:2008, ISO 9004:2009 provides guidance to organizations, supporting the achievement of sustained success through a quality manage-ment approach. It is applicable to any organization, regardless of size, type, and activity (ISO 2010b).

ISO 14000

The ISO 14000 family of standards establishes the framework for environmental management systems. An environmental management system is designed to ensure an environmentally friendly product throughout the entire life cycle. Table 2 summarizes the various ISO 14000 standards that are included in the Environmental Management System and in the ISO 14000 Model.

Two standards in the ISO 14000 group that are of particular importance to the safety professional are ISO 14001:2004 and ISO 14004:2004. Both have recently undergone revisions. These standards establish the framework for an environmental management system (EMS). ISO 14001:2004 specifies the requirements for an EMS that provides a framework for an organization to control the environmental impact of its activities, products, and services, and to continually improve its environmental performance.

ISO 14001:2004 specifies requirements for an EMS that enables an organization to develop and implement policies and objectives that take into account the legal and other requirements the organization subscribes to, and information about significant environmental aspects. It applies to the environmental aspects that the organization has identified as being those it can control and those that it can influence. It does not itself state specific environmental performance criteria. ISO 14001:2004 is applicable to any organization that wishes to establish, implement, maintain, and improve an environmental management system, to assure itself of conformity with its stated environmental policy, and to demonstrate conformity with ISO 14001:2004 by (ISO 2004b):

- making a self-determination and a self-declaration
- seeking confirmation of its conformance by parties having an interest in the organization, such as customers

TABLE 2

The ISO 14000 Family of International Standards (ISO 2009)

Designation	Publication Title
ISO 14001:2004	Environmental management systems – Requirements with guidance for use
ISO 14004:2004	Environmental management systems – General guidelines on principles, systems, and supporting techniques
ISO/DIS 14005	Environmental management systems – Guidelines for the phased in implementation of an environmental management system
ISO/CD 14006	Environmental management systems – Guidelines on ecosystems
ISO 14015:2001	Environmental management – Environmental assessment of sites and organizations (EASO)
ISO 14020:2000	Environmental labels and declarations – General principles
ISO 14021:1999	Environmental labels and declarations – Self-declared environmental claims (Type II environmental labeling)
ISO 14024:1999	Environmental labels and declarations – Type I environmental labeling – Principles and procedures
ISO 14025:2006	Environmental labels and declarations – Type III environmental declarations – Principles and procedures
ISO 14031:1999	Environmental management – Environmental performance evaluation guidelines
ISO/AWI 14033	Environmental management – Quantitative environmental information – Guidelines and examples
ISO 14040:2006	Environmental management – Life cycle assessment – Principles and framework
ISO 14044: 2006	Environmental management – Life cycle assessment – Requirements and guidelines
ISO/WD 14045	Eco-efficiency assessment – Principles and requirements
ISO/TR 14047: 2003	Environmental management – Life cycle assessment – Examples of application of ISO 14042
ISO/TS 14048:2002	Environmental management – Life cycle assessment – Data documentation format
ISO/TR 14049:2000	Environmental management – Life cycle assessment – Examples of application of ISO 14041 to goal and scope definition and inventory analysis
ISO 14050:2009	Environmental management – Vocabulary
ISO/CD 14051	Environmental management – Material flow cost accounting – General principles and framework
ISO/TR 14062:2002	Environmental management – Integrating environmental aspects into product design and development
ISO 14063: 2006	Environmental management – Environmental communication – Guidelines and examples
ISO 14064-1:2006	Greenhouse gases – Part 1: Specification with guidance at the organization level for quantification and reporting of greenhouse gas emissions and removals
ISO 14064-2:2006	Greenhouse gases – Part 2: Specification with guidance at the project level for the quantification, monitoring and reporting of greenhouse gas emission reductions or and removal enhancements
ISO 14064-3:2006	Greenhouse gases – Part 3: Specification for the validation and verification of greenhouse gas assertions
ISO 14065: 2007	Greenhouse gases – Requirements for greenhouse gas validation and verification bodies for use in accreditation or other forms of recognition
ISO/CD 14066	Greenhouse gases – Competency requirements for greenhouse gas validators and verifiers document
ISO/WD 14067-1	Carbon footprint of products – Part 1: Quantification
ISO/WD 14067-2	Carbon footprint of products – Part 2: Communication
ISO/AWI 14069	GHG-Quantification and reporting of GHG emissions and organizations – Guidance for the application of ISO 14064-1
ISO 19011:2002	Guidelines for quality and/or environmental management systems auditing
ISO Guide 64:2008	Guide for the inclusion of environmental aspects in product standards

Key to Abbreviations: AWI = Approved Work Item., CD = Committee Draft, DIS = Draft International Standard, TR = Technical Report, WD = Working Draft

- seeking confirmation of its self-declaration by a party external to the organization
- seeking certification/registration of its environmental management system by an external organization.

ISO 14004:2004 provides guidance on the establishment, implementation, maintenance, and improvement of an environmental management system and its coordination with other management systems. The guidelines in ISO 14004:2004 are applicable to any organization, regardless of its size, type, location, or level of maturity. While the guidelines in ISO 14004:2004 are consistent with the ISO 14001:2004 environmental management system model, they are not intended to provide interpretations of the requirements of ISO 14001:2004 (ISO 2004b).

REFERENCES

Al-Mutairi, A., and J. M. Haight. 2009. "Predicting Incident Rates." *Professional Safety* 54 (9):40–48.

American Industrial Hygiene Association (AIHA). 2005. *American National Standard for Occupational Safety and Health Management Systems*. Fairfax, VA: AIHA.

American Society for Testing and Materials (ASTM). 1995. *Manual on Presentation of Data and Control Charts*. Philadelphia, PA: ASTM.

British Standards Institution (BSI). 2010. *BS OHSAS 18001: Occupational Health and Safety* (accessed November 21, 2010). www.bsigroup.com/en/ Assessment-and-certification-services/management-systems/Standards-and-Schemes/BSOHSAS-18001/

Hays, William. 1988. *Statistics*. Orlando, FL: Holt, Rinehart and Winston.

International Organization for Standardization (ISO). 2004a. *Overview of the ISO System*. www.iso.org/iso/ en/aboutiso/introduction/index.html#two

_____. 2004b. *ISO 14001: 2004: Environmental Management Systems—Requirements for Guidance and Use*. www.iso. org/iso/en/CatalogueDetailPage.CatalogueDetail? CSNUMBER=31807&ICS1=13&ICS2=20&ICS3=10& scopelist=ALL

_____. 2009. *Environmental Management: The ISO 14000 Family of International Standards*. Geneva, Switzerland: ISO.

_____. 2010a. *ISO 9000 Essentials*. www.iso.org/iso/iso_ catalogue/management_standards/iso_9000_iso_ 14000/iso_9000_essentials.htm

_____. 2010b. New edition of *ISO 9004* maps out the path forward to "sustained success." www.iso.org/ iso/pressrelease.htm?refid=Ref1263

Iyer, P. S., J. M. Haight, E. Del Castillo, B. W. Tink, and P. W. Hawkins. 2004. "Intervention Effectiveness Research: Understanding and Optimizing Industrial Safety Programs Using Leading Indicators." *Chemical Health & Safety* 11(2):9–20.

Juran, Joseph M., and A Blanton Godfrey. 1999. *Juran's Quality Handbook*. New York: McGraw-Hill.

Lack, Richard W. 2002. *Safety, Health, and Asset Protection*. Boca Raton, FL: Lewis Publishers.

Mohamed, Sherif. 2002. "Safety Climate in Construction Site Environments." *Journal of Construction Engineering & Management* 128(5):375–385.

Occupational Safety and Health Administration (OSHA). 1998. *Publication 2552: Training Requirements in OSHA Standards and Training Guidelines*. Washington, D.C.: OSHA.

_____. 2004. *Safety and Health Management eTool*. www.osha.gov/SLTC/etools/safetyhealth/ components.html

_____. 2008a. *Voluntary Protection Programs (VPP): Policies and Procedures Manual* (OSHA Directive Number CSP 03-01-003). Washington, D.C.: OSHA.

_____. 2008b. *Consultation Policies and Procedures Manual* (OSHA Directive Number CSP 02-00-002). Washington, D.C.: OSHA.

Petersen, Dan. 1996. *Analyzing Safety System Effectiveness*. New York: Van Nostrand Reinhold.

Pierce, F. David. 1995. *Total Quality for Safety and Health Professionals*. Rockville, MD: Government Institutes.

Shewhart, Walter. 1931. *The Economic Control of Quality of Manufactured Product*. New York: Van Nostrand and Company.

Swartz, George. 2000. *Safety Culture and Effective Safety Management*. Chicago, IL: National Safety Council.

Weinstein, Michael B. 1997. *Total Quality Safety Management and Auditing*. Boca Raton, FL: CRC Press LLC.

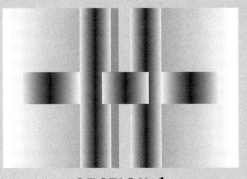

SECTION 1

MANAGEMENT OF SAFETY ENGINEERING WORK

LEARNING OBJECTIVES

▌ Describe the concepts and framework related to the management of safety engineering work.

▌ Describe the role of safety in the system life cycle.

▌ Identify some of the professional organizations, federal agencies, resources, references, and publications for safety engineering practices and management.

▌ Define various management approaches used for major systems.

BEST PRACTICES

Linda Rowley

THIS CHAPTER PROVIDES an overview of the best practices in the management of safety engineering work and includes a general overview of basic safety engineering concepts and principles, references to regulations and standards, and management practices. In this chapter, the management elements in a comprehensive framework are grouped and summarized to provide a general description of safety engineering and its interfaces with the organization. Best practices in safety engineering work are developed from research, lessons learned in past experience, and examining successful models. In one perspective, a best practice could be an applied methodology or a standard practice in the development of a system. From another perspective, best practices are constantly evolving, where both process and product benefit from keeping two goals at the forefront: safety and efficiency.

The field of engineering is involved with the application of mathematical, physical, and scientific principles used to plan, design, and build systems. There are traditional fields of engineering, such as civil, electrical, industrial, mechanical, and chemical, as well as specialized fields such as information systems technology, aerospace, nuclear, medical, construction, mining, and safety. Safety engineering is a specialized field that applies engineering principles, criteria, and techniques to identify and eliminate hazards and manage risk.

System safety is a management framework that facilitates safety engineering work, including the review and decision-making process of identifying, evaluating, and controlling hazards, and managing risks from concept through system disposal. Although the identification of hazards, risks, and corrective actions can be applied to existing systems, system safety engineering is ideally applied to new designs, facilities, and processes. Including safety as part of the system design is considerably more efficient and cost effective than retrofitting or adding safety features to a system.

The terms safety engineering and system safety are often used interchangeably, but there is a subtle difference. *Safety engineering* draws upon analytical techniques and tools, such as fault tree analysis and failure modes and effects analysis, to enhance the design and operation of a system. *System safety* is the holistic framework that facilitates the management of hazards for the life cycle of a system or product. Managing safety helps to identify and monitor hazards; increase efficiency; and control costs to operate and maintain a system safely in its intended environment with minimal risk to users, the general public, property, and the environment.

According to Clemens and Simmons (2002):

> System safety has two characteristics: (1) it is a doctrine of management practice that mandates that hazards be found and risks controlled; and (2) it is a collection of analytical approaches with which to practice the doctrine. Systems are analyzed to identify their hazards, and those hazards are assessed for a single reason: to support management decision making.

This chapter focuses on the framework, process, and management of safety engineering work, identifying the principles and best practices in management. As Leveson states (2004):

> Whereas industrial (occupational) safety models focus on unsafe acts or conditions, classic system-safety models instead look at what went wrong with the system's operation or organization to allow the accident to take place.

Best practices are dynamic organizational learning systems achieved by benefiting from previous experiences, acquiring new information through research or reviewing the literature, benchmarking and measuring performance, and committing to learning and continuous improvement. Various organizational examples in this chapter highlight the structure and principles of common and accepted practices in safety engineering management, references to governmental requirements and professional organizations, and publications as resources for lessons learned and best practices.

The management system structures the process for managing safety engineering activities. The frame-work, including leadership, the formal structure, communications, training, and risk-based decision making, is critical in managing safety engineering work.

SAFETY ENGINEERING IN THE SYSTEM LIFE CYCLE

System safety is a comprehensive approach for integrating safety as part of the design—and implementing requirements throughout other phases—in the life cycle of a system, product, process, or facility. The primary function of system safety is to identify and control hazards in each phase of the life cycle, from concept through decommissioning and disposal. In system development, anticipating potential hazards and conditions is a key aspect of safety engineering work. It is a challenge to anticipate the hazards of a system before it is developed; however, safety engineering activities designed into each phase promote a systematic process of anticipating and identifying hazards as the system is developed. According to Brauer (1990), "System safety is . . . the systematic, forward-looking identification and control of hazards. . . ." Safety engineers assess the existing and potential conditions that could affect a system.

There are four major phases of development in a system life cycle: (1) concept, (2) system development, (3) production and deployment, and (4) sustainment and disposal.

Each phase includes safety engineering tasks that result in a formal decision about proceeding to the next phase. A system-safety management plan should be developed during the concept phase in order to design safety into the system and maintain it throughout the system's life. Incorporating system safety early in development increases the probability that hazards can be addressed more economically and with greater efficiency. A formal decision earmarks the acceptance of risk(s) to that point of development or operation.

Risk can have many different meanings (Main 2004), and the perception of risk is often related to the perspective of the assessor. For example, risk perceived from a fire or health perspective would be different than risk perceived from a financial or security perspective. In safety, risk is based on the probability and severity of a hazard or unsafe condition. Risk is commonly categorized by high, medium, and low risk where quantitative and qualitative data support the categorization of risk. There are variations on a risk model that might include additional risk categories such as negligible, very low, and extremely high. The risk-management matrix provides a consistent method of evaluating and managing hazards for that system, or could be used as an organizationwide risk-assessment method. Three fundamental best practices emerge in managing safety engineering work: (1) a common definition of risk and methodology for assessing hazards; (2) collaboration, allowing the integration of safety engineering into each phase of design and development; and (3) risk decisions for each hazard.

Incorporating safety early in system development increases the probability that hazards will be addressed in each development phase. The opportunities for timely and cost-effective solutions are addressed in early design stages rather than in later phases that potentially have significant impact on development, schedules, and costs. According to Beohm (Marshall 2000), "Safety engineers and professionals should be involved in the conceptual stages of any project design until its final commissioning to ensure that safety is an integral part of that product."

The management or project plan identifies safety engineering requirements for the project, usually for the following activities:

- design, construction, operation, and modification of facilities and structures
- new product design, development, or acquisition
- new process or change
- redesign of a facility or process

Many organizations have established policies and requirements for system safety in the concept stage, from which a requirements document can be formulated. System-safety requirements also apply to subsystems and components, which are assessed both individually and wholly to determine interoperability and interfaces with other components within the entire system. Each phase of development ideally includes risk decision making at the system and subsystem levels.

The management structure and processes vary among organizations, but the commonalities are consideration of safety in the planning stage and a deliberate process of evaluation and decision making. A best practice in managing safety engineering work is a structured management model that facilitates the process for early and continuing involvement of safety engineering.

Management tools, such as the National Aeronautics and Space Administration's (NASA) *Systems Engineering Handbook* (NASA 2007) and *System Safety Handbook* (NASA 1999) provide a systematic approach to managing systems governed by NASA from concept through final disposition. The system-safety framework is the premise NASA established to manage safety engineering work in its systems and facilities. According to NASA, "The System Safety Program Plan (SSPP) is the most important element in implementing a system safety program" (NASA 1999, p. 4-2). Safety engineering work is included in each phase of the life cycle of a system or facility. The management framework for each project identifies key activities and responsibilities for each phase of the life cycle. The major components of the SSPP are:

- Establish the objectives.
- Define responsibilities for performing safety tasks.
- Identify interfaces with other disciplines and organizations.
- Define the tasks to achieve the objectives.
- Specify the management review process and controls.
- Determine the methods for conducting safety analyses.

Federal government system-safety requirements standardize the planned approach for safety engineering work within its organizations, schedules, activities, and decision making. For example, the management process for the Department of Defense (DOD), found in Military Standard 882E, is the structure for managing safety engineering work from concept through all phases to disposal (DOD 2000). There are eight requirements used for each system:

1. Establish the system-safety approach. This is the management plan that defines the

requirements and milestones for how safety will be integrated in system developments and how risks will be identified, communicated, accepted, and tracked.

2. Identify hazards through safety engineering methods that could occur in hardware, software, operations and use, and the environment.

3. Assess the risk in terms of severity and probability to determine the potential impact of each hazard. In MIL-STD 882E, a standard risk-assessment matrix is used to provide consistency in risk analyses and decisions.

4. Identify risk mitigation measures and alternatives. The order of priority for identifying alternatives and reducing risk is:
   (a) design safety into the system
   (b) use safety devices
   (c) provide warning devices
   (d) use procedures and training to reduce risk

5. Reduce unacceptable risks, using the order of prioritization.

6. Verify risk control measures through testing, inspection, and other methods, that show the control measures work as intended and do not introduce other unanticipated hazards.

7. Establish formal risk acceptance at an appropriate level of management.

8. Track all hazards throughout the life cycle of a system, including the hazards of disposal.

This management approach can be universally used for any industrial application of safety engineering work.

The National Institute of Building Sciences (NIBS) promotes an integrated team approach to buildings and their components.

These examples demonstrate a structure of established regulatory and industry procedures and system safety models that facilitate the management of safety engineering work. The formal structure provides a path that incorporates collaboration and integration of safety engineering activities, especially important in complex systems that have high risks. Management tools, such as plans and schedules, should be tailored for specific systems. One management tool that is often used is a project plan that schedules various activities and timelines in each phase of development. Project management principles are universal tools that can be applied to any system, building, process, or product.

Safety engineering work is facilitated through sound management principles that provide the framework of the management system, which includes the following activities:

- *Planning:* Beginning during the concept phase, it is included for each phase of system development, and is modified for continuous improvement throughout the life cycle of the system.

- *Organizing:* Management structure, system-safety process, people, resources, and activities.

- *Budgeting:* The costs of system development, testing, and operations of the system from concept through final disposition, including maintenance, replacement, and decommissioning.

- *Communicating:* A formal structure of written documents concerning the policies, procedures, development, hazards, and risk decisions that supplement informal communications, such as problem solving.

- *Decision making:* A formal process aligned within the system-safety program that determines the criteria for decision making, including the decision authority levels, actions taken, timelines, and risk decision(s) (acceptance or alternatives).

- *Change management:* The written process and implementation of changes within the organization or in the system life cycle.

- *Implementing:* A formal management structure that defines roles and responsibilities.

- *Evaluating:* Both informal and formal methods of monitoring and assessing safety engineering work, activities, decisions, and the efficiency of the system-safety process.

While the management plan does not usually determine the analytical methods for the implementation of safety engineering at a project level, it offers a structure for integrating safety engineering into the process in the context of evaluating risks and making decisions at strategic points in a system's development.

Formal decision making is a key component of system safety. A risk-assessment matrix, which includes the identification, evaluation, and prioritization of hazards, is used to make risk decisions.

Risk management is concerned with three primary goals: (1) managing hazards, (2) designing an efficient system, and (3) cost-efficiency.

ORGANIZATIONAL MANAGEMENT AND SAFETY ENGINEERING

Leadership and Organizational Management

Leadership is a fundamental component of the organizational and safety culture. A written policy statement, usually in the form of the organizational vision, mission, policies, and procedures, sets the direction for the strategic plans, guiding principles, and expectations for the organization. A written statement of the executive leadership's commitment, by itself, does not determine the culture, but it is a major influence in shaping the management systems and organizational culture. The leaders of the organization—top executive(s), board of directors, or owner(s)—must communicate, by word and action, a commitment to safety. For example, the National Safety Council (NSC) uses the phrase "the 3 E's of Safety" (engineering, education, and enforcement). The first "E," engineering, is the preferred choice in eliminating or mitigating hazards in a system. Where it is not feasible to engineer hazards from the design or operation of a system, education is used as an alternative and supplementing method to inform users of hazards. Lastly, the third "E," enforcement of the requirements, includes supervision and monitoring.

At the organizational level and in the system-safety plan, it is important to articulate organizational values and priorities. "The causes of accidents are frequently, if not always, rooted in the organization—its culture, management, and structure" (Leveson et al. 2004, 1). In studies of companies with exceptional safety performance, four common characteristics were identified (Marshall 2000):

1. Strong management commitment
2. Efficient hazard identification
3. Efficient employee communication and involvement

4. Integration of safety into the larger management system

For example, NASA leadership has established the following high-level safety objectives for managing hazards (NASA 2008):

1. Protect public health
2. Protect workforce health
3. Protect the environment
4. Protect a program (systems and infrastructures needed to execute a mission) and public assets

NASA asserts that (NASA 2008, 5):

. . . to properly support key design and operational decisions, it is necessary that design and operational alternatives are analyzed not only with respect to their impact on the mission's technical and programmatic objectives, but also with respect to their impact on these high-level safety objectives.

Hazard identification is the primary activity in safety engineering work. While the organizational culture influences the priorities and decisions made during system development, management has a direct relationship with safety activities, resources, schedules, and decisions. The management framework incorporates and addresses resource allocation and other management issues that arise from four sources of failure (Haimes 2009, 25):

1. Hardware failure
2. Software failure
3. Organizational failure
4. Human failure

The system-safety program provides a mechanism for managing safety engineering work by aligning activities and resources within a planned timeframe.

There are likely to be multiple, and sometimes competing, perspectives and objectives. An essential element of system safety involves making decisions that eliminate hazards or reduce the frequency and/or consequences of accidents involving hazards to an acceptable level by introducing hazard control measures and modifying system design and/or procedures. The organization of the system-safety program is critical to:

1. Integrating safety engineering functions with the development of a system

2. Making risk decisions at each phase of development

According to Haimes (2009, 3), "Uncertainty colors the decision-making process regardless of . . ." the involvement of one or more parties; economic, sociopolitical, or geographical issues; science and technology; power and stakeholder involvement. Decision tools are helpful in establishing the criteria to make decisions about whether hazards are eliminated, mitigated, transferred, or accepted. Consequently, risk decision authority is an important element of the system-safety process.

In a report about NASA's safety culture, Leveson wrote that culture is embedded in routine, everyday activities, as well as in the organizational structure (2004): ". . . all aspects of the culture that affect safety must be engineered to be in alignment with the organizational safety principles." Common engineering methods, such as fault tree analysis (FTA) and failure modes and effects analysis (FMEA), are components of a system safety program within a comprehensive organizational safety structure. Leveson (2004) further states:

> Management, resources, capabilities, and culture are intertwined, and trying to change the culture without changing the environment within which the culture operates is doomed to failure. At the same time, simply changing the organizational structures—including policies, goals, missions, job descriptions, and standardized operating procedures related to safety—may lower risk over the short term, but superficial fixes that do not address the set of shared values and social norms are very likely to be undone over time.

A safety culture is complex; however, the organization's management structure and practices are significant factors in influencing the safety culture.

Culture is a pattern of shared basic assumptions that members of a group perceive, think, and feel in solving problems (Schein 1993). According to Schein, who is credited with coining the term *corporate culture*, a culture is comprised of three main components: (1) assumptions, (2) espoused values, and (3) artifacts and behaviors. Safety engineering work is largely influenced by the culture of the organization. The management structure, including goals, policies, plans, procedures,

resources, scheduling, and other tools, are artifacts—visible and tangible activities that influence the culture. The three components are interdependent entities that collectively create an environment that affects individuals, work, and the organization.

Safety culture is a term that was created in 1989 in a report by the International Atomic Energy Agency (IAEA) after the Chernobyl nuclear accident (IAEA 1989). According to the IAEA, a safety culture is the characteristics and attitudes of the organization and individuals concerning the perception of the value and prioritization of safety. Similarly, another definition was created after the NASA Columbia accident as "the subset of organizational culture that reflects the general attitude toward and approaches to safety and risk management" (Leveson et al. 2005, 5). A safety culture is complex and unique within each organization. Creating and sustaining a safety culture is challenging, especially so in organizations with diversity in geographical locations, contractor support activities, multiple operations, and other variables. The overall organizational safety culture is less likely to be changed, or developed, as easily as the management structure and resources.

However, the organization's management structure and practices are significant factors in influencing the safety culture. The management framework has a direct effect on the process of performing safety engineering work. In addition, the management framework has a dual effect, indirectly affecting the culture, as well as being indirectly affected by the culture.

The best practice for optimizing safety engineering work is to create an organizational culture that embraces safety. This practice takes a multipronged approach in planning and implementing the three components that create an environment where safety engineering work is esteemed as a critical function in developing a product, facility, or system. Safety engineers and managers may have divergent perspectives in optimal solutions for system safety. As stated by Main (2004, 381):

> Engineers typically have a strong passion for technical accuracy . . . conversely, managers and implementers tend to focus on value and effectiveness and often lack passion for technical accuracy. Managers may willingly accept some inaccurate but effective solutions that are easily implemented.

The best approach for a particular company is the method that works best in the organizational culture and design processes (Main 2004, 423).

PLANS, RESOURCES, AND COSTS

The primary purposes of safety engineering work are to prevent loss and optimize efficiency. Management of safety engineering work involves planning, budgeting, scheduling, and weighing risks in each phase of the system. Establishing criteria for decisions during the planning phases of system safety creates an objective method for weighing the costs and risks in the management of the hazards. Planning includes establishing guidelines and parameters within given cost and time constraints. Turner (2003) cautions that "the most important question to ask of any practice is the size of the bill."

The budget for any system, facility, or product includes cost and time consideration on two levels. First, there must be adequate resources allocated for safety engineering during each phase of development. For example, in the concept phase, a preliminary hazard analysis serves as a basis to create a system-safety plan. In addition to establishing milestones in each phase of system development, there is an opportunity to minimize costs and maximize efficiency by considering other disciplines that would enhance working groups.

Second, cost is part of the risk evaluation and decision for each hazard. It is likely that most people would be able to use more resources, but it is usually not efficient or feasible to eliminate all hazards in a system. Using the principles of risk management, risks may be transferred, controlled, or accepted. Cost and schedules are considered in a risk decision, but should not be the primary determinants in system development. Errors, time pressures, inadequately trained personnel, and unscheduled downtimes can have adverse effects on costs and schedules, indirectly contributing to the potential for accidents or oversights and elevating system costs.

There are numerous examples where resources, in terms of budget and time, have been cited as contributing factors in a system catastrophe. Leveson and Cutcher-Gershenfeld (2004) noted that one of the lessons learned in the accident analysis of the Columbia accident was that "budget cuts without concomitant cuts in goals led to trying to do too much with too little" (Leveson and Cutcher-Gershenfeld 2004, 1). Another example of a catastrophic accident occurred at the BP Texas City refinery in Texas City, Texas, in 2005. Among numerous root and contributing causes of the accident, the U.S. Chemical Safety Board (CSB) report found that risks were oversimplified and BP failed to address serious safety hazards (CSB 2005, 186), concluding that "budget cuts impaired process safety performance" (CSB 2005, 210).

There is much to be learned from catastrophic accidents concerning the importance of plans and resources for safety engineering work. A best practice in managing safety engineering work is to develop a system-safety management plan that includes adequate resources for resolution of serious hazards.

FEDERAL REGULATIONS AND RESOURCES

System-safety requirements are mandated for critical systems that can adversely affect life, health, property, operations, and the environment. In addition to regulatory requirements, federal agencies that develop systems provide a framework and guidance for managing safety engineering work for the respective systems they develop. The framework and guidance would include such elements as policies, procedures, handbooks, responsibilities, tasks, and other such elements.

The following government organizations regulate and oversee the development, operation, and disposal of certain critical systems. Commercial firms and other contractors implement government regulations but do not regulate the affected industry. Government organizations and industries develop provisions to implement federal regulations and may exceed minimal standards.

The Code of Federal Regulations (CFR) represents the standards and requirements of executive departments and federal agencies that are generated from federal laws. For example, the Occupational Safety and Health Administration (OSHA), created by the Occupational Safety and Health Act of 1970, establishes standards for workplace safety and health, and is an administrative branch of the Department of Labor. The law establishes the requirements, while other organizations, such as the American National Standards Institute (ANSI), the Institute of Electrical and Electronics Engineers, Inc. (IEEE), and the American Society of Safety Engineers (ASSE), develop standards, practices, guidelines, and other tools organizations can use to comply with the requirements and industry practice.

Below are some of the federal government agencies and regulations for system-safety requirements:

- Department of Defense Instruction (DoDI): DoDI 5000.1, The Defense Acquisition System; DoDI 5000.2, Operation of the Defense Acquisition System; and Military Standard 882D, DoD Standard Practice for System Safety

- Department of Transportation, Federal Aviation Administration (FAA): 14 CFR 1, Aeronautics and Space, FAA *System Safety Handbook*

- Department of Transportation, National Highway Traffic Safety Administration (NHTSA): Federal Motor Vehicle Safety Standards (FMVSS) 49 CFR 5 and 301

- Environmental Protection Agency (EPA): 40 CFR 68, Chemical Accident Prevention Provisions

- Food and Drug Administration (FDA): 21 CFR 807.90, Pre-Market Notification for Medical Devices; Part 210, Current Good Manufacturing Practice in Manufacturing, Process, Packing, or Holding of Drugs; 21 CFR Part 211, Current Good Manufacturing Process for Finished Pharmaceuticals

- Nuclear Regulatory Commission (NRC): 10 CFR 70.62, Safety Program and Integrated Safety Analysis; 10 CFR 70.72, Facility Changes and Change Process

- Occupational Safety and Health Administration (OSHA): 29 CFR 1910.119, Process Safety Management; 29 CFR 1910.147, Control of Hazardous Energy

- United States Patent and Trademark Office: *Life Cycle Management Manual*

Many organizations use voluntary guidelines and industry consensus standards to enhance capability, maximize resources, and mitigate hazards, thereby minimizing the necessity of redesign for correcting hazards and reducing other costs that may adversely affect people, property, or the environment.

INDUSTRY STANDARDS AND PROFESSIONAL ORGANIZATIONS

In addition to the mandatory federal regulations, organizations advance industry standards, research, and current information through publications, guidelines, and practices developed by technical experts from government, industry, academia, and other stakeholders. Professional nonprofit organizations also publish timely peer-reviewed articles from their members. A few that publish professional journals in addition to other member services are listed below. These journals are excellent resources for standards and practices that have been developed and recommended by technical and scientific committees.

- The American National Standards Institute (ANSI), a nonprofit organization, coordinates and publishes voluntary standards that exceed regulatory requirements. Experts from industry, academia, and government work on technical committees to develop consensus standards. One of the recent publications, *ANSI Z-10, Occupational Health and Safety Management Systems*, was created through a partnership with the American Industrial Hygiene Association (AIHA). ANSI has numerous committees, subcommittees, and publications.

- The American Petroleum Institute (API) is the national trade association for the oil and natural gas industry and produces quality standards for the industry. One of its standards is *Specification for Quality Programs for the Petroleum, Petrochemical and Natural Gas Industry* (API 2007), which includes the requirements of the International Organization for Standardization (ISO) 9001 and additional quality assurance requirements for the oil and gas industry. The API does not regulate the industry; however, their guidance documents provide a systematic approach to integrating safety, health, and environment considerations for equipment, products, and services in the global industry.

- The American Society of Safety Engineers (ASSE) is a nonprofit professional safety organization that advances research, technical publications, and other initiatives concerning protection of people, property, and the environment.

- The American Society for Testing and Materials (ASTM) is an international organization that publishes technical standards and specifications for materials, products, systems, and services. In addition to its library of standards, ASTM publishes several technical journals.

- The Institute of Electrical and Electronics Engineers, Inc. (IEEE) is a nonprofit professional organization that develops international standards for the advancement of technology, particularly in areas such as aerospace systems, telecommunications and information technology, biomedical engineering, and power generation. The standards are developed from research and technical committees comprised of technical experts.

- The International Standards Organization (ISO) is an international consortium that develops technical standards by consensus. The standards define specifications and criteria for the classification of materials, manufacture and supply of products, testing and analysis, terminology, and services. Although the ISO is not an enforcement agency, ISO 9000 certification is an international quality benchmark that verifies conformance to ISO standards.

- The National Fire Protection Association (NFPA) is an international nonprofit organization for fire, electrical, building, and public safety. The NFPA forms technical committees, adopts and publishes standards, provides training, and is a global leader in the prevention of fire and related hazards and building safety standards. The NFPA publishes standards such as the *National Fire Codes*, the *National Electric Code*, and the *Life Safety Code* through its technical committees.

- The Society of Automotive Engineers (SAE) is an international nonprofit organization that advances the engineering practices of mobility systems. Its technical committees publish specifications and guidance for materials, products, processes, and procedures for powered vehicles.

- The Society of Fire Protection Engineers (SFPE) is an nonprofit international organization that supports practitioners in fire protection engineering. Technical committees develop and publish guidelines and practices for fire protection designs and services.

Several of these nonprofit organizations develop, adopt, and publish industry standards. All use technical expertise from industry, government, academia, and other stakeholders in developing models and best practices for managing safety engineering work.

Approaches to Managing Safety Engineering Work

Safety engineering is managed and structured like other business plans within the context of an organization and its system-safety program. A business plan implements a strategy "to look ahead, allocate resources, focus on key points, and prepare for problems and opportunities" (Berry 2004). The foundation for a business plan includes a mission statement, goals, responsibilities, a decision process, a budget, and performance measurements. A system-safety plan is similar to a business plan in its overall structure and essential management elements. Effective management of safety engineering work requires similar planning, allocation of resources, human resource management, and performance measurements. In addition, management of safety engineering work addresses communications, which may be accomplished by using an established software program and writing reports.

Besides outlining the steps and key decision points in a given management model, the system-safety plan should identify the plan's interactions with other key functions. Some organizations use internal system-safety plans, but if they contract to provide a service for another organization, it is prudent to examine the interface points. Many other system or process management models use common approaches in assessment strategies, including a life-cycle framework, early integration, risk management, decision points, performance assessments, user/operator/stakeholder feedback, and continuous improvement.

One of the best practices in the management of safety engineering work is forming a cross-functional team, often referred to as a working group, which encourages collaboration and communication. A team approach allows the disciplines to design and evaluate a system, and communication is often facilitated with design reviews and periodic presentations.

A multidisciplinary team-based approach to life-cycle management creates synergism in assessing identified, unknown, and potential hazards that may have an adverse effect on people, property, and the environment. As stated by Belke (2000), "... various elements are generally not independent from one another; a significant interrelationship usually exists between each of them, and all of the elements need to work well together, or accidents can happen." A major benefit in using a multidisciplinary team is to identify a broader range of alternatives to eliminate or minimize hazards. Unintended consequences could result from mitigating hazards in one area that could create problems in another. For example, in the design of a new high-pressure research facility in the United Kingdom, a multidisciplinary team was formed to address both system development and operations. There were a series of modifications to both equipment and the facility. The working group was an essential part of the engineering design throughout the process. The group made it possible to identify alternative equipment configurations that met operational needs within a new facility (Philbin 2010).

RISK MANAGEMENT IN A MULTIDISCIPLINARY ENVIRONMENT

Risk management is a process that is used in several disciplines as an analytical method to evaluate requirements, costs, and risks, and to make decisions about the system. Often, each engineering discipline will use different models for risk assessment. It is beneficial to identify the various engineering disciplines that will be involved in the development of a system and

use a common risk-assessment matrix upon which to evaluate hazards.

Research and case studies of the experiences of many organizations demonstrate that consideration and integration of safety engineering and other related disciplines facilitate hazard identification and corrective actions, which are especially important during early phases when corrective actions can be less complex and costly.

A best practice in managing safety engineering work is to be aware of other disciplines and of opportunities to collaborate or coordinate information with them. For example, environmental engineering, the application of science and engineering, studies systems and processes that mitigate harm to the environment. Environmental concerns considered early in the design can address systems and processes that may affect air, ground, water, hazardous waste, or human health.

Most systems will require human involvement in some aspect of operations, maintenance, or disposal, thus allowing a potential exposure to hazards, or the possibility of human error. The field of human factors engineering is involved with the control of hazards in a human–machine interface through design. Scientific and engineering methods are used to assess the potential for human error and equipment or system design hazards with the goal of designing jobs, machines, operations, environments, and work systems for compatibility with human capabilities and limitations. Many ergonomic concerns, such as musculoskeletal disorders (MSDs), high noise levels, or eye hazards, may be minimized by utilizing human factors engineers to assess the risks that may affect the user or operator of the system. For example, the seat dimensions, head and leg room, and placement and illumination of visual displays and operator controls in aircraft cockpits are designed to fit aviators. The goal of the system is to maximize the space and to consider the tasks and operations in the cockpit in order to minimize human error in both routine and emergency situations.

Collaboration with other organizations improves each organization's ability to identify potential hazards in a system. The Department of Defense (DOD), Federal Aviation Administration (FAA), and National Aeronautics and Space Administration (NASA) jointly developed a publication on engineering design criteria and guidelines entitled *Human Engineering Design Data Digest* (2000). This publication provides quantitative human engineering design criteria and guidelines for use during system, equipment, or facility design and assessment. In the management of safety engineering work, the collaboration and use of publications, databases, and other methods that help to identify hazards is a best practice that improves safety and efficiency.

Other engineering disciplines also enhance system design and efficiency. Every change in materials, equipment, process, or operation in a system's life cycle should be assessed by a safety engineer to identify potential hazards that may impact the system.

A COMPREHENSIVE MANAGEMENT FRAMEWORK

The field of safety has emerged from a need to reduce accidents, minimize losses, prevent harm, and increase efficiency. In industrial safety, that need has eventually materialized into laws and regulations that standardize requirements for various hazardous working conditions. From that perspective, the federal government has specified the requirements and enforced the laws and regulations, thus building the foundation for industrial safety management. In contrast, system safety has evolved from responsible organizations that have a need to produce a safe system or product. Historically, organizations with the greatest need to produce safe systems have been developers in the aerospace, aviation, missile, and nuclear industries, primarily government and government contractors. The concept of system safety has grown and expanded to other industries, such as transportation; however, the structure and implementation of system safety is dependent on organizational requirements rather than law.

Generally, the framework for managing safety engineering work commonly includes the following elements:

1. Defining roles and responsibilities
2. Determining requirements and criteria
3. Allocating resources
4. Identifying a strategy and process to identify hazards and manage risk
5. Measuring performance
6. Facilitating communication, information exchange, and a feedback loop
7. Facilitating participation, involvement, and commitment to safety and health at all levels in the organization

There are numerous ways to manage safety engineering work. Organizational procedures vary on the management structure, safety engineering methodologies, risk categories, and other elements of system safety. Organizations such as the DOD, FAA, NASA, DOE, DOT, and others have similar system-safety programs and regulations that provide a comprehensive framework for managing safety engineering work for the systems they develop.

In private industry, organizations also establish the parameters for developing new systems, and, as with the federal government agencies, each within their scope of authority. MacCollum suggests using a similar methodology for the construction industry (MacCollum 2008, 26): "The application of system safety principles has been largely limited to the aerospace and electronic community. These principles need to be adopted by forward-thinking design and build contractors."

Although each organization varies in its mission, collaboration and communication within industries serve to help and encourage organizations to use and improve both management and safety engineering work that results in systems that cost less and are safer to build, operate, and maintain. In the construction industry, a long-standing organization, the National Institute of Building Sciences (NIBS), was established in 1974 to serve as an interface between government and the private sector. Their mission is to serve the nation by advancing knowledge in the building sciences and technology to enable organizations to identify and resolve issues for the construction of safe, affordable structures for housing, commerce, and industry (NIBS 2011). Through the various committees comprised of public and private industry representatives, the organization develops and publishes consensus standards that facilitate communication and an integrated approach to building safe structures.

However, although such industry consensus standards promote sound concepts and standards, each organization must determine the structure for management and implementation within their organizations. As Vincoli stated, ". . . no matter how exact and comprehensive a design or operating safety program is considered to be, the proper management of that system is still one of the most important elements of success" (Vincoli 1997, 5).

Organizations that achieve the greatest success in developing and maintaining safe systems recognize that the management framework and safety engineering work are two components of a comprehensive system. The third intangible component that is highly influential in how the work is carried out, and the decisions made concerning the system, is the organizational culture.

CONCLUSION

This chapter discusses the best practices in managing safety engineering work. There is a difference between the definition of system safety and safety engineering. The subtle distinction is that system safety is defined as the management system, and safety engineering is the application of safety and engineering within the management framework.

Best practices in the management of safety engineering work are based on sound business principles and administration. There are many ways to manage safety engineering work, using a variety of sources for information, including regulatory agencies, consensus standards, and professional organizations and publications, all of which are intended to facilitate an environment of continuous learning and improvement. There are three fundamental components in successfully managing safety engineering work that will reap the greatest benefit to the organization and the system: (1) organizational culture, (2) management framework, and

(3) safety engineering practices. The three components are intertwined and interdependent.

At an organizational level, a safety culture fosters a dynamic learning environment committed to continuous improvement through the integration of safety management into all facets of work planning and execution. The comprehensive framework is a structured model that integrates safety as part of the design and throughout other phases in the life cycle of a product, process, or facility. The primary function of system safety is to identify and control hazards in each phase of the life cycle, from concept through decommissioning and disposal.

A management system provides a process for planning, organizing, budgeting, and aligning resources within time and cost constraints. Within these major functions, there are various elements that define the management process and tasks, including decision making, implementation, and evaluation.

This chapter shows how safety engineering work without a supportive organizational culture can influence risk decisions concerning cost and schedule. Similarly, the best organizational culture or management system without the technical expertise of safety engineering methodology can contribute to the failure in any system. As stated by Main: "The best approach for a particular company is the method that works best in the organizational culture and design process" (Main 2004, 423).

REFERENCES

American Petroleum Institute (API). *Recommended Practice for Development of a Safety and Environmental Management Program for Offshore Operations and Facilities* (accessed February 1, 2011). www.api.org/Standards/epstandards/upload/75_E3.pdf

———. *Specification for Quality Programs for the Petroleum, Petrochemical and Natural Gas Industry* (accessed February 3, 2011). www.api.org/Standards/faq/upload/valueofstandards.pdf

Belke, James C. 2000. *Chemical Accident Risks in U.S. Industry: A Preliminary Analysis of Accident Risk Data from U.S. Hazardous Chemical Facilities* (accessed February 3, 2011). www.toxic.dead-planet.net/pdfs/stockholmpaper.pdf

Berry, Tim. 2004. *Hurdle: The Book on Business Planning.* Eugene, OR: Palo Alto Software, Inc.

Brauer, R. 1990. *Safety and Health for Engineers.* New York: Van Nostrand Reinhold.

Clemens, P., and R. Simmons. 2000. *System Safety Scrapbook* (accessed February 3, 2011). www.fault-tree.net/papers/clemens-safety-scrapbook.pdf

Department of Defense (DOD). 2000. *Human Engineering Design Data Digest* (accessed February 7, 2011). www.dtic.mil/cgi-bin/GetTRDoc?AD=ADA467401&Location=U2&doc=GetTRDoc.pdf

_____. 2005. Military Standard 882E, *Standard Practice for System Safety* (accessed January 17, 2011). www.system-safety.org/Documents/MIL-STD-882E-Feb05.doc

Food and Drug Administration (FDA). *Facts About Current Good Manufacturing Practices (CGMP)* (accessed February 7, 2011). www.fda.gov/Drugs/DevelopmentApprovalProcess/Manufacturing/ucm169105.htm

Haimes, Yacov Y. 2009. *Risk Modeling, Assessment, and Management.* Hoboken, NJ: John Wiley & Sons.

Leveson, N. 2004. *A New Accident Model for Engineering Safer Systems* (accessed February 9, 2011). sunnyday.mit.edu/accidents/safetyscience-single.pdf

_____. 2009. *Engineering a Safer World: System Safety for the 21st Century* (accessed February 9, 2011). sunnyday.mit.edu/book2.pdf

Leveson, N., and J. Cutcher-Gershenfeld. 2004. *What System Safety Engineering Can Learn from the Columbia Accident* (accessed February 10, 2011). sunnyday.mit.edu/papers/issc04-final.pdf

Leveson, N., J. Cutcher-Gershenfeld, B. Barrett, A. Brown, J. Carroll, N. Dulac, L. Fraile, and K. Marais. 2004. "Effectively Addressing NASA's Organizational and Safety Culture: Insights from Systems Safety and Engineering Systems." Paper presented at the Engineering Systems Division Symposium, Massachusetts Institute of Technology, Cambridge, MA, March 29–31, 2004 (accessed March 17, 2011). sunnyday.mit.edu/papers/esd2-columbia.doc

MacCullom, D., and R. Davis. 2008. "Engineering Principles for Safer Design." Presented at the Professional Development Conference of the American Society of Safety Engineering June 9–12, 2008, Las Vegas, NV.

Main, B. 2004. *Risk Assessment: Basics and Benchmarks.* Ann Arbor, MI: Design Safety Engineering, Inc.

Marshall, G. 2000. *Safety Engineering.* 3d ed. Des Plaines, IL: American Society of Safety Engineers.

National Aeronautic and Space Administration (NASA). 1999. DHB-S-001, *System Safety Handbook.* hnd.usacc.army.mil/safety/RefDocs/FASS/NASA%205Systems%20Safety.pdf

_____. 2008. NPR 8715.3, *General Safety Program Requirements* (retrieved January 3, 2011). www.hq.nasa.fov/office/code/doctree/87153.htm

_____. 2007. SP-2007-6105 Rev. 1, *System Engineering Handbook.* education.ksc.nasa.gov/esmdspacegrant/Document/NASA%20SP-2007-6015%20rev%201%20Final%2031Dec2007.pdf

National Institute of Building Sciences (NIBS). 2011. *Whole Building Design Guide* (accessed April 12, 2011). www.nibs.org

Nuclear Regulatory Commission (NRC). 2005. *Safety Program and Integrated Safety Analysis* (accessed February 7, 2011). www.nrc.gov/reading-rm/doc-collections/cfr/part070/part070-0062.html

Philbin, Simon P. 2010. "Developing an Integrated Approach to System Safety Engineering." *Engineering Management Journal* 22.2(2010): 56–67.

Roland, Harold E., and B. Moriarty. 1990. *System Safety Engineering and Management.* 2d ed. Hoboken, NJ: John Wiley & Sons, Inc.

Schein, E. H. 2004. *Organizational Culture and Leadership.* 3d ed. San Francisco, CA: John Wiley & Sons, Inc.

Stephans, Richard A. 2004. *System Safety for the 21st Century: The Updated and Revised Edition of System Safety 2000.* Hoboken, NJ: Wiley-Interscience.

Turner, R. 2003. "Seven Pitfalls to Avoid in the Hunt for Best Practices." *IEEE Software* 20(1):67–69.

Vincoli, J. 1997. *Basic Guide to System Safety.* New York: John Wiley & Sons.

Wasson, C. 2006. *System Analysis, Design, and Development: Concepts, Principles, and Practices.* Hoboken, NJ: John Wiley & Sons, Inc.

APPENDIX: SELECTED REFERENCES, PUBLICATIONS, AND ORGANIZATIONS

The following references are a few of the organizations and publications where the reader can find best practices in systems and engineering.

American Chemistry Council (ACC). *Model of Responsible Care*. www.americanchemistry.com

American Institute of Chemical Engineers (AIChE). *Technical Management of Chemical Process Safety*. www.knovel.com/knovel2/Publisher.jsp?PublisherID=101253

American National Standards Institute (ANSI). www.ansi.org

American Petroleum Institute (API). www.api.org

American Society of Civil Engineers (ASCE). *Journal of Construction Engineering and Management*. www.asce.org/asce.cfm

American Society of Engineering Education (ASEE). www.asee.org

American Society of Heating, Refrigeration, and Air Conditioning Engineers (ASHRAE). www.ashrae.org

American Society of Mechanical Engineers (ASME). www.asme.org

American Society of Mechanical Engineers, Safety Engineering and Risk Analysis Division (SERAD). www.asme.org/divisions/serad

American Society of Safety Engineers (ASSE). www.asse.org

Architectural Engineering Institute (AEI). www.content.aeinstitute.org/intro.html

Department of Defense (DOD). *Defense Acquisition Guidebook*, "Systems Engineering." www.defenselink.mil/pubs/archive/html

Department of Defense (DOD). Ergonomics Working Group, *Best Practices*. www.ergoworkinggroup.org/ewgweb/IndexFrames/index3.htm

Department of Defense (DOD), Human Factors Engineering Technical Advisory Group. *Human Engineering Design Data Digest*. www.hfetag.dtic.mil/docs/pocket_guide.doc

Department of Energy (DOE). DOE P 450.4, :"Safety Management System Policy." www.directives.doe.gov/pdfs/doe/doetext/neword/450/p4504.html

Electric Power Research Institute (EPRI). www.my.epri.com

Federal Aviation Administration (FAA). *System Safety Handbook*. www.faa.gov/library/manuals/aviation/risk_management/ss_handbook

Food and Drug Administration, Center for Drug Evaluation and Research. *Current Good Manufacturing Practices (CGMP) Regulations: Division of Manufacturing and Product Quality*. www.fda.gov/cder/dmpq

Food and Drug Administration (FDA), Center for Drug Evaluation and Research. *Good Laboratory Practices, A Risk-Based Approach to Pharmaceutical Current Good Manufacturing Practices (CGMP) for the 21st Century*. www.fda.gov/cder/gmp

Food and Drug Administration (FDA). *Good Laboratory Practices (GLP)*. www.fda.gov/ora/compliance_ref/bimo/glp/default.htm

Human Factors: The Journal of the Human Factors and Ergonomics Society. www.hfes.org/web/AboutHFES/history.html

Institute of Electrical and Electronics Engineers (IEEE). www.ieee.org

Institute of Physics, Nanotechnology. www.nanotechweb.org/

International Ergonomics Association. 2000. *The Discipline of Ergonomics*. www.iea.cc/

International Standards Organization (ISO). www.iso.org

Johnson, Paul W. *ePORT, NASA's Computer Database Program for System Safety Risk Management Oversight (Electronic Project Online Risk Tool)*. National Aeronautics and Space Administration. ntrs.nasa.gov/archive/nasa/casi.ntrs.nasa.gov/20080030091_2008022873.pdf

Joint Commission Accreditation of Healthcare Organizations (JCAHO). www.jcaho.org

Journal of Architectural Engineering. www.pubs.asce.org/journals

Mechanical Engineering Magazine Online. www.memagazine.org

National Aeronautics and Space Administration (NASA). *Systems Engineering Handbook*. www.ntrs.nasa.gov/archive/nasa/casi.ntrs.nasa.gov/19960002194_1996102194.pdf

National Fire Protection Association (NFPA). www.nfpa.org

National Nanotechnology Initiative (NNI). www.nano.gov

Society of Automotive Engineers (SAE). www.sae.org

System Safety Society. www.system-safety.org

U.S. Department of Energy (DOE), Nuclear Criticality Safety Program. www.ncsc.llnl.gov

SECTION <u>2</u>
HAZARD COMMUNICATION
AND RIGHT-TO-KNOW

Regulatory Issues

Cost Analysis and Budgeting

Benchmarking and Performance Criteria

Best Practices

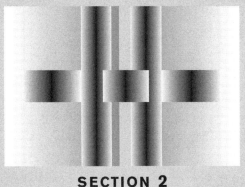

LEARNING OBJECTIVES

▌ Learn how to implement and comply with the OSHA *Hazard Communication Standard* 29 CFR 1900.1200 (OSHA 1983).

▌ Become familiar with hazard communications for products, environments, and locations *not* within an OSHA-controlled workplace, including established methods for providing general chemical product information (ANSI Z129.1 2010); standards for environmental, facility, and product signage and labeling (ANSI Z535 series 2011); and standards more closely related to vehicular applications (*Manual on Uniform Traffic Control Devices* 2009).

▌ Learn how labeling and material safety data sheet (MSDS) standards and guidelines are gradually changing to the Globally Harmonized System (GHS).

REGULATORY ISSUES

James M. Miller

THIS CHAPTER IS concerned with hazard communications, with an emphasis on the standards and regulations that address such communications. Most of the chapter addresses the Occupational Safety and Health Administration's promulgated *Hazard Communication Standard* (HazCom or HCS), dealing primarily with chemical hazards. But it also includes a broader overview of warnings applicable to several other types of hazard communications that are often confronted in one's work and nonwork environments.

Hazard communication should be viewed as a broad term that identifies information about hazards of many types. The goal of such information is to create an awareness that will help protect not only human safety and health but also physical property, vehicles, machinery, processes, and the environment. Ultimately, any hazard communication is directed toward humans with the hope that they might respond in a way that will increase the likelihood of avoiding a particular hazard. The common channels through which such information is conveyed include environmental and facility signing, product labeling, operator and instruction manuals, specialized safety documents, formalized training, and personal communications. All of these typically have imbedded within them both warning and instructional information. Think of hazard communications as both "warnings" about the possible presence of hazards and "instructions" for remedial action to avoid or minimize the risk associated with such hazards.

The modern movement toward providing hazard communications started to gain momentum in the 1960s and early 1970s with the passage of congressional acts such as the Consumer Product Safety Act (CPSA), the Motor Vehicle Safety Act (MVSA), and the Occupational Safety and Health Act (OSH Act). The health regulations promulgated under OSHA in the mid-1980s, section

29 CFR 1910.1200, focused on the premise of the *worker's right to know*, and that section was titled "Hazard Communication." In retrospect, using this term was unfortunate; it probably should have been more specifically identified as "Health Hazard Communication." As a consequence, in any type of chemical health setting, the term "hazard communication" has been broadly used to refer to the OSHA promulgated 29 CFR 1910.1200 (OSHA 1983). However, outside of the OSHA setting, the term is used more generally to refer to all of the types of communications about many hazards. Therefore, within this or any writings about hazard communications, one must correctly identify the type of hazard being addressed. For example, there are environmental hazard communications, safety hazard communications, health hazard communications, processing hazard communications, and equipment hazard communications, to name a few. This chapter turns first to a discussion of early health hazard considerations that led to the OSHA (Health) *Hazard Communication Standard* (HazCom) (OSHA 1983).

EARLY HISTORY OF CHEMICAL HAZARDS

Chemical Hazards in the Pre-OSHA Era

Providing information about chemicals to users is a tradition that goes back centuries. Manufacturers and distributors have always had an interest in defining the characteristics of the chemical products they make and distribute. Chemical manufacturers are in business to sell chemicals, and such chemicals will not be bought if manufacturers do not have specification data that deal with the functional and physical characteristics of each chemical. Thus, there were early versions of abbreviated chemical data sheets that had information about health and safety hazards along with physical properties. Such safety data, until recently, was voluntarily developed and distributed as a part of doing business as a chemical manufacturer or distributor. That there are now regulatory requirements for such information has only slightly changed the format of these earlier safety data sheets and the types of information they provide. However, there are those who allege that the purposes of these sheets

should be much broader in scope than tradition or current regulations require. Thus, an understanding of the development of the chemical data sheet is essential, particularly in the legal environment, to appreciate what it was intended to do, both historically and currently.

The formative period in the history of chemical data sheets was from the early 1900s through about 1968. As this period evolved, professional, trade, industrial, university, insurance, and government organizations gradually began to take an interest in providing information about both the physical characteristics and the potential health hazards associated with chemical usage. In 1938, the National Conference of Governmental Industrial Hygienists first issued maximum allowable concentrations of chemicals for human exposure. In 1944, the Manufacturing Chemists Association established their Labels and Precautionary Information Committee. A few years later in 1946, they began to publish what was to become a tradition for the next 30 years, their Chemical Safety Data Sheets, the first of which was for formaldehyde (Kaplan 1986).

One academic individual stood out in these early years, the industrial hygienist Warren Cook of the University of Michigan, who in 1947 compiled the early listings of maximum allowable concentrations (MACs). These were compiled among the industrial hygienists and toxicologists of that day. It was also in the 1940s that insurance companies had an interest in providing hazard information about chemicals through their American Association of Casualty and Safety Companies (AACSC). Initially called "Special Hazard Bulletins," they were renamed "Chemical Hazard Bulletins" in 1951 and were distributed to the AACSC's insured companies, who in turn distributed them to end users of hazardous chemicals (Kaplan 1986).

The U.S. government also took a role in providing health hazard information with initial efforts housed in the U.S. Department of Labor (DOL). In 1945, DOL began to publish a series of documents under the title "Controlling Chemical Hazards." The first of these was on ammonia. How exposure levels were measured and reported changed in the years 1958–59, and the term maximum allowable concentration was changed to threshold limit value. About ten years later, it was changed to time-weighted averages as OSHA and the industry began using the personal dosimeter, which could measure workplace exposure concentrations over a full 8-hour shift (Kaplan 1986).

One industry that received early attention from the government in the 1950s was the maritime industry. Because of the number of incidents, the DOL established a maritime safety office, headed by Joseph LaRocca and Edward C. March, to investigate maritime and dock accidents. They found the cause of many accidents to be related to hazardous chemicals and began researching the types of chemical data sheets used by the manufacturing industry. Some 18 years later, in August 1968, LaRocca and Van Atta produced the first governmental format for chemical information sheets with categories of recommended information. It was published in 33 FR 12008 as an amendment to 29 CFR, Parts 1501, 1502, and 1503 (Shipbuilding, Shipbreaking, and Ship Repairing) (Kaplan 1986). It was identified as Form No. LSB-00S-4, and employers in the covered industries were to collect information about the chemicals within their respective maritime workplaces. To do this, they were to use Form LSB-00S-4 or to collect these same categories of information and place them into optional formats. It was likely that these required types of information were solicited from chemical manufacturers, distributors, trade sources, and insurance companies. It is important to note that even these early regulatory responsibilities required employers to gather information but did not require manufacturers to provide it. There is no information on whether this requirement was enforced or whether the main intent of these efforts became absorbed into the regulations of the act that followed. This act was the OSH Act of 1970 and, with its enactment, the world of worker safety and health was forever changed.

Post-OSHA and Before the HCS Standard (1970–1985)

With the passage of Public Law 91-596 in December 1970, the Occupational Health and Safety Act, the OSH Act, as it is known today, was established. Relative to hazard communication, the act states that all occupational health and safety standards "shall prescribe the use of labels or other appropriate forms of warning as are necessary to insure that employees are apprised of all hazards to which they are exposed, relevant symptoms and appropriate emergency treatment, and proper conditions and precautions of safe use or exposure" (OSH Act, Section 6, Paragraph 7). This provision of the OSH Act was to be implemented by employers. It did not put requirements on manufacturers to provide chemical information. However, one can presume information from manufacturers was being requested by those employers at the same time manufacturers were voluntarily providing such information in conjunction with regular customer technical services.

To provide and further promote the idea of readily available chemical information, the form developed for maritime employers (LSB-00S-4) was considered as something that might be useful across many industries, so it was adopted by OSHA and renamed Form OSHA-20 in May 1972. Another step toward providing chemical information came in 1974 when the National Institute for Occupational Safety and Health (NIOSH) published a document intended for OSHA, "A Recommended Standard: An Identification System for Occupationally Hazardous Materials" (NIOSH 1974). It included recommendations for warning labels and chemical data sheets (48 FR 53280). It was OSHA's decision not to act on this proposal at that time, and the NIOSH recommendations did not become part of a proposed standard until several years later.

Then in 1976 Congressman Andrew Maguire of New Jersey and a health research group petitioned OSHA to issue a standard requiring the labeling of all workplace chemicals. During the same time period, the House of Representatives' Committee on Government Operations recommended that OSHA enforce the health provisions of the Occupational Safety and Health Act by requiring manufacturers to disclose any toxic ingredients in their products and to disclose this information to employees (47 FR 12092). By January 1977, OSHA responded and published in the Federal Register an advanced notice of proposed rulemaking (ANPR) regarding chemical labeling. The ANPR notice requested comments and recommendations from the public regarding the need for such a standard along with information that should be included in such a standard (42 FR 5372-5374, 34). Four years later, in January 1981, OSHA published a notice of proposed rulemaking (NPR) that would require employers to assess workplace hazards under a predetermined set of criteria. The proposed standard did not make material safety data sheets (MSDSs) mandatory, and it was withdrawn a month later for further consideration (48 FR 53280, 34). It was the following March 1982 that OSHA published a "final proposal" for the *Hazard Communication Standard*. It required chemical manufacturers to assess the hazards of all chemicals that they produced. Furthermore, all employers were to establish hazard communication programs for their employees. Under this proposed standard, an important change was that the MSDS would now be mandatory (47 FR 12092), but it was several years before this became a reality, due to various legal challenges.

THE HAZARD COMMUNICATION STANDARD IS ENACTED

On November 25, 1983, OSHA published in the Federal Register, Vol. 48, the actual *Hazard Communication Standard*, 29 CFR Part 1910.1200. This initial standard applied only to standard industrial classification (SIC) codes 20 through 39. As of November 25, 1986, it required MSDSs to be provided by only manufacturers and distributors for their customers and employees. Even prior to this effective date, during 1985, there was a judicial review of this same HazCom standard. Because this original standard covered only manufacturing and distributors, OSHA was asked by the U.S. Court of Appeals to reconsider this limited breadth. Then, in August 1987, OSHA published a final rule incorporating the changes suggested by the Court of Appeals. The revised standard expanded the scope to all industries where employees were exposed to hazardous chemicals (52 FR 31852). After various court challenges, it eventually

became effective January 30, 1989. On another front, in September 1985, the OSHA staff published OSHA Form 174, a blank MSDS sheet that incorporated all of the MSDS requirements of the *Hazard Communication Standard*, although it was not necessary to use this form to provide the required information. When completed correctly, an MSDS prepared using Form 174 contains all the information required by OSHA. However, Form 174 does not use the more organized and comprehensive 16-section format and substantial changes that the Global Harmonization System (GHS) will require in the 16-section format. As noted earlier, Form 174 was structured after the earlier Form LSB-00S-4. An example of Form 174 appears as Appendix A.

HAZCOM STANDARD OVERVIEW AND RESPONSIBILITY

The *Hazard Communication Standard* was based on the philosophy that employees have both a need and a right to know the identities of chemicals and the associated hazards of those chemicals to which they are exposed when working. They also have a right to know what protective measures are available to prevent adverse effects from occurring. Dr. Eula Bingham, Assistant Secretary of Labor for OSHA in the late 1970s, was a strong promoter of this philosophy. The major administrative interpretations of the HCS were formulated during this period of time to provide employees with the information they needed to know about their workplace health hazards. The rules specifically address the evaluation and communication of chemical hazard information to workers. The standard has been represented by analysts as incorporating a "downstream flow of information," which means that producers of chemicals have the primary responsibility for generating and disseminating information, whereas users of chemicals must obtain the information and transmit it to their own employees.

It should be obvious to anyone who looks at a chemical's hazard information that the evaluation of chemical hazards involves a multitude of technical concepts, and this evaluation process is one that requires the professional judgment of experienced experts familiar with a particular chemical or a particular chemical family. That is why the HCS is designed so that employers who simply use chemicals but do not produce or import them are not required to evaluate the hazards of those chemicals.

Once a hazard determination is made, it continues to be the responsibility of the manufacturers and importers of the chemicals to provide updated hazard information to employers purchasing and using their chemical products. On the other hand, employers who do not produce or import chemicals need only to focus on those parts of the rule that deal with establishing a workplace program and communicating pass-through hazard information to their workers.

Because of the extensive compliance requirements within OSHA's health hazard communications standard, employers and chemical manufacturers carry a heavy burden of responsibility that is hardly matched by the requirements of any other type of health, safety, or environmental hazard regulation. The dominance of health hazard communication requirements within OSHA becomes further emphasized by OSHA's records, which reflect that violations of 29 CFR 1910.1200 have typically been second only to scaffolding in the number of citations issued annually by OSHA compliance officers.

Before moving into the next section, which provides some specifics of compliance, there are certain historical clarifications that should be noted. In the current forensic environment, workers' exposures to hazards are being reviewed retrospectively to include their past as well as their present and future work careers. The role that product hazard information in various forms has played in this review has come under scrutiny because hindsight seems so much clearer than foresight. During the period before 1987, some factions point to certain inadequacies of labeling or to MSDS material as not complying with OSHA. But before this time there was no compliance required by OSHA, as noted in several places in this chapter. On the other hand, even when compliance was not mandatory, there were extensive voluntary efforts by chemical producers, distributors, professional organizations, trade associations, and insurance interests to create

the common practice of providing chemical hazard information to purchasers and users. But again, it was only after the enactment of the OSHA HCS from 1987–89 that it became mandatory to provide such information to employees. To summarize, before the November 1987–89 effective dates for the HCS, manufacturers, importers, and distributors were not required under OSHA to provide (a) any material safety data sheets for chemicals under their manufacture or distribution; (b) specific categories of health hazard information; or (c) health hazard information in a certain format.

Federal Versus State Program Requirements

As this chapter proceeds to discuss the implementation of the HCS requirements, there is one caveat that could affect certain practitioners. That is the existence of OSHA-approved state plans. When operating with employees in state plan states, one must obviously comply with that state's requirements, which may be slightly different from the federal requirements. However, to qualify for a state plan, a state must provide rules (regulations) that are "at least as effective as" the federal OSHA regulatory requirements. Some states, such as California, have selected requirements that go beyond those of the federal program. A few of the state-plan states actually had hazard communication or right-to-know laws prior to the effective date of the federal OSHA rule. Currently, about half the states have some type of OSHA-approved state plan. However, some states such as Connecticut, New Jersey, and New York, as well as the Virgin Islands, have plans that cover only public-sector (state and local government) employment. The specifics of state plans are not provided or further addressed in this chapter. Thus, employers in state-plan states should contact their respective state OSHA Offices or Web sites for applicable requirements.

The chapter next turns to a description of the OSHA *Hazard Communication Standard* as it now exists and how one can, in general, implement a plan that will likely satisfy the OSHA compliance requirement. Recognize that, over the next ten years, this standard is expected to evolve and resemble the GHS.

HazCom Standard Requirements under Federal OSHA

As of 2010, the HazCom standard applies to all businesses where hazardous chemicals are used in the workplace. A *hazardous chemical* is defined by OSHA as "any liquid, solid, or gas that could present a physical or health hazard to an employee" (OSHA 2002, 4–5). Examples of hazardous chemicals include cleaning agents, degreasers, flammables, greases, paints, pesticides, aerosols, and compressed gases.

The provisions outlining the hazard communication program compliance requirements are found in the standard located at 29 CFR 1910.1200 (OSHA 1983). A key focus of these requirements is the employer's HazCom program. The specifics of such a program are in paragraphs (e) through (h) in particular, but the following list of headings includes all paragraphs within 29 CFR 1910.1200, including (e) through (h):

(a) purpose
(b) scope and application
(c) definitions
(d) hazard determination
(e) written hazard communication programs
(f) labels and other forms of warning
(g) material safety data sheets
(h) employee information and training

Paragraphs (e), (f), (g), and (h) are frequently cited as the heart of the *Hazard Communication Standard*. However, 29 CFR 1910.1200(b), "scope and application," and 29 CFR 1910.1200(c), "definitions," should be used as references to help explain the breadth of coverage of all of the provisions. Volumes have been written for employers about how to comply with HazCom. The following version is a list suggested by OSHA (OSHA, 2000, 16):

- Obtain a copy of the HCS rule.
- Read and understand the requirements.
- Assign responsibility for tasks.
- Prepare an inventory of chemicals.
- Ensure that containers have labeling.
- Obtain the MSDS for each chemical.
- Prepare a written program.
- Make MSDSs available to workers.

- Conduct training of workers.
- Establish procedures to maintain the current program.
- Establish procedures to evaluate effectiveness.

This chapter identifies fives tasks that embody the essence of this list:

Task 1. Develop a written HazCom plan/program.
Task 2. Create an up-to-date hazardous chemical inventory.
Task 3. Have all hazardous chemicals properly labeled.
Task 4. Make accessible to employees an MSDS for every chemical that is covered by the standard.
Task 5. Properly instruct, train, and provide required information to all affected employees.

The chapter will now focus on assisting management in implementing these five primary tasks of a HazCom program. Each task involves a major commitment of time and resources from management.

Implementation of a HazCom Program

Task 1. The Written HazCom Program

For the fiscal year 2009, hazard communication was the third most frequently cited standard by OSHA. Failure to develop and maintain a written program was and is the most pervasive type of violation, with failure to provide training a close second. Establishing programs that include training will not only help eliminate these violations, but may also reduce other violations that are causally related to injuries and illnesses suffered by employees who are not receiving adequate training. Additionally, establishing written programs with training is likely to provide protection against many willful violation claims (Keene State College 2006, 2). One should be aware of OSHA's proposal in September of 2009 to align the standard with the United Nations' Global Harmonization System (GHS) of Classification and Labeling of Chemicals (OSHA 2009). This has yet to be acted upon in final rulemaking.

Consultants and OSHA administrators agree that the first task for employers using hazardous chemicals is to develop the written program, and the most important aspect of the written program is to designate a responsible administrator. That individual will be responsible for oversight and implementation of each of the five tasks listed above.

The overall written plan does not have to be lengthy or complicated. It is intended to be a blueprint for implementation of a program and to provide assurance to inside management and outside observers that all aspects of the HazCom requirements have been addressed. The written program must describe how the requirements for labels (and other forms of warnings), material safety data sheets, and employee information and training are going to be met in a facility.

Preparation of the written plan can be done most easily using good resources. Because there were so many citations issued for noncompliance with the HCS and many misunderstandings about the requirements, OSHA responded with extensive information to assist employers in their compliance efforts. To this end, there are many publicly available and reproducible bulletins offered by OSHA in electronic formats. Several of these have been used in the preparation of this chapter, and they are cited within. Among the key documents that would be useful to the program administrator are the following (OSHA 2000):

- All about OSHA, OSHA 2056
- Chemical Hazard Communication, OSHA 3084
- Consultation Services for the Employer, OSHA 3074
- Employee Workplace Rights, OSHA 3021
- Employer Rights and Responsibilities Following an OSHA Inspection, OSHA 3000
- How to Prepare for Workplace Emergencies, OSHA 3088
- OSHA Inspections, OSHA 2098
- Personal Protective Equipment, OSHA 3077
- Respiratory Protection, OSHA 3079

These and other OSHA documents can be located at www.osha.gov/ and www.osha-slc.gov/. Single hardcopies can be obtained free of charge from the OSHA Publications Office, P.O. Box 37535, Washington, D.C. 20013-7535; a self-addressed mailing label is requested along with your solicitation.

Integration into a Sample Program

Complying with the many OSHA guidelines involves compiling information and integrating it into a comprehensive written program. This integration might best be illustrated through an example program (see Sidebar). Several federal, state, and private example programs can be found via the Web. The example template program presented in the Sidebar has been adapted from a publicly available California Occupational Safety and Health Administration (CalOSHA) document intended to assist program administrators to satisfy both CalOSHA and federal requirements. Of course, employers must tailor this and any program to accommodate their individual operations and regulatory needs. Just reading through the template itself is an excellent tutorial for understanding the scope of the HazCom program and responsibilities placed on the administrators of the program.

Task 2. Hazard Evaluation and Chemical Inventory: A "Tiered" Approach

The second major task in setting up a HazCom program is the chemical hazard evaluation and inventory process. This process is intended to result in a complete inventory of chemicals used in a particular workplace and other chemicals to which employees might be exposed. In light of the hundreds of chemicals that could possibly be present in an employer's establishment, a systematic means is necessary to survey the candidate chemicals to determine those that have been identified as occupationally hazardous. To this end, OSHA has attempted to assist by creating a document titled "Draft Guidance for Hazard Determination" (OSHA 2002). This document attempts to provide a methodology for creating a hazardous chemical inventory list for an entire facility.

The hazard evaluation process recommended by OSHA has been labeled as a tiered step approach. This means that the thoroughness to which a chemical must be evaluated depends on factors such as

SIDEBAR

Example Program Template for the XYZ COMPANY

To enhance our employees' health and safety, our company has developed and implemented and now maintains a hazard communication program as required by federal OSHA 29 CFR 1900.1200 (and this state's regulations). The hazard communication manager, [insert name here], has full authority and responsibility for implementing and maintaining this program. We provide information about the hazardous substances in our workplace, the associated hazards, and the control of these hazards through a comprehensive hazard communication program that includes the elements in the following list.

1. List of hazardous substances

   (Person/position) will prepare and keep current an inventory list of all known hazardous substances present in our workplace. Specific information on each noted hazardous substance can be obtained by reviewing the MSDSs (see Attachment C, "Hazardous Substance Inventory List Sample" [not included in present chapter]).

2. Proposition 65 list of chemicals [California Only]

   (Person/position) is responsible for obtaining updates of Proposition 65 listed chemicals and providing new information to affected employees. In the case of newly added chemicals to the Proposition 65 list, warning requirements take effect twelve months from the date of listing.

3. Material Safety Data Sheets (MSDSs)

   [Person/position] is responsible for obtaining the MSDSs, reviewing them for completeness, and maintaining the data sheet system for our company. In the review of incoming data sheets, if new and significant health or safety information becomes available, this new information is passed on immediately to the affected employees by additional training sessions, posting of memos, and other means of communication. Legible MSDS copies for all hazardous substances to which employees of this company may be exposed are kept in [list all locations here]. MSDSs are readily available for review to all employees in their work area and during each work shift. If MSDSs are missing or new hazardous substances in use do not have MSDSs, or if an MSDS is obviously incomplete, please contact [person/position] immediately, and a new MSDS will be requested from the manufacturer. If we are unable to obtain the MSDS from the vendor within 25 calendar days of the request, we will either call or write to our local federal or state compliance office.

   If we use alternatives other than paper MSDSs—computer or microfiche machines with printers or telefax machines—we will make sure that employees have ready access to and know how to operate these devices for retrieval and printing of legible hard copies. Our back-up system in the event of failure of the primary MSDS retrieval system will require employees to request paper MSDSs by telephone. An MSDS hardcopy will be provided to the requester as soon as possible after the telephone request is made.

4. Labels and other forms of warning

   Before hazardous substance containers are released to the work area, it is the policy of our company that [person/position] will verify that all primary and secondary containers are labeled as follows:

   • Identity of the hazardous substance(s)
   • Applicable hazard warnings
   • Name and address of the manufacturer

   To address exposures to (California Proposition 65-type) chemicals, [person/position] will provide clear and reasonable warnings to individuals prior to exposure by means of posting signs conspicuously, labeling consumer products, and training employees. If applicable, [person/position] will arrange for labels, signs, and other warnings to be printed in other languages.

5. Employee information and training

   Employees are to attend a health and safety training session set up by [person/position] prior to starting work. This training session will provide information on the following:

   • The requirements of the hazard communication regulation, including the employees' rights under the regulation
   • The location and availability of the written hazard communication program
   • Any operation in their work area, including nonroutine tasks, where hazardous sub-

stances or Proposition 65 carcinogens or reproductive toxins are present and exposures are likely to occur

- Methods and observation techniques used to determine the presence or release of hazardous substances in the work area
- Protective practices the company has taken to minimize or prevent exposure to these substances
- How to read labels and review MSDSs to obtain hazard information
- Physical and health effects of the hazardous substances
- Symptoms of overexposure
- Measures employees need to put into practice to reduce or prevent exposure to these hazardous substances by engineering controls, work practices, and use of personal protective equipment
- Emergency and first-aid procedures to follow if employees are exposed to hazardous substances
- The location and interpretation, if needed, of warning signs or placards to communicate that a chemical known to cause cancer or reproductive toxicity is used in the workplace
- Additional training whenever a new hazard is introduced into the workplace or whenever employees might be exposed to hazards at another employer's work site

6. Hazardous nonroutine tasks

Periodically, our employees are required to perform hazardous nonroutine tasks. Prior to starting work on such projects, affected employees will be given information by their supervisor on hazards to which they may be exposed during such an activity. This information will cover the following:

- Specific hazards
- Measures the company has taken to reduce the risk of these hazards, such as providing ventilation, ensuring the presence of another employee, providing a respiratory protection program, and establishing emergency procedures
- Required protective/safety measures

7. Labeled/unlabeled pipes (if applicable)

Above-ground pipes transporting hazardous substances (gases, vapors, liquids, semi-liquids, or plastics) shall be identified in accordance with established standards for "Identification of Piping." The standard to be followed is ANSI A13.1, American National Standard Scheme for Identification of Piping Systems.

Other above-ground pipes that do not contain hazardous substances but that may have associated hazards if disturbed or cut (e.g., steam lines, oxygen lines) shall be addressed as follows:

Before employees enter the area and initiate work, [persons/position] will inform them of the following:

- The location of the pipe or piping system or other known safety hazard
- The substance in the pipe
- Potential hazards
- Safety precautions

8. Informing contractors

To ensure that outside contractors work safely in our plant and to protect our employees from chemicals used by outside contractors, [person/position/department] is responsible for giving and receiving the following information from contractors:

- For hazardous substances, including (California Proposition 65-type) chemicals, to which contractor employees may be exposed while on the job site as well as substances they will be bringing into the workplace, we will provide contractors with information about our labeling system and give them access to MSDSs.
- Precautions and protective measures the employees may take to minimize the possibility of exposure include the following: _____

If anyone has questions about this plan, please contact [person/position]. Our plan will be maintained by [person/position] to ensure that the policies are carried out and the plan is effective.

_____

(Signature of Owner or Management Representative)

(Adapted from California Department of Industrial Relations 2000, 17)

the common knowledge regarding the chemical, whether its health effects are under scientific review, and how prevalent the chemical is in a particular workplace. This process can be systematized into the following tiered set of steps (OSHA 2002, 12):

Step 1. Create the Exhaustive Inventory List

Often one can start with the purchasing department to determine all the chemicals and chemical products that have been purchased. Nearly any powdered, gaseous, or liquid product and some solid products will qualify for this initial list. The list should not be limited to raw materials used in production but should also include items to which employees may be exposed through maintenance, construction, or even office-work contact. For items produced in a particular facility, there will be potential for chemical exposure during handling, shipping, storage, waste disposal, and recycling. And, of course, those chemical items being shipped to customers will have to include MSDS sheets, just as the chemicals received within the facility will have to have MSDS sheets. It quickly becomes apparent how large and complex these lists can become. In similar industries or places of business, it is common for lists to be shared, as long as proprietary information is not involved. Trade associations are often in a position to assist in providing such lists among their members that have similar chemical inventories.

Step 2. Identify the "Floor" Chemicals

At this second step, one begins to identify the hazardous nature of certain chemicals. It begins with determining from governmental sources whether the chemical is part of the "floor" of chemicals to be considered hazardous in all situations. This floor of chemicals has been identified as originating from three sources, which include the following:

1. Any substance for which OSHA has either a permissible exposure limit (PEL) in 1910.1000 or a comprehensive substance-specific standard in Subpart Z. (This includes any compound including these substances and where OSHA would sample to determine compliance with the PEL.)

2. Any substance for which the American Conference of Governmental Industrial Hygienists (ACGIH) has a threshold limit value (TLV) in the latest edition of their annual list and any mixture or combination of these chemicals.

3. Any substance that the National Toxicology Program (NTP) or the International Agency for Research on Cancer (IARC) has found to be a suspected or confirmed carcinogen or any substance that OSHA regulates as a carcinogen.

At this level of review one would also check the NIOSH Registry of Toxic Effects of Chemical Substances (RTECS) to see if any hazards are indicated that do not appear in the previously listed sources. If there are, further investigations should be done to evaluate the hazards. It has been noted by OSHA that the NIOSH-generated RTECS, though useful as a screening device, should not be considered a definitive source for establishing a hazard because it consists of data that has not been evaluated (OSHA 2002, 16).

Step 3. Analyze the Data Collected about the Chemicals

The third step involves analyzing the collected data. This step is the most demanding in technical expertise. The HCS requires that chemical manufacturers and importers conduct a hazard determination to determine the level to which physical or health hazards exist. It is likely to require the services of outside expert consultants.

Step 4. Document the Process and Results Obtained

This fourth step focuses on documenting the findings for each chemical. This is an important step because all other steps will be wasted if findings are not documented carefully. Good documentation will assist in preparing labels and MSDSs, maintain a record for future reference and updating, and defend the decision regarding how the chemical hazards are handled.

Keeping Inventory Current

A continuing challenge with any inventory is that it can change on a daily basis. This is true also with the chemicals passing through an organization. The HazCom manager must set up a system to track the new chemicals entering an organization and the ones no longer being used. An efficient way to do this is through monitoring the products and vendors passing through the purchasing department. In theory, most companies have formal procedures for what items are purchased and through which channels or vendors those items may be acquired. A close relationship with the purchasing department will greatly assist the manager of the chemical inventory list. Many companies are now using bar-coding systems to create the chemical inventory libraries. On the other hand, in small companies where there is no purchasing department, then the chemical list manager must communicate with the numerous persons who have the authority to order products for offices, production buildings, or anywhere on the premises.

Task 3. Proper Chemical Container Labeling

The third primary task in the HazCom program is making sure all chemical containers are properly labeled. Although most containers are typically thought of as being some type of open or closed can of a certain size, material within piping systems may also be thought of as a container. The following discussion first addresses the usual can-type containers. It will be followed by specific standards dealing with pipe labeling.

Based on OSHA standards, each individual container must be marked. The formal requirement comes under OSHA 29 CFR 1910.1200, *Hazard Communication Standard*, in paragraph (f), "Labels and Other Forms of Warnings": "Each container of hazardous chemicals is to be labeled, tagged or marked with the following: (i) Identity; (ii) Appropriate hazard warnings; (iii) Name and address of manufacturer" (OSHA 1994, 947).

Interpretations made by OSHA have been broader than these three requirements might imply. OSHA has administratively stated that the labels must also include hazard warnings appropriate for employee protection. The hazard information and warnings can contain any type of message, words, pictures, or symbols that provide at least general information regarding the hazards of the chemical(s) in the container and any targeted organs affected. Employers are re-

quired to use legible labels and other forms of warning that hopefully can clearly and quickly communicate the identity and hazards of chemicals in the workplace. Labels and other forms of warnings are to be conspicuously placed on containers so that the message is readily visible. If a business employs a large number of non-English-speaking employees, employers have the option to use a combination of symbols, warning signs in English and other languages, and any other means necessary to ensure that their employees understand the dangers present in the workplace. On stationary process containers employers can use signs, placards, and other options in lieu of labels as long as the required information is included. Finally, employers must also relabel containers whenever labels are damaged or defaced.

In California, additional labeling requirements are applicable for those specific chemicals listed under the substance-specific health standards as referenced in the California Code of Regulations at T8 CCR, Article 110, "Regulated Carcinogens" (California Department of Occupational Safety and Health, n.d.).

Labeling Exemptions (OSHA)

As has been suggested, there are exemptions to the requirement that each individual in-plant container be labeled (OSHA 1998, 6). This can be an unnecessary burden and may not lead to increased safety under certain circumstances. These exemptions are as follows:

- Employers can post signs or placards that convey the hazard information if there are a number of stationary containers in a work area that have similar contents and hazards.
- Employers can substitute various types of standard operating procedures, process sheets, batch tickets, blend tickets, and similar written materials for container labels on stationary process equipment if they contain the same information and if the written materials are readily accessible to employees in the work area.
- Employers are not required to label portable containers into which hazardous chemicals are transferred from labeled containers if the portable containers are intended only for the

immediate use of the employee who makes the transfer. This is sometimes interpreted as a chemical within a portable container that is for immediate use during a single shift by a single employee who performs the transfer himself or herself.

Chemicals regulated by the following acts do not require their own OSHA-style HAZCOM warning labels because the respective acts controlling them likely have their own labeling specifications. From 29 CFR 1910.1200(f)(4), the acts listed are as follows:

- Toxic Substances Control Act
- Federal Food, Drug, and Cosmetic Act
- Virus-Serum-Toxin Act
- Federal Alcohol Administration Act
- Consumer Product Safety Act
- Federal Hazardous Substances Act
- Federal Seed Act

Although OSHA is very strict about there being labels on chemicals in and around the workplace, the requirements for the actual formatting and content of the label are fairly broad. The general language requiring "appropriate hazard warnings" is very nonspecific. On the other hand the chemical manufacturers and affiliated organizations have been concerned for decades about the specifics of what information should be provided for a chemical. They have stated these recommendations through the American National Standards Institute (ANSI) committees responsible for the standard titled ANSI Z129.1, *American National Standard for Hazardous Industrial Chemicals—Precautionary Labeling* (2000, 6).

Labels for Chemicals Based on ANSI Z129.1

For any commercial- or industrial-type chemical, the most respected standard for communicating information about that chemical is ANSI Z129.1. This standard has evolved after extensive research and committee deliberations. That research had as its objective the construction of labels that would not only have the essential information about the chemical, but also provide hazard communication with language that the average chemical worker would likely understand. The requirements of the standard, though

voluntary, have received wide support from the industry. The requirements themselves existed before the OSHA requirements and have continued concurrent to the OSHA HazCom standards. In fact, one of the reasons the OSHA chemical labeling requirements are minimal is that most chemical manufacturers followed the ANSI Z129.1 standard even before OSHA and have included extensive amounts of information about their product. Most managers can expect to find this more extensive information on the labels they encounter. Purchasers of chemicals would expect the types of information in the list following the next paragraph to be on the respective labels if the ANSI Z129.1 standard has been followed by the originator. If such information is not on the label, equivalent language can often be found on the MSDS sheet for that chemical. It would also be reasonable to request missing information from the chemical manufacturer or distributor.

The standard categories of information recommended in ANSI Z129.1 for labels are provided in the following list. Explanations of those categories are also provided as abstracted from the standard itself (ANSI 2006). There is no recommended format or order for these categories. Of course, how many of the different categories of information are included may depend on the space available on the container:

> *Product Name or Identification (Identity of Hazardous Components).* Identification of the chemical product or its hazardous components shall be adequate to allow selection of proper action in case of exposure. The chemical name should be used for a single chemical substance. For mixtures, use the chemical names of the components contributing substantially to the hazards of the mixture.
>
> *Signal Word.* The signal word shall indicate the relative degree of an immediate hazard in diminishing order and may use an exclamation mark for emphasis after the signal word.
>
> *Statement of Immediate Hazard(s).* The statement of hazard shall give notice of the hazard(s) that are present as determined by the hazard evaluation.

Precautionary Measures. These supplement the statement of hazard by briefly providing measures to be taken to avoid injury from physical or health hazards.

Delayed Hazard(s) Label Statement. Longer-term potential health effects.

Instruction in Case of Contact or Exposure (Including First Aid and Antidotes). Instructions in case of contact or exposure shall be included where the known or potential adverse effects of contact or exposure warrant immediate treatment and where simple measures may be taken before professional medical assistance is available.

Notes to Physicians. If a specific, effective antidote is known and can be administered by medical personnel, include it on the label.

Fire Instructions. Include simple and brief instructions in case of fire. These are intended to provide persons who handle containers during shipment and storage with appropriate instruction for confining and extinguishing fires.

Spill or Leak Instructions. Include methods for handling spills or leaks to allow immediate action to contain spills.

Container Handling and Storage Instructions. Include these to provide additional information for chemicals requiring special or unusual handling and storage procedures.

References. May include a reference to an additional label, MSDS, technical bulletin, and so on.

Additional Useful Statements. Reserved for any other statements the manufacturer chooses to include.

Name, Address, and Telephone of Chemical Company. Include the name and address of the manufacturer, importer, or distributor on product labels leaving the workplace and intended for outside sale or distribution.

(Adapted from ANSI 2006)

Special situations arise when chemicals are bought in large bulk volumes and then divided into smaller quantities by distributors, such as in 1-, 5-, and 50-gallon barrels for liquids or dry chemicals in smaller packages. Also, chemicals that are by-products of production processes and that are either in storage or in transition awaiting disposal or recycling have very special labeling and handling requirements. Such labeling is aimed at the protection of environment, water, personnel, and physical facilities. Regulations dealing with the management of such by-products exist at both the federal and state levels.

An extremely useful feature of ANSI 129.1 deserves special notice. This feature has been useful to label and sign designers, as well as those involved in warning-label and sign litigation. The standard has over 225 examples of hazard communication phrases that have been divided by the type of hazard one might want to address. Many of these phrases have been tested with worker populations for understandability. Consequently, the phrases have found their way into all types of safety communications, and the authors of such communications can rest somewhat easy in knowing that they are choosing phrases that have had some peer review and have possibly been tested.

Other Systems of Labeling

The safety manager will also see other systems of labeling on products entering the plant. These include the national fire rating (NFR), the hazardous materials identification guide (HMIG), and right-to-know (RTK) systems.

To satisfy the OSHA HazCom standard, personal preference determines which system or combination of systems are adopted since OSHA does not require a specific format as of this printing. RTK labels list the chemical name, common name or synonym, signal word, hazard information, precautionary measures, first-aid procedures, and the CAS number. No chart for interpretation of hazards is necessary. Personal protection pictorials can be added to the RTK system for additional worker awareness (Lab Supply Safety 2007).

The NFR system uses a hazard-rating colored diamond code for ranking the health, flammability, and reactivity of hazardous chemicals in the presence of fire. Substances are assigned a rating of 0–4, with 4 being the most hazardous. Several pictorials alert workers to hazards such as water reactive and radioactive (Lab Supply Safety 2007).

The HMIG system is similar to the NFR system, except the label is in a color bar format and is rectangular, rather than diamond, in shape. The definition of the health ratings is not based on fire exposure, but on acute and chronic hazards present in normal day-to-day operations. It includes twelve icons for personal protective equipment (Lab Supply Safety 2007).

After reviewing these several types of chemical labeling, one can understand why OSHA has not been specific as to a given format and content. Each manufacturer has thus far had the right to choose the system that best fits a particular chemical. The safety manager will see all these types of labels in his plant, all of which will likely comply with OSHA. Unfortunately, a mixture of label styles will likely lead to some uncertainty and confusion on the part of the workers—just what the OSHA act seeks to avoid.

Labeling for Piping

A type of hazardous chemical labeling that is not addressed in OSHA is that which identifies chemicals contained in pipes. However, there are some specific standards dealing with above-ground pipe labeling. For example, in California, as noted in the example program template presented earlier, it is specifically stated that above-ground pipes transporting hazardous substances (such as gases or vapors, liquids, semiliquids, or plastics) shall be identified in accordance with T8 CCR, Section 3321, "Identification of Piping." This requires identification through one or more of the following methods (California Occupational Safety and Health n.d.):

1. Complete color-painting of all visible parts of the pipe may be used.
2. Alternately, color bands, preferably eight to ten inches wide, at various intervals and at each outlet valve or connection may be used. Where identification is provided by complete color painting or by color bands, a color

code shall be posted at those locations where confusion would introduce hazards to employees.
3. One may also put several of the names or abbreviations of the transported materials lettered or stenciled on the pipe near the valves or outlets.
4. Finally, one may use tags of metal or other suitable material naming the transported material and fastened securely to the system on or near the valve. The tag legibility must be maintained.

On a national level there are voluntary consensus standards that recommend color-coding of pipes based on the materials they are carrying. Even where such identification is not required, it is still a good practice to install such an identification system. The U.S. national standard is ANSI A13.1-2007, the *American National Standard Scheme for Identification of Piping Systems* (2007).

The ANSI standard for pipe identification is a widely used guideline in determining pipe-identification requirements. The purpose of the standard is to "assist in identification of hazardous materials conveyed in piping systems and their hazards when released in the environment." Pipes are defined as "conduits for the transport of gases, liquids, semiliquids or fine particulate dust." This ANSI standard recommends that pipes be marked with a legend indicating the name of the contents and arrows showing the direction of flow of the material. A color is used in combination with the legend to identify the characteristic hazards of the contents. The labeling needs to be applied close to valves, flanges, branches, where changes in direction occur, wherever pipes pass through walls, and at 50-foot intervals on straight runs. In 2007, the new edition of the standard changed the color scheme requirements for labels. Previous versions of the standard included only four colors for identifying pipes. The new label color requirements are based on the characteristic hazards of the contents. These are the classification of materials and designated colors (ANSI 2007):

- Flammable Fluids (Color field: yellow. Lettering: black)

- Toxic or corrosive fluids (Color field: orange. Lettering: black)
- Combustible fluids (Color field: brown. Lettering: black)
- Potable, cooling, boiler feed, and other water (Color field: green. Lettering: white)
- Compressed air (Color field: blue. Lettering: white)
- Fire quenching fluids (Color field: red. Lettering: white)

Task 4. Chemical Material Safety Data Sheets (MSDSs) and Their Accessibility

The fourth major task in the HazCom program deals with material safety data sheets, and this can involve their design, collection, maintenance, distribution, and accessibility. As indicated in the early portions of the chapter, chemical (or material) safety data sheets are a vital part of employee right-to-know programs, such as the OSHA HazCom. The MSDS has legal significance relative to the tort liability of manufacturers or processors who actually develop chemicals for eventual use or distribution. The adequacy of MSDS information often comes into question in such litigation. However, the focus of the present discussion is on compliance with the OSHA health hazard communication requirements. It should be noted, however, that any proposed criteria used to test MSDS adequacy under litigation and the common law can be quite different from adequacy under OSHA, unless, at some point, there is a government-mandated pre-exemption.

The first step in designing how chemical information should be presented to users within an MSDS is to decide on a format within which to present the chosen information. A standardized format was early seen as a way to make the technical information easier for users to read. Therefore, as discussed previously, OSHA established a voluntary format for MSDSs in the 1970s and called it OSHA Form 20, and a later version of a standardized format appeared in 1985 as Form 174 (see Appendix A). This two-page form includes spaces for each of the items included in the MSDS requirements of the standard. It was to be filled in with the appropriate information as determined by the man-

ufacturer or importer. However, some in the regulated community did not find the OSHA Form 174 suitable to their needs. They were looking for a more comprehensive, structured approach for developing clear, complete, and consistent MSDSs.

To accomplish this objective, the Chemical Manufacturers Association (now known as the American Chemistry Council) formed a committee to establish guidelines for the preparation of MSDSs under the committee structure of the American National Standards Institute (ANSI). This effort resulted in the development of what is now known as ANSI Z400.1, *American National Standard for Hazardous Industrial Chemicals Material Safety Data Sheets—Preparation* (2004). Employers, workers, healthcare professionals, emergency responders, and other MSDS users participated in this development process. The standard established a 16-section format for presenting information. If one follows the recommended format, the information of greatest concern to workers is featured at the beginning of the data sheet, including information on ingredients and first-aid measures. More technical information that addresses topics such as the physical and chemical properties of the material, along with toxicological data appears later in the MSDS. The 2004 revision included several changes, most importantly improving hazard communication and aligning the standard with the recommendations for safety data sheets in the Globally Harmonized System for Hazard Classification, Communication and Labeling (GHS) and reordering the MSDS sections so Hazards Identification appears before Composition Information. The major sections of the ANSI Z400.1 standard follow. A detailed description of each appears in Appendix B.

- Section 1: Chemical Product and Company Identification
- Section 2: Hazards Identification
- Section 3: Composition, Information on Ingredients
- Section 4: First-Aid Measures
- Section 5: Fire-Fighting Measures
- Section 6: Accidental Release Measures
- Section 7: Handling and Storage

- Section 8: Exposure Controls, Personal Protection
- Section 9: Physical and Chemical Properties
- Section 10: Stability and Reactivity
- Section 11: Toxicological Information
- Section 12: Ecological Information
- Section 13: Disposal Considerations
- Section 14: Transport Information
- Section 15: Regulatory Information
- Section 16: Other Information

The ANSI Z400.1 standard also includes guidance on the appearance and reading level of the text in order to provide a document that would likely be understandable to readers. OSHA allows this format to be used to comply with the HCS because it generally includes the OSHA required information (ANSI 2004).

These sixteen sections differ only slightly from comparable sections appearing in the OSHA Form 174. Table 1 compares the ANSI and OSHA formats for MSDS creation. Note that a manufacturer is allowed a wide judgment in choosing what to include in an MSDS, although certain specific items are mandatory.

An employer who is not a chemical manufacturer or supplier is not expected to generate the information for MSDS sheets. Rather, the section descriptions listed above represent the information an employer would expect to be provided in whatever format is chosen by a manufacturer for its MSDS.

Comparison to European Safety Data Sheet

The European Commission in its initial Commission Directive 91/155/EEC stated that it is "defining and laying down the detailed arrangements for the system of specific information relating to dangerous preparations in implementation of Article 10 of Directive 88/379/EEC (31991L0155)" (EC 1991). To implement this directive, Europe essentially adopted the ANSI Z400.1 approach with an identical set of sixteen required sections (ANSI 2004). However, in 2007, the European Union (EU) regulation concerning the registration, evaluation, authorization, and restriction of chemicals (REACH) came into force. This law

overtook the EU's provisions for SDS; therefore, Directive 91/155/EEC was repealed. The statutory basis for SDSs is laid down in Article 31, "Requirements for Safety Data Sheets," of REACH, and Annex II details the requirements for the compilation of an SDS in accordance with this article. REACH still maintains the division into 16 sections; however, Section 2, "Composition and Information on Ingredients," and Section 3, "Hazards Identification," have been reversed in order (EC 2001). Although the titles to the sections are the same, the particular requirements are described in a more specific and less liability-guarded terminology. Those manufacturers supplying to Europe will also be interested in when and how the SDSs (safety data sheets) must be provided. This is stated in the most recent referred-to directive as follows. Note, however, that this directive is being revised due to various parts of the GHS proposals:

Article 1:1 . . . the manufacturer, importer or distributor, shall supply the recipient who is a professional user of the substance or preparation, with a safety data sheet containing the information set out in Article 3 and the Annex to this Directive, if the substance or preparation is classified as dangerous according to Directive 67/548/EEC or European Parliament and Council Directive 1999/45/EC. (European Commission 2001, 2)

Article 3: The safety data sheet referred to in Article 1 shall contain the following obligatory headings: [Numbers 1–16 are listed in the standards at this point within the directive and are identical in title to the ANSI 400.1 sections]. (European Commission 1991, 2)

An interesting observation has been included in the EEC directive that reflects the reality of member-nation differences in language. The EEC openly recognizes language-translation differences and states, "Chemical safety data sheets are published under several names, such as: international chemical safety card, ICSC; chemical safety card; chemical info-sheet; material safety data sheet, MSDS; product safety data sheet; health and safety data sheet" (EC 1991).

It is also interesting that the EEC recognizes two different types of chemical safety data sheets: (1) chemical safety data sheets prepared by working groups of experts containing information based on

TABLE 1

Comparison of ANSI Z400.1, OSHA, and European MSDS Specifications

ANSI Z400.1(2004–) MSDSs–Preparation and Communication Standard, Directive 91/155/EEC (1991)–SDS Safety Data Sheets Directive	U.S. Dept. of Labor OSHA Hazard (29 CFR 1910.1200) Subpart Z	U.S. Dept. of Labor OSHA Form OSHA 174 (1985)
Section 1: Product and Company Identification	Identification	Identity
	Name, Address, Manufacturer Telephone #	Section I. Manufacturer Information
	Date of preparation	
Section 2: Hazards Identification	Carcinogenicity: Listing of Hazardous Chemical	
Section 3: Composition/Information on Ingredients		Section II. Hazardous Ingredients/Identity Information
		Section III. Physical/Chemical Characteristics
Section 4: First Aid Measures	Emergency and First Aid procedures	
	Primary Routes of Entry OSHA PEL, TLV	
Section 5: Fire Fighting Measures	Physical Hazards (Fire, Explosion, and Reactivity)	Section IV. Fire and Explosion Hazard Data
Section 6: Accidental Release Measures		Section VIII. Control Measures
Section 7: Handling and Storage	Safe Handling and Use	Section VII. Precautions for Safe Handling and Use
Section 8: Exposure Controls/Personal Protection	Control Measures, PPE	
Section 9: Physical and Chemical Properties	Physical and Chemical Characteristics	Section III. Physical/Chemical Characteristics
Section 10: Stability and Reactivity	Physical Hazards	Section V. Reactivity Data
Section 11: Toxicological Information	Health Hazards (signs/symptoms, exposure)	Section VI. Health Hazard Data
Section 12: Ecological Information		
Section 13: Disposal Considerations		
Section 14: Transport Information		
Section 15: Regulatory Information		
Section 16: Other Information		

laboratory tests and checked knowledge and (2) chemical safety data sheets prepared by the manufacturer or retailer. EEC further suggests that "validated" data sheets on pure substances are available—for example, from the International Programme on Chemical Safety (IPCS) or from national institutions such as the Canadian Centre for Occupational Safety and Health. The EEC suggests that these can be used by manufacturers as basic information sources when they create chemical safety data sheets for their own products.

By way of comparison, this EEC approach to chemical information is presented along with the ANSI and OSHA formats in Table 1. It is noted, however, that the European and U.S. regulations are under revision as various provisions of the GHS are adopted. The reader should follow these developments, as they are not complete as of the publication of this Handbook.

Comparison to Canadian MSDSs

Canada's right-to-know legislation is the Workplace Hazardous Materials Information System (WHMIS) (Health Canada 1988). In Canada, every material that is controlled by WHMIS must have an accompanying MSDS. Nine categories of information must be present on an MSDS in Canada. These categories are specified in the Controlled Products Regulations (CPR) and include the following (Department of Justice Canada 1985):

1. Product information: product identifier (name) and manufacturer and supplier names, addresses, and emergency phone numbers.
2. Hazardous ingredients
3. Physical data
4. Fire or explosion hazard data
5. Reactivity data: information on the chemical instability of a product and the substances it may react with

6. Toxicological properties: health effects
7. Preventive measures
8. First-aid measures
9. Preparation information: who is responsible for preparation and date of preparation of MSDS

Many products are imported from and exported to the United States using the 16-heading format used under ANSI Z400.1. Canadian authorities have indicated that this 16-heading format is acceptable in Canada if two conditions are met. First, all the required information specified under Column III of Schedule I of the Canadian Controlled Products Regulation (CPR) must be addressed; also, all headings and subheadings that are on the MSDS must be addressed by providing the required information or by stating that the information is not available or not applicable, whichever is appropriate (Canadian Centre for Occupational Health and Safety 2006). Second, the statement "This product has been classified in accordance with the hazard criteria of the CPR, and the MSDS contains all of the information required by the CPR" must appear under the section heading "Regulatory Information" (Canadian Centre for Occupational Health and Safety 2006). This is an interesting type of self-certification not yet found in other countries.

A conclusion one could draw from this is that, for chemicals being shipped to Canada or abroad to Europe, one could use essentially the same MSDS as would be prepared for the United States under ANSI Z400.1, with some small changes to accommodate the local regulations or customs. It is noted, of course, that translations into country-specific languages may be necessary. Thus, although there are no multilingual requirements for chemicals distributed in the United States, there will be non-English-language requirements for some other countries.

In Canada, the GHS will affect how chemicals are classified, and label requirements will change with the addition of a few new requirements. An interim Canadian policy has been established to permit the use of GHS-formatted safety sheets in Canada. Reg-ulatory proposals to update WHMIS were anticipated in 2010.

Global Harmonization System (GHS) Evolution

Hazard communication systems are rapidly evolving, as various governments and organizations consider the proposals brought forward within the Global Harmonization System (GHS). The goal of this chapter is to give the reader an introduction to what is happening and what may be coming with the GHS. Unquestionably, the GHS is rapidly becoming a factor in providing hazard communications about chemicals and other products around the world.

The GHS began as a result of the recognition by the United Nations for the need to harmonize the separate systems between countries. It began in 1992 at the United Nations, and its goal was to have a system in place by 2000. The work groups involved produced a proposal, which was adopted in December 2002 under what is now called the "Purple Book." While sizable, this is a very understandable document intended for use by practitioners, regulators, and standards committees. The GHS is slowly being adopted; New Zealand, Japan, Korea, and Taiwan have already adopted it. Also, provisions within the GHS are regularly included in standards in both Canada and the United States, and this proposal is likely to change the way hazards are communicated across the globe over the next twenty years. The GHS is an international system under the United Nations Subcommittee for GHS. It has as its objective the establishment of new rules for hazardous chemicals in transportation, workplace use, and consumer use, and there are special rules for pesticides. The GHS includes new MSDS or SDS requirements and new hazard symbols. Its scope includes classifying chemicals, symbols for hazards, labeling requirements, and MSDS requirements. The hope is that it will replace the patchwork of regulations across the globe, all of which cover uses of similar chemicals.

Key to the GHS system is its new chemical classification methodology, based on both the physical and health hazards associated with any particular chemical. It also establishes a new labeling program that includes such elements as: product identifier/ingredient disclosure, supplier identification, symbols/hazard pictograms, signal words, hazard statements, and precautionary information. Keep in mind that these are applicable to transportation, workplace, and consumer environments and would supersede the individual standards for each application that countries like the United States currently have in place.

The model for SDS or MSDS requirements is similar to the International Labour Organization (ILO) and ANSI 16-heading format, but is different from OSHA Form 174. It should be anticipated that chemical suppliers using OSHA Form 174 or some other arbitrary format will be rewriting their MSDS materials to the 16-section format within the next several years.

Chemical labeling will also have to be changed under the GHS. Standardized signal words, hazard symbols, and risk phrases will be required. Suppliers of labels under the GHS system will have to reevaluate their product's hazards and redo all their labels whenever the GHS is made mandatory, regardless of what format they are currently using.

The U.S. government is now in the process of adopting certain provisions of the GHS and looking at integrating various "building blocks" of the GHS into their present requirements. An Advanced Notice of Proposed Rulemaking (ANPR) came out in 2006, which stated the OSHA position relative to the GHS and how it might affect the current OSHA HazCom regulations. The U. S. Department of Transportation (DOT) has been more aggressive in considering parts of the GHS and has adopted several of its elements within rulemaking number HM-2151. The U. S. Environmental Protection Agency (EPA) is in the process of holding public meetings relative to the potential use of the GHS in its requirements. The U.S. Consumer Product Safety Commission (CPSC), which has responsibility for the Hazardous Substances Act, is also currently evaluating to what extent they want to follow or adopt certain aspects of the GHS.

Within the Canadian government, both Health Canada and Transport Canada have indicated a commitment to incorporating changes to their regulations that reflect the GHS proposal.

In summary, there are few parts of either the U.S. or Canadian government regulations pertaining to chemical and product hazards that will not be impacted by adoption of all or parts of the GHS. A monumental education process for suppliers and users will soon be forthcoming, as parts of the GHS are adopted. Such adoption will also put heavy burdens on the consensus standards organizations to modify their standards to reflect such global changes in hazard communication.

Employee Access to MSDS Data—Electronic Access

From the very onset of the employee-right-to-know movement in the 1970s, unions and other employee groups wanted to know the specifics about the chemicals to which they were being exposed. However, once this information was collected by employers and input into possibly hundreds of sets of MSDS sheets, how was the employer to make this information practically available to workers in any location where an employee might be working? Adequate distribution and the continual updating became quite the challenge. How physically close this information had to be to any particular employee became open for compliance interpretation. Fortunately, the electronic era assisted in accommodating this concern in the late 1990s, and OSHA compliance administrators have cooperated. A 1998 news release from OSHA addressed the issue within the title "New OSHA Directive Makes It Easier for Employers to Comply with Hazard Communication Standard" (OSHA, April 7, 1998).

The directive addresses the issue of electronic access to MSDSs, indicating that in addition to hardcopies, employers may provide MSDSs to employees through computers, microfiche machines, the Internet, CD-ROM, and fax machines. It does insist that employers using electronic means must ensure that reliable devices are readily accessible in the workplace at all times; that workers are trained in the use of these devices, including specific software; that there is an adequate back-up system in the event of the failure of that system, such as power outages or online access delays; and that the system is to be part of the overall hazard communication program for the workplace. Additionally, the employees must be able to access hardcopies of the MSDSs and, in medical or fire emergencies, employers must immediately be able to provide copies of MSDSs to medical or fire personnel.

OSHA believes this type of electronic implementation more fully carries out the intent of the regulation by allowing a much broader and more user-friendly access, and it facilitates employers and chemical manufacturers in timely updating and enhancements. It also facilitates an information channel that can expand its coverage well beyond the mandatory requirements of the HazCom itself.

Trade-Secret Protection

Some chemical manufacturers understandably resist the idea of providing overly specific information about products that they consider trade secrets. This concern has been recognized by both the federal government and certain states. It is covered under 29 CFR 1910.1200(i):

> The chemical manufacturer, importer, or employer may withhold the specific chemical identity, including the chemical name and other specific identification of a hazardous chemical, from the MSDS.

Under the trade-secret provision, manufacturers, importers, or employers who wish to withhold the specific identity of a hazardous chemical from the MSDS must meet specific requirements as outlined in 29 CFR 1910.1200(i), including the following: (a) the MSDS must state that the specific identity of the chemical mixture is being withheld as a trade secret, but all other MSDS categories must be addressed; and (b) trade-secret information must be released in certain circumstances.

Information on the specific chemical identity of a trade-secret substance may be requested in medical emergencies as well as in nonemergency situations. In the case of a medical emergency, the chemical identity must be immediately disclosed to medical personnel. In nonemergency situations, disclosure shall be made to health or safety professionals and to employees and their designated representatives upon a written request that explains why the disclosure of the specific

chemical identity is essential and describes the procedures by which the disclosed information will be kept confidential. It is also noted that a trade secret cannot typically include chemical identity information that is already discoverable through laboratory qualitative analysis (OSHA 2005).

Employee Understanding of MSDS

One of the more controversial issues is the difficulty some employees have understanding a label, MSDS, or other type of work chemical specification. A training program will have as one of its objectives the explaining of this information to the employees. The International Labour Organization (ILO) has proposed a useful set of questions that could either be asked of workers to determine their level of understanding or be used by workers as a self-test.

General
   Do you have the right safety data sheet for the chemical of interest?
   Do you have an up-to-date sheet?
Potential Hazards
   Can this chemical explode?
   Is this chemical unstable? If so, under which conditions?
   Can this material react with other chemicals? If so, which ones?
   Is there a possibility of mixing during storage?
   Can this chemical harm your health?
   Do you know the symptoms which may warn you of overexposure?
Preventive Measures
   Does your worksite need engineering controls?
   Does this material require special handling precautions?
   Do you need protective equipment?
   Do you need to be careful when mixing this chemical with any other chemicals?
   Does this material require special storage conditions?
Emergency Measures
   Do you know what to do in case of a fire or explosion?

Do you know the fire-extinguishing
method for this chemical?

Do you know the first-aid measures
needed in case of an overexposure?

Do you know what to do in case of a spill
or leak?

Do you know where the emergency
response equipment is and how to use it?

(ILO 2004, 10)

Online Access to MSDS and Other Information

The availability of MSDS and other information has
mushroomed in the past few years. There are Web
sites now advertising free availability to literally millions of MSDS sheets and other HCS materials. Not
only have general lists been compiled, but individual
companies and manufacturers also have freely made
MSDS information available for the products they are
responsible for. The reader wanting a quick overview
of MSDS availability via the Internet is encouraged
to visit the following URL: www.ilpi.com/msds/#
Internet. In addition, Table 2 has been compiled by this
author as an extensive Web-site listing of sites, active
as of this writing, that provide access to vast amounts
of MSDS and other HCS materials.

Task 5. Training Programs

The heart of right-to-know legislation is the training
and education that provides knowledge in a form
workers can appreciate, understand, and apply. Because of the importance of this education, there is an
abundance of commercially purchasable materials
and services to satisfy these requirements. Considerable free material is also available online from private
organizations willing to provide training services.
The material that follows in this chapter is intended
to give insight into (a) OSHA requirements, (b) the
OSHA criteria established to measure compliance, and
(c) assistance OSHA provides to employers for the
purposes of complying. From the employer's perspective, training has been a significant financial burden
because of the paid time away from work that employees spend in such programs. However, this burden
may be lightened with an improved safety and health

record for the workforce, which may in turn reduce
other costs such as worker compensation rates.

OSHA compliance activities for the HCS in general have focused strongly on the required training
programs under the act. Consequently, failure to have
adequate training has become a major source of noncompliance citations. Compliance officers are given
the following guidelines to look for when examining
an employer's training program. An OSHA publication,
*Inspection Procedures for the Hazard Communication Stan-
dard*, outlines these guidelines by indicating what a
training program is expected to contain (OSHA 1998):

- a summary of the standard and this company's
  written program
- the chemical and physical properties of hazardous materials (e.g., flash point, vapor pressure, reactivity) and methods that can be used
  to detect the presence or release of chemicals
  (including chemicals in unlabeled pipes)
- the physical hazards of the chemicals in the
  work area (e.g., potential for fire, explosion)
- the health hazards, including signs and symptoms of exposure, of the chemicals in the work
  area and any medical condition known to be
  aggravated by exposure to these chemicals
- procedures to protect against chemical hazards
  (e.g., required personal protective equipment
  and its proper use and maintenance; work
  practices or methods to ensure appropriate use
  and handling of chemicals; and procedures
  for emergency response)
- work procedures to follow to assure protection when cleaning hazardous chemical spills
  and leaks
- the location of the MSDSs, how to read and
  interpret the information on labels and
  MSDSs, and how employees may obtain
  additional hazard information

Designing a Training Program

At the time of the introduction of the HCS, the OSHA
training requirements of the regulation were not well
defined and not well understood. Currently, these
requirements are carefully specified and examples of

complete programs, including visuals, are available through numerous sources. Many training programs are accessible online free of charge. In 2003, OSHA took the lead by providing a "Draft Model Training Program for Hazard Communication" (2003). This model is complete with a day-by-day subject outline, PowerPoint slides, movies, and study/test questions to assure that the students have an adequate level of understanding. The program is available online at www.osha.gov. Of course this generic program cannot satisfy the detailed operations of specific employers. Thus, each program must be customized regardless of whether the OSHA model program is used or not. Such customization requires the HAZCOM program manager to be aware of the individual requirements of training. Such training must explain and reinforce the information presented to employees through the written mediums of labels and material safety data

TABLE 2

Sources of Online Information for MSDSs, Labeling, and Training Programs

Locating or Providing MSDSs

Web Site Address	Organization	Description
www.msds.com/	MSDS Solutions	Site houses over 2,000,000 MSDSs—English, German, Chinese, Dutch, Spanish, and French.
www.ilo.legacy/english/protection/safework/cis/products/icsc/dtasht/index.htm	International Occupational Safety and Health Information Centre	Describes what chemical safety cards are and their purpose.
http://www.rmis.com/db/dbchemicals.htm	Risk Management Internet Services	Conduct online searches of numerous chemical databases to obtain information related to material safety data sheets (MSDS). Has some international links.
www.ccohs.ca/products/msds	Canadian Center for Occupational Health and Safety	MSDS database gives instant access to the most up-to-date (more than 280,000) MSDSs from 2,000 North American manufacturers and suppliers. Provides link for MSDSs in French.
www.msdssearch.com/backgroundN.htm	MSDS Search	Find links/information on every aspect of MSDSs, including how to read, write, understand, and train employees to meet the HazCom standard.
http://hazard.com/msds/	Vermont Safety Information Resources	Searchable MSDS database of chemicals and chemical compounds.
www.ilpi.com/msds/index.html	Interactive Learning Paradigms Incorporated—Safety Emporium	Contains a listing of more than 100 free sites you can access to find MSDSs on the Internet.

Creating an MSDS

Web Site Address	Organization	Description
www.ess.co.at/RISK/MSDS/msds.html	Environmental Software and Services	Site provides a listing of the 16 articles required by EU's Directive 91/155/EEC.
2001/58/EC- http:eur-lex.eu/smart/cgi/sga_doc?smartapi!clexapi!prod!CELEXnumbdoc&numdoc=201L0058&model==guichett&lg=en		Can download Directive 2001/58/EC, which amended 91/155/EEC from the European Union Web site. Sets out the requirements for the information that should be included in a safety data sheet. Employer responsibilities outlined in detail in Directive 98/24/EC.
http:eur-lex.europa.eu/LexUriServ/LexUriServ.do?uri=CELEX:31998L0024:En:HTML		
http://ccinfoweb.ccohs.ca/help/msds/msdsINTGUIDE.html	Canadian Centre for Occupational Health and Safety	'Site provides a summary of "The MSDS; A Basic Guide For Users—International Version."

Creating an MSDS *(Continued)*

Web Site Address	Organization	Description
www.ilpi.com/msds/ref/chip.html	Chemicals Hazard and Information and Packaging for Supply Regulations (CHIP). Interactive Learning Paradigms Incorporated- Safety Emporium	Great Britain's law governing MSDSs (among many other items) is the Chemical Hazard and Information and Packaging for Supply Regulations (CHIP)
www.ilpi.com/msds/ref/ghs/html	Safety Emporium	Provides links to several sites/pages detailing the Globally Harmonized System (GHS).
www.ccohs.ca/oshanswers/legisl/msds_prep.html	Canadian Centre for Occupational Health and Safety	Aids writers in identifying the specific types of information required in MSDSs used in Canada, the United States, and the European Union.
http://ccinfoweb.ccohs.ca/help/msds/msds CDNREQE.html		Site provides a brief summary of Canadian requirements.
www.msdssearch.com/backgroundN.htm	MSDS Search	Find links/information on every aspect of MSDSs.

Chemical Labeling

Web Site Address	Organization	Description
www.rmis.com/sites/chemichemi.php	Risk Management Internet Services	Guidance on the required information for chemical hazard label systems for DOT, HMIS, NFPA diamond.
www.apps.kemi.se/nclass/default.asp	Nordic Council of Ministers (European Chemicals Bureau)	Provides up-to-date list of the legally required harmonized classifications and labelling for substances in the EU.
www.umanitoba.ca/admin/human_resources/ ehso/WHMISHandbook.pdf	University of Manitoba	Site provides link to a Workplace Hazardous Materials Information System (WHMIS) handbook.
www.hc-sc.gc.ca/ewhisemt/occup-travail/ whmis-simdut/index_eng.php	Health Canada	Canadian legislation overing the use of hazardous materials in the workplace. Closely parallels the U.S. Hazard Communication Standard.
http://ecb.jrc.ec.europa/eu/classification-labelling Click on the "Search ClassLab" tab and then the "Search Annex 1 button" to perform the search.	European Commission Joint Research Centre	Provides informationand links to classification and labelling requirements for dangerous substances and preparations.
www.msdssearch.com/backgroundN.htm	MSDS Search	Find links/information on every aspect of MSDSs, including how to read, write, understand, and train employees to meet the HazCom standard.
www.hc-sc.gc.ca/ahc-asc/intactiv/ghs-sgh/ implement/tor/ghs1_e.html	Health Canada	Provides information on the Globally Harmonized System for Hazard Classification and Labeling, defining and classifying hazards, and communicating information on labels and safety data sheets.
www.osha.gov/dsg/hazcom/global.html	Occupational Safety and Health Administration (OSHA)	OSHA's information page; links to information on the GHS.

Hazard Communication Program Training

Web Site Address	Organization	Description
www.freetraining.com/osha/hazcom/hazmenu.htm		Free hazard communication training course covers labeling, MSDSs, physical hazards, health hazards, and protective measures.
www.osha-safety-training.net	National Safety Compliance	Offers OSHA compliance and training resources for all workplaces and employers.
www.free-training.com/		Offering free online training courses available in various formats.
www.lni.wa.gov/Safety/TrainTools/Trainer/kits/hazcom	Washington State Department of Labor and Industries	Free hazard control training kit containing Powerpoint presentation and script.
www.msdssearch.com/backgroundN.htm	MSDS Search	Find links/information on every aspect of MSDSs.

sheets. They must also learn how to apply this information in their workplace. Labels and material safety data sheets will be successful only when employees understand the information presented and are aware of what actions should be taken to avoid or minimize both exposure and the likely occurrence of adverse effects.

Training helps to integrate and classify the many pieces of information that relate to chemical hazard communication. In a typical workplace, a worker may be confronted with posted hazard warnings, signs, tags, incoming labels, workplace labels, MSDSs, manuals that explain the company hazard communication program, lists of chemicals, and information furnished by the union. This wide variety of communications will differ in format, content, and reading level. These differences can obscure the important hazard communication message; thus, integration of such information through training programs is essential.

Training sessions also provide a forum for employees to share their health and safety concerns and to obtain answers from managers and occupational health and safety professionals. Employees can also share their ideas and job experiences, which often include acquired expertise in dealing with potentially hazardous situations in their work environments.

Specific Requirements

Paragraph (h) of the HCS (29 CFR 1910.1200) addresses employee information and training. The requirements reflect the overall purpose of the standard. There are certain key words and phrases in this requirement on which OSHA has focused. (They are indicated in bold.) These key words and phrases have been identified in this integrated version of paragraph (h) (OSHA 1994):

  a. First, employers shall provide employees with **effective** information and training on hazardous chemicals **in their work area** at the **time of their initial assignment**, and whenever a **new physical or health hazard** that employees have not been previously trained about is introduced into their work area. Information and training may be designed to cover **categories of hazards** (such as flammability or carcinogenicity) or **specific chemicals. Chemical-specific information must always be available through labels and material safety data sheets**.

  b. Second, employees shall be **informed** of: the requirements of this section; any **operations in their work area** where hazardous chemicals are present; the **location and availability** of the written hazard communication program, including the required list of hazardous chemicals, and material safety data sheets that describe them.

  c. Third, employee **training** shall include at least: **methods and observations** that may be used to detect the presence or release of a hazardous chemical in the work area (such as monitoring conducted by the employer, continuous monitoring devices, visual appearance or odor of hazardous chemicals when being released, etc.); the **physical and health** hazards of the chemicals in the work area; the **measures employees can take to protect themselves** from these hazards, including specific procedures the employer has implemented to protect employees from exposure to hazardous chemicals, such as appropriate work practices, emergency procedures, and personal protective equipment to be used; and the **details of the hazard communication program** developed by the employer, including an explanation of labels and material safety data sheets, and how employees can obtain and use the appropriate hazard information.

OSHA's Interpretation of Key Training Requirements

In order to give guidance to both employers attempting to comply and officers active in compliance activities, OSHA has provided some interpretation of the key words/phrases from the previous extract.

Effective means that the information and training program must work. Employees must carry the knowledge from the training into their daily jobs. For example, if asked, they should know where hazardous chemicals are present in their work area, and should also know how to protect themselves.

In their work area means just what it says. The information and training must be specific to each work area. You cannot inform only at training about general hazards found in work areas; you have to address the potential hazards that employees are actually going to encounter.

Time of initial assignment. This means that new employees must be informed and trained before going on the job, so that they are not faced with unknown hazards.

New physical or health hazard. Sometimes new hazardous chemicals are introduced into the workplace, and sometimes employees are assigned to new jobs that involve potential exposure to new hazards. Either way, no employee should be in the position of encountering unfamiliar or unknown hazards.

Categories of hazards. OSHA is aware that workplaces may contain so many different chemicals that it would be difficult and confusing to attempt to train employees about each one separately. Fortunately, many chemicals fall into categories, such as flammables or acids and bases. In these instances, it is not only acceptable but also more effective to discuss the hazards of the category as a whole. If individual chemicals within a category present a special safety or health hazard, these unique properties must be pointed out.

Specific chemicals are those that don't belong in a category or should be singled out for some other reason. For example, they may present a special hazard, or be represented in great quantity in the workplace.

Informed. Providing information is not quite the same as training, but we have included both under the general term "training"

in this Model Training Program. It means that employees must know what the standard means and where things are kept. Information can be furnished with the help of signs, notices, handouts, or other means. Whatever information measures are chosen, however, they must be effective. For example, employees should be able to tell you where the written program is housed, and also to locate the material safety data sheet collection.

Operations in their work area. This phrase points again to the need to be specific in the information and training program. Generalities about operations that have no relevance to specific employees are not sufficient.

Location and availability must again be specific. For example, the written hazard communication program may be kept in Building A or in the supervisor's office, where it must be available at **all** times. Employees should know exactly where it is and how to gain access.

Training. This term covers anything that is done to impart new knowledge or skills or to refresh employees' memories on previously learned knowledge or skills. It can best be imagined as bridging the gap between what employees know now and what they have to know to identify hazards and protect themselves against chemicals. Many different training methods and media can be used to achieve this goal.

Methods and observations are any active or passive means that can be used to detect the presence or release of a hazardous chemical. For example, some chemicals can be detected by their odor, color, or other unique properties.

Physical and health hazards. These terms apply only to the physical and health hazards of chemicals. A physical hazard is associated with a chemical that is a combustible liquid, a compressed gas, explosive, flammable, an organic peroxide, an oxidizer, pyrophoric, unstable or water-reactive. All these can harm as a result of physical reaction. **Health hazard**

means that exposure to the chemical can cause acute or chronic health effects. Examples are carcinogens and eye irritants.

Measures employees can take to protect themselves. These can include any type of control, including everything from learning the meaning of emergency signals to observing "No Entry" areas or selecting the correct personal protective equipment.

Details of the hazard communication program. This allows employees to learn what label statements mean, what information can be found in the material safety data sheet, and how to find out if a chemical presents a potential hazard. (OSHA 2003, I-2.)

As indicated earlier, to assist employers with limited technical resources and to illustrate training that would satisfy the regulation, OSHA developed an example training program. This is complete with a schedule of topics, slides to accompany lectures, and quizzes to measure comprehension. This program can be obtained directly from OSHA.

Eight lessons have been developed within this program. These lessons and the approximate time for each are listed below.

Lesson A:	1 hour	Understanding the Hazard Communication Standard
Lesson B:	1 hour	Understanding the Material Safety Data Sheet
Lesson C	1 hour	Understanding Labels
Lesson D	1 hour	Understanding Health Information
Lesson E	90 minutes	Understanding Flammables and Combustibles
Lesson F	1 hour	Understanding Corrosives
Lesson G	90 minutes	Understanding Reactive Chemicals
Lesson H	1 hour	Understanding Toxic Chemicals
	9–10 hours	Approximate total lesson time (not including breaks)

The proposed contents for each of these lessons are listed in Appendix C. The topics within the contents provide what OSHA expects of employers in the way of a comprehensive training program. Such expectations are not to be taken lightly by the safety or health professional in charge of such training, and strong consideration should be given to using the OSHA model training program as a foundation from which to work.

Compliance Results and Assistance from OSHA

Over the years the General Accounting Office (GAO) and OSHA have done surveys and analyzed inspection data to determine levels of compliance with HCS. They found a substantial number of employers out of compliance, especially small employers with fewer than twenty employees. OSHA inspections of particular work sites are often selected because of accidents, complaints, or the hazardousness of the industry. In the early 1990s, OSHA found 26 percent of all inspected work sites out of compliance with at least one HCS requirement (United States GAO 1991, 3). In surveying a random sample of employers, GAO found 58 percent of small employers and 52 percent of all employers to be out of compliance with key requirements of HCS (United States GAO 1991, 3).

GAO issued reports identifying the difficulties small employers were said to be experiencing in complying with the HCS. The findings were based on the results of the employer survey mentioned previously. Forty-five percent of those in compliance with the HCS considered the standard to have a positive effect on employees, compared with only 9 percent who viewed the effect as negative. Almost 30 percent of employers reported that they had replaced a hazardous chemical with a less hazardous chemical substitute because of information presented on an MSDS (United States GAO 1991, 4).

Almost 70 percent of small employers complying with the HCS reported no difficulty in maintaining MSDSs and providing access for employees. Larger employers reported comparatively more difficulty, likely because of a need to manage a larger quantity of MSDSs and to provide access to a greater number of employees. Half of all large employers reported that they had 250 or more MSDSs. With regard to training, almost 80 percent of small employers complying with the HCS reported some difficulty. Insufficient training expertise and complex MSDSs were cited as particular problems (OSHA, March 2004).

The GAO findings generally indicated that non-compliance with the HCS resulted largely from lack of knowledge about the requirements of the standard, rather than difficulty in complying with the provisions of the standard. These results pointed toward greater outreach assistance efforts as a way to improve compliance. After these studies, OSHA continued to make extensive efforts to provide helpful materials to assist employers to comply with the various provisions of the HCS. This is reflected in the materials offered on their Web site and through hardcopy versions available for the referenced materials within this chapter.

This completes the chapter's five tasks addressing hazard communication compliance with OSHA. However, one can see from the listing of desired training topics proposed by OSHA (see Appendix C) that the expected scope of employee knowledge about safety and health goes well beyond that which is only within the OSHA regulations. Other standards and regulations that will be encountered by employees both on and off company premises are included within the topics of the suggested training materials. Consequently, the following sections have been developed to cover standards addressing several of the other types of hazard communication that are not covered under OSHA, for example, accident-prevention signs, general chemical labeling, safety posters, lockout tagging, barricade tapes, and highway hazard signs and vehicle communications.

OTHER HAZARD COMMUNICATIONS: SIGNAGE AND LABELING

Pre-OSHA Signage

The importance of accident-prevention signs to worker safety had been recognized by the early 1900s. By the 1930s to 1940s, the National Safety Council and insurance companies had assumed an important role in creating, promoting, and distributing safety-related information such as posters. During this time there was little research as to what type of signage design might be the most effective under a particular circumstance and context. Today, extensive research has suggested four attributes can be analyzed in any safety- or health-related labeling, signage, or other instructional materials. These include text (and cognitive aspects of messages), symbols (usage and meaning), format (layout and presentation), and location (geographical placement and environmental factors). For every type of safety communication developed, these attributes have to be addressed, and the number of such communication types is vast. One can think of scores of examples where persons are exposed to signage in their daily occupational and personal lives. To appreciate the breadth of this exposure, Appendix D has been developed to list numerous types of primarily hazard communications. There are warning and instructional communications that have been given special attention through government and voluntary standards organizations. Only a few of them are discussed in this chapter, but the scope of hazard warnings is clearly very broad.

Coverage of Standards—Any Standard

Understanding and properly applying standards covering the areas in Appendix D requires knowledge of the intent of the various provisions within a standard, in terms of coverage and specificity. Signage standards range all the way from being extremely specific and very detailed to being very nonspecific and with limited details. It is useful to think about classifying whole standards, or provisions within standards, in terms of (a) coverage (horizontal versus vertical) and (b) degree of specificity (performance versus specification). OSHA refers to such a classification system in its publication 92-14 (May 1996), but such a classification system applies regardless of whether it is a voluntary consensus standard (such as ANSI or ASTM) or a mandatory government regulation (such as OSHA, EPA, or CPSC).

The concept of the *horizontal* standard indicates application to a breadth of industry or across product categories (e.g., all machine guarding, all chemical hazard warnings, or all electrical safety). On the other hand, a *vertical* standard means it is more specific to a particular industry, type of operation, or a specific chemical (e.g., shipbuilding, welding, woodworking machines, benzene, or asbestos).

Relative to a standard's degree of specificity, consensus organization's standards are more likely to be of a *performance* nature to give applicators a breadth of flexibility in achieving a design adaptable to their company (e.g., automobiles must meet a crashworthy test at 5 mph, regardless of their design). On the other hand, government-mandated standards are often of a *specification* nature that, among other things, facilitates enforcers to judge compliance more easily (e.g., worker exposure to benzene shall not exceed 1 part per million (PPM) as a time-weighted, 8-hour average).

Government and consensus organizations must determine whether each standard, subsection, and provision will have a horizontal or vertical scope and then determine if the specificity of it will be based on performance or design. Nearly all standards have within them a mixture of these classifications across their various provisions, and the practitioner must try to ascertain what the intent of the developers was relative to these potential formats.

Most signing standards promulgated by consensual organizations are horizontal in structure, applying to a breadth of signing categories (e.g., all environmental or facility signing). Consensus standards are also more likely to be of a performance nature to give applicators a breadth of flexibility in achieving a design adapted to their company.

Early Industrial Accident-Prevention Signs

Many think of the United States of America as being innovative in its approach to industrial safety and health communications since 1970. However, the reader may be surprised by some of the contents of a publication dated 1914 and published by the Accident Prevention Department of the National Association of Manufacturers. It is titled "Preventive Appliances," and the publication abounds with quotations that could well have been published contemporarily 98 years later. Consider the following example:

> The use of danger signs has a very important place in a campaign for safety, serving as a warning to point out an existing danger, and . . . with the weight of opinion among safety engineers and others connected with the safety movement . . . the color green having come into general acceptance as signifying safety . . . the red color that indicates danger. (National Association of Manufacturers 1914, 1)

The National Safety Council, in its early safety and health role, provided a large selection of safety posters covering a wide variety of potential hazards. This effort was well underway by 1927, as indicated by a *National Safety News* article from that era (Mathieu 1927).

> The National Safety Council (NSC) posters are too well known to be described here. The hundred of thousands ordered each month show they serve a useful purpose.
> It remains then for our silent salesman to bridge the gap between safety meetings and other safety activities. This silent salesman is the safety poster.
> Posters must be changed frequently, the oftener, the better, within reasonable limits.
> We must remember the danger of leaving it up too long, for this is one case where our adaptiveness will work against us. (Mathieu 1927, 17–18)

If one looks at examples of posters from this era, an appreciation is gained of how sophisticated the designs were, even without having the benefit of our *modern* research input. More recent research has only validated the experiential knowledge applied to the designs of accident-prevention signs created in this earlier era.

The NSC posters often used cartoon-type drawings to depict various safety circumstances, and they gave accompanying descriptions suggesting preventive actions. These cartoon-type drawings could be viewed as the predecessors of nontextual symbols used internationally today. The early signs also revealed an important recognition that has since been called *human factors*. Namely, there was a sensitivity for understanding the capabilities and limitations of the various target recipients of safety information—humans. For example, a 1937 National Safety Congress presentation focused on longshoremen workers. "Longshoremen, as a class, are distinct from types of men found in other industry. . . . there are posters with safety slogans that 50 per cent of them can neither read nor understand" (Ames 1937, 358).

The response to such a situation was to create cartoon characters, such as the "Ozzie" used by the Travelers Insurance Company. Ozzie would be shown performing unsafe acts leading to an accident. As an indication of how effective this portrayal was, workers who had tendencies to commit unsafe acts were themselves called "Ozzies" by other workers, and not in a complimentary way (Ames 1937, 358).

The standards for signing can easily be traced back 50 years. For example, the United States of America Standard Institute's (USASI) "Specifications for Accident Prevention Signs" was already in its second revision in 1968 (1968a). According to the standard, it was mutually agreed that signage was one of the "oldest items of safety equipment" used. Also, within this standard, there was evidence that the sponsors had identified objectives and desired outcomes that are currently known as *effectiveness*. For example, one part of the standard expressed, "Uniformity of signs, intelligently located and properly worded, should provide an automatic warning, caution, or notice to all employees no matter where they work with a meaning that is clearly understood immediately" (USASI 1968a, 7).

A Movement toward Uniformity

The above showed early recognition of the importance of uniformity in hazard communication signs at all industrial levels. Guidelines for this uniformity came in a 1941–42 version of an American Standards Association (ASA) standard, Z35.1, *American Standard Specifications for Industrial Accident Prevention Signs*. After many years of use and subsequent deliberations, this ASA Z35.1 standard was revised in 1959 under the same title.

The early versions of ASA Z35.1 standards were specifically developed for hazard communications in workplaces. It is interesting that in the 1959 revision of the same American Standard Z35.1, the now well-known radiation symbol first appeared after its approval by ASA (ASA 1959, 9).

Contrary to how plaintiff lawyers try to convince juries, these initial signing standards were never intended to be applicable to labels on products. This is understandable since there were no other safety communication standards applicable to product labels in this era. As a consequence, many attempted to extrapolate the specifications within the Z35.1 signage standards and apply them to product warning labels. It was not until the 1991 ANSI Z535.4 standard that consumer-product warning labels were specifically addressed (ANSI 1991a–e).

Signage Standardization

Evolution of ANSI (ASA to USASI to ANSI)

It was about the time of World War II that a renewed interest in safety signage began. With a preexisting organization like the ASA already in place, it was a logical place for additional signing standardization to begin.

Current-day researchers attempting to trace the changes in consensual signing standards throughout the years are confronted with the name changes of the standards-generating organizations. Namely, early standards for safety colors were developed as an American War Standard at the request of the War Department, which was in power throughout World War II. This color standard was adopted in 1945 by the previously mentioned American Standards Association (ASA). The ASA was reconstituted as the USA Standards Institute (USASI) in August 1966 and later as the American National Standards Institute (ANSI) in October 1969 (ANSI 1979). Interestingly, although an organization's name may change throughout the life of a given standard, the standard's designated number typically does not change.

Consolidation under the ANSI Z535 Series

The ANSI Z535 series (2011) has become a set of systematic guidelines for designing any type of word-based hazard communication, whether signs, labels, tags, tapes, manuals, or instructions. The series could have been written as one standard, rather than six separate standards, and covered all the listed types of hazard communication channels. Regardless of the communication type, the designer is confronted with the same set of general questions, which the current ANSI Z535 series is now able to answer:

1. *What should the parts of the communication be?* Answer: For one-page communications there should be a two- or three-panel display consisting of an enlarged signal-word panel; a panel with verbiage describing the hazard, potential consequences, and preventive measures; and, optionally, a symbol that may also have a few words with it identifying what hazard or preventive measure the symbol represents.

2. *What color combinations should be used?*
   Answer: The standard Z535.1 (2006, R2011)
   specifies which colors are recommended for
   different parts of the design.

3. *If one uses a symbol, what are the rules of
   use, and how should it be displayed?* The
   answer is in Z535.3 (2011b), which gives the
   criteria for safety symbol usage.

4. *Are there recommendations specific to the
   type of communication one is designing for a
   particular application?* Answer: Yes, although
   the design procedure is the same and uses
   similar criteria, there are slight differences
   based on the application. These slight differences are spelled out in the separate standards
   dealing with the following: Environmental
   and Facility Safety Signs (Z535.2, 2011a);
   Product Safety Signs and Labels (Z535.4,
   2011c); Safety Tags and Barricade Tapes
   (Z535.5, 2011d); and Other Collateral Materials (Z535.6, 2011e).

A somewhat controversial fifth question could
be asked at this point, even though it digresses from
the present discussion:

5. *How will the Globally Harmonized System's
   (GHS) recommendations affect the design and
   acceptability of "Environmental and Facility
   Safety Signs" and "Product Safety Signs and
   Labels"?* Answer: As described later in this
   chapter, the international directions for such
   designs are slightly different from that described within the ANSI Z535 series. There
   are cultural reasons for many of the differences,
   which U.S. governmental and standardization
   organizations have been slow to recognize.
   As a result, there will be alternative formats,
   which are likely to be acceptable across
   international borders.

The scope of the GHS proposal will be discussed
later in this chapter.

As noted, the first four of these questions could
have been dealt with more efficiently in one standard
with several sections. However, it was more feasible

under the ANSI committee political structure to divide
the guidelines into six separate standard areas and to
assign appropriate experts to respective committees.
The misfortune is that a designer will probably have
to have all these standards available for study so that
no specification is overlooked.

Many different hazard communication applications are portrayed in the various signs in Appendix D
in this chapter. For all these applications, the U.S.
signing designers had moved in a common direction.
That common direction was the ANSI Z535 series. For
nearly twenty years this series of standards has become
universally respected, and it has been used for guidance
across broad classifications of safety information. The
series is obtainable in electronic or hardcopy versions
from the ANSI organization at www.ansi.org or through
the Secretariat for the Z535 standards (National Electrical Manufacturers Association, 1300 North 17th
Street, Rosslyn, VA 22209).

This entire series of ANSI Z535 standards began
with the ANSI Z35.1 1941–42 standard on accident-
prevention signs:

- Z535.1 (2006, R2011)—**Safety Color Code**
  (This first historical standard was published
  as Z35.1 in 1941–42. It was updated in 1979
  and combined into this present standard in
  1991.)

- Z535.2 (2011a)—**Environmental and Facility
  Safety Signs** (ANSI Z35.1-1972 and Z35.4-1972
  were updated and combined into this standard
  in 1991 with the latest revision in 2007.)

- Z535.3 (2011b)—**Criteria for Safety Symbols**
  (new in 1991 with the latest revision in 2007.)

- Z535.4 (2011c)—**Product Safety Signs and
  Labels** (new in 1991 with latest revision in
  2011.)

- Z535.5 (2011d)—**Safety Tags and Barricade
  Tapes (for temporary hazards)** (ANSI Z35.2-
  1974 was updated and combined into this
  standard in 1991 with the latest revision in
  2007.)

- Z535.6 (2011e)—**Product Safety Information
  in Product Manuals, Instructions, and Other
  Collateral Materials** (new in 2006.)

For the scholar and researcher as well as the serious applications person, there are excellent references provided at the end of each of these standards. Such references have been either cited within the standards themselves or utilized as foundations for specific provisions. Just looking over the list of these references allows one to appreciate how intertwined standards for signage have become. Such intertwining is positive because it has led to consistency across many, though not all, arenas and applications. Because of the importance of these references, they have been compiled and provided in Appendix E to this chapter, titled "References in the ANSI Z535-2011 Series."

This chapter is no substitute for having the complete set of ANSI Z535 standards available for review. It addresses only certain aspects of the standards. The focus of this chapter has been on the hazard communications dealing with the occupational and commercial applications as opposed to the household and consumer applications. Hence, the ANSI Z535.4 standard on product safety signs and labels will not be emphasized. Instead, the ANSI Z535.2 standard on environmental and facility signs will be used to illustrate the design options available. Within the Z535.2 standard there are about fifteen parameters that the sign designer has limited options to manipulate. As these are discussed, remember that they are the same parameters that are applicable to product labeling or almost any type of visual hazard communication.

About the ANSI Z535 Series

The major types of hazard communications covered in the ANSI Z535 series are environmental signage and product signage. The difference in these is spelled out in the following section.

Environmental or Product Safety Signs

Even among the safety communications experts, there remains an assemblage of terms whose definitions are still gray, including *warnings* (verbal, written, contextual, auditory, etc.), *warning labels, signs, signage, instructions, safety data sheets, placards, tags, safety information, important information, safety tape, paperless warnings,* and *computer on-screen product information.*

To distinguish environmental signing from product signage and labeling, one can think of products as completed functional units or components that are purchased from, or supplied by, an entity outside an immediate organization. As such, the signing that was placed on the product before it was delivered to a customer is usually referred to as *product labeling.* The supplied product then already has a type of signage (or labeling) prior to the time it enters onto a premise, into a facility, or anywhere in its applications environment.

On the other hand, *environmental signage* involves the communication of information that an end user, facilities manager, premise owner, or environmental administrator determines as necessary for the safety and health of humans (or other living organisms) in a particular domain. This differentiation will become apparent as the Z535.2 standard is discussed further.

From Z535.2, an "environmental safety sign" is a "sign or placard in a work or public area that provides safety information about the immediate environment" (ANSI 2007, 4). And a "product safety sign," is defined in the same Z535.2 standard as a "sign, label, or decal affixed to a product that provides hazard and safety information about that product" (ANSI 2007, 4).

Safety signs, both environmental and product, are categorized in ANSI Z535.2 as being in one of the following seven categories: (1) DANGER, (2) WARNING, (3) CAUTION, (4) NOTICE, (5) safety instructions or safety equipment location, (6) fire safety, or (7) directional arrow signs. Among these, the signal words in uppercase letters designate the level of hazard seriousness. The specific definition associated with each of these types of sign is provided in the following list (ANSI 2007, 4).

1. **DANGER sign:** Indicates a hazardous situation that is to be limited to the most extreme situations. If not avoided, it *will* result in death or serious injury.
2. **WARNING sign:** Indicates a hazardous situation that, if not avoided, *could* result in death or serious injury.

3. **CAUTION sign:** Indicates a hazardous situation that, if not avoided, could result in minor or moderate injury. It may also be used without the safety alert symbol as an alternative to "NOTICE:" "NOTICE" is the preferred signal word to address practices not related to personal injury. The safety alert symbol should not be used with this signal word. As an alternative to "NOTICE," the word "CAUTION," without the safety alert symbol, may be used to indicate a message not related to personal injury.

4. **NOTICE sign:** Notice signs are used for precautions not related to personal injury, and the safety alert symbol is not used with this signal word.

5. **Signs for safety instructions or safety equipment location:** Signs used to indicate general instructions relative to safe work practices or indicate the location of safety equipment.

6. **Fire safety signs:** Signs used to indicate the location of emergency fire-fighting equipment. (*Note:* These signs indicate the location of, but not the directions to, the equipment).

7. **Directional arrow signs:** Signs used to indicate the direction to emergency equipment, safety equipment, and other locations important to safety.

Designing Hazard Communication Signs

Unless mandated by government regulations, the use of signage for the environment or products is voluntary. Nevertheless, the use of signs and posters to provide hazard communications is widespread and often effective both in providing valuable safety and health information and in constantly reminding employees of actions they need to take for their own well-being. However, if it is decided to use signage, the consensus has been that it is preferable for such signage to be standardized along certain guidelines that might improve their potential effectiveness. To this end, the ANSI standard Z535.2 provides guidelines for sign designers.

A better understanding of the standard can be achieved if one arbitrarily divides it into four categories of features: (1) sign classification, (2) configuration of panels, (3) content of panels, and (4) display method.

If one analyzes the ANSI Z535.2 standard further, it becomes apparent that there are at least fifteen parameters regarding these features over which the designer has control as indicated below:

1. *Sign classification.* At the onset, the designer confronts the issue of what type of sign is needed (parameter 1). The choices are danger, warning, caution, notice, general safety, fire safety, or directional.

2. *Configuration of panels.* Signage is typically formatted in a 3-panel display layout. Although the standard notes several acceptable configurations for this layout, each of these layouts will typically include a signal-word panel (parameter 2), symbol/pictorial panel size (parameter 3) as specified in Z535.3 (ANSI 2007), and the word-message size (parameter 4). Even at this initial stage the designer must consider the overall desired or allowable physical size of the sign given environmental (or product-size) limitations.

3. *Content of Panels.* The panel content parameters include color choice (parameter 5) in accordance with Z535.1 (ANSI 2006), choice of signal word (parameter 6), shapes of directional arrows, if used (parameter 7), choice of symbols or pictorials (parameter 8), letter style (parameter 9) and letter size (parameter 10), choice of text message (parameter 11), and possible use of multilingual formats (parameter 12).

4. *Display Method.* This designation includes: sign placement within an environment so that persons might see it (parameter 13); illumination on a sign under limited natural-lighting conditions (parameter 14); and contrast (parameter 15).

As a beginning to the design process, there are twelve acceptable format or layout examples provided in Z535.2, suggesting the variety of ways the panel components—signal-word panel (#2), symbol/pictorial panel (#3), and word message (#4)—might be laid out. Only in the case of fire safety or signs and labels is a panel format without a signal-word panel (#2) recommended (ANSI 2007, 10, 17).

The preceding discussion illustrates that there is a very systematic way to conceive and design signs for various purposes. Dividing the decision making into the suggested fifteen parameters also provides a methodology for documenting how the various components of a sign (or label) evolved. It is noted that, if the question of "adequate warnings" arises in the litigation arena, the systematic approach laid out here leads to a documentation trail that, though optional, will be highly valuable in the litigation discovery process.

Safety Symbols

According to ANSI Z535.3, "Safety symbols are an *optional* component of the multi-panel safety sign, label, and tag formats described in the ANSI Z535.2, ANSI Z535.4, ANSI Z535.5 standards. Although the international trend is to rely much more heavily on symbols to transcend the language barriers, symbols usually consist of a black image (or safety red image for some symbols) on a white background" (ANSI 2007, 3).

If a safety symbol is utilized, it may be used with or without additional verbiage to describe the nature of the hazard being addressed by a particular symbol. The ANSI standard has a clear requirement that, if a symbol is to stand alone without explanatory verbiage, then it must have been tested for its "demonstrated understandability." This involves passing an "85% recognition test" as described in the ANSI Z535.3 standard (ANSI 2007, 21). There are 24 such pretested successful symbols provided as examples in the ANSI Z535.3 standard. These may be used by any designer without further testing. Along with these tested symbols, references are given as to which researcher or author conducted the successful testing (ANSI 2007, 40–53).

"Other symbols," as defined in the standard, are those that have not passed this level of "understandability" with a sample population. For all these other symbols that have not been successfully tested, it is required that additional explanatory word messages be provided to assist in explaining the intent of the symbol. Note that such testing can be done by private concerns, consultants, or research organizations, or taken from published results, as long as the procedural guidelines explained in ANSI Z535.3 have been followed. In support of these sections on ANSI Z535 labeling, three examples are provided. Figure 1 shows three symbols (labeled A, B, and C) that have been tested in accordance with ANSI Z535.3 and can be used without any text explanation as to their related hazard. The reader is cautioned that the philosophy

A

B

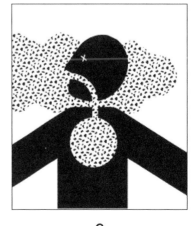

C

FIGURE 1. ANSI-tested safety symbols (*Source:* ANSI Z535.3, 2007)

and criteria associated with symbol usage is changing internationally even as this Handbook is published.

Figure 2 is the CPSC- and major manufacturers-approved ANSI Z535-style label that appears on all-terrain vehicles sold in the United States. It was developed and tested by this author not only for symbol recognition but also for user comprehension and understanding, where its score was in the 90 percent range. Figure 3 provides an example of an ANSI-formatted electrical hazard lockout label.

Choice of Signal Word

In any of the specifications for signs, labels, tags, or tape, emphasis has been placed on the choice of signal word for *alerting* persons regarding the level of hazard they may be about to face. Early research did *not* indicate a preferred signal-word prioritization scheme. The hypothesis has been that the continued, consistent use of certain signal words for particular purposes would eventually cause the exposed subject populace to learn the significance of these prioritizations (e.g., that DANGER always suggests a hazard with a greater potential consequence than WARNING). Although there are no recent studies to test this hypothesis, this differentiation continues to be the accepted convention. Consequently, the definitions and use of these signal words have become consensually accepted even outside the scope of ANSI. The following definitions are consistent with the types of signs presented earlier (ANSI 2007, 18–19).

> **DANGER** indicates a hazardous situation which, if not avoided, *will* result in death or serious injury.

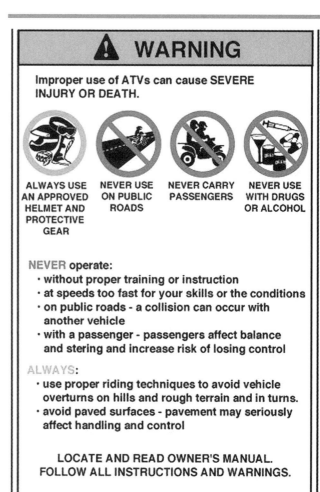

FIGURE 2. Example of ANSI-formatted ATV safety label (*Source:* ANSI Z535.4, 2007)

> **WARNING** indicates a hazardous situation which, if not avoided, *could* result in death or serious injury.
> **CAUTION (with the safety alert symbol)** indicates a hazardous situation which, if not

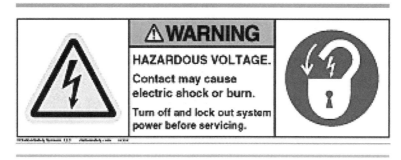

FIGURE 3. Example of ANSI electrical hazard lockout label (*Source:* ANSI Z535.4, 2007)

avoided, may result in minor or moderate injury.

CAUTION indicates a hazardous situation which, if not avoided, may result in minor or moderate injury. Without the safety alert symbol, it is used to address practices not related to personal injury.

NOTICE is used to address practices not related to personal injury.

Safety instruction or safety equipment location signs indicate general instructions relative to safe work practices or indicate the location of safety equipment.

The Safety Colors Standard

The use of colors in safety communication efforts has been extremely important. However, for those who have never reviewed the standard, there are many misunderstandings about the ANSI Z535.1 *Safety Colors* standard (2006), which neither indicates where a particular color should be used nor defines the significance of any given color. Rather, it is a specification standard that can be used to *manufacture* a certain color or verify that a given safety color has been achieved. There are ten such safety colors named. Where they are to be used is described in other standards. With this caveat in mind, the early history of the standard, described below, can be appreciated.

The Safety Color Code, was part of the *American War Standard*, which reportedly began in 1946 under committee procedures of the ASA and with the NSC as sponsor. This evolving effort was approved by ASA as the Z53 standard on September 11, 1953 (explaining the "53" designation). The 1979 version of ASA Z53.1 was the fourth revision and last in the series before the merging of several standards occurred under the Z535 series of 1991. The Z53.1 then took on the designation ANSI Z535.1, *Safety Color Code* (ANSI 2006, foreword, v). In 2006, the name of the standard was changed from *Safety Color Code* to *Safety Colors*.

In 1979, the ANSI Z53 Committee on Safety Colors was combined with the ANSI Z35 Committee on Safety Signs to form the ANSI Z535 Committee on Safety Signs and Colors. This committee still manages the entire ANSI Z535 series (ANSI 2006, foreword, v).

As indicated by this history, it was recognized early that individuals would learn to rely on the color coding, and such coding can even be applied to objects not featuring any word description, such as fire hydrants or facility piping.

The standard color specifications can be used across various types of safety information and safety-related objects, and they are frequently used within specifications originating from different governmental or organizational structures. They are also a mandatory reference for printers responsible for creating safety signage, labels, and other safety information.

As noted, other standards in the Z535 series recommend the circumstances in which a particular color from this set should be chosen. The standard color set itself is provided in Munsell Notation Specifications (ANSI 2006, 7) and also the Equivalent Commission Internationale de L'Eclairage (CIE), "Data Specifications" (ANSI 2006, 7). Besides specifying these colors, methods are given for testing, including visual evaluation. The set of ten primary color specifications for "safety colors" includes SAFETY RED, SAFETY ORANGE, SAFETY BROWN, SAFETY YELLOW, SAFETY GREEN, SAFETY BLUE, SAFETY PURPLE, SAFETY WHITE, SAFETY GRAY, and SAFETY BLACK. In addition to the color specs, the same Z535.1 standard provides recommendations for illumination and contrast (ANSI 2006).

The Z535.2 standard for environmental and facility signage utilizes a majority of the safety colors in its combinations of guidelines. Appendix F has been constructed to indicate the breadth of color combinations recommended in ANSI Z535.2. Each signal word is the beginning of the color combination for that respective type of sign. The required colors for background to the signal word, messages, background to messages, safety symbols, and background to symbols all have been specified for that type of sign. These combinations are shown on the table in Appendix F.

Signage Research References

The Z535 series standard has evolved from meetings where the communication scientists associated with signs and labeling and those persons actually involved in the design and application of such signage have tried to find common ground. Obviously, not all results found from research have made their way into these standard guidelines, and committees for such standards have not necessarily been in agreement as to what from the science should be included in any particular standard. Nevertheless, it is notable that the standards have listed in their appendices the primary references upon which some of the specifications were based. To assist the reader in being aware of these critical references, a table summarizing all the references cited by the ANSI Z535 committees has been prepared by this author and appears in Appendix E of this chapter under the title "References in the ANSI Z535 2006, 2007 Series." The various topics addressed in the standards, including the parameters used to design hazard communications, were further researched and presented in the book *Warnings and Safety Instructions— An Annotated Bibliography* (Miller and Lehto 2001), which reviewed 1200 such references.

Signage for Temporary Hazards—Tags and Tape

An early target in accident-prevention efforts was the class of accidents that occurred to persons involved in hazards created by temporary circumstances in the workplace. In 1968, USASI responded to these accidents with the initiation of standard USAS Z35.2, *Accident Prevention Tags* (1968b). This tracked the guidelines of its sister standard USAS Z35.1, *Accident Prevention Signs* (1968a). It found its way into the ANSI Z535 series of standards in 1991 as Z535.5, *Accident Prevention Tags (for Temporary Hazards)*, where it was made consistent with the other standards in this series. In the 2002 version of Z535.5, an additional type of signage was included, safety tags, and the standard was renamed: Z535.5 *Safety Tags and Barricade Tapes (for Temporary Hazards)* (ANSI 2007).

What distinguishes this type of hazard communication from others is discussed in the introduction to ANSI Z535.5 (2007): "Safety tags and barricade tapes are a means of alerting persons to temporary hazards often associated with construction, equipment installation, maintenance, repair, lockout or other transient conditions." It further explains that these are "not to be used in place of a permanent sign or label intended for hazards in normal use, operation or maintenance."

The same guidelines of design discussed under Z535.2, *Environmental and Facility Safety Signs*, can also be applied to both safety tags and barricade tape. Namely, the format includes a signal word, safety symbol, and message block. Thus, the fifteen parameters of design discussed earlier should also be considered in the design of accident-prevention tags and barricade tape. The barricade-tape format is unique in that it naturally has a more horizontal presentation and is expected to be repeated throughout the length of the tape. Thus the target audience of such tape may see the warnings repeated dozens of times.

Safety tags, besides providing warning information, are also used to signal the dysfunction of a piece of equipment. Some tags are attached to a lockout device for the equipment. This makes only the person named on the tag solely responsible for removing the tag before any energizing occurs because this person will have the only unlocking key. An interesting suggestion made in the appendix of the Z535.5 standard is that a photograph of the person responsible for the lockout be placed on the tag as an easier way to locate that individual on a large job site where workers may not be known by name (ANSI 2007, 18). Safety tags are also an important safety measure used in the ANSI and OSHA machine-guarding standards. Mechanical, chemical, and electrical systems having maintenance performed on them have been the subject of multitudes of accidents when they have not been safety tagged and locked out. Thus, the importance of this type of hazard communication cannot be overemphasized. Figures 4 and 5 represent examples of lockout and barricade tape warnings, respectively.

Other Types of Hazard Communication

Besides the requirements necessary for OSHA compliance in the workplace, there are many other circumstances within which hazard communication is important, and there were standards and practices in place to provide such warnings long before OSHA existed. One very prominent standard that was discussed earlier in the chapter was ANSI Z129.1, *American National Standard for Hazardous Industrial Chemicals— Precautionary Labeling* (2006). Another standard related to chemical hazard communication is the mandatory standard administered by the U.S. Department of Transportation, Bureau of Motor Carrier Safety (BMCS). It involves the labeling of vehicles that are carrying hazardous materials.

Placarding and Labeling of Hazardous Materials (49 CFR Chapter 1, Part 172)

The objective of this standard is to identify what chemicals are contained and being transported in over-the-road vehicles. It also addresses the level of hazard associated with the chemicals in those vehicles. The type of labeling and placarding required within these standards is very precisely defined in terms of colors, size, placement, and terminology. Because of the dif-

FIGURE 4. Example of ANSI-formatted lockout/tagout safety tag (*Source:* ANSI Z535.5, 2007)

FIGURE 5. Examples of barricade tape (*Source:* ANSI Z535.5, 2007)

ferences in jurisdiction and enactment dates, these standards have not been promulgated to be complementary to the ANSI Z535 series, ANSI Z129.1, or the *Manual of Uniform Traffic Control Devices* (MUTCD) standards, discussed in the next section. Colors are specified in accordance to Munsell notations and the Commission Internationale de L'Eclairage (CIE) specifications, but the colors are not the same as those referenced in the ANSI Z535.1 *Safety Color Code*. The description of all DOT hazardous chemical labeling and placarding requirements can be found in 49 CFR Chapter 1, Part 172 (1–704) and its appendices (OSHA 1976). Again, it is noted that these standards are in transition to make them consistent with international changes in signing.

Manual on Uniform Traffic Control Devices (MUTCD) Signage

The last of the U.S. standards addressed in this chapter is the MUTCD. It has importance in this discussion of hazard communication because of its extensive coverage and use. Although one sees a large volume of various signs and labels in relation to the work and home environments, there is also an incredible number of signs in the environment, which encompasses all highways and destination areas traveled to by the public.

The need for uniform standards in and around public highways and other public areas was recognized as early as 1927 for rural highways and 1930 for urban highways. At that time several early organizations joined efforts and eventually published the original edition of the *Manual on Uniform Traffic Control Devices* in 1935 (Federal Highway Administration (FHWA) 2009, I-1).

The MUTCD is underwritten by the Federal FHWA, which administers the MUTCD through the Code of Federal Regulations. All states are required to adopt a manual with specifications substantially similar to and consistent with guidelines provided in the current revision of the MUTCD (FHWA 2009, 2). Therefore, the MUTCD represents a mandated set of standards whose enforcement and implementation has been decentralized to state governments. Although its title might imply "traffic control," its scope goes far beyond that, and its guidance plays an important continuing role in hazard communication.

As was noted with placarding and labeling of hazardous materials (49 CFR Chapter 1, Part 172), the MUTCD actually originated before the ANSI Z535 series of standards.

Consequently, there has been no effort to make the MUTCD compatible with the ANSI Z535 series, and there probably is no necessity for the two to be complementary given that their respective functions are generally far removed from one another. On the other hand, the idea of standardizing signage formats, signal words, and colors so that people become uniformly knowledgeable about safety communications is somewhat undermined by the differences.

Unique to the MUTCD system is the importance of shape coding, which is not used in the Z535 series, but does appear in the current and proposed international signing guidelines. To accompany the MUTCD shape coding, there are colors that correspond to the shapes used. Anyone who has ever taken a state driver's license exam has been tested on MUTCD signage shapes and colors.

One area that does have some interesting overlap is the use of symbols. The ANSI Z535.3 requirement that symbols used alone must pass a recognition test is not specified as part of MUTCD. Instead, there are over 125 symbols that have been identified as acceptable for use across the various types of signage that MUTCD covers. One could conclude that the MUTCD is the most highly developed system for hazard communication in the United States. Its methods of communicating important safety and directional information are also likely the best understood of any safety system in the United States. The MUTCD special features involving designated colors and shapes have made this system unique. They have been summarized in Appendix G.

International Standards Organization (ISO) 3864—Safety Colors and Safety Signs

Many companies in this country are known as multinational corporations, or they do business with an international clientele. Consequently, such globalization requires the safety professional to recognize and

sometimes accommodate for international standards for signage, labeling, and warnings. As noted in the discussions of the chemical MSDS materials, there has almost been a consensus regarding the content and format of hazard and physical properties information presented with chemicals. Europe and several other country groups have created standards quite similar to the ANSI 400.1 (2004). Hence, satisfying the chemical labeling and information requirements of these other countries is quite similar to satisfying the OSHA requirements in this country.

Existing in parallel to the ANSI Z535 series but quite different in content are some of the standards generated by the International Standards Organization (ISO). One such is the ISO 3864 standard *Safety Colours and Safety Signs* (2002). This standard was developed by the Technical Committee ISO/TC 80 in November of 1979. It was widely accepted by many countries, but countries such as the United States and Sweden initially disapproved of it (ISO 1984a, foreword). Today, it still maintains high acceptability among many countries, including most of Europe as well as Mexico and South Africa. This is the preferred format in the European community because of the concentration of diverse languages and because it focuses on universal symbols *without* words.

In 1998, the ISO subcommittee in charge of the ISO 3864 standard recognized the need to divide the standard into two parts: one for safety signs in the workplace and public areas and another for product safety labels (Peckham 2008, 1). ISO 3864, *Graphical Symbols—Safety Colours and Safety Signs: Part 1: Design Principles for Safety Signs in Workplaces and Public Areas*, was developed in 2002. Together with ISO 7010, it cancels and replaces ISO 3864:1984, which has been technically revised (ISO 2002, foreword). *Graphical Symbols Safety Colours and Safety Signs—Part 2: Design Principles for Product Safety Labels*, was first published in 2004 and reaffirmed without changes in 2010. The United States was instrumental in writing Part 2 of ISO 3864, the goal being to write a standard that would incorporate existing formats currently defined in both ISO product-specific standards and in the ANSI Z535.4 standard. In the ANSI Z535 standards, the safety alert symbol is used in the signal word panel to indicate the risk of personal injury. In ISO 3864, the triangle with an exclamation mark is defined as the general warning sign and indicates the risk of personal injury. When it came time to illustrate the use of signal words for product safety labels, the writers of ISO 3864-2 insisted that the triangle-with-exclamation-mark symbol appearing in the severity panel be identical to the ISO 3864-1 warning sign. As of the 2006 publication of ANSI Z535 standards, both ISO and ANSI have format options that are identical in every respect (Peckham 2008, 5).

The ISO is still responsible for publishing this standard, which defines the design criteria for *international* safety signs. It is a graphic-only approach intended to communicate the safety label's message quickly and without the use of words. Three geometric shapes are defined for use in graphic symbols. The circular form is used to surround symbols designating a prohibition or mandatory action, the triangle is used to designate warnings, and rectangular shapes are used to surround informational or instructional information (ISO 2002, 4). A color-coding scheme is also built into the standard: red for stop and prohibition, blue for mandatory action, yellow for caution and risk of danger, and green for a safe condition (ISO 2002, 4).

Figure 6 illustrates the three categories of ISO safety symbols, which are defined by both their shape and their color:

- Warning signs must be yellow triangles with a black border. The graphic must be black (Figure 6A).

- Prohibition signs are white circles with the familiar red circle and slash. Again, the graphic must be black. Each prohibition sign illustrates a prohibited activity (Figure 6B).
- The mandatory action signs are blue circles with white graphics and no border. Each sign indicates an action that must be performed for the safe use of the product (Figure 6C).

ISO 4196: Graphic Symbols—Use Of Arrows

An interesting companion document to ISO 3864, also with a first edition date of 1984, is the ISO 4196 *Graphical Symbols—Use of Arrows* (1984b). Based on its introduction, this standard was developed and agreed on to "promote the use of a reduced number of arrow forms as graphical symbols" (ISO 1984b, 1). Its scope was to "lay down the basic principles and the proportions to be adopted when designing graphical symbols which incorporate an arrow, or arrows, to indicate various movements, forces, or function to be indicated" (ISO 1984b, 1). Although it was international in its use and approved by European, Japanese, and South African countries, the United States neither approved nor disapproved of the standard (1984b, foreword). There is nothing comparable in the ANSI series of standards that deals only with arrows; however, ANSI Z535.2 includes a small section on arrow designation.

This introduction to international signs and labels suggests quite a different philosophy that other countries have relative to the design of signs and warnings. On the one hand, through U.S. standards committees

FIGURE 6. Example of ISO labels (*Source:* ISO 3864:1; ISO 3864:3)

and litigation, extensive amounts of information about a hazard have come to be expected on a label or sign. One expects an attention-getting signal word, description of the hazard, consequences in the form of potential injury, and what preventive action is in order. Other countries have products more likely to be distributed or exposed to nationals of several countries who may understand only a single native language. In such cases, repeating a warning in a multitude of languages may not be feasible with signage space restrictions. It is logical, then, that a system based on symbols and shapes would make more sense and likely be more effective among a multiple-language population of users.

One consequence of this philosophy is that hazard communications on equipment and nonchemical products that cross international borders into the United States will likely need to be reviewed and possibly modified by a safety professional. Label and signage changes may be necessary for products imported as well as for those exported. This necessity has been recognized by some of the ANSI signage committees, and changes have already been made to draft standards of the ANSI Z535 series that incorporate the international approach, placing more emphasis on symbols and shapes. While the above international standards were active as of the publication of this Handbook, the reader is strongly advised to stay abreast of the evolution caused by the Global Harmonization System (GHS) discussed earlier in this chapter. It may radically change the approach now used internationally for hazard warnings.

Advertising and Electronic Hazard Warnings

One contemporary type of hazard communication that often goes unmentioned in traditional safety research circles is that which accompanies advertising or which appears in some electronic form. Because of both governmental and common law, advertisers must provide warnings about certain potential hazards associated with the use of a product they are trying to sell.

The advertising that was used to sell products 50 years ago typically did not provide communications relating to the hazards intrinsic to a particular product. However, in the late 1960s the federal government started requiring safety information about smoking to appear in product advertising. Currently, safety information appears abundantly in the advertising of many product types. Such information is used to warn of the health or safety aspects of a product's use; to deter certain types of behavior (e.g., use of drugs, alcohol while driving, and cigarettes); and to prevent target groups of individuals from using certain products (e.g., "not intended for use by small children" or "use only with parental or adult supervision"). There are no known consensus standards that directly apply to solely advertising-type communications as of this printing.

Another type of contemporary hazard communication is that appearing in some electronic form, sometimes referred to as "paperless warnings." As an example, marketing people, in selling products for and through computers, are frequently not providing any paper warnings or operating instructions with their product other than what might appear on the packaging. Instead, the product may have only a CD containing warnings and instructions, or one may receive a video. On some products one is referred to a product Web site to find current information about new safety warnings, recalls, warranty, repair, maintenance, and operating instructions. Warnings are also now often being incorporated anywhere television-type monitors appear for public information, such as in retail stores, on electronic billboards, in airports and train stations, and at major sports arenas. Even facilities such as fast food restaurants and bowling alleys now heavily use monitors to provide various safety and instructional information. Finally, one cannot escape Internet searches with pop-up windows with various sorts of advertising and other unsolicited information, which also can contain hazard communications.

These expanding possibilities for providing hazard communication and training give safety and health professionals additional opportunities for bringing messages to employees and nonemployees in a facility as well as to the public outside the occupational environment. How this new era of electronic media will impact the hazard communication standards of such organizations as ANSI and ISO is only now being initially looked at by the respective committees, who in the past have been concerned only with static information appearing on signs, labels, or paper.

CONCLUSION

A first goal of this chapter was to provide guidance to those responsible for OSHA compliance with the *Hazard Communication Standard*, 29 CFR 1900.1200 (1983). The emphasis of this standard is, of course, the recognition and control of chemical hazards in the workplace and satisfying every employee's right to know about chemical exposure while working. As noted earlier, to accomplish this, the professional would have to accomplish five primary tasks: (1) developing a written health hazard communication (HazCom) plan/program; (2) creating an up-to-date hazardous chemical inventory; (3) having all hazardous chemicals properly labeled; (4) making accessible to employees an MSDS for every chemical that is covered by the standard; and (5) properly instructing, training, and providing required information to all effected employees. In this chapter, information useful to complying with each of these five steps was provided along with Internet and paper references for obtaining additional assistance.

Not every professional reading this chapter will be concerned with responsibility for HazCom compliance. Thus, a second goal of the chapter was to address hazard communication outside of the "OSHA box," that is, to review how hazard communication is accomplished for products, environments, and locations other than within a U.S. OSHA-controlled workplace. Consequently, the chapter introduced standards that establish methods for providing general chemical product information (ANSI Z129.1 2006); standards for environmental, facility, and product signage (ANSI 2006, 2007); and standards more closely related to vehicular applications and travel within this country (MUTCD 2009).

What is certain in this global economy is that one cannot avoid confronting the issue of imported or exported products (or workers). Thus, familiarization with hazard communication norms for other countries and other languages is becoming a necessity. Imported products will have to be reviewed as to the hazard

information that accompanies them, and this information may have to be revised to meet new U.S. standards, which adopt some proposals within the Global Harmonization System (GHS). Products to be exported will also have to be modified to satisfy the new hazard communication standards of other countries, which may now reflect changes due to the GHS. Although the chapter discussed how similar MSDS standards were across countries, it also indicated how dissimilar on-product warnings were. The U.S. standards emphasize detailed verbiage to explain hazards, whereas the non-U.S. standards, such as those within the ISO, emphasize symbols and shapes. Achieving a higher level of international consistency is the goal of the GHS, which many countries are now in the process of reviewing for possible adoption.

Finally, it has been known for some time that presenting hazard information training through the use of videotape-type formats has been effective and useful. However, the expanded use of hazard communications through digital displays, monitors, computers, and other dynamic electronic means is an arena that has only recently started to get the attention of standards committees and researchers. Research may prove that these digital devices are the most effective means of communicating hazard information to a population that voluntarily gives priority attention to electronic visual media. Designers of hazard communications will undoubtedly have to incorporate these popular digital display devices into their warning, training, and instructional programs.

REFERENCES

Accident Prevention Department of the National Association of Manufacturers. 1914. "Signs and Their Value in the Prevention of Accidents." *Preventative Appliances, Supplement to American Industries*, May, pp. 1–4.

American National Standards Institute (ANSI). 1979. Z53.1-1979, *Safety Color Code for Marking Physical Hazards*. New York: ANSI

———. 2010. ANSI Z400.1/Z129.1-2010, *Hazardous Workplace Chemicals—Hazard Evaluation and Safety Data Sheet and Precautionary Labeling*. Washington, D.C.: Chemical Manufacturers Association.

———. 2006 (R 2011). Z535.1, *Safety Colors*. Washington, D.C.: NEMA.

_____. 2011a. ANSI/NEMA Z535.2-2011, *Environmental and Facility Safety Signs*. Washington, D.C.: NEMA.

_____. 2011b. ANSI/NEMA Z535.3-2011, *Criteria for Safety Symbols*. Washington, D.C.: NEMA.

_____. 2011c. ANSI/NEMA Z535.4, *Product Safety Signs and Labels*.Washington, D.C.: NEMA.

_____. 2011d. ANSI/NEMA Z545.5-2011, *Safety Tags and Barricade Tapes (For Temporary Hazards)*. Washington, D.C.: NEMA.

_____. 2011e. ANSI/NEMA Z535.6, *Product Safety Information in Product Manuals, Instructions, and Other Collateral Materials*. Rosslyn, VA: NEMA.

American National Standards Institute (ANSI)/American Society of Mechanical Engineers (ASME). 2007. A13.1-2007, *Scheme for Identification of Piping Systems*. New York: ANSI.

American Standards Association (ASA). 1941. Z35.1-1941, *American Standard Specifications for Industrial Accident Prevention Signs*. New York: ASA.

_____. 1959. Z35.1-1959, *American Standard Specifications for Industrial Accident Prevention Signs*. New York: ASA.

Ames, F. 1937. "The Value of Safety Posters in Accident Prevention." Transactions of 26th National Safety Congress, Kansas City, Missouri. National Safety Council, Inc., pp. 357–359.

California Department of Industrial Relations. 2000. *Guide to the California Hazard Communication Regulation*. Sacramento: California Department of Industrial Relations.

California Occupational Safety and Health Administration (CalOSHA). n.d. *Regulated Carcinogens*. Title 8 CCR, Article 10. Sacramento: CalOSHA.

_____. n.d. *Identification of Piping*. Title 8 CCR, Section 3321. Sacramento: CalOSHA.

Canadian Centre for Occupational Health and Safety (CCOHS). 2007. *OSH Answers, Material Safety Data Sheets (MSDSs)—Creating* (retrieved October 3, 2011). www.ccohs.ca/oshanswers/legisl/msds_prep.html

_____. 2009. *Globally Harmonized System (GHS)* (retrieved October 2011), www.ccohs.ca

Centers for Disease Control and Prevention (CDC). n.d. *International Chemical Safety Cards: Description*. NIOSH and International Programme on Chemical Safety (IPCS) (retrieved October 1, 2011). www.cdc.gov/niosh/ipcs/ipcscard.html

Chapanis, A. 1965. "Words, Words, Words." *Human Factors* 7: 1–17.

Compliance Center, Inc. 2011. *GHS Awareness for Canada and United States* (retrieved October 2011). www.compliancecenter.com

Department of Justice, Canada. 1985. *Hazardous Products Act, Part II. Controlled Products* (R.S. 1985, c. H-3) (retrieved November 2006). http://laws.justice.gc.ca/en/H-3

European Commission (EEC). 1991. *Commission Directive 91/155/EEC of 5 March 1991 defining and laying down the detailed arrangements for the system of specific information relating to dangerous preparations in the implementation of Article 10 of Directive 88/379/EEC* (retrieved October 2011) www.reach-compliance.eu/english/legislation/docs/launchers/launch-91-155-EEC.html

_____. 2001. *Commission Directive 2001/58/EC of 27 July 2001 amending for the second time Directive 21/155/EEC defining and laying down the detailed arrangements for the systems of specific information relating to dangerous preparations in implementation of Article 14 of the European Parliament and Council Directive 199/45/EC and relating to dangerous substances in implementaiton of Article 27 of Council Directive 67/548/EEC (safety data sheets)* (retrieved October 1, 2011) www.reach.sgs.com/documents_directive_2001_58_ex.pdf

Federal Highway Administration, U.S. Department of Transportation. 2009. *Manual of Uniform Traffic Control Devices (MUTCD 2009)*. Washington, D.C.: U.S. Government Printing Office.

Gullickson, R. 1996, May. *Reference Data Sheet on Material Safety Data Sheets*. Glenview, IL: Meridian Engineering and Technology.

Health Canada. 1988. *Hazardous Products Act*. Ottawa, Ontario: Health Canada.

International Labour Organization (ILO). 2004, November 11. "Chemical Safety Cards." In *Basics of Chemical Safety*. Geneva: International Occupational Safety and Health Information Centre (retrieved January 2007). www.ilo.org/public/english/protection/safework/cis/products/safetym/msds.htm

International Standards Organization (ISO). 1984a. ISO 3864-1984, *Safety Colours and Safety Signs*. Switzerland: ISO.

_____. 1984b. *Graphical Symbols—Use of Arrows*. ISO 4196-1984(E). Switzerland: ISO.

_____. 2004. ISO 3864:2-2004, *Graphic Symbols—Safety Colours and Safety Signs--Part 2: Design Principles for Product Safety Labels*. Geneva, Switzerland: ISO.

_____. 2006. ISO 3864:3-2006, *Graphic Symbols—Safety Colours and Safety Signs: Part 3: Design Principles for Use in Safety Signs*. Geneva, Switzerland: ISO.

_____. 2011. ISO 3864:1-2011, *Graphic Symbols—Safety Colours and Safety Signs--Part 1: Design Principles for Safety Signs in Workplaces and Public Areas*. Geneva, Switzerland: ISO.

Kaplan, S.A. 1986. *Development of Material Safety Data Sheets*. 191st ACS meeting (retrieved 2006). www.phys.ksu.edu/area/jrm/Safety/kaplan.html

Keene State College. 2006. *Most Frequently Cited Serious Violations* (retrieved November 2006). www.keene.edu/conted/FY%202005%20MFC%20General%20Industry.ppt

Lab Safety Supply. 2007. *Labeling for Hazardous Communication: Document #200* (retrieved January 2006). www.labsafety.com

_____. 2010. Document #203, *ANSI Pipe Marking Standards* (retrieved June 2010). www.labsafety.com

Mathieu, A. 1927, August. "Bridging the Gap in Safety Education." *National Safety News*, pp. 17–18.

Miller, J. M., and M. R. Lehto. 2001. *Warnings and Safety Instructions—Annotated and Indexed*. 4th ed. Ann Arbor, MI: Fuller Technical Publications.

National Institute for Occupational Safety and Health (NIOSH). 1974. *A Recommended Standard . . . An Identification System for Occupationally Hazardous Materials* (retrieved 2006). www.cdc.gov/niosh/75-126.html

Occupational Safety and Health Administration (OSHA). 1976. 49 CFR 172. *Hazardous Materials Table, Special Provisions, Hazardous Materials Communication.* Washington, D.C.: Office of the Federal Register.

_____. 1983. 29 CFR 1910.1200. *Hazard Communication.* Washington, D.C.: Office of the Federal Register.

_____. 1994. 29 CFR 1901.1200. *Hazard Communication, Final Rule.* Federal Register 59 (27). Washington, D.C.: OSHA.

_____. 1996, May. *Setting Occupational Safety and Health Standards.* Washington, D.C.: OSHA.

_____. 1997, May 23. *Hazard Communication: A Review of the Science Underpinning the Art of Communication for Health and Safety.* Washington, D.C.: OSHA.

_____. 1998. OSHA 3084, *Chemical Hazard Communication* (retrieved 2006). www.osha.gov/Publications/osha3084.pdf

_____. 1998, March 20. CPL 02-02-038-CPL 2-2.38D, *Inspection Procedures for the Hazard Communication Standard* (retrieved 2006). www.osha.gov

_____. 1998, April 7. *New OSHA Directive Makes It Easier for Employers to Comply with Hazard Communication Standard.* OSHA news release. Washington, D.C.: OSHA.

_____. 2000. *Hazard Communication: Guidelines for Compliance OSHA 3111* (retrieved 2006). www.osha.gov/Publications/osha3111.pdf

_____. December 2002. *Draft Guidance for Hazard Determination* (retrieved 2006). www.osha.gov

_____. 2003. *Draft Model Training Program for Hazard Communication* (retrieved 2006). www.osha.gov/dsg/hazcom/MTP101703. pdf

_____. 2004, March. *Hazard Communication in the 21st Century, Executive Summary* (retrieved 2006). www.osha.gov

_____. 2005. *A Guide to the Globally Harmonized System of Classification and Labeling of Chemicals (GHS)* (retrieved October 2011). www. osha.gov/hazcom/ghs.html

Nolan, T. J. 1960, October. "Revised Standards for Safety Signs." *National Safety News*, p. 206.

Peckham, Gregory. 2008. ISO 3864, *Part 2: The New International Standard for Product Safety Labeling* (retrieved November 2010). www. clarionsafety.com/assets/common/pdf/whitepapers/3864-2.pdf

United States of America Standards Institute (USASI). 1968a. USAS Z35.1-1968, *Standard Specifications for Accident Prevention Signs.* New York: USASI.

_____. 1968b. USAS Z3521-1968, *Standard Specifications for Accident Prevention Tags.* New York: USASI.

United States General Accounting Office. 1991. GAO/HRD-92-8, *OSHA Action Needed to Improve Compliance with Hazard Communication Standard.* Washington D.C.: U.S. Government Printing Office. www.gao.gov/

APPENDIX A

OSHA Form 174

Material Safety Data Sheet
May be used to comply with
OSHA's Hazard Communication Standard,
29 CFR 1910.1200. This Standard must be
consulted for specific requirements.

U.S. Department of Labor
Occupational Safety and Health Administration
(Non-Mandatory Form)
Form Approved
OMB No. 1218-0072

IDENTITY (As Used on Label and List)	Note: Blank spaces are not permitted. If any item is not applicable, or no information is available, the space must be marked to indicate that.

Section I

Manufacturer's Name	Emergency Telephone Number
Address (Number, Street, City, State, and ZIP Code)	Telephone Number for Information
	Date Prepared
	Signature of Preparer (optional)

Section II - Hazard Ingredients/Identity Information

Hazardous Components (Specific Chemical Identity; Common Name(s))	OSHA PEL	ACGIH TLV	Other Limits Recommended	% (optional)

Section III - Physical/Chemical Characteristics

Boiling Point		Specific Gravity (H_2O = 1)	
Vapor Pressure (mm Hg.)		Melting Point	
Vapor Density (AIR = 1)		Evaporation Rate (Butyl Acetate = 1)	

Solubility in Water

Appearance and Odor

Section IV - Fire and Explosion Hazard Data

Flash Point (Method Used)	Flammable Limits	LEL	UEL

Extinguishing Media

Special Fire Fighting Procedures

Unusual Fire and Explosion Hazards

Section V - Reactivity Data

Stability	Unstable		Conditions to Avoid
	Stable		

Incompatibility *(Materials to Avoid)*

Hazardous Decomposition or Byproducts

Hazardous Polymerization	May Occur		Conditions to Avoid
	Will Not Occur		

Section VI - Health Hazard Data

Route(s) of Entry:	Inhalation?	Skin?	Ingestion?

Health Hazards *(Acute and Chronic)*

Carcinogenicity:	NTP?	IARC Monographs?	OSHA Regulated?

Signs and Symptoms of Exposure

Medical Conditions Generally Aggravated by Exposure

Emergency and First Aid Procedures

Section VII - Precautions for Safe Handling and Use

Steps to Be Taken in Case Material Is Released or Spilled

_____

_____

_____

Waste Disposal Method

_____

_____

Precautions to Be Taken in Handling and Storing

_____

_____

Other Precautions

_____

_____

Section VIII - Control Measures

Respiratory Protection *(Specify Type)*

Ventilation	Local Exhaust	Special
	Mechanical *(General)*	Other

Protective Gloves	Eye Protection

Other Protective Clothing or Equipment

Work/Hygienic Practices

Section IX - Special Precautions

Precautions to Be Taken in Handling and Storing

_____

_____

Other Precautions

Each MSDS must be reviewed for correctness and completeness every three years.

Reviewed by _____   Reviewed by _____

Revision date_____   Revision date _____

APPENDIX B

The ANSI Z400.1 Sections

Section 1: Chemical Product and Company Identification. Names the material and relates the MSDS with the label and shipping documents. Must also have a mailing address and telephone number for the manufacturer or distributor.

Section 2: Hazards Identification. Describes the material's appearance, odor, and health, physical, and environmental hazards that may be of concern for emergency response personnel.

Section 3: Composition, Information on Ingredients. Identifies the hazardous components of the material. If non-hazardous ingredients are listed, they should be listed separately. Chemical Abstract Service (CAS) numbers should be included, as well as OSHA permissible exposure limits and American Conference of Government Industrial Hygienists (ACGIH) TLVs. If the identity of any ingredient is claimed to be a trade secret, it should be so indicated in this section.

Section 4: First Aid Measures. This section should include emergency and first aid procedures. It should be in layman's language and easy to understand, and procedures for each potential route of exposure should be included. A "Notes to Physicians" subsection should be included if such information is available.

Section 5: Fire Fighting Measures. This section should describe fire and explosive properties of the material, extinguishing media to be used, and fire-fighting instructions. It applies to anyone who may be in the area of the fire.

Section 6: Accidental Release Measures. This section is intended for emergency response personnel.

Section 7: Handling and Storage. This section provides guidelines for minimizing any potential hazards from storing the material. It should include information to minimize handling when appropriate and conditions such as temperature, inert atmosphere, and conditions to avoid.

Section 8: Exposure Controls, Personal Protection. Discusses the degree of engineering control that may be needed when handling the material and the personal protective equipment that should be used if there is a potential for exposure above the regulatory or suggested limits. Exposure guidelines, such as OSHA PELs and ACGIH TLVs, should be included in this section.

Section 9: Physical and Chemical Properties. These properties should be included to assist users to determine proper handling and storage. Appearance, odor, physical state (liquid, solid, gas), pH, vapor pressure and density, melting and freezing point, solubility, and specific gravity should be included. Additional properties may be included if they are useful.

Section 10: Stability and Reactivity. This section should describe conditions that may result in a potentially hazardous reaction, such as evolution of hazardous gases, production of heat, or other hazardous conditions.

Section 11: Toxicological Information. This section should include any known information resulting from animal testing or human experience on the toxicity of the material. Also included would be information on its potential for causing cancer. Data should be included for acute, subchronic, and chronic exposures, if available.

Section 12: Ecological Information. This section should list impacts to the environment that may occur if the material is released to the environment or in evaluating waste treatment practices.

Section 13: Disposal Considerations. This section is intended to provide guidance to environmental and other technical people responsible for waste management for the product.

Section 14: Transport Information. This section should provide information concerning classification for shipping the material. It should include U.S. Department of Transportation (DOT) classifications or an indication that it is not regulated. It may include information for shipment into other countries.

Section 15: Regulatory Information. This section should contain information regarding the regulatory status of the material. It should include OSHA and EPA regulations. It may also include other regulatory agencies, and state agencies, if appropriate.

Section 16: Other Information. This section is intended for other material that the preparer feels is pertinent and that should not be included in the other fifteen sections. For example, it may include label information, hazard ratings, revision dates, and references to other related information.

APPENDIX C

Sample Training Program Contents

Lesson	Lesson module	Topics covered
Lesson A	Understanding the Hazard Communication Standard	
1 hour		Identification of responsible staff
		Identification of hazardous chemicals in workplace
		Written program
		Labels and other forms of warning
		Material safety data sheets
		Information and training
		A training video and quiz are included in lesson
Lesson B	Understanding the Material Safety Data Sheet	
1 hour		Purpose of the MSDS
		Contents of MSDS
		Requirements: identity used on the label
		Requirements: physical and chemical characteristics
		Requirements: health hazards
		Requirements: routes of entry
		Requirements: exposure limits
		Requirements: carcinogens/potential carcinogens
		Requirements: safe handling procedures
		Requirements: control measures
		Requirements: emergency and first-aid procedures
		Requirements: identity of responsible party and date of preparation
		A training video and quiz are included in lesson
Lesson C	Understanding Labels	
1 hour		Requirements: three pieces of information
		Sample label
		Requirements: labels on incoming containers
		Requirements: stationary containers
		Requirements: transfer containers
		Exceptions
		Labeling and placarding systems: ANSI
		Labeling and placarding systems: NFPA
		Labeling and placarding systems: HMIS
		Labeling and placarding systems: DOT labels
		Labeling and placarding systems: DOT placards
		A training video and quiz are included in lesson
Lesson D	Understanding Health Information	
1 hour		Dose–response relationship
		Exposure limits
		Routes of entry
		Acute effects
		Chronic effects
		Toxic and highly toxic chemicals
		Carcinogens
		Corrosives
		Irritants

Lesson	Lesson module	Topics covered
		Sensitizers
		Target organ effects
		Controls
		A training video and quiz are included in lesson
Lesson E	Understanding Flammables and Combustibles	
90 minutes		Definitions of flammables and combustibles
		Types of flammables and combustibles
		Flammable aerosol
		Flammable gases
		Flammable gases: physical properties and hazards
		Flammable gases: health hazards
		Flammable gases: methods of detection
		Flammable gases: emergency and handling procedures
		Flammable gases: first-aid procedures
		Flammable liquids
		Flammable liquids: physical properties and hazards
		Flammable liquids: health hazards
		Flammable liquids: methods of detection
		Flammable liquids: personal protective equipment
		Flammable liquids: emergency and handling procedures
		Flammable liquids: first-aid procedures
		Combustible liquids
		Flammable solids
		Flammable solids: physical properties and hazards
		Flammable solids: health hazards
		Flammable solids: methods of detection
		Flammable solids: emergency and handling procedures
		Flammable solids: first aid procedures
		A training video and quiz are included in lesson
Lesson F	Understanding Corrosives	
1 hour		Health effects
		Methods of detection
		PPE
		First-aid procedures
		Spill, leak, and disposal procedures
		A training video and quiz are included in lesson
Lesson G	Understanding Reactive Chemicals	
90 mins		Reactive chemicals in the work area
		Physical properties and hazards
		Health hazards
		Methods of detections
		PPE
		Emergency and handling procedures
		First-aid procedures
		A training video and quiz are included in lesson
Lesson H	Understanding Toxic Chemicals	
1 hour		Toxic chemicals/carcinogens in mixtures
		Toxic chemicals in work area

Lesson	Lesson module	Topics covered
		Routes of entry
		Physical hazards
		Health hazards
		Methods of detection
		PPE
		Emergency and handling procedures
		First-aid procedures
		A training video and quiz are included in lesson
9–10 hours	Approximate Total Lesson Time (without breaks included)	

Note: Adapted from *Draft Model Training Program for Hazard Communication,* by Occupational Safety and Health Administration, n.d.

APPENDIX D

A Taxonomy of Environmental, Facility, and Electronic Signing

Private-Residence Premise Signing
- swimming pools/spas
- trespassing prevention
- animal/property hazard

Commercial Premise Signing/Markings
- parking lots
- chemical storage (i.e., MSDS info)
- open areas/landscaping
- construction
- trespassing prevention
- informational/directional signs
- crosswalk/crossing vehicle

Signing Inside Commercial Buildings
- employee and visitor protection
    - danger/caution/safety signs
    - fire and emergency procedures (i.e., MSDS info)
    - personal protective equipment
    - informational/directional signs
    - accident prevention tags (safety tags/ barricade tapes)
    - temporary hazards
- process-related signing
    - process instructions
    - material handling procedures
    - environmental contamination prevention (i.e., MSDS info)
    - quality control procedures

Advertising and Electronic Media Warnings
- billboard footnote warnings
- magazine/paper footnote warnings
- software computer warnings

- e-commerce warnings
- product video tapes
- point-of-purchase video
- sports facility monitors

Public Notification Signing
- public buildings
    - informational/directional signs
    - fire and emergency signs
    - parking
    - egress/ingress
- recreational facilities signing
    - swimming pools/spas
    - parks/playgrounds
    - sports facilities
    - directional signs for hiking/bicycling trails
    - public boating, fishing, and beach areas
- public highway and road signs
    - traffic control and safety
    - pedestrian control and safety
    - informational/directional signs
    - temporary hazards/road construction
    - parking on city streets
    - school and pedestrian crossings
    - hazardous materials being transported

Environmental Dangers and Emergencies Signing
- weather warnings/natural disasters
- littering/landfill signs
- air pollution/smog warnings
- chemical spills and contamination (i.e., MSDS info)
- radiation/biohazard

APPENDIX E

References in the ANSI Z535 2006, 2007 Series

Author/Org	Title/Date	Primary Reference	Also Referenced In
Akerboom et al.	Products for Children: Development and Evaluation of Symbols for Warnings, 1995	Z535.3	
ANSI	D10.1-1966: Adjustable Face Vehicle Traffic Control Signal Heads, 1970	Z535.1	
ANSI	C95.2-1982: Radio Frequency Radiation Hazard Warning Symbol, revised 1999	Z535.1	Z535.2
ANSI	N2.1-1989: Radiation Symbol	Z535.1	Z535.2
ANSI	Z129.1-2000: Hazardous Industrial Chemicals— Precautionary Labeling	Z535.1	Z535.2, Z535.3, Z535.5
ANSI	A13.1-2002: Scheme for the Identification of Piping Systems	Z535.1	
ANSI/ASSE	Z244-2003: Control of Hazardous Energy Lockout/Tagout and Alternative Methods	Z535.1	
ANSI/ASTM	D1535-97: Standard Practice of Specifying Color by the Munsell System	Z535.1	
ANSI/NFPA	70 (1990) National Electrical Code	Z535.2	
ANSI/NFPA	70 (2002): National Electrical Code	Z535.2	
ANSI/SAE	S276.2: Slow Moving Vehicle Identification Symbol, 1968	Z535.2	
Assoc. of American Railroads	Standard Code—Operating Rules, Block Signal Rules, Interlocking Rules	Z535.1	
ASTM	D4956-95 99a: Standard Specification for Retrore-flective Sheeting for Traffic Control	Z535.1	
ASTM	D1729-3 2003: Visual Appraisal of Colors and Color Differences of Diffusely-Illuminated Opaque Materials, 2003	Z535.1	
ASTM	D4086-92a(03): Visual Evaluation of Metamerism, 2003	Z535.1	
ASTM	E1164-02: Obtaining Spectrophotometric Data for Object Color Evaluation, 2004	Z535.1	
ASTM	E308-01: Computing the Colors of Objects Using the CIE System, 2001	Z535.1	
ASTM	D2244(2002): Test Method for Calculation of Color Differences from Instrumentally Measured Color Coordinates	Z535.1	
ASTM	E991-98: Color Measurement of Fluorescent Specimens, 1998	Z535.1	
Brugger	Public Information Symbols: A Comparison of ISO Testing Procedures, 1994	Z535.3	
CIE	39.2-1983: Recommendations for Surface Colours for Visual Signalling	Z535.1	
Code of Federal Regulations	Title 49, Parts 100–199: Hazardous Materials Warning Placards and Labels	Z535.1	
Collins	Use of Hazard Pictorials/Symbols in the Minerals Industry, 1983	Z535.3	
Collins et al.	Safety Color Appearance Under Selected Light Sources, 1986	Z535.2	Z535.5
Collins, Lerner, and Pierman	Symbols for Industrial Safety, 1982	Z535.3	

Author/Org	Title/Date	Primary Reference	Also Referenced In
Deppa and Kalsher	Safety Symbols in the ANSI and ISO Standards—Do People Understand Them? 2006	Z535.5	
Deppa and Martin	Human Factors Behind the Improved ANSI Z535.3 Label Standard for Safety Symbols, 1997	Z535.3	
Dreyfuss	Symbol Sourcebook—An Authoritative Guide to International Graphic Symbols, 1972	Z535.3	
FAA	AC 70 7460-1: Obstruction Marking and Lighting	Z535.1	
Federal Specification	KKK-A-1822: Ambulance Blue and Orange, 1994	Z535.1	
FMC Corp.	Product Safety Signs and Labels, 1978	Z535.3	
FMC Corp.	Product Safety Sign and Label System, 1985	Z535.4	Z535.5
Frascara and Yau	Evaluation and Development of Safety Symbols, Part 1: Evaluation of Existing Graphic Symbols for Safety, 1986	Z535.3	
Frascara and Yau	Evaluation and Development of Safety Symbols, Part 2: Evaluation of Safety Symbols, Appropriateness Ranking Tests, and Comprehension Recognition Tests, 1986	Z535.3	
General Services Admin.	Colors, Federal Standard 595B, 1994	Z535.1	
Grund	Lockout/Tagout, The Process of Controlling Hazardous Energy, 1995	Z535.5	
Hale Color Chart	Safety Color Tolerance Charts/Highway Color Tolerance Charts	Z535.1	
Howett	Size of Letters Required for Visibility as a Function of Viewing Distance and Observer Visual Acuity, 1983	Z535.2	Z535.4, Z535.5
ISO	3864: Safety Signs and Colors, 1984	Z535.2	Z535.3, Z535.5
ISO	3864:1: Graphic Symbols—Safety Colours and Safety Signs—Part 1: Design Principles for Safety Signs in Workplaces & Public Areas, 2002	Z535.3	Z535.5, Z535.6
ISO	3864:2: Graphic Symbols—Safety Colours and Safety Signs—Part 2: Design Principles for Product Safety Labels, 2006	Z535.3	Z535.6
ISO	3864:3 Graphic Symbols—Safety Colours and Safety Signs—Part 3: Design Criteria for Graphic Symbols Used in Safety Signs, 2004	Z535.5	
ISO	7010:2003 Graphical Symbols—Safety Colours and Safety Signs—Safety Signs Used in Workplaces and Public Areas, 2003	Z535.5	
ISO	11684: 1995 Annex D—Principles and Guidelines for Graphical Design if Hazard Pictorials	Z535.3	
ISO	Technical Report 7239: Development and Principles for Application of Public Information Symbols, 1984	Z535.3	
ISO	9186-2001: Graphical Symbols—Testing Methods for Judged Comprehensibility and for Comprehension	Z535.3	

Author/Org	Title/Date	Primary Reference	Also Referenced In
Lirtzman	Validation of Proposed Symbols for Precautionary Labeling of Hazardous Industrial Chemicals, 1987	Z535.3	
Magurno et al.	Iterative Test and Development of Pharmaceutical Pictorials, 1994	Z535.3	
Miller, Lehto, and Frantz	Instructions and Warnings, the Annotated Bibliography, 1990	Z535.5	
Munsell Laboratory	Munsell Book of Color	Z535.1	
Nat. Conf. On School Transportation	Minimum Standards for School Buses, revised 1970	Z535.1	
NFPA	291-1988: Uniform Marking of Fire Hydrants	Z535.1	
NFPA	1901-1985: Automotive Fire Apparatus	Z535.1	
NFPA	178-1986: Symbols for Fire Fighting	Z535.2	Z535.5
Olglay	Safety Symbols Art: Camera-Ready and Disk Art for Designers, 1995	Z535.3	
Olglay	Safety Symbols Art: The Testing Protocol, Materials & Results, 1996	Z535.3	
Smith	Letter Size and Legibility, Human Factors, 1979	Z535.2	Z535.4, Z535.5
Snap-On Tool Corp.	Safety Symbol Identification Survey, 1994	Z535.3	
Standard Solutions	The Standard Solutions Symbol Reference Manual, 1995	Z535.3	
Stds. Assoc. of Australia	AS 2342 Part 3: Test Procedures for Evaluating Graphic Symbols and Symbol Signs, 1980	Z535.3	
UL	UL969-1995: Standard for Marking and Labeling Systems	Z535.4	
U.S. Coast Guard	COMDTINST M16500.3A: Aids to Navigation—Technical	Z535.1	
U.S. Coast Guard	Colored Elastomeric Film, Specification G-ECV-473, 1992	Z535.1	
U. S. Dept. of Transportation, FHA	Manual on Uniform Traffic Control Devices for Streets and Highways, 2009	Z535.1	Z535.2
Virzi	Streamlining the Design Process: Running Fewer Subjects, 1990	Z535.3	
Westinghouse	Westinghouse Product Safety Label Handbook, 1981	Z535.4	
Wolff	A Study of the Effect of Context and Test Method in Evaluating Safety Symbols, 1995	Z535.3	
Wolff and Wogalter	Test and Development of Pharmaceutical Pictorials, 1993	Z535.3	
Zwaga	Comprehensibility Estimates of Public Information Symbols, 1989	Z535.3	
Zwaga et al.	Public Graphics, Visual Information for Everyday Use, 1994	Z535.5	

APPENDIX F

Color Combinations Used in ANSI Z535 Series
(Abstracted from ANSI Z535.2, 2007)]

SIGNAL WORD	SIGNAL WORD COLOR	SIGNAL WORD BACKGRND	SAFETY ALERT SYMBOL COLOR	SAFETY ALERT SYMBOL BACKGRND	MESSAGE COLOR	MESSAGE BACKGRND	OPTIONAL SAFETY SYMBOL/ PICTORIAL COLOR	OPTIONAL SAFETY SYMBOL/ PICTORIAL PANEL BACKGRND
DANGER	WHITE	SAFETY RED (rectangular background)	SAFETY RED	WHITE	BLACK or RED or WHITE	BLACK OR RED ON WHITE OR WHITE ON BLACK	BLACK, SAFETY RED, OR BLACK and SAFETY RED	WHITE
WARNING	BLACK	SAFETY ORANGE (rectangular background)	SAFETY ORANGE	BLACK	BLACK or WHITE	BLACK on WHITE OR WHITE on BLACK	BLACK	WHITE
CAUTION	BLACK	SAFETY YELLOW	SAFETY YELLOW	BLACK	BLACK or WHITE	BLACK on WHITE OR WHITE on BLACK	BLACK	WHITE

SIGNAL WORD	SIGNAL WORD COLOR	SIGNAL WORD BACKGRND	SAFETY ALERT SYMBOL COLOR	SAFETY ALERT SYMBOL BACKGRND	MESSAGE COLOR	MESSAGE BACKGRND	OPTIONAL SAFETY SYMBOL/ PICTORIAL COLOR	OPTIONAL SAFETY SYMBOL/ PICTORIAL PANEL BACKGRND
CAUTION (property damage)	BLACK	SAFETY YELLOW	none	none	BLACK or WHITE	BLACK on WHITE OR WHITE on BLACK	BLACK	WHITE
NOTICE signs	white italics	SAFETY BLUE	none	none	SAFETY BLUE or BLACK	WHITE	SAFETY BLUE or BLACK	WHITE

(ANSI 2007, 5–7)

APPENDIX G

Usage of Color and Shapes in MUTCD Signage Systems

(Abstracted from *Manual on Uniform Traffic Control Devices* 2009)

Color Code	Functional Uses	Color Uses	Shape Code	Sign Classifications
YELLOW	General warning	Used as background color for warning signs and for school signs	PENNANT SHAPE/ ISOSCELES TRIANGLE (Longer axis horiz)—NO PASSING	WARNING SIGNS
RED	Stop or prohibition	Used only as background color for STOP, multiway supplemental plates, DO-NOT-ENTER messages, WRONG WAY signs and on Interstate route markers, as legend color for YIELD signs, parking prohibition signs, and the circular outline and diagonal bar prohibitory symbol	OCTAGON (STOP ONLY) EQUILATERAL TRIANGLE (1 point down)—YIELD	REGULATORY SIGNS
BLUE	Motorist services guidance	Used as background color for information signs related to motorist services and evacuation route marker	PENTAGON (Pointed up)—School, county route sign	MOTORIST SERVICE SIGNS, TOURIST-ORIENTED SERVICES
GREEN	Indicated movements permitted, direction guidance	Used as background color for guide signs, mileposts, legend color w/ white background for permissive parking regs and circular outline permissive symbol	RECTANGLE— Regulatory series, Guide series, Warning series	GUIDE SIGNS— CONVENTIONAL ROADS, EXPRESSWAY, FREEWAYS
BROWN	Recreational/ cultural interest	Used as background color	TRAPEZOID— Recreational series	RECREATIONAL/ CULTURAL-INTEREST AREA SIGNS
ORANGE	Construction and maintenance warning	Used as background color for construction and maintenance signs ONLY	DIAMOND— WARNING Series	CONSTRUCTION/ MAINTENANCE
BLACK	Regulation	Used as background on ONE WAY signs, certain weigh station and night speed limit signs; also used as message. On white, yellow, and orange signs	CROSSBUCK (2 rectangles in an X configuration)— Grade Crossing	REGULATORY SIGNS

Color Code	Functional Uses	Color Uses	Shape Code	Sign Classifications
WHITE	Regulation	Used as background for route markers, guide signs, fallout shelter directional sign, and regulatory signs, except STOP signs, and for the legend on brown, green, blue, black, and red signs.	CIRCLE—GRADE CROSSING,	REGULATORY SIGNS
PURPLE				
YELLOW-GREEN	School signs	Used as background color		
LIGHT BLUE	Unassigned			
CORAL	Unassigned			

(FHWA 2009, 2A-1, 2N-09)

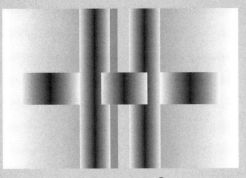

LEARNING OBJECTIVES

■ Be able to apply essential cost analysis of SH&E issues consistent with the culture of the organization, demonstrating fiscal value.

■ Understand and identify which components of a hazard communication program cost money, and how to assign a dollar value to those components.

■ Understand and calculate the value of your time in a company, and how to identify and value the various costs and benefits that accrue to the company for designing and implementing any safety program.

■ Explain why basic budgeting practices are insufficient to demonstrate the value added to the company by a hazard communication program.

■ Identify and explain the essential differences between cost effectiveness, cost-benefit and net-present-value analyses, and how each may be used to evaluate the impact of the hazard communication program to the company.

COST ANALYSIS AND BUDGETING

James D. Ramsay and Anthony Veltri

THIS CHAPTER PRESUMES you, the reader, are a safety, health or environmental (SH&E) professional or leader in charge of coordinating safety programs and managing personnel and training in your company. Because you realize the Code of Federal Regulations (CFR) for general industry standards apply to your company, are detailed and required by law, you work hard to make sure your company is in as complete a state of compliance as possible, and as often as possible. The *Hazard Communication Standard* (HazCom), 29CFR 1900.1200, is a large and especially complex standard covering the some 650,000 chemicals used in industry today. As a result, one would expect the HazCom to be one of the most-cited standards each year. Indeed, in fiscal year 2009, the HazCom was the third most-frequently cited standard and the ninth most-expensive citation (OSHA 2010).

Although staff positions, SH&E practitioners and management often operate under different realities and with different professional obligations. As convincing as it may be to the SH&E professional that a state-of-the-art HazCom program should be designed and implemented, it may not always appear that way to upper management; or, if it does, that it is worth the organizational resources allocated to the HazCom program. The OSH Act itself has traditionally been a source of support for SH&E practitioners who have had to convince management to design and run SH&E programs simply. However, even though the law still exists, conventional wisdom suggests that the threat of inspection is not always enough of a motivation for management to support SH&E activities at the work site. Today, SH&E practitioners still compete for resources, employee time, and management support. In this sense, the ability to demonstrate the economic value that your SH&E program will add to the organization could enhance your ability to win the support of management. Hence, safety becomes a managed initiative like each of the other initiatives within the organization (Petersen 2005), as opposed to being merely a checklist used to avoid federal citations. Demonstrating how your activities add economic worth to the company can be a valuable tool. Therefore, economic defense of SH&E programs is a core competency of SH&E practitioners (Adams 2002).

The safety department and all of its programs compete for limited employee time and attention; in addition, safety programs need to demonstrate they add value to the organization. Hence, safety must be fully integrated into the prevailing management philosophy and most standard operating procedures, such as employee job descriptions, union contracts, and so on; thus, safety must work with every other functioning unit within a company for time and resources. In this sense, safety may be viewed by some as an add-on, or something employees need to do in addition to their jobs. Further, because it is difficult to charge the endline consumer for safety, in a competitive market the cost of running a safety program is sometimes seen as a sunk cost, or simply as money down the drain. As a functional unit within the company, safety must demonstrate to management that it is an investment center, not a cost center (Behm, Veltri, and Kleinsorge 2004; Veltri & Ramsay 2009).

BUDGETING BASICS AND TYPES OF COST ANALYSIS

Effective budgeting in an organization is an essential skill for today's SH&E practitioner. Successful SH&E practitioners understand how money and organizational resources flow within their companies, and successful implementation of their programs is based on this understanding. It is no longer sufficient to simply ask for resources to do the job you've been hired to do. Cost analysis provides strategies and methods that will allow the SH&E practitioner to successfully argue for money, to access employees while at work, and to access the other resources needed to operate a state-of-the-art safety program (Arrow et al. 1996). This section covers basic components of organiza-

tional budgeting, the various costs used in cost analyses, as well as several forms of cost analysis, including cost-minimization analysis, cost-effectiveness analysis, and cost-benefit analysis.

Traditional Budgets

The *American Heritage Dictionary* defines a *budget* as either: (a) an itemized summary of estimated or intended expenditures for a given period, along with proposals for financing them; or (b) a systematic plan for the expenditure of a usually fixed resource, such as money or time, during a given period; or (c) the total sum of money allocated for a particular purpose or period of time.

Organizations sometimes use a wide variety of budgetary processes and financing logic. Conventional wisdom indicates that budgets are developed for specific time frames (for example, six months, a year, or two years) and are usually based on last year's performance and experience. They are developed and predicated on the assumption that the coming year will look like the previous year. Embedded in the traditional budget is a generic growth factor that can be tied to organizational performance or other socioeconomic trends. In this way, traditional budgets tend to concentrate on the incremental costs associated with a project from year to year, over the lifetime of the project (Ross et al. 2007). Needless to say, this is a potential complication when you are establishing a traditional budget for a program that is designed to be resourced and implemented over a multiyear period, the way many SH&E programs might be.

Therefore, traditional budgets can present an inadequate logic for an SH&E program generally, and for a HazCom program in particular. The reason is that programs as large and as complex as HazCom cannot be completely implemented, nor their benefits evaluated, within a given fiscal year. Training and record-keeping requirements occur annually but vary in their scope given changes in employee demographics, changes in chemicals used in production, and so on. Traditional budgets can also include separate budgets for specific and distinct projects.

Zero-Based Budgets

The zero-based budgeting (ZBB) process is common in many public or municipal centers or agencies. They require the manager of the budget to justify the entire budget, purchase by purchase, project by project, line item by line item, dollar by dollar, each time the budget is prepared. In this way, each project must define a timeline and specific and measurable goals or objectives, activities, and required resources and their costs. Together, these components constitute a *decision package*. Astute managers tie each decision package to the organization's mission as tightly as possible (Deming 1986). As such, cost or expenditure estimates are created from scratch for each budget period and for each decision package. Indeed, this is the root of the name for this budgetary process, zero-based budgeting.

The next step in the ZBB process normally involves an organizationwide ranking of each decision package, meaning that each decision package is compared to the others; indeed, this is an opportunity for the safety professional to demonstrate the value added of their program relative to other programs. Although the ranking criteria are specific to each organization, they sometimes include the degree of fit between the decision package and the organization mission, the consequences to the organization if the decision package is eliminated (or not done), or whether the decision package is the most efficient way of addressing the proposed problem.

If a decision package is accepted, it is usually resourced, that is, given monetary and other resources (staff, physical space, materials, consultants, and so on) requested in the decision package. However, some managers realize that since the actual allocated budget for a given decision package might be less than the amount requested, they have learned to strategically request a greater budget than is needed, hoping the allocated amount will indeed be sufficient. Of course, the reader should suspect that gaming a ZBB system in this way may not always work. It is typically best to consider individual items within a budget and their relative contribution to the overall objectives of the SH&E program for the coming year when deciding whether and how to trim suggested budgets.

Ultimately, ZBBs can facilitate an SH&E manager's ability to participate in organizationwide planning and policy development. In addition, ZBBs tend to minimize the main weakness of traditional budgets, namely, the need for traditional budgets to concentrate on incremental costs for multiyear programs. At one level, and because training requirements are performance-based and should occur annually, the HazCom lends itself nicely to a zero-based budgeting format. However, the best way to budget for your HazCom program is to find a way to fit the program expenses into the budgeting format used by management.

The Budgetary Bottom Line

There are several important characteristics to keep in mind about budgets. First, budgets are typically inadequate to support cost analyses (Levin and McEwan 2001) because they usually do not include the estimates of specific components of a given program. For example, the costs associated with material safety data sheet (MSDS) development may not be a line item on the safety department budget, but it is an essential component in the HazCom program. Second, according to Levin and McEwan (2001), most budgets include plans for how resources would be allocated during a given fiscal period rather than a classification of expenditures after a given program has already occurred. Hence, the SH&E practitioner will need to search elsewhere for the cost inputs needed to conduct a cost analysis. As a direct consequence of finding organization-specific costs to be used in the cost analysis, the level of the department's fiscal accountability improves as well. Fiscal accountability improves because cost analysis will show quantitatively what the organizational resources that have been allocated are buying the company in return.

TYPES OF COSTS USED IN COST ANALYSES

Within the scope of budgets lies the concept of costs. Since there are many kinds of costs in organizations, the major types will be briefly discussed below. A *fixed cost* is a cost (or budget line item, or unit cost) that does not vary in size as either levels of production or levels of sales vary. Examples of fixed costs include rent, insurance, and taxes. In contrast, a *variable cost* is a cost (or budget line item, or unit cost) that will vary in some logical way as either production or sales vary. Examples of variable costs include production supplies, fuel or electricity, and labor (Levin and McEwan 2001). *Total cost* can refer to either the sum of fixed plus variable costs in an accounting sense, or in an investment sense, the total amount spent on that investment or project. An *opportunity cost* is the cost to an organization of the next best option available to them that they forego when they decide to pursue a particular project or option (Drummond et al. 2005). Although opportunity costs are important to include in a cost analysis in order to aid decision making, they do not usually appear in financial statements such as income statements or balance sheets.

It might not be a simple or straightforward exercise to monetize (to convert an asset or thing into a dollar value) or establish a dollar value for an opportunity cost. The *cost of capital* is the opportunity cost of a specific project or investment. That is, it is the rate of return (the value returned to the company attributable to a specific project or investment expressed as a percentage of the total amount invested in the project) that the company would otherwise be able to earn as the investment or project, assuming both projects have the same level of risk to the company (Drummond et al. 2005). An employee's *salary* refers to the annual wages paid to each employee, in dollars, for services rendered to the company. *Fringe benefits* refer to all nonsalary compensations paid to the employee each year, and include things like health insurance and retirement contributions by the company. In cost analyses, the term *loaded salary* refers to the combination of salary plus benefits received by the employee per year, and *loaded hourly salary* refers to the combination of salary plus fringe benefits, but on an hourly basis (Nas 1996).

Establishing Prices for Activities in a Cost Analysis

Once you identify the type of costs in a cost analysis, the next step is to establish a monetary value for each

cost or benefit. This process is sometimes referred to as *cost valuation*. There are two main methods used in cost analysis to establish a monetary value for both costs and benefits. These methods are establishing the *market price* or establishing the *shadow price*.

Establishing shadow prices can be challenging, since the method is used for costs or benefits that do not have clear market values, or the market value for a cost or benefit is spurious due to significant market imperfections, such as imperfect information about buyers or that there are too few buyers or sellers to safely assume perfect market conditions. Hence, for the purposes of this chapter, we will concentrate on using market values to establish a monetary value for both the costs and the benefits in the cost analysis. Market prices are simple to obtain, and serve as fairly reliable indicators of the true value of a good, service, cost, or benefit. Establishing fair market value for personnel, physical plant components, or supplies can be done accurately and has the advantage that they automatically include the idiosyncratic peculiarities of a given region of the country or of a given industry.

The SH&E practitioner is strongly encouraged to ask for assistance from either the finance department or the human resources department (or both) when attempting to establish the market value of a cost or benefit for use in a cost analysis. In addition, it would be wise to consult with the finance and HR departments in order to determine if there are in-house values for specific components in the cost analysis. Indeed, the sentiment that SH&E professionals need to act more strategically was echoed by the article, "The Versatile SH&E Pro" (Lawrence 2008). An example would be establishing the value for the opportunity cost of having employees attend an MSDS training seminar.

Types of Cost Analysis

It should be noted at this point that cost analysis is a large and complex field used by many industries to optimally characterize the incremental value added by a potential project or proposed capital acquisition. This section is not intended to be a thorough review of economic analysis. Indeed, the opening chapter of this text is meant to be a more comprehensive review of the use of cost analysis in SH&E. Therefore, this section offers a selective primer on cost analysis in order to equip the SH&E practitioner to better justify and evaluate HazCom programs offered at the work site.

Cost or economic analysis is arguably as much art as science (Drummond et al. 2005). Indeed, the study of cost analysis could be characterized with the following quote taken from Aristotle:

> Therefore in discussing subjects, and arguing from evidence, conditioned in this way, we must be satisfied with the broad outline of truth . . . for it is a mark of the trained mind never to expect more precision in the treatment of any subject than the nature of that subject permits. (Rackham 1934, 7–8).

If they do accurately characterize cost analysis, these words may seem to cast a rather gloomy picture. The intent is not to discourage the reader before we start! Indeed, the intent is to convey the notion that anyone using cost analysis in industry will need to make assumptions as they go. Such assumptions will concern the value of the costs or benefits being evaluated, which costs and benefits should be included in the analysis, which discount rates to use, how best to offer specific programs or parts of specific programs, and when these options should be included in the cost analysis, and so on. And, like many things in life, the outputs will only be as good as the inputs. Hence, the better the financial or budgetary data a company has about its processes, the better the cost and benefit estimates will be, and therefore the better, or more robust, the cost analysis will be.

Ultimately, cost analysis attempts to address the following questions: who should do what, with which resources, and with what relation to other organizational activities? The law of modern business is resource scarcity. *Resource scarcity* simply refers to the notion that organizations exist to make money, and everything that happens inside an organization is directed and designed to make money, but there is never enough money to do everything that needs to be done. Hence, cost analysis enables the comparative analysis of alternative courses of action in terms of each course's costs and consequences.

However, although you can sometimes arrive at the same conclusion using different types of cost analyses, not all cost analyses are the same. Nor are they designed to be. There are usually good reasons

why an SH&E practitioner should use one and not another type.

The next section discusses two main methods of cost analysis: cost-effectiveness analysis and cost-benefit analysis. Each of these methods measures costs, or inputs, in dollars, but vary by how they measure consequences, or the outputs of a project. Both can be applied to the economic evaluation of HazCom programs. Which is used depends on the sensibilities and skill level of the SH&E practitioner, the amount of time available to perform the analysis, the availability of data to support the analysis, the availability of alternatives to the project being evaluated, and the subject of the evaluation.

Cost-Effectiveness Analysis (CEA)

CEAs are meant to compare alternatives that share a single common effect (for example, cases of disease averted) that may differ in magnitude, or the degree to which each alternative is able to achieve the outcome (Drummond et al. 2005, Ross et al. 2007). Although outcomes across alternative courses of action or projects can be similar, the fact that various alternatives will develop outcomes of different magnitudes distinguishes a CEA from a *cost-minimization analysis* (CMA). CMAs are a separate type of cost analysis that focus the comparison of two or more alternatives that accomplish not only identical outcomes, but also outcomes to the same degree. Because of this characteristic, the basis of the cost analysis is reduced to merely a comparison of the total cost of each alternative, with the least costly option being the preferred option.

The results of a CEA can be stated as costs per unit of a natural effect (for example, cost per unit drop in diastolic blood pressure, or cost per ten employees trained to manage existing MSDSs and to create new ones) or as effects per unit cost (for example, percentage reduction of accidents gained per dollars spent on HazCom training). According to Drummond et al. (2005), CEAs can be performed if either of the following conditions is met:

- There is one, clear objective to the project or the intervention which can be used to assess the effectiveness of the intervention.

• There are many objectives, but it is believed that each objective or option achieves the same effect roughly to the same extent.

For example, suppose there are three methods available to educate employees on chemical labeling. The end result of each education program is virtually the same by design, but each of the three training options vary in the use of supplies, length, and intensity. The SH&E practitioner can use CEA to determine the optimal training program given this specific endpoint. If the programs transcend the current fiscal year, the inputs (costs) and the outputs (the effects) need to be put into today's dollars, which will require the practitioner to discount them. Discounting is more fully addressed in the next section.

Cost-Benefit Analysis (CBA)

By contrast, cost-benefit analyses (CBAs) are used when you are not sure if the consequences of alternative programs are identical, or it is not possible to reduce the outcomes of interest to one common effect (Drummond et al. 2005, Ross et al. 2007). For instance, how might you compare a hypertension screening program aimed at preventing premature death to an influenza immunization program aimed at reducing disability days? The answer is to standardize the units or the dimension of the outputs. Hence, CBAs require that all inputs and all outputs (benefits) need to be in dollars. So, all costs and all consequences from each program need to be monetized. Further, if the program transcends the current fiscal year, both the costs and the benefits need to be in today's dollars, which, like multiyear CEAs, requires discounting.

CBAs provide an indication of the absolute benefit of a program in addition to the program's relative contribution. For example, CBAs implicitly assume that the alternative is a do-nothing (or a no-cost, no-benefit) approach. That is, the difference between the benefits attributable to the program and the costs of having to design, implement, and evaluate the program is compared to the costs to the firm of not running the program. CBAs can be evaluated as:

• a cost/benefit ratio
• a net present value (NPV)
• a comparison of the calculated internal rate of return (IRR) to the market rate of return, or some other predetermined rate of return, such as one that is specific to the industry or to the organization

Each of these evaluative forms, or decision rules as they will be referred to later, is discussed in more detail in the next section. Figure 1 summarizes the main components of both CEAs and CBAs.

Inputs and Outputs to a Cost Analysis

Once the decision has been made to pursue either a CEA or a CBA, the next important step is to identify the inputs to be monetized. Levin and McEwan (2001) refer to the inputs as the ingredients method to a cost analysis. The ingredients method requires the SH&E practitioner to fully describe each project in terms of

Type of Analysis	Valuation of Inputs (costs)	Identification of Consequences	Valuation of Consequences
CEA	Today's dollars	Single common effect to each alternative	"natural units" like disability days avoided
CBA	Today's dollars	≥1 effect not necessarily common—common effects may be achieved to various degrees	Today's dollars

FIGURE 1. Essential components of CEAs and CBAs (Adapted from: Levin and McEwan 2001.)

the supplies (personnel, materials, space, time, and so on) it requires.

In order to facilitate a more complete and responsible cost analysis, the thoughtful SH&E practitioner collects the necessary input data in a systematic way, which not only legitimizes the actual value placed on each input, but which will also facilitate a *sensitivity analysis* (explained in the next section). Each input should be carefully identified and include the following information:

- a high estimated dollar value and a low estimated dollar value
- source of the valuation estimate
- date of the valuation

Figure 2 presents the suggested structure for the ingredients method.

While a detailed listing of each alternative's required inputs is critical, a similar listing of the expected consequences of each alternative is also critical. This is perhaps the trickiest part of the cost analysis so far, both in terms of identifying the consequence and in terms of monetizing that consequence. You do not want to claim that your intervention program can cure

everything. On the other hand, if the consequences are found lacking in magnitude, it is quite logical to expect that they will be less than the inputs, and therefore render the program cost-ineffective or not cost-beneficial.

In order to identify the expected consequences, carefully analyze the nature of the inputs and decide exactly what they are designed to achieve. A partial list of consequences you might expect to accrue from a well-designed and compliant HazCom program would include the following (OSHA 2000, OSHA 2006a):

- fewer accidental chemical injuries
- increased job satisfaction (less fear, lower stress, less absenteeism)
- decreased turnover
- increased retention and better chemical hazard recognition (via exam)
- increased productivity

Once identified, each consequence is monetized. Constructing an outputs table, as was done for the inputs (see Figure 2), is advisable. To help determine the value for each consequence, the SH&E practitioner will likely use internal company financial data,

Input	Cost – hi ($)	Cost – lo ($)	Reference	Date
MSDS binders	10 @ 5.50 ea.= 55.00	10 @ 4.45 ea.= 44.50	Staples®	Nov 11, 2009
Chemical Labels	37.00/100	22.70/100	LSS.com	Nov 23, 2009
Training video	307.00	307.00	LSS.com	Nov 23, 2009
Personnel*	58.60	42.50	HR dept.	Dec 5, 2009
Spanish MSDS pocket dictionaries	35 @ 5.70 ea.= 199.50	24 @ 6.20 ea.= 148.80	LSS.com	Nov 23, 2009
MSDS cabinet	193.00	178.00	LSS.com/Staples®	Dec 7, 2009
Totals				

* Cost of personnel attending the HAZCOM training assumes average loaded salary of between $42.50/hr. and $58.60/hr. based on seniority of those present.

FIGURE 2. The ingredients method for input determination

Workers Compensation data, healthcare utilization data from the company's healthcare (or third party) administrator, as well as any other historical data (that is, what it cost in the past) at his or her disposal.

At this point, an economic evaluation of a HazCom program is almost underway. There are, however, a few more details requiring attention before one can actually complete the analysis.

STRATEGIES AND TOOLS IN COST ANALYSIS

Whether you use CEA or CBA as a cost-analysis strategy, there are two core questions the SH&E practitioner needs to address about the project under consideration. First, what is the likelihood that the program will take more than the current fiscal year to complete? Second, what is the likelihood that the program's costs and consequences might occur at different points in time? Although there are some SH&E programs that might be perfectly designed, implemented, concluded, and evaluated within the current fiscal year, most SH&E programs are probably more accurately thought of as longer-term, or ongoing endeavors. As such, most SH&E programs will require long-term financial and philosophical commitment from management.

The upside is that such SH&E programs will also produce superior and sustainable results. Given this kind of multiyear perspective, the differential timing of when costs occur and when consequences may occur, leads to a discussion of the financial concept of *discounting*. Discounting is central—not only to HazCom programs specifically, but to SH&E programs in general.

Discounting and Present Value

Discounting is a simple mathematical process that responds to the time preference for money—that is, a dollar today is usually preferred to a dollar next year (Drummond et al. 2005, Ross et al. 2007). Discounting enables one to talk about all the associated costs and consequences of a program, regardless of when they

occur, with a standardized time frame. In other words, discounting is the process by which the present value is determined (Drummond et al. 2005). Although discounting is a manageable concept, and mathematically straightforward, it becomes a bit more complex when one needs to determine a discount rate. The choice of a discount rate is addressed below in the *sensitivity analysis* section.

Equation 1 is commonly used to discount a stream of either inputs (costs) or consequences (benefits or effects) over time.

$$PV = \sum_{i=1}^{N} F_n (1 + r)^{-n} \qquad (1)$$

Where PV is the present value of a sum F, r is the discount rate as a decimal, and n is the year in which the sum occurs, ranging from year 1 (n = 1) to the last year (N) (Drummond et al. 2005).

Notice that the summation operator requires each numerator to be divided by the quantity $(1 + r)$ raised to the year in which the sum occurs. For example, to accomplish an MSDS maintenance program each year for the next 3 years, you determine that this part of your HazCom program will cost $650 the first year, $500 in year 2, and $1750 in year 3. What is the present value of the costs of the 3-year MSDS training program?

To solve for the PV, you need to first decide what to use for a discount rate. Assume you would like to take a conservative approach at first. In this case, it would be logical to use the prevailing U.S. Treasury-bill (T-bill) rate (Drummond et al. 2005). Note that T-bills will be reported at the current or today's rate, or a longer-term average rate, such as three, six, or nine months. Any of the longer-term average rates will suffice. The T-bill rate is considered the least risky investment rate, since purchase of such bills is virtually risk-free. Assuming that the three-month average T-bill rate is 5.5 percent, and using the formula above:

$$PV = \{\$650/(1 + 0.055)^1 + \$500/(1 + 0.055)^2 + \$1750/(1 + 0.055)^3\}$$

$$PV = \{\$616.11 + \$449.23 + \$1490.32\} = \$2555.66$$

Notice how different the discounted sum is from the direct linear sum of the undiscounted cost figures, {\$650 + \$500 + \$1750} = \$2900. In addition, the reader may note that larger discount rates favor large projects whose benefits are more distant, whereas lower discount rates favor projects with staged investments and shorter expected payback. This is why the use of multiple discount rates in a sensitivity analysis is warranted in all cost analyses.

Determining the present value of the cost stream or the benefit stream is perhaps half the game. A more interesting question now becomes obvious, how does one use cost analysis to actually decide if a proposed project should be invested in or not?

Decision Rules

In any cost analysis, you need to articulate the rationale for accepting or rejecting a particular project ahead of time. There are three basic decision rules: the net-present-value rule, the benefit/cost ratio rule, and the internal rate-of-return rule (Nas 1996). Each is discussed below.

Decision Rule 1—Net Present Value

In one sense, net-present-value (NPV) analysis is used to determine the feasibility of a project, and can be considered a special case of CBA because its inputs and outputs are in dollars (Drummond et al. 2005). To calculate the NPV of a project or proposal, all costs and all benefits need to be identified and monetized for each year of the project. Once this is done, the project's costs are subtracted from the benefits for each year, forming the annual net benefit (NB). The NB is treated the same way the sum was treated in the present-value example above. That is, the NB is discounted each year using the present-value formula. In addition, an NPV calculation requires the practitioner to identify and monetize the initial, or one-time-only, expenses associated with the project. The initial expenses are subtracted from the sum of the present values of each year's NB to form the net present value of the project.

The traditional formula for the NPV is represented by Equation 2.

$$NPV = -I_0 + \sum_{(i=1)}^{N} \frac{NB_n}{(1 + r)^n} \qquad (2)$$

Where NPV is the net present value of a net benefit NB in year n, I_0 is the initial investment, r is the discount rate as a decimal, and n is the year in which the sum occurs, ranging from year 1 (n = 1) to the last year (N) (Drummond et al. 2005).

For example, continuing with the example above, suppose that, in addition to the cost data, you determine that your HazCom program will require a one-time cost of \$400 in supplies, binders, pamphlets, gloves, and so on at the beginning of the first year. Further, you expect that the program will yield no benefits the first year, but by having successfully trained people to use gloves, the company could save \$1200 in year two and \$2500 in year three in lost-time productivity that has been traditionally experienced due to skin allergies from poor chemical handling practices. Hence, the three NBs would be:

$NB_1 = (\$0 - \$650)$; $NB_2 = (\$1200 - \$500)$; and $NB_3 = (\$2500 - \$1750)$

$NB_1 = -\$650$; $NB_2 = \$700$; and $NB_3 = \$750$

In order to determine the three-year NPV using the above data and using the same discount rate of 5.5 percent, we first need to discount each NB and add them:

Discounted sum of NBs = {$-\$650/(1.055)^1 + \$700/(1.055)^2 + \$750/(1.055)^3$}

Next, we need to figure in the initial, one-time-only cost of \$400, that is, an $I_0 = \$400$:

$NPV = -\$400 + \{-\$616.11 + \$628.92 + \$638.71\}$
$= \$251.52$

Using the NPV as a decision rule is relatively straightforward. A project with a positive NPV is accepted, a project with a negative NPV is rejected, and a project with a zero NPV is up for debate, as the project neither costs the company money nor makes it money. Caution is in order here. The NPV tends to be lower at higher discount rates. In addition, there are always *intangibles* that qualify each and every cost-analysis decision. More will be said about intangibles a bit later.

Decision Rule 2—The Benefit/Cost Ratio

The benefit/cost ratio (B/C), also known as the *profitability index* (Nas 1996) is another decision rule you might use to determine whether or not a program gets funded or cut. According to Nas (1996), the B/C can be calculated in a variety of ways as follows:

$$B/C = \text{PV of } B_t / \text{PV of } C_t$$
$$\text{or } B/C = \text{PV of } NB / I_0$$

or the net benefit/cost ratio is determined as:

$$\text{Net } B/C = NPV / \text{PV of } C$$

Using our example above, and assuming an $I_0 = \$400$, Table 1 summarizes the NPV and the C/B rules as well as the effect on the NPV of changes in discount rate. One can easily see that, as the discount rate increases, the NPV of any project goes down; hence, the benefit/cost ratio of that project will be lower.

The evaluation of the B/C ratio is straightforward and logically similar to the evaluation of the NPV analysis. That is, you would accept a project if the B/C ratio is greater than 1.0. Note that both the B/C ratio and NPV decision rules are sensitive to changes in discount rates, that is, they both get smaller as the discount rate goes up. This phenomenon necessitates the use of multiple discount rates in all sensitivity analyses. Moreover, the outcome of any cost

analysis is quite sensitive to the discount rate used. In this sense, all responsible cost analyses will use more than one discount rate. Making sure all your eggs are not placed in one basket is the essence of a sensitivity analysis.

Decision Rule 3—The Internal Rate-of-Return Rule

The last decision rule is the use of the *internal rate of return* (IRR). The IRR is defined as the discount rate for which an NPV is zero (Nas 1996). From the NPV formula above, if you set the NPV = 0 and proceed to solve for r, you would determine the IRR. In our example, the IRR is 18.545 percent. The IRR rule is an indication of the relative merit of a project, and states that projects are accepted if the IRR exceeds the market rate of return or some other internally determined (or required) rate of return (Nas 1996) such as the *minimum acceptable rate of return* (MARR). The MARR is the cost of capital that a potential investment must promise in order for the market value of the firm to at least remain unchanged. The MARR then acts as a threshold against which the IRR of all projects can be compared, thus facilitating an organizationwide ranking of projects.

Nas (1996) points out that the IRR decision rule is potentially problematic. That is, use of the IRR can be complicated by comparing projects of different magnitudes. For instance, a project with a large IRR might not be better (more cost-beneficial) than a project with a lesser IRR if the large project also has high costs and yields NBs in the thousands of dollars, while the project with the lesser IRR yields NBs in the tens of thousands of dollars. Further, Nas (1996) suggests that, if a project has a nonconventional benefit stream over time, it might be possible to calculate more than one IRR. Clearly, such a situation would render the IRR rule inconclusive.

For these reasons, and when there are few limitations on the availability of resources, the NPV rule tends to be the most robust cost-analysis decision rule. In contrast, with limited budget, the IRR rule might be superior. In the final analysis, the SH&E practitioner needs to make investment/noninvestment decisions based on not only a solid cost-analysis decision rule,

TABLE 1

The Effect of Discount Rates on the NPV (Assume $n = 3$ years, $I_0 = \$400$ and $d = 5.5\%$; 7.5%)			
Discount Rate	PV of $NB_{1,2,3}$	NPV	B/C (as PV of NB/I_0)
5.5%	$651.52	$251.52	1.629
7.5%	$604.80	$204.80	1.512

Assuming an initial investment of $150,000, a NB=$13,500 each year, various interest rates and a project lifetime of 30 years.				
Discount Rate	**PV $**	**NPV $**	**B/C (=PV/I$_o$)**	**Comments**
4	*233,442*	*83,442*	*1.556*	*Best NPV*
6	185,825	35,825	1.238	
8	151,980	1,980	1.013	
8.14	*150,000*	*0*	*1.000*	*IRR*
10	127,263	−22,737	.848	

FIGURE 3. The relationship between r, PV, NPV and B/C (Data adapted from Nas 1996)

but also on the intangibles inherent in the project. Intangibles will be discussed later.

To summarize, Figure 3 shows the relationship between various discount rates: the PV, the NPV, and the IRR.

Risk, Uncertainty, and Sensitivity Analyses

Risk and uncertainty surround our everyday existence. Although uncertainty is nothing new to those who own or manage businesses, it is essential to account for it in any cost analysis (Drummond et al. 2005, Nas 1996). The reality is that management support, data, and overall economic conditions are each dynamic and therefore subject to change over time. In addition, employee compliance to training and your programming effectiveness are not givens. For example, each component in a cost analysis is subject to judgment and change, from the choice of a discount rate, to how benefits are identified and monetized, to how often you run each component within a program—which of course affects the total cost of your program as well as the potential benefits the program accrues to the organization. As an example of the latter, consider that it might be logical to continue offering training and education programs about chemical safety in a company. The question

then becomes, at what point will continuous training cease to produce commensurate gains in health and safety?

Sensitivity analysis provides techniques that will address the inherent volatility in all cost analyses (Drummond et al. 2005, Ross et al. 2007). For example, instead of using point estimates for each cost or each benefit, or even a discount rate, it is often preferable (and professionally more appropriate) to use a range of estimates. It is advisable that all cost analyses incorporate at least three levels of sensitivity analysis. The three levels of a sensitivity analysis include:

1. Performing the cost analysis with at least two different discount rates—for instance, use the three-month T-bill rate and perhaps another rate provided by your company's finance or accounting department (Drummond et al. 2005, Ross et al. 2007, Nas 1996).
2. Using high and low estimates for each cost and each monetized benefit, again construct a table as demonstrated in Figure 2.
3. Vary the sequence of which programs are run, how often they are run, and the content of each program—all of which will alter the cost and benefit streams over time.

The interested reader is referred to the solution to Question 9 in the Instructors' Guide as an example of a sensitivity analysis conducted within an NPV cost analysis.

Indeed, spreadsheets make it easy for sensitivity analyses to model at least three possible eventualities, including:

- *Pessimistic case.* This eventuality is modeled as nothing works: essentially, you spend money and produce no discernable improvement in the exposure level faced by employees. That is, following the SH&E intervention program, the recordable injury rate due to the exposure remains unchanged.
- *Optimistic estimate.* This eventuality is where you are able to achieve the highest estimable gains in health by virtue of the SH&E program intervention. For example, a 90 percent reduction in occupational dermatoses due to a glove-and-hand-washing program.
- *Most likely case.* This is the most probable level of improvement, due to the SH&E program modeled as a discernable improvement in specific metrics, such as recordable incidents due to the exposure. However, there remains a solid percentage of injuries you feel are logically preventable, but which were not eliminated due to the SH&E program.

Break-Even Analysis

Break-even analysis is a fairly straightforward method to help determine the time between profitability and nonprofitability (Bragg 2000). Break-even analysis is done in order to determine either the length of time needed to run a project before the project begins to save the company money, or to calculate the number of widgets that need to be produced and sold in order to become profitable (Bragg 2000). The point at which the sum of all related costs equals all pertinent benefits (or monetary consequences) of a program is the break-even point (Bragg 2000).

Figure 4 illustrates a graphical solution for a break-even analysis.

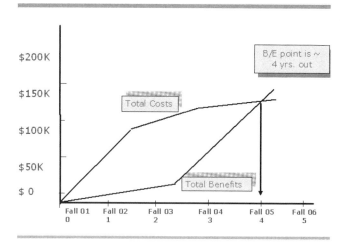

FIGURE 4. Graph of a sample break-even analysis

Break-even charts typically plot the cost curve and benefit curve over the same time frame, with money as a function of time. When these intersect, the corresponding point on the X-axis is the break-even point. In SH&E programs, it is not unusual, indeed it is mostly the case, that the cost curve is superior to the benefits curve initially. This is true simply because health benefits typically take some time to develop substantially enough to begin to actually save the company large sums of money. In this sense, it is particularly important for management to take a long-term perspective of the SH&E programs, and thereby turn SH&E programming into an investment center as opposed to a cost center.

As opposed to a graphical determination of the break-even point, a second way to view the break-even point of a project is by a numerical analysis. This method is often useful when you determine ahead of time whether it is possible to even start a project. For example, consider the following data from a wellness program:

Company X has 125 employees who work full time. The results of a recent health risk assessment (HRA) indicate that there are fourteen people who are clinically hypertensive, and therefore would benefit from a hypertension management program. You decide to design and implement a hypertension intervention program. After researching the various options, you determine that the total cost of the hypertension program you want to run will be $10,000. Similarly, you determine through company healthcare utilization data that, although it varies from employee to employee, the median incremental cost of hypertension to the company is $400 per employee.

The break-even point in this situation is determined as:

B/E = {the costs to the company/median cost per employee of having hypertension}

B/E = $10,000/$400

B/E = 25 cases

This hypertension program cannot support itself economically, since 25 employees need to be hypertensive, but the in-house HRA data suggest only fourteen are in fact hypertensive and therefore eligible for the program. Realize that this program might still be acceptable as a loss leader (that is, a net loss by itself, but an effective draw into other activities).

Therefore, with any break-even analysis, asking whether breaking even is necessary is logical and, in fact, helps to position the break-even analysis within the larger context of work.

Intangibles

In all cost analyses, intangibles need to be identified and figured into the accept/not accept decision process. Intangibles are any factors that are not *easily quantifiable* but which may accrue as either benefits or costs to an organization, its employees, or the community, by implementing the project—or by failing to implement it. Examples include increased morale, good will, doing what's right regardless of cost (social responsibility), and the notion of loss leaders. It is not illogical for a company to accept a project with a zero NPV, or even a slightly negative NPV, in order to achieve a different, greater end. Hence it is wise for the SH&E practitioner to always develop a list of intangibles for each project or investment he or she would like to evaluate with cost analysis.

The next section briefly reviews the essential components of a HazCom program in order to highlight the ability of cost analysis as an evaluation tool.

HAZARD COMMUNICATION PROGRAM BASICS: PINPOINTING THE COSTS

Other chapters in this unit serve to present a more thorough analysis of the components of the HazCom. These chapters discuss the regulatory, engineering, benchmarking, and performance indicators applicable to HazCom. Hence, the main purpose of this section is not to detail the HazCom standard itself, but instead to highlight specific areas of HazCom in order to help the SH&E practitioner think of HazCom as an economic entity, rather than simply a mandated compliance program.

Hazard communication has been a standard compliance program since its inception in 1983 (OSHA 2006b). Otherwise known as the workers' right-to-know standard, HazCom primarily refers to a chemical management program designed to facilitate safe handling, use, and disposal of work-related chemicals by those who are exposed to them in the work site by virtue of their position descriptions. Effective HazCom training is critical to successful compliance (OSHA 2006a, OSHA 2004). Diligent paperwork, record keeping, and documentation are central to effective training (OSHA 2004). In short, although the HazCom is one of many compliance programs an SH&E practitioner will need to implement and manage, it could easily be nearly a full-time job by itself if the company is large. As such, it is essential that the SH&E practitioner uses CBA tools to demonstrate the value of HazCom to the organization ownership. Adding value is the best means to secure enthusiastic support from upper management. This is where cost analysis comes in. Successful cost analysis is dependent on the ability to identify which inputs and which outputs of a proposed SH&E program should be included in the analysis and how you monetize each of these (Drummond et al. 2005, Arrow et al. 1996).

Proper compliance with the HazCom requires an ongoing series of activities, many of which will be real costs to an organization, above and beyond the cost of production (OSHA 2004). In this sense, you could say that any successful HazCom program depends on the complete buy-in from every employee in an organization. In *Hazard Communication Guide-*

lines for Compliance, OSHA recommends the following checklist of eleven activities to ensure compliance with the HazCom (OSHA 2000, 16):

1. Obtain a copy of the HazCom rule.
2. Read and understand all requirements.
3. Assign responsibility for each task.
4. Prepare an organizationwide inventory of all chemicals.
5. Ensure every container is labeled.
6. Obtain an MSDS for each chemical in the organization.
7. Prepare the written HazCom program.
8. Make MSDSs available to each employee on every shift.
9. Conduct and record employee training.
10. Establish procedures to maintain the current program over time.
11. Establish procedures to measure efficacy of the training program.

An Example of Cost Analysis Applied to the HazCom

The above eleven components of HazCom provide several clues as to how you would determine the cost of implementing a HazCom program. Perhaps the best way to connect a HazCom program to cost analysis is by way of an example. What follows is a description of the development of a series of programs, or interventions, designed to bring a company into more complete compliance with HazCom. Both the inputs and a select set of outputs of this process will be identified and monetized in order to structure a CBA. The result will not be an exhaustive analysis of all phases of the HazCom program as it may appear in a company, but rather the result will be a six-step process toward a HazCom cost/benefit analysis (Ramsay and Jones 1998).

Step 1—Initial Exposure Assessment

Step 1 involves identifying who is exposed to worksite chemicals by virtue of their position descriptions, the degree to which they are exposed, and the nature of their exposure, and what the possible program content might look like. This step can be thought of as an initial financial assessment of the prevailing exposures in the organization *before* specific SH&E training and educational programs take place. That is, Step 1 targets specific exposures for remediation, and thus establishes the baseline against which your program will be evaluated following its implementation.

Step 2—Monetizing the Exposures

Step 2 involves determining the cost to the organization due to the exposure(s) that you have targeted to remediate in Step 1. To facilitate the necessary sensitivity analysis, the SH&E practitioner should collect both a high estimate as well as a low estimate for the cost to the organization of each exposure. The SH&E practitioner should identify and quantify these costs as either *direct* or *indirect* costs. *Direct costs* include the medical and legal claims associated with the adverse outcomes associated with the illnesses or injuries associated with inadvertent overexposures of the employee. *Indirect costs* include hiring and replacement costs; turnover and absenteeism; lost time due to inefficiencies of new employees; production losses; cost of administrative handling of the claims, including supervisor involvement in hiring and retraining; and the costs of lowered morale and higher stress.

Estimation of these costs is not easy since, as mentioned in the budgeting section, some companies might not collect this kind of data in a concerted, thoughtful way. Hence, you likely will not be able to reliably identify and monetize each type of direct or indirect cost. Still, the practitioner will likely be able to generate best-guesses from past medical records; for instance, several examples of what heart attacks have typically cost your organization. As average values are more susceptible to extreme individual values, try to use the median cost of the examples you can find.

For example, historical data, conversations, and past experience might reveal the median cost of a chemical spill in a given department to range from approximately $15,000 to $25,000 per person per year in direct medical costs to the organization, and another $30,000 to $50,000 per person per year in indirect costs. Although such guesstimates might not be perfect monetization of the true financial burden to the company due to a chemical spill, it is a good start and might indeed reflect the best data available to your cost analysis. Establishing at least a high- and low-end estimate of the costs to the organization is central to your ability to conduct a sensitivity analysis. In turn, a proper and thorough sensitivity analysis will add robustness and credibility to the overall cost analysis.

The bottom line in Step 2 is that the past costs of injuries and illnesses will adequately proxy the benefits attributable to the HazCom intervention program because, presumably, the company will not experience the same accident/incident experience once the employees have been better trained and better educated. As such, an organization is better able to avoid the same frequency and the same severity of its past experience. And, as the reader will see shortly, improving on an organization's past incident experience will become the bases of how you estimate the benefits of any SH&E program.

Step 3—Establish the PV of the Program Costs

Step 3 involves estimating the present value of both the direct costs and indirect costs of the supporting activities and materials of your involvement in the HazCom program for each year of the program's lifetime. In this step, just as in Step 2, the SH&E practitioner should obtain both a high- and a low-end estimate for each specific cost. The direct costs of your involvement include calculating your loaded hourly salary, and indirect costs include estimating the per-person cost to the organization for their involvement in each phase of the HazCom program.

Next, the costs are annualized and summed. For instance, in the case of an organization that uses a zero-based budgetary process, even though the program might require a multiyear implementation, all of the costs would be for the current budget year only.

Last, a discount rate is identified and used to establish the present value of the annualized costs of the multiyear program. It is advisable to use at least two discount rates in all cost analyses, effectively creating another level of a sensitivity analysis. The first discount rate is traditionally the risk-free rate on U.S. T-bills as described earlier. The second should be a rate chosen by management that perhaps more accurately reflects the cost of capital to the organization.

Step 4—Program Evaluation

Step 4 involves a reevaluation of the costs to the organization by the exposures or hazards that exist after the HazCom program has been run, and then to monetize each benefit. Presumably, the exposure level that remains following the HazCom training and educational intervention is measurably less than it was when initially assessed in Step 1.

There are several ways you might proxy an improved exposure level following the implementation of any given SH&E program. For instance, a lesser exposure level might be indicated by the value (economic or intangible) to the organization of increased knowledge and skill among its exposed employees, decreased workers' compensation claims, a decreased experience rating, fewer lost-time accidents, more near-miss reports, higher job satisfaction, improved morale, less absenteeism, less presenteeism, and a quantifiable decline in the number of reportable injuries and/or illnesses, each directly due to the HazCom program. Associating a dollar value with each of these benefits that closely reflects the cost of these benefits to the company monetizes them and allows them to be used in the calculation of a benefit/cost ratio. In this way, Step 4 is designed to capture, quantify, and monetize the improved risk position of the organization due to the HazCom intervention program.

CAUTION: REMEMBER, in addition to varying the individual cost and benefit estimates and using at least two discount rates to establish the PV of the cost and benefit streams, a more thorough and defensible sensitivity analysis will also vary the magnitude and frequency of various program costs and the subsequent expected benefits, among other components of the specific program.

Step 5—Establish the PV of the Program Benefits

Once the benefits of the HazCom program have been identified in Step 4, Step 5 involves calculating the present value of each benefit. In this step, as in Step 2, it is prudent to establish both a high- and low-end estimate for each benefit that was attributable to the organization by virtue of the HazCom program. Once monetized, and once the SH&E practitioner determines when each benefit occurs over the lifetime of the program, the benefit stream needs to be discounted into

STEP	ACTIVITY	RESULT
1	Organization-wide HazCom exposure assessment.	Of 100 employees, approximately 25% (n = 25) are at risk of chemical handling exposures. These employees should be educated and trained in the safe handling, use, disposal of each chemical they're required to use.
2	High and low estimated per person cost to the firm of the exposure; e.g., safe chemical handling. Use data from past WC claims or other healthcare utilization records and other company data as available to identify what costs have been in the past => avoided past costs = benefits of your program.	**Direct** => high = $25,000/person/year || low = $15,000/person/year **Indirect** => high = $50,000/person/year || low = $30,000/person/year TOTAL = **(direct + indirect)** => high = $75,000/person/year => low = $45,000/person/year

3	Estimate costs of **your involvement** for the year + **supporting activities & materials.**
	
	Assume all 25 employees at risk of chemical over-exposures will participate in each of the 4 intervention programs and that your total time is approx. 800 hours for the year.
	
	Calculate the present value of both the high and low cost estimates to implement all HazCom intervention programs.
	
	PV_c = Present value cost
		Direct => ($13.94/hour)(800 hrs./year) = $11,152/yr.
		Indirect => costs due to your programming, materials, supplies, opportunity costs, etc.
		    Stress management, basic HAZCOM => high $55/person || low $22/person
		    Chemical spill training => high $225/person || low $75/person
		    Chemical labelling training => high $135/person || low $22/person
		    MSDS management => high $8/person || low $4/person
		
		TOTAL = **(direct + indirect)**
		=> high = $21,727/25 people/year
		=> low = $14,227/25 people/year
		
		HIGH PV_c = $21,727/(1+.04)^1 + $21,727/(1+.04)^2 + $21,727/(1+.04)^3$
		= $60,294
		
		LOW PV_c = $14,227/(1+.04)^1 + $14,227/(1+.04)^2 + $14,227/(1+.04)^3$
		= $39,481

4	Upon reassessment of company data, determine the number of avoided cases due to the HazCom program.	25 employees are trained and evaluated, assume no change in injury or illness rate the first year, but 2 injuries are avoided the second year, and 2 more in year 3 => 0 avoided cases in year 1, 2 avoided cases in year 2 and 2 avoided cases in year 3.
5	Calculate the present value of both the high and low benefits estimates expected due to avoided cases. PV_B = Present value benefit	HIGH PV_B = 0($75,000)/(1+.04)^1 + 2($75,000)/(1+.04)^2 + 2($75,000)/(1+.04)^3$ = $272,032 LOW PV_B = 0($45,000)/(1+.04)^1 + 2($45,000)/(1+.04)^2 + 2($45,000)/(1+.04)^3$ = $163,220
6	BENEFIT/COST = PV_B / PV_c	HIGH B/C => $272,032/$39,481 = $6.84 to $1 LOW B/C => $163,220/$60,294 = $2.71 to $1

FIGURE 5. How to calculate a benefit/cost ratio for a HazCom program (Adapted from Ramsay and Jones 1998.)

today's dollars, that is, the PV of the benefit stream needs to be calculated. The same discount rates used to calculate the PV of the cost stream should be used to determine the PV of the benefit stream.

Step 6—B/C Ratio Calculation

Step 6 involves calculating two distinct benefit/cost (B/C) ratios for each discount rate used. First, calculate a high B/C ratio by dividing the present value of the high estimate of the benefits identified in Step 5 by the present value of the low estimate of the costs identified in Step 3. The second benefit/cost ratio is the low B/C ratio, which is derived by dividing the present value of the low estimate of the benefits by the present value of the high estimate of the costs.

Figure 5 presents an example of these steps given one discount rate. Notice that it may first appear that such cost-analysis logic may be appropriate in years for which there are injuries, illnesses, and so forth, that are averted due to the safety professional's programming. However, this should not be the interpretation. The core logic of NPV analysis is that cost savings may or may not be uniform over time; rather, it may be the case that it takes several years to improve the health status of a population of employees enough to offset the costs of that improvement. Hence, over the lifetime of a set of interventions, some years may be "more productive" than others in the sense that more health is saved, which would be seen by higher cost savings and, ultimately, a higher benefit/cost ratio.

RELATING YOUR HAZCOM PROGRAM TO MANAGEMENT

Conventional wisdom might suggest that prevailing organizational culture is a powerful driver of organizational effectiveness, including all elements of employee health and safety, product or service quality, and the impact on the environment. There may be no greater influence on SH&E programs at the work site today than the prevailing organizational culture. Virtually every component of an SH&E program is affected by the culture; its resources, access to data, access to employees, purchasing, and the professional development opportunities of the SH&E practitioner, to name a few.

In this sense, a few words about organizational culture and its potential impact on the success of a Haz-Com program are warranted.

In a classic piece of scholarship, Daft (2004) defines organizational culture as "the set of key values, guiding beliefs and understandings shared by members of an organization." Organizational culture involves shared values that create normative pressure to behave and understand organizational realities in a particular way. In this sense, organizational culture implies a level of standardization in:

- communication
- unwritten traditions and unspoken feelings
- rites, ceremonies, myths, and symbols
- personal interpretation and experience

Thus, the main role of organizational culture is to serve as a normative guide and to control employee behavior. It is logical to realize that organizational culture affects job satisfaction, morale, production, absenteeism, presenteeism, and the general esprit de corps of a company.

Wiener and Vardi (1990) suggest that culture can be viewed as the glue that holds an organization together and that organizational culture has two basic components:

1. The substance or the networks of meaning contained in its ideologies, norms, and values
2. The form or the practices whereby these meanings are expressed, affirmed, and/or communicated to members

Further, Wiener and Vardi (1990) also suggest that a person's behavioral intention is determined by:

1. The attitude toward performing the act is a function of beliefs concerning the consequences of the act and their value to the person.
2. The subjective norm is a function of a person's beliefs about what others view as important to the person—doing something because someone you respect thinks it is important.

Ultimately, therefore, the culture will impact the health and safety of each employee. Furthermore, only upper management can really change the prevailing culture. Hence, influencing upper management becomes a key initiative of the safety professional.

In addition, the SH&E professional is reminded at this point of the hierarchy of controls; that is, one should always pursue engineering controls (including substitution, isolation, and elimination) before either administrative (or work-practice) controls, or before personal protective equipment (PPE). Using the tenets of prevention through design (PTD) requires that engineering controls are employed to their maximum extent first, followed by work-practice controls that eliminate dangerous exposures or, at least, greatly minimize them. Indeed, by the time the SH&E professional provides PPE, they need to acknowledge that they are putting employees in harm's way. Clearly, establishing a NPV analysis of a hazard communication program that is inclusive of a combination of controls is both logical and judicious. What, then, might be the implication to SH&E practitioners wanting to successfully sell their HazCom program to management, or at a minimum, to demonstrate the value their programs add to the organization? Quite simply, acknowledging how the culture of an organization affects employee behavior, and realizing who sets and changes culture, are each central to the success of any SH&E program. So, the question really reduces to how an SH&E practitioner might influence upper management. This is where the utility of cost analysis (and NPV analysis by extension) comes in. Knowing that management is influenced by what makes and what loses money, SH&E professionals should always budget, design, implement, and evaluate their programs economically, using the tools and strategies of cost analysis.

References

Adams, S. 2002. "Financial Management Concepts: Making the Bottom-Line Case for Safety." *Professional Safety* (August:) pp. 23–26.

Arrow, K., M. Cropper, G. Eads, R. Hahn, L. Lave, R. Noll, P. Portney, M. Russell, R. Schmalensee, V. Smith, and R. Stavins. 1996. "Is There a Role for Benefit Cost Analysis in Environmental Health and Safety Regulation?" *American Association for the Advancement of Science Reprint Series* (April 12) 272:221–222.

Behm, M., A. Veltri, and I. Kleinsorge. 2004. "The Cost of Safety." *Professional Safety* (April) pp. 22–29.

Bragg, S. 2000. *Financial Analysis: A Controller's Guide*. New York: John Wiley & Sons.

Daft, Richard. 2004. *Management* 7th ed. Mason, OH: Thomson Southwestern.

Deming, W. E. 1986. *Out of the Crisis*. Cambridge, MA: Massachusetts Institute of Technology, Center for Advanced Engineering Study.

Drummond, M., M. J. Sculpher, G. W. Torrence, B. J. O'Brien, and G. L. Stoddart. 2005. *Methods for the Economic Evaluation of Healthcare Programmes*. 3d ed. Oxford England: Oxford University Press.

Lawrence, T. 2008. "The Versatile SH&E Pro." *Professional Safety*, May 2005.

Levin, H. M., and P. McEwan. 2001. *Cost Effectiveness Analysis; Methods and Applications*. 2d ed. Newbury Park, CA: Sage Publications, Inc.

Nas, T. 1996. *Cost Benefit Analysis: Theory and Application*. Newbury Park, CA: Sage Publications.

Occupational Safety and Health Administration. 2000. *Hazard Communication Guidelines for Compliance*. OSHA 3111 (retrieved November 12, 2007). www.osha.gov/Publications/osha3111.html

_____. 2004. *Hazard Communication in the 21st Century Workplace* (retrieved May 2006).www.osha.gov/dsg/hazcom/finalmsdsreport.html

_____. 2006a. *Draft Model Training Program for Hazard Communication* (retrieved May 2006). www.osha.gov/dsg/hazcom/MTP101703.html

_____. 2006b. *Hazard Communication: Foundation of Workplace Chemical Safety PRograms* (retrieved May 2006). www.osha.gov/SLTC/hazardcommunications/

_____. 2010. *Most Frequently Cited Standards*. OSHA Web site (retrieved Sept. 2010). www.osha.gov/dcsp/compliance_assistance/frequent_standards.html

Petersen, D. 2005. "Safety Improvement: Perception Surveys Can Reveal Strengths and Weaknesses." *Professional Safety*, January 2005.

Rackham, H. 1934. *Aristotle in Twenty-three Volumes XIX—The Nicomachean Ethics*. Cambridge, MA: Harvard University Press.

Ramsay, J., and J. Jones. 1998. "Using Behavior Staging to Evaluate the Economic Effect of Worksite Health Promotion." *American Journal of Health Studies* 14(2).

Ross, S., R. Westerfield, B. Jordan, and J. Jaffe. 2007. *Corporate Finance: Core Principles and Applications*. Boston, MA: Mcgraw Hill Press.

Veltri, A., and J. Ramsay. 2009. "Economic Analysis of Safety, Health and Environmental Issues and Practices." *Professional Safety*, Sept. 2009.

Wiener, Y,. and Y. Vardi. 1990. "Relationships Between Organizational Culture and Individual Motivation: a Conceptual Integration." *Psychological Reports* 67:295–306.

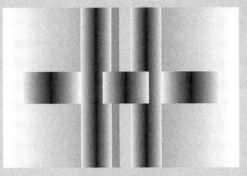

LEARNING OBJECTIVES

▌ Know and understand the basic components of the *Hazard Communication Standard* (HCS) and what is required for compliance.

▌ Be able to evaluate the quality of hazard communication program practices as well as the level of their compliance with OSHA directives.

▌ Understand the steps with which one may institute a hazard communication program within a company.

▌ Recognize the upcoming changes in the Globally Harmonized System (GHS).

BENCHMARKING AND PERFORMANCE CRITERIA

David Fender and Hamid Fonooni

THE *HAZARD COMMUNICATION STANDARD* (HCS), also referred to as HazCom or Workers' Right to Know, was established by OSHA in 1983 (OSHA 1996) to protect workers' safety and health in the United States. Following the establishment of the HCS, in 1986, the EPA established the Emergency Planning and Community Right-to-Know Act, also known as SARA Title III (EPA 1986). HCS, found in 29 CFR 1910.1200, is a performance-based standard, which means that it allows flexibility in meeting its expectations. Requirements, rather than being iron-clad, can be adapted to meet the needs of particular workplaces. However, this flexibility also makes it difficult to know exactly what should be done to be in compliance with various aspects of the standard or to follow the overall intent of the standard in various safety and health issues. Each company must use its own judgment in implementing an appropriate and effective program that adequately protects its employees.

Benchmarking means identifying, understanding, and adapting best practices from other organizations in order to improve the operation's performance. Benchmarking in the HCS area is a little more difficult, however, because the HCS is an OSHA standard, and it exerts a strong influence over companies' practices, regardless of their "best practice." Therefore, this chapter will frequently list a best practice in a particular area that is the generally accepted way companies comply with the particular issue while protecting their employees.

INTRODUCTION

According to OSHA, the HCS "is based on the simple concept that employees have both a need and a right to know the hazards and the identities of the chemicals they are exposed to when working. In addition, they need to know what protective measures are available to prevent adverse effects" (OSHA 1993). Although the concept is simple, complying fully with the technical requirements of the standard—as well as meeting the spirit of the standard—can be much more difficult. This is generally not because the requirements are obscure, or hard to understand, but because consistent implementation of necessary policies can prove a challenge. This difficulty is illustrated by HCS's consistent citation as one of the most common violations encountered in OSHA compliance inspections, especially in terms of lack of training and of inadequate record keeping (Galt 2006).

Compliance with HCS requires continuous effort. It is unlikely that one would find every one of a group of fifteen randomly selected chemicals within a company in full compliance. Compliance with HCS comes by means of firm policies understood by all employees and management that are continuously kept in mind and updated or revised when necessary. Information in this chapter will help companies stay in compliance and aid safety, health, and environmental (SH&E) practitioners in designing and implementing HCS programs, as well as help workers protect themselves from chemical hazards at work sites.

The following sections of this chapter address what to look for when auditing for compliance, and outline what best practices are for maintaining material safety data sheets (MSDSs), labeling, training, and measuring, and what changes to expect in the HCS.

OSHA is pursuing changes in the HCS through implementing the Globally Harmonized System (GHS), which is being promulgated by the United Nations. As this chapter is being written, OSHA is taking comments on the proposed rule, making it impossible to specifically address the actual changes here. OSHA has stated that it does not intend to adopt all of the GHS but will adopt the portions applying to labeling and MSDSs, and these changes will also affect training. In the final part of this chapter, the upcoming Globally Harmonized System (GHS) is addressed. OSHA is currently proposing a two-year adoption period for GHS with complete adoption to be in place potentially by 2015 (OSHA 2010b).

SAFETY AUDITS
OSHA Guidelines

It is always a good idea to review or audit a program periodically to make sure that policies and procedures are being properly implemented and are working as intended. Compliance checklists are available from many sources. Federal—and some state—OSHA programs publish checklists, which are also available from commercial sources and from certain noncommercial sources, such as universities. OSHA publications are available at the OSHA Web site: www.osha.gov.

Every audit is best when conducted systematically. Initially, review the written program for needed changes, and then review the various aspects of the written program to ascertain levels of compliance. Review training to ensure that the proper subjects are being taught, and talk to employees to discover how well they comprehended their training. Inspect labels in work areas for appropriateness. Finally, inspect inventory areas where chemicals are stored or used and compare their contents to MSDS sheets to discover if proper MSDSs are available.

OSHA publishes *Hazard Communication: A Compliance Kit* (OSHA 1999a). This publication gives detailed information about all aspects of hazard communication and is broken into sections. OSHA also publishes its inspection procedures in the document CPL 02-2-038 (OSHA 1998a). This document provides a sample written hazard communication program as well as inspection criteria. The following information is based on OSHA's inspection criteria document, which is a good guideline for program compliance. After highlighting each item of concern, an example will be given of best practices.

The Written Program

Exactly who, what, and how the company HCS program will be conducted must be stated in the written program. Other companies' written programs may be useful as well. Obtain these by networking with other safety professionals. But be very cautious about using another company's plan—do not automatically assume that it is correct or that it will meet your needs. Always tailor others' ideas to your company's needs to ensure that your written program complies with regulations.

A written program must contain the following elements. Best practice: use copies of programs from other companies and follow the guidelines in the hazardous communication compliance kit (OSHA 1999a).

Labels and Other Forms of Warning

Designate, whether by name or by position, the person(s) responsible for ensuring labeling of in-plant containers. Also designate, by name or position, the person(s) responsible for ensuring the labeling of shipped containers (likely individuals in the receiving section).

Describe the labeling system(s) used by the company, specifying the elements of a label and any graphic symbols used. Although generally best practice is to use the labels that come with products, do not use inadequate product labels.

SIDEBAR

The written program should not be a document that exists merely to fulfill government requirements; it should match the company's way of business and overall culture. The more realistic a plan is, the more likely it will be followed, and the more useful it will be. Use the your company's personnel titles and the actual names of departments, buildings, and areas. If your company uses the term "foreman" instead of "first-line supervisor," then use "foreman." If a building is named, use its most commonly recognizable name. If the building has an official name but is commonly known under another name, use both. Clarity is essential.

If your company operates in a more streamlined manner and does not have front-line supervisors, give responsibilities to workers that are consistent with the company's daily business—but realize that this may require additional training so that workers can fully understand and perform their duties. A plan works best when it fits in with the company culture.

Describe any written alternatives to labeling of in-plant containers, such as tanks, where applicable. For more information see "Exceptions" under "Best Practices of Labeling." Best practice is to simply describe what is done. Because many operations do not need alternative labeling systems, this section may not be applicable.

Establish procedures for reviewing and updating label information. Best practice is to state exactly how the company updates information when changes occur. In many cases, information will be from an MSDS.

Material Safety Data Sheets

Material safety data sheets are a significant part of the HCS and must be correctly handled to maintain compliance. The person(s) responsible for obtaining/maintaining the MSDSs must be designated in the written program by name or position, and by area of responsibility if applicable.

How the data sheets will be maintained is important (such as in three-ring binders in work areas, in a pick-up truck at the job site, or available via fax, email, or internet) and what procedures govern the electronic retrieval of MSDSs (be very specific in stating how someone can get an MSDS), including back-up systems used in the event of failures in primary electronic equipment (many companies have a master paper copy maintained in a specific place against just such an occurrence), and how employees may obtain access to MSDSs. Best practice is to specifically address how the data sheets are maintained and how employees gain access to them. If MSDSs are kept in notebooks next to a hazardous material cabinet, it should be stated where employees can find the notebooks as well as how to find a specific MSDS. Although there are many ways of doing this, one common method is to number MSDSs and compile an index sheet in the front of each notebook listing MSDSs by names and numbers. A good reference guide for MSDSs can be found in *Hazard Communication: A Compliance Kit* (OSHA 1999a).

If the list of MSDSs is not received with the initial product shipment, the best practice is to refuse shipment. If this is impossible, a designated space should be labeled as a repository area where items without MSDSs are stored unused until MSDSs are received. An individual must be designated as responsible for acquiring the MSDSs for such products. It is also a good idea to establish the length of time products can be held without MSDSs before being either returned or properly discarded.

Training

Training is an important aspect of the HCS, and its requirements are very specific (OSHA 1999a). The person responsible for training must be identified by name or position and should be someone with comprehensive knowledge of the standard and the company procedures, as well as someone who understands the hazards posed by the chemicals. This will commonly be someone responsible for managing safety (OSHA 2004).

The format of the training program must be explained. The best practice is to detail how training will be conducted (whether by means of audiovisuals, classroom instruction, or similar methods). Initial instruction should primarily use a face-to-face instructor in a classroom environment. Although other means may be suitable during refresher training, someone must be readily available to answer employees' questions.

List the procedures used to train new employees at the time of their initial assignment as well as the procedures for training employees when new hazards are introduced into the workplace. Both best practice and OSHA require training prior to any chemical exposure. Because MSDSs can be complex and confusing documents, employees must understand how to read them, even when they do not understand all the technical terms. Employees do not need to be introduced to every MSDS. The same MSDS for a chemical the workers use should be presented when demonstrating how to read an MSDS. Address how employees will be trained when new chemicals are introduced. If chemicals pose new hazards to workers, it may be best to conduct a training session for employees who will be affected. If a chemical with similar hazards is already used, it may be sufficient to inform employees of the new chemical orally or in a memo. No mat-

ter how training is done, companies are responsible for ensuring that their employees understand chemical hazards and how to protect themselves from them (OSHA 2004).

As applicable, write procedures to train employees about new hazards to which they may be exposed when working on or near another employer's worksite (in other words, hazards introduced by other employers than their own). Best practice is to address the standard operation procedure used in such a scenario.

The written training plan should address:

- Safe work practices for conducting operations in work areas where hazardous chemicals are present. This will vary from company to company and will depend entirely on the hazards posed by the chemicals that are present.
- The location of the written hazard communication program and general information regarding the company program. Best practice is to state where the document can be found and to provide a general overview of the program.
- The location of the listing of hazardous chemicals and MSDS sheets, and how to get an MSDS. The best practice is to clearly state where these documents are kept in the company and to explain the specific procedure for obtaining an MSDS.
- How to detect the presence, or release, of a hazardous chemical. This will depend upon the chemicals present.
- The physical and health hazards of the various chemicals in the work area. This will depend upon the chemicals present.
- How employees can protect themselves from hazards, such as by safe work practices, emergency procedures, and PPE. This will depend upon the chemicals present.
- The labeling system and what its terms and graphic symbols mean. Best practice is to directly address the specific terms and graphic symbols, explaining what they mean in understandable terms.

Additional Topics to Be Reviewed

According to OSHA standards, a *hazardous chemical* is any chemical that poses a physical hazard or a health hazard. A *physical hazard* is posed by any chemical that scientifically valid evidence identifies as a combustible liquid, a compressed gas, an organic peroxide, or an oxidizer, or is explosive, flammable, pyrophoric, unstable (reactive), or water-reactive. A *health hazard* is posed by a chemical that statistically significant evidence, based on at least one study conducted in accordance with established scientific principles, associates with the occurrence of acute or chronic health effects in exposed employees. Health hazards include chemicals that are carcinogens, are toxic or highly toxic agents, or are reproductive toxins, irritants, corrosives, sensitizers, hepatotoxins, nephrotoxins, neurotoxins, agents acting on the hematopoietic system, or agents that damage the lungs, skin, eyes, or mucous membranes (29 CFR 1910.1200). Appendix A of 29 CFR 1910.1200 provides further definitions and explanations of the scope of health hazards covered by the standard, and Appendix B describes the criteria to be used to determine whether or not a chemical is considered hazardous for purposes of this standard.

The best source of information about hazards posed by a chemical is its MSDS, where its health and physical hazards will be listed. This is also the best source of information for employees along with labeling on containers.

For the company to best protect its employees, additional topics may need to be addressed in training. Hazardous chemicals must be listed on site. Best practice is to use the list of hazardous chemicals as the starting point for developing a written plan. A program cannot be properly written until all on-site chemicals are identified and the hazards associated with those chemicals are known. This list must be updated as each new chemical is introduced into the workplace.

Outline methods by which the employer will inform employees of the hazards of nonroutine tasks. Best practice is to ensure that these methods include procedures addressing how employees will be informed of potential hazards at other worksites they may visit, including multiemployer worksites.

Inform employees of the hazards associated with chemicals contained within pipes in their work areas. Best practice is to start with the MSDS for the chemicals and add any other appropriate issues, such as stating the chemical's behavior under pressure or heat.

Ensure that the written plan includes the methods the employer will use at multiemployer worksites to inform other employers of any precautionary measures necessary for the protection of employees. Best practice is to address this in the written plan and during employee training. Normally the management personnel of the company should inform the management personnel of the other employers of the hazards posed by chemicals in use, although the exact procedure may vary from employer to employer.

The methods an employer will use to inform other employees about the labeling system in use should be clearly described. The best practice is to provide written documentation and to document who received it and when it was provided.

The written program should be made available to employees and their designated representatives upon request. Best practice is to specifically address who is responsible to respond to such a request and to answer questions.

Labels and Other Forms of Warning

Labels or other markings on each container must include identification information and appropriate hazard warnings describing the effects of the hazardous chemical on vital organs. Labels on shipped containers must also include the name and address of the chemical manufacturer, importer, or otherwise responsible party.

Containers must prominently display legible labels written in English, and optionally in other appropriate languages. Labels must be cross-referenced with MSDSs and with the list of hazardous chemicals. Best practice is to ensure that some key term, such as a chemical name, is used both on the MSDS and the hazardous chemical list. This name may be a generic (i.e., common) name, such as "Acetone," or a trademarked name, such as "Super Purple Solvent." To differentiate between similar common names, it is a good practice to indicate the manufacturer, as in "Acme Acetone 1402."

Containers of unusual shape or proportion that do not easily accommodate a legible label may take alternative labels, such as a tag on a collapsible plastic container.

It is a good idea to occasionally evaluate the effectiveness of labeling systems in the organization, the training programs, and the MSDS procedures. Evaluation should include the presence of labels on containers and the presence of necessary information. Interviews with employees should be conducted with the purpose of determining their familiarity with the hazards posed by the various chemicals in their workplace. This evaluation should be done at least annually and affect all potentially exposed employees. An effective labeling system ensures that employees are aware of the hazardous effects (including those upon target organs) of the chemicals to which they may be exposed (OSHA 1999a).

Material Safety Data Sheets (MSDSs)

This section will discuss material safety data sheets and their specifications. Employers must have an MSDS for each hazardous chemical on site. Best practice is to use the list of chemicals as a guide to what MSDSs are necessary. Although MSDSs are only required for hazardous chemicals, it is a good idea to have an MSDS for every chemical, confirming that it is not hazardous and providing information to answer employees' questions.

Each MSDS must contain information accurately addressing *at least* the twelve elements required by the standard at 1910.1200(g)(2)(i)–(xii), which include chemical identity, components, physical and chemical characteristics, physical hazards, health hazards, primary routes of entry, PEL and TLV, whether listed as a carcinogen, safe handling methods and precautionary measures, control measures, emergency and first aid procedures, and the date of preparation of the MSDS. The name, address, and telephone number of the manufacturer, importer, or party otherwise responsible for preparing the MSDS should be provided. Best practice for seeing if any information is missing or incorrect is to contact the manufacturer or distributor for a current MSDS.

Employers who work on a multiemployer worksite and bring hazardous chemicals onto that site must inform other employers of the presence of those chemicals and the availability of appropriate MSDSs. If the employer uses a general contractor or other employer as an intermediary for storing and providing MSDSs, and that intermediate employer has agreed to hold and provide ready access to MSDSs, the intermediate employer becomes the controlling employer and is responsible for ensuring the availability of the MSDSs. If MSDSs are not available because a subcontractor failed to make them readily accessible, that subcontractor is responsible for any OSHA violations.

Employee Information and Training

The HSC requires that certain information and training be provided to all employees exposed or potentially exposed to hazardous chemicals. Employees must be informed and aware of the hazards to which they are exposed. They must know how to obtain and use information on labels and MSDSs, and must know and follow appropriate safe work practices established by the company.

According to OSHA's *Inspection Procedures for the Hazard Communication Standard* (1998a), compliance officers should ask the following questions to determine the adequacy of a company's training program. These questions are also a good guide for companies.

- Has a training and information program been established for employees exposed to hazardous chemicals?
- Is this training provided at the time of an employee's initial assignment and again whenever a new hazard is introduced into work areas?
- Have all new employees at this location received training equivalent to the required initial assignment training?
- If electronic access to MSDSs is relied upon at a workplace, have employees been adequately instructed how to retrieve the information?

Information and training must be provided to employees about the hazards or potential hazards posed by all chemicals in their work areas. The information should include hazards associated with by-products and hazardous chemicals introduced by another employer, provided that these are known to be present in such a way that employees may be exposed to them under normal conditions of use or in a conceivable emergency situation.

Exceptions

There are several exceptions to MSDS requirements in the OSHA standards that are listed in this section.

Hazardous waste. Hazardous waste is exempted from the standard when subject to regulation by the Environmental Protection Agency (EPA) under the Resource Conservation and Recovery Act (RCRA). If the waste is not regulated under RCRA, then the requirements of the standard apply. More information can be viewed on the EPA's Web site at www.epa.gov.

Consumer products. A substance is considered a consumer product if it is (1) defined as such under the Consumer Products Safety Act, (2) used in the workplace as intended by its manufacturer, and (3) used with the same frequency and duration of exposure expected of a typical consumer. Chemicals that do not satisfy all these requirements are not exempt from the HCS; instead, they need to be included in the HCS program. One area that commonly does not meet the requirements is the third requirement "duration of exposure expected of a typical consumer." Using a chemical product to clean a single desk in a residential environment results in a different level of exposure than if the same product is used to clean multiple desks in a company setting. Best practice is to incorporate the chemical into the HazCom program if there is any doubt about its status.

Articles. By definition, a manufactured item is exempted as an article if "under normal conditions of use it does not release more than very small quantities, e.g., minute or trace amounts of a hazardous chemical . . . and does not pose a physical hazard or health risk to employees" [29 CFR 1910.1200(c)]. An item may appear to meet the definition of an "article" but may produce a hazardous by-product during normal processing. If cutting, burning, heating, or otherwise processing the article results in exposure of employees to a hazardous chemical, but such processes are not considered part of its normal conditions of use, the item is an article under the standard and is therefore exempted.

Conditions of use. Because of their conditions of use some products otherwise considered articles are not exempt. Examples include:

1. Bricks for use in construction operations, because, under normal conditions of use, bricks may be dry cut, drilled, or sawed, and the clay slurry of wet cutting (when dried) releases dust containing crystalline silica.
2. Switches with mercury in them that are installed in a maintenance process when it is known that a certain percentage break under normal conditions of use.
3. Lead acid batteries having the potential to leak, spill, or break during normal conditions of use, including conceivable emergencies. Lead acid batteries also have the potential to emit hydrogen, which may result in a fire, or an explosion, upon ignition.

Wood and wood products. Wood and wood products, including lumber that will not be processed, in cases when the chemical manufacturer or importer can establish that the only hazard they pose to employees is inherent in their flammability or combustibility, do not require MSDSs. However, the wood and wood products exemption was never intended by OSHA to exclude wood dust from coverage (OSHA 1998a). The permissible exposure limits for wood dust in the HCS program must be included on the MSDS, which will usually be developed by the sawmill, the distributor, or the first employer to handle or process the raw material in such a way that the hazardous chemical is "produced" and released into the work environment. After an MSDS is created for a wood product, retailers or distributors are required to pass on the MSDS to employers just as they would for any other chemical. Further, any chemical additives present in the wood that present a health hazard must also be included on the MSDS and labeled as appropriate [29 CFR 1910.1200 (b)(6)(iv)].

Particulates not otherwise regulated (PNOR). Particulates not otherwise regulated are exempt unless evidence exists that they present a health or physical hazard, as determined by studies or research performed by the manufacturer or by others. For these chemicals, the PNOR PEL must be included on the MSDSs. OSHA includes in PNOR "[a]ll inert or nuisance dusts, whether mineral, inorganic, or organic, not listed specifically by substance name" [Footnote(f) (29 CFR 1910.1000; Table Z-1–Table Z-3, Limits for Air Contaminants)].

BEST PRACTICES FOR MAINTAINING A MATERIAL SAFETY DATA SHEET

An MSDS for Every Hazardous Chemical

A hazardous chemical is one associated with a physical or health hazard [29 CFR 1910.1200(c)]. The employer is required to have an MSDS for each hazardous chemical in the workplace, except when these chemicals are only handled in sealed containers, as in a retail store. Manufacturers, importers, or distributors are required to provide an MSDS with each hazardous chemical they sell to a commercial company. Best practice is to establish policies requiring an MSDS the first time a product is received on company property. When products are shipped to the company, the shipper is required to provide the MSDS with the first shipment and the most recent MSDS with the first shipment after an update [29 CFR 1910.1200(g)(6)(i)]. In cases where products are purchased and brought onto company property by company personnel, firm procedures must require trained personnel to acquire the MSDS upon product purchase [29 CFR 1910.1200 (g)(7)]. MSDSs are not required to be maintained for any chemicals that are not covered by the *Hazard Communication Standard*, such as those in food, drugs, and cosmetics.

Some items, such as office supplies, may not arrive with an MSDS. Retailers of office supplies should be able to provide the MSDSs for products they sell, or manufacturers will provide MSDSs if requested.

MSDSs for products such as whiteout and copier toner are almost always available at manufacturers' Web sites.

Although some products do not require an MSDS because they fall under the exceptions previously mentioned (being a consumer product or an article; see exceptions under "Safety Audits" above), best practice is to incorporate all chemicals into the HazCom program and to have MSDSs available for each, allowing the company to review all products for hazards and acting as reassurance for any employee dubious about the safety of a particular chemical.

Sometimes incomplete MSDSs will be received. If a piece of missing information is deemed critical by the company, the product should be retained unused until the missing information has been supplied by the manufacturer or distributor. If the information is not forthcoming, the company will need to decide whether to use the chemical or to dispose of it and find a substitute. Best practice is to refuse to use any chemical not accompanied by all critical information, allowing the company to stay in complete compliance with the HCS.

Immediate Employee Access to an MSDS

MSDSs are maintained either as paper copies or in electronic storage. If a company has only a small number of chemicals, paper copies will likely be easiest. Electronic storage raises considerations of the availability of computer terminals and the ability of employees to use them, as well as the expense involved in operating them. Both methods are acceptable to OSHA, so companies will have to determine which is most appropriate and useful for them.

According to 29 CFR1910.1200(g)(8), the employer is required to make MSDSs readily and immediately accessible to all employees. This accessibility may be in the form of a hardcopy of each MSDS, or through other means. The employer may use electronic storage, microfiche, or other methods to maintain and provide access to MSDSs so long as no barriers to immediate employee access exist in any workplace (OSHA 1995). Immediate access to MSDSs means that employees must be able to access them without involving an intermediary of any sort (OSHA 1999b). Regardless, although MSDSs *must* be in English, languages in addition to English need not (but may) be used.

Periodic chemical inventories (at least annually) must ensure that MSDSs for all chemicals are available, that all unlabeled chemicals are eliminated, and that unneeded chemicals are removed. After the inventory is completed, a current MSDS for every chemical must be verified as available and up to date. Best practice is to reduce chemical inventories as much as possible, which can greatly assist in reducing the MSDS maintenance and storage burden. Small quantities of chemicals should be especially questioned.

Paper Copies

The most common method of keeping MSDSs available for all hazardous chemicals is to keep paper copies of MSDSs specific to a particular area in 3-ring binders in the area so that all employees on each shift and in each location always have access to the MSDSs. Although making MSDSs available in binders is both simple and effective, the need for employees to *easily* find any particular MSDS requires the provision of some type of indexing system. The easiest index system is to list the chemicals alphabetically.

Large work areas or multiple buildings will require additional sets of binders, making it difficult to keep all the binders updated. Companies should have someone designated in each department or work area to maintain the MSDS binders and to coordinate them with the company safety office. A good rule of thumb is that an employee should not have to walk more than one minute to access one of the binders. Separate buildings must have their own sets of binders, as should separate operations (for example, a paint shop or the maintenance division).

Electronic Storage

More and more companies are storing MSDSs electronically. In cases of electronic storage, the terminals necessary for accessing the information must be located in employee work areas in such a way as to provide ready access to each employee. Further-

more, employees must know how to look up, and be able to look up, a particular chemical's MSDS at any time without assistance. This requirement will affect employee training.

Database software, such as *Microsoft Access*, may be used to store the information, and several companies provide software for just this purpose. Some software scans the original MSDS and stores the resulting images for retrieval. Many companies make their MSDSs available on their Web sites for download, most commonly in Adobe Acrobat (*.pdf) format. These can then be indexed by other software. Some software companies, after receiving a list of chemicals, will set up a custom electronic database of MSDSs, updating it as necessary. Other software requires manual entry of information from MSDSs into a database. However, this is very time-consuming and disconcertingly prone to error in its transference of liability to the company if an error in data entry occurs. It is considered a best practice to use electronic systems that use and display the manufacturer's original MSDSs.

Another example of a software-based solution uses an automated chemical inventory management system that not only keeps a real-time record of the chemical inventories but also automatically searches for the latest MSDS for each chemical. These systems are much more likely to result in accurate chemical inventories and proper MSDS availability if properly implemented and maintained. This type of service has to be customized to some extent for each company and, if the company has many MSDSs, may require specialized scanners and other hardware, making this a somewhat expensive solution. Yet this type of chemical inventory and MSDS system management is currently the best system for total chemical control and compliance.

Because electronic methods are constantly changing, any recommendation regarding specific software will quickly become outdated, so the best way to approach this is to find out what other companies are using and to research the variety of software solutions currently available. What works best will depend upon the company and resources available.

When electronic means are used, an adequate back-up system for rapid access to hardcopies of

MSDSs must be available and accessible in case of a failure of the primary system. Employees must know what the back-up system is and know how to use it. Transmission of information via telephone is not adequate. Best practice is to have paper copies of all MSDSs available for back-up and emergency purposes. The back-up files should be indexed for rapid identification of specific chemicals. How items are indexed is not important so long as individuals understand the indexing system and how to use it. Alphabetical indexing is most common; or each MSDS could be numbered and then appear on a master index with the numbers listed after the product names or manufacturer or other organizing item.

Access of MSDS by Mobile Employees

Employees who work at more than one site during a work shift must be able to obtain MSDS information immediately in an emergency. MSDSs may be kept at the primary workplace facility so long as the employer has a representative available at all times to ensure ready access to this information. Mobile employees, such as linemen, who move frequently from location to location, are the employees to whom an employer is allowed to transmit hazard information via voice communication. The employer must address, in the written hazard communication program, the means by which MSDS information will be conveyed to remote worksites.

BEST PRACTICES OF LABELING

This section will discuss some best practices of labeling, including basic requirements, exceptions, sealed containers, and labeling of laboratories.

Basic Requirements

Every container of hazardous chemicals in a workplace must have a legible label written in English (and in other languages if desired) identifying the chemical name and the health hazards associated with it, including its effects on target organs. It must also display the supplier's name and address.

Exceptions

This section will discuss the exceptions to the HCS's labeling requirements. Portable containers are exempt if they are intended for immediate use by employees transferring hazardous chemicals into them from labeled containers. Therefore, a mechanic could use an unlabeled quart container to hold a small quantity of solvent for use in a job. Although it is best to label containers frequently used in this manner, such labeling is not mandatory.

Stationary process containers are exempt if the employer uses signs, placards, batch tickets, or other written materials identifying the containers and conveying the information normally required. For example, a stationary 200-gallon tank containing a hazardous chemical needs only a sign mounted on the container that displays the information outlined in the "Basic Requirements" section above.

Products regulated by the federal Food and Drug Administration (FDA) or the U.S. Department of Agriculture (USDA) are also exempt, including food, drugs, insecticides, cosmetics, medical products, distilled spirits, and common consumer products. Although the labeling requirements of HCS do not apply to these types of products, the labels that come affixed to these products should be left intact and may be required by other regulations.

Sealed Containers and Laboratories

Other rules specifically address sealed containers—containers in storage or handling that will not be opened—and laboratories. Warning labels must remain on the containers in the state in which they are received. Any MSDSs received should be retained by employers and made available to employees in the manner previously discussed. If an employee so requests, obtain an MSDS for a sealed container, even if the chemical is not being used. Fortunately, because most labels supplied by manufacturers tend to meet federal labeling requirements, best practice is for the company to retain original labels on containers. If labels must be generated at the work site, refer for information to the chemical's MSDS, or request a new label from the manufacturer.

TRAINING AND MEASURING WORKER COMPREHENSION

OSHA has specific requirements regarding employee training, some of which are intended to ensure that trained workers comprehend the training they receive. This section will discuss training considerations, the sources of training material, required training content, and measurement of employees' comprehension of their training. Another source for training information can be found in ANSI/ASSE Standard Z490.1, *Criteria for Accepted Practices in Safety, Health, and Environmental Training* (ANSI/ASSE 2009).

Training Considerations

MSDSs alone are not sufficient to ensure that workers understand chemical hazards. On average, the information on a typical MSDS was found to be about one-third incomprehensible to workers (Kolp et al. 2007). Furthermore, a study by Houts and McDougall (2007) demonstrated that "Workers' response to notification about health effects from exposure to toxic materials is determined not just by the content of the message but also by the 'context' within which notification occurs . . . [which includes t]he workers' prenotification knowledge, attitudes, and experiences concerning environmental health risks in general as well as the health problem that is the subject of the notification." Hence, what workers already "know" affects how they perceive and act upon the information presented. Thus, knowing one's audience, knowing the training that has occurred before the upcoming session, knowing the prevailing organizational culture and management philosophy, and knowing as much about what does and what does not work in a particular organization is critical to effective training.

Training is usually more effective when it is interactive and uses trainer-intensive delivery methods in small group settings. A study performed by Robins et al. (1990) showed that using these methods in hazard communication training increased employee knowledge and improved work practices over a 2-year period after training. An excellent health information program operated by AT&T Bell Laboratories found that the keys to a successful program are involving appropriate subject-matter experts and receiving strong management support (Brooks et al. 1994).

Sources of Material

Training material is readily available for worker HCS training. Products may be purchased from commercial sources, and the government publishes materials that are made freely available. OSHA has quite a bit of useful training material. One publication, entitled *Draft Model Training Program for Hazard Communication* (OSHA 2004), has very detailed suggestions for training, including transparency masters. The Mine Safety and Health Administration (MSHA) publishes a training guide, OT 49, *Telling Miners About Chemical Hazards*. The State of Oregon's safety program offers guideliness to hazard communication compliance and training materials (OR-OSHA 2004), and many other states make similar materials available. Appendix E of the HCS Standard (20 CFR 1910.1200 Appendix E) is entitled "Guidelines for Employer Compliance" and is available at the OSHA Web site.

Appendix E contains the following sections, which have been adapted from the OSHA guidelines.

Required Training

Effective training and information must be provided to all employees about the hazardous chemicals in their work areas. In order to be effective, OSHA requires that employees, after completing their training, will understand the hazards of chemicals they are working with and how to protect themselves (PPE use), will know how to read and use labels and MSDSs, and will know where to obtain substance-specific information on labels and MSDSs.

Information and training may be provied either regarding individual chemicals or categories of hazards (such as flammability or carcinogenicity). If only a few chemicals are used in the workplace, discussing each one individually may be as practical as it is appropriate. In cases where large numbers of chemicals are used, however, or in which the chemicals in use change frequently, training may be addressed instead to general categories of hazards (flammable liquids, corrosive materials, carcinogens, and so on) [29 CFR 1910. 1200 AppE (4)(c)]. When deciding exactly how to train, best practice is to keep in mind that the purpose of the training is for the employees to know the hazards and how to protect themselves, and then to conduct training in such a way that employees will be able to safely work with the chemicals in use.

Training must be provided when an employee is assigned to an area with chemical hazards, whether temporary, short term, or long term, and when a new physical or health hazard is introduced into a work area. Training records must be kept that note when each employee was last trained.

Required Training Content

OSHA requires that certain items be covered in training. The general requirements of the OSHA *Hazard Communication Standard*, as per 29 CFR 1910.1200(h)(2), include covering the physical and health hazards of the chemicals in an employee's work area and how these chemicals may be detected (by monitoring devices, by smell, and so forth). Workers must be informed about how they can protect themselves (by using safe work practices, emergency procedures, or PPE). An explanation of the chemical labeling system, of MSDSs, and of how to get hazard information as well as general information about the employer's hazard communication program, must be provided. Workers must also be made aware of the location and availability of MSDSs, of the list of hazardous chemicals in the workplace, and of the employer's written hazard communication program.

Measuring Comprehension

Chemical hazards are communicated to workers to ensure that they fully understand the risks and hazards of the chemicals they work with and are thus able to make informed decisions to protect themselves (Nicholson 2000). Cox and Tait (1998) state that risk communication has no value unless it actually informs or changes behavior in order to ensure

safety and is thus about "winning hearts and minds," not merely about providing information.

According to Sadhra et al. (2002), the best results of communicating hazard information are subject to several considerations. Individuals communicating the information must be credible, skillful, and knowledgeable, and the message should directly address the needs and circumstances of employees. The perceived importance of the message affects how employees receive it.

The form in which a message is delivered makes a difference—and face-to-face delivery is the most effective approach. Characteristics of the receiver, such as age, intelligence, and personality, affect the way training is received. These characteristics must be taken into account when training is being planned and is underway. The values, needs, and interests of employees affect how they receive training. The better employees are understood, the more specifically training can be designed for maximum effectiveness.

How individuals and groups of employees (subcultures) perceive safety affects how receptive they are to safety messages. Individuals unfamiliar with hazardous activities, as well as individuals so familiar that they are blasé about the hazards, may not truly understand aspects of training, or may believe it does not apply to them. Becoming familiar with the way employees think about the hazards connected with their jobs will allow trainers to adapt training to each group of employees for maximum effect.

Each worker may react uniquely to HazCom training, even when given the same information about workplace hazards (Cox et al. 2003). Although these differing behavioral responses result from a variety of factors, many of which are outside the workplace, the company is responsible for ensuring that individuals understand hazard information. In a study performed by Sadhra et al. (2002) of electroplating workers working with chromium, nickel, and hazardous chemicals, it was shown that various workers in the same company had different understandings of the hazards of their work environment, including misunderstandings of words such as "long-term" versus "short-term" and "acute" versus "chronic." This demonstrates the need to use terms and language that workers understand. Workers also tended to be concerned most about short-term, immediate risks, such as acid burns, whereas safety experts were more concerned about the long-term, carcinogenic nature of chemicals. This study also showed that the workers tended to learn much more from each other than from written information or training provided by company management. Because new workers learned most of what they knew about the hazards of their jobs from their senior workers, if the senior workers had incorrect understandings of workplace hazards, new workers likely adopted the same erroneous views.

Methods of measuring individual work comprehension can vary. Written tests or quizzes may be given, but in industry settings these types of instruments may not provide optimum feedback and may only indicate how good an individual is at taking a test or how well an employee can read—not what employees really know and can do. If written quizzes are used, it must be remembered that the purpose is not to see how well someone does on a test, but whether they understand key information. Only questions about essential information should be asked; trivia should be ignored. A passing score must be established. Note that if questions are asked only about essential information *and* one or more questions are missed, an employee is demonstrating a lack of understanding of an essential safety issue. Because of this, a passing score may need to be 100 percent. One way to achieve perfect scores on tests of essential information is to perform a post-test review that can ensure that employees understand the information they previously failed to comprehend.

A more reliable way to measure comprehension (see "Required Training Content" for topics workers should understand) is to talk to workers in their work areas. A few weeks later, ask individual workers questions at their job sites. Ask them to identify the hazards of a particular chemical, and ask them how they can protect themselves against those hazards. Ask them what particular symbols or terms on chemical labels mean. Identify chemicals and have them demonstrate how to find MSDSs. Ask questions using variable phrasings and from different points of view to accurately determine whether incorrect answers are merely based on misunderstand-

ings of terms. If workers do not understand key points, it is best to briefly inform them at that time, keeping a positive attitude and a friendly, open approach.

Training must be provided to employees at the time of their initial assignment and again whenever new physical or health hazards are introduced into their work area [29 CFR 1910.1200(h)(1)]. No records are required to be kept documenting training, but best practice is to keep such records for monitoring purposes [29CFR 1910.1200, App E(4)(C)]. Record keeping will vary by company policy, but it should minimally keep track of names, work units, and dates of training.

GLOBALLY HARMONIZED SYSTEM (GHS)

In 1992, at the United Nations Conference on Environment and Development (also called the Rio Earth Summit), an initiative was taken to design a system to protect human health and the environment by establishing a single global system to classify chemical hazards, to provide standard hazard labeling, and to provide uniform safety data sheets (SDSs). This initiative turned into action and soon became known as the United Nations' Globally Harmonized System for the Classification and Labeling of Chemicals (GHS) (UNECE 2009b). The GHS evolved through a series of international meetings of the Committee of Experts. At this point, the third revised edition of the GHS was published in July 2009 and is available (UNECE 2009a).

Although international organizations and governments are the primary audience for the GHS, industry and other private and public entities will eventually implement requirements that will be developed and adopted in the future. The GHS also provides a basis for harmonization of rules and regulations on chemicals at the national, regional, and worldwide level. It is also an important factor for trade facilitation.

The GHS will have a significant impact on the U.S. OSHA *Hazard Communication Standard*, and on the chemical industry that manufactures and supplies chemicals; it will also impact the users of chemicals. From their production to handling, transport, and use, chemicals present potential dangers to human health and the environment. People of any age all over the world with different languages, cultures, and social and economic conditions, including illiterates, face dangerous products daily (chemicals, pesticides, and so on).

Why Is the GHS Needed?

It is impossible for each country to identify and specifically regulate every hazardous chemical product. For instance, in the United States, it is estimated that there are about 945,000 such products. Regulating requirements for identification and information to accompany such products should provide needed protection. Global systems that have adopted harmonized requirements for hazard definition and information will impact not only this protection, but also trade between countries.

How Does the GHS Impact the HCS?

The United States currently has regulatory requirements that address concerns in different agencies; several agencies will therefore be affected by adoption of the GHS—for example, the Pesticides Program in the Environmental Protection Agency, the Hazardous Materials Regulations in the Department of Transportation and the Consumer Product Safety Commission, as well as the Occupational Safety and Health Administration. Currently, each of the above-mentioned agencies has adopted independent regulations that differ from the others, creating a rather cumbersome and inefficient process for domestic producers who must classify and label the same hazardous product multiple times.

Since OSHA's HCS has performance-oriented requirements for labels and material safety data sheets, communication should address inconsistencies among the users of labels and the MSDSs. Labeling provisions are the major difference between the HCS and the GHS. Adoption of the GHS should help comprehensibility and facilitate compliance. There will be a substantial impact on OSHA, since HCS requires labels and MSDSs for over seven million workplaces and about 945,000 hazardous chemical products.

It should be also noted that the HCS refers to lists of chemicals in hazard determination and uses them to establish a "floor" of covered chemicals. The floor was included in the HCS to address concerns about self-classification by manufacturers. However, the GHS does not have similar provisions. There are more detailed hazard determination provisions in the GHS addressing those concerns, which is the reason for removing the floor provisions.

The Scope of the GHS

The GHS covers all hazardous chemical substances, dilute solutions, and mixtures. The substances that would be directly impacted by adoption of GHS are: pharmaceuticals, food additives, cosmetics, and pesticide residues in food. These substances will not be covered at the point of intentional intake but will be covered where workers may be exposed, and in transport. There are some exceptions regarding the acute toxicity and environmental effects. The GHS includes five categories of acute toxicity effects for each route of entry, which are intended to protect children from consumer products. However, it is not likely that OSHA will cover all five categories when adopting the GHS. In addition, it covers aquatic toxicity, which requires environmental information on MSDSs. OSHA does not have jurisdiction on environmental information; therefore, it may not adopt aquatic toxicity criteria or require environmental information on MSDSs. However, all of the other criteria seem to be relevant to the workplace, and OSHA expects to adopt them.

Testing of Chemicals

Under the current HCS requirements, chemical manufacturers can base their evaluations on currently available data. However, the GHS does not require any testing of chemicals to determine their hazards. The criteria for classification of health hazards are test-method neutral. Any scientifically valid test data can be used.

Mixture Provisions

The HCS is based on either test data for the mixture as a whole, or a percentage cut-off approach. The GHS employs a tiered approach, allowing extrapolation of data from similar mixtures, an additivity formula for acute toxicity, and a varied cut-off approach.

Labels

HCS has performance-oriented labels that allow almost any method of conveying hazards. However, the GHS has specific harmonized provisions for pictograms, hazard statements, and signal words. The GHS also has suggested precautionary statements that are not yet harmonized, but are expected to be in the future. Manufacturers and importers should expect substantial change from current requirements. Labels must include: (1) product identifier, (2) signal word, (3) hazard statement(s), (4) pictogram(s), (5) precautionary statement(s), and (6) supplier information (OSHA 2010c).

Material Safety Data Sheets

The HCS allows any order of information on MSDSs. However, the GHS specifies the order of information, which is consistent with industry approaches in ANSI and ISO. This should help to improve comprehensibility and issues regarding accuracy of the information (OSHA 2010c).

Advanced Notice of Proposed Rulemaking (ANPR)

The ANPR presents information relevant to the provisions of the GHS that OSHA expects to adopt. The ANPR covers background and history of the *Hazard Communication Standard* and the Globally Harmonized System of Classification and Labeling of Chemicals. A comprehensive document with information regarding GHS can be found on the OSHA Web site at www.osha.gov/dsg/hazcom/ghs.html.

Summary and the Future

The major elements of hazard communication consist of proper labeling, MSDS availability, and effective training. Understanding what has to be done to comply with the HCS is not difficult. A little study and review of this OSHA standard and its interpretations will provide a good understanding of its requirements. Where it becomes more difficult is in creating and keeping a good inventory of chemicals and in properly continuing management of the MSDS program, including training. As stated in the beginning of the chapter, compliance with OSHA, as well as best practice, indicates that anyone in the company having anything to do with hazardous chemicals must always follow established procedures in procuring, storing, using, and disposing of them. Because of this, effective training is essential.

As of this writing, OSHA has issued proposed rulemaking and held informal hearings to make the HCS consistent with the Globally Harmonized System of Classification and Labeling of Chemicals (GHS) adopted by the United Nations in 2003 (OSHA 2009, 2010a, and 2010b). Modifying the standard will change the criteria for classifying health and physical hazards, will lead to adoption of standardized labeling requirements, and will require a standardized order of information for safety data sheets (SDSs). Part of this modification is a concept called *control banding*, which identifies chemical risks based on the process, task, material characteristics, control, and quantity used ("Control Banding" 2005). If all these proposed changes occur, employees may be able to more easily understand labels and MSDSs and more clearly explain chemical hazards present at their work sites. Employers will have access to new standardized MSDS formats and label requirements and, after retraining employees, benefit by simplified compliance requirements and improved chemical safety.

References

American National Standards Institute (ANSI)/American Society of Safety Engineers (ASSE). 2009. *Z490.1-2009, Criteria for Accepted Practices in Safety, Health, and Environmental Training*. Des Plaines, IL: ASSE.

Brooks, L., S. Merkel, M. Glowatz, M. Comstock, and L. Shoner. "A Comprehensive Reproductive Health Program in the Workplace." *American Industrial Hygiene Association Journal* (April 1994) 55:352–357.

"Control Banding." *Professional Safety*, 22:68–69.

Cox, P., J. Niewohner, N. Pidgeon, S. Gerrard, B. Fischhoff, and D. Riley. 2003. "The Use of Mental Models in Chemical Risk Protection: Developing a Generic Workplace Methodology." *Risk Analysis*, 23(2):311–324.

Cox, S., and R. Tait. 1998. *Safety, Reliability and Risk Management.* 2d ed. Oxford: Butterworth Heinemann.

Environmental Protection Agency (EPA). 1976. Resource Conservation and Recovery Act, 40 CFR 239–282. Washington, DC: U.S. Government Printing Office.

_____. 1986. Superfund Amendments and Reauthorization Act (retrieved December 28, 2010). www.epa.gov/superfund/policy/sara/htm

Galt, D. 2006. "Effective Hazcom Training." *Industry Safety and Hygiene News* (October 2006), p. 46.

Houts, P., and V. McDougall. 2007. "Importance of Evaluating the Context Within Which Notification Occurs." *American Journal of Industrial Medicine* 23(1):205–210.

Indiana University. 2003. *Hazard Communication Program Audit Form.* www.ehs.indiana.edu/WorkerSafety/HazcomAuditform.pdf

Kolp, P., B. Sattler, M. Blayney, and T. Sherwood. 2007. "Comprehensibility of Material Safety Data Sheets." *American Journal of Industrial Medicine* 23(1):135–141.

Mining Safety and Health Administration (MSHA). 2002. OT 49, *Telling Miners About Chemical Hazards.* www.msha.gov/REGS/COMPLIAN/Guides/Hazcom/HazComToolKit.pdf

Nicholson, P. J. 2000. "Communicating Occupational and Environmental Issues." *Occupational Medicine* 50: 226–230.

Occupational Safety and Health Administration (OSHA). 1993. Fact Sheet 93–26, *Hazard Communication Standard,* www.osha.gov/pls/oshaweb/owadisp.show_document?p_table=FACT_SHEETS&p_id=151

_____. 1995. *Compliance with the Occupational Safety and Health Administration's (OSHA) Hazard Communication Standard (HCS) and the Requirement for Material Safety Data Sheets (MSDS). OSHA Standard Interpretation.* www.osha.gov/pls/oshaweb/owadisp.show_document?p_table=INTERPRETATIONS&p_id=21743

_____. 1996. 29 CFR 1910.1200 App E, "Guidelines for Employer Compliance." Washington, D.C.: U.S. Government Printing Office.

_____. 1998a. CPL 02-2-028, *Inspection Procedures for the Hazard Communication Standard,* March 20. www.osha.gov/pls/oshaweb/owdisp.show_document?p_table=DIRECTIVES&p_id=1551

_____. 1998b. OSHA 3084, *Chemical Hazard Communication.* Washington, D.C.: U.S. Government Printing Office.

_____. 1999a. OSHA 3104, *Hazard Communication: A Compliance Kit.* Washington, D.C.: Government Printing Office.

_____. 1999b. OSHA 3104, *Employee Access to MSDSs Required by 1910.1200 vs. 1910.1020. OSHA Standard Interpretation,* December 7. www.osha.gov/pls/oshaweb/owadisp.show_document?p_table=INTERPRETATIONS&p_id=22830

_____. 2004. *Draft Model Training Program for Hazard Communication.* www.osha.gov/dsg/hazcom/MTP101703.html

_____. 2009. *HCS/GHS Proposed Regulation September 30, 2009.* www.osha.gov/dsg/hazcom/hcs_reg_text_093009.pdf

_____. 2010a *OSHA Announces Informal Public Hearing on Hazard Communication Rule (retrieved November 15, 2010).* www.osha.gov/pls/oshaweb/owadisp.show_document?p_table=NEWS_RELEASES&p_id+17028

_____. 2010b. OSHA 10-44, *U.S. Labor Department's OSHA Announces Informal Public Hearing on Hazard Communication in Pittsburgh on March 31 (retrieved November 15, 2010).* www.osha.gov/pls/oshaweb/owadisp.show_document?p_table=NEWS_RELEASES&p_id=17277

_____. 2010c. "A Guide to The Globally Harmonized System of Classification and Labeling of Chemicals (GHS)" (retrieved November 15, 2010). www.osha.gov/dsg/hazcom/ghs.html

Oregon OSHA. 2004. Publication 2034, *Hazard Communication: A Guide to Safe-Work-Practices.* www.orosha.org/pdf/pubs/2034/pdf

Robins, T., M. Hugentobler, M. Kaminski, and S. Klitzman. 1990. "Implementation of the Federal Hazard Communication Standard: Does Training Work?" *Journal of Occupational Medicine* 32(11):1133–1140.

Sadhra, S., J. Petts, S. McAlpine, H. Pattison, and S. MacRae. 2002. "Workers' Understanding of Chemical Risks: Electroplating Case Study." *Occupational Environmental Medicine* 59:689–695.

Smith, Sandy. 2002. "HAZCOM Pays Off at the Cary Co." *Occupational Hazards* (December 2002), pp. 31–34.

United Nations Economic for Europe (UNECE). 2009. *Globally Harmonized System of Classification and Labeling of Chemicals (GHS) (retrieved March 18, 2009).* www.unece.org/trans/danger/publi/ghs/ghs_welcome_e.html

_____. 2010. *Globally Harmonized System for Classification and Labeling of Chemicals, Historical Background (retrieved November 15, 2010).* www.unece.org/trans/danger/publi/ghs/histback_e.html

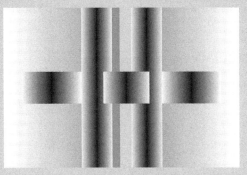

LEARNING OBJECTIVES

- Identify best practice standards.

- Understand the administrative issues involved in hazard communication (hazcom).

- Identify training issues for different types of work sites and learn how to prepare training, education, and/or instruction programs.

- Understand the development, use, and limitation of material safety data sheets (MSDSs).

- Understand the complexities of labeling and signage.

- Develop some strategies for evaluating the quality of training programs.

- Recognize when to do training of first responders and clinical emergency responders.

- Explain the strengths and weaknesses of different training formats.

- Understand some of the strategies for evaluating the quality of training programs.

BEST PRACTICES

Sharon Campbell

THERE ARE MANY issues involved in hazard communication, including providing adequate information at the work site; training workers effectively and efficiently; obtaining, maintaining, and providing 24/7 access to MSDSs that actually have useful information; and properly labeling and storing hazardous chemicals. As all safety professionals know, the *Hazard Communications Standard* (HCS) regulations are minimum standards, and there are a host of other issues that need to be considered as well to meet best practice standards. And now, the *Globally Harmonized Standard* (GHS), *REACH*, *control banding*, and *responsible care* are all considerations.

But first, what are *best practice* standards? Keep in mind that best practices can change regularly, with new benchmarks being set as safety professionals constantly go beyond minimum standards or as government changes the laws. The following are some criteria:

1. The program meets the basic legal requirements set by the Occupational Safety and Health Administration (OSHA) and the Environmental Protection Agency (EPA).
2. The program goes beyond the basic requirements to include the realities of the workforce: varied languages and cultures; different levels of literacy, ages, concerns, and abilities.
3. The program goes beyond the basic requirements to include everyday realities:

   - international work sites and workforces
   - transport of hazardous materials
   - the emergence of terrorism
   - biological hazards
   - the need to deal with chemically, biologically, and radiologically contaminated disaster sites

327

- the emergence of new technologies
- the education of various people beyond the workforce

There are other measures of excellence, and many safety professionals, especially members of the Voluntary Protection Program Participants Association (VPPPA), strive for and attempt to achieve these standards of excellence. It is recommended that an organization check the criteria and actions of like companies and safety professionals to increase the organization's own practices over time.

These practices will change over time, and what works for one organization may or may not work for another. As technology, knowledge, materials, education levels, management techniques, tools, and the rest of the work world change, the safety professional must continually reevaluate *best practices* and how they can and must change and improve.

First, this chapter looks at administrative issues; next, it discusses the available educational materials and processes, such as MSDSs, other publications, and training programs. The section after that looks into training practices, labeling, symbols and language; and, finally, the chapter looks at emerging issues traditionally not addressed in the hazcom training materials.

Administrative Issues

Basic compliance is not difficult. O'Brien (2001) has a checklist for HCS compliance:

- Know the regulations.
- Identify responsible staff.
- Identify and list all chemicals.
- Write the plan.
- Maintain good labeling on containers.
- Provide quick access to MSDSs for all employees on all shifts.
- Train all employees on all possible chemical exposures.
- Frequently review and revise the program.

No sweat, right? But to go further and become world class, using best practices, look at each of the above in detail.

Know the Regulations

Obviously, to comply with the HCS, safety professionals first have to know and understand the regulations. Any set of regulations has its own ambiguities and gray areas that, in any given situation, could "sort of" apply. Also, like any set of regulations, these will change from time to time. Keeping up is essential. Safety professionals with questions can ask OSHA for advice on compliance. OSHA provides free, confidential expertise, which is primarily aimed at smaller businesses.

The OSHA consulting branch is separate from the enforcement branch, which changes the dynamics from an OSHA-complaint inspection. When called, the consulting branch does require some commitment for compliance. "Your only obligation will be to commit yourself to correcting serious job safety and health hazards—a commitment which you are expected to make prior to the actual visit and carry out in a timely manner" (OSHA 2007a). Be aware, though, that "In rare instances, the consultant may find an 'imminent danger' situation during the walk-through. If so, you must take immediate action to protect all employees. In certain other situations that would be judged a 'serious violation' under OSHA criteria, you and the consultant are required to develop and agree to a reasonable plan and schedule to eliminate or control that hazard. The consultants will offer general approaches and options to you" (OSHA 2007a). It is also advisable to look to the future. Many countries have specific standards for their MSDSs and they are not the same. Because of the difficulty multinational companies or those selling to a large international market experience in complying with every single variation, an international mandate to develop a globally harmonized system for hazard classification and labeling was adopted in 1992 (OSHA 2009). It is clear now that MSDSs will eventually reflect whatever standard the global-harmonization project sets.

SHE practitioners responsible for writing MSDSs or labels need to look at the proposals and see if they can implement the probable requirements now. Is there new technology for delivering MSDS information quickly and easily on the horizon? If a new computer system is needed, it would be farsighted to identify the availability of new technology now to maximize future access, as would planning training programs with an eye on the future.

Any SHE professional required to write MSDSs needs to be properly trained to do so. There are training courses available from numerous sources, such as the Society for Chemical Hazard Communication; Interactive Learning Paradigms Incorporated, which offers advice but no courses; Chemical Plant Safety Resources, which offers a book with templates; Denehurst Chemical Safety, Ltd.; and others. The American National Standards Association (ANSI) has a publication that gives the current standards. Any course taken should include the GHS and other relevant standards.

Identify Responsible Staff

Choose carefully. Make sure the person selected is qualified for the hazcom position. Consider also whether or not this person is qualified to do the labeling as well. What if nobody is particularly qualified? Some good options include hiring a qualified consultant, at least for providing oversight on the program. If the designated employee is approaching qualified status, have the person get the additional training needed to fill in knowledge gaps. If the employee knows chemistry but not the regulations, that situation could be correctable. If the employee knows the regulations, but not chemistry, team the person up with someone who does, or find someone else, because it would take too long to turn a regulatory specialist into a chemist. These staffers do not have to be on site all the time, as long as the entire program is running correctly.

Identify and List All Chemicals

This can be a daunting task, and one that also requires competent personnel. It may not seem that way to a nonchemist, but someone unfamiliar with chemical nomenclature making chemical lists can make all kinds of mistakes, necessitating a major or complete redo of the inventory. Facilities with only a relatively small number of chemicals on site are in good shape.

The logistics are pretty easy, and the extent of chemical expertise needed is limited. On the other hand, large research facilities, where each lab has thousands of different chemicals, most in very small quantities, *definitely* require someone competent. Either way, make sure all the MSDSs for all the chemicals are on site, or provide continuous access to them.

Consider finding some system—a bar-code system, for instance—for maintaining lists of chemicals if there are a lot of them, so that what has been consumed, discarded, or acquired is frequently updated. Centralizing purchasing, if practical, would be helpful for the acquisition department.

Write the Plan

It is not necessary to reinvent the wheel. Available prewritten plans from various vendors can be customized. Be sure to check the credentials of the plan developers, though, and make sure that the plan is appropriate for the facility. Whether or not a premade plan is selected, Pinto has simplified the plan's requirements (Pinto 1999):

- a list of the employees in charge of all the various responsibilities
- a list of all hazardous chemicals
- the source and methods for obtaining MSDSs, including a protocol if the MSDS is not received with the initial purchase; list precisely how employees can access them and how they can review and update procedures and schedules
- labeling procedures for generic containers with hazardous chemicals
- information and training procedures for workers so they can protect themselves from the hazards
- procedures for informing workers about the hazards of nonroutine tasks
- a respiratory protection program, including detailed standard operating procedures (SOPs) for selection and use of respirators
- a personal protective equipment (PPE) program, including the provision of and training in the use of PPE other than respirators

- a blood-borne pathogen (BBP) program (29 CFR 1910.1030 requires such a program if safety professionals can "reasonably anticipate skin, eye, mucous membrane or parenteral contact with blood or other potentially infectious materials that may result from the performance of an employee's duties")
- a confined spaces program
- any other OSHA standards that apply to the operation

Whoever writes the program should keep in mind that OSHA inspectors should find the program easy to evaluate, which would also make it easier for people to use. They will evaluate the plan to verify compliance. To that end, 3E safety and transportation specialists Burns and Beckel recommend including copies of posters, signs, and training materials, or at least referencing their location in the plan (Burns and Beckel 2001). The virtue of referencing such materials within the written program instead of inserting them is that it eliminates the need to include extensive details.

Keep in mind that any program must be updated as problems, changing conditions, and changing personnel require. At the least, establish a schedule and procedure for updating. Some mechanism for reporting problems, glitches, and suggestions that will filter up to the person/people responsible is essential to optimize the Hazard Communication Program.

As part of the continual reevaluation of HCS compliance, use safety inspections to monitor the effectiveness of the program as well as the training and understanding of individual employees (whether they are "getting it") (IOMA, Inc. 2001). Test individual employees on inspections: ask if they know the hazards of the chemicals they use; what PPE they need; what to do if chemicals are spilled; how to decontaminate themselves and/or the facility, if necessary; and so on. Get specific, and make sure they understand what the rating scales actually mean, for example. If an employee, because he or she is not working with hazardous chemicals, happens not to be wearing PPE when the safety professional is making rounds, make the employee demonstrate the wearing of the PPE. As gaps in knowledge are discovered, revise the training program.

In addition, consider performing systematic job safety analyses (JSAs) in order to regularly ensure that job descriptions adequately identify inherent hazards and that employees have adequate understanding to be able to avoid those hazards.

TRAINING MATERIALS AND REQUIREMENTS
Requirements and Optional Training

The requirements for chemical safety training are pretty much laid out by federal and state OSHAs, the Department of Transportation (DOT), and the EPA in their regulations based on the chemical inventory. (See appropriate references in this book.) However, do not forget to find out what other legal requirements may apply to the organization's operations. There may be local fire department and even city environmental and safety regulations to consider.

Another training issue to consider is the need to train, or at least inform, local emergency responders and medical providers in the event of an emergency, disaster, or terrorist attack. While they may not need the same training as employees, appropriate people who are kept informed of chemicals and other hazards on site, could make a big difference in an emergency. Consider offering more detailed training to selected responders. Invite them to see the layout and quantity of hazardous materials so they are prepared in the event of an emergency.

Do not forget contractors doing work on the site. For example, in one lawsuit, a contractor, Hydroblast, was hired to pressure test the tubes in a heat exchanger system with the chemical solvent, Selexol, in it ("Nobody told *me* . . . ," n.d.; 10th U.S. Circuit Court 1998). The owner of Hydroblast was told of the hazards of Selexol. The contractor's foreman asked a plant employee if there was anything harmful in the tubes and was told there was not. The warning did not get to the foreman and crew from the president of Hydroblast. Relying on the employee's word, the crew did not wear protective coveralls when working, and used only face or eye protection. Selexol was blown from the tubes during testing for some unspecified and possibly unknown reason, drenching the plaintiffs. As they did not realize it was hazardous, they did not know to promptly get cleaned off and thus sustained unspecified ill effects. Had the foreman insisted on seeing the MSDS he would have had the crew wear PPE. Had the employee who assured the foreman the chemical was not hazardous also insisted on seeing the MSDS, accurate information would have been given to the contractor's employees. The take-home lesson here is that every party should carefully read the MSDSs and not take anyone's word on the actual level of hazard.

Participating on the local emergency planning committee (LEPC) can be a good way to get to know the local fire and police departments. The committees are made up of local emergency responders, with representatives from the fire department, the sheriff's department, the police department, and so on, as well as industry representatives, citizens, and others. Safety professionals may also want to let local emergency providers know what resources can be contributed to them if needed, in terms of equipment, supplies, and trained and willing people. Consider cross-training between companies if each company's people might get involved in a nearby company's emergency involving hazardous materials they do not have on site. It would be a good idea to investigate potential legal liabilities in planning these activities in case unwanted events occur during training or other activities.

Medical providers may or may not be aware of the acute and chronic effects of exposures of a company's major hazardous materials and processes. Local emergency providers should know at least how to get crucial information quickly, and how to gain access to the pertinent MSDSs. Knowing how to read them could make a difference in a serious emergency. In addition, enhancing one's emergency management plan and emergency response capabilities can be a direct result of working with your local LEPC.

BARRIERS TO MSDSs AND OTHER SAFETY INFORMATION

A *barrier* does not necessarily mean a locked door. As Geller has pointed out repeatedly for years, and as one knows from personal experience, safety needs to be convenient (Geller 2003). It was not until this author, a certified safety professional who relies on her eyes

to hear, due to her lifelong hearing loss, put a set of chemical splash goggles in each bathroom (for cleaning agents), laundry room (for bleach), garage (for solvents, paint, etc.), and kitchen (for splattering hot oil) that she finally started using eye protection every time it was required. Why would any SHE professional think his or her employees will do any better when it is inconvenient to get to the MSDSs?

Geller recommended in 2003 that companies set up "a behavioral inconvenience scale" ranging from one (very easy) to 10 (most difficult). Ask the employees to rate the ease of access to the MSDS locations (and other safe work behaviors—the technique has broad applications) on all shifts, at all locations. Consider asking other parties that might need fast access to them, such as emergency responders and medical personnel, to do the same. Identify the barriers and eliminate them if feasible and reasonable. Hanging a pile of MSDSs from each cleaning cart eliminates access barriers for the cleaning staff, but it is clearly excessive. And if they cannot read or understand the MSDSs hanging there, that is still a profound barrier.

MSDS Issues

Who Wrote this Thing, Anyhow?

Good question! Perhaps more pertinent is the question of the qualifications of the person who wrote the MSDSs that people are relying on in a facility (OSHA 2004b). Another issue to consider is whether the document is actually complete. Thomas G. Grumbles, CIH, president of The American Industrial Hygiene Association (AIHA), testified to the Committee on Health, Education, Labor and Pensions Subcommittee on Employment Safety and Training of the United States Senate at the March 24, 2004, Hazard Communication hearing (henceforth referred to as the Enzi Hearing); he pointed out that the HCS does not address that issue. Reasonably enough, the AIHA believes that the quality of MSDSs will be increased if the authors are competent and are provided with guidelines on the preparation and maintenance of MSDSs. While it is not currently possible to demand that suppliers reveal the bona fides of their MSDS writers, participation in the lengthy process of developing standards, or at least offering strong suggestions, for the qualifications of

MSDS creators and on the preparation and maintenance guidelines will improve the quality of MSDSs in the future, and make them more useful and reliable. Consider joining such committees to have a voice in this important issue.

Fortunately, there are sources for training materials and courses on MSDS writing. The Society for Chemical Hazard Communication offers courses on MSDS preparation, REACH, GHS, and many other pertinent areas. Interactive Learning Paradigms Inc., offers a very useful MSDS "Frequently Asked Questions"page, and OSHA and the Canadian Centre for Occupational Health and Safety make information on this topic available.

Why They Need to Be Correct and Understood by Users

Testimony at the Enzi Hearing by Carolyn W. Merritt, former chair and chief executive officer of the U.S. Chemical Safety and Hazard Investigation Board (CSB) was stark. She testified that "Our investigations show that lives continue to be lost in accidents because chemical hazards are not being effectively communicated in the workplace. Among accidents we have investigated, faulty communication of material hazards contributed to 12 deaths among workers and 79 injuries to workers, first responders and members of the public" (Merritt 2004).

In two of nineteen major accidents, no MSDSs were provided at all; in two more, MSDSs were provided but employees were not trained in their use. Two other accidents resulted from a failure to provide product-flammability data; three more were caused by lack of information on reactivity; one resulted from language barriers; and three major dust explosions in 2003 resulted from failure to warn of that hazard.

A two-year study from 2000 to 2002 found that, over the past twenty years, unreliable reactive hazard information led to 167 serious incidents, resulting in 108 deaths and extensive injuries and property damage. The problem is that information on the hazards from mixing or blending chemicals is not included in the MSDSs (Merritt 2004).

Some of the more spectacular cases investigated by the CSB include:

- A complete lack of MSDSs led to the BLSR Operating, Ltd., blast, when two tanker trucks delivering flammable gas condensate waste for disposal allowed the waste to run over open ground into a trench, which is the usual practice for nonflammable drilling mud. Nobody knew the waste was highly flammable. Three workers died and four were seriously burned.

- Waste chemicals reacted in the basement of a mixed-use building in the Chelsea neighborhood in New York City, causing damage as high as the fifth floor of the building, and injuring 36 people, including 14 members of the public. Not only were there no MSDSs, but even if there had been, many of the workers would not have understood them due to language barriers.

- Four workers died and six were injured when a worker restarted a mixer containing solidified explosive material at a company that reclaimed military munitions. MSDSs were only available in English, and most employees understood only Spanish.

- A fine plastic powder used to make rubber goods exploded in a medical rubber plant, killing six, injuring dozens, and causing hundreds to lose their jobs. The dust, which nobody knew was potentially flammable, had accumulated over a manufacturing area at the plant. In this case, the manufacturer of the powdered polyethylene included a warning in its MSDS, but the plant's source was a formulation company, which turned powder into a water-based slurry and neglected in its MSDS to inform end users that, when dried, the product could release potentially explosive dust.

- Another dust explosion involved powdered resin used as a fiberglass insulation binder. The MSDS understated the hazard, indicating that its powder was "combustible," but did not mention that the powder's catastrophic potential was the dust allowed to accumulate. Seven people died and more than 30 others were injured.

Far too many people have died or been maimed because of controllable hazards caused by chemicals they did not understand for a variety of reasons.

Lack of Clarity

OSHA has long required employers to provide MSDSs for all the chemicals on the premises and in use, but what good are these MSDSs to the average employee, particularly in an emergency, if they are written in technical language unfamiliar to most employees, and the formats are confusing at first glance? Language barriers can also exist. These issues have been addressed repeatedly, and OSHA requires training, not merely the handing out of MSDSs (OSHA 2007b). While employees can be trained to read them, safety professionals cannot give them the chemical, medical, and technical background to understand what they read (Campbell 1992, Pullen 2003).

OSHA-sponsored research confirmed that workers understand only about 60 percent of the health and safety information presented (Fugoto and Fung 2002). This is not particularly disturbing, but what is scary is the results of a 1990 study by the Printing Industries of America, which found that workers with fifteen or more years of education (i.e., at least some college and more) were able to understand only two-thirds of the MSDS information (Fugoto and Fung 2002).

Under the HCS, all chemicals produced in or imported into the United States that could harm employees who are exposed to them under normal conditions of use or in a foreseeable emergency must have MSDSs that are readily available to employees. There should be no *barriers*, such as having to ask a supervisor for it, not having easy access to it, or not being trained to access electronic MSDSs (Ernst 2003). Backup systems and power must be available for electronic access.

Some confusion results from the fact that there is no single, approved, standard format for the MSDS, and there are a variety of other complaints (Minter 2003):

- "A specific improvement would be to actually write them to help the user in their use of the chemical rather than as lawsuit protection . . . " (safety consultant).
- "They should be written in 'plain, layman's English' because most employees do not

understand some of the technical language in MSDSs" (industrial hygienist in the petrochemical industry).
- "They are too general and include boilerplate phrases with little useful information, such as specifying the use of 'chemical-resistant gloves'" (industrial hygienist).
- "PPE requirements should be specific for large or small quantities of a substance. . . . A worker would need skin protection against phenol regardless of the quantity used because it can be absorbed through the skin, but PPE levels would vary for methyl alcohol, depending on the amount in use" (safety professional).
- " . . . they simply are not consistent. . . . When training employees, it is difficult for them to understand why they cannot just go to section 'X' in every MSDS to find PPE and section 'Y' to find physical properties" (safety professional).
- Errors in MSDSs were responsible for at least one explosion—at the Morton International plant in Patterson, New Jersey—that injured nine people. In that particular case, a chemical with a reactivity rating of "4" (most reactive) was described as a "0" on the MSDS, and the boiling point was off by 230°C. Doubtless other errors in MSDSs have caused many less spectacular mishaps.

OSHA and Industry Response to MSDS Problems

Some of these concerns are being addressed directly by OSHA, which is developing an enforcement initiative on the adequacy of MSDSs. OSHA will select certain chemicals, identify some critical phrases, words, and so on, that should be in accurate MSDSs; OSHA will also train compliance officers to inspect the MSDSs they find ("Hazard communication via material safety data sheets," 2004). If they find deficiencies, the employer will *not* be fined; OSHA will instead notify the manufacturer of the chemical and order a correction. If the manufacturer fails to correct the MSDS, it can be cited under the HCS, but the employer relying on the accuracy of the MSDSs is not culpable.

Of course, safety professionals who spot something wrong, or confusing, or who have other reason to question the MSDS should contact the source of the erroneous MSDS immediately and resolve any problem ("Questions and answers . . . " 2004). Certainly, if a compliance officer found out that a safety professional had misgivings about an MSDS and failed to attempt to resolve them, the safety professional could risk being cited.

Often the issue concerns a lack of clarity rather than outright error. Many safety professionals are tempted to rewrite or create a *summary sheet* for their employees. It is a risky thing to do. As Glenn Trout of MSDSonline pointed out in a series of questions and answers, " . . . if you edit, augment, or change an MSDS you may become liable for the content of the MSDS" ("Questions and answers . . . " 2004). Do it right and there is no problem. Do it wrong and bad things could happen. In addition to the risk of unexpected consequences, there is a risk of incurring an OSHA citation or fine, and the potential for civil and criminal liability for any errors introduced. Safety professionals who go beyond their personal level of expertise could even incur individual liability.

Creating Simplified MSDSs

As Judy Hoffman, manager of public affairs for a chemical manufacturer, pointed out, "In the case of the chemical industry, [effective communication with the press and public at large] will be required at the time of a chemical incident" (Hoffman 2003). She found a single-page Chemical Information Sheet, or Layman's Language MSDS on benzene very useful when addressing a local citizens' meeting on benzene's possible impact on groundwater. The company continued the practice for twelve other chemicals of public concern due to either toxicity or the quantity used.

Hoffman addressed the concern about the correctness of the information quite simply: three chemical experts took her, a chemical layperson, through each section and explained what they meant. She wrote down what they said and drafted her Layman's Language Chemical Information Sheet using a simplified format, which they used for all thirteen of the chemicals.

Just five categories were addressed:

1. *Product name.* This included the common name, phonetic pronunciation guide, and other names of the chemical, as well as physical properties, such as appearance and odor. Both company and everyday uses are described; and if the product was commonly used by the public, that information helped people see why the chemical was important.
2. *Storage.* Besides the quantity of chemical on site, the safety measures used to keep it safe are included. For instance, if the liquid is in double-lined vessels with dikes equipped with foam fire protection system and storage-tank vents connected to a vapor-collection system, people feel a lot better about having it relatively close to them.
3. *Exposure limits.* Besides the numbers, they have an explanation of what an exposure limit is and the typical worker exposure at the facility and the amount measured at their fence line.
4. *Health hazards.* No sugarcoating here! But adding safety precautions and reassurance that the public is very unlikely to be exposed to harmful levels helps soothe anxiety.
5. *Emergency response.* First-aid measures and when to seek medical attention are key points here. The option of giving firefighting techniques here is not always used, because the authors assume that fire fighters can read actual MSDSs and make the right decisions. It is not known how valid this assumption might be in areas with a small volunteer firefighting force; when deciding what to include, consider the sophistication of local fire companies likely to get involved in an incident.

At the bottom of each form is information on contact persons who can provide more details or explanations, preferably a direct-dial number rather than the general switchboard. This approach for educating employees requires contact information on people who can be reached at any time.

This concept has not caught on since it was first proposed. Clearly, it would be impossible to do this for everything. However, for special situations, such an approach can be quite valuable—for example, if the entire concept was developed to aid in communications during a crisis. Should an unwanted event occur involving just one or a few chemicals, this would be very useful in communicating with reporters and the general public.

It could also be useful for communicating effectively with cleaning crews, clerical staff, and others with extremely limited exposure to hazardous chemicals.

How to Evaluate MSDSs

Look at the company's MSDSs and see if they meet everyone's needs. As this venture can require expertise beyond that of the average safety professional, and could involve scrutinizing thousands of documents, many safety professionals choose to leave this chore to experts in chemical safety and hazardous materials information management ("Questions and answers [on MSDSs]" 2004). However, there are aspects that safety professionals can, and should, evaluate.

- Do they clearly communicate the hazard characteristics of the material?
- Do they address preventive measures?
- Do they address PPE, if pertinent? Do they address first aid in enough detail in the event of exposure?
- Are they available in the employees' languages? If not—and they probably are not, unless only English speakers are in the workforce—make sure that a truly bilingual employee is on site at all times, one who can translate *accurately and completely*. Alternately, arrange for an off-site professional translation provider to be readily available at all times, advises Michael Beckel, supervisor of training at the 3E Company (Burns and Beckel 2001).

Still using hardcopy MSDS? As long as they are readily and immediately available without barriers to all employees in event of an emergency, there is nothing wrong with that, especially if only a small number of people are involved. They do present problems, though ("Questions and answers . . . " 2004). David Lochridge, General Manager of Production of Dolphin Software, advises a regular audit for accuracy and completeness. Are all pages still readable? Photocopies and printouts deteriorate, get holes punched in them, have stuff spilled on them, and can become otherwise illegible or lose information. Are they complete, with all the pages there? Are they current? Have a system for regular updating and replacement of MSDSs. Consider requiring an annual updating from all manufacturers. Lochridge does suggest that electronic text is the best option for utilizing MSDSs, though. It is possible to do a quick electronic search of the document for pertinent information rather than having to read through the whole thing, to mention but one advantage.

Make sure that every other legal entity that needs the MSDSs has them. Local fire regulations may require that the fire department have access to them, and the EPA's SARA Title III requires that they have the company chemical inventory. It is not that much harder to give them the MSDSs (Ernst 2003). If there are plants in other countries, they may have requirements for providing chemical inventories and MSDSs to some of their agencies.

Look at the MSDS collection in light of the following suggestions for people who develop them, and contact the sources to improve their MSDSs in future drafts. Feel free to send them a copy of these pages to help them in the future.

Who Should Be Developing MSDSs?

Anyone asked or assigned to develop MSDSs should first consider carefully if he or she is qualified. If there is any question or doubt, do not do it (Grumbles 2004). Seek out a qualified consultant instead. There are too many poor-quality MSDSs out there. As John Henshaw, Assistant Secretary Of Labor for Occupational Safety and Health, testified before the Subcommittee On Employment, Safety and Training Committee on Health, Education, Labor and Pensions for the U.S.

Senate in 2004 (Henshaw 2004), "Disparity in the qualifications of those who prepare MSDSs is another significant reason for variability in quality. OSHA's HCS does not address the qualifications needed to prepare an MSDS. Those who write MSDSs come from a wide variety of educational backgrounds, and there is little training available that is specific to this task. Accurately depicting the health effects of chemicals requires a technical background to review relevant scientific literature. Large chemical manufacturers often have multidisciplinary staffs of experts devoted to this task, but smaller manufacturers may not have such resources. Thus, the disparity in qualifications can lead to differences in the quality of information included in an MSDS."

Generally expertise comes from backgrounds such as toxicology, chemistry, or industrial hygiene. The Society for Chemical Hazard Communication has a series of professional development courses on labels and MSDSs, and it would be reasonable to insist that whoever writes the MSDSs is qualified. For those who do have the technical qualifications, DeChristopher and this author have some suggestions for them ("Questions and answers . . ." 2004).

- Select and use one standard format. The American National Standards Institute (ANSI) developed a format in 1993, ANSI Z4001-1993, that has sixteen parts to it. There may be others that work better for a particular company's products, and the movement for a globally harmonized hazcom system needs to be considered in selecting a format.
- Do not leave out any information for a particular section; if it is not relevant to the chemical in question, leave it in the form but enter N/A (not applicable) since it is not. That way the user does not have to wonder if the writer was just spacing that section out or if it really is not applicable.
- Format the document so that the margins allow for fax lines and holes for binders.
- Use a sans-serif font large enough for folks with aging eyes to read. The document does not have to be kept to the fewest possible number of pages. Trees are a renewable resource, employees are not. Besides, most people are accessing the information electronically, so there are not many trees involved any more.
- Clearly mark the manufacturer name, the product name, and the revision date on the top of the MSDS. Consider adding the appropriate categories as well, as this is the future of making MSDSs readily usable.
- Be sure to include page number and the total number of pages on multipage MSDSs. A notation like "Page 1 of 3 pages" lets the reader know how many pages are involved and if any of them are missing. If there is only "Page 1" and "Page 2," the reader cannot know that page 3 is missing without that information.
- Did the product name change? Be sure to put the former name up there, too, for ease of updating. Also, the user may still have a stock of the older version in the storeroom.
- For all ingredients, make sure the chemical name(s) are listed under "CAS #" (which must be carefully verified at www.chembiofinder.com or some such Web site before listing); the annotation should include the percentage or range of percentages of chemicals in the product. Using the range allows the actual formula to be kept a trade secret if necessary. Some food manufacturers who vary the source of particular ingredients, such as sugars, list all the possible sugars that they might use on their labels to avoid having to produce new labels for each batch that varies. This tactic may work for MSDS for products that vary slightly from batch to batch.
- Include units of measure for physical data. If the MSDS says that the density = 4, that does not tell the user much. Four what? lb/gal? gm/l? If the melting point = 100 degrees, is that Celsius or Fahrenheit? It makes sense to list both temperatures since Americans have resolutely avoided going metric, unlike the rest of the world. Similarly, volumes and weights would be better understood by more

CASE STUDY

The BP Approach to MSDS Generation

BP, a chemical-manufacturing company, now sees the need for generating MSDSs as a company core competency and even a competitive advantage (Buxbaum 2001). The Swindon, a UK-based company, cuts costs, increases efficiency, and supports its marketing efforts by incorporating concepts of hazardous material regulations and handling in the product design process. The commitment of BP to be an environmentally sensitive oil company made hazardous material compliance so important that it acquired and implemented an e-business system that ensures compliance with

the assorted environmental regulations worldwide.

Burmah Castrol, before BP acquired it, had developed a single MSDS system to eliminate the need for seventeen different systems deployed around the world. BP has implemented this system, now known as the ClearCross Materials Compliance System, for all its global MSDS requirements.

The software lets the companies generate MSDSs in more than twenty languages and in compliance with the regulatory requirements of 30 countries. Instead of taking days to produce an MSDS, it takes minutes, and eliminates the previous $100 translation costs. By combining access to current regulatory

requirements with a database of product-formulation templates that are used to generate the forms, language translation, and document-management functions, ClearCross not only ensures regulatory compliance, but lets the company develop its products so that they are acceptable worldwide. They might formulate a product for, say, Germany, and find that it cannot be used in the United States. This situation led to additional costs to reformulate the product.

BP chemists now first use Clear Cross to cross-reference ingredients against the worldwide regulations and work problems out *before* developing the product, which provides even more of a competitive advantage.

users if they are given in both English and metric units.

- Tell the user if the product is a solid, liquid, or gas. That way, MSDS reviewers do not have to go hunt down the actual product if it is not in front of them or they do not know that information. It also helps emergency responders, medical providers, and LEPCs.
- Fagotto and Fung recommend watching the level of the language used as well (O'Brien 2001). Keep it simple for the reader. Slicing onions causes lacrimation, as do many chemicals. People without a medical background probably will not understand that it just means that they cause tears. Use standard and basic language, so that such words as "poison" mean the same thing for every MSDS regardless of source.
- New discoveries regarding hazards of various chemicals are made frequently. If new information comes out about something with an MSDS, it absolutely, positively must be updated to reflect that discovery within three months ("Hazard Communication via MSDSs" 2004). Distribute the update promptly to all customers; do not just wait until an annual updating comes around.

Due to the imminent implementation of the Globally Harmonized Standard (GHS), MSDSs will need to comply with those new regulations. While OSHA has not yet (as of the publication of this Handbook) adopted the GHS requirements for their HCS, it is this safety professional's opinion that they certainly will do so. (EHS World.net 2010). It is easier to implement them into an MSDS now then to have to go back and redo what has already been written.

Areas of Frequent Confusion about the HCS and MSDSs

Robert A. Ernst, associate editor at J. J. Keller and Associates, answered some common questions about MSDSs (Ernst 2002).

- Who else needs the MSDSs? Under EPA's SARA Title III, MSDSs must be available as part of compliance. Some states and municipalities have additional requirements.
- Is a specific format required? No, but ANSI Z400.1-1993 is recommended; with the global standardization movement, any such format would minimize work in future revisions.
- Which MSDSs must be kept? Under the HCS, an MSDS should be kept for chemicals defined

as hazardous, but before throwing away the MSDS for nonhazardous chemicals, keep in mind that medical records, air sampling, and other exposure data must be retained for 30 years. MSDSs are identified as exposure records. Considering that many chemicals not initially recognized as hazardous are eventually found to be so, it is not a bad idea to keep all the MSDSs. Also, sometimes certain populations are found to react badly to "nonhazardous" chemicals, or to hazardous chemicals at exposure levels far below those that harm most other people.

- MSDSs for consumer products are not required if used only for the intended purpose and for the expected duration. If bathroom cleaners are used to clean the bathrooms daily, no problem. If it turns out that one brand of bathroom cleaner solves some problem and an employer is buying it in 55-gallon drums for constant use, then MSDSs must be obtained and retained.

- Must MSDSs be produced when catastrophes happen? Not under HCS, as access is required only under "normal conditions" or in the event of foreseeable emergencies. OSHA does not expect people to foresee major fires, earthquakes, or other catastrophes, such as planes flying into the facility. However, EPA's SARA Title III does require that at least local emergency responders have a list of chemical stocks, and preferably the MSDSs themselves. With modern computers this need not be an onerous requirement.

- There are many ways to get MSDSs, including by fax, e-mail, database access, and hardcopy. However, manufacturers cannot require customers to, for instance, buy the latest computer and software, which is the only way they can access the manufacturer's shiny new database. If the MSDSs are needed in some other format, the manufacturer must supply it.

- If a company chooses to add or substitute its name and remove the manufacturer's name from the MSDS or product label, the company can do so. There may be copyright issues, though. Buying two chemicals from two different manufacturers and combining them along with some other stuff into a new product makes it mandatory to change the name to a new brand and write a new MSDS. But it better be right, because the manufacturer is now the responsible party if there are any deficiencies or errors on the MSDS or labels.

- What if the chemical in question is a drug? The manufacturer needs to evaluate the hazard level, and if the level is of concern, safety professionals need to maintain the MSDS, with one exception: if the drug is a solid and packaged for direct administration to the patient.

How Should Employee Access to the MSDS Collection Be Arranged?

In the good old days, the MSDSs were in a binder (or two, or three, or a dozen, or more), arranged in alphabetical order, and put in the safety office or some central location where they gathered dust. Some intrepid souls tried putting them on microfiche to save space, but if the power was out when someone needed to access them, the person was out of luck, unless he or she had very good eyesight. Every now and then, when someone thought of it, the MSDS would be updated, certainly every decade or so. The EHS professionals would try to remember to remind Purchasing to request the company in question for the MSDSs and get them to the safety professionals, but such intentions mostly got buried in the urgent business of the day. Then the safety office was locked as everyone went home for the day and nobody would be able to get to them or remember where they were kept, unless someone stuck around for some reason. If the dust did not get too thick because someone actually looked at the MSDSs occasionally, pages went missing, got ripped, and got coffee stains on them, rendering parts of them illegible. And, of course, the one that was urgently needed was either missing or completely out of date because there was no system in place to ensure the collection woud be complete and current.

This scenario might be why OSHA instituted the MSDS access requirements for the HCS. Such mismanagement was not acceptable then, and similar mismanagement of MSDSs today can lead to serious citations. The paper-binder method of access remains an option. If there are relatively few chemicals and the work site is small, with only one shift, that method is a very reasonable solution. Of course, that is not often the case!

Establish a system that provides

- access to all MSDSs by all employees at all times
- the ability to access and send information to places such as fire departments and emergency rooms in minutes
- a plan that keeps all MSDSs current
- a way to ensure that MSDSs are accurate and complete

Luckily, this burden is not one OSHA can issue citations for; nevertheless, everyone needs accurate information for obvious reasons.

If this sort of record keeping sounds complicated, it is, and a perfect job for a computer. Indeed, electronic access is the only reasonable solution for workplaces with large chemical inventories, multiple shifts and languages, and lots of square footage. There was some confusion as to whether some form of electronic access met OSHA requirements, but OSHA regulation 29 CFR 1910.1200(g) permits alternatives to paper copies as long as there are no barriers to immediate employee access (Galt 2003). Keep in mind that local jurisdictions, which may require access to a company's MSDSs, may still require paper copies on site (Hoffman 2003). Check with them to see what they require and whether a planned electronic-access system will be acceptable to them.

There are many ways to electronically access MSDSs:

- fax on demand
- Web sites
- CD-ROM
- e-mail

Each of these has its strengths and weaknesses. With the fax-on-demand service, which requires a subscription, the only equipment required are a telephone and a fax machine, or a computer equipped with fax capabilities. Making the system accessible for employees requires only that the service number be on each telephone and that there is a way to get the fax with reasonable ease. In a large facility, a single fax machine per building or department might be enough, or one in each room might be required. Telephones should be much closer to employees than the fax machine. The fax service is responsible for keeping the data sheets current and may have professionals who can answer questions medical personnel might have for treating exposed employees.

Web sites and CD-ROMs require computer access (and subscriptions), with all the potential issues involved. The right machines, printers, and software must be selected, and all employees must know how to use them. There are many vendors of MSDS electronic access to select from. Weadock points out, "the trick is finding one that does not create more work or require an extensive orientation to operate" (Weadock 2003).

Here are some factors to consider in selecting a vendor for electronic MSDSs:

- How easy is it for the average employee who may only have occasion to use this system once a year to learn and retain?
- How easy is it to actually find the information needed? What if only a trade name is available, or an internal number, or just the CAS number? What if the person looking cannot quite remember how to spell the darned thing?
- Can it be found by location on the site?
- Can the user know when the MSDS was last revised?
- How often is the subscription database updated? Monthly? Weekly? Daily?
- How can the MSDS be transmitted? Can it be e-mailed, printed, and saved to create an internal MSDS database?
- Does it provide a reasonably complete ingredient list of the product (within trade-secret limitations)?

- Is there a link to click on to get the same information in simplified form, or in another language?
- What is the procedure if the subscription database does not have an MSDS requirement? Can one be ordered, and if so, can the status of the request be determined?
- Is there a number to call to get questions answered? How about faxed information? How many calls are included in the subscription, and what happens if it is necessary to go over the allotted number of calls?
- Is there a way for disabled employees to access the information? Can a deaf employee use the TTY to call? Can a visually impaired employee get a large-type printout or magnify the image on screen?
- What happens if the computers crash, or the electricity goes out? Can the binders be dusted off, or is there some provision for other access to the MSDSs? One solution might be to ensure that someone off site can access the subscription service, so if the power is out in one location, the information can be transmitted by telephone, if nothing else.
- What happens if the electronic information supplier's computers go down? Do they have a viable back-up system?

When selecting an electronic MSDS vendor, be sure that the information can be readily accessed no matter what else is going on. Safety professionals need to be confident that their provider will be able to give the most up-to-date information when needed, in whatever language that may be required.

LABELING ISSUES

How hard can it be to make a label? Surprisingly, it can be quite a challenge according to Ernst (2003), who explained the general requirements. Labels cannot conflict with the requirements of the Hazardous Materials Transportation Act (49 U.S.C. 1801 et seq.) and with OSHA requirements in 29 CFR Subpart Z. There might also be potential DOT and EPA labeling requirements to be aware of.

In 1910.1200, OSHA requires that hazardous material containers be "labeled, tagged or marked" with the identity of the hazardous chemical, directions for recommended use, and information on handling and storage. The requirement also calls for appropriate hazard warnings or words, pictures, symbols, or a combination of these, to provide information regarding the hazards of the material in the container and the name and address of the manufacturer. There is a labeling exemption for when employees take some of the material in a portable container that will be used *immediately* without being passed on to another worker. While this may be legal, it is not necessarily very smart. Should an emergency occur during the shift, it may be necessary for someone else to know what the material is, and it is generally a bad idea to let someone change his or her safety behavior for specific occasions.

Employers cannot remove or deface labels on incoming containers unless they are immediately relabeled. Burns and Beckel suggest keeping a supply of duplicate labels near the containers so that employees who spot a problem can immediately apply a clean, legible label (Burns and Beckel 2001). A similar approach to applying labels to transfer containers would keep employees from developing two different labeling procedures and doing the wrong thing at the wrong time.

None of this happens without planning, though. James E. Roughton (2002), M.S., C.S.P., a safety professional for Safety Management Systems, recommends the following:

- designating specific individual(s) responsible
- describing the labeling system used
- describing written alternatives to labeling the containers
- creating procedures to review and update labeling information when necessary

Even though all this sounds straightforward, the nuts and bolts of exactly what needs to be on the label is not. The list of colors, symbols, and pictograms that are mandated vary according to country, and there is little information on how effective these colors and symbols are in conveying crucial information. Concerns about these and other issues were addressed in the Report of the Hazard Communication Workgroup to the National Advisory Committee on Occupational Safety and Health (NACOSH) from 1996 (NACOSH 1996). Two specific concerns with graphics and color coding could arise. Aside from the different standards for graphics and symbols in different countries, one symbol study by the National Bureau of Standards for the National Institute of Occupational Safety and Health (NIOSH) in 1982 (Publication Report No. NBSIR 82-4285) found that several widely used symbols, some mandated by DOT, had a relatively poor performance. A similar study in 1986 found that only four hazards were recognized by the symbols used, and not all symbols for the same hazard were understood. The hazards studied were toxicity, corrosivity, oxidation, flammability, sensitization, explosivity, reactivity, and irritation. The take-home message for safety professionals is that it is necessary to train people on the meaning of these symbols.

Fortunately, the GHS simplifies both training and actual label-making. Symbols, signal words, and hazard-statement words are all specified, so only one version needs to be trained for or used.

Color coding is a good idea and generally effective, but it only works if the individual can perceive the color. Color alone is not sufficient; a symbol must be included, or words, or both. When considering the additional complications of literacy and languages, labeling issues, and global-harmonizing issues, it is clear that those responsible need to stay on top of the new requirements being developed. There may well be future changes down the road, but with the dust settling on the GHS, things should be fairly calm in the next few years. After all, the GHS was first proposed in 1992 and even OSHA has not yet finished adopting it as of the publication of this Handbook.

In the meantime, the ANSI Z535, 2002 standard on effective warnings provides specific guidelines for setting up signs and labels (Cheatham, Shaver, and Woglater 2003). It suggests specific colors, backgrounds, and words as follows:

- *Format:* large enough to be seen; text left-justified; messages oriented to read left to right; and the most information put on top

- *Wording:* avoid unnecessary words; use short sentences; be explicit with instructions; use short, familiar words; avoid jargon and abbreviations unless users are trained to recognize them; use bulleted lists; use active voice rather than passive voice; use concrete words; and avoid ambiguity

- *Signal words:* danger = immediate hazard that will cause death or serious injuries; warning = potentially hazardous situation that may cause death or serious injuries; caution = potentially hazardous situation that may result in minor or moderate injury

- *Pictorials:* use only tested symbols

- *Color:* Red panel should be used with "Danger." Orange goes with "Warning," and yellow with "Caution." If human injury is a concern, use an alert or signal icon, which is a triangle surrounding an exclamation point in the panel. There is software that will let safety professionals print their own signs and labels quickly, economically, and in compliance with most regulations. Put safety instructions in green with white lettering (Wagshol 2003).

The ANSI Z535 series of standards have been updated, different sections in 2006, 2007, and 2008 (ANSI 2006–2008). It is reasonable to assume that the committee responsible for these standards will be revised to incorporate the GHS provisions in the future, so safety professionals need to make sure that they are meeting the future requirements.

Do not forget the National Fire Prevention Association signs (Wagshol 2004). The familiar blue/red/yellow/white signs with the numbers 0–4 in the first three, and assorted letters clarifying the exact hazard in the white are lifesavers for employees and fire fighters. Blue means health hazard, red represents fire hazard, yellow stands for reactivity or instability, and white reflects a specific hazard, such as an oxidizer. The higher the number, the more severe the hazard.

One can assume that the NFPA standards will be aligned with the GHS as well. Dr. David Michaels, the Assistant Secretary for OSHA, indicated that he and NFPA President Jim Shannon can collaborate on formal feedback on each other's standards development. ("We're in the business of protecting working people" 2010.) That suggests that safety professionals can look for a similar alignment of NFPA standards with the GHS where applicable.

Safety professionals in charge of developing pictorial symbols should check out the Wolf and Wolgarter paper from Human Factors (Wolff and Wolgarter 1998). Where the GHS do *not* apply, these considerations should be applied. They detail research-evaluating methods for testing comprehension of pictorial symbols, and look at context and test methods. In this case, *context* means the presence or absence of photographs depicting the probable environments where the symbol would be seen. This is not a task to be approached casually. ANSI's Z535.3 (1991) and the Organization for International Standardization's ISO 3864 (1984) advises that symbols must be, respectively, at least 85 percent or 67 percent correctly recognized by users ("reach a criterion of").

Warnings are important, but they often fail. Even with the best warnings, with symbols and pictorials understood by 100 percent of employees, people will not go against their innate predisposition to use the easy way of doing things just because a sign warns against something (Green 2004b). The workplace needs to be engineered for maximum safety.

It is also important that safety professionals be aware of some of the many reasons why warnings will fail. Some decisions that potential sign readers make are mentioned by Marc Green, a cognitive psychologist who consults on accidents and safety. People see a sign and ask themselves the following questions:

- Should I invest the effort to read the warning? Mental costs are calculated, and if the font is too small and difficult to read, or it has low contrast or too little white space, or if it is too long or in all capitals, then some will decide that the effort is not worth it and ignore the written warning.
- How risky do things actually appear? If direct observation reveals obvious hazards, such as open flames, sharp edges, moving mechanical parts, etc., then the observer is more likely to read the warning. But if the observer does not see anything obvious, then the person probably will not read the warning. This is counterproductive, as posted signs are more often about the hidden hazards than the obvious ones.
- Will compliance with the warning hinder the easy attainment of my goal? If so, is the gain in safety worth the hindrance? The user will consider if there is an alternative means for reaching the goal. The easier the alternative, the more likely the user is to use it. This is all a matter of perception, but it is also a valuable tool for increasing compliance. For instance, Green cites a library with "do not use cell phone" signs all over, but on each floor they have a small room into which a phone user can step. If the person had to leave the building to make a call, compliance would probably be much less likely. Make the safety connection. For instance, if people need to wear safety glasses before entering an area, put a box of them under the sign telling them to put the glasses on.
- Is there any risk? Many people simply fail to perceive the risk that is present, and if they have done something unsafely repeatedly and gotten away with it, they will disregard warnings.
- Is the risk immediate? If it is not, the likelihood of compliance with warnings plummets. Green cites the example of the warnings for health consequences of cigarette smoking. As syndicated humorist Dave Barry suggested, cigarette smoking would likely end overnight if the package warnings read "WARNING: cigarettes contain fat!" (Barry 2007).
- Are there too many warnings around here? The more warnings for low-probability events, the less likely people are to heed any of them.
- Some people may decide that they can "control" the risk. For instance, someone might dive in a no-diving area under the illusion that they can do a shallow dive and avoid the hazard.

- People use *cognitive shortcuts* that affect decision making and lead to erroneous decisions. People will seek out *confirmation bias* and look for information that confirms their preconceived belief and avoid contrary evidence. If the person decides there is little risk, the person will ignore warnings.
- Adaptation leads to the literal inability to perceive the signs. They can focus on the task and see nothing around them, actually look at a sign but fail to see it, and/or start reacting automatically to situations and quit seeing things around them to varying degrees.
- For a really effective sign program, and to maximize the impact of signs, working with the way people really are is the place to begin. Certainly, changing signs periodically is a good starting place, and consulting experts to help maximize the program could be a good investment.

International Issues

Global Harmonization System

Rare is the workplace whose chemicals come entirely from U.S. manufacturers who sell only to local markets. For everyone else, this can be a big headache. The United States is not the only country requiring MSDSs, and any manufacturer in any country with an international market has difficulties with the different requirements of different countries. The logical solution is for the stakeholders to come together and develop a single worldwide standard.

This logic was recognized long ago, and the United States and many other countries have endeavored to reach some consensus on a globally harmonized system for the classification and labeling of chemicals since 1992 (Markiewicz 2003c). In 2002, the United Nations adopted the GHS. Now available for worldwide implementation, the goal was for the system to be fully operational by 2008. ("MSDS Global Harmonization Legislation Planned" 2004). While that goal has not been met, imminent adoption of the GHS is coming, and SHE professionals need to plan on it becoming the worldwide standard.

The United States is not alone in adopting and adapting the GHS into their regulations. Canada and Mexico are working diligently to do so—and apparently so is the rest of the world. The North American Free Trade Act (NAFTA) is putting pressure on the United States, Canada, and Mexico to adopt the guidelines. Other countries are using the GHS because of international trade and the United Nations' adoption of it. This will affect every safety professional to some degree.

REACH

GHS is not the only international issue of concern for looking at best practices in hazard communications. The U.S. EPA and the European governments lack basic safety data on more than 85 percent of chemicals in commerce, which is a concern to both the United States and the European Union (Working Group on Community Right-to-Know 2007). The European Commission is taking a new approach called REACH (Registration, Evaluation, and Authorization of Chemicals), which will require the chemical industry to prove that chemicals are safe before they can be used or marketed, regardless of how long they have been in use.

- *Registration* will require manufacturers and importers to present basic data on the health and environmental hazards of the chemicals.
- *Evaluation* will require European Union member countries to assess the chemicals against basic safety standards.
- *Authorization* will require that chemicals failing to meet basic safety not be used unless specifically authorized.
- *Chemical safety* must be proven before a chemical or product can be marketed—no data, no marketing.

These data will be invaluable in selecting chemicals for continued use, and in refining further understanding of any necessary precautions once they are available.

Luckily, the standardized sixteen-section format for the GHS safety data sheets is very similar to the ANSI Z4001-2004 MSDS standard. Two headings are reversed as the sole change. As OSHA has not mandated the ANSI form, when the United States adopts the GHS, there should be little logistical difficulty (OSHA 2004b).

However, there will be some problems that the International Chemical Safety Card (ICSC), the equivalent of the MSDS, will pose because of reproductive hazard listings (Markiewicz 2003c). In the United States there are strict legal prohibitions against treating pregnant employees in a discriminatory fashion, but the ICSCs emphasize the reproductive hazards and use the words "unborn child" in the warnings. The final upshot was that the GHS kept this terminology, however unpopular it is in the United States (Markiewicz 2009).

The other problem is that the ICSCs use as exposure limits the MAK, which are used in Germany and several other countries (Markiewicz 2003c). This is on top of the other exposure standards.Threshold-limit data are used worldwide, from Great Britain (MEL), France (FR-VLE and FR-VME), Germany (MAK), Japan (JP-OEL), Sweden (SE-STEL), and the United States (TLVs) (Ovid.com 2010). It is possible that all exposure-limit systems may need to be used in MSDSs, or a reconciliation of all the systems can become another great global standardization task.

Another consideration is that, due to genetic differences, different populations may actually require different exposure levels. This is quite challenging, since people from different parts of the world do not stay home. Safety professionals, particularly toxicologists, need to team up with geneticists and learn to identify the genes associated with heightened susceptibility to specific chemicals. Once this is done, and people are properly tested, there can be much more confidence that the exposure limits are actually providing the safety employees need. There is much more work to be done with global understanding and standardization for all safety professionals.

The REACH legislation applies only to chemicals made in quantities greater than one ton per year, which have "proven or suspected hazardous properties" (Durodié 2003). Writers for the Society for Risk Analysis have raised some valid concerns.

• What logistical resources are needed to do this?

While the costs to industry were not addressed in this particular paper, British researchers commissioned by the UK government pointed out that some 30,000 substances are covered and required to be tested by 2012. If, as expected, the number of chemicals with "suspected hazardous properties" grows dramatically, the problem will be worse. This is not logistically feasible, as there are only sixteen contract research organizations within the EU able and willing to do the testing. Furthermore, the number of graduate chemists is falling. The report cited by Durodié suggests that if the legislation were narrowed to the 10,000 chemicals produced in quantities greater than 10 tons per year, testing could be completed by 2017. While the United States has more testing facilities and chemists, it will doubtless have proportionally more chemicals to be tested as well should this idea spread.

Then there is the matter of the sheer number of animals needed for the testing, which is estimated to be 45.8 million rodents and 4.4 million fish. Since 1981, testing for all new substances and those older ones on the priority list required only about 870,000 vertebrates. This report does not mention the need to deal with the animal rights organizations that would doubtless become very loudly involved.

Financially, the initial testing is estimated to be 8.7 billion Euro. This does not include verification and reporting. The real question here is whether this animal testing will reveal anything that is not already known. Consider that most of these chemicals have been in use for a quarter-century or more and have been consumed or used for billions of hours by humans. The science of epidemiology has become very sophisticated, and it stands to reason that if there was a large amount of damage to human health, it would have become very apparent by now. The bottom line is that our life expectancy has increased dramatically, which would not be the expected result if the entire population was showered with large amounts of toxins daily. One of the expressed concerns is toxicity due to endocrine disruption, which is not tested for in the proposed program. Data are showing increasing numbers of young people reaching puberty at younger and younger ages, but this development can easily be explained by the improvement in nutrition of the present generation over that of previous ones. It is possible that environmental chemicals that interfere with or enhance this process may even be beneficial. Clearly, this will neither be easy nor inexpensive to research, and the matter has not even been addressed by the current legislation (Durodié 2003):

- Is REACH going to benefit society?

What happens if people are given hazard information that ends up labeling contact-lens solution and toothpaste as *explosive* because the products include small concentrations of hydrogen peroxide? In this author's opinion, generally speaking, nothing good can come of it. As it is, people are sometimes literally "worried sick" about very tiny risks, and society has a poor grasp of the effects of the psychosocial environment on physical and mental health. This opinion is supported by a great deal of research on the effects of warnings. There is the problem of "crying wolf," which leads people to disregard warnings of such things as potential tsunamis. Thousands of Japanese ignored evacuation orders after a massive earthquake ("'Cry Wolf' effect" 2007). One town, Kushiro, had just 0.25 percent of its 13,400 coastal residents report to evacuation centers. Apparently, the rest stayed home and monitored the situation on TV, which is clearly a recipe for disaster, given the rapidity and catastrophic consequences of these giant waves.

Human-factors research also consistently finds that warnings are often ineffective in changing people's behavior. There are a variety of reasons for this, but it boils down to the fact that people are not rational, logical animals. As was pointed out earlier in this chapter, they figure out the cost of obeying versus the benefit of ignoring the warning, have a very poor grasp of statistics, think they have more control over a situation than they do, and quit seeing the warnings in short order (Green 2004a, b). The bottom line for the average person is that warnings are

common, while accidents are rare. Most people go through life bombarded by warnings but have few major accidents (Green 2004b).

Also, consider the level of education of the average person, which seems to be trending downward in the United States, particularly with respect to science education. Furthermore, most of those responsible for bringing the news to the general public have a poor understanding of science, leading to even more distortion of risk and hazard information. The difference between correlation and causation seems to be a particularly difficult concept for both the news media and the average person to grasp, a concept that is absolutely crucial for making educated decisions.

Finally, putting resources into tests of doubtful significance could mean they will not be available to tackle real and known risks and problems. This safety professional believes that it is inevitable that the REACH program will be proposed in some form for the United States, and all safety professionals should consider lending their considerable expertise to the debate to follow.

The manufacturers' costs of the REACH program are huge. In 2008, new fees were established for the registration process. "The basic registration fee will range from 1600 for substances produced in volumes below ten tonnes to 31000 for those above 1000 tonnes. Joint registration charges are somewhat less, from 1200 for substances produced in volumes below ten tonnes to 23250 for those above 1000 tonnes. SMEs' fees are further reduced, depending upon whether the company is 'small,' 'medium,' or 'micro-sized' and whether it notifies alone or jointly with other similarly-sized companies." (New REACH fees expensive, 2008). These fees are actually lower for non-EU companies, but the economic impact will be substantial.

It would be reasonable for safety professionals to anticipate disruption in supplies down the road, as some companies decide it is too expensive to sell to and through the EU. Other companies will make substitutions to reduce costs, which will be another concern for safety professionals.

Control Banding

Rather than controlling employee exposures chemical by chemical, control banding is designed so that people with less expertise in toxicology and industrial hygiene are able to make better decisions about how and how much to prevent employee exposure to chemicals (Jackson 2002). Developed in the United Kingdom and adopted by some European countries, the *R phrases* (risk phrases), which describe the most important hazards of a chemical that must be assigned to potentially harmful chemicals by the manufacturer of the chemical in Europe are used to determine control measures. The user finds the R phrases for the chemical using the label or MSDS supplied by the chemical supplier and looks for the R phrases in the list of hazard groups. Exposure potential is then assessed, taking into consideration the quantity and the dustiness/volatility. Considering both hazard level and exposure potential, a simple table suggests either control measures or that the users consult an expert. The controls are described in control guidance sheets, which comprise both general information and, for commonly performed tasks, more specific advice. The options, aside from consulting an expert, include "Employ good industrial hygiene practice," "Use local exhaust ventilation," and "Enclose the process."

One problem is that users may not always know when they need to consult an expert. The ASSE testimony in the Enzi hearing commented that "[s]ome chemicals, though included in certain bands, may cause reactions outside the norm of the band and require unique responses that banding simply will not address. Care must be taken to ensure that control banding is used with this kind of warning always in mind" (ASSE 2004). Another problem is that OSHA's permissible exposure limits (PELs) are not incorporated into the European scheme. Should this be incorporated into U.S. regulations, that would need to be remedied. It also appears that idiosyncratic reactions between chemicals are also not considered.

Control banding is one effective tool for those individuals with little education to understand the risks of the chemicals and processes they work with.

The ASSE Board of Directors, in a position statement adopted in 2005, stated (ASSE 2005):

> It is suggested that, as OSHA and MSHA proceed, work should be initiated to revise the HazCom Standard to incorporate the model of Control Banding. One key element currently excluded in the Control Banding models is the issue of physical hazards such as flammability. The agencies should investigate and propose a model to incorporate this information.

In January 2005, an article by Paul Oldershaw stated that control banding has an important place in this world (Oldershaw 2005).

According to Oldershaw, some experts do not like control banding because they see it as an attempt to carry out a risk analysis without the necessary expertise. This is incorrect, as the process defaults to directing the user to seek expert advice. Others see it as not how toxicology should be carried out. Control banding builds on much of the same information for limit-setting and chemical classification. And "[o]thers say it is an 'interesting idea, but couldn't work here,'" while still others see control banding as cutting across legal duties linked to compliance with exposure limits.

Yet, Oldershaw concludes, "If this position, frozen by tradition or law, prevails then we will never be effective in addressing the risks to many workers, in most of the world, who have no access to the skills and resources to turn exposure limits into effective control" (Oldershaw 2005).

There is little evidence that much progress has been made in implementing control banding since then, certainly not in the United States. Safety professionals may be under the impression that U.S. employers have the resources to educate/train employees and do not need control banding. This is a flawed assumption. Small businesses may have MSDSs available, but owners seldom understand them and certainly cannot train their employees. Nor do they generally hire safety professionals on a consulting basis to fill in their personal knowledge gaps. The United States is also full of employees for whom English is not a first language, or who have poor literacy skills, or who are simply too busy with other things in their lives to acquire the expertise they need.

Organizations Working to Unify and Simplify Regulation Compliance

Life for chemical companies became more difficult with increasing sales to international customers. The regulations for any one product depends on the point of sale rather than origination, and hazard communication information needs to be in more and more local languages. As the increasing complexity of the hazard communication challenges becomes apparent, at least one organization has been formed to deal with the confusion of differing regulations (Harries and Baker 2004). Worldwide Environmental Regulatory and Compliance Solutions (WERCS) came into being in 1984 with the aim of providing software tools and services to automate the authoring, distribution, and management of MSDS and other hazard communication documents. This is no small challenge, as it involves some 1500 sets of regulations worldwide and no fewer than 4500 information phrases in over 40 languages.

Currently based in New York City, WERCS now has an office in Belgium, and is partnering with a UK-based company, MAP80, which is a market-leading software developer. The new company is called Prisym Chemica.

Health Canada, OSHA, the American Society of Safety Engineers (ASSE), the National Safety Council (NSC), the Society for Chemical Hazard Communication (SCHC), and the American Chemical Society (ACS) are among the many organizations that are helping members to comply with the new international regulations. Safety professionals with questions do not have to look far to find them.

If any person or organization has a particular stake in the outcome of the reconciliation of the assorted regulations, they should definitely get involved with an organization working on the many issues.

MSDS Training Materials

A cursory search showed a dearth of books on the subject. However, there is a great deal of software and interactive Web-based training materials available, each with its own strengths and weaknesses. Safety professionals need to carefully evaluate their choice based on the information in the next section of this chapter on effective training as well as in other appropriate chapters of this Handbook.

TRAINING ISSUES AND TECHNIQUES
What Is Really Going On?

A lovely, refined, middle-aged woman, a native of the Philippines, learned English as her second language. One day at a party, she was struggling to use the line "Let me live in the house by the side of the road and be a friend to man" that comes from the Sam Walters Foss poem, "The House by the Side of the Road."

She mentally plugged in a literal translation of the words and said she would like to "live in the house by the side of the road and be friendly to men." It was an accurate translation by dictionary definition, but did not convey the meaning found in the poem. Similarly, because the thesaurus lists the words "training," "instruction," and "education" as being roughly equivalent, one could easily confuse the three and commit an equivalent faux pas in hazcom training programs.

Education is a long-term process, dependent on the life experiences of the trainee (Tapp 2004). Most people go through life doing unsafe things and having nothing untoward happen. Safety professionals need to continue training and try to overcome the difficult burden of good luck.

Instruction teaches the learner not just the "what" but the "why" and "how," points out that employees not only need to be taught how to lift safely, but how to apply that information to their actual job and in unusual situations (Tapp 2004).

Training is what is done when the goal is to get an employee to do something specific, such as drive or operate a machine. However, the ultimate goal is to create a change so that the learner continually does what the trainer wants him or her to do. Besides knowing how to read an MSDS, safety professionals also need trainees to read and heed them on a regular basis. People should practice as well as train successfully.

While OSHA only requires *training*, safety professionals need to remember to use instruction and education as well. This requires frequent reinforcement, successive training sessions, and overcoming good luck.

Markiewicz addressed the issue of whether training is actually the solution to the problem (Markiewicz 2003a). While in this case OSHA mandates training, it is important to look beyond the regulatory requirements and analyze whether the training will *fix* the safety hazards. Markiewicz uses the example of a request by a plant manager to *train* the employees to use the bonding strap when filling transfer containers with flammable fluids. The safety professional needs to look deeper and ask questions. Can the hazard be eliminated by substituting a nonflammable fluid? If bonding straps are required, who is responsible for maintaining them? Is anyone? Is there a procedure for this? Is there accountability for failure to do so? How does the entire system work? Are all the related issues covered?

With MSDS training, it is important to start at the top, questioning the need for the hazardous materials and identifying their handling and disposal processes as well as their use. When the entire system has been addressed, then it is time to work on the mandated training.

Planning the Training Content

While some specifics are mandated, dig deeper. The following are some questions to ask (Lewis 2003):

- What is needed? Who needs to be trained and what do they need to know? How will a "successful performance" be defined? Under what conditions will the trainees have to work? Are there different populations that will need different approaches and materials?
- What are the characteristics of the trainees? How much experience do they have? Are they literate? Is English their first language? Do they have disabilities?
- What constraints are there? What is the deadline? Must training be done in relays or can everyone go at once? Are there different loca-

tions? What training resources and equipment is available?

Define the Objectives

Anne Lewis, a developer of safety training materials, lists five to consider:

- *Terminal Objectives:* what the trainee needs to be able to demonstrate at the end
- *Critical Objectives:* things that the trainee absolutely, positively needs to master or risk causing injury to people or property
- *General Objectives:* things that the trainee needs to know to avoid causing operational interruptions
- *Minor Objectives:* things that are not critical to safety, property, or operations but are good to know
- *Enabling Objectives:* objectives within a set of objectives that support the attainment of the terminal goals. As everyone has time constraints, it is important to prioritize; hence, the minor objectives should be at the bottom of the pile.

How does all of this apply to hazcom training? Luckily, safety professionals do not have to reinvent the wheel because OSHA has published its "Draft Model Training Program for Hazard Communication" (OSHA 2004a). Most things need to be adapted for specific circumstances, but this is a good template to begin with.

Look beyond the training mandates for hazcom, others apply, and there may be some overlap in requirements (McKinnon 2003). McKinnon suggests that all the training needs be analyzed and combined into an integrated whole. If respirator training is on the list, perhaps it can be part of the hazcom training, for example. Or perhaps confined space training can be combined with the hazcom training for the chemicals in question.

McKinnon also says it is important to ensure that the trainers be competent and prepared for all segments of the training. It may require a team training approach.

As a final step in planning a training program, a decision should be made between teaching the hazards of each chemical, or hazard-category training (Sapper 2002). Sapper points out that it is not legally necessary to train employees on every single individual chemical. It is not practical to train employees in each of hundreds or thousands of different chemicals, if that many are present.

Despite this, some OSHA compliance officers have given citations based on the assumption that the requirement is for chemical-specific training. The source of the confusion lies in paragraph (h)(3) of the *Hazcom Standard*, which states that the training must include "[t]he physical and health hazards of the chemicals in the work area," the "measures employees can take to protect themselves from these hazards," and "the [m]ethods and observations that may be used to detect the presence or release of a hazardous chemical." What they miss is paragraph (h)(1), which states that "Information and training may be designed to cover categories of hazards (e.g., flammability, carcinogenicity) or specific chemicals. Chemical-specific information must always be available through labels and material safety data sheets." Even in 1983 the preamble to the original version of the training provision also stated that the option of training by categories of hazards was always available.

The 1994 amendment should keep OSHA compliance officers from issuing erroneous citations, but confusion remains as a result of some decisions made by the Occupational Safety and Health Review Commission on cases that occurred before 1994. In addition, OSHA compliance directives and training materials that are at odds with the plain language of the regulations have been issued, much to the consternation of employers. In a hotly disputed case, *Secretary of Labor v. Cagle's, Inc.*, OSHRC Docket No. 98-485, which attracted many *amici curiae* briefs supporting Cagle's, Inc., the seven-member OSHRC unanimously decided in 2006 that chemical-category training complies with the OSHA requirements (Sapper 2006).

Planning the Training Methods

There are a variety of options for training employees to read MSDSs. There is the old standby, classroom training, which is rapidly falling into disfavor as new technologies are developed. Videos are also popular, and there is the newer computer-based training using either CDs or the Web. Which is best? All of them! Just not necessarily for everyone. How to decide? Look at the trainees and their issues.

Trainee Characteristics to Consider

Language Issues

Perhaps the most important characteristic is the native language of the trainees. If it is not English, which is the language most MSDSs are in, there is a twofold problem. First, safety professionals in the United States still usually attempt to train in English, the language that such trainees will understand to varying degrees. Second, the content of the information is such that they literally may not be able to understand it even if it were presented in their native language. The obvious solution is to get the MSDSs in their native language, which is quite easy. A fast Internet search of "MSDS translation" turned up 94,500 hits, with at least two dozen companies that offer the service. Now comes the problem of selecting the vendor. It is best to hire a consultant fluent in both languages, and, ideally, also familiar with the technical terms used in MSDSs to evaluate the quality of the translation. It would also be a good idea to hire someone fluent in both languages to actually do the training.

One such service is LanguageLine Services, www.languageline.com (Schierhorn 2002). Using a speakerphone, the supervisor explains to the translator what she needs the employee to understand, and after that translation is complete, she has the translator ask the worker to repeat what was said. She stresses the importance of confirming employee understanding, whether the training is done in person or by telephone. Besides simply having the employee verbally repeat, she has the employee actually demonstrate his or her understanding of working with chemicals. Along with safety manuals, safety signage and labels need translation as well.

Luckily there are more and more paper and online bilingual resource materials, particularly in Spanish. OSHA has a Web page, www.osha.gov, and a toll-free number that links employees to Spanish-speaking

OSHA officials; the site also has a Spanish version of the OSHA 10-Hour Construction Outreach course, among others.

Of course, Spanish is not the only language found in the U.S. workplace. Here are the top ten foreign languages spoken by U.S. residents over five years old (Tompkins 1996):

- Spanish
- French
- German
- Italian
- Chinese (which has many dialects)
- Tagalog (Filipino)
- Polish
- Korean
- Vietnamese
- Portuguese

Although it is important to use bilingual training materials, keep in mind that translated materials are often scaled-down versions of the English materials. The New York State Health Department has reduced MSDS information to generic terms in the employee's native language, and it provides the sheets in both English and Spanish. Neville C. Tompkins (1996), safety and health consultant and trainer in Cedar Run, New Jersey, has some additional suggestions to maximize understanding:

- Use line drawings, sketches, and photos to emphasize key points.
- Use examples with videos or photos taken on the job.
- Use real-life examples or accidents at the trainees' workplace.
- Include safety signs and symbols with the training presentation.
- Use non-English teaching materials with minimal technical jargon and matching key English words side-by-side with the translated word.
- Put English words on the left-hand side of the page and the second language on the right, so workers can quickly spot the corresponding English word.
- Use native-speaking "buddies" to reinforce training.

- Use trainers who are fluent in the trainee's native language. A safety trainer with the Labor Occupational Health Program at the University of California, Berkeley, advises against using simultaneous translations, as it is slower and reduces interaction with trainees.

Weissman (2003) has some additional suggestions:

- Speak slowly, not loudly. Repeat important points using different words. Make sure the trainer can understand the questions from trainees with heavy accents before they answer them.
- Use simple language, avoiding acronyms, jargon, and slang.
- Demonstrate, do not just tell. Consider using one skilled employee to demonstrate during the explanation period.
- Use props. This livens up the presentation and makes difficult concepts clear. For example, Weissman uses balloons and cookies to illustrate the difference between inhaling and ingesting.
- Encourage class participation. Have class members pair up and practice what was taught, and ask leading questions of observing employees who might not want to speak up and comment on errors. For instance, if the exercise is putting on respirators and one of the pair does not put his straps on properly, ask the other "How should he have put that on?" This will show whether they have understood the exercise even if they do not speak up.
- Use pictures and diagrams.
- Give handouts.
- Make the information relevant to the trainee, both on and off the job. Tell them that hazard communication skills can help them keep their family safe at home, for example.
- Conduct follow-ups a day or two, a week, and a month later. Call, e-mail, or visit and ask them questions. This will not only show whether they have learned and retained the material, but it will also reinforce the idea that what they have learned is important.

Cultural Issues

Language can be the least of the problems (Kalaroa 2004). There can be cultural issues as well. For instance, in some cultures, asking questions in a training class can cause loss of face. Willingness to wear PPE can be derailed by cultural machismo. Asking questions, or, worse, a trainer correcting an error can be a formidable challenge in the Japanese culture. While the easy way out is to refuse to hire someone in the first place, on safety grounds, Nancy Kalaroa, loss-control coordinator for The Protector Group Insurance Agency, Inc. advises against it. Some courts have found language discrimination to be the same as discrimination based on race or national origin. She suggests working with the community in question in a holistic manner, including offering English as a second language (ESL) classes to the employees. Safety professionals need to recognize that language barriers will be a continuing problem as the pool of available English-speaking employees continues to shrink for many types of jobs and locations (Pierce 2003).

Pierce, a safety consultant with more than 30 years of experience, worked with a company that tried the above measures in vain. They found that their undesirable statistics, such as high injury rates—as high as five times the average injury rate for its SIC—failed to go down, and they had increasing quality issues and personnel-relations problems. Pierce decided to see if low English proficiency was really the source of the problem. He concluded that the "fixing the worker" approach of trying to more or less force workers to learn English was a failure. It was definitely time to try something new.

Looking at the entire work environment and the work itself proved to be the key. The workers continued with the ESL classes, but this time with concrete objectives tied to the specific language the employees needed to know for work. Other crucial system strategies designed to reduce the problems at the worker/work interface include the following:

- removing barriers to leadership and information that created confusion, ignorance, and lack of companywide focus
- removing environmental and cultural barriers to good team dynamics
- removing work barriers that make workers unable to be successful in doing the work
- removing individual barriers to worker progress and success

Notice that the last item on the list focuses on the individual. The specifics of implementing these strategies were complicated and are detailed in Pierce's paper. The results: English proficiency went up eight percent, monthly injuries were cut in half, error rates decreased by 15 percent, turnover leveled off, productivity rose 7 percent, and employee-relations issues decreased by half.

While getting employees to look at problem solving from a systems viewpoint was expected to be difficult, that factor proved to be minimal as employees became excited and energized by the process. However, management proved to be the big barrier, as it was difficult to get some of the middle managers to let go of traditional problem-solving techniques, but upper management was committed to the new systems approach and prevailed (Pierce 2003).

Clearly, simply assuming that the problem is language barriers is not the route to safety or business success. Language barriers do need to be addressed, but within a more comprehensive framework.

Literacy Issues

Just because trainees speak English, even fluently, it does not necessarily follow that they read well. Trainees may have issues such as dyslexia or some other learning disability, poor vocabulary, or just poor reading skills. They may also be learners who absorb information best if they hear it as opposed to see it. Some people not only need to see or hear, or both, but they also need to actually handle things to learn. They need to see, hear about, and feel the PPE needed. Actual practice donning the PPE is essential for them. The simple solution here is to offer the information in all the ways that people learn. Using standard techniques for people who do not speak English as their native language will address these issues easily.

True Comprehension of Terms

Unfortunately, hazard communications contain adverbs and adjectives that are *fuzzy* in meaning. In a complicated

CASE STUDY

A Successful Construction Safety Program for Hispanic Workers

The safety training program instituted in 2002 at the Dallas-Fort Worth Airport (DFWA) has proven to be successful in reversing the trend of Hispanic workers' increasing on-the-job death rate (Nash 2004). The urgency of the situation was undeniable; of the 277 Hispanic construction workers killed in 2002, 81 died in Texas, 36 in California, and another 20 in Florida. While the construction fatality rate for all workers has increased by only 1.2 percent since 1997, the increase for Hispanic workers was a frightening 46.9 percent, prompting the Hispanic Contractors Association de Tejas (HCAT) to declare a "state of emergency." Javier Arias, chair of HCAT, declared a special state of emergency for the Dallas-Fort Worth area because more construction fatalities had occurred there since 2000 than in any other metropolitan area.

The DFWA Capital Development Program implemented a special training program for all its employees, but the emphasis was on making sure that each person understood the training so they could apply it on the job. While the safety training program was not the only reason for the success, the program has been very successful. Where the incident rate of total OSHA recordables nationally has been 6.9, at DFW it was 4.2 per 100 full-time workers. The lost-workday case rate at DFW is a mere 0.4, compared with 3.4 nationally. The average cost of a Workers' Compensation claim is more than 15 percent lower than the Texas average.

Perhaps the most important step, said Keith Smith, EHS manager for Dallas-based Austin Commercial, one of the two general contractors for the project, was that they enforce a single, universal safety program for all subcontractors on the site, as Pierce had advised in his first system strategy. This eliminated the problems of confusion, ignorance, and a lack of projectwide focus. This they accomplished via a "wrap-up" insurance program, and they enforced a mandatory 40-hour bilingual safety training program for each and every employee regardless of which contractor they worked for.

Training is conducted in both Spanish and English, using both instructors and curriculum developers who are not only bilingual but also from the culture of the workers, and, preferably, who have also worked in construction. English speakers are taught some crucial, life-saving Spanish terms, such as "peligro" (danger) and "cuidado" (be careful). Training materials include printed material workers can take on the job, too. Workers get cards with Spanish-to-English on one side and English-to-Spanish on the other.

Due to language issues, written tests for comprehension were not an option, so each student was made to demonstrate his or her understanding. For instance, the instructor might demonstrate the proper use of fall-protection equipment, and students must then demonstrate that they can also use it properly in a special classroom "laboratory." A similar approach can be used with hazcom and MSDS training.

The cultural issues are equally important in the outstanding safety record of this project. Arias explained one particular cultural issue that has huge safety implications. "Maybe it's machismo, maybe it's because our fathers told us if you want to help someone you do not say no, or maybe its fear we'll lose our job, but often we do not want to say, 'No.'" More practically, Dean Wingo, OSHA's area director for the Fort Worth office, explained, "If a hammer falls apart, you'll find the Latino has found a way to tape it back together, whereas an American worker will come up to you and say, 'You give me this piece of crap and I can't do my job!'" An important part of the training program is to overcome the cultural aversion to saying "no" and make it clear that they will not get fired for reporting unsafe acts or conditions. To further clarify that it is safe, the airport set up a confidential hotline so workers could report problems safely.

These people do not make the mistake of thinking that all Latino or Hispanic workers share the same cultural customs, either. Javier Maldonado, a manager of field engineers who also took the 40-hour course, pointed out that "Some workers, such as those from Panama, may want to be greeted first instead of just told, 'You are doing something wrong.'" Come to think of it, this is not a bad approach for every employee! A little courtesy goes a long way in any culture.

Similarly, all Oriental workers do not share the same culture. Take the time to learn about the cultures that the employees come from to maximize safety for all of them.

All this training does not come cheaply. They spend about $500 per employee on tuition for the 40-hour OSHA course, plus the wages earned. Nor is it a one-time thing. Using a continuous quality-improvement process, they determine how the training is affecting the workers' safety behavior on the job, and when they identify a weakness, they provide additional training. They also have weekly safety meetings to reinforce the lessons and address emerging job hazards. Pre-task, they communicate in English and Spanish, sometimes in writing.

If safety professionals analyze this program, they will see that it follows Pierce's four systems steps. Since this company went far beyond simply addressing language barriers, that accounts for some of their success.

and lengthy paper, Lehto, House, and Papastavrou (2000) discuss the degree to which people understand the meaning of such phrases as "prolonged exposure, safe, weak, strong, extremely, lightly, poorly or adequate." The purpose of using such fuzzy qualifiers is to convey more information with fewer words, but how much information they actually convey to the readers of MSDSs or other safety information is virtually unknown. One very important issue that needs to be considered is context. "Small shrimp" and "small whale" convey very different visual images, for example.

If providing extensive contextual information on MSDSs were required, it would make content that is already long, even longer, if not far too long for most readers. One question addressed in this paper is whether it is necessary to provide this very bulky contextual information to clarify the meaning of these and similar terms. Luckily, these authors conclude that training and worker knowledge can eliminate the need to provide contextual information. People designing hazcom training programs might find it worthwhile to use this paper to help them clarify the fuzzy terms in their programs.

Disabled Trainees

Another concern is disability among the trainees. This author has spent fifteen years studying disabilities and their impact on safety. She also has personal expertise in several disabilities, including hearing loss. Generally speaking, the older the workers, the more likely it is that they have some disabilities. Successful training will be most impacted by hearing loss. People with serious hearing loss, particularly deaf people, are not the biggest problem, as they know they have a problem and take steps to deal with it. They may not know the best ways to address their hearing loss and maximize understanding in a variety of situations, though. They may still be bluffing and pretending to understand. Post-training testing will assist safety professionals in detecting these problems.

One problem that presents a real challenge is training those people with moderate or mild hearing loss, people who are still in denial about the fact. Since the average person spends seven years that way, this is a significant problem. They pretend to understand when spoken to, and when they finally get hearing aids they often continue to pretend. They seldom know about the strategies and equipment available for maximizing understanding and remain at a serious disadvantage, especially in noisy situations. Providing them with equipment and communication strategies will greatly help increase their comprehension. Clearly, the level of denial of hearing loss shows that the use of *captioned* training materials only should be a minimum requirement when evaluating possibilities. Again, testing is essential to verify that they have heard and understood what was actually said.

There are many other disabilities that can impact the ability of a trainee to learn. Vision impairment, diabetes, heart disease, multiple sclerosis, and other serious illnesses and conditions can all affect the ability to learn and may necessitate accommodations, such as needing shorter training sessions, large-print materials or recorded training materials, and additional memory aids. Safety professionals need to identify individual concerns that can affect training and work around them. Work with disability experts to determine accommodations both for training and for doing the job.

If there is an employee who needs to use a wheelchair or other mobility device, such as a scooter, do not assume that the training setup is accessible. What is accessible for one person using a wheelchair may not be for another. Often, people can get into the training room but not the bathroom, or they may not be able to reach or use the computer keyboard, if some training is done that way. Have each individual do a roll-through of all the training facilities before the training session and test them to make sure they can do everything they need to do and get everywhere they need to. *Hint:* if some part of the training facility is inaccessible, get it fixed or move the training session!

Do not assume that the company does *not* have employees with disabilities in the workforce. Most disabilities are invisible, so the trick is to identify them. In many cases, the employee will have to let safety professionals know they have special needs. This, in turn, requires an employer who will not proceed to find excuses to fire them after they identify themselves. Even though this is highly illegal, it does happen, and disabled people are very aware of such situations even if others do not recognize them. If this is the situation, there will be people who do not understand all the training because their needs are not accommodated.

Other Training Issues to Consider

Communicating Risk and Hazard Information to First Responders and Clinicians

If there are some extraordinarily hazardous materials that could end up affecting employees, first responders, and/or members of the public, consider training at least the first two groups in the hazards, how to protect themselves in event of a problem, first aid, and treatment for exposures. This population should be relatively easy to train as they have professional expertise. Under the Emergency Planning and Community Right to Know Act of 1986, safety professionals must establish an emergency planning program where the total amount of any extremely hazardous substance is equal to or exceeds the threshold planning quantity, which is specified in the Act (House 2002). Including formal training would be a worthwhile exercise so that bad situations are not made worse.

One should think long and hard about the training of the public, as most have a great deal of difficulty understanding the difference between hazard communication and risk. If there is an unusual situation, such as that of the Chemical Depot in Pueblo, Colorado, which houses very large quantities of mustard gas, there is no choice. However, this is not a job for amateurs; get a consultant who has expertise in educating without unduly alarming the public. To evaluate the consultant, or if someone without the necessary expertise must do the job, Petroff (2004) has written an outstanding paper on making risk communication effective without scaring people unnecessarily. This is strongly recommended reading.

Petroff advises accepting and involving the public as a partner, planning carefully and evaluating those efforts, listening to their specific concerns, being honest, frank, and open, working with other credible sources, meeting the needs of the media, and speaking clearly and with compassion. This author recommends addressing the misinformation put out by the ignorant and those with other agendas. They will likely surface and must be neutralized to prevent panic.

In this post-9/11 world, security considerations may also influence what and how much to say to whom.

STORAGE ISSUES

One weakness in most labeling and MSDS information is a failure to make clear what should not be stored near what. How near is "near"? What should be in ventilated hazardous material storage cabinets? According to Brown, most of the information needed is in state, city, or even county fire codes. Safety professionals do need to be in contact with local officials, but Brown provides some guidelines (Brown 2005).

One commonly overlooked requirement of fire codes is keeping "incompatible materials" separate. Incompatible materials are defined as "materials which, when in contact with each other, have the potential to react in a manner that generates heat, fumes, gases or by-products which are hazardous to life or property" (Brown 2005). Separation options include the following:

- segregation by a distance of not less than 20 feet
- isolation by a noncombustible partition, extending not less than 18 inches above and to the sides of the stored materials
- storage in hazardous materials storage cabinets
- storage of compressed gases in gas cabinets or enclosures with exhausts

However, incompatible materials cannot be stored within the same cabinet or enclosure with exhaust.

Hazardous material storage and areas where they are used and dispensed have other requirements as well, including:

- the use of noncombustible, liquid-tight doors

- appropriate spill control and secondary containment
- high-level, low-level temperature and pressure-limit controls
- standby and emergency power
- other requirements, such as signage and lighting

Larry Garcia, hazmat instructor at the OSHA Region 10 Education Center in Seattle, advocates making this part of the training very memorable (Nightswonger 2000). To that end, he demonstrates what can happen when storing an oxidizer with a reactive material. He mixes incompatible materials, fire breaks out, and, as he says, "It's a pretty visual recollection for the students."

CONDUCTING TRAINING

Knowing what information the training needs to cover, pertinent characteristics about the trainees, and just who needs training means it is time to tackle this project. There are many techniques:

- face-to-face classroom training
- videotapes
- computer-based training
- hands-on training
- Web-based training
- video- or audio-conferencing

As most readers work with adults, it is important to understand a bit about how people learn. Generally, people remember

- 10 percent of what they read
- 20 percent of what they hear
- 30 percent of what they see
- 50 percent of what they both see and hear
- 70 percent of what they say when they speak
- 80 percent of what they actually do
- 90 percent of what they say as they actually do it (Grieff 2003)

This is the reason why the advice was always "to learn something, teach it!" And do not overlook the "forgettery" factor, either. Many students have had the experience of taking an exam and realizing directly afterward that they would fail it if they had to take it again; the details had disappeared from memory the moment the exam was over. They may have retained a portion of the information, but they would have to relearn much of it. The average student forgets as much as 47 percent of what he or she just learned in the classroom in as few as twenty minutes, and 80 percent just 31 days later. Classroom training alone hardly seems worthwhile, does it?

Also, consider these four key principles from Malcolm Knowles, a leader in the field of adult education (Tapp 2004):

- *Readiness:* The students need to open their minds to what they have to learn. In essence, Knowles suggests "selling" them on the importance of the information.
- *Experience:* What do they already know? Present the training so it is neither over their heads nor insultingly simple.
- *Autonomy:* While the training may be mandatory, increase their freedom of choice by making the training interactive and providing opportunities for them to make their own decisions.
- *Action:* Successful on-the-job applications.

In-Person, Classroom Training

If the option to do classroom-type, in-person training is selected, numerous experts have all kinds of suggestions. This topic is discussed extensively in the chapter on conducting and documenting training. Trainers who are not comfortable presenting in front of groups must do something about it. Join Toastmasters. Take a course. Get a coach. In the meantime, get someone with appropriate expertise and presentation skills to do the classroom training until presentation skills are acquired. Safety and hazcom training is too important to let it be diluted by a poor instructor.

One good source of off-the-shelf training materials is the Texas-based Association of Reciprocal Safety Councils, which has developed a 4.5-hour course to meet the classroom training requirements of OSHA standards (OSHA 2007a). One senior OSHA compliance officer who was invited to see the training saw only one very minor error, and very highly recommended this course. Local safety councils will offer this training, or know how to contact someone who does this type of training.

One innovative approach to training is to transform a hot-work-permit training program to make it specific to the unique needs of the workplace (Donnelly 2003). Instead of routinely discussing the permit process and answering a few questions, Donnelly found a doll-house designer who helped him make an accurate scale model of the workplace from a mid-range-cost doll house. The artist included miniature items such as employees, welding equipment, 55-gallon drums, welding blankets, and fire extinguishers. The designer even came to the work site to make the model more accurate. They put in safety signs and posters, labels, and so on, even overhead wiring! This could be applied to the hazcom training. Instead of standing in front of the class and talking, Donnelly arranged the model to reflect problems for the students to identify.

Interestingly, the students in the exercise even spotted safety problems that the instructor had not included in the exercise! Training in groups of two or three, intensive discussions on different ways to address the safety problems while filling out the company hot-work permit were very educational. Best of all, the students described the experience as "cool," "fun," and a "great idea."

Web-Conferencing

Web-conferencing has some complicated technological requirements, but it can save considerable travel time. The interactive component is maintained. However, keep in mind that many people need to see the speakers' faces, as the audience is relying on speech-reading. When considering audio-conferencing, remember that this shuts out everyone with even a small hearing loss. Generally, this author strongly advises against considering this technology for hazcom training.

If the infamous PowerPoint training is selected, here are some important tips from Tapp (2003b):

- Use both PowerPoint and interactive training. Use the slide to illustrate, then have the trainees "do."
- Do not overuse it! Instead of putting all the information on the slides, use the slides as reminders of what needs to be covered.

- Print out the slides and use them as handouts. This lets the trainee make notes as they go.
- Use interesting templates and backgrounds. However, be sure that the printed handouts are still legible. It may be necessary to use both an interesting template for the presentation and a simple one for the handouts.
- Make the reading easy. Use a few words in large print. This is where the handouts let the trainee make notes as the trainer comments on the few words on the screen.
- Use contrasting colors. Do not get too fancy or make the presentation difficult to read. Get some feedback on legibility *before* the presentation.
- Use pictures! Use, for instance, clip art, plant-site photos, or cartoons. These can be animated, too. But do not get carried away. If it does not add to the message, pass it up.
- Use the slides as the outline, rather than the entire content. Although this was recommended earlier, it is important.
- Add movies and animation to increase interest.
- One nice thing about PowerPoint is that it can be e-mailed to let people go through the training on their own time. Obviously, if this option is selected, there must be much more information on the slides than if the slides were just notes to remind the presenter what to say. Alternately, talking characters that can lead others through the training can be added in the absence of a trainer.

PowerPoint can also be put on a laptop for road trips, or burned onto a CD for distribution. This lets trainees work through it on their own time. However, they miss out on the opportunity for interactive training.

Videos are very important training tools, but it is not reasonable to expect that safety trainers can just sit people down in front of the monitor and leave. As a part of a well-planned hazcom training program, videos can provide variety to the training sessions. Be very sure that *all* of the videos are open-captioned, and in Spanish if needed. The majority of videos this author has seen have extensive portions that show everything but the face of the speaker, and this situation makes it highly unlikely that anyone with even a slight hearing loss will understand everything. Even if the face is shown all the time, the ability to speech-read varies greatly. Do not rely on closed-captioning, either. Not every trainer knows to turn it on, so just having every video open-captioned takes the whole issue off the table. At the very least, insist on closed-captioning, and that all trainers turn the captioning on every time, whether someone requests it or not.

An experienced and knowledgable person should screen the video for accuracy and relevance before use as well. Look for parallels in the video with this particular workplace, and do not hesitate to stop the video to point those out.

If there is a video with errors in it, what should safety professionals do? It could serve as a bad example, so be sure to notify the producer. Once training is done using other materials, showing the trainees the video with the error on it should demonstrate if they learned what they should have. Just in case they did not, of course, be sure to point out the error if nobody else does.

Computer-Based (CBT) and Web-Based Training (WBT)

Online training is an increasingly popular option, and the quality of some of these training programs is outstanding. There are some advantages to these, not the least of which can be cost. Perry compares multimedia and classroom instruction in three areas: cost, instruction, and administration (Perry 2003).

Instruction refers to how the instruction is accomplished. *Cost* refers to the impact of training on the bottom line, or the cost of training. *Administration* refers to tasks related to managing the logistics of training, such as scheduling, making training accessible, tracking student progress, and posting results.

Multimedia appears to be the big winner in terms of apparent cost. Savings result from less money spent on instructors, renting facilities, and travel and lodging for students. Training takes less time, productivity is not lost due to travel, and many administrative costs, such as grading tests by hand, are bypassed. Using computer-based training simulations avoids taking expensive or scarce equipment out of service,

or risking damage, and also reduces student exposure to hazardous training environments.

The bottom line is that the U.S. Coast Guard found the HH60J helicopter CBT flight-simulator training program saved more than $11 million in a three-year period (reported in 1992). Federal Express estimated savings of over $100 million in a 1990 publication. However, it is interesting that these examples are over ten years old, and few companies have to train their employees to fly choppers. This raises questions as to the cost-effectiveness of simulation training for situations where failure is far less catastrophic and/or expensive. It is possible that the improvements in computers, software, video games, and related expertise could make simulators less expensive to develop and use in the future.

Perry explains that custom multimedia courses developed for a specific company are cost-effective after about 1000 students. Off-the-shelf courseware can have a much lower break-even point, depending on the cost of the software and the computer systems required (Perry 2003).

What about instructional quality? Obviously, pre-programmed courseware is consistent, so there is no worry about the quality of the trainers or the completeness of the content. Employees can go through it at their own pace, reviewing as needed when they might not be willing to ask questions of an on-site trainer. Attendance is documented by the employees' log-on information, and in both cases the students need to take and pass tests to verify understanding. Perry also reports that students who used multimedia retain 25–50 percent more content than those who had classroom learning.

Provided that the material is completely accessible to every trainee, even those with hearing and/or vision loss, multimedia instruction can be superior in imparting information. It keeps people interested as the media changes, it provides immediate feedback for effective reinforcement, and student-progress monitoring not only documents the ability of the student to understand but also the effectiveness of all the components of the training. If something is not working, it is quickly apparent, which is not always the case with in-person trainers.

In terms of administration, life is simpler as long as the training technology does not require massive investment in new computer hardware and software. It is not necessary to get enough people together to form a cost-effective class, rent space, and set up schedules around production needs. And tracking and reporting features are built into the multimedia software. Training can be done anywhere the student and a computer can connect. Students are also reported to be more satisfied and motivated to use the multimedia learning tools.

Whether or not multimedia is superior for the average student, this author is not aware of any studies involving people training multilingual and multicultural employees, particularly those who are not already pretty comfortable with computers and generally literate. When comparing CD-ROM training versus Web-based training, Perry (2003) points out the strengths and weaknesses of each:

- CD-ROM training allows for a wider range of sophisticated teaching designs; it has fewer restrictions on media such as video and audio due to lack of bandwidth (not every location has high-speed Web access!); and it allows for more types of interactivity in test questions and exercise types

Web-based training, on the other hand:

- costs less to develop and distribute
- allows immediate updates and revisions to courseware
- makes the content available on a wider range of computer platforms, such as Windows, Mac, O/S 2, and Unix
- makes assessment and certification easier, and harnesses the use of electronic conversations to increase interactivity
- improves access to useful Web sites that could not be accessed via CD-ROM
- makes courseware more accessible as a resource and reference

Switching from Classroom to Computer

Anyone considering making the move from classroom-based to computer-based training needs to think care-

fully. Tapp (2003a), CSP, suggests starting with ten questions:

1. Does the content require interaction? If so, Tapp recommends using CBT, provided a method of interaction with a qualified trainer is provided. OSHA approves of access via a telephone hotline. If students must demonstrate their ability to put on and remove PPE, it will not do the job alone.

2. Would employee understanding of training materials be improved if they learned in a group? For instance, if the training group is a mix of experienced and new employees, the new employees can learn a lot from the experienced employees, and hence CBT is not a good solution.

3. How motivated are the trainees? They need to *want* to learn to make the effort. At least an in-person instructor can serve as a motivator, and a good one will ensure that the least motivated still learn.

4. Does the training need to be given in a convenient location? If there are different workplaces and shifts to consider, CBT solves a lot of logistical issues.

5. Will there be resistance to CBT? Some people do not know how to use a computer, and are afraid of embarrassment. Others like the social aspects of classroom training, and do not want to feel isolated at a computer. Consider incorporating some CBT with the classroom training to decrease resistance for future training.

6. Will the managers be resistant? They may not feel confident that their employees will be adequately supervised or trained, so they may need to be educated about process and effectiveness.

7. How disparate is the safety education level between trainees? If there is a great gap, CBT can let the more advanced students skip to their level of knowledge and the beginners slog through the rest of it without boring the advanced students to tears.

8. How permanent is the information of the course? If it changes fast, it can be expensive to make changes to some CBT technologies,

but not Web-based. The logistics of tracking whether the trainees are updated appropriately do become an issue, however.

9. Is the workforce multilingual? Tapp recommends CBT in their native language. However, make sure the translations are accurate, and if some of the less-often required languages are involved, it may be difficult to find appropriate CBT. Another concern is if the student truly understands the content.

10. How many people need to be trained? The larger the class, the more cost-effective CBT can be.

Whatever the decision, Tapp emphasizes that it is important to evaluate the training and the methods and document how it is all working. If the decision to transition to CBT is made, Perry concurs with Tapp, who recommends taking it slowly (Perry 2003). Perry suggests conducting pilot projects, which will build momentum and support in the organization by proving the technology. His paper includes a chart for deciding if and when to move to multimedia training.

As with any other change, there can be some organizational challenges, most of which have already been discussed. One additional, very important piece of advice for getting through the transition is to provide troubleshooting guides (Hall 2003). There will be questions, glitches, and other problems. Have both paper/computer information and a phone number or e-mail address of someone who can get back to users. However, this author strongly recommends providing phone contact *at all times* if that is when the training is happening. Waiting for an e-mail response when students are angry and frustrated is not the way to make friends and influence trainees, or trainers, for that matter.

Situated Learning

Before leaving the issue of hazcom training, readers should be made aware of a very interesting paper in *Professional Safety* (Machles 2003). In this thought-provoking paper, Machles suggests approaching safety training from the standpoint of the learner rather than the teacher, using the apprentice model instead of the training model. Rather than training with learning principles added, focus on learning with teaching principles added. Clearly, Machles points out, only 10 to 15 percent of the content from training conducted in the workplace is retained after one year, yet most workers are safe. Where are they getting the other 90 percent of the information? Not from the classroom. Rather, they learn through *situated learning*, the term Machles uses to describe the learning that occurs while interacting with other, more seasoned members in the situation.

OSHA requires classroom and/or e-learning, but the degree of situated learning that occurs in the rest of the trainees' world would be worth considering. This paper discusses a pilot biotech respirator-use situational training program that may or may not have applications to other hazcom training programs. Interestingly, the approach taken by John Donnelley in the hot-work-permit training discussed above is situated learning.

Evaluating the Training

With the hazcom training program set up and running smoothly, it is time to move on to the next item on the company's "to-do" list.

Not quite. As Roger D. Evans asks, "Employee training absorbed? Or water off a duck's back?" (Evans 2003). As a safety consultant, he has interviewed many employees and found that trainees were too often made to sit down in front of videos and left alone, after being given a ten-question multiple-guess test that he describes as "so ridiculously easy that, even without seeing the video, a person of average intelligence could pass with a seven out of ten score." Worse, too, many employers have no system to retest those who fail or to provide—never mind require—additional training. In some cases, the company does not even have a pass-or-fail policy.

The solution? Evans recommends that management representatives take the training, preferably unannounced, with the new employees, and grade the content and the trainer. Regularly review the materials and upgrade them if needed. Evans emphasizes that employers need to set training requirements based on what is needed for a safe operation, not just what is required by law.

Somewhat more tangibly, Leese (2004) offers a checklist to evaluate safety training. Her checklist covers such issues as:

- ensuring that regulatory requirements are met
- planning meeting content in terms of what the students need to comprehend
- varying the training formats
- measuring against specific training goals

This is a useful beginning list to set up a more comprehensive checklist for workplace-specific needs.

SECURITY ISSUES

Back in the good old days before 9/11, the real concern was making sure the public knew what sort of nasty stuff was in their neighborhood so they could, in theory, protect themselves in the event of an unwanted incident. Now, however, safety professionals need to be aware that the right-to-know information can be, and has been, tragically abused. The EPA used to require that "worst-case scenarios" be available to the public, but that has been changed because of concerns that the information would serve as a recipe for disaster (Sissell 2004). There is currently some litigation on the matter, but the EPA still does require an executive summary.

Unfortunately, safety professionals must also cope with the fact that hazardous materials can be stolen and used to wreak havoc, death, and mayhem if steps are not taken to prevent this theft. While it is beyond the scope of this chapter to discuss in detail, clearly safety professionals need to work with their security counterparts.

As with safety, a certain amount of common sense goes a long way when it comes to security issues. Consider that someone intends to cause harm using the organization's materials that have been released. These people can embrace a wide variety of causes. Petroff, in a paper on hazardous materials, military policing, and military intelligence addresses this con-

CASE STUDY

Using Hazcom Training to Sell Safety

Terry L. Mathis (2004), safety consultant and software expert and president of Integrated Performance Technologies, Inc., advocates some major paradigm shifts in hazcom (and other) training. Mathis reports on how a safety consultant, who stepped in at the last minute for a stranded trainer, used the mandated hazcom training session to also get employee input and stress the importance of helping the organization reach its goal. The result? Trainees reported feeling engaged in the training for the first time in years, several stated goals for applying the training, and most mentioned "being more serious about safety" after the experience.

Obviously, the one-time training would not sustain the effect, so Mathis' client had the consultant train his supervisors in the same materials and assigned them to discuss both the materials and vision in weekly toolbox training. He also made posters and wrote a letter in the company newsletter about the training and plans to involve the site manager in the next annual training. This company moved from "going through the motions" to using training to sell safety.

How do they do this? First, training sessions include a brainstorming session on how improving safety benefits both employees and the company, with real data from accidents, near misses, and unsafe acts. The workplace-specific training and personal benefits to the trainees make the safety strategies more relevant to the trainees.

Second, the company coupled mandated training on a specific subject with organizational needs around the subject, and used the training to accomplish both goals. One chemical plant planned to modify its MSDS program for computer access, so the organizers took the opportunity to include the new system and, importantly, to gather worker feedback on the proposed changes. Final modifications reflected the worker feedback. This can be inverted as well. If a new situation requires training, couple the needed training with any mandated regulatory training.

Third, look at training as only an initiation tool. Reminders and refreshers must be provided at least monthly. Furthermore, provide on-the-job reminders that translate classroom training into safe behavior.

Finally, make the training more or less continuous. Use regular meetings, communication tools, and even casual conversations to maintain focus and attention on organizational goals. One tool a company is using toward this end is a *shirt-pocket checklist*, which includes three or four safety-focus items over which the workers have control. Using a behavior-based safety approach, employees fill out the card based on what s/he sees fellow workers doing during the shift and turns the cards in so the company can measure progress on safety strategies.

cern (Petroff 2003). Some people he suggests worrying about include:

- criminals
- disaffected persons (insider threat)
- paramilitary forces such as militias and hate groups
- protesters for causes such as politics, the environment, or animal rights
- terrorists with political, religious, or single-issue motives, such as above

Consider the physical safety and protection from theft of the hazardous materials. Check Web access to ensure, at least, that people with malevolent intentions cannot access information from the outside. Work with Web security experts. Work with Human Resources to see if there are unstable employees who may pose a security hazard. Be sure that the safety department has input regarding security issues. The usual conflicts of security wanting doors locked and safety wanting people to have an escape route generally play out in a variety of ways.

Petroff recommends that companies integrate security into the hazardous materials management plan in a methodical, deliberate, and ongoing manner, utilizing local security experts such as the police or sheriff's departments, or the expertise of the Local Emergency Planning Committee. The goal is to implement measures that deter, detect, delay, or defeat the threat. Deterrence is improved by using highly visible measures and randomness. Use the same general procedure as risk management:

- Assess the threat.
- Assign specific physical security duties.
- Conduct security planning, both personnel and physical.
- Conduct risk analysis.
- Identify essential or vulnerable areas.
- Designate restricted areas.
- Coordinate security efforts.
- Establish physical security responsibilities for the operating staff.
- Employ physical and procedural security measures.
- Conduct inspections and surveys.

Regulations from Homeland Security will continue to evolve as terrorists use different tactics and strategies. Safety professionals must work with their counterparts in security to make sure that both are complying with the current regulations.

If, for some reason, someone is suspicious of a fellow employee, or someone else, do not just brush it off. Refer the concern to the security department, and let them check it out.

EMERGING CONCEPTS AND ISSUES
Data Sheets for Processes and Tools

The concept of hazard communication can be extended beyond using the MSDS concept just for *hazardous materials*. How about *hazardous processes*? Morse, Warren, Cherniack, Fletcher, and Peterson (2001) described a process for creating ergonomic data sheets to battle work-related musculoskeletal disorders (WRMSDs). In this very interesting paper, the authors developed a six-part ergonomic data sheet (EDS) for hand tools. The sections include:

- tool description
- basic information on ergonomics
- a warning of known and suspected WRMSDs associated with both general hand tools and the specific ones addressed in the EDS
- recommended work practices for risk reduction
- a checklist of potential ergonomic risk factors associated with the specific tool, combined with relevant design features of the tool
- results of several standardized tests quantifying ergonomic risk factors, comparing this tool with similar tools

The concept could be extended to other situations, such as climbing ladders, working at heights, entering confined spaces, and more. Taking the opportunity to generalize the MSDS format and concept and applying them to other types of safety data sheets would bring the benefits of continuity across all the safety education programs. Consider engaging employees in expanding the data-sheet concept.

Unfortunately, there is no evidence as of August 2010 that this particular concept has been followed.

If it has, it has not been written about in the safety trade magazines. On the other hand, these data sheets look an awful lot like a job safety analysis (JSA), so perhaps this is the case of a redundant concept.

Unknown Risks from New Technologies

Innovation will never cease, and one will always have unknown hazards with new technologies and inventions. When the semiconductor industry developed, it seemed that, with the clean-room technology, it was a very safe industry. Time has proven us wrong, as unexpected health effects resulted from the use of new chemicals.

One area of current concern is nanotechnology. NIOSH officials are currently working on guidelines for best practices in handling nanotechnology materials ("NIOSH working on safety guidelines for nanotechnology" 2004). Under research are issues such as predicting the types of exposure and the exposure routes of nanomaterials; this information will help determine the control measures. As nanotechnology is used more and more, the safety research in this area is heating up. Safety professionals involved in this particular area need to be diligent in keeping abreast of the new research.

As new materials and technologies develop, safety professionals need to be alert to the development of new hazardous materials and processes and need to anticipate solutions as well.

Handling Major Disasters and Their Clean Up

The collapse of the World Trade Center Towers taught safety professionals both short-term and long-term lessons on hazard communication. Given the magnitude of the task of the initial rescue, recovery, and clean up, there were remarkably few serious, immediate injuries. The teamwork of safety professionals, fire fighters, construction and operating engineers, safety equipment suppliers, and so on, was outstanding. However, the long-term health effects of the clean up have been significant, and are still not clearly understood. They may not be clearly understood for decades, particularly the health effects on residents near the site who were exposed to unknown quantities of who knows what (Lyman 2003; "September 11, 2001, Ground Zero" 2003).

It has become clear that many of the people working both in rescue and clean up are suffering from long-term lung injuries. What additional steps beyond providing PPE safety professionals could have taken in that awful tragedy and afterwards are unclear, but there are always lessons to be learned.

The *opportunity* to learn from this tragedy and plan for safer managing of serious disasters is one that safety professionals must not miss. Learning how to better evaluate hazards and communicate them is important so that immediate and long-term casualties can be minimized. Safety professionals must remember to balance accurate communication of hazard and risk with the concern for needless panic that would only compound the problem.

Biological Terrorism

Both the nation and its organizations do not really have much of a handle on coping with biological terrorism, and it is necessary to do so soon. The logistics of vaccinations and tracking disease incidence seem to have been reasonably well planned for, but the political and military need to control population movement very early in a bioterrorism incident appears not to have been addressed at the local, state, or federal level. Should such an incident occur, it would be a good idea for Homeland Security and emergency management experts, regulators, the media, and safety professionals to have considered ways to restrict the movements of their own employees to protect them from exposure.

This consideration could include setting policies in conjunction with the safety professionals' security counterparts, establishing ways to enforce the policies (potentially up to and including at gunpoint), and stockpiling and rotating supplies and materials to shelter the work population on site for a reasonable period of time. Should the biological organism be particularly virulent, a situation that will be evident within a few days, the shelter planning need not include much time beyond that.

A communication system for employees to contact loved ones is essential, and there are many more concerns. Working with local medical, military, and law-enforcement personnel, plus a good lawyer or two to address potential concerns about the legality of forcing employees to remain on site via policies and enforcement plans may save many lives in the future.

Whatever policies and procedures are selected, it is crucial that the employees *and their families* understand the necessity of the decisions and how those decisions can save the lives and health of everyone involved. As usual, the more employee input there is in these plans, the better.

One possible application for an HCS does apply to the selection of PPE against the possibility of a bioterror attack. Steve Williams, CHMM, founder and president of Bighorn Environmental Safety and Health, LLC, in Oregon, is a former state trooper and fire chief who develops and delivers antiterrorism curriculum for the U.S. government. As an expert on emergency planning and response, Williams points out that by analyzing the biological agent involved, it is possible to decide what level of protection first responders need to use (Williams 2003). Until the actual hazard is identified, Williams suggests using EPA Level A, fully encapsulated chemical protective clothing and self-contained breathing apparatus. Afterward, this can be modified to what is actually required. For example, consider the mailed anthrax attack of September 18, 2001. Five people died and at least thirteen others were sickened, and there was a great deal of confusion nationwide ("Anthrax Attack" 2007). Mail was cross-contaminated, Capitol Hill was severely disrupted, and people were frightened and inconvenienced; a

CASE STUDY

Hazard Communication Plan Pays Off Big at a Small Company

A comprehensive hazard communication plan that involves employees, the community, and the fire department has paid off for the Cary Company, a 42-employee chemical distributor in Addison, IL (Smith 2002). This 107-year-old company has a comprehensive hazcom program that includes

- extensive new employee training in Right-to-Know, OSHA, and DOT regulations
- an extremely well-maintained library of some 2500 MSDSs
- a partnership with the Addison Fire Department
- training for each new chemical or hazard as it is introduced into the workplace
- employee training in reading MSDSs
- a complete chemical labeling program
- ongoing education for both employees and management

What has been particularly valuable to the company is its ongoing relationship with the Addison Fire Department. The Cary Company has provided the fire department with a facility for emergency re-

sponse training exercises. They also notify the fire department when regulations they must comply with change, which Logistics and Regulatory Coordinator Dave Meehan makes sure he keeps up with. To do this, he attends "train the trainer" courses each year. The company has complete credibility with the fire department as a result. They know that the company has never tried to get around regulations.

In return, the fire department conducts approximately biannual inspections of the emergency shut-off valves for the gas and electricity, chemical storage locations, emergency-response equipment, and MSDSs. In addition, new fire fighters are brought out to look over the facility as they are hired. The biggest favor the fire department did was assist the company when it decided to construct a new 140,000-square-foot warehouse building with a HAZMAT room that could store 300,000 gallons of chemicals in 55-gallon drums. The National Fire Protection Association (NFPA) Code 30 has stringent regulations. In this case, they called for explosion-proof lighting, explosion-proof outlets, and an explosion-proof heating and cooling system that would add $100,000 to the construction costs. By telling the local fire department what they were going to store in the room, the fire

fighters helped design the room so that it met NFPA standards but did not have to be explosion-proof.

Instead of the explosion-proof equipment, the room contains an in-rack foam suppression system and an early suppression system in the general storage area designed to spray twice as much water as a normal fire protection sprinkler sprays. Besides a dike in the HAZMAT room to contain any spills, the warehouse has heat sensors, eleven hose stations, 54 fire extinguishers, and a fire protection room with a dedicated phone line, alarm, and electrical circuits. The fire department keeps a key to the fire protection room so emergency responders have 24-hour access to the MSDSs, maps showing electrical power switches, and emergency-contact phone numbers.

Besides saving a substantial amount of money when building the new warehouse, the company sees many other advantages. Company president Bill Cary points out that their hazcom program "helps differentiate us from many of our competitors, . . . reduce[s] accidents and injuries, saving us money, and our customers trust us to provide them with the most current, accurate information available for the chemicals they purchase from us."

great deal of money was spent cleaning up contaminated locations. Some confusion lay in the question of what PPE was needed to protect people from this? Protection levels finally moved down from EPA Level B clothing to Level C with N95 air-purifying respirators with HEPA filters (Williams 2003).

The HCS needs to discuss what level of protective gear is needed, how to decide this, what is appropriate for different organisms, and what guidelines and equipment are needed for dealing with the heat-stress problems of the chemical protective clothing. Methods for decontamination should also be included. As always, the necessary respirator-fit tests, as well as tests for any PPE, are required in advance of the need to use them.

Effects of Chemicals on Reproduction and Nursing

Dan Markiewicz, CIH, CHMM, CSP, an occupational health, safety, and environmental consultant, wrote an outstanding series on reproductive hazards and breastfeeding in *ISHN*. While these are not *new* issues, they are reemerging. In March 2004, IBM settled a lawsuit over whether or not a child's birth defects were caused by on-the-job exposure of the pregnant mother (Markiewicz 2004a). Even though the amount of the settlement was not revealed, the lawsuit called for $100 million in damages. Then there is the popularity of breastfeeding, which is causing some concern about the presence of chemicals in breast milk (Markiewicz 2004b). Markiewicz points out that safety professionals have no idea what the answers to very important questions are. Some of those questions are:

- Will breast milk be safe for infant consumption if the employer is in full compliance with OSHA chemical exposure standards?
- Do MSDSs provide enough information to determine if a chemical may concentrate in breast milk?
- Are there any recommended biological exposure indices for workplace chemicals in breast milk?
- Has the FDA set "safe limits" of industrial/environmental chemicals in breast milk?

These questions and the complicated legalities need to be addressed by employers. And these issues cannot be resolved by simply firing or refusing to hire pregnant women and nursing mothers. That would be difficult to explain to the Equal Employment Opportunity Commission and then to a judge and jury. Markiewicz suggests a set of flow charts to help evaluate the level of concern in worker populations and workplaces and a series of proactive steps for protecting both workers and company resources (Markiewicz 2003b). At some point, safety professionals may need to put this type of information into their hazcom training.

Biological Hazards

Molds and bacterial organisms such as *Legionella*, which causes a lung infection fatal in 15 percent of cases, popularly known as Legionnaires' disease after the famous outbreak, are recurring problems that are relatively easy to prevent (Morris and Shelton 2003, Pinto and Fennema 2003). Some 10,000 to 100,000 cases occur per year, according to the Centers for Disease Control and Prevention (CDC). Estimating 25,000 cases per year, Morris and Shelton (2003) point out that while they are no longer media-worthy, they are almost entirely preventable.

Two illnesses are caused by *Legionella*: Legionnaire's and the milder but more virulent Pontiac fever (Morris and Shelton 2003). Even though fewer than 5 percent of exposed individuals develop Legionnaire's, the flu-like Pontiac fever develops in approximately 95 percent of exposed individuals. None of these patients has died, but the cost of having so many employees out with an entirely preventable disease is high in terms of both business continuity and suffering.

Water is the growth medium here, and when it is aerosolized it can infect people. Cooling towers, evaporative condensers, humidifiers, potable water heaters and holding tanks, pipes containing stagnant warm water, showerheads, faucet aerators, decorative fountains, nebulizers, mister reserves, and whirlpool baths need to be monitored. The prevention is pretty simple: good, routine, preventative maintenance programs.

Of course, routine, preventative maintenance can be one of the first things management will let slide or even cut when money gets tight and emergencies occur.

Consider putting together a Hazard Control Sheet on this and other biological hazards, complete with the health hazards, costs, if available (consult Human Resources for costs of absenteeism), information on the maximum acceptable bacteria counts, any maintenance procedures required to prevent the problems and at what required intervals. This will emphasize the importance of maintenance for both management and the employees who need to carry it out.

Similarly, mold is a water-related biohazard. One particularly devastating form, *Stachybotrys*, is responsible for profound health effects (Pinto and Fennema 2003). Clearly, it is crucial to take complaints of health problems, such as frequent illnesses in the employees, seriously and resolve them quickly. Unfortunately, too many building managers, insurance companies, and builders do not take water leaks and indoor air-quality complaints seriously enough. Here, too, an HCS spelling out the potential consequences of ignoring and under-remediating water in the building would be called for. It should also include the proper procedures for ensuring that all the water is thoroughly dried out in the event of a water problem, which will ensure that proper procedures will be followed and mold problems prevented rather than having to raze the building later, which is the worst-case possibility. The HCS may or may not have much influence with insurance companies whenever water leaks occur.

The threat of a pandemic flu is increasing as the world shrinks. The H1N1 strain of flu (known as swine flu) was extremely virulent, as well as the H5N1 or avian flu—especially in countries where livestock (such as swine), birds, and people mix together. Combined with ever-cheaper air travel, the potential for a pandemic increases. There was a worldwide scare in 2009 of an H1N1 pandemic that could have been as disastrous as that of 1917–1918. Because of massive inoculation programs and public health actions to prepare and protect especially the most at-risk individuals, such as the young, elderly and those with preexisting conditions, the outbreak was far less serious than it might have been (CDC 2010). In any case, safety professionals need to stay aware of future potential for pandemics and epidemics and be prepared to manage that risk.

CONCLUSION: THE FUTURE OF HAZARD COMMUNICATION

Nobody can say for sure what direction hazard communication will take, but safety professionals can rely on the hazard-communication aspect of their jobs becoming more and more complex as knowledge expands on the health and safety hazards of various new and existing materials, processes, and organisms; on effective adult education; and on effective communication skills. Safety professionals do not just have to *keep up*, they have to *stay ahead*!

REFERENCES

10th U.S. Circuit Court. 1998. *Formal chemical warning could be modified by employee's verbal statement* (retrieved May 28, 2007). www.toxicmold.org/documents/0280.pdf

American National Standards Institute (ANSI). 2006–2008. 200601007. Z535, *Safety Color Codes*. Washington, D.C.: ANSI.

American Society of Safety Engineers (ASSE). 2004. "Statement of the American Society of Safety Engineers to the Committee on Health, Education, Labor and Pensions Committee, Subcommittee on Employment, Safety and Training on Hazard Communication in the Workplace" of the United States Senate hearing on Hazard Communication in the Workplace (retrieved August 20, 2004). www.asse.org/ngcomm115.htm/

_____. 2005. Position Statement: "Control Banding and the Future of the HazCom Standard." Approved June 2005 (retrieved August 28, 2010). www.asse.org/professionalaffairs_new/positions/hazcom.php

Anthrax Attack. 2007 (retrieved February 27, 2007). www.biblia.com/terrorism/anthrax.htm

Barry, Dave. 2005. *D Minus 1 Day to the Fabulous Demystifying Divas Plus One Gentle, Caring Takeover of WitNit* (retrieved January 17, 2007. witnit.blogspot.com/2005/06/dave-barry.html

Brown, Robert. 2005. "Managing Hazardous Materials: The Missing Link." *2004–2005 Supplement Buyer's Guide* 73(7):102.

Burns, Jacki, and Michael Beckel. 2001. "Saving Cash with Compliance." *Occupational Health and Safety*, September 1, 2001, p. 180.

Buxbaum, Peter. 2001. "Handle with Care." *Line 56 Magazine, the E-business Executive Daily* December 2001 (retrieved February 12, 2005). www.line56.com/articles/?NewsID-3203/

Campbell, Sharon Lynn. 1992. "A New Look for the MSDS." *Occupational Health and Safety*, June 1992, pp. 62–67.

Centers for Disease Control (CDC). 2010. *The 2009 H1N1 Pandemic: Summary Highlights, April 2009–April 2010* (retrieved August 30, 2010) www.cdc.gov/h1n1flu/cdcresponse.htm

Cheatham, Deane, Eric Shaver, and Michael Woglater. 2003. "Developing Effective Warnings for the Workplace." *Occupational Health and Safety*, June 2003, pp. 28–32.

"'Cry Wolf' Effect Sees Thousands Ignore Tsunami Warnings after Massive Quake." 2007. *The Mainichi Newspapers*, January 14, 2007, p. 2A (retrieved February 24, 2007). www.mdn.mainichi-msn.co.jp/national/news/20070114p2a00m0na009000c.html

Donnelly, John C. 2003. "The Hot Work House." *Occupational Health and Safety*, October 2003, p. 18.

Durodié, Bill. 2003. "The True Cost of Precautionary Chemicals Regulation." *Risk Analysis* 23(2):389–398.

Ebara v. AMOCO Production Company. 1998. United States Court of Appeals Tenth Circuit, No. 98-2189, D.C. No. CIV 96-838-LH (retrieved January 21, 2005). www.kscourts.org/ca10/cases/1999/06/98=2189.htm

Ernst, Robert. 2002. MSDS FAQ's: "Taking the Mystery out of Material Safety Data Sheets." *ISHN*, January 2002, pp. 37–38.

_____. 2003a. "Hazard Communication." *Compliance Magazine*, July 2003, p. 8.

_____. 2003b. "The ABCs of MSDS." *ISHN*, September 2003.

Evans, Roger D. 2003. "Employee Training Absorbed? Or Water Off a Duck's Back?" *Facility Safety Management*, December 2003, pp. 45–47.

Fagotto, Elena, and Archon Fung. 2002. "Improving Workplace Hazard Communication." *Issues in Science and Technology*, Winter 2002–03:63–69.

Galt, David L. 2003. "Electronic MSDS: Do You Still Need a Paper Trail." *ISHN*, March 2003, pp. 42–44.

Geller, Scott. 2003. "Pardon the Inconvenience." *ISHN*, March 2003, pp. 14–16.

Green, Marc. 2004a. *The Psychology of Warnings* (retrieved January 21, 2007). www.visualexpert.com/Resources/psychwarnings.html

_____. 2004b. "Why Warnings Fail." *Occupational Health and Safety*, February 2004 (retrieved February 27, 2007). www.stevenspublishing.com/Stevens/OHSPub.nsf/frame?open&redirect=and www.stevenspublishing.com/Stevens/OHSpub.nsf/PubArchive?openview

Grieff, Jacque S. 2003. "How to Find Training That's Right for You." *Occupational Health and Safety*, April 2003, pp. 86–97.

Grumbles, Thomas G. 2004. Testimony before the Committee on Health, Education, Labor and Pensions' Subcommittee on Employment Safety and Training at the United States Senate Hearing on "Hazard Communication in the Workplace" on March 24, 2004.

Hall, Mike. 2003. "10 Tips for Launching a Successful E-learning Program." *Compliance Magazine*, February 2003, pp. 18–19.

Harries, Karen, and John Baker. 2004. "Information Overload?" *European Chemical News*, February 23, 2004, p. 1.

"Hazard Communication via Material Safety Data Sheets." 2004. *Facilities Safety Management*, June 2004, pp. 36–37.

Henshaw, John L. 2004. Statement of John L. Henshaw, Assistant Secretary of Labor for Occupational Safety and Health before the Subcommittee on Employment, Safety and Training, Committee on Health, Education, Labor and Pensions, United States Senate on March 25, 2004 (retrieved January 16, 2007). www.osha.gov/pls/oshaweb/owadisp.show_document?p_table=TESTIMONIES&p_id=349

Hoffman, Judy. 2003. "Communication Strategy: Hazardous Materials and the Public—JCH Enterprises." *Chemical Market Report*, March 2003, p. 10.

House, Matthew. 2002. "Provisions for Emergency Response and Community Right to Know." *Journal of Occupational Health & Safety*, November 2002.

Jackson, Heather. 2002. "Control Banding: Practical Tools for Controlling Exposure to Chemicals." *Asian-Pacific Newsletter on Occupational Safety and Health* 9:62–63 (retrieved January 23, 2005). www.ilo.org/public/english/protection/safework/ctrl_banding/practools.pdf

Kalaroa, Nancy. 2004. "Breaching the Language Barrier." *Occupational Health and Safety*, June 2004, pp. 60–65.

Leese, Carolyn. 2004. "Evaluating Your Safety Training." *Compliance Magazine*, February 2004, pp. 18–19.

Lehto, Mark R., Theresa House, and Jason D. Papastavrou. 2000. "Interpretation of Fuzzy Qualifiers by Chemical Workers." *International Journal of Cognitive Ergonomics* 4(1):73.

Lewis, Anne. 2003. "Training Done Right." *ISHN*, May 2003, pp. 33–34.

Lyman, Francesca. 2003. *Messages in the Dust: Lessons Learned, post-9/11, for Environmental Health* (retrieved March 3, 2007). www.neha.org/9-11%20report/index-FContents.html

Machles, David. 2003. "Situated Learning: New Approach to SH&E Training Focuses on Learning." *Professional Safety*, September 2003, pp. 22–28.

Markiewicz, Dan. 2003a. "Beware of the Training Trap: Training Is Not Always the Cure-all Employers Expect." *ISHN*, December 2003.

_____. 2003b. "Breast Milk and Working Women: How Can an Employer Protect this Food Source." *ISHN*, February 2003, pp. 18–20.

_____. 2003c. "Ready for a New World Order? The Impact of Globally Harmonized Hazard Communication." *ISHN*, April 30, 2003, pp. 18–20.

_____. 2004a. "The $100-Million Wake-up Call." *ISHN*, April 2004, pp. 17–19.

_____. 2004b. "Uncertainty over an Emerging Risk: How to Protect Employees Who Breastfeed." *ISHN*, July 2004, pp. 16–18.

_____. 2010. "Managing Best Practices: Workplace Developmental Hazards," *ISHN*, March/April 2010 (retrieved August 28, 2010). www.ishn.com/Articles/Column/BNP_GUID_9-5-2006_A_10000000000000713529

Mathis, Terry L. 2004. "Golden Opportunity: Use Compliance Classes to Reach Your Strategic Safety Goals." *ISHN*, June 2004, cover.

McKinnon, Stephanie H. 2003. "Improving Your Safety, Health and Environmental Training." *EH&S Products*, (October) 1:12.

Merritt, Carolyn W. 2004. Testimony to the Committee on Health, Education, Labor and Pensions Subcommittee on Employment Safety and Training of the United States Senate Hearing on "Hazard Communication in the Workplace," on March 24, 2004 (retrieved May 28, 2007). www.csb.gov/news_releases/docs/CSBFinalTestimonyMSDS32404.pdf

Minter, Stephen G. 2003. "Will OSHA Act to Improve MSDS?" *Occupational Hazards*, September 2003, p. 8.

Morris, George K., and Brian G. Shelton. 2003. "*Legionella* Bacteria in Environmental Samples: Hazard Analysis and Suggested Remedial Actions." *Compliance Magazine*, January 2003, pp. 32–34.

Morse, Timothy, Nicholas Warren, Martin Cherniack, Frederick Fletcher, and Donald Peterson. 2001. "The Creation of Ergonomic Data Sheets for Hazard Communication of Work-Related Musculoskeletal Disorders." *Applied Occupational and Environmental Hygiene*, August 2001, pp. 823–831.

"MSDS Global Harmonization Legislation Planned." 2004. *Flashpoint Lube News*, March 30 2004.

Nash, James L. 2004. "Construction Safety: Best Practices in Training Hispanic Workers." *Occupational Hazards*, February 2004, pp. 35–38.

National Fire Protection Association (NFPA). 2010. "We're in the business of protecting working people." *NFPA Journal*, March/April 2010 (retrieved August 29, 2010). www.nfpa.org/archivedJournalList.asp?categoryID=1991&src=NFPAJournal

National Institute of Occupational Safety and Health (NIOSH). 2004. "Working on Safety Guidelines for Nanotechnology." *ISHN*, July 2004, p. 8.

"The New REACH Fees Regulation: Expensive and Flawed." May 9, 2008 (retrieved August 29, 2010). www.wilmerhale.com/publications/whPubsDetail.aspx?publication=8230

Nightswonger, Todd. 2000. "Are You Storing Hazardous Materials Safely?" *Occupational Hazards*, June 2000, pp. 45–48.

O'Brien, Daniel Patrick. "Easing Your Hazcom Headaches." 2001. *ISHN*, January 2001, p. 45.

Occupational Safety and Health Administration (OSHA). 2004a. *Draft Model Training Program for Hazard Communication* (retrieved October 23, 2004). www.osha.gov/dsg/hazcom/MTP101703.html/

_____. 2004b. *Hazard Communication in the 21st Century Workplace* (retrieved October 23, 2004). www.OSHA.gov/dsg/hazcom/finalmsdsreport.html

_____. 2007a. *Consultation Program* (retrieved January 12, 2007). www.osha.gov/dcsp/smallbusiness/consult.html

_____. 2007b. *Hazard Communication* (retrieved January 17, 2007). www.osha.gov/SLTC/smallbusiness/sec16.html

_____. 2009. *The Globally Harmonized System for Hazard Communication*, revision 3 (retrieved August 30, 2010). www.osha.gov/SLTC/hazardcommunications/global.html

Oldershaw, Paul. 2005. "Control Banding—Threat or Benefit," *OHS World*, January 2005 (retrieved August 28, 2010) www.sheilapantry.com/oshworld/focus/2005/200501.html

"OSHA's No. 1 Target (and Your Top Safety Priority) Made Easier." 2001. *Ioma's Safety Director's Report*, March 2001, pp. 6–10.

Perry, Terrell L. 2003. "Torn over Training? Studies Have Shown Technology-Based Training Costs Can Be 25 Percent to 75 Percent Lower Than Classroom Instruction." *Occupational Health and Safety*, November 2003, pp. 80–82.

Petroff, Dale M. 2003. "Security of Hazardous Materials." *Occupational Health and Safety*, April 2003, pp. 44–48.

_____. 2004. "Risk Communication: Effective Education: The Goals of Risk Communication Are to Ensure Responders Have the Information They Need and to Prevent Panicked Reactions by the Public." *Occupational Health and Safety*, May 2004, pp. 66–72.

Pierce, F. David. 2003. "Low English Proficiency & Increased Injury Rates." *Professional Safety*, August 2003, pp. 40–45.

Pinto, Larry. 1999. "Larry Pinto: Company Safety Programs That Must Be in Writing." *Pest Control*, March 1, 1999.

Pinto, Michael A., and Cherie Fennema. 2003. "Mold and Bleeding Lungs: Another Connection?" *Occupational Hazards*, May 2003, pp. 55–58.

Powell, Isaac. 2003. "Ask the Experts: Hazard Communication." *Compliance Magazine*, August 2003, p. 5.

Pullen, Matthew. 2003. "Sorting Out the MSDS Mess." *ISHN*, June 2003, pp. 41–42.

"Questions and Answers [on material safety data sheets]." 2004. *ISHN*, June 2004, pp. 32–36.

The Report of the Hazard Communication Workgroup to the National Advisory Committee on Occupational Safety and Health (NACOSH). September 12, 2006 (retrieved March 3, 2007). www.osha.gov/SLTC/hazardcommunications/wgfinal.html

Roughton, James E. 2002. "Creating a Successful HazCom Program." *Plant Safety & Maintenance*, December 28, 2002, pp. 31–33.

Sapper, Arthur G. 2002. "Legal Affairs." *Occupational Hazards*, August 2002, pp. 43–44.

_____. 2006. "OSHA's HazCom Standard Does Not Require Chemical-Specific Training." *Occupational Hazards*, December 12, 2006.

Schierhorn, Carolyn. 2002. "Hazardous Duty." *Health Facilities Management*, July 2002, pp. 37–40.

"September 11, 2001, Ground Zero." 2003. *Journal of Environmental Health* (December 2003) 1:32.

Sissell, Kara. 2004. "Right-to-Know Activists Consider Lawsuit over RMP Data." *Chemical Week*, April 28, 2004, p. 13.

Smith, Sandy. 2002. "HAZCOM Pays Off at the Cary Co." *Occupational Hazards*, December 12, 2002 (retrieved April 16, 2006). www.occupationalhazards.com/articles/5279

_____. 2004. "Breakthrough Safety Management." *Occupational Hazards*, June 2004, pp. 41–44

Tapp, Linda. 2003a. "Computer-Based Training: Ten Questions to Help Determine If It's Right for You." *ISHN*, May 2003, pp. 35–36.

_____. 2003b. "Nine PowerPoint Tips." *ISHN*, October 2003, pp. 36–38.

_____. 2004. "Do Your Employees Need Training, Instruction or Education?" *ISHN*, February 2004, pp. 28–29.

Tompkins, Neville C. 1996. "Lessons in Many Languages Can Boost Workplace Safety." *HR Magazine*, March 1,

1996 (retrieved February 27, 2007). www.findarticles.com/p/articles/mi_m3495/is_n3_v41/ai_18251531

"U.S. GHS Implementation," 1010. *Silver Platter Guides* (retrieved August 28, 2010). www.ovid.com/site/products/fieldguide/dose/TLV_Threshold_Limit_Values.jsp

Wagshol, Marcia. 2003. "Using Signs and Symbols to Communicate Safety." *ISHN*, November 2003, pp. 35–37.

_____. 2004. "Putting a Label on Safety." *ISHN*, July 2004, pp. 27–28.

Weadock, Valerie. 2003. "MSDS Technology Made Simple." *Occupational Health and Safety*, April 1, 2003, p. 26.

Weissman, Barry R. 2003. "Ten Classroom Tips for Training Non-English Speaking Employees." *ISHN*, October 2003.

Williams, Steve. 2003. "The Threat of Bioterrorism," *ISHN*, May 2003, pp. 43–45.

Wolff, Jennifer Snow, and Michael S. Wolgarter. 1998. "Comprehension of Pictorial Symbols: Effects of Context and Test Method." *Human Factors*, June 1, 1998, p. 173.

Working Group on Community Right-to-Know. 2007. *Registration, Evaluation and Authorization of Chemicals* (retrieved March 3, 2007). www.crtk.org/detail.cfm?docID=23&cat=international

Appendix: Additional Resources

International Hazard Communication

American National Standards Institute (ANSI), www.ANSI.org. They have current information on the status of the U.S. adoption of the GHS.

Canadian Centre for Occupational Safety and Health, www.ccohs.ca

Chemical hazard communication site lists Web sites from all over the world at www.unitar/org/cwm/GHS-CD/cat5.html

ChemicalPlantSafety.net is a chemical plant safety blog. It includes a lot of information, and one entry, http://chemicalplantsafety.net/msds/writing-msds-using-msds-template is particularly valuable. You can also get quite a few MSDSs.

Denehurst Chemical Safety, Ltd., www.denehurst.co.uk/. This is a consulting firm that offers help to the chemical industry.

Globally Harmonized System for the Classification and Labeling of Chemicals. International Labor Organization Draft Integrated Proposal, www.unece.org/trans/danger/publi/ghs/implementation_e.html. This has all the information on which countries have implemented the GHS.

Global MSDS, Ltd., Environmental Insight. www.globalmsds.com

Interactive Learning Paradigms, Inc., www.ILPI.com, offers custom training programs.

Samples of International Chemical Safety Cards. They do not replace MSDSs (NIOSH version: www.cdc.gov/niosh/ipcs/icstart.html) (OSHA version: www.osha.gov, under the index for "Hazard communications." Also includes OSHA's explanation for the GHS.)

Society for Chemical Hazard Communication, www.schc.org

United Nations Economic Commission for Europe, www.unece.org/trans/danger/publi/ghs/officialtext.html

The Wercs, Ltd., e-mail: info@thewercs.com; Web site: www.thewercs.com

MSDS Databases

3E Company of Carlsbad, CA, provides services for environmental, health, and safety (EH&S) related compliance management, including: global regulatory research; MSDS authoring, distribution, and management; transportation; emergency response; training; regulatory reporting; and hazardous waste management.

Environmental Support Solutions of Tempe, AZ, provides software in two integrated suites.

OHS-MSDS-SUM, just the summary sheets; and PESTLINE-OHS, agricultural chemical product ingredients (MSDS-PEST). All are updated weekly.

STN International offers Occupational Health Services databases, MSDS-OHS, complete identification.

Risk Communication

Sheldon, Keith. 1996. "Credibility Is Risky Business." *Communication World*, April 1, 1996.

This is an interview with Vincent T. Covello, an expert on risk communication and media relations, who has advice on communicating with members of the public in a credible way.

SECTION 3
ENVIRONMENTAL MANAGEMENT

Air Pollution Control and Mitigation

Water and Wastewater

Solid Waste

Hazardous Waste

Hazardous Material Spills and Response

Management Systems

SECTION 3
ENVIRONMENTAL MANAGEMENT

LEARNING OBJECTIVES

▌ Develop a better awareness of the air pollution problem and the need for prevention and control.

▌ Be able to identify regulatory and compliance issues related to controlling and preventing air pollution associated with industrial operations.

▌ Internalize basic information for assisting, evaluating, and selecting air pollution control equipment and systems.

▌ Become familiar with guidelines for evaluating air pollution control systems and programs.

AIR POLLUTION CONTROL AND MITIGATION

Anthony J. Joseph and Tyler Nguyen

REVIEWING THE DEVELOPMENT of environmental issues over the past century, it can be said that the first period was characterized by the growth of a conservation movement that focused mainly on protection of wild and scenic areas and a general appreciation of nature in a rapidly urbanizing world. This began in the 1890s and lasted until the early 1960s. The second development, which lasted from roughly 1964 until the early 1990s, focused primarily on pollution control and remediation—reducing *point source* emissions into air, land, and water. Today, recognizing that air pollution is not simply industrial emissions, but a by-product of the social demands of living, pollution prevention is the method of dealing with environmental degradation.

The information presented in this chapter was extracted primarily from published works, such as the *Handbook of Environmental Health and Safety* (Koren and Bisesi 1995) and *Air Pollution Control* (Cooper and Alley 2002), as well as those found on the Environmental Protection Agency (EPA) Web site (www.epa.gov). Additional information was extracted from the chapters on air pollution and air pollution control in the *Encyclopaedia of Occupational Health and Safety* (ILO 1993) and from the *Handbook of Environmental Health and Safety Principles and Practices* (Koren 2003).

AIR POLLUTION CONTROL APPROACHES AND MEASURES

Two approaches are used for control and prevention of harmful effects from poor air quality:

1. air quality management
2. best practicable means

Air quality management aims at the preservation of environmental quality by prescribing the tolerated degree of pollution, leaving it to the public and local communities to devise and implement programs and actions that will ensure that the maximum accepted degree or level of pollutants in the air is not exceeded.

The best practicable means approach stresses that the air pollutant emissions should be kept to a minimum. This is defined through emission standards for single sources of air pollution. An emission standard is a limit on the amount or concentration of a pollutant emitted from a source.

In the author's opinion, among the many factors that must be considered in order to select the most adequate air pollution control strategy are:

- geographical situation and meteorology
- number of sources and their relative location to each other and to the surrounding communities
- type of sources and effluents
- characteristics of the pollutants involved
- degree of control required
- socioeconomic aspects and priorities

HISTORY OF AIR POLLUTION

The following is a historical review of air pollution and a statement of the importance of controlling air pollutants.

Notable Incidents

Air quality issues prior to and including industrial contributions were primarily concerned with *air abatement* issues. These included residential fuels, burning of coal, peat, and wood in urban areas, with contributions from trade industries such as metallurgy, ceramics, tanning, smelting, and woodworking. Kanarek (2004) noted that, between the 1880s and the 1940s, the United States saw no penalties for violation of early laws prohibiting the burning of peat and coal during designated times, for ore smelting in 1900–1930s that created pollutants such as sulfates, lead, zinc, and nickel, or for increased smog from electrical power plants and motor vehicles.

In the 1930s, Meuse Valley, Belgium, experienced a disastrous air pollution event caused by a combination of industry, dense population, and climatic conditions. Considered one of the first modern air pollution events, Meuse Valley, a densely populated and highly industrialized area, experienced a climatic event during the winter—high barometric pressure that created a thermal inversion. This temperature inversion restricted stack emissions from an industrial plant from dissipating into the atmosphere. The result was an inversion layer within the valley, consisting of smog comprised of sulfur dioxide and sulfuric acid mist; the evaporation of water from the nearby river also contributed to this development. Sixty-three people died, along with cattle, rats, and birds. Others experienced sore throat, shortness of breath, cough, phlegm, nausea, and vomiting.

In 1952, the Great London Smog occurred as a result of (among other factors) Londoners burning bituminous (soft, high-sulfur) coal. This led to:

- a temperature inversion, creating five days of the worst smog ever seen (smog = smoke + fog)
- a halt in public transportation
- a spike in the death rate and increased instances of bronchitis, coronary disease, myocardial degeneration, and pneumonia

Another historic air pollution incident occurred in 1948 in Donora, Pennsylvania. Located in the Monongahela River Valley, Donora was an industrialized city of approximately 14,000 people that had a steel mill industry, which smelted ore and burned coal within blast furnaces. On October 26, a stable temperature inversion, lasting nearly six days, trapped sulfur dioxide and zinc emissions within the valley, resulting in twenty deaths and hundreds of illnesses, with over 1500 requiring medical assistance. The U.S. Public Health Service became involved in what was recognized as air-pollution-caused incidents. There is some controversy as to the cause of the deaths—either fluorides or sulfur mists—and it is a question that is still unresolved today. Other notable air pollution incidents include the 1976 Seveso, Italy, dioxin release that exposed tens of thousands of humans and farm animals; the 1984 methyl isocyanate release in Bhopal, India, which was reported to have killed over two thousand people; the Chernobyl radioactive release in Russia in 1985; and the most recent World Trade Center disaster on September 11, 2001, which released asbestos and particulate matter, contributing to what is referred to today as the "World Trade Center Cough."

History of Pollution-Related Regulations

The Air Pollution Control Act of 1955

Enacted on July 14, 1955, the Air Pollution Control Act (P.L. 81-159) was the first federal legislation to address the national environmental problem of air pollution. It was "to provide research and technical assistance relating to air pollution control" (AMS 2002), providing funds for research in air pollution. The act "left states principally in charge of prevention and control of air pollution at the source" (Schnelle and Brown 2002). It declared that air pollution was a danger to public health and welfare, but preserved the "primary responsibilities and rights of the States and local government in controlling air pollution" (EPA 1955). The act set the federal government in a purely informational role, authorizing the U.S. Surgeon General to conduct research, investigate, and pass out information "relating to air pollution and the prevention and abatement thereof" (EPA 1955). However, the Air Pollution Control Act of 1955 contained no provisions for the federal government to actively combat air pollution by punishing polluters (Schnelle and Brown 2002).

California was the first state to act against air pollution. The metropolis of Los Angeles had begun to notice deteriorating air quality. Several geographical and meteorological problems unique to the Los Angeles area exacerbated the air pollution problem. Under the Air Pollution Control Act of 1955, research was federally funded to assist states in assessing air pollution sources and identifying the range of general health effects on urban populations.

Clean Air Act of 1963 and Amendments (1965–1969)

Eight years later, Congress passed the Clean Air Act of 1963 (CAA 1963). This act dealt with reducing air pollution by setting emissions standards for stationary sources such as steel mills and power plants. The CAA 1963 was the first federal legislation to address air pollution control. It established a federal program within the U.S. Public Health Service and authorized research into techniques for monitoring and controlling air pollution. In 1967, the Air Quality Act was passed in order to expand federal government activities. In accordance with this law, enforcement proceedings were initiated in areas subject to interstate air pollution transport. As part of these proceedings, for the first time the federal government conducted extensive ambient monitoring studies and stationary source inspections. Mobile sources of air pollution were not covered, although they are the largest source of many dangerous pollutants. Amendments to the Clean Air Act were passed in 1965, 1966, 1967, and 1969 (EPA 1971; Kanarek 2004).

These amendments authorized the Secretary of the Health, Education, and Welfare (HEW) Department to set standards for auto emissions, expanded local air pollution control programs, established air-quality control regions (AQCR), set air-quality standards and compliance deadlines for stationary source emissions, and authorized research on low-emission fuels and automobiles. Again, funding was made available to states and local authorities to assist in implementing programs, enforcing regulations, and supporting research programs into pollution control technologies.

The 1965 amendment created the President's Science Advisory Committee, which published a report entitled "Restoring the Quality of our Environment" (EPA 1971). The report identified numerous major sources of environmental contamination: municipal and industrial sewage, animal wastes, municipal solid wastes, mining wastes, and unintentional releases, which included automobile exhaust, smokestack emissions, pesticide mists, and agricultural chemicals that drained into waterways, among other things. The main report contained subpanel reports on soil contamination, the potential for global warming by carbon dioxide, the effects of chlorinating wastes, the health effects of environmental pollution, and the effects of pollutants on organisms other than man. Also in 1965, automobile emissions were added under the Motor Vehicles Air Pollution Control Act (EPA 1971; Kanarek 2004). Standards mirroring the California auto emissions requirements, which included emission control devices such as catalytic converters, were set as guidelines for other states to follow.

One of the first attempts toward identifying regional contributions of air pollution was made through the Air Quality Act of 1967. States were given regional designations by the Secretary of Health, Education, and Welfare and were tasked with identifying regional contributions affecting air quality. Regional boundaries were set, which created published criteria for sulfur oxide (SO_x) emissions and particulate matter. Also coming into play was the inclusion of climatic influence on the interboundary transport of air pollutants, including to and from Mexico and Canada.

Clean Air Act of 1970 (CAA 1970)

The year 1970 brought about the most radical environmental steps to date. The National Environmental Policy Act (NEPA) was formulated to emphasize a need for active participation of the national government in the protection of natural resources (EPA 1970). NEPA served as the conduit for the formation of two historic governmental agencies, the Council on Environmental Quality (CEQ) and the EPA, resulting in the passage of the CAA 1970. The enforcement of the CAA 1970 was the responsibility of the EPA.

The provisions within the CAA 1970 created:

- *The National Ambient Air Quality Standards* (NAAQS), establishing the six criteria pollutants: SO_x, nitrogen oxide (NO_x), particulate matter (PM10), lead, volatile organic compounds (VOCs), and carbon monoxide (CO)
- state implementation plans (SIPs) for the identification and regulation of stationary and mobile sources of pollution
- new source performance standards (NSPS) for all major stationary sources of air pollution
- requirements for best available control technology (BACT), including engineering technology to reduce pollutants, as well as requirements for administrative compliance through alternative fuels
- regulation of eight *National Emission Standards for Hazardous Air Pollutants* (NESHAPs): asbestos, vinyl chloride, radio nuclides, arsenic, mercury, beryllium, radon, and benzene
- increased enforcement authority of the EPA

- control technology guidelines (CTGs) for specific-source industrial categories

The CAA 1970 sought to tighten standards for air pollutants and enforcement that had failed under the 1967 Air Quality Act. By 1970, fewer than three dozen air quality regions had been designated, as compared to the anticipated 100. Not a single state had developed a full pollution control program. The CAA 1970 went from regional to national air quality standards, with Congress imposing statutory deadlines for compliance with emission standards.

1977 Amendments to the 1970 Clean Air Act

The amendments of the 1970 CAA, written in 1977, added provisions that utilized monitoring data to categorize air quality within regional boundaries. Areas were designated as attainment, nonattainment, or unclassified (EPA 1970; Kanarek 2004). The prevention of significant deterioration (PSD), an amendment to maintain regions that currently met or exceeded the NAAQS, was also established. The amendments required construction permits for new or modified stationary sources categorized as *major*, to include the installation of BACT for large industries and power plants. The 1977 CAA amendments, while tightening some standards under the PSD, also relaxed the enforcement authority of the EPA at the state level, allowing individual SIPs to set extended timeframes for implementing air quality emission standards for vehicles and industry.

Clean Air Act of 1990 (CAA 1990) and Amendments

Since 1970, the CAA has provided the primary framework for protecting the environment and people from the effects of air pollution. The CAA requires the EPA to significantly reduce daily, "routine" emissions of the most potent air pollutants. These routine emissions are defined as substances that are known or suspected to cause serious health problems such as cancer or birth defects. The CAA 1990 refers to these substances as "hazardous air pollutants," commonly referred to as toxic air pollutants or, simply, air toxics. Prior to 1990 the EPA set standards for each toxic air pollutant, based on its particular health risks. This approach proved difficult and minimally effective at reducing emissions. As a result, when amending the CAA in 1990, Congress directed the EPA to use a technology- and performance-based approach to significantly reduce emissions of air toxics from major sources of air pollution, followed by a risk-based approach to address any remaining, or residual, risks (EPA 1990; Kanarek 2004).

Standards are developed under the technology-based approach for controlling the routine emissions of air toxics from each major type of facility within an industry group (or source category). These standards are known as maximum achievable control technology (MACT) standards. They are based on emission levels already achieved by the better-controlled and lower-emitting sources in an industry. This approach provides a level economic playing field by ensuring that facilities employing cleaner processes and good emission controls are not disadvantaged by competitors with poorer controls.

In setting MACT standards, the EPA does not generally prescribe a specific control technology. Instead, whenever feasible, the agency sets a performance level based on technology or other practices already used by the industry. Facilities are free to achieve these performance levels in whatever way is most cost-effective for them. The deadline for companies to submit detailed applications for permits, under which state air agencies would determine their hazardous air pollutant (HAP) emission limits on a case-by-case basis, was scheduled for May 15, 2002; on April 5, 2002 it was extended to May 15, 2004. The promulgation delay by the EPA forced industry and the state air agencies to make MACT determinations in the absence of a specific rule, or based on proposed rules, rather than a final rule. Due to the dynamic nature of this standard, it was advisable to evaluate its applicability on a case-by-case basis as it applies to a facility. The EPA projected that, once fully implemented, these standards would cut emissions of toxic air pollutants by nearly 1.5 million tons yearly.

The CAA 1990 and its amendments introduced some major changes, holding states responsible for implementing and enforcing the act; conducting hearings for permits to build power or chemical plants, and setting fines for violating air pollution limits. However, the ultimate responsibility for enforcing the CAA remains with the EPA. States were allowed to establish standards more stringent than federal standards and were also required to develop SIPs. These plans provide information on how the state will comply with the requirements of the CAA. States are required to involve the public through hearings and commenting opportunities in the development of their SIP. The EPA must approve all SIPs. In states with no approved SIP, and the federal CAA is enforced.

In 1990, provisions written in the previous titles of CAA 1970 were enhanced to include nine more titles (EPA 1990):

1. Attainment of the 1970 *National Ambient Air Quality Standards* (NAAQS), and timeframes for compliance
2. New emission reductions from mobile sources of air pollution
3. Emission control standards for the 189 identified toxics under the *National Emission Standards for Hazardous Air Pollutants* (NESHAP)
4. Acid rain deposition and transport from sources of SO_x and NO_x
5. Permit requirements for stationary sources
6. Identification and reduction of stratospheric ozone-depleting chlorofluorocarbons (CFCs)
7. EPA enforcement rights
8. Miscellaneous issues
9. Research programs aimed at the reduction of air pollution

The 1990 Clean Air Act Amendments (CAAA) introduced the "Haze and Visibility Rule," later adopted in 1999, which seeks to reduce smog and soot problems by emphasizing PM10 and ozone. Congress also introduced another version of control technology for both stationary and mobile sources called "best available retrofit technology" (BART), which was applied to 26 source categories and was finalized in April 2005 (EPA 2005a).

A somewhat controversial emissions trading initiative was introduced in 2003 by the Bush administration as an alternative to provisions in the CAA of 1990. The Clear Skies Act (CSA) was introduced in Congress in 2005, though never passed as law; it was supposed to dramatically and steadily cut power-plant emissions of three of the worst air pollutants (EPA 2005c). President Bush indicated that the CSA would do the following:

- Cut sulfur dioxide (SO_2) emissions by 73 percent from current emissions of 11 million tons to a cap of 4.5 million tons in 2010 and 3 million tons in 2018.
- Cut emissions of nitrogen oxides (NO_x) by 67 percent, from current emissions of 5 million tons to a cap of 2.1 million tons in 2008 and 1.7 million tons in 2018.
- Cut mercury emissions by 69 percent—the first-ever national cap on mercury emissions. Emissions would be cut from current emissions of 48 tons to a cap of 26 tons.

Opponents contended that the emissions trading under the CSA would change the CAA limits. CSA would loosen the cap on NO_x to 2.1 by 2008; and on SO_x (acid rain) emissions to 4.5 million tons by 2010. There is no limit set on CO emissions because it is a voluntary program. By the fifteenth year of the Bush plan, there would be an estimated 450,000 more tons of NO_x, one million more tons of SO_x, and 9.5 more tons of mercury in the environment (Sierra Club 2004). The Bush administration has declined signing the Kyoto Protocol, a global warming reduction document entered into by other countries (West 2005). The CSA is a separate U.S. plan allowing the President to manage ozone and NO_x emissions independently of international scrutiny (Kanarek 2004; EPA 2005c; Montague 1999).

FEATURES OF THE CLEAN AIR ACT AMENDMENTS OF 1990 (CAAA 1990)

The federal CAAA 1990 was expanded from six titles to nine. The intent of CAA 1970 was to enhance air quality management with the introduction of specific pollutant criteria, state monitoring programs, stationary permitting, and federal enforcement rights. It failed to address improvements to human health and the environment from acid rain, regional smog, and air toxics, resulting in the amendments. Unfortunately, the 1990 amendments failed to address two increasingly prominent global air pollution problems: greenhouse gas emissions and mercury pollution. Carbon dioxide (CO_2) is the most important of these

emissions, and, as noted earlier, electric power plants emit one-third of the total carbon dioxide emissions in the United States. Mercury pollution from coal combustion is becoming a crucial regional and global issue because of contamination of essential food supplies (Wooley 2000).

Major features of the CAAA 1990 are discussed under the following headings:

- *National Ambient Air Quality Standards* (NAAQS)
- Mobile Sources: Vehicle Emissions
- Hazardous Air Pollutants (HAPs)
- Acid Deposition
- Stratospheric Ozone and Global Climate
- Air Pollution Control Research

National Ambient Air Quality Standards (NAAQS)

In 1971, then-EPA-administrator William Ruckelshaus announced that NAAQS had been established. The standards applied to six criteria pollutants:

- sulfur oxides (SO_x)
- particulate matter (PM10, particulate matter 10 microns or less in diameter)
- carbon monoxide
- photochemical oxidants (ozone)
- nitrogen oxides (NO_x)
- hydrocarbons (ozone precursor)

This occurred in response to the requirement that the administrator publish, within thirty days of December 31, 1970, air quality standards for mobile and stationary sources that contribute to air pollution. By 1978, the EPA had revised the NAAQS to include lead as a recognized health hazard, particularly for children.

In 1978, the EPA published a list of nonattainment areas within the country, regions that had not met the NAAQS for the six specified criteria. Many reports across the country indicated that the targeted deadlines were unattainable as originally envisioned. In addition, it appeared that the Clean Air Act Amendments of 1977 (CAAA 1977) did not provide the most

TABLE 1

Six Criteria Pollutants, Major Emission Sources, Chemical Interactions, and Potential Control Technologies

Criteria Pollutant	Source(s) & 1997 Emission Estimates (short tons per year)	Basic Chemical Reactions	Control Technology/ Main Options
Sulfur dioxide (SO_2) Corrosive gas	Transportation: 1.4 Fuel Combustion: 17.3 Industrial Processes: 1.7 Miscellaneous: 0.0 Total: 20.4 % of 1970 Total: 65%	Reacts in the atmosphere to form acid rain $S + O_2 \rightarrow SO_2$ $SO_2 + H_2O \rightarrow H_2SO_4$	Scrubbing
PM10 Particulate matter, as a solid or vapor between 0.1–0.00005 mm	Transportation: 0.7 Fuel Combustion: 1.1 Industrial Processes: 1.3 Miscellaneous: 0.0 Total: 3.1 % of 1970 Total: –	Coarse: road dust, sea spray, construction Fine: fossil fuel combustion from autos and industry	Mechanical separators, fabric filters, electrostatic precipitators, and wet scrubbers.
Carbon monoxide (CO) Odorless gas emitted from fossil fuel combustion, primarily autos	Transportation: 67.0 Fuel Combustion: 4.8 Industrial Processes: 6.1 Miscellaneous: 9.6 Total: 87.5 % of 1970 Total: 78%	CO does not react readily in the atmosphere $CO + O_2 \rightarrow CO_2$	Promote complete combustion or oxidation.
Ozone (O_3) Troposphere ozone gas is a contributor to smog	Transportation: 7.7 Fuel Combustion: 0.9 Industrial Processes: 9.8 Miscellaneous: 0.8 Total: 19.2 % of 1970 Total: 70%	$NO + HC + Sunlight \rightarrow NO_2 + O_3$	Reduce emissions of its precursors
Nitrogen dioxide (NO_2) Reddish-brown gas generated from fossil fuel combustion	Transportation: 11.6 Fuel Combustion: 10.7 Industrial Processes: 0.9 Miscellaneous: 0.3 Total: 23.5 % of 1970 Total: 116%	$NO + HC + O_2 + Sunlight \rightarrow NO_2 + O_3$(ozone) $NO_2 + H_2O \rightarrow$ nitric acid (acid rain) $NO_2 + cation \rightarrow$ particulate matter	Combustion modifications and flue gas treatment.
Lead (Pb) Toxic blue-gray metal	Transportation: 0.00052 Fuel Combustion: 0.00050 Industrial Processes: 0.0029 Miscellaneous: 0.0 Total: 0.0039 % of 1970 Total: 1.7%	Tetraethyl-lead in gasoline $Pb(C_2H_5)_4$	Substitution

(Adapted from Fleagle and Businger 1980)

effective means to handle the problems associated with ozone nonattainment areas. Under CAAA 1990, designated nonattainment areas were given clarification that revised the mechanism used to meet attainment deadlines. The previously defined nonattainment areas were further subcategorized based upon severity of pollution, deadlines were revised, and sanctions, originally reserved for nonattainment, were used to ensure compliance with the CAA 1990.

Criteria Pollutants

Table 1 presents the six criteria pollutants, major emission sources, chemical interactions, and some potential control technologies.

NAAQS Nonattainment Areas

The CAAA 1990 required states to revise their SIPs to meet the national primary and secondary ambient air quality standards. Title 42, Section 7410, states that "Each State shall . . . submit to the Administrator . . . after the promulgation of a national primary ambient air quality standard . . . a plan which provides for implementation, maintenance and enforcement of such primary standard in each air quality control region within such State." Additionally, under the prevention of significant deterioration (PSD) requirements within the act, states must prohibit any source which contributes significantly to nonattainment in, or interfere with the maintenance by, any state with respect to any such national primary or secondary ambient air quality standard. Classifications within regions where the six criteria pollutants of the NAAQS apply were identified as nonattainment, attainment, and reclassified. Within the nonattainment classification were further area classes identified as marginal, moderate, serious, severe, or extreme for the particular criteria pollutants for ozone. The designated areas within regions were also required to address cross-jurisdictional air pollution. "The boundaries of serious, severe, or extreme nonattainment areas located within metropolitan statistical areas (MSAs) or consolidated metropolitan statistical areas (CMSAs) are to be expanded to include the entire MSAs or CMSAs." This led to an expansion of geographic areas classified as "nonattainment" (DOE OHSS 1996).

The EPA maintains a Web site providing yearly data from different geographic areas within the United States. Air quality data can be retrieved for the entire country by EPA region, state, and county. The data includes emission and monitoring information on pollution sources and concentrations. Emissions data are estimates provided by the computing of annual data from individual sources, such as power plants, industry, and vehicles. Monitoring data is compiled from designated outdoor monitoring stations situated in 4000 strategic areas throughout the country. Ambient air quality information is supplied to the EPA by the states, and a yearly summary for individual stations is generated.

Monitoring sites report data to the EPA for six air pollutants termed *criteria pollutants* because of the requirement that the EPA describe the characteristics and potential health and welfare effects of these pollutants. It is on the basis of the criteria that standards are set or revised. These are:

- carbon monoxide (CO)
- nitrogen dioxide (NO_2)
- ozone (O_3)
- sulfur dioxide (SO_2)
- particulate matter—PM10 and PM2.5, which are acronyms for particulate matter consisting of particles smaller than 10 and 2.5 micrometers, respectively.
- lead (Pb)

One might expect that the EPA would track emissions of the same six criteria air pollutants. However, ozone is not emitted directly but forms through chemical reactions of organic compounds with nitrogen oxides in the air, mediated by sunlight. The EPA tracks emissions of lead only as a hazardous air pollutant, defined as a pollutant to which no ambient air quality standard is applicable and that may cause or contribute to an increase in mortality or in serious illness. Ammonia reacts with nitric and sulfuric acids in the atmosphere to form fine particulate matter, so the EPA tracks ammonia emissions. Thus, the EPA tracks emissions data of the following air pollutants (EPA 2004b):

- carbon monoxide (CO)
- sulfur dioxide (SO_2)
- particulate matter (PM10 and PM2.5) and three precursors/promoters of criteria air pollutants:
- volatile organic compounds (VOC)
- nitrogen oxides (NO_x)
- ammonia (NH_3)

Mobile Sources: Vehicle Emissions

The CAA 1970 required emission reductions from automobile exhaust—considered a major contributor to nitrogen oxides (NO_x), hydrocarbons (HCs), and carbon monoxide (CO).

The act directs the EPA to prescribe the following (EPA 1971):

- standards to reduce emissions of CO and HC by 90% from 1970 model levels in the 1975 model autos
- NO_x standards, reduced by 90% from 1971 model levels, to take effect in 1976 model year
- a description by companies of the basic techniques being explored to meet emission standards

EPA sent this requirement to 28 automobile manufacturers; however, delays in meeting the CAA 1970 requirements occurred in part because of the failure of the automobile industry to meet emission-reduction standards and in part because of the energy crisis of the 1970s. By 1975, the oxidation catalytic converter was introduced on newer vehicles. Additionally, gasoline suppliers were to reformulate leaded gas (introduced in 1923); the purpose was to eliminate lead by the introduction of alternative fuels. Even with the phase-out of leaded gasoline in the United States by 1986, it was estimated that the use of lead had deposited seven million tons of non-degradable lead throughout soils, water, and indoor soot (Western Houston Association Issues 2003). Note that between 1975 and 1988 there was a 99 percent reduction in leaded gas.

The CAAA 1990 set more stringent emission standards for automobiles and some categories of light trucks for further reduction in pollutants from mobile sources. CAAA 1990 also required:

- stricter emission standards
- stricter standards for gasoline and diesel fuel
- programs for enforcement of the development of vehicles designed to operate on "clean" fuels (methanol, ethanol, propane, natural gas, and electricity)

The CAAA 1990 also used emission standards compliance in the levying of major highway funding to the states under Transportation Conformity (Section 176(c)). This encourages states to continue to reduce emissions of the six criteria pollutants (NAAQS), in keeping with the maintenance of attainment areas, primarily by encouraging programs within their SIPs that promote car-pooling, gas conservation, and mass transit.

Hazardous Air Pollutants (HAPs)

Hazardous air pollutants, or air toxics, are known or suspected to cause cancer or other serious health problems related to (for example) reproduction and birth and also to affect the environment adversely. The presence of HAPs in the air is more localized than are the criteria pollutants, and HAPs are usually found at highest levels close to their sources. Examples of air toxic pollutants include benzene (found in gasoline), mercury (from coal combustion), perchloroethylene (emitted from some dry-cleaning facilities), and methylene chloride (used as a solvent by a number of industries). Most air toxics originate from manmade sources, including mobile sources such as cars, trucks, and construction equipment; stationary sources such as factories, refineries, and power plants; and indoor sources such as some building materials and cleaning solvents (EPA 2005b).

In 1985, the EPA set forth a strategy for the identification and reduction of HAPs, or air toxics, from specific major and minor stationary source categories. This applied to operational emissions and accidental releases. The strategy went from focusing on categories of chemicals to focusing on specific pollutants emitted by industry, power plants, and waste combustors. Included in the strategy were mobile sources and fuel refineries. The 1985 strategy outlined the following efforts (EPA 1997):

- expanding the focus of the national air toxics control program from solely regulating individual pollutants to also regulating multiple pollutants from different source categories
- expanding the program to reduce risk in specific communities having air toxic problems
- increasing federal support of state air toxic programs, allowing states to improve their capabilities to deal with air toxics within their borders

- improving emergency preparedness and response at all levels of government for sudden, accidental releases of HAPs
- beginning new efforts to give the public the information needed to prevent, prepare for, and respond to toxic accidents

The CAA 1990 began focusing on HAPs emitted by specific major and area source categories, based upon the size of the industry and its potential to emit toxic air pollutants. The following is a summary of the requirements of Title 42, Section 7412, of the CAA:

- Require emission controls for major sources, defined as stationary sources with the potential to emit 10 tons per year or more of any hazardous air pollutant or 25 tons per year or more of any combination of hazardous air pollutants.
- Regulate 189 (now 188) listed hazardous air pollutants under Title 42, Section 7412.
- Revise the list to include pollutants found through scientific study to adversely affect human health and the environment.
- Identify major or area (nonmajor) categories of emissions in accordance with established emission standards.

Along with the identification of source categories, MACT for the reduction and control of emissions included, but was not limited to, end-of-the stack controls, material substitution, recovery/recycling, and chemical use reductions within processes. Emission standards for source categories that emit HAPs must, within reasonable cost constraints, include provisions to reduce pollutants in accordance with established pollutant limits. Hence, control technology should:

- reduce the volume of, or eliminate emissions of, such pollutants through process changes, substitution of materials, or other modifications
- enclose systems or processes to eliminate emissions
- collect, capture, or treat such pollutants when released from a process, stack, storage, or fugitive emission point

- reduce pollutants through design, equipment, work practice, or operational standards (including operator training or certification)
- employ a combination of the above

When developing a MACT standard for a particular source category, the EPA looks at the level of emissions currently being achieved by the best-performing similar sources through clean processes, control devices, work practices, or other methods. These emission levels set a baseline (often referred to as the MACT floor) for the new standard. At a minimum, a MACT standard must achieve, throughout the industry, a level of emissions control at least equivalent to the MACT floor. The EPA can establish a more stringent standard when it makes economic, environmental, and public-health "sense."

The MACT floor is established differently for existing sources and for new sources.

- For existing sources, the MACT floor must equal the average emission limitations currently achieved by the best-performing 12 percent of sources in that source category, if there are 30 or more existing sources. If there are fewer than 30 existing sources, then the MACT floor must equal the average emission limitation achieved by the best-performing five sources in the category.
- For new sources, the MACT floor must equal the level of emissions control currently achieved by the best-controlled similar source.

Wherever feasible, the EPA writes the final MACT standard as an emissions limit (i.e., as a percent reduction in emissions or a concentration limit that regulated sources must achieve). Emission limits provide flexibility for industry to determine the most effective way to comply with the standard.

Acid Deposition

Acid deposition, or acid rain, is addressed under Title IV of CAAA 1990, which calls for regulatory programs to control emissions of sulfur dioxide (SO_2) and nitrogen dioxide (NO_2). Sulfur dioxide reacts in the atmosphere in the presence of water to form sulfuric acid, and nitrogen dioxide reacts with sunlight to form tropospheric ozone, with atmospheric moisture to form nitric acid, and with cations in the atmosphere to form particulate matter in the form of gases of sulfates and nitrates (PM10 and PM2.5). The primary sources of SO_2 and NO_2 come from the combustion of fossil fuels such as coal and oil used to generate electricity at power plants. EPA regulations require that major sources, such as power plants, install continuous monitoring devices to measure the quantities of emissions. The goal of emission standards was to reduce NO_2 emissions by 10 million tons in 2000 and SO_2 emissions by 10 million tons below the 1980 standards (EPA 2005a).

Emissions trading was established as a form of reduction strategy whereby plants that reduce emissions below their allotted standards could sell their excess to other power plants and industries unable to meet source category emission standards. Under the Acid Rain Program of the Clean Air Markets Division, major reductions of sulfur dioxide and nitrogen dioxide from electric utilities were achieved through a new approach to environmental protection that featured market incentives. This nationwide cap-and-trade method of regulation has resulted in significant environmental progress and cost savings. Under the emissions-trading program, each allowance permits a unit to emit one ton of SO_2 during or after a specified year. For each ton of SO_2 emitted in a given year, one allowance is retired, that is, it can no longer be used. The program acts almost like a stock, where companies and the public may purchase units, resell them, create accounts, or, in some instances, retire the units. Utilities are limited to 8.95 million allowances per year (EPA 2005).

Acid-Rain Deposition Mapping

The U.S. Geological Survey (USGS) provides tracking data and other information on precipitation deposition of rain, sleet, and snow by monitoring location and identifies areas impacted by sulfur and nitrogen deposition. The USGS also includes recent reports and presentations on the effects of pollutant deposition.

Atmospheric Deposition of Air Toxics to the Great Lakes and Coastal Waters

Under the CAAA 1990, the EPA and the Under Secretary of Commerce of Oceans and Atmosphere must create a report that identifies the effects of air toxics on the Great Lakes as well as the Chesapeake Bay, Lake Champlain, and coastal waters. The study must use the existing national monitoring stations for the Great Lakes region and deploy an atmospheric monitoring network for coastal waters. By 1993, and on a biennial basis thereafter, pursuant to Section 7412 (6)(m), the Under Secretary of Commerce for Oceans and Atmosphere must use monitoring data to create a report to be submitted to Congress that identifies atmospheric impacts to the Great Lakes, Chesapeake Bay, Lake Champlain, and coastal waters. The report must:

- assess the contribution of atmospheric deposition to pollution loadings
- identify impacts to the environment and public health of any pollutant that is attributable to atmospheric deposition
- describe the sources of any pollution
- assess whether pollutant loadings cause or contribute to overshooting of drinking water standards or water quality standards
- indicate whether any federal law revisions are required to ensure protection of human health and the environment

Since 1990, the EPA has issued three reports to Congress on the deposition of air toxics and their detrimental effects on the Great Waters (i.e., the Great Lakes, the Chesapeake Bay, Lake Champlain, and coastal waters). In these reports, the EPA lists fifteen pollutants of greatest concern, most of which have a tendency to persist in the environment and accumulate in organisms such as fish. The pollutants of concern are metals (mercury, cadmium, lead), dioxins, furans, polycyclic organic matter, polychlorinated biphenyls (PCBs), pesticides (such as chlordane and DDT/DDE), and nitrogen compounds. Nitrogen compounds from the deposition of air toxics can intensify nutrient enrichment (or eutrophication) of coastal water bodies.

EPA's most recent report, issued in 2000, provides an update on atmospheric deposition of pollutants to the Great Waters and identifies activities that will reduce these pollutants (EPA 2000; Kanarek 2004).

Several of the MACT standards are expected to substantially cut emissions of mercury, dioxins, and other pollutants of concern to the Great Waters from sources such as municipal waste combustors and medical waste incinerators. Compared to the 1990 baseline, these alone account for almost 30 percent of mercury emissions and over 70 percent of dioxin emissions nationwide (EPA 2005a).

Mercury Emissions from Coal-Fired Electric Utilities

Mercury is one of the 188 listed toxic air pollutants. It is of concern because it does not degrade in the environment but persists. The largest emitters of mercury are electric utility plants (primarily coal-fired plants), which are estimated to emit approximately one-third of all manmade mercury in the United States. The EPA reported in 2004 that reduction achievements exceeded expectations. The Institute of Clean Air Companies (ICAC) reported that the air pollution control industry had already achieved commercial readiness of mercury control and measurement technologies and could surpass the level of reductions proposed by the EPA in the December 2003 Utility Mercury Reduction Rule. Multiple mercury control technologies are available at a reasonable cost for a range of coals and equipment. Mercury reductions of 50 percent (24 tons of emissions) are achievable by 2008 to 2010, and with flexibility in the rule, a 70 percent reduction (14 tons of emissions) is achievable. Continuous emission measurement systems (CEMS) for mercury are available and provide the technology needed to document compliance, improve process controls, and support the emissions certainty needed for regulatory flexibility such as trading programs (ICAC 2004).

Integrated Urban Air Toxics Strategy

A key component of future efforts to reduce air toxics is the integrated urban air toxics strategy, released by the EPA in July 1999. The strategy presents a framework to address air toxics in urban areas and builds on the substantial emission reductions already achieved in cars, trucks, fuels, and industries such as chemical plants and oil refineries. The strategy outlines actions to further reduce emissions of air toxics and to improve the EPA's understanding of the health risks posed by air toxics in urban areas. The goals of the strategy are to reduce the risk of cancer by 75 percent and to substantially reduce noncancer risks associated with air toxics from commercial and industrial sources. The strategy also reflects the need to address any disproportionate impacts on sensitive populations, including children, the elderly, minorities, and low-income communities (EPA 1999).

The reduction of SO_2 and NO_2 emissions, both of which had specific timeframes for emissions reduction, is set on a phase-in schedule (Wikipedia 2005b):

- Phase I began in 1995 and affected 263 units at 110 (mostly coal-burning) electric utility plants located in 21 eastern and midwestern states.
- An additional 182 units joined phase I of the program as substitution or compensating units, bringing the total of phase I–affected units to 445. Emissions data indicate that the 1995 SO_2 emissions at these units nationwide were reduced by almost 40% below their required level.
- Phase II, which began in 2000, tightened the annual emission limits imposed on these large, higher-emitting plants and also set restrictions on smaller, cleaner plants fired by coal, oil, and gas, encompassing over 2000 units. The program affects existing utility units serving generators having an output capacity of greater than 25 megawatts, as well as all new utility units.
- The act also called for a 2-million-ton reduction in NO_x emissions by the year 2000. A significant portion of this reduction has been achieved in coal-fired utility boilers that were required to install low NO_x burner technologies and to meet new emission standards.

Stratospheric Ozone and Global Climate

Title VI of CAA 1990 describes the requirements for identifying stratospheric ozone-depleting substances, the monitoring of class I and class II chemicals, and phase-out schedules for these substances. Class I substances include CFCs, or chlorinated compounds, that have mostly been phased out from production, with some exceptions. Class II substances include HCFCs, which are slated for phase-out by 2030. Ozone-depleting potential factors were established by the EPA in determining the effects of the most harmful substances. Federal measures to control emissions that impact stratospheric ozone depletion take the initiative to

- create area classifications of nonattainment for ozone within state and interstate boundaries
- establish control technology guidelines (CTGs) for the reduction or elimination of ozone-depleting gases
- identify the sources of ozone depletion—i.e., volatile organic compounds (VOCs), nitrogen dioxides (NO_2), carbon dioxide (CO_2), and their precursors

Ozone Classifications for Boundary/Interboundary Attainment

Ozone (O_3) is a primary component of smog. Ozone is described in its naturally occurring state and as a toxic chemical pollutant. In the naturally occurring state, ozone exists as a thin layer between the troposphere and the stratosphere, acting as a filter for harmful ultraviolet (UV) radiation. As a toxic chemical, O_3 is created when organic compounds—such as hydrocarbons emitted from the combustion of gasoline and solvents and nitrogen dioxides from fuels

combustion—combine with UV rays to form the unstable gas O_3. This can be written chemically as

$$NO_2 + \text{sunlight} \rightarrow NO + O \qquad (1)$$
$$O + O_2 \rightarrow O_3$$

In 1989, the CAA prescribed classifications of areas for attainment of design values of ozone concentrations, set in parts per million (ppm). Under Title 42 (Section 7511) of the 1990 CAA, attainment dates for each classification were established for state compliance as presented in Table 2. Anticipating the challenge to achieve these targeted dates, provisions were set for extended dates of attainment and for subsequent reclassifications of nonattainment areas.

Control Technology Guidelines (CTGs)

Sources of volatile organic compounds (VOCs), which include manmade organic compounds such as gasoline, solvents, and other hydrocarbons, received CTGs to begin implementation within three years of the November 1990 CAAA. The amendments brought into regulation an additional eleven source categories for which VOC emissions had not been previously set.

Under the CTGs, the EPA is required to periodically review sources and modify the listing according to the determination of VOC contribution toward ozone attainment. Those source categories that are priority contributors in ozone nonattainment areas include power plants, hazardous waste incinerators, and industries considered major sources (depending upon tons/emissions of VOCs), such as aerospace, shipbuilding, and chemical manufacturing facilities. These major source categories emit VOCs from such operations as degreasing, paint-spraying, and coating operations, with aggregate contributions of 25 tons of VOCs or more yearly. Such facilities are required to implement a progression of control technologies based upon available technology, from RACT to the more aggressive BACT and MACT, as prescribed by CTGs (EPA 1997).

Key Sources of Ozone Depletion

Title 42, Section 7511, of the CAA 1990 further defines the potential of consumer or commercial products to release VOCs. This applies to "any substance, product

TABLE 2

Attainment Dates for State Compliance with Ozone Values

Area Class	Design Value (ppm)	Primary Standard Attainment Date
Marginal	0.121–0.138	3 years after November 15, 1990
Moderate	0.138–0.160	6 years after November 15, 1990
Serious	0.160–0.180	9 years after November 15, 1990
Severe	0.180–0.280	15 years after November 15, 1990
Extreme	0.280 and above	20 years after November 15, 1990

(Adapted from *Federal Register* 2001)

(including paints, coatings and solvents) or article (including any container or packaging) held by any person, the use, consumption, storage, disposal, destruction, or decomposition of which may result in the release of VOCs." This has been of particular importance within industries such as the aerospace industry that ship degreased components that frequently undergo scrutiny for VOC because of the use of chlorinated solvents.

As required under the CAAA, by 1993, the EPA had to generate a report detailing the contribution of various sources under the categories of consumer and commercial products and identify sources with the potential for exceeding ozone levels in noncompliance with NAAQs. These reports divide the source categories into groups with emissions comprising 80 percent VOCs and assign a priority and incremental timeline for VOC reduction.

Although CFCs and HCFCs have received the most international attention, the increasing use of fossil fuels in the United States and, particularly, in developing countries has also been recognized as a major contributor to global warming. The burning of fossil fuels, which include oils, coal, and natural gas, contributes much carbon dioxide to the atmosphere. The estimated CO_2 in the atmosphere has increased since industrialization in the 1860s. Many environmental groups and organizations, such as the Sierra Club, identified the United States as a major contributor to CO_2, stating that "[t]he US has four percent of the world's population yet emits 25% of the global warming pollution. Power plants emit 40% of US carbon dioxide pollution, the primary global warming pollutant. In 1999, coal-fired power plants alone released 490.5 million metric tons of CO_2 into the atmosphere (32% of the total CO_2 emissions for 1999)" (Sierra Club 2004).

There have been a number of new requirements proposed or already implemented regarding greenhouse gas (GHG) emissions. In the United States, on November 8, 2010, the EPA finalized a rule regarding reporting requirements for the petroleum and natural gas industry under 40 CFR Part 98, the regulatory framework for the Greenhouse Gas (GHG) Reporting Program.

This final rule requires petroleum and natural gas facilities that emit 25,000 metric tons or more of carbon dioxide (CO_2) equivalent per year to report annual methane (CH_4) and CO_2 emissions from equipment leaks and venting, and emissions of CO_2, CH_4, and nitrous oxide (N_2O) from gas flaring and from onshore petroleum and natural gas production stationary and portable combustion emissions and combustion emissions from stationary equipment involved in natural gas distribution.

Emerging industries (such as solar panel and semiconductor) and traditional ones (such as aluminum) use perfluorocarbons (PFCs) in their manufacturing processes. PFCs are fluorocarbons, compounds derived from hydrocarbons by replacement of hydrogen atoms by fluorine atoms. PFCs are made up of carbon and fluorine atoms only, such as octafluoropropane, perfluorohexane, and perfluorodecalin. Aluminum and semiconductor industries are greatly affected by controlling PFC emissions (EPA 2011).

Air Pollution Control Research

CAA 1990 provisions included the use of public and private funds for air pollution prevention, especially for

- research
- investigations
- training
- advisory committees for technical issues
- alternate fuels research
- alternative vehicles research

To achieve these provisions, the EPA was required to establish a program that supports the research and transfer of air pollution prevention and control technologies and systems. Specifically, the EPA was required to:

- promote facilities research and monitoring, as well as scientific studies and public surveys into the effects of air pollution on human health
- provide federal technical and financial assistance to the states' environmental protection agencies or other "public or private agencies, institutions and organizations and individuals" (EPA 1990a)

- work collaboratively with the states to identify specific air pollution contributions and sources; identify solutions for preventing air pollution from affecting communities
- create diverse panels of experts (Department of Defense, Department of Energy, the National Aeronautics and Space Administration, and the National Oceanic and Atmospheric Administration) to conduct research analysis
- provide means for training individuals in air pollution recognition and prevention

In addition, the agency was required to collect and distribute results of investigative air pollution studies and reports and to make them available to the public.

Throughout the CAA of 1990, several requirements are given for the generation of reports periodically updated over a series of years. These include:

- air modeling and data management
- atmospheric effects of pollutants
- trend analysis for ozone, VOCs and reactivity, nitrogen dioxides, sulfur dioxides, carbon dioxide, and particulate emissions
- national/international networks dealing with the effects of pollutants on human health and on ecosystems

A large portion of funding has been allocated to to foster a better understanding of the properties of ozone-depleting chemicals for analysis of inventory and chemical reactivity. Every five years the EPA must submit a report to Congress on the progress and effectiveness of monitoring programs, research committees, data generation, and overall regulatory control of air pollution programs.

Clean Air Act Achievements

Total emissions of the six criteria air pollutants identified in the Clean Air Act dropped again in 2003; air in the United States was the cleanest it had been in three decades. Annual emission statistics for these six pollutants are considered major indicators of the quality of the nation's air because of their importance for human health and the existence of their long-standing national standards.

Emissions have continued to decrease even as the U.S. economy has increased by more than 150 percent. Since 1970 (changing numbers to reflect the 1970 baseline), the aggregate total emissions for the six pollutants (carbon monoxide, nitrogen oxides, sulfur dioxide, particulate matter, volatile organic compounds, and lead) have been cut from 301.5 million tons per year to 147.8 million tons per year, a decrease of 51 percent. Total 2003 emissions were down 12 million tons since 2000, a 7.8 percent reduction (Sierra Club 2004; EPA 2004).

Benefits of the Clean Air Act from 1990 to 2020

The EPA develops periodic reports that estimate the benefits and costs of the Clean Air Act. The main goal of these reports is to provide Congress and the public with comprehensive, up-to-date, peer-reviewed information on the Clean Air Act's social benefits and costs, including improvements in human health, welfare, and ecological resources, as well as the impact of the act's provisions on the U.S. economy. This report is the result of *The Benefits and Costs of the Clean Air Act—Second Prospective Study from 1990 to 2020* (EPA 2011).

The CAAA of 1990 augmented the significant progress made in improving the nation's air quality through the original Clean Air Act of 1970 and its 1977 amendments. The amendments built on the existing structure of the original Clean Air Act, but went beyond those requirements to tighten and clarify implementation goals and timing, increase the stringency of some federal requirements, revamp the hazardous air pollutant regulatory program, refine and streamline permitting requirements, and introduce new programs for the control of acid rain and stratospheric ozone depleters.

The main purpose of this report was to document the costs and benefits of the 1990 CAAA provisions incremental to those costs and benefits achieved from implementing the original 1970 Clean Air Act and the 1977 amendments. The analysis estimates the costs and benefits of reducing emissions of air pollutants by comparing a "with-CAAA" scenario that reflects expected or likely future measures implemented under the CAAA with a "without-CAAA" scenario that freezes the scope and stringency of emission controls at the levels that existed prior to implementing the CAAA.

There are six basic steps undertaken to complete this analysis:

1. air pollutant emissions modeling
2. compliance cost estimation
3. ambient air quality modeling
4. health and environmental effects estimation
5. economic valuation of these effects
6. results aggregation and uncertainty characterization

The results of the analysis make it abundantly clear that the benefits of the CAAA exceed its costs by a wide margin, making the CAAA a good investment for the nation. The report estimates that the annual dollar value of benefits of air quality improvements will be quite substantial, and will grow over time as emission control programs take full effect, reaching a level of approximately $2.0 trillion in 2020.

These benefits will be achieved as a result of CAAA-related programs and regulatory compliance actions, estimated to cost approximately $65 billion in 2020. Most of these benefits (about 85%) are attributable to reductions in premature mortality associated with reductions in ambient particulate matter; as a result, researchers estimate that cleaner air will, by 2020, prevent 230,000 cases of premature mortality in that year. The remaining benefits are roughly equally divided among three categories of human health and environmental improvement: (1) preventing premature mortality associated with ozone exposure; (2) preventing morbidity, including acute myocardial infarctions and chronic bronchitis; and (3) improving the quality of ecological resources and other aspects of the environment, the largest component of which is improved visibility.

The wide margin between estimated benefits and costs and the results of an uncertainty analysis suggest that it is extremely unlikely that the monetized benefits of the CAAA over the 1990 to 2020 period reasonably could be less than its costs, under any alternative set of assumptions conceived (EPA 2011).

ENVIRONMENTAL AND HUMAN EFFECTS

Toxic Air Pollutants

Most toxic air pollutants originate from manmade sources that include mobile sources such as cars, trucks, and construction equipment; stationary sources such as factories, refineries, and power plants; and indoor sources such as some building materials and cleaning solvents. Some air toxics are also released from natural sources that include volcanic eruptions and forest fires (EPA 1991; EPA 2005a).

The Clean Air Act of 1990 identifies 188 air toxics from industrial sources (EPA 2005a). The EPA has identified 21 pollutants as mobile source air toxics, including benzene (a known human carcinogen), formaldehyde, acetaldehyde, 1,3-butadiene, and diesel particulate matter.

In addition, in 1999 the EPA listed 33 urban hazardous air pollutants that pose the greatest threats to public health in urban areas. The list of HAPs considered emissions from major, area, and mobile sources, including acetaldehyde, ethylene oxide, acrolein, formaldehyde, acrylonitrile, hexachlorobenzene, arsenic compounds, hydrazine, benzene, lead compounds, beryllium compounds, manganese compounds, 1,3-butadiene, mercury compounds, cadmium compounds, methylene chloride, carbon tetrachloride, nickel compounds, chloroform, polychlorinated biphenyls (PCBs), chromium compounds, coke oven emissions, polycyclic organic matter (POM), quinoline, dioxin, 1,1,2,2-tetrachloroethane, ethylene dibromide, vinyl chloride, propylene dichloride, perchloroethylene, trichloroethylene, 1,3-dichloropropene, and ethylene dichloride (EPA 2004b).

People who are exposed to toxic air pollutants at sufficient concentrations and for sufficient durations may be at increased risk of developing cancer or experiencing other serious health effects. Depending on which air toxics an individual is exposed to, these health effects can include damage to the immune system, as well as neurological, reproductive (e.g., reduced fertility), developmental, and respiratory problems. A growing body of evidence indicates that some air toxics (e.g., DDT, dioxins, and mercury) may disturb hormonal (or endocrine) systems. In some cases, this happens by pollutants either mimicking or blocking the action of natural hormones. Health effects associated with endocrine disruption include breast cancer, reduced male fertility, and birth defects. In addition to the hazards of being exposed to air toxics, there are also risks associated with the deposition of toxic pollutants onto soils or surface waters. These pollutants, through plants and animals, are magnified as they work their way up the food chain. Like humans, animals may experience health problems because of air toxic exposure.

The following is a summary of common air pollutants, their major sources, and their environmental and health effects (Koren and Bisesi 1995; EPA 2005a):

1. Ozone: ground-level ozone is the principal component of smog
   Source: chemical reaction of pollutants; VOCs and NO$_x$
   Environmental effects: ozone can damage plants and trees; smog can reduce visibility
   Health effects: breathing problems, reduced lung function, asthma, eye irritation, stuffy nose, reduced resistance to colds and other infections, may speed up aging of lung tissue
2. Volatile organic compounds (VOCs): the EPA does not list VOCs as criteria air pollutants
   Source: VOCs are released from burning fuel (for example, gasoline, oil, wood, coal, natural gas), solvents, paints, glues, and other products used at work and at home; cars are a significant source of VOCs that include such chemicals as benzene, toluene, methylene chloride, and methyl chloroform
   Environmental effects: in addition to ozone (smog) effects, some VOCs (such as ethylene and formaldehyde) may harm plants
   Health effects: in addition to ozone (smog) effects, many VOCs can cause serious health problems, including cancer
3. Nitrogen dioxide (one of the NO$_x$)
   Source: burning of gasoline, natural gas, coal, oil, and so on; cars are a significant source of NO$_2$
   Environmental effects: nitrogen dioxide is an ingredient of acid rain (acid aerosols), which can damage trees and lakes and reduce visibility
   Health effects: lung damage, illnesses of the respiratory system
4. Carbon monoxide (CO)
   Source: burning of gasoline, natural gas, coal, oil, and so on
   Health effects: reduces ability of blood to bring oxygen to body cells and tissues (cells and tissues need oxygen to work); carbon monoxide may be particularly hazardous to people who have heart or circulatory (blood vessel) problems or who have damaged lungs or breathing passages
5. Particulate matter (PM-10); (dust, smoke, soot)
   Source: burning wood, diesel, and other fuels; industrial plants; agriculture (plowing, burning off fields); unpaved roads
   Environmental effects: particulates are the main source of visibility-reducing haze
   Health effects: nose and throat irritation, lung damage, bronchitis, early death
6. Sulfur dioxide
   Source: burning of coal and oil, especially high-sulfur coal from the eastern United States; industrial processes (paper, metals)
   Environmental effects: SO$_2$ is an ingredient in acid rain (acid aerosols) that damage trees and lakes and reduce visibility
   Health effects: breathing problems; possible permanent damage to lungs
7. Lead
   Source: leaded gasoline (being phased out), paint (houses, cars), smelters (metal refineries); manufacture of lead storage batteries
   Environmental effects: can harm wildlife
   Health effects: brain and other nervous-system damage (children are at special risk); some lead-containing chemicals cause cancer in animals; lead also causes digestive and other health problems

Toxic pollutants in the air, or deposited on soils or surface waters, can have a number of environmental effects. The EPA *Health Effects Notebook* concluded that deposited air toxics contribute to birth defects, reproductive failure, and disease in animals. Persistent toxic air pollutants are of particular concern in aquatic ecosystems because the pollutants accumulate in sediments and may biomagnify in tissues of animals at the top of the food chain to concentrations many times higher than the original concentration in the water or air. Toxic pollutants that mimic hormones also pose a threat to the environment. In some wildlife (e.g., birds, shellfish, fish, and mammals), exposures to pollutants such as DDT, dioxins, and mercury have been associated with decreased fertility, decreased hatching success, damaged reproductive organs, and altered immune systems.

The primary source of information used by the EPA to develop these findings is its Integrated Risk Information System (IRIS) (EPA 2007), a database that summarizes available toxicity data and contains EPA's assessment of the data; it also contains secondary sources, such as EPA's Health Assessment Documents, Drinking Water Criteria Documents, Health Effects Assessment Summary Tables (HEAST), and the Agency for Toxic Substances and Disease Registry (ATSDR) Toxicological Profiles (CDC 2007). In addition, databases such as the Hazardous Substances Data Bank (HSDB), which contains summaries of peer-reviewed literature (NLM n.d.) and the Registry of Toxic Effects of Chemical Substances (RTECS) (CDC n.d.), which lists toxic effects of chemicals (and which is not peer reviewed), were used.

The EPA has developed a National-Scale Air Toxics Assessment (EPA 1999), a nationwide analysis of air toxics. It uses computer modeling of the 1996 National Emission Inventory (NEI) air toxics data as the basis for developing health-risk estimates for 33 toxic air pollutants (a subset of the Clean Air Act's list of 188 air toxics plus diesel PM). The national-scale assessment is intended to provide state, local, tribal, and other agencies with a better understanding of the risks of inhalation exposure to toxic air pollutants from outdoor sources. It will help the EPA and states prioritize data and research needs to better assess risk in the future, and it will also provide a baseline to help measure future trends in estimated health risks.

Three air toxics (formaldehyde, chromium, and benzene) appear to pose the greatest nationwide carcinogenic risk. The EPA generates maps showing the distribution of relative cancer risk across the continental United States, with 20 percent of counties containing almost three-fourths of the U.S. population at high risk. This map does not include the potential risk from diesel exhaust emissions, because existing health data are not sufficient to develop a numerical estimate of cancer risk for this pollutant. However, exposure to diesel exhaust is widespread, and the EPA has concluded that diesel exhaust is a likely human carcinogen and ranks with other substances that the national-scale assessment suggests pose the greatest relative risk. One air toxic, acrolein, is estimated to pose the highest potential nationwide risk for significant, chronic, and adverse effects on health after cancer.

This technical assessment represents an important step toward characterizing air toxics nationwide. It is designed to help identify general patterns in air toxics exposure and risk across the country, and it is not recommended as a tool to characterize or compare risk at local levels (e.g., to compare risks from one part of a city to another). More localized assessments, including monitoring and modeling, can be obtained from local radio and TV weather reports of daily air quality levels and air pollution forecasts in the area, as well as from newspapers and online sources, including the EPA (www.epa.gov/airnow/) and the American Lung Association (2000). Many of these online sites provide ambient air quality data on a state-by-state basis throughout the United Sates, including:

- outdoor air quality
- outdoor air pollutants
- children and ozone air pollution fact sheet
- air toxics
- carbon monoxide
- lead
- outdoor air pollution fact sheet
- ozone
- nitrogen dioxide
- particulate matter
- sulfur dioxide
- particle pollution fact sheet
- ozone fact sheet
- diesel exhaust and air pollution

- the air quality index
- Clean Air Week®: American Lung Association® Survey, and Air Quality Index Backgrounder
- air quality index fact sheet
- selected key studies on particulate matter and health

Acid Rain

Acid rain causes acidification of lakes and streams and contributes to the damage of trees and sensitive forest soils. In addition, acid rain accelerates the decay of building materials and paints, including irreplaceable buildings, statues, and sculptures that are part of our nation's cultural heritage. Prior to falling to the earth, SO_2 and NO_x gases and their particulate matter derivatives, sulfates and nitrates, degrade visibility and public health.

The Acid Rain Program confers significant benefits on the nation. Reducing SO_2 and NO_x will significantly improve many acidified lakes and streams so that they can once again support fish life. Visibility will improve, allowing for increased enjoyment of scenic vistas across our country, particularly in national parks. Stress to forests that populate mountain ridges from Maine to Georgia will be reduced. Deterioration of our historic buildings and monuments will be slowed. Most importantly, reductions in SO_2 and NO_x will reduce fine particulate matter (sulfates, nitrates) and ground-level ozone (smog), improving public health (EPA 2004a).

Greenhouse Effect

Gaseous components in the atmosphere, generated from such sources as fossil-fuel combustion from electrical power plants and emissions from automobiles, when combined with sunlight, create what is known as the "greenhouse effect." Since the 1860s, with the increase in fossil-fuel combustion for power and industrialization, emissions from these sources of greenhouse gases have contributed to significant levels of CO_2, NO_x, and methane. Table 3 shows average emission values in 1998 compared to pre-1750 levels. Emissions from these sources and from natural sources, such as

volcanic activity and deforestation, have over time contributed to the warming of the earth (Sierra Club 2004). The pre-1750 values are based on scientists piecing together a picture of the earth's climate dating back decades to millions of years by analyzing a number of surrogate, or "proxy," measures of climate such as ice cores, boreholes, tree rings, glacier lengths, pollen remains, and ocean sediments; they have also done so by studying changes in the earth's orbit around the sun (NRC 2006, Wikipedia 2005a).

According to the NASA Astrobiology Institute (2005), most of the energy from the earth that affects weather comes from the sun. The planet and its atmosphere absorb and reflect some of the energy. The absorbed energy tends to produce warming, and the reflection or radiation of energy allows the planet to cool. The balance between absorbed and radiated energy determines the average temperature. The radiation balance can be altered by factors such as the intensity of solar energy, reflection of energy by clouds or gases, absorption of energy by various gases or surfaces, and emission of heat by various materials. A balance is continually found based on sunlight, depth, and density of atmospheric areas with various amounts of gases, clouds, and aerosols, and where seasons alter the ground cover. The planet is warmer than it would be in the absence of the atmosphere. Emissions of greenhouse gases tend to dissipate over time. These gases can be reabsorbed from the atmosphere through a series of natural physical and biological processes that include photosynthesis, oceanic activity, and climatic changes. The destruction of the ozone has been recognized as a phenomenon affecting global climate, arguably due to anthropogenic activities.

TABLE 3

Comparison of Average Emissions of Carbon Dioxide, Methane, and Nitrous Oxide—1750 to 1998

Gas	Current (1998) Amount by Volume	Increase Over Preindustrial (1750)	Percentage Increase
Carbon dioxide	365 ppm	87 ppm	31%
Methane	1745 ppb	1045 ppb	150%
Nitrous oxide	314 ppb	44 ppb	16%

(Adapted from Wikipedia 2005b)

Some scientists believe that climactic change due to rising temperatures is a natural progression that follows the cycle of earth's evolution. As with many fields of scientific study, there are uncertainties associated with the science of climate change. This does not imply that scientists do not have confidence in many aspects of climate science. Some aspects are known with virtual certainty, because they are based on well-known physical laws and on documented trends. Current understanding of many other aspects of climate change ranges from *likely* to *uncertain*. In short, a number of scientific analyses indicate, but cannot prove, that rising levels of greenhouse gases in the atmosphere are contributing to climate change, as some theories assert. In the coming decades, scientists anticipate that as atmospheric concentrations of greenhouse gases continue to rise, average global temperatures and sea levels will continue to rise as a result, and precipitation patterns will change (EPA 2006b).

Increased global industrialization has created international concerns, such as the potential effects of global warming associated with emissions and such as changes in the distribution of endemic diseases as concluded by the National Research Council (NRC 2006). The understanding of the relationship betweem weather/climate and human health is in its infancy, and the health consequences of climate change are still poorly understood. Worldwide concerns have, however, resulted in multinational policies such as the Montreal Protocol (UNEP 2000). The Montreal Protocol is an international policy for broad-based cooperation in the phase-out of Class 1 CFCs and Class 2 HCFCs over a scheduled period. The policy is an effort to eliminate chlorinated and fluorinated chemical compounds that contribute to the depletion of stratospheric ozone. The United States signed the Montreal Protocol of CFCs in 1988, with the anticipation of the signatory concurrence of over 59 countries by 1989. The United States further set a goal to eliminate the five CFCs under the protocol by 2030.

CONTROL TECHNOLOGIES AND METHODS

Today most of the air pollution in the United States is directly related to combustion of fuels for transporta-tion, production of electricity, and manufacturing. As discussed in previous sections of this chapter, air pollution is a global concern. Recognizing the complexity of reducing or preventing air pollution, this section briefly discusses advantages and disadvantages of using different types of air pollution control equipment for major pollutants linked to stationary sources. The major air pollutants are particulates, sulfur dioxide, carbon monoxide, nitrogen oxides, and volatile organic compounds. Mathematics and engineering formulae are only introduced in this section to support or clarify concepts. A detailed discussion of the engineering design, operations, maintenance, and selection of air pollution control equipment is beyond the scope of this chapter. Recommended readings may be found in Appendix A at the end of this chapter.

Air pollution control can be achieved using isolation, substitution, treatment, or prevention techniques. Treatment is by far the technique most frequently used. Prevention is the preferred method. It is best achieved through proper planning, proper equipment maintenance, and adequate placement of various industrial sources. In general, air pollution is reduced by using many of the techniques known today, and specific controls are available for most industries.

Basic Science

Understanding and knowledge of some key scientific concepts are essential for determining the best control and preventions solutions for air pollution. Hence, this section will briefly introduce vital concepts of the atmosphere, gas law, concentration measurements in gases, material and energy balances, characteristics and behavior of particles, and engineering economics as they pertain to air pollution. Only frequently used formulae will be identified and discussed; a full discussion of these topics is beyond the scope of this chapter. The information in this section is extracted from the textbook, *Basic Physical Chemistry for the Atmospheric Sciences*, by Peter V. Hobbs (2000).

The Atmosphere

Air under dry ambient conditions consists of a number of gases, including nitrogen (78%), oxygen (21%), carbon dioxide (0.03%), and less than 1% of argon, neon, helium, crypton, and xenon. Oxygen oxidizes other substances by serving as an electron acceptor that bonds with them. Air also contains varying amounts of water vapor and a variety of natural and artificial pollutants. Dispersal of air pollutants is based on the stability of the air, thermal and mechanical turbulence, mixing depths, inversion, wind direction, wind speed, time of day, season, weather, land topography, and local obstructions that cause crosscurrents.

The rate that air temperature decreases as altitude increases is called the adiabatic lapse rate, theoretically 5.4°F for every thousand feet in dry air. Therefore, if air is permitted to rise without any heat exchange because of its environment, as the pressure decreases, the air expands and cools, and vice versa. However, the actual air temperature often changes with altitude at a higher rate than the theoretical rate. When such a situation exists, the air is said to be unstable, and warm surface air rises rapidly. This instability is good because it creates an up-and-down mixing of air currents that dilutes air pollutants.

Thermoturbulence is the rapid mixing of hot and cold air. The mixing depth of the air usually extends several thousand feet during the daylight hours of the summer and a few hundred feet during the winter, when the sun contributes less heat. At night, the air close to the earth is cooled by contact with it, but the air higher up stays relatively warm. This causes a minimal level of mixing, thereby concentrating the pollutants close to the surface of the earth. Winds at the surface and at higher elevations are important factors in determining the rate at which concentrations of pollutants can be dispersed. Note that the upward dispersion of pollutants is more effective than horizontal dispersion. Whenever the temperature at higher altitudes is greater than at the lower altitude, a temperature inversion is created that forms a "lid" and prevents vertical mixing (Fleagle and Businger 1980).

Weather has an effect on the degree of pollution in the air and the interaction of pollutants. Rain or snow will precipitate pollutants, making air cleaner but causing surface pollution. Fog, the condensation of water vapors in the air, contains aerosols (tiny suspended solid or liquid particles), but smog is a combination of smoke or chemicals and fog. As aerosols cool, the moisture in the air adheres to them. Fog can convert harmful gases, such as sulfur dioxide and nitrogen dioxide, into even more harmful chemicals, such as sulfuric acid, nitric oxide, and atomic oxygen (which reacts with oxygen molecules and other constituents of air emissions to form a variety of products, including ozone). Ozone is harmful and associated with highly complex, undesirable reactions in the atmosphere.

The Gas Law

Recall the gas law for an ideal gas

$$PV = nRT \qquad (2)$$

where P is the absolute pressure (atm), V is the volume (in liters), n is the number of moles (gmol), R is the ideal gas law constant equal to 0.08206 L-atm/gmol-K, and T is the absolute temperature (in degrees Kelvin). Note that in air pollution calculations, normal temperature of 25°C (298°K) and pressure of one atmosphere are used instead of the standard values of 0°C (273°K) and one atmosphere. Hence the volume per gram mole (V/n) is equal to 24.45 L/gmol, instead of the standard 22.4 L. The standard gas law equations are applicable for ideal gases, but air is not composed of ideal gases.

The gas law can be rewritten in terms of the mass density (ρ)g/L

$$\rho = M/V = P(MW)/RT \qquad (3)$$

where M is the mass of the sample (g) and MW the molecular weight of the gas (g/gmol).

Concentration Measurements in Gases

Common units used in air pollution to quantify concentration are parts per million (ppm) = (volume of pollutant/total volume of gas mixture) $\times 10^6$, and micrograms per cubic meter (μg/m³).

From the gas law, the concentration of a pollutant as a fraction of the total gas volume is expressed as

$$C_{ppm} = 10^6 V_p/V_t \qquad (4)$$

where V_p is the volume of the pollutant and V_t is the total volume.

Converting from volume (ppm) to mass ($\mu g/m^3$),

$$C_{(\mu g/m^3)} = 1000\ C_{ppm}\ MW_p/24.45 \tag{5}$$

where MW_p is the molecular weight of the pollutant.

Material and Energy Balances

The law of conservation of mass and energy is the basis for material and energy balance calculations, which can be expressed as:

$$\text{Accumulation} = \text{Input} - \text{Output} + \text{net generation} \tag{6}$$

For steady-state operation, all operating parameters are time-independent, and accumulation is equal to zero. In selecting and sizing most air pollution control equipment, steady-state conditions are assumed. Some exceptions to this generalization are encountered in the design of direct-fired dryers, incinerators, and adsorbers. It is necessary to define the system and its boundaries in such a way as to make maximum use of the information available on the system. To achieve this, draw a sketch of the process and then identify and label all entering and existing streams, performing material and energy balance calculations. Note that the pollution control engineer will be better equipped to perform the calculations. Because minimizing the use of energy is critical, a basic understanding of energy fundamentals is a prerequisite for good design. See the suggested reading for additional textbooks on this subject. For steady flow systems, the enthalpy (H) of a substance is a physical property and a function of the conditions at a point; hence, absolute enthalpy (H) is given as

$$H = U + PV \tag{7}$$

where U is the internal energy of the fluid per unit mass and PV is as previously defined. Note that absolute enthalpies are not used, but rather a difference in enthalpy between a desired point and a standard reference point; thus, reference to change in enthalpy (ΔH) is used in calculations.

$$\Delta H = H_a - H_b \tag{8}$$

where the subscripts a and b denote desired and standard points, respectively.

In performing energy calculations, absolute enthalpies are not used, but rather difference in enthalpies between a desired and a standard reference point. For example, enthalpy for steam and water can be found in standard steam tables.

CHARACTERISTICS AND BEHAVIOR OF PARTICLES

Polluting particles are composed of a variety of artificial and natural substances of varying sizes in different states. Collectively, they are called particulates and are often divided into smoke, fumes, dust, mist, and particles. Extracted from Lapple (1961), the following are some technical definitions for the various particulates:

- Smoke is both solid and liquid particles under 1 micron (μm) in diameter—usually less than 0.05 μm in diameter.
- Fumes are solid particles under 1 μm in diameter that are formed as vapors condense or as chemical reactions take place. Fumes are emitted by many industrial processes, including smelting and refining, both of which generate metallic oxide fumes.
- Solid particles are more than 1 μm in diameter and are generally referred to as dust. Dust may be formed from solid organic or inorganic matter by natural attrition or through innumerable industrial and agricultural processes when a parent material is reduced in size through some mechanical process, such as crushing, drilling, grinding, or friction.
- Mist is made up of liquid particles up to 100 μm in diameter. It is released industrially in such operations as spraying, splashing, foaming, and impregnating, or is formed by the condensation of vapor in the atmosphere or by the effect of sunlight on automobile exhaust. As mist evaporates, a more concentrated liquid aerosol or mist is formed.

Particulate size and, to a lesser degree, chemical state influence its divisions and behavior. For example, larger particulates (5–30 μm), when inhaled, tend to affect the upper nasal airways through inertia, but smaller particulates are deposited in the lungs. Through diffusion or Brownian movement, particles 0.1–1 μm in size tend to accumulate in the alveolar region. These particulates may cause localized irritation or lung disease or may be absorbed into the circulatory system, ultimately causing systemic problems. When particulates are emitted into the air, their properties and effects may change. These changes can result in detrimental effects. For example, the particles in the emission may break up, forming very small aerosols (from 0.001 to 0.1 μm in diameter) that act as nuclei on which vapor condenses relatively easily. This is the case with the formation of fogs, ground mists, and rain.

Particulates must be separated from a fluid as part of a pollution control system. So considering a particle in motion relative to a fluid, either the particle or the fluid or both can be moving relative to an absolute frame of reference. The fluid exerts an opposing force on the particle, termed *drag force*. Separating particles from the fluid will require external forces, causing impaction, interception, or diffusion. These forces must be greater than the drag force. Applying, for example, Stokes' law, Cunningham's correction to Stokes' law, Newton's law of turbulent flow, the laws of transitional flow, and the drag coefficient, the settling velocity of particles can be determined—a necessary parameter for selecting pollution control devices. Discussion of these topics is beyond the scope of this chapter but is covered in college physics textbooks and the air pollution design textbooks cited in the references and recommended readings.

Engineering Economics

In this section, some key concepts such as depreciation, optimization, incremental rate of return, and payout period will be briefly defined. These terms are frequently used in the financial analysis of alternatives. See the recommended readings for books on this subject.

There are several financial techniques and tools that range in sophistication from simple payback (investment/annual net savings) or rate of return

(average annual net savings/total investment) to more accurate calculations, such as net present value (NPV) or internal rate of return (IRR), which take into account the time value of money. Regardless of which calculations are used, the most important part of a financial analysis is the estimation of project costs and benefits.

Only those incremental costs associated with the alternative should be included when determining the financial ramifications of the investment on the company. In other words, include only those costs that arise from an alternative and would not exist if the alternative were not pursued. These costs are generally dominated by direct costs, such as engineering fees, equipment purchases, supplies, contractor fees, costs of off-site training for employees, lost production resulting from disruption of production during project installation and learning curve, and ongoing maintenance of new equipment. Costs that do not change as the result of an investment decision are irrelevant to the decision. For example, overhead costs that may be allocated to an alternative, but which would exist regardless of the alternative, should not be included in a financial analysis because they are not incremental costs.

It is difficult to accurately estimate total benefits resulting from installation of air pollution control equipment. However, it is a critical step in the corporate capital-investment decision-making process to estimate all costs and benefits related to a proposed investment before the investment is made. Enhanced corporate image is one benefit that a company will probably not attempt to quantify, but it will still be taken into account qualitatively when making decisions with environmental benefits.

Return on Investment

Because return on investment (ROI) is a concept that determines viability in equipment purchase, maintenance, and replacement, these factors should be considered:

- ROI speaks the business language of safety.
- ROI illustrates a measure of profitability.
- ROI provides a consistent accounting method.

- ROI justifies equipment and program resource expenditures.
- ROI determines needs that go beyond operations and allow for payback potential.

To calculate the time value of money for pollution control equipment, assess the projected costs and savings associated with the equipment. The equipment must fit the requirements. Other tangible elements of the equipment need to be be defined. Benefits that derive from the use of equipment in terms of operational efficiency and savings should be communicated to management to secure support. NOTE: This calculation is drawn from Mr. David Pais' presentation to the American Society of Safety Engineers Greater San Jose Chapter meeting, February 8, 2011, and a college course in Engineering Economics.

Depreciation

Pollution control equipment decreases in value with time. This decrease in value is a noncash cost. Assuming straight-line depreciation (normal practice), the asset value after n years in service is equal to

$$V_n = V_i - d_n \text{ or } V_i(1 - f)^n \tag{9}$$

where V is the value in dollars, d is the annual depreciation in dollars, f is the fixed percentage factor; subscripts n and i are years in service and initial value, respectively. Factoring in salvage average (s) the annual depreciation is equal to $(V_i - V_s)/n$ (Sepulveda et al. 1990).

The following is a simple example. In 2000, companies X and Y bought identical cyclone spray chambers that cost $150,000 each. In both applications, the service life was estimated to be five years with zero salvage value. The corporate income tax rate for both companies was 50 percent. Company X used straight-line depreciation and Company Y used the modified accelerated cost recovery system (MACRS method). How much more money did Company Y save over the first three years of service based on its depreciation procedure?

Solution:

Depreciation claimed by Company X:
$150,000/5 \times 3 = $90,000$

Depreciation claimed by Company Y:

From the MACRS tables, the depreciation in the first three years totals 76% of the initial cost.

$150,000 \times 0.76 = $114,000$

Because the corporate tax rate for each company is 50%, Company Y saved

$0.50 \times ($114,000 - $90,000) = $12,000.$

Note that as a practical matter, most companies use the most advantageous method of depreciation allowed by law for tax purposes, whereas engineers typically use straight-line depreciation for evaluation of alternative cases.

Optimization

Optimization can be broadly defined as the determination of a highest or lowest quantifiable parameter over a range. Thus a problem can be maximized for profit or minimized for loss.

Minimization is the act of finding the numerically lowest point in a given function, or in a particular range of a given function.

The following is a simple example. Select the best replacement fabric bag from three different types that are available for the fabric filter, given the estimated total cost (capital and operating) per square yard and the manufacturer's rated pressure drop for each after 1000 cubic feet of dust-laden air has been filtered, as shown in Table 4.

Select the best system based on the optimum criterion stating that the best system is the one with the lowest total cost per pressure drop. Based on this criterion, option A is the best, because cost per pressure drop is the least. Note carefully in using this technique that the process design that provides the lowest total cost may differ from the one that provides the best operating efficiency.

TABLE 4

Type	Cost	Pressure Drop (psi)
A	$350	1.5
B	$360	0.9
C	$370	0.92

Incremental Rate of Return on Investments

The incremental rate of return on investment can be defined as the annual profit from incremental investment divided by incremental investment. In this technique, alternatives are selected based on profit and the least total investment.

The following is a simple example. A company invited bids for supplying a cyclone to control dust from its operations. The lowest bid on a cyclone that would meet all control requirements is for a carbon-steel cyclone with an installed cost of $50,000. The cyclone has a service life of five years. A second bid received is for a stainless-steel cyclone at an installed cost of $80,000 and guaranteed for ten years, which is projected to lower maintenance costs by $2000 per year. Both cyclones are estimated to have zero salvage value. If the company currently receives a 10 percent return before taxes on all investments, which cyclone should be purchased?

Solution:

Depreciation on carbon-steel cyclone = $50,000/5 = $10,000 per year

Depreciation on stainless-steel cyclone = $80,000/10 = $8000 per year

Total yearly savings with stainless-steel cyclone = ($10,000 − $8,000) + 2000 = $4000 per year

Incremental investment = $80,000 − 50,000
$$= \$30,000$$

Incremental rate of return on investment = $4000/$30,000 × 100 = 13.3%

As the incremental return exceeds company requirements, the higher bid should be accepted. Note that, in this case, even if the incremental return did not appear to be acceptably high, further consideration must be given to the stainless-steel cyclone because, presumably, a second carbon-steel cyclone would need to be purchased after five years.

Payout Period

Payout period is a measure of profitability in terms of length of time required to recover the fixed capital investment. It can be defined as

$$\frac{\text{Fixed capital expenditure}}{(\text{average annual profit} + \text{average annual depreciation})}$$

Most companies assume that depreciation is linear over a fixed number of years, as allowed by governmental regulations.

Air Pollution Control Devices

In principle, air pollutants are controlled at the source or diluted after emission into the atmosphere. Source pollution control is accomplished by preventing the pollutant from forming. This can be achieved by changing existing industrial operations through modification or replacement of raw materials, fuels, equipment, or production methods; developing new products or processes that minimize air pollution problems; developing equipment that destroys, alters, or traps pollutants; and destroying, masking, or counteracting odorous materials.

Control of Particulates

Particulates are emitted in the gases or smoke from smokestacks. Koren and Bisesi (1995) concluded that a considerable quantity of particles could be removed from gas streams by applying the following principles:

1. Sufficiently reducing the velocity of the gas to allow the particles to settle by gravity (for example, a settling chamber)
2. Suddenly changing the direction of the gas flow to cause the particles to flow straight ahead because of inertia (for example, a cyclone or louver collector)
3. Filtering of dust-laden gas (for example, bag-house collectors)
4. Electrostatically charging particles to cause the charged particles to be attracted to objects with opposite charge (as in electrostatic precipitators)

Applying these principles, different styles and types of particulate control equipment can be developed. The major types are mechanical separators, such as gravity settlers, cyclones, fabric filters, electrostatic precipitators, and wet scrubbers. The following is a brief description of the operating principles of the above-mentioned control equipment. Examples and illustrations are available on the Internet that can aid in the understanding of the description and operations.

A *gravity settler* is a large chamber in which gas speed is slowed, allowing particles to settle.

A *cyclone* causes the entire gas stream to flow in a spiral pattern inside a tube. Affected by centrifugal force, the larger particles move outward and collide with the wall of the tube, falling down to the bottom of the cyclone, where they are removed. The cleaned gas flows out of the top of the cyclone. It is important to prevent moisture condensation within the tubes or cyclone area. Multi-tube cyclones are more efficient than the single-tube cyclones and may be used for final particulate collection. The efficiency of the multi-tube cyclones depends mainly on the velocity of the gas coming in, the diameter and length of the individual tubes, and the range of the particle size in the gas stream. Higher inlet gas velocities, smaller tube diameters, and longer tube lengths increase particle removal efficiency and resistance to gas flow. The major advantages of cyclones are low capital cost, ability to operate at high temperatures, and low maintenance requirements; the major disadvantages are low efficiencies and high operating costs.

A *fabric filter*, typically called a *bag-house* collector, operates on the same principle as a vacuum cleaner. Air carrying dust particles is forced through a cloth bag. As the air passes through the fabric, the dust accumulates on the cloth, providing a cleaned air stream. The dust is periodically removed from the cloth by shaking or by reversing the airflow. At times, the inert gas is pretreated or precleaned before it comes to the fabric filter. It is important to prevent moisture condensation within the bag-house or the filter area, which can otherwise cause collected particles to plug the bags. The collection efficiency of fabric filters is dependent upon the character of the fabrics used, the particle size distribution, and the porosity of the dust cake. Particulate matter removal efficiencies of greater than 99.9 percent are achieved in a variety of applications of the fabric filters known as HEPA filters, which are high-efficiency particulate air filters. The major advantages of fabric filters are

high collection efficiencies and the ability to operate on a wide variety of dust types in a wide range of volumetric flow rates. The major disadvantages are required large floor areas, the inability to operate in moist environments, the potential of harm through high temperatures or corrosive chemicals, and the potential for fire or explosion.

An *electrostatic precipitator* (ESP) applies electrical force to separate particles from the gas stream. A high voltage drop is established between electrodes, and particles passing through the resulting electrical field acquire a charge. The charged particles are attracted to and collected on an oppositely charged plate, and the cleaned gas flows through the device. Periodically, the plates are cleaned by rapping to shake off the layers of accumulated dust, which is collected in hoppers at the bottom of the device. ESPs are used in a variety of industries and operations, such as the aluminum, pulp and paper, cement, gypsum, iron, and steel industries. They are also used in sulfuric acid recovery; asphalt blowing stills; phosphoric acid production; tar and oil recovery from waste, fuel, or gases; phosphate rock crushing; and coal-fired boiler operations. The collection efficiency of an electrostatic precipitate is dependent on the characteristics of the particulates: their size and electrical resistivity and the amount of collection electrode-plate surface area used. Particle-removal efficiencies of more than 99.9 percent have been achieved in some of these processes. The major advantages of ESPs are very high efficiencies, the ability to handle large volumes with low pressure drop, the dry collection of valuable materials or wet collection of fumes and mists, low operating costs (except at high efficiencies), and the potential for use in a wide range of gas temperatures. Major disadvantages are high capital costs, high space requirements; the inability to control gaseous emissions, inflexibility in operating conditions, and low efficiency for particles with high electrical resistivity.

A *wet scrubber* applies the principles of impaction and interception of dust particles through droplets of water. The heavier water droplets are easily separated from the gas by gravity. The solid particles can then be independently separated from the water, or the water can be otherwise treated before reuse or discharge.

Wet scrubbers are also used for the abatement of acid fumes generated from heated acid baths. In some cases, chemical treatment of the wet-scrubbing media is needed to adjust the pH level and optimize abatement efficiencies. A wet scrubber is a collection device that uses an aqueous stream or slurry to remove particulate matter and gaseous pollutants. Scrubbers are classified by energy consumption in terms of gas-phase pressure drop. Performance of typical wet scrubbers is affected by gas velocity, liquid-to-gas ratio, particle-size distribution, and inlet gas particulate-matter concentration. The gas-phase pressure drop is usually the major factor affecting the removal of the particulates. Wet scrubbers are best used for the collection of hygroscopic and corrosive submicron particles, such as those found in the phosphate fertilizer and in the lime, asphalt, and metal industries. The major advantages of wet scrubbers are their abilities to handle mists and flammable and explosive dusts, to cool hot gases, to provide gas absorption and dust collection in a single unit, and to neutralize corrosive gases and dusts. Their major disadvantages are that effluent liquids can present water pollution problems, their high potential for corrosion, the possible contamination of collected particulates (thus rendered unrecyclable), the necessity of protecting them from freezing, and the expense of disposing of waste sludge.

Each particulate air pollution control problem is unique and can only be resolved through engineered solutions. Note that cost efficiency is critical in designing a system; the following are broad generalities for identifying possible air pollution control alternatives. The overall collection efficiency of a system composed of two or more devices in series is not the sum or product of the efficiencies of each device. It is the total mass collected as a fraction of the total mass entering the first device. Mechanical collectors are typically much less expensive and moderately efficient than other types of equipment. They are better used for large particle removal than for fine dust and are often used as precleaners, especially when dust loading is high. Fabric filters tend to be costly and have very high efficiencies but are usually limited to dry, low-temperature conditions, although able to handle many different types of dust. Electrostatic pre-cipitators are costly, relatively inflexible to changes in process operating conditions, and they can handle very large volumetric flow rates at low pressure drops while achieving very high efficiencies. Wet scrubbers can be very costly to operate because of high pressure drops but can achieve high efficiencies. One of their major advantages is that some gaseous pollutants can be removed simultaneously with the particulates, but they also produce a wet sludge that can present additional disposal problems.

Control of Gases

Carbon monoxide and nitrogen oxides (NO_x) are controlled by process modifications that include combustion control through proper use of temperature, oxygen, time, turbulence, and catalysis; absorption of gases by use of water or other liquids; adsorption of gases on activated carbon, silica gel, lithium chloride, and activated alumina; and controlled stack emission. With proper selection of adsorbing or adsorption material, and contact time between the material and vapor-laden exhaust stream, high collection efficiency can be achieved.

Flue Gas Desulfurization

Sulfur oxide emissions are controlled by flue gas desulfurization scrubbing systems. The two major systems are wet-scrubbing and spray-drying systems. The wet flue gas-desulfurization scrubbing process includes lime and limestone, nonregenerable sodium alkali, dual alkali, magnesium oxide, and Wellman–Lord. A major disadvantage is the large quantities of waste generated.

Control of Volatile Organic Compounds

Volatile organic compound (VOC) control systems rely upon the concept of chemical reaction. When the reaction involves organic hydrocarbons, the process is called oxidation. In the VOC oxidation process, heat and oxygen are added to the hydrocarbons to create the oxidation reaction. One of the most used oxidation methods for air pollution, as opposed to bulk liquids or solids, is incineration, specifically termed vapor incineration, or thermal oxidizers, or afterburners. Some VOC thermal abatement devices are optimized with pre-heaters or heat exchangers to improve fuel efficiency. In some cases, the heat generated can be used for operation of other equipment, such as water boilers, and so on. Note that vapor incinerators can sometimes be used successfully for air polluted with small particles of combustible solids or liquids, as well as for odor control. The process design of a vapor incinerator requires determining a temperature of operation along with a desired residence time and then sizing the device with the proper flow velocity. Controlling temperature, turbulence, and time are the key elements for achieving high process efficiency. Alternatives to incineration are recovery of the vapors, and liquid absorption coupled with either recovery or chemical oxidation. Some volatile organic compounds can also be abated through the use of carbon absorption systems.

Selection of the proper piece of equipment depends on such factors as mode of operation (continuous or intermittent), oxygen content, and the concentration of the VOC (Hemsath and Susey 1972). One of the drawbacks of thermal oxidation of VOCs is the generation of other pollutants such as nitrogen oxides (NO_x). This should be considered in the selection of abatement devices. Proper selection and proper sizing are very important when trying to minimize the overall cost of the incineration option. For this reason, it is desirable to keep the volume of the stream to be treated as low as possible. However, most insurance regulations limit the maximum VOC concentration in such streams to 25 percent of the lower explosive limit (LEL) of the VOC. Even so, many process streams encountered in industry have concentrations of 5 percent or less of the LEL. If the process stream could be concentrated from 5 percent up to 25 percent of the LEL (for instance, by reducing the flow rate of dilution air), the total volume to be incinerated would drop by 80 percent. Hence, the process exhaust stream must be characterized to determine the most appropriate VOC control technology available to best suit the application. The first step in characterizing the exhaust stream is to establish the current operating parameters, such as volumetric flow, volatile organic compound loading, and any other inorganic contaminants that might exist. The following is a list of con-

siderations for determining the best cost-effective VOC control system:

- initial capital cost for the VOC system
- annual operating cost for VOC system
- annual maintenance cost for VOC system
- reliability of equipment vs. plant requirements for process run time
- the system's capture efficiency
- required destruction-rate efficiency for compliance with regulations
- flexibility for future operation of the plant's process

Innovative Air Pollution Control Devices

The number of innovative air pollution control devices is increasing sharply. The following are five examples identified by Koren and Bisesi (1995):

1. Vaporsep™ Membrane Process
   This device was developed by Membrane Technology and Research, Inc., and uses synthetic polymer membranes to remove organic vapors from contaminated air streams. The process generates a clean air stream and a liquid organic stream for reuse or disposal. Air laden with organic vapor reaches one side of a membrane 10 or 100 times more permeable to the organic compound than to the air. The membrane separates the gas into two streams: a permeate stream containing most of the organic vapor and a clean residual air stream. The organic vapor is condensed and removed as a liquid; the purified air stream may be vented or recycled. It can treat most air streams containing flammable or nonflammable halogenated and nonhalogenated organic compounds, including chlorinated hydrocarbons, chlorofluorocarbons (CFC), and fuel hydrocarbons.

2. TiO₂ Photocatalytic Air Treatment
   This device was developed by Matrix Photocatalytic Inc. It uses a titanium dioxide (TiO_2) photocatalytic air treatment technology to remove and destroy volatile and semi-

volatile organic compounds from airstreams. The technology is an ambient temperature, solid-state process in which contaminated air flows through a fixed TiO_2 catalyst bed activated by light. Typically, destruction of organic contaminants occurs in fractions of a second. The TiO_2 photocatalytic air-treatment technology can effectively treat dry or moist air. The technique has been demonstrated to purify streams directly, thus eliminating the need for condensation. Systems treating 100 cubic feet per minute of exhaust air have been successfully tested on vapor-extraction operations, air-stripper emissions, steam from desorption processes, and VOC emissions from manufacturing facilities.

3. Bio-scrubber

This device was developed by the Aluminum Company of America. It uses a bioscrubber to digest hazardous organic emissions from soil, water, and air decontamination processes. The bioscrubber consists of a filter with an activated carbon medium that supports microbial growth. This unique medium, with increased microbial population and enhanced bioactivity, converts diluted organics into carbon dioxide, water, and other non-hazardous compounds. The filter provides biomass removal, nutrient supplement, and moisture addition. The technique is especially suited to treating streams that contain aromatic solvents, such as benzene, toluene, xylene, alcohols, ketones, hydrocarbons, and others.

4. Acoustic Barrier Particulate Separation

Developed by General Atomics, Nuclear Remediation Technologies Division, acousic barrier particulate separation separates particulates in a high-temperature gas flow. The separator directs an acoustic waveform against the gas flow, causing particulates to move opposite the flow. Eventually, the particulates drift to the wall of the separator, where they aggregate and precipitate into a collection hopper. The acoustic barrier separator differs from other separators in that it combines both high-efficiency and high-temperature capabilities. It can treat off-gas streams from thermal desorption, pyrolysis, and incineration of soil, sediment, sludge, and other solid wastes. It is a high-temperature, high-throughput process with high-removal efficiency for fine dust and fly ash.

5. Reactor/Filter System

This device was developed by the Energy and Environmental Research Corporation. It is designed to treat gaseous and entrained particulate matter emissions from the primary thermal treatment of sludge, soils, and sediments. It is used to remove entrained particulates, volatile toxic metals, and condensed-phase organics present in high temperature (800–1000°C) gas streams.

Best Practices

The practices in air pollution control are very diverse and technologically challenging, requiring specialized knowledge and skills. For the safety professional with the responsibility of environmental compliance, five key themes are recommended for adopting the best practices:

1. Using an integrated approach and the best technology available
2. Performing a comprehensive financial analysis
3. Continuously conducting surveillance and evaluations
4. Developing comprehensive air pollution control programs
5. Capturing and destroying fugitive emissions

An Integrated Approach

The EPA reports that since 1990 technology-based emission standards for industrial and combustion sources have proven extremely successful in reducing emissions of air toxics. The following two examples developed by the American Council for an Energy-Efficient Economy (ACEEE 1997) illustrate how industries implement projects; they also illustrate overall corporate strategies that profit from the synergies of energy efficiency, pollution prevention, process efficiency, and increased productivity. Note that the U.S. Department of Energy collaborates with U.S. industry to implement energy-efficiency demonstration projects in operating plants. At the end of each collaborative project, an assessment is conducted, and the results published if qualified as a best practice (DOE 2005).

These two projects developed many best practices and equipment, clearly underscoring the fact that air pollution prevention best practices must be identified in relationship to productivity, investment, and energy efficiencies. Below are two examples extracted from the DOE document on best practices.

EXAMPLE 1

Bowater, Inc., manufactures market pulp, newsprint, and coated magazine paper. During the processing of green wood chips (half water and half fiber), the water is converted to steam as the fibers are separated, processed, and pumped to paper machines to be converted to paper stock. By converting steam into energy, the company captured the energy lost in this low-pressure steam it vented from its seven thermomechanical pulping (TMP) refiner lines. The company installed two mechanical vapor recompression (MVR) heat pumps that efficiently converted the 19 psig steam at 250°F to 57 psig steam at 470°F. The converted steam was used to power the drying stage of the paper-production operations. The MVR compressor also had a turndown of 50 percent, allowing it to adapt to changing amounts of steam, which optimized energy use.

The major achievements cited in the DOE report were:

1. Annual energy savings of $1 million paid back the $1.5 million investment in 1.5 years.
2. About 200 gallons of turpentine (a TMP by-product) is recovered daily for resale, reducing atmospheric emissions and providing additional income.
3. By preventing steam from escaping, 100 gallons of water per minute is saved, saving about $144 per day.

4. Controlling the steam vapor once it is released into the atmosphere reduces the plant's noise level.

EXAMPLE 2

Cominco America, Inc., produces ammonia for fertilizer, which uses water and gas fuel to generate steam. Process condensate is generated as wastewater, which is managed by a holding pond and injection wells. Cominco retained an engineering consultant, M.W. Kellogg Co., to reengineer its ammonia plant to reduce fuel and make up water consumption.

Fuel consumption was reduced by replacing existing plant parts with newer material that improved heat transfer. Convection-section and heating-coil modules were replaced with more efficient units that reduced heat and improved heat transfer, which reduced NO_x emissions and fuel consumption. The ammonia-converter reactor was modified with new equipment to reduce steam consumption. These new designs not only reduced fuel consumption but also increased productivity. Major achievements cited in the DOE report were:

1. Natural gas consumption declined 22 percent (1 billion cubic feet per year), saving over $1.7 million per year.
2. NO_x emissions declined 35 percent.
3. Average annual water usage for steam production was reduced by more than 110 million gallons, saving $65,000 per year.
4. Additional savings came from reduced disposal costs of wastewater into injection wells.
5. $16 million in capital costs were recovered in approximately six years.

Financial Analysis

The financial analysis of an efficiency project is the basis for making the investment decision. Hence, considering the cost of alternative control methods and technologies using a quantitative technique such as incremental analysis to determine the best choice is essential. Incremental analysis is a very simple method for determining the best rate of return on investment (ROI), and ensures that each increment of investment will provide an acceptable return. Cooper and

Alley (2002) suggested the following procedure for comparing alternatives:

1. Select the acceptable unit with the lowest installed cost as the base case and designate it as, say, "Alternative 1."
2. Designate higher-cost alternatives in order of increasing cost and designate them with distinguishing names.
3. Calculate the incremental rate of return on investment (ROI) between Alternative 1 and the next higher-cost identified alternative. If the ROI is acceptable, Alternative 2 now becomes the base case. If the ROI is not acceptable, Alternative 1 remains the base case and Alternative 2 is discarded.
4. Calculate the ROI between the next alternative and the base case. If the ROI is acceptable, Alternative 3 becomes the new base case. Again, if the ROI is unacceptable, Alternative 3 is discarded.
5. Continue this process until all alternatives are evaluated.

Surveillance and Evaluation

The EPA recommends that inspections and evaluations of emissions be conducted regularly to determine the level of air quality, the level of pollutants, and adherence to the established air quality standards. It is important when conducting the detailed survey to ensure that the site selection for sampling is made in such a way that it reflects the entire network design, that it is a representative sample consistent with objectives, and that the sampler considers the meteorological and topographical restraints as well as the sampling schedules. Sampling must be collected accurately and without contamination by skilled and trained individuals. Analysis and evaluation of the sample must be accurate, and the data-handling and evaluation systems must be accurate and consistent. The initial major step in surveillance and evaluation is proper planning. Planning is the advance thinking and organizing of a sequence of actions needed to accomplish the proposed objectives and to communicate the information to other individuals.

The planning of the survey must include the selection of the site for sampling, the sampling equipment to be used, the actual sample collection, the sample analysis, data processing, data evaluation, and comprehensive report writing.

The major objectives for monitoring air pollution include:

- providing an early warning system for potential health effects
- assessing air quality against standards
- tracking air pollution trends and specific polluters

Monitoring may also be required as part of the equipment permit requirements (EPA 1997).

Air Pollution Control Programs

A good program must include legal authority to institute and carry out a pollution control program and a continuing air quality monitoring program, to establish an emission-source inventory and continuously update it, to develop air quality goals and standards based on air quality criteria, to inculcate a thorough understanding of local meteorological conditions and their relationship to the movement of air pollutants, to make land-use planning decisions based on air quality control and other environmental factors, to develop good public information and educational programs, to train available personnel in the use of monitoring equipment, samplers, and laboratory analysis of pollutants, to implement air-use plans for existing industries, to approve plans for new industries, and to identify polluters and use enforcement techniques when needed to achieve compliance.

The management of air resources to protect the health and welfare of people must be carried out through the joint efforts of local, state, and federal agencies, the industry, and the population at large.

Fugitive Emissions

Process fugitive emissions come from a process or piece of equipment away from the main vent or stack. The fumes escape from valves, pumps, compressors, access ports, and feed or discharge ports of a process. Control techniques include leak detection and repair programs to seal the leaks. Further, the use of sophisticated pump seals, as well as valve and valve seals, can reduce emissions. Control techniques for organic or inorganic vapor emissions from area fugitive sources such as lagoons and ponds are very difficult to implement. The best approach is to reduce sharply the hazardous pollutant before it goes to the lagoon or pond and becomes a hazardous air pollutant.

CONCLUSIONS

The information related to air pollution presented in this chapter is intended to increase awareness of the problem and of the need for prevention and control. It also identified regulatory and compliance issues related to controlling and preventing air pollution associated with industrial operations. The chapter provided basic information for assisting, evaluating, and selecting air pollution control equipment and systems and guidelines for evaluating air-pollution control systems and programs. Most air pollution is directly related to combustion of fuels for transportation, production of electricity, and manufacturing, all reflections of the social demands of the way we live. Air pollution is a global concern that creates a need for international strategies and agreements. Toxic air pollutants may cause cancer or other serious health problems, as well as adverse environmental and ecological effects. Hence, air pollutants must be controlled at the source or diluted before being emitted into the atmosphere. Preventing pollutants from forming is the preferred method.

Challenges associated with the control of air pollution over the coming decades are complex and are likely to require mitigation strategies. These strategies not only require the understanding of the dispersion and interaction of multiple pollutants over national and international airsheds but also of the effects on human health and ecosystem conditions that arise from simultaneous exposure to multiple pollutants. Designing air pollution control systems and selecting the best air pollution control equipment requires engineering knowledge, which may be beyond the grasp of many safety professionals and is also beyond the scope of one chapter. However, an understanding of basic technological concepts and terms is essential for ensuring pollution control, productivity, investment, and energy efficiency.

Acknowledgment

I gratefully recognize the contributions from Moira McCue, MS, Adjunct Instructor of ESH, University of Connecticut, in the writing of this chapter.

REFERENCES

American Council for an Energy-Efficient Economy. 1997. *The Integrated Approach: Case Studies* (retrieved October 23, 2005). www.aceee.org/p2/p2cases.htm

American Lung Association. 2000. *Outdoor Air Quality* (retrieved October 6, 2005). www.lungusa.org / site/apps

American Meteorological Society (AMS). 2002. Legislation: *A Look at Air Pollution Laws and Their Amendments* (retrieved October 22, 2005). www.ametsoc.org/ sloan/cleanair/cleanairlegisl.html

Centers for Disease Control (CDC). Agency for Toxic Substances and Disease Registry (ATSDR). 2007. *Toxicological Profile Information Sheet.* www.astdr.cdc. gov/toxprof.html

_____. National Institute for Occupational Health and Safety (NIOSH). *Registry of Toxic Effects of Chemical Substances (RTECS).* www.cdc.gov/niosh.rtecs/ default.html

Cooper, D., and F. Alley. 2002. *Air Pollution Control—A Design Approach.* 3d ed. Illinois: Waveland Press.

Department of Energy (DOE) Office Pollution Prevention. 2005. *Best Practices* (retrieved November 21, 2005). www.hss.energy.gov

_____. Office of Health, Safety and Security (OHSS). 1996. *Environmental Policy and Guidance: Clean Air Act.* (January 25) (retrieved October 18, 2005). www.eh. doe.gov/oepa/workshop/envlawsregs256/caa.ppt

Environmental Protection Agency (EPA). 2005a. *About Air Toxics, Health and Ecological Effects.* (retrieved October 18, 2005). www.epa.gov/air/toxicair/newtoxics.html

_____. 2005b. *Acid Rain* (retrieved November 18, 2005). www.epa.gov/airmarkets/index.html

_____. 1991. EPA 450/3-90-022, *Air Pollution and Health Risk.* (retrieved October 23, 2005). www.epa.gov/oar/ oaqps/air_risc/3_90_022.html

_____. 1955. Air Pollution Control Act (APCA). P.L. 84-159. Washington, D.C.: EPA.

_____. 1967. Air Quality Act. P.L. 90–148. Washington, D.C.: EPA.

_____. 1999. *Air Toxics: National-Scale Air Toxics Assessment* (retrieved November 29, 2007). www.epa.gov/ ttn/atw/nata/1999

_____. 1963. Clean Air Act of 1963 (CAA 1963). P.L. 88-206. Washington, D.C.: EPA

_____. 1970a. Clean Air Act of 1970 (CAA 1970). P.L. 91-604. 7401 *et seq.* Washington, D.C.: EPA

_____. 1990a. Clean Air Act Amendments of 1990 (CAAA). P.L. 101-549. Washington, D.C.: EPA

_____. 2005c. Clear Skies Act of 2005. S.B. 131 (107th Congress). Washington, D.C.: EPA.

_____. 2006. *Climate Change.* (retrieved November 15, 2006). www.epa.gov/climatechange/index.html

_____. 2000. EPA-453/R-00-005, *Deposition of Air Pollutants to the Great Waters—3rd Report to Congress.* www.epa.gov/oar/oaqps/gr8water

_____. 2004a. *EPA Acid Rain Program* (retrieved October 22, 2005). www.epa.gov/airmarkets/arp/index.html

_____. 2004b. *Air Data.* (retrieved October 18, 2005). www.epa.gov/airmarkets/acidrain

_____. 1997. *EPA Announces National Strategy for Toxic Air Pollutants* (retrieved October 22, 2005). www.epa.gov/history/topics/caa70/16.htm

_____. 2005c. *EPA Clean Air Act.* (retrieved October 20, 2005). www.epa.gov/history/topics/caa70

_____. 1971. *EPA History: Hearing Set on Automobile Pollution Control* (retrieved October 21, 2005). www.epa.gov/history/topics/caa70/05.htm

———. 1970b. National Environmental Policy Act (NEPA). P.L. 91-90, 42 U.S.C. 4347. Washington, D.C.: EPA

_____. Technology Transfer Network. 2006. *Air Toxics: List of 33 Urban Air Toxics.* (retrieved November 3, 2006). www.epa.gov/ttn/atw/urban/list33.html

_____. 2011. *The Benefits and Costs of the Clean Air Act— Second Prospective Study from 1990 to 2020* (retrieved April 27, 2011). www.epa.gov/sect812/prospective 2-2.html

Fleagle, R. G., and J. A. Businger. 1980. *An Introduction to Atmospheric Physics.* 2d ed. New York: Academic Press.

Hemsath, K. H., and P. E. Susey. 1972. "Fume Incineration in Theory and Practice." Paper presented at the 71st National Meeting of the American Institute of Chemical Engineers, Dallas, TX, February 20–23.

Hobbs, P. V. 2000. *Basic Physical Chemistry for the Atmospheric Sciences.* Cambridge, UK: Cambridge University Press.

The Institute of Clean Air Companies (ICAC).2004. *Viewpoint on Hazardous Air Pollutants* (retrieved October 23, 2005). www.icac.com/i4a/pages/index.cfm? pageid=3397

International Labour Office (ILO). 1993. *Encyclopaedia of Occupational Health and Safety, Volume I, A-K.* 3d ed. Geneva, Switzerland: ILO. (AUTHOR: Review 1998 edition of this and revise accordingly.)

Kanarek, M. 2004. *History of the Air Pollution Problem* (retrieved October 19, 2005). www.admin.pophealth. wisc.edu/marty/phs502

Koren, Herman. 2003. *Handbook of Environmental Health and Safety Principles, Volume II.* 2d ed. Chelsea, MI: Lewis Publishers.

Koren, H., and M. Bisesi. 1995. *Handbook of Environmental Health and Safety, Volumes I and II.* 3d ed. Boca Raton, FL: Lewis Publishers.

Lapple, C. E. 1961. "Characteristics of Particles and Particle Dispersoids." *Stanford Research Institute Journal* 5:94.

Montague, P. 1999. *The Waning Days of Risk Assessment* (retrieved October 17, 2005). www.rachel.org/bulletin/ index.cfm?St=2

National Aeronautics and Space Administration (NASA). *Astrobiology Institute, Ames Research Center.* (2005) (retrieved October 4, 2005). www.nai.arc.nasa.gov

National Library of Medicine (NLM). Toxocology Data Network (TOXNET). *Hazardous Substances Data Bank.* www.toxnet.nlm.nih.gov

National Oceanic and Atmospheric Administration (NOOA). 2002. *Fact Sheet: President Announces Clear Skies and Global Climate Changes* (retrieved October 20, 2005). www.whitehouse.gov/news/releases/2002/ 02/20020214.html

National Research Council (NRC). 2006. *Surface Temperature Reconstructions for the Last 2,000 Years.* Washington, D.C.: National Academy Press.

Sepulveda, J. A. et al. 1990. *Schaum's Outline Series Theory and Problems of Engineering Economics.* New York: McGraw-Hill.

Sierra Club. 2004. *Air Pollution Facts. Clean Air Resources.* (retrieved October 17, 2005). www.sierraclub.org/ cleanair/factsheets

United Nations Environmental Programme (UNEP), Ozone Secretariat. 2000. *The Montreal Protocol on Substances that Deplete the Ozone Layer.* Nairobi, Kenya: UNEP. (retrieved November 28, 2007). www.unep.org/OZONE/pdfs/MontrealProtocol 2000.pdf

West, L. 2005. *About: Environmental Issues. Should the United States Ratify the Kyoto Protocol?* (retrieved October 19, 2005). www.environment.about.com/ od/kyotoprotocol/i/kyotoprotocol.htm

Western Houston Association Issues. 2003. *EPA Reports on Clean Air Act* (retrieved October 21, 2005). www.westhouston.org/epa_report.htm

Wikipedia. 2005a. *Greenhouse Gas.* (retrieved October 19, 2005). www.en.wikipedia.org/wiki/Greenhouse_ gas

_____. 2005b. *Image: Global Carbon Emission by Type.* (retrieved October 19, 2005).www.en.wikipedia.org/ wiki/Image:Global_Carbon_Emission_by_Type.png

Wooley, D. R. February 2000. *A Guide to the Clean Air Act for the Renewable Energy Community* (retrieved October 20, 2005). www.repp.org/repp_pubs/articles/ issuebr15

APPENDIX: RECOMMENDED READING

Cengel, Y. A., and M. A. Boles. 2008. *Thermodynamics: An Engineering Approach with Student Resources DVD.* 6th ed. Boston: McGraw-Hill Higher Education.

Cheremisinoff, N. P. 2002. *Handbook of Air Pollution, Prevention and Control.* Boston: Butterworth-Heineman.

De Nevers, N. 2000. *Air Pollution Control Engineering.* 2d ed. Boston: McGraw-Hill.

Licht, W. 1988. *Air Pollution Control Engineering: Basic Calculations for Particulate Collection.* 2d ed. New York: Decker.

Moran, M .J., and H. N. Shapiro. 2000. *Fundamentals of Engineering Thermodynamics.* 4th ed. New York: Wiley.

Mycock, J. C., J. D. McKenna, and L. Theodore. 1995. *Handbook of Air Pollution Control Engineering and Technology.* Boca Raton, FL: CRC Press.

Newnan, D. G., T. G. Eschenbach, and J. P. Lavelle. 2004. *Engineering Economic Analysis.* 9th ed. New York: Oxford Univ. Press.

Park, C. S. 2004. *Fundamentals of Engineering Economics.* Upper Saddle River, NJ: Pearson/Prentice Hall.

Park, C. S., and G. P. Sharp-Bette. 1990. *Advanced Engineering Economics.* New York: Wiley.

Schnelle Jr., K. B., and C. A. Brown. 2002. *Air Pollution Control Technology Handbook.* Boca Raton, FL: CRC Press.

Stern, A. C., ed. 1976. *Air Pollution. Volume 7, Supplement to Measurements, Monitoring, Surveillance, and Engineering Control.* 3d ed. New York: Academic Press.

_____. 1976. *Measurements, Monitoring, Surveillance, and Engineering Control.* New York: Academic Press.

Smith, J. M., H. C. Van Ness, and M. Abbott. 2005. *Introduction to Chemical Engineering Thermodynamics.* 7th ed. Boston: McGraw-Hill.

Sullivan, W. G., E. M. Wicks, and J. Luxhoj. 2006. *Engineering Economy.* 13th ed. Upper Saddle River, NJ: Pearson/Prentice Hall.

Van Ness, H. C. 1983. *Understanding Thermodynamics.* New York: Dover.

Wang, L. K., N. C. Pereira, Y. Tse-Hung, and K. H. Li, eds. 2005. *Advanced Air and Noise Pollution Control.* Totowa, NJ: Humana Press.

_____. 2004. *Air Pollution Control Engineering.* Totowa, NJ: Humana Press.

White, J. A., M. H. Agee, and K. E. Case. 1998. *Principles of Engineering Economic Analysis.* 4th ed. New York: Wiley.

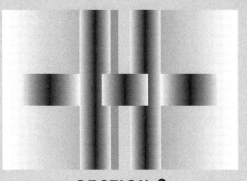

LEARNING OBJECTIVES

▌ Recognize the federal laws that govern water and understand the difference between the Safe Drinking Water Act (SDWA) and the Clean Water Act (CWA).

▌ Examine the wastewater discharge permit system and know the difference between the permits for direct dischargers and indirect dischargers.

▌ Understand the basic parameters of the pretreatment system.

▌ Understand the basic concepts of sampling and analysis.

▌ Consider how current wetlands management rulings might impact industry.

▌ Be exposed to a number of wastewater treatment technologies.

WATER AND WASTEWATER

Judy Freeman

THE MAJORITY OF AMERICANS living and working in cities get their water from municipal water supplies derived from surface water sources. Thus, the responsibility for providing safe drinking water to employees and clean process water for operations is not an issue for most environmental health and safety (EHS) managers in the United States, unless they are located in rural areas. How that water is used inside the facility and the quality of the water as it leaves in the form of waste, however, is the ultimate responsibility of the EHS manager.

In rural areas there are fewer people, but more water sources. Most workplaces that draw drinking water and process water from groundwater wells are subject to regulations. For these, the quality of water coming into the workplace, as well as that going out, must be assessed, maintained, and controlled by EHS personnel.

WATER-QUALITY REGULATORY ISSUES

In general, the quality of the water coming into the facility is ruled by the Safe Drinking Water Act (SDWA 1974), and the quality of the water going out is ruled by the Clean Water Act (CWA 1956). Both laws have something to say about how water is used in the facility. In most states, the laws are enforced at the state level. This means that state law may well be stricter than federal law.

Most people in the United States get their water from surface water sources managed by community water systems. Thus, the regulatory demands of the SDWA 1974 are beyond their control and responsibility.

However, where the water for a facility does not qualify as a community water system, the owner or individual responsible for that water source has the responsibility to maintain it according to SDWA regulations (SDWA 1986; SDWA 1996). The act covers water sources—primarily groundwater wells but also streams, ponds, and lakes—that meet the definition of "a public water system that is not a community water system and that regularly serves at least 25 of the same persons over 6 months per year" (SDWA 1974). States may independently impose restrictions on noncommunity water systems or stricter regulations on community water systems than those of the SDWA.

The SDWA addresses the quality of water in the public water supply. As noted, "public" here does not necessarily mean owned by the public, but rather used by it. The objective of the SDWA is to protect public water supplies from harmful contaminants by requiring the suppliers of water to achieve established standards (SDWA 1974).

Originally passed in 1974 and amended in 1986 and 1996, the SDWA controls community public water systems, defined as those which provide water to the public for human consumption and have at least 15 service connections or serve at least 25 individuals for at least 60 days a year. A community water system may include private sources (SDWA 1974; SDWA 1986; SDWA 1996). The SDWA does not have jurisdiction over nonpublic water supplies, which may include private residential wells, and individual schools, churches, motels, and some commercial or industrial facilities where use might be described as more incidental. A workplace where employees routinely use water for drinking and washing would probably not qualify as incidental use.

An EHS manager with responsibility for a plant should ensure that such sources fall within acceptable limits. Further, operators of facilities whose operations could impact the quality of a drinking water aquifer over which they reside must take precautions to avoid allowing chemical releases that will damage this resource. Such operations controls include:

- adequate containment of chemical storage should catastrophic failure occur
- knowledge of any aboveground or underground chemical/petroleum storage tanks

that are on site. What is their content? age? condition?
- knowledge of the particular aquifer that feeds the facility, and what other pollutants may have been or are contaminating the common resource

In addition to establishing standards and treatment requirements for drinking water, the SDWA controls underground injection of waste and protects groundwater. It covers:

- improperly disposed-of chemicals
- animal waste
- pesticides
- human waste
- wastes injected underground
- naturally occurring contamination

EHS directors have the responsibility for ensuring that both water taken into the plant and wastewater discharged from the plant are within regulation. Underground injection of wastewater is highly regulated and should be contemplated carefully, if at all. The risk of potential contamination of a groundwater or surface water source should be understood.

States are granted *primacy*, or the authority to implement the SDWA by establishing water-quality standards that are at least as stringent as those imposed by the Environmental Protection Agency (EPA). Their role is then to enforce the law by providing oversight to the operations of water systems.

The SDWA directs the EPA to set water-quality levels for both man-made and naturally occurring contaminants based on health-related science. Currently, the EPA has standards set for 90 chemical, microbiological, radiological, and physical contaminants in drinking water. These are listed on the EPA's Web site, which may be found in the reference section at the end of this chapter.

National Primary Drinking Water Regulations (NPDWR) (EPA 1975) and National Secondary Drinking Water Regulations (NSDWRs) (EPA 2007) both are established, but only NPDWRs are enforceable; secondary levels are for guidance only.

NPDWRs establish maximum contaminant levels (MCLs) for certain specific drinking water contaminants. Other constituents are controlled using specific required treatment techniques in order to achieve the established standards (EPA 1975). NSDWRs address aesthetic values in a water supply, such as color, odor, taste, or turbidity. They must be considered for guidance only, because their values are not enforceable (EPA 2007).

Maximum contaminant level goals (MCLGs), based on the most stringent standards that would limit potential health effects, are established as goals rather than enforceable limits (EPA 1975). MCLs are required to be set as close to MCLGs as feasible. Decisions regarding feasibility take the cost of best available treatment technology into account when establishing limits.

The SDWA amendments (1986) resulted in the establishment of 83 contaminant levels, and the 1996 amendments added 20 more (see Table 1).

The 10 percent of Americans whose water comes from private wells (individual wells serving fewer than 25 persons) are not required to be protected by these federal standards. People with private wells are responsible for making sure that their own drinking water is safe. Some states do set standards for private wells, so well owners should check their state requirements. The EPA recommends testing water *at least* once per year to see if it meets federal and state standards (EPA 2006b).

Environmental health and safety directors of facilities that draw water from nonpublic water systems must be aware of the limits of their particular states. Further, in order to protect the health of their employees or the public who may use their facility, regular testing and compliance with the standards of the act are recommended.

Water Sampling

Where a company manages a private water source, routine sampling is recommended as a minimum and may be mandated by state law. This requires sampling of the water source, whether surface water or groundwater. Additionally, where chemical releases

TABLE 1

Regulated Chemicals under SDWA

Organics

Benzene	Di(2-ethylhexyl)adipate
Carbon tetrachloride	Di(2-ethylhexyl)phthalate
Chlorobenzene	Dibromochloropropane (DBCP)
1,2-Dichlorobenzene	Dinoseb \4\
1,4-Dichlorobenzene	Diquat
1,2-Dichloroethane	Endothall
cis-Dichloroethylene	Endrin
trans-Dichloroethylene	Ethylene dibromide (EDB)
Dichloromethane	Glyphosate
1,2-Dichloropropane	Heptachlor
Ethylbenzene	Heptachlor epoxide
Styrene	Hexachlorobenzene
Tetrachloroethylene	Hexachlorocyclopentadiene
1,1,1-Trichloroethane	Lindane
Trichloroethylene	Methoxychlor
Toluene	Oxamyl
1,2,4-Trichlorobenzene	PCBs \3\ (as decachlorobiphenyl)
1,1-Dichloroethylene	PCBs \3\ (as Aroclors)
1,1,2-Trichloroethane	Pentachlorophenol
Vinyl chloride	Picloram \4\
Xylenes (total)	Simazine \2\
2,3,7,8-TCDD (dioxin)	Toxaphene
2,4-D \4\	Total trihalomethanes
2,4,5-TP \4\ (Silvex)	
Alachlor \2\	
Atrazine \2\	
Benzo(α)pyrene	
Carbofuran	
Chlordane	
Dalapon	

Inorganics

Antimony	Nitrate
Arsenic	Nitrite
Asbestos	Selenium
Barium	Thallium
Beryllium	Coliform
Cadmium	Turbidity
Chromium	
Cyanide	
Mercury	
Nickel	

from spills or leaking underground storage-tank incidents are suspected of contaminating groundwater, whether a water source or not, groundwater sampling is required to make that determination.

Equipment required for sampling groundwater from an established monitoring well includes a water-level indicator, a bailer, a rope, and possibly a pump. Equipment used to test water quality in the field includes a thermometer, a pH meter, and a conductivity meter. Turbidity meters, dissolved oxygen meters, and oxygen reduction potential (ORP) meters are also used.

Measurements in the field are used not only to test the targeted parameters, but also to determine the stability of the water. If meter readings fluctuate from one reading to the next, the water has not yet stabilized and samples should not be drawn until the readings are consistent.

Sampling protocol is to move from clean wells to the dirty ones and from up-gradient to down-gradient to minimize the chance of cross-contamination. Bailing water from the well should be performed with care to minimize both turbulence and volatilization of chemicals. The bailer should be tied securely to the rope so it does not slip off and remain in the well. Pumps may be used to retrieve water where flow is less generous, and to conduct well development.

Upon completion of the drilling and construction of a well, well development must occur to remove foreign matter, including sediments from the well walls and water that may have been used in drilling. The well must be purged prior to sampling to ensure that the water being sampled is representative of the aquifer. Samples must be taken according to EPA protocol and must be refrigerated immediately. A chain of custody must be maintained (Bodger 2003).

WASTEWATER

The objective of the Clean Water Act (CWA 1977) is to restore and maintain the integrity of the nation's waters. Specific goals of the act, established to achieve this objective, are to eliminate discharge of pollutants; to make water quality fishable and swimmable; and to reach zero discharge, that is, to eliminate any discharge of toxic pollutants in toxic amounts. The target dates set for these goals were passed in the mid-1980s, but even though compliance has not been reached, the goals remain the same.

When the CWA took effect, only 33 percent of the nation's waters were fishable and swimmable; 460,000 acres of wetlands were lost annually. Soil

erosion into lakes and rivers was estimated at 2.25 billion tons. Phosphorus and nitrogen levels were high. Only 85 million people were served by sewage treatment (Cox 2000).

Since that time, approximately 60–65 percent of the nation's waterways are fishable/swimmable. The amount of wetland reduction has decreased to about 70,000 to 90,000 acres annually. Soil erosion is down to 1.5 billion tons. Phosphorus and nitrogen levels are reduced, and 173 million people are served by sewage treatment.

Legislative History

The first U.S. water legislation was the Rivers and Harbors Act (1894), which prohibited unauthorized obstruction or alteration of the nation's waters. This was followed by the Refuse Act (1899), which prohibited discharge of refuse that would affect the course, location, condition, or physical capacity of navigable waters. It mandated comprehensive programs to reduce pollution in interstate waters.

The Water Pollution Control Act (WPCA 1948) serves as the regulatory framework upon which subsequent laws have been developed. Under the Federal Water Pollution Control Act (FWPCA 1956), water-quality standards were based on desired uses of receiving waters: drinking water, recreation, navigation, body contact, and fishing. The Clean Water Restoration Act (CWRA) of 1965 was the first to require states to set standards for interstate waters that would be used to determine actual pollution levels. These laws were generally ineffective because of political, technical, and legal weaknesses, designated uses designed to attract industry, lack of information on effects of industrial discharges, and inadequate consideration of aquatic ecosystems (CWRA 1965).

With the 1972 amendments, the CWA incorporated the philosophy that no one has the right to pollute. The only acceptable reason for water pollution might be the limits of control technologies. For the first time, nationally uniform industrial limits were established. It was also this law that established the system of National Pollutant Discharge Elimination

System (NPDES) permits. Also for the first time, secondary treatment was required for publicly owned treatment works (POTWs). The act established a construction grants program to upgrade community sewage treatment systems. The act also established a watershed management system, which covers the country's river basins and regions. Enforcement authority was vested in the administrator of the EPA.

Previous versions of the CWA had focused primarily on conventional pollutants such as biological oxygen demand and suspended solids, but the 1977 amendments expanded the EPA's program to focus on control of toxic substances and required promulgation of pretreatment standards for 65 priority pollutants in (now) 34 industrial categories. Technology-based controls were imposed on industry with the standard set at the best practicable control technology (BPT) currently available. By 1983, the EPA had raised the bar again to a standard of compliance representing the best available technology (BAT) economically achievable. The 1987 amendments established a program aimed at focusing on the improvement of waterways that were expected to remain polluted even after the most stringent technology-based requirements were met. Particular attention was to be given to areas such as Chesapeake Bay and the Great Lakes. Furthermore, the 1987 law imposed additional regulations on stormwater.

How the System Works

The Clean Water Act (CWA 1977) regulates industry in two ways. Direct dischargers (or point sources of pollution) are required to secure a NPDES permit (EPA 2006a). Indirect dischargers—those discharging into a sewer leading to a publicly owned treatment works (POTW)—are required to meet another set of pollution limits on their wastewater (EPA 1982). In order to meet these limits, these industries must pretreat their wastes before discharging them into the sewers. They may also be required to have a permit from the POTW, which, in turn, has its own NPDES permit for its treated effluent. A regulated facility

may have an NPDES permit, a POTW permit, or both.

Direct Dischargers

Primarily, the CWA limits discharges into the nation's waterways through the act's NPDES system. Under the NPDES permit program, every point-source facility is required to obtain an NPDES permit from the EPA or state agency (whichever has primacy in that state). A point source is one that discharges directly into the waterway.

NPDES permits allow industrial facilities to discharge a specified volume of wastewater, containing specified pollutants, from a specified outfall.

NPDES permit applications are required for process and nonprocess wastewater, and the requirements are slightly different for each, as well as for all other miscellaneous categories of entities regulated by these permits.

Other limits are also generally set in the permit, such as volume, duration, visual appearance, pH, temperature, sampling and reporting protocols, and frequency. Regulated waste streams requiring a NPDES permit include industrial process waters, noncontact cooling water, boiler blowdown, and stormwater runoff.

Pollution limits in the NPDES permit are based on multiple requirements, with the most stringent requirements imposed in most cases. They incorporate federal effluent guidelines and toxic standards, state effluent standards, and, potentially, water-quality-based limits. The list of priority pollutants must be considered, as well as categorical standards. Limits may be stated in terms of the volume of a pollutant in the waste stream or as a concentration of the pollutant—or, as is usually the case, as both.

Indirect Dischargers

Indirect dischargers, those discharging into the local POTW (sewage treatment plant), are also required to achieve technology-based effluent limits and minimum treatment requirements. Known as the pretreatment program, industrial users (IUs) discharging into the sanitary sewer system account for about 80 percent of the nation's wastewater flow (EPA 1982). Permits are issued by the POTW.

The POTW has its own NPDES permit, and its treatment of incoming wastewater provides one basis for its effluent limits under that permit. IUs are prohibited from any discharges to the POTW that may cause a *pass-through* or *interference* violation. A pass-through, either by itself or in combination with other wastewater with which it commingles in the treatment plant, is a violation of the POTW's NPDES permit. Interference inhibits or disrupts the POTW's treatment process. Also of concern is the solid waste left after treatment has occurred—sludge, the disposal of which is also regulated. Substances that alter the sludge and render the POTW unable to dispose of it by reuse are in violation.

Certain industries are targeted as categorical dischargers and as such are subject to the categorical pretreatment standards, which establish set effluent limits for them (see Table 2). The effluent limits are based on technology-based limits analogous to BAT.

TABLE 2

Regulated Chemicals under Pretreatment Standards

1. Acenaphthene	36. Fluoranthene
2. Acrolein	37. Haloethers (other than those listed elsewhere; includes chlorophenylphenyl ethers, bromophenylphenyl ether, bis(dichloroisopropyl) ether, bis(chloroethoxy) methane, and polychlorinated diphenyl ethers)
3. Acrylonitrile	
4. Aldrin/Dieldrin	
5. Antimony and compounds	
6. Arsenic and compounds	
7. Asbestos	38. Halomethanes (other than those listed elsewhere; includes methylene chloride, methylchloride, methylbromide, bromoform, and dichlorobromomethane)
8. Benzene	
9. Benzidine	
10. Beryllium and compounds	
11. Cadmium and compounds	39. Heptachlor and metabolites
12. Carbon tetrachloride	40. Hexachlorobutadiene
13. Chlordane (technical mixture and metabolites)	41. Hexachlorocyclohexane
14. Chlorinated benzenes (other than di-chlorobenzenes)	42. Hexachlorocyclopentadiene
15. Chlorinated ethanes (including 1,2-di-chloroethane, 1,1,1-trichloroethane, and hexachloroethane)	43. Isophorone
	44. Lead and compounds
	45. Mercury and compounds
16. Chloroalkyl ethers (chloroethyl and mixed ethers)	46. Naphthalene
17. Chlorinated naphthalene	47. Nickel and compounds
18. Chlorinated phenols (other than those listed elsewhere; includes trichlorophenols and chlorinated cresols)	48. Nitrobenzene
	49. Nitrophenols (including 2,4-dinitrophenol and dinitrocresol)
19. Chloroform	50. Nitrosamines
20. 2-Chlorophenol	51. Pentachlorophenol
21. Chromium and compounds	52. Phenol
22. Copper and compounds	53. Phthalate esters
23. Cyanides	54. Polychlorinated biphenyls (PCBs)
24. DDT and metabolites	55. Polynuclear aromatic hydrocarbons (including benzanthracenes, benzopyrenes, benzofluoranthene, chrysenes, dibenz-anthracenes, and indenopyrenes)
25. Dichlorobenzenes (1,2-, 1,3-, and 1,4-di-chlorobenzenes)	
26. Dichlorobenzidine	
27. Dichloroethylenes (1,1- and 1,2-dichloroethylene)	56. Selenium and compounds
28. 2,4-Dichlorophenol	57. Silver and compounds
29. Dichloropropane and dichloropropene	58. 2,3,7,8-Tetrachlorodibenzo-p-dioxin (TCDD)
30. 2,4-Dimethylphenol	59. Tetrachloroethylene
31. Dinitrotoluene	60. Thallium and compounds
32. Diphenylhydrazine	61. Toluene
33. Endosulfan and metabolites	62. Toxaphene
34. Endrin and metabolites	63. Trichloroethylene
35. Ethylbenzene	64. Vinyl chloride
	65. Zinc and compounds

(*Source*: EPA 2007)

These limits may be reduced where the POTW demonstrates the capacity to treat and remove named pollutants. The POTW can also set more stringent local limits for problem pollutants and to achieve the POTW's program objectives: specifically, its compliance with its own permit limits under NPDES and sludge disposal regulations.

Limits into the POTW are established so that the POTW can maintain its own NPDES permit, can keep the POTW system operating effectively, and can meet its sludge disposal limits.

The list of regulated chemicals provided derives from EPA's Model Pretreatment Ordinance. Each municipality that operates a POTW will have its own ordinance, which may be more stringent than that of the federal government.

The Industry's Relationship with the POTW

Industry is prohibited from discharging anything into the system that will affect operations of the POTW. These systems aerate wastes in an aerobic digestion process, which uses bacteria to convert waste. Many chemicals, in sufficiently large quantities, can kill off these beneficial bacteria and cause the sewage treatment plant a costly and painful restart.

The POTW will also set local limits based on the technology they have in place to treat a facility's discharge. Any chemical that cannot be removed by the POTW, passing through the system, is prohibited to be discharged. A facility is also prohibited from discharging into a POTW a waste stream containing chemicals that the POTW *can* remove, but which will end up in the sludge, if that discharge will cause the POTW to be in violation of its federal sludge disposal requirements. Local POTW discharge limits must be at least as stringent as the federal rules and must take into account the capabilities of the local POTW to eliminate the toxic contaminates present in the waste.

It may be worth noting here that there is no black box that makes waste disappear. It can be converted to other forms, and the most toxic elements can be removed and disposed of in other ways, but what goes into the system comes out of the system in one way or another. Aerating volatile organic compounds in a sewage treatment plant may take them from a liquid form to an aerosol or a gas, but in that case they simply become air pollution instead of water pollution.

If a company has an NPDES permit, or a permit to discharge into the local POTW, it will likely be required to perform sampling and analysis for conventional pollutants—biochemical oxygen demand (BOD), total suspended solids (nonfilterable) (TSS), pH, fecal coliform, oil and grease—as well as for categorical standards for that particular industry and compliance standards for anything else the POTW believes it might expect to be in the waste stream that they do not want to have to deal with. Some of these are regulated as user charge items and some as compliance items.

The POTW has a responsibility under the Section 204(b)(1)(A) of the Clean Water Act, as a condition of receiving federal funding for wastewater treatment works, to charge each recipient of waste treatment services its proportionate share of the costs of operation and maintenance of waste treatment services provided to it. User charges are not compliance items but rather cover the costs of volume and pollution loading the POTW can remove, such as BODs, chemical oxygen demands (CODs), and TSSs.

Compliance items are those that are either categorical standards or items that cause the POTW problems. These include limits on heavy metals, pH, extreme temperatures, sulfide compounds, and a number of other organic and inorganic compounds.

Over the years that these laws have been enforced, most industrial dischargers have come to understand what it takes to stay out of trouble with the local POTW (for example, maintaining an efficient wastewater treatment system, reporting within deadlines, and maintaining good communication with inspectors). However, as in any process, errors occur. When compliance excursions occur, those responsible in the plant must take responsibility and fix the problem. Failure to do so will usually result in problems with the POTW that are worse than the one that was ignored.

Permit Applications

Permits may be required from the EPA (state or federal, in the case of direct dischargers) or from the local POTW (for dischargers into the local sewer system). Specifics of these applications differ, but both processes have common elements.

Applications will contain detailed information, including:

- outfall location with drawings
- average flows and treatment, intermittent flows, and maximum production capacity
- current upgrade activities
- effluent characteristics

The process of effluent characterization requires a baseline monitoring of at least the following:

- biological oxygen demand (BOD)
- chemical oxygen demand (COD)
- total organic carbon (TOC)
- total suspended solids (TSS)
- ammonia (N)
- temperature (summer and winter)
- pH

Other effluent characterization, including quantitative data, may be required for each specified pollutant from each outfall containing wastewater. Specified pollutants are likely to include:

- processes in specific industry categories
- organic toxic pollutants
- specified pesticides
- toxic metals
- cyanide
- total phenols
- any other Appendix D parameter that the applicant might have reason to discharge from any outfall

Waivers from particular requirements of an application are available from the EPA Regional Administrator for individual point sources, particular industries, or targeted pollutants under certain circumstances.

Examples of discharge permit applications may be found on the EPA's Web site (EPA 2010).

Permit Conditions

Most of the authority under the Clean Water Act is allocated to state agencies (with strong oversight from the federal EPA). States set water-quality standards—subject to federal approval—for waterways based on their use. The EPA can assume authority where state standards are deemed inadequate. It is important to keep in mind that the EPA has broad discretionary authority to impose a variety of restrictions on facilities as it deems appropriate.

Permit Limit Framework

The EPA's effluent limits are based on the levels of compliance the EPA has determined can be achieved at various levels of treatment technology. Technology-based treatment requirements set the minimum level of control that must be imposed in a permit.

When the rules under the CWA were first promulgated, all dischargers were responsible for achieving the best practicable control technology (BPT) currently available. After 1983, compliance was based on the best available technology (BAT) economically achievable. A less stringent standard of best conventional pollutant-control technology (BCT) applies to conventional pollutants (biological oxygen demand, total suspended solids, fecal coliform, pH, and oil and grease). None of these standards apply to new sources, which must meet an even higher standard of best available demonstrated control technology. In general, these limits are set to reflect the levels that, in the EPA's assessment, an industry could achieve with the specified levels of pollution control in place. To reiterate, while the limits are based on the technology, compliance is going to be determined by what comes out of the plant as effluent. BPT standards are established by surveying particular industries to identify the better-run facilities and mirror their achievements.

At the BAT level, maximum feasible pollution reduction should be achieved. These standards are based upon a number of factors beyond choosing the technology that provides the maximum pollution removal, including energy usage, other environmental impacts, and cost. The standards are required to be economically achievable. The BCT category was developed in order to impose a cost-reasonableness standard on conventional pollutants.

An effluent limit is set based upon the maximum allowance of a pollutant without exceeding the standard for the receiving waters. Permit limitations based on chronic health effects are defined as 4-hour averages; acute health effects are defined as 1-hour or 24-hour limitations. A dilution factor is calculated based upon the proposed pollution load and the rate of flow of the receiving stream.

The CWA has anti-backsliding provisions in order to assure continuous improvement of the nation's waterways. This means that new and renewing permits cannot be issued or reissued with lower limits. States establish a total maximum daily load (TMDL), the maximum allowable pollution load for a specific waterway in order to try to achieve water-quality standards.

Toxicity-based limitations are also used. Whole effluent toxicity (WET) imposes requirements for sampling and monitoring the effluent. Effluent toxicity tests involve exposing selected species of aquatic life to the proposed concentrations of effluent to determine the consequences of short- and long-term exposures.

Effluent Limits

As noted, these discharge standards are technology-based; that is, the EPA establishes effluent guidelines that incorporate discharge limits for specific types of industries (see Table 3). Categorical dischargers will be subject to the specific limits of their industry sector. Other local limits are particular to a specific POTW and their ability to treat the wastes from their service sector.

In addition to chemical sampling, the permittee may be required to maintain limits on water volumes, temperature, and pH, as well as on chemical constituency.

The EPA has issued effluent guidelines for over 50 industrial categories (see Table 4).

Sampling and Monitoring

Permit conditions for either direct or indirect discharge will likely require routine sampling and monitoring of

TABLE 3

Industrial Categories

Dairy products processing	Mineral mining and processing
Grain mills	Centralized waste treatment
Canned and preserved fruits and vegetables processing	Metal products and machinery
Canned and preserved seafood processing	Pharmaceutical manufacturing
Sugar processing	Ore mining and dressing
Textile mills	Transportation equipment cleaning
Cement manufacturing	Paving and roofing materials (tars and asphalt)
Concentrated animal feeding operations (Cafo)	Waste combustors
Electroplating	Landfills
Organic chemicals, plastics, and synthetic fibers	Paint formulating
Inorganic chemicals manufacturing	Ink formulating
Soap and detergent manufacturing	Concentrated aquatic animal production
Fertilizer manufacturing	Gum and wood chemicals manufacturing
Petroleum refining	Pesticide chemicals
Iron and steel manufacturing	Explosives manufacturing
Nonferrous metals manufacturing	Carbon black manufacturing
Phosphate manufacturing	Photographic
Steam electric power generating	Hospital
Ferroalloy manufacturing	Battery manufacturing
Leather tanning and finishing	Plastics molding and forming
Glass manufacturing	Metal molding and casting
Asbestos manufacturing	Coil coating
Rubber manufacturing	Porcelain enameling
Timber products processing	Aluminum forming
Pulp, paper, and paperboard	Copper forming
Meat and poultry products	Electrical and electronic components
Metal finishing	Nonferrous metals forming and metal powders
Coal mining	
Oil and gas extraction	

(*Source*: California State University 1996)

wastewater discharges in order to comply with the permit. Samples must be representative of the monitored activity. How the sample is taken, whether it is a grab or a composite, and the frequency and duration of sampling are all regulated. Monitoring records are required to be maintained for 5 years (or longer where required by 40 CFR 503). These records must be provided to the EPA as required and upon request.

Sampling Safety

Safe work practices must be maintained during sampling procedures. If sampling requires entering a manhole, confined space regulations must be followed (29 CFR 1910.146). All potential confined space atmospheres should be tested and appropriate ventilation

TABLE 4

Effluent Characteristics from Various Industries

Industry	Effluent Characteristics
Automotive	Oil and grease, phenols, metals, BOD, COD, acids, toxic organics
Bakery	Fats, oil and grease
Batteries	Acids, metals
Chemicals, organic	Toxic organics, BOD, COD, acids, metals
Chemicals, inorganic	Acids, metals, TDS, ammonia, phosphate
Electrical and electronics	Metals, acids, SS, toxic organics, fluoride
Electroplating and metal finishing	Acids, metals, cyanide, toxic organics
Foods	BOD, COD, SS, alkalies, oil and grease
Leather tanning and finishing	BOD, SS, chromium, oil and grease, sulfide, fecal coliforms
Metals (primary metals, smelting, and refining)	Acids, metals, BOD, COD, SS, phenols, cyanide, sulfide, ammonia
Mining	Acids, metals
Paints	BOD, COD, SS, toxic organics, copper, lead, mercury
Petroleum	Oil and grease, BOD, COD, acids and alkalies, metals, sulfide, ammonia, phenols, mercaptans, heat
Pharmaceuticals	BOD, metals
Plastics and synthetics	BOD, COD, SS, toxic organics
Power generation (utilities)	Heat, oils, SS, TDS, metals, chlorine, PCBs
Pulp and paper	Acids, alkalies, BOD, COD, wood preservatives
Rubber	BOD, SS, oil and grease
Textiles	COD, chromium, phenol, sulfide, dyes
Wood products	SS, oil and grease, BOD, COD, wood preservatives

(*Source*: California State University 1996)

employed, as necessary, prior to entry. Personal protection equipment (PPE) appropriate to the specific risks of the company must be worn and must include safety shoes, gloves, eye protection, and respiratory protection where required.

There are hazards that are unique to each industry, which should be known, understood, and addressed prior to conducting sampling activities at that facility. It is not possible to list all of these hazards, which may be as diverse as high-voltage electricity in metal finishing shops to slips, trips, and falls.

Sampling generally means end-of-pipe sampling, but routine monitoring of system operations is also

required (California State University 1996). Flow and pH charts, flow-meter calibrations, temperature, conductivity, lower explosive limit (LEL), and oxidation reduction potential are all possible sampling protocols that may be required.

Odor detection can also alleviate problem areas or even emergency response situations. Organic material can accumulate in waste treatment lines and release hydrogen sulfide into the atmosphere. The odor of rotten eggs should act as a trigger to test for the presence of hydrogen sulfide gas, which is the most common toxic gas encountered while sampling wastewater. Although its strong odor is readily identified, olfactory fatigue occurs at high concentrations and at continuous low concentrations. For this reason, odor is not a reliable indicator of hydrogen sulfide's presence and may not provide adequate warning of hazardous concentrations (CDC/ATSDR 2011). The recommended exposure limit (REL) of the National Institute of Occupational Safety and Health (NIOSH) for hydrogen sulfide is 10 ppm (CDC 1994); the immediately dangerous to life and health (IDLH) limit is 100 ppm (NIOSH 1997).

Other gases that may be of concern in sampling include hydrogen cyanide, having a threshold limit value (TLV) of 10 ppm (NIOSH 1997). Hydrogen cyanide gas can be generated when discharged from improperly treated metal-finishing wastewater and then combined with acidic wastewater in the system. Exposure to cyanide gas can be fatal. Chlorine gas can be encountered in a wastewater treatment system that uses it for cyanide destruction. The NIOSH limit for chlorine is 0.5 ppm (NIOSH 1997).

Other chemicals that may be encountered in sampling activities include corrosives, solvents and flammable materials, poisonous and toxic chemicals, and infectious agents.

Sampling Protocol

Samples may be collected as *composites* or *grab samples*. Composites are defined as "a collection of individual samples obtained at regular intervals, usually every one or two hours during a 24-hour time span. Each individual sample is combined with the others in proportion to the rate of flow when the sample was collected. Equal volume, individual samples also may be collected at intervals after a specific volume of flow passes the sampling point or after equal time intervals and still be referred to as a composite sample. The resulting mixture (composite sample) forms a representative sample and is analyzed to determine the average conditions during the entire sampling period" (California State University 1996).

Composites may be flow-weighted averages or time-weighted averages (TWAs). Grab samples are collected as single samples taken all at one time. A composite is a number of flow-weighted (taken from discharges of equal flow) or time-weighted (taken from discharges at equal time intervals) grab samples. Composites are more representative than grab samples.

Sampling for total toxic organics must be conducted with care to minimize volatilization of the chemicals; such samples should be refrigerated and immediately transported to the laboratory.

Where baseline monitoring reflects pollutants present only in traces, infrequent sampling may be sufficient. Where pollutants are discharged near limits, more frequent sampling may be required to avoid violations.

Sampling should be representative of operations. Where operations fluctuate either seasonally or cyclically (over the course of a week or a month), samples should be collected to reflect those fluctuations.

Samples should be analyzed by a certified laboratory qualified to conduct the necessary tests using U.S. EPA–approved methods. Appropriate containers, properly labeled and preserved, must be used. A chain of custody must be maintained.

Treatment

Each facility must design its own wastewater treatment system to address its own physical layout and permit limits. For a more thorough discussion of wastewater treatment, see the "Applied Scientific and Engineering Principles" section.

Inspection

The permittee must allow access to authorized representatives of the EPA (including the POTW) to review records; inspect facilities, equipment, and

operations; and sample and monitor for any substance (40 CFR 122.41(i)). POTWs will generally perform routine inspection of each significant industrial user at least once annually, including sampling for constituents listed in the permit.

Receptionists and security guards should be trained to handle unannounced visits, to request identification, and to notify EHS staff promptly. Note that, if the individual normally responsible for escorting inspectors is not available, the inspector still has the right to inspect the facility. The facility should be prepared to supply a back-up escort. Denial of access is a permit violation.

The inspector may wish to review records, including logs of flow measurements, pH, flow-meter calibrations, process upsets, MSDSs, and liquid waste hauler's manifests to gain additional knowledge of the plant's operation. A facility inspection will generally at least include inspection of the company's outfall(s), but a complete facility tour may be requested.

Should violations be found in the POTW's sampling, the company may be issued a citation for a violation. Additional sampling and monitoring may be required until the company has shown compliance.

Reporting

A facility is required to notify the EPA or its authorized representative of:

- any planned physical alterations or additions to the permitted facility if the changes might prompt the EPA to reassess the facility as a new source or if the change will have significant impact on the nature or quantities of the pollutants discharged
- any incidents of noncompliance

Each reporting agency will have its own set of requirements.

Enforcement

As with all other aspects of regulatory compliance, an EHS director must be aware of aspects of law that may be industry- or region-specific.

Either the EPA or, where appropriate, the state agency or local POTW can enforce against Clean Water Act violations. Facilities that experience violations will be required to increase sampling, monitoring, and reporting activities until the facility has demonstrated to the permitting agency its return to compliance. Criminal and civil penalties may be sought and fines of at least $1000 per day for each violation may be imposed for any negligent or intentional violation.

Environmental law is complex and confusing. When there is doubt about the law, the company's attorney should always be consulted. It should be remembered that environmental liability may "pierce the corporate veil." That means that an EHS director, company officer, or board member may be personally liable for information appearing above his or her signature, or for actions taken by company personnel. Further, the Clean Water Act is enforceable not only for wanton acts, but for negligence; lack of knowledge about the law is not a defense.

OTHER WATER REGULATIONS
The Oil Pollution Act

The Oil Pollution Act (OPA), Section 311 of the Clean Water Act, prohibits discharge of oil or hazardous substances into navigable waterways (OPA 1990). Congress passed OPA in August 1990, partially in response to the *Exxon Valdez* spill in 1989.

The law was based on damage that was caused by one cargo-hold load of oil in the 1989 spill. This assumption grossly underestimated the potential for release into the waters of the United States, as was experienced in the Gulf of Mexico following the explosion of the Deepwater Horizon oil-drilling platform on April 20, 2010, and subsequent release of an estimated 4.9 million barrels of oil before the well was capped on July 15, 2010. As of June 2011, the impact assessment and investigation of this incident is ongoing, but it is clear that the incident overwhelmed the environmental health and safety systems in place at the time. The social, political, and legislative response to this disaster will inform how

future catastrophic releases are addressed (Freeman 2011).

It is in the best interests of all stakeholders that a thorough and scientific analysis be conducted to enhance decisions regarding continued efforts to improve the environment in the Gulf region, and future legislation and regulatory rulemaking regarding how such incidents are addressed.

One of the components of this law relates to spill control, listing 300 substances considered hazardous when spilled. Exceeding threshold limits for these substances must prompt a call to the National Response Center.

Spill Control

A spill prevention, control, and countermeasure plan (SPCC) is required at sites where petroleum products exceed the designated minimum quantities (1320 gallons above ground; 42,000 below ground; 660 gallons in a single aboveground tank) The plan must cover the facility components that are specifically designed to control spills—both on-site control measures and off-site clean-up measures. The plan must be updated every 3 years (EPA 2002a). A facility response plan is required of "any non-transportation-related on-shore facility that, because of its location, could reasonably be expected to cause substantial harm to the environment by discharging oil into or on the navigable waters or adjoining shorelines" (EPA 2002a).

Spills that are discharged to the local POTW in excess of reportable limits require that the POTW be notified so that it can take evasive action. This is a self-reporting system, and failure to notify can result in civil or criminal penalties.

Components of the SPCC Plan

A spill prevention, control, and countermeasure (SPCC) plan must be carefully thought out, prepared in accordance with good engineering practices, and have full approval of management at a level necessary to commit the necessary resources. Where the potential exists for equipment failure to result in a spill event, the plan should include a prediction of direction and rate of flow and the total quantity of oil that could result.

Containment sufficient to handle predictable spills should be provided. Such containment could include dikes, berms, or retaining walls; curbing; culverts, gutters, or other drainage facilities; wiers or booms; spill diversion ponds; retention ponds; and sorbent materials. Where facilities are located off shore, containment may also include sumps and storage tanks.

The plan should also address controls and monitoring for:

- facility drainage
- bulk storage tanks, underground storage tanks, aboveground storage tanks
- material transfer and pumping operations
- tank-car and tank-truck loading and unloading

Oil production, pipelines, and drilling facilities have their own specific rules.

Inspections must be made and records kept in accordance with the facility's own plans. Security, consisting of fencing and gates, must be present. Valves must be locked. Lighting must be appropriate for night on-site facility response. Personnel must be trained to operate equipment in such ways as to prevent discharges, and plans to do so should be reviewed. Each facility should have a designated person accountable for oil-spill prevention.

The plan must be amended whenever there is a change in facility design, construction, or operation that materially affects the facility's potential for discharge of oil. Amendments must be made within six months of such changes.

APPLIED SCIENTIFIC AND ENGINEERING PRINCIPLES

Although the regulatory framework dictates standards for water quality for consumption and effluent limits for discharge, how those values are maintained from withdrawal to discharge is a function of wastewater management engineering.

Before population growth and industrial development began to overtax natural systems, streams, rivers, wetlands, ponds, and lakes had more capability for eliminating contamination. Wetlands still provide more benefits than just serving as important habitats for wildlife; they contribute water storage to reduce flood risk and are a natural buffer to pollution.

Wetlands Management

The Clean Water Act addresses the maintenance of the nation's wetlands. This is important for flood-control issues as well as for a healthy environment. This section on wetlands management is added here, however, not only to recall the importance of wetlands in environmental management but also to point out the potential difficulties in constructing on wetland properties.

The definition of a protected wetland has undergone a legal shift as a result of a series of Supreme Court cases. In 2001, the Supreme Court heard *Solid Waste Agency of Northern Cook County v. Army Corps of Engineers*. In this case, the solid waste agency had petitioned for the construction of a landfill. In the period between the application for the landfill and the court case which followed, the unused property, which had previously been a quarry, became a wetland and home to a rookery and endangered species birds.

The Army Corps of Engineers declined the permit and based their jurisdiction on the definitions of "waters of the United States" under the Clean Water Act. The Supreme Court reversed the 6th Circuit Court, which had upheld the Corps' jurisdiction in the case, taking the position that isolated wetlands did not constitute navigable waters as defined in the Clean Water Act.

Decisions handed down on June 16, 2006, in *Rapanos v. United States* and *Carabell v. United States* left many unanswered questions as to what is a protected wetland under the law. The question comes down to what is considered "navigable waters," and whether wetlands are adjacent to or connected to navigable waters. In *Rapanos*, the connection was remote, consisting of a series of about 20 miles of ditches and canals through which the water from the wetlands had to meander before reaching navigable waters. In *Carabell*, the wetland in question was adjacent to a ditch that eventually emptied into navigable waters, but there was no direct connection, and a berm separated the ditch from the wetlands.

The Court split three ways in its findings, with no majority achieved. Four justices sided with one opinion, which would have severely limited the Corps' jurisdiction over wetlands. A dissenting opinion would have upheld the Corps' jurisdiction. One justice wrote a solitary opinion that "waters of the United States" includes not only navigable waters, but also nonnavigable waters that have a "significant nexus" to navigable waters. Such a nexus might include wetlands, which "either alone or in combination with similarly situated lands in the region, significantly affect the chemical, physical, and biological integrity of other covered waters more readily understood as 'navigable.'" This decision, because it mediates between the two sides, will be the one that stands. The result, then, is that the Corps must determine whether a "significant nexus" exists on a "case-by-case basis." Thus, the Corps might be said to have jurisdiction over the two cases heard, but because this standard was not applied, the cases were remanded to the lower court (Murphy 2006).

Wastewater Management

The first step in wastewater management is an understanding of the character of, and the water and wastes in, the water being discharged. As with other wastes, prevention is the first line of defense. That includes reducing the amount of water going through the system, as well as the volume of waste materials it contains. Waste reduction options include product reformulation, product substitution (replacing toxic materials with those that are less so), process redesign, process control, and waste concentration.

Waste recovery technologies that operate on a closed-loop system to reuse water and product in the system are often more cost effective and environmentally sound than end-of-pipe treatment technologies. Where waste products are of no use to producers, most state EPAs provide waste recycling services that find users for many waste products.

Housekeeping measures that minimize spillage, check for leaks, and make minor process changes can help to keep costs under control. Further management of wastewater depends upon the volume of water flow and concentration of waste materials in the flow.

Consideration must be given to total, average, and peak flows, for which there will likely be permit limits. Total flows are used to calculate user charges. The average daily flow is often used to size a waste treatment system for optimal efficiency. Peak flow is used to size pumps, pipes, and flow metering devices, and should be reflected in the company's waste treatment capacity (California State University 1996).

Wastewater is classified by its chemical, physical, and microbial characteristics. Chemical characteristics include organics (BOD, COD), heavy metals and inorganics, cyanide, toxics, oil and grease, and pH. Physical characteristics include solids (settleable, suspended, colloidal, and dissolved), odor, temperature, and color. Microbial characteristics include bacteria, particularly pathogens (California State University 1996).

Wastewater Treatment

Treatment options must be designed to correspond with the flow, composition, and effluent limits of the waste stream, which is unique to each individual company.

Waste treatment technologies may be grouped into five categories:

1. physical treatment
2. chemical treatment
3. biological treatment
4. land treatment
5. thermal treatment.

The following discussions of waste treatment technologies have been adapted by Michael C. Lee, Richard G. Wilson, and Douglas K. Garfield (California State University 1996). This series of manuals provides a very detailed overview of wastewater treatment operations for the reader seeking more thorough knowledge.

The waste treatment operator at a facility needs a thorough knowledge of the waste stream, the specific technology and operation of the waste treatment operation in use to handle it, and what to do when the system does not work as it should. While it may be useful in considering what additional technologies might enhance a company's current waste treatment system, it is not necessary for a waste treatment operator to have the knowledge of how every type of waste treatment system works in order to be an effective employee. The following provides many of the highlights.

Physical Treatment

Physical treatment includes those processes that separate waste stream constituents or change their form without altering their chemical structure. These processes include equalization, screening, filtration, evaporation, distillation, adsorption, and stripping.

Equalization is performed in a tank, a sump, a basin, or an elongated pipe, and might be used to mix rather than separate constituents in order to neutralize them by mixing acid and basic materials, or by releasing materials slowly that might otherwise cause a shock to the system if released all at once.

Screening removes large particles from the waste stream. This may be accomplished with a rotating drum that is coated with a screen medium through which the water passes. Solids are scraped off the filter as it rotates. A vibrating or stationary screen is tilted so that solids fall off one side.

In a *sedimentation* system, suspended solids are removed by a clarifier, which is a holding tank or basin that allows gravitational settling to occur. Often, a series of baffles and weirs direct the water flow, separate the liquids from the solids, and contribute to the collection and thickening of the settled solids. A *flocculant* (lime, aluminum sulfate, or ferrous chloride) is introduced at the inlet to agglomerate the solid particles so that they can settle faster. Material collected from the settling operation is often still very wet, so additional sludge dewatering must be incorporated at the end. Such systems generate sludge that must then be disposed of.

Flotation is a process for removing solids and oil and grease by introducing air bubbles to the discharge to induce floating. This method is particularly useful for lighter materials that do not lend themselves to sedimentation methods.

Filtration separates liquids and solids by using various types of filtration media. Filters are used to achieve a greater level of separation in the wastewater following clarification or to further dry solids that have been removed from a clarifier.

Evaporation heats a waste solution or slurry in order to condense and concentrate wastewater solutions. Although an expensive alternative, it can be used to concentrate and recycle rinse waters and to recover valuable constituents.

Distillation is used primarily in oil refineries and chemical plants to separate organic liquids at different boiling points.

Adsorption separates constituents by passing them through a filtration medium—usually activated carbon, which has a large surface area per unit of mass. Organic contaminants are removed by adsorbing (clinging) to the surface of the carbon granules. It is effective with dilute concentrations of organic contaminants (solvents, pesticides, PCBs, and phenols), especially nonbiodegradable organics, and some inorganic contaminants, such as cyanide and chromium.

Stripping removes volatile components of wastewater through treatment with a stripping fluid using steam or air.

Reverse osmosis removes or recovers dissolved organic and inorganic materials, particularly soluble metals and most total organic carbon. The process involves pressure filtration through a semipermeable membrane at a pressure greater than the natural osmotic pressure caused by the dissolved materials in the wastewater. It is often used for ultrafiltration to achieve high purity of water.

Solvent extraction is used to remove organic substances through the use of an immiscible solvent (one that normally forms a separate phase) with the waste stream. Added to the wastewater, it combines with the organics and is then extracted through a series of mixing and settling operations. In addition, it is often used in removing phenol from coke industry waste and toxic dyes.

Chemical Treatment

Chemical treatments alter the chemical structure of the constituents to remove them from the waste stream prior to discharge to render the resultant solution less hazardous. These are normally easy to implement but result in sludges.

Neutralization is used to adjust the pH of wastewater by adding acids or bases to produce a neutral solution. Sulfuric and hydrochloric acids are commonly used for neutralization of alkaline streams, and sodium hydroxide (caustic soda), calcium hydroxide (hydrated lime), calcium oxide (quicklime), calcium carbonate (limestone), sodium bicarbonate (soda ash), and ammonia are used to neutralize acids.

Precipitation removes soluble compounds by forming an insoluble precipitate through the addition of a chemical. When lime or caustic soda is added to metal-bearing wastewater, hydroxide precipitates form. The resulting material is removed as a solid. Precipitation is used in the iron, steel, and copper industries to remove metals from pickling wastewater, in metal finishing to remove spent metals from rinse water, and in the inorganic chemical industry in a number of applications.

Ion exchange is accomplished with ion-exchange resin beads composed of synthetic molecular weight polyelectrolytes that are insoluble in water. These beads contain a loosely held ion in their structure that can be exchanged for another ion of the same charge. Cationic resins generally exchange hydrogen ions (H^+) for other positive ions such as metal ions, and anionic resins exchange hydroxyl ions (OH^-) for negative ions such as carbonate. These resins can be designed to be very selective in the ions they remove so that systems can be tailored to a specific application. The liquid is passed through a fixed bed of natural or synthetic resin. One type of ion contained in the water is adsorbed onto an insoluble solid material and replaced by an equivalent quantity of another ion of the same charge. Inorganic material in the solu-

tion attaches to the resin and moves from the solution to the resin bed. This technology is effective in handling cyanide and chromium waste streams and in separating metals from mixed metal waste streams. It makes the most sense when metal-bearing waste streams are of high value. However, its disadvantages include its cost, the need to treat regenerate solutions, the need to prefilter prior to ion exchange, the downtime required for regeneration, and upper concentration limits beyond which the process is not feasible.

Oxidation/reduction refers to processes that involve the exchange of electrons to convert toxic compounds into simpler, less toxic chemicals. Common applications of oxidation include conversion of cyanide to cyanate (and then to nitrogen gas and carbon dioxide) and conversion of sulfide to sulfate or elemental sulfur in a two-step process: first, cyanide to cyanate at a pH of 10 to 11; and, second, cyanate to nitrogen at a pH of 8.5. Common reduction applications include the conversion of hexavalent chromium to trivalent chromium. Trivalent chromium precipitates out and can be removed as a solid at a pH of 8 to 8.5, while hexavalent is soluble in water over a wide range of pH levels.

Dechlorination strips chlorine atoms from highly chlorinated toxic compounds, such as PCBs and chlorinated pesticides, producing nontoxic residue.

Biological Treatment

The biological treatment of wastewater involves processes that decompose organic wastes through a variety of methods. These technologies do not usually add microbes but rather encourage the growth and use of the microbes that are already there in order to achieve consumption of a contaminant. There are *designer bacteria* that can be added to a waste stream to handle its particular constituency. In addition to the organic wastes that this technology can address, nitrogen and sulfur compounds can benefit from its application. However, this technology uses living organisms that can die if not properly cared for through feeding and watering.

In *stabilization ponds*, wastes are allowed to decompose biologically over a long period of time. These ponds may be aerobic, aerobic–anaerobic, or anaerobic. In an aerobic pond, bacteria and algae biodegrade the wastes.

Aerated lagoons treat waste on a flow-through basis using the same biological processes that are used by activated sludge systems. This technology has a long retention time while organic matter decomposes. It has been used to treat wastewaters from petroleum, textile, and refinery wastes but is not recommended for waste having high solids or metal content, or for mixed organic wastes.

Activated sludge converts organic matter in a waste stream to carbon dioxide and simpler organics under organic conditions. The technology has been successfully applied to refinery, petrochemical, and other biodegradable organic wastewaters.

Trickling filters consist of a bed of rock or synthetic material with attached bacteria. As wastes are trickled through, the bacteria decompose them.

Anaerobic digestion metabolizes organic matter in the absence of free or dissolved oxygen. The process provides a high degree of waste stabilization with a low production of biological sludges. The end products of this process are methane gas, carbon dioxide, and microbial cell mass. It has traditionally been used for treatment of municipal wastewater sludges. Additional discussion of anaerobic treatment technologies and the potential for energy recovery may be found in the "Best Practices" section.

Land Treatment

In a land-farm treatment scenario, waste, soil, climate, and biological activity all interact to degrade, immobilize, or deactivate waste constituents. Waste may be applied on or into the soil and regularly tilled to enhance biological degradation or left to evaporate and degrade biologically. Waste biosludges, tank-bottom sludges, separator sludge, emulsion solids, and cooling-tower sludges are all appropriate targets, as long as they are biodegradable and organic. Oily wastes from petroleum refinery operations treat waste in this manner. Again, this technology depends upon living organisms. Extreme temperature fluctuations or toxic content in the waste can interfere with this biological activity and render the site useless. Odors and air pollution from volatilization of some chemicals may also be a problem.

Thermal Treatment

Thermal technologies apply temperatures above 300°F/150°C to reduce the volume and break down toxic components of wastes into simpler, less toxic forms. It is applicable for a wide variety of wastes. Energy may be recovered in the process. Thermal treatment can occur in the presence of oxygen (incineration) or in the absence of oxygen (pyrolysis).

The downside to thermal technologies, particularly for wastewaters, is the need for supplemental fuel. It has proven costly for treatment of sludges because they are wet. Air emissions are a concern with these technologies, and siting and permitting may be particularly difficult.

Example: Electroplating

The metal-finishing industry is representative of regulated water-using industries in many ways. Electroplaters are defined as "dischargers of pollutants in process wastewater resulting from the process in which ferrous or nonferrous base material is electroplated in copper, nickel, chrome, zinc, tin, lead, cadmium, iron, aluminum or any combination thereof" (EPA 1986). The category consists of plating, anodizing, metal coating, etching, electro-less plating, and printed circuit-board manufacture. An electroplating operation is a categorical discharger with established compliance sampling deadlines and limits.

In an electroplating operation, items are submerged in a series of baths to perform cleaning, etching, plating, and rinsing operations. Items may be cleaned to remove machine oil and dirt prior to plating, and in this stage solvents may be used. In etching operations, acid solutions are added to remove metal from certain areas of the item. In the plating operation, an electric current is run through the bath and the metal adheres to the item being plated. The item to be plated must be rinsed in clean water after

TABLE 5

Categorical Standards for Electroplaters

Conventional pollutants

Biochemical oxygen demand (BOD)	pH
Total suspended solids (nonfilterable) (TSS)	Fecal coliform
	Oil and grease

Metals

Total cyanide	Zinc
Copper	Lead
Nickel	Cadmium
Chrome (total and hexavalent)	Total metals

Total toxic organics

Acenaphthene	1,2-Dichloropropane	N-Nitrosodi-n-propylamine	Vinyl chloride (chloroethylene)
Acrolein	1,3-Dichloropropylene	Pentachlorophenol	Aldrin
Acrylonitrile	(1,3-dichloropropene)	Phenol	Dieldrin
Benzene	2,4-Dimethylphenol	Bis(2-ethylhexyl) phthalate	Chlordane (technical mixture
Benzidine	2,4-Dinitrotoluene	Butyl benzyl phthalate	and metabolites)
Carbon tetrachloride	2,6-Dinitrotoluene	Di-n-butyl phthalate	4,4-DDT
(tetrachloromethane)	1,2-Diphenylhydrazine	Di-n-octyl phthalate	4,4-DDE (p,p'-DDX)
Chlorobenzene	Ethylbenzene	Diethyl phthalate	4,4-DDD (p,p'-TDE)
1,2,4-Trichlorobenzene	Fluoranthene	Dimethyl phthalate	Alpha-Endosulfan
Hexachlorobenzene	4-Chlorophenyl phenyl ether	1,2-Benzanthracene	Beta-Endosulfan
1,2-Dichloroethane	4-Bromophenyl phenyl ether	(benzo(a)anthracene)	Endosulfan sulfate
1,1,1-Trichloroethane	Bis (2-chloroisopropyl) ether	Benzo(a)pyrene (3,4-benzopyrene)	Endrin
Hexachloroethane	Bis (2-chloroethoxy) methane	3,4-Benzofluoranthene	Endrin aldehyde
1,1-Dichloroethane	Methylene chloride	(benzo(b)fluoranthene)	Heptachlor
1,1,2-Trichloroethane	(dichloromethane)	11,12-Benzofluoranthene	Heptachlor epoxide
1,1,2,2-Tetrachloroethane	Methyl chloride (chloromethane)	(benzo(k)fluoranthene)	(BHC-hexachlorocyclohexane)
Chloroethane	Methyl bromide (bromomethane)	Chrysene	Alpha-BHC
Bis(2-chloroethyl) ether	Bromoform (tribromomethane)	Acenaphthylene	Beta-BHC
2-Chloroethyl vinyl ether (mixed)	Dichlorobromomethane	Anthracene	Gamma-BHC
2-Chloronaphthalene	Chlorodibromomethane	1,12-Benzoperylene	Delta-BHC
2,4,6-Trichlorophenol	Hexachlorobutadiene	(benzo(ghi)perylene)	(PCB-polychlorinated biphenyls)
Parachlorometacresol	Hexachlorocyclopentadiene	Fluorene	PCB-1242 (Arochlor 1242)
Chloroform (trichloromethane)	Isophorone	Phenanthrene	PCB-1254 (Arochlor 1254)
2-Chlorophenol	Naphthalene	1,2,5,6-Dibenzanthracene	PCB-1221 (Arochlor 1221)
1,2-Dichlorobenzene	Nitrobenzene	(dibenzo(a,h)anthracene)	PCB-1232 (Arochlor 1232)
1,3-Dichlorobenzene	2-Nitrophenol	Indeno (1,2,3-cd) pyrene	PCB-1248 (Arochlor 1248)
1,4-Dichlorobenzene	4-Nitrophenol	(2,3-o-phenylene pyrene)	PCB-1260 (Arochlor 1260)
3,3-Dichlorobenzidine	2,4-Dinitrophenol	Pyrene	PCB-1016 (Arochlor 1016)
1,1-Dichloroethylene	4,6-Dinitro-o-cresol	Tetrachloroethylene	Toxaphene
1,2-trans-Dichloroethylene	N-Nitrosodimethylamine	Toluene	2,3,7,8-Tetrachlorodibenzo-
2,4-Dichlorophenol	N-Nitrosodiphenylamine	Trichloroethylene	p-Dioxin (TCDD)

(*Source*: EPA 2011)

each step. The process requires large volumes of water that are eventually discharged as wastewater after the potency of the solution has been exhausted.

The list of contaminants that must be removed from electroplating-system wastewater prior to discharge represent many of the EPA's targeted chemicals, including cyanide, oil and grease, high pH, total toxic organics (TTOs), and metals such as copper, nickel, chrome, zinc, cadmium, lead, and iron. In lieu of TTO monitoring, the POTW may allow the IU to provide an affidavit certifying it has not discharged any TTOs since its last filing period (see Table 5).

Electroplaters are required to implement process controls and pretreatment technologies to achieve discharge limits. Conventional pretreatment technology for an electroplater consists of the addition of chemical reagents that react with soluble pollutants, followed by settling, resulting in the production of insoluble, metal-laden sludges. The wet sludge is dewatered or thickened and then disposed of in a landfill (Campbell and Glenn 1982). A determination must be made as to whether sludges constitute a hazardous waste; the material must be treated based on that determination.

Wastewater entering the treatment system at an electroplating shop will first be screened to remove large debris. Cyanide will be treated first—and separately to avoid mixture with other substances, which could prove more harmful. Hexavalent chrome, because of its toxicity, will be treated next.

Wastewater will move into primary treatment, or clarification, where solid matter will settle out or float to the surface for separation. Solids may be dissolved or suspended, and treatment protocols are different for each. Dissolved solids are those left after suspended solids have been filtered or settled out. Secondary or biological treatment will introduce beneficial bacteria that will eat the organic material remaining in the wastewater.

In larger, more complex facilities, the sludge will be sent for digestion and dewatering. Tertiary treatment is generally saved for municipal wastewater treatment facilities, and more sophisticated ones at that. However, as more cost-effective tools are sought in order to stay competitive, and as energy costs rise, biological treatments that capture energy may prove more cost effective for some wastes than traditional pipeline solutions.

Reverse osmosis has been used effectively in the electroplating industry to remove TOC, copper cyanide, zinc, and nickel. Reverse osmosis was discussed previously in the "Applied Science and Engineering Principles" section.

Electrolytic recovery, also known as *cementation*, is a process in which electrochemical reduction of metal ions at the cathode reduces those ions to elemental metal. This technology is generally used to pull metal ions from solution.

Other technologies, such as ion exchange, will remove metals for recycling. These are in use currently in certain plants and central recovery facilities. However, they are considered cost effective only for those metals of high recovery value.

PERFORMANCE MEASUREMENT AND BENCHMARKING

Discharge limits draw the line in the sand for industry. Over the line is bad; inside is good. But on either side of that simple equation are fluctuations in values that are the result of very specific conditions of operation. Perhaps pH goes down when temperature goes up. If bottles are left unstopped, chemicals volatize. A pump jams and leaves a tank full of grass clippings to create some serious odor. The hotter the sun, the lower the pH, the faster the chemicals in the bottle evaporate, and the quicker the neighbors complain about the smell.

Treatment performance ebbs and flows because of any number of factors. The job of the system operator is to know why the system ebbs and flows, what its potential ranges are, and how to keep operation within a range of tolerable limits.

Maintenance of an effective wastewater treatment facility requires vigilant oversight. If the system is sized appropriately and designed properly, and the operator is well trained on the system, it is left to the operator to maintain it and keep it functioning. Records of all treatment-system upsets should be maintained and excursions investigated. If the treatment system is undersized or poorly designed, changes must be made to bring the facility into compliance.

Statistical process control measures can be used to track system effectiveness and target points of concern. System effectiveness often follows a standard bell-curve distribution, peak performance occurring at a particular point when system chemicals are new, there is a storm event that dilutes process flows, or the plant is down for clean up. Monitoring the activities that coincide with poor performance can help to determine what changes must be made.

Overall system effectiveness can be further refined by tracking individual process lines, specific constituents, or a particular time of day when values tend to be higher. Often, by careful monitoring of such variables, a minor change in process flow can have a greater impact on compliance.

COST ANALYSIS AND BUDGETING

The goal of a waste management system is to use the most cost-effective combination of management options to handle waste streams within the confines of applicable regulations. Large capital expenditures are by no means the only way to achieve this (Campbell and Glenn 1982). The seemingly smallest and cheapest of acts can have monumental impact. Simple housekeeping practices can show immediate return in terms of cost control. How corn meal is washed down the drain during clean up in a tortilla factory, for instance, can mean a major dollar difference in user charge fees. Table 6 provides a listing of anticipated capital and operating costs for the installation or retrofitting of a water treatment system.

When waste treatment equipment must be purchased or retrofitted, major capital expenditures are often involved. The price will range (depending upon the size of the system and its functionality) from a small holding tank to capture and treat small quantities of material in the back of a shop to vast municipal waste treatment systems with many employees, but the purpose is the same.

It is wise to seek the counsel of a qualified wastewater treatment engineer. If treatment must be installed, the type of system, the cost of maintenance and operations, and the amount of waste that will require hauling will greatly affect long-term costs. Where a strategy means lower capital costs, perceived savings may be quickly offset by high operating and disposal costs. It is usually best, unless acting as a wastewater management engineer, to hire a company with the ability to handle the entire job in a turnkey fashion. Make sure the bid includes all components such as piping and installation. Beware of unexpected costs: for example, the excavation of the old system to find the contamination its operation left. It should also be noted that it is often more cost effective to plan for future growth than to retrofit systems every few years. Where new technologies

TABLE 6

Anticipated Costs of a Waste Treatment System Installation or Retrofit

Capital Costs	Operating Costs
Wastewater treatment system, engineering, and installation	Wastewater treatment chemicals
Trucks, as needed	Sludge hauling/transportation costs
	Sludge disposal costs
	POTW user charges
	Permit and license fees
	Fixed costs
	Sampling and analytical costs
	Utility costs

(*Source*: Freeman 2008)

are considered, it is prudent to lease equipment or require performance guarantees.

The POTW will charge the company discharging into its system for the costs of treating its wastes. Thus, measures that minimize the amount of water used, and the contributions of BOD or COD, suspended solids, and other user charge items will have an effect on these costs. Wherever possible, waste minimization is always cheapest.

Various treatment technologies create sludges, which must be hauled away and disposed of. Costs of both transportation and disposal continue to increase. Some waste treatment systems require large amounts of electricity, costs of which will also escalate. Technologies that convert waste to energy are preferred for this reason, where feasible.

BEST PRACTICES

As the wastewater treatment industry matures, many of the practices outlined in this chapter have become commonplace in water-using industries. New and improved wastewater treatment technologies continue to be developed that provide new opportunities to minimize product loss and waste and to do so in a cost-effective manner.

Objective analysis of most of the nation's water suggests that point-source pollution is by and large under control.

However, emergency situations, such as the explosion in the Gulf of Mexico, can arise from circumstances not imagined nor adequately planned for. Development of technologies that allow drilling in deeper and more difficult places than ever before brings new responsibilities for minimizing impact to area waters. EHS directors who are involved with EHS operations that push boundaries must be aware and address their unique issues.

Further, nonpoint-source pollution continues to be a problem in the nation's waters. Nitrates and phosphorus from agricultural irrigation runoff, stormwater runoff from roads and into surface water, and leaks and spills into groundwater all usually occur without the benefit of sewage treatment systems. The EPA has established a number of regulations for the agricultural sector and continues to monitor the impact of these sources on water quality. The EPA has increased its scrutiny of the agricultural sector for its contributions to these environmental problems and continues to monitor the impact of these sources on water quality. How these problems are solved is currently beyond the control or direct concern of most EHS personnel at most industrial sites. However, it is incumbent upon every EHS manager to recognize his own company's potential for off-site contamination and to control for it.

The impact of Environmental Management Systems, ISO 14001, on wastewater treatment systems continues to increase, as is discussed in other chapters of this book.

There has been growing awareness of unmeasured and unregulated chemicals that flow through POTWs untreated. Among these are nanoparticles and endocrine disrupters, including the pharmaceuticals for human and animal hormones. These may be passed through the body or flushed down the toilet unused. They are not treated by the POTW, and there are no standards for municipal discharge. However, concerns do exist about the impact of these hormones on public health, and research has begun.

Issues related to sustainability, including old concepts of conservation and resource management—but with the addition of sustainable development and the incorporation of new technologies—is a burgeoning area of environmental management. Increased awareness of global climate-change issues, international energy demands, and environmental indicators that continue to decline worldwide are driving such changes.

On the forefront of these changes is the use of waste products as fuels in digester and gasification projects that mine our waste products for their resource value. Production of ethanol from waste cornhusk rinses may at this time be more expensive than refining oil drawn from the ground, but will likely not always be so. These are not new ideas, but they are being approached with new fervor.

Industry Innovation

Each industry brings its own contribution to the pollution loading in our waterways—and new solutions. When technical innovation reaches the marketplace, EHS concerns must be identified and addressed.

Automated process control of wastewater systems allows continuous monitoring to catch and correct fluctuations in wastewater discharge, engendering greater compliance, as well as cost containment, since chemicals are metered out only as needed.

CONCLUSION

Water is a nonrenewable resource that must be monitored and controlled to maintain a healthy environment. Federal, state, and municipal laws are in place to facilitate this. It is the responsibility of EHS staff to determine how its facility is impacting local water sources and to take the necessary steps to comply.

IMPORTANT TERMS

Aerobic: With oxygen

Anaerobic: Without oxygen

Anti-backsliding: A provision of the Clean Water Act whereby renewals of NPDES permits cannot be issued to dischargers using any limits but final limits, unless it can be shown that the process has undergone substantial change.

Average monthly (or weekly) discharge limitation: The highest allowable average of daily discharges over a calendar month (week), calculated as the sum of all daily discharges, divided by the total number of daily discharges measured during that month (week) (40 CFR 122.2).

Best available technology (BAT): The best technology, treatment technique, or other means available, taking cost into consideration. For the purpose of setting MCLs for synthetic organic chemicals, any BAT must be at least as effective as activated carbon (40 CFR 141.2).

Biological (or biochemical) oxygen demand (BOD): The quantification of the amount of dissolved oxygen needed to satisfy the metabolic rate of microorganisms living in aerobic conditions. Wastewater with a high loading of organic material will reduce oxygen levels in receiving waters, leading to eutrophic conditions. BOD testing will calculate the amount of decompostable material in wastewater by measuring the amount of oxygen (mg/L) used over a period of 5 days at 20°C.

Blowdown: The minimum discharge of recirculating water for the purpose of discharging materials contained in the water, further buildup of which would cause concentration in amounts exceeding limits established by best engineering practice (40 CFR 401.11).

Categorical pretreatment standards: Industry-specific wastewater discharge standards (40 CFR 403-471).

Chemical agent: That element, compound, or mixture that coagulates, disperses, dissolves, emulsifies, foams, neutralizes, precipitates, reduces, solubilizes, oxidizes, concentrates, congeals, entraps, fixes, makes the pollutant mass more rigid or viscous, or otherwise facilitates the mitigation of deleterious effects or the removal of the pollutant from the water. Chemical agents include biological additives, dispersants, sinking agents, miscellaneous oil-spill control agents, and burning agents, but do not include sorbents (40 CFR 300.5).

Coliform: A type of bacterium that is an indicator of possible pathogenic bacterial contamination.

Community water system: A public water system that serves at least 15 service connections used by year-round residents or regularly serves at least 25 year-round residents (40 CFR 141.2).

Conventional pollutant: The following comprise the list of conventional pollutants designated pursuant to section 304(a)(4) of the CWA: BOD, TSS, pH, fecal coliform, oil and grease.

Daily discharge: Discharge of any pollutant measured during a calendar day or any 24-hour period (40 CFR 122.2).

Direct discharge: Discharge of a pollutant (40 CFR 122.2).

Discharge: Any spilling, leaking, pumping, pouring, emitting, emptying, or dumping. This also means the addition of any pollutant to the waters of the United States. This includes addition of pollutants from surface runoff. It may also mean substantial threat of discharge. Discharge also refers to introduction of pollutants into a POTW from any nondomestic source of the act (40 CFR 112.2, 122.2, 300.5, 307(b), (c) or (d), and 403.3).

Disinfection: The process that inactivates pathogenic organisms in water by chemical oxidants or equivalent agents (40 CFR 141.2).

Effluent: Liquid waste, treated or untreated, from sewage or industrial process or treatment.

Effluent limitation: Any restriction imposed on the quantities, discharge rates, and concentrations of pollutants discharged from point sources into waters of the United States, contiguous zones, or the ocean (40 CFR 401.11).

Effluent standard: "Any effluent standard or limitation which may include a prohibition of any discharge, established or proposed to be established for any toxic pollutant under Section 307(a) of the Act" (40 CFR 122.2).

Filtration: A process for removing particulate matter from water by passage through porous media (40 CFR 141.2).

Finished water: Water that is introduced into the distribution system of a public water system and is intended for distribution and consumption without further treatment, except as necessary to maintain water quality in the distribution system (e.g., booster disinfection, addition, or corrosion control chemicals) (40 CFR 141.2).

Ground water: Water in a saturated zone or stratum beneath the surface of land or water (40 CFR 101.12).

Hazardous ranking system: The method used by the EPA to evaluate the relative potential of a hazardous substance release to cause health or safety problems, or ecological or environmental damage (40 CFR 300.5).

Indirect discharge: The introduction of pollutants into a POTW (40 CFR 403.3).

Indirect discharger: A nondomestic discharger introducing "pollutants" to a POTW (40 CFR 403.3).

Industrial user: A source of indirect discharge (40 CFR 403.3).

Inorganic waste: Waste material containing substances of mineral origin.

Interference: A discharge that inhibits or disrupts the POTW, its treatment processes or operations, or its sludge processes, use, or disposal, and therefore is a cause of a violation of the POTW's NPDES permit or the prevention of sewage-sludge use or disposal (40 CFR 403.3).

Local limits: Specific prohibitions or limits on pollutants or pollutant parameters developed by a POTW.

Maximum contaminant level (MCL): The maximum permissible level of a contaminant in water that is delivered to any user of a public water system. It is required to be as close to MCLG as possible (40 CFR 141).

Maximum contaminant level goals (MCLGs): The most stringent drinking water standards at which no known or anticipated adverse effect on the health of persons would occur, plus an adequate margin of safety. Maximum contaminant level goals are nonenforceable health goals (40 CFR 141).

National Pollution Discharge Elimination System (NPDES): The national program for issuing, modifying, revoking and reissuing, terminating, monitoring, and enforcing permits, and imposing and enforcing pretreatment requirements under sections 307, 402, 318, and 405 (40 CFR 122.2).

National pretreatment standard: Any regulation containing pollutant discharge limits promulgated in accordance with Section 307(b) & (c) of the Act.

Navigable waters: Waters of the United States.

New source: Any facility from which there is or may be a discharge of pollutants and the construc-

tion of which commenced after effluent standards were proposed for the discharges of its operation (40 CFR 307).

Noncommunity water systems: A public water system that is not a community water system. A noncommunity water system is either a "transient noncommunity water system (TWS)" or a "non-transient noncommunity water system (NTNCWS)" (40 CFR 141.2).

Noncontact cooling water: Water used for cooling that does not come into direct contact with any raw material, intermediate product, waste product, or finished product.

Nontransient noncommunity water systems (NTNCWS): A public water system that is not a community water system and that regularly serves at least 25 of the same persons over 6 months per year. Workplaces with over 25 employees will be thus classified (40 CFR 141.11).

Nonpoint sources: Pollution from diffuse sources, not a point source.

Oil: Oil of any kind in any form, including but not limited to petroleum, fuel oil, sludge, oil refuse, and oil mixed with wastes other than dredge spoil (40 CFR 112.2). The definition is slightly different under OPA, which specifies that the Act does not include petroleum, including crude oil or any fraction thereof, which is specifically listed and designated as a hazardous substance under CERCLA (40 CFR 311(a)(i)).

Organic waste: Waste material derived mainly from animal or plant sources, including petrochemical derivatives.

Pass through: A discharge which exits the POTW into waters of the United States in quantities or concentrations which, alone or in conjunction with a discharge from other sources, is a cause of a violation of the POTW's NPDES permit (40 CFR 403.3).

Pathogenic organisms: Bacteria or viruses that can cause disease.

Permit: An authorization, license or equivalent, and control document issued by the EPA or an approved state (40 CFR 122.2).

pH: Measurement of the acid–base condition of a liquid on a scale of 0 to 14, with 0 being the most acidic, 14 being the most basic, and 7 neutral.

Point source: Any discernible, confined, and discrete conveyance, including but not limited to any pipe, ditch, channel, tunnel, conduit, well, discrete fissure, container, rolling stock, animal feeding operation, landfill leachate collection system, vessel, or floating craft (40 CFR 122.2).

Pollutant: Any material that can contaminate water.

Pollution: Any man-made or man-induced alteration of the chemical, physical, biological, or radiological integrity of water (40 CFR 401.11).

Pretreatment: The reduction of the amount of pollutants, the elimination of pollutants, or the alteration of the nature of pollutant properties in wastewater prior to, or in lieu of, discharging or otherwise introducing such pollutants into a POTW (40 CFR 403.3).

Pretreatment standard: Any regulation containing pollution discharge limits promulgated by the EPA in accordance with Sections 307(b) and (c) of the Act that applies to industrial users of a publicly owned treatment works. It further means any state or local pretreatment requirement applicable to a discharge and which is incorporated into a POTW under Section 402 of the Act (40 CFR 117).

Primary treatment: Treatment by screening, sedimentation, and skimming adequate to remove biochemical oxygen-demanding material and suspended solids, and disinfection where appropriate.

Process wastewater: Any water that comes, during manufacturing or processing, into direct contact with or results from the production or use of any raw material, intermediate or final product, by-product, or waste (40 CFR 122.2).

Publicly owned treatment works: A facility owned by a state or municipality that includes any devices and systems used in the storage, treatment, recycling, and reclamation of municipal sewage or industrial wastes of a liquid nature (40 CFR 403.3).

Receiving water: The waters of the United States into which treated or untreated wastewater is discharged.

Secondary treatment: A wastewater treatment process that converts dissolved or suspended materials into a form more readily separated from the water being treated.

Sedimentation: A process for removal of solids before filtration by gravity or separation.

Septage: The liquid or solid material pumped from a septic tank, cesspool, or similar domestic sewage treatment system (40 CFR 122.2).

Septic: A condition produced by anaerobic bacteria that creates a heavy oxygen demand.

Sewage sludge: Any solid, semisolid, or liquid residue removed during the treatment of municipal wastewater or domestic sewage (40 CFR 122.2).

Significant industrial users: All categorical dischargers, plus companies discharging over 25,000 gallons per day or those whose discharge is of concern to the POTW.

Stabilize: To convert to a form that resists change.

Toxic pollutant: Any pollutant thus identified in the Act (40 CFR 122.2, 307, 405(4)).

Transient noncommunity water system (TWS): A noncommunity water system that does not regularly serve at least 25 of the same persons over six months per year (40 CFR 141.11).

Technology-based treatment requirements: The minimum level of control that must be imposed in a permit (40 CFR 125.3).

Variance: Any mechanism or provision that allows modification to or waiver of the generally applicable effluent limitation requirements or time deadlines of CWA (40 CFR 122.2).

Waters of the United States: All waters which are, were, or may be used in interstate or foreign commerce. These waters are specified as all waters that are subject to the ebb and flow of the tide. These include interstate waters such as wetlands and all other waters—including interstate lakes, rivers, streams, mudflats, sandflats, wetlands, sloughs, prairie potholes, wet meadows, playa lakes, and natural ponds—the use of which would or could affect interstate or foreign commerce. Specifically excludes cooling ponds operating as waste treatment systems (40 CFR 122.2).

Water-quality standards: "Provisions of the State or Federal law which consist of a designated use or uses for the waters of the United States and water quality criteria for such waters based upon such uses. Water quality standards are to protect the public health or welfare, enhance the quality of water and serve the purposes of the Act" (40 CFR 131.2)

Wetlands: Areas that are inundated or saturated by surface or groundwater at a frequency and duration sufficient to support a prevalence of vegetation typically adapted for life in saturated soil conditions (40 CFR 122.2).

REFERENCES

Agency for Toxic Substances and Diseases (ATSDR). 2011. *Toxic Substances Portal: Hygrogen Sulfide* (accessed May 31, 2011). www.astdr.cdc.com/mmg/mmg.asp?id+385&id=67

Bodger, K. 2003. *Fundamentals of Environmental Sampling.* Lanham, MD: Government Institutes.

California State University Sacramento, School of Engineering. 1996. *Pretreatment Facility Inspection.* 3d ed. Washington D.C.: U.S. Environmental Protection Agency.

Campbell, M. E., and W. M. Glenn. 1982. *Profit from Pollution Prevention, A Guide to Industrial Waste Reduction and Recycling.* Toronto, Ontario, Canada: Pollution Probe Foundation.

Cox, D. B. 2000. *Hazardous Materials Management Desk Reference.* New York: McGraw-Hill.

Environmental Protection Agency (EPA). 1975. 40 CFR 141.2. "National Primary Drinking Water Regulations; Definitions." Washington, D.C.: EPA.

_____. 1982. 40 CFR, Subchapter N. "Effluent Guidelines and Standards." Parts 401–424. Washington, D.C.: EPA.

_____. 1986. 40 CFR 413, *et seq.* "Electroplating Point Source Category." Washington, D.C.: EPA.

_____. 2006a. 40 CFR 125. "Criteria and Standards for the National Pollutant Discharge Elimination System." Washington, D.C.: EPA.

_____. 2006b. *Safe Drinking Water Act 30th Anniversary, Drinking Water Standards & Health Effects.* www.epa.gov/safewater/privatewells/index2.html

_____. 2007. 40 CFR 143. "National Secondary Drinking Water Regulations." Washington, D.C.: EPA.

_____. 2008. *Effluent Characteristics from Various Industries.* www.epa.gov/waterscience/guide/industry.html#exist

_____. 2010. *NPDES Permit Program Basics.* www.cfpub.epa.gov/npdes/home.cfm?program_id=45

_____. 2011. "Effluent Guidelines: Electroplating (40 CFR 413) (retrieved November 8, 2011). www.epa.gov/scitech/watertech/guide/eletroplating/index.cfm

Freeman, Judy. 2011. "What Oil?" *EnviroMentor,* vol. 10, no 2.

Murphy, J. 2006. *"Rapanos v. United States:* Wading Through Murky Waters." *National Wetlands Newsletter* 28(5):1, 16–19.

National Institute of Occupational Safety and Health (NIOSH). 1997. *NIOSH Pocket Guide to Chemical Hazards.* Washington, D.C.: Government Printing Office.

Occupational Health and Safety Administration (OSHA). 1994. *Documentation for Immediately Dangerous to Life and Health (IDHLs): Hydrogen Sulfide* (accessed May 31, 2011). www.cdc/niosh/idhl/7783064.html

_____. 1998. 29 CFR 1910.146, *Permit-Required Confined Spaces.* Washington, D.C.: OSHA.

Rapanos v. United States. 2006. 547 US 715. 376 F3d 629 (No. 04-1034) and 391 F3d 704 (No. 04-1384). Vacated and remanded.

Solid Waste Agency of Northern Cook County v. Army Corps of Engineers. 2001. 531 US 159, 191 F3d 845. Reversed.

U.S. Congress. 1977. *Clean Water Act of 1977.* P.L. 95-217. Washington, D.C.: Government Printing Office.

_____. 1965. *Clean Water Restoration Act.* P.L. 89-753. Washington, D.C.: Government Printing Office.

_____. 1948. *Federal Water Pollution Control Act* (FWPCA). P.L. 80-845. Washington, D.C.: Government Printing Office.

_____. 1972. *Federal Water Pollution Control Act of 1972.* P.L. 92-500. Washington, D.C.: Government Printing Office.

_____. 1972. *Federal Water Pollution Control Act Amendments.* P.L. 92-500. Washington, D.C.: Government Printing Office.

_____. 1990. *Oil Pollution Act* (OPA). P.L. 101-380. Washington, D.C.: Government Printing Office.

_____. 1899. *Protection of Navigable Waters and of Harbor and River Improvements, Generally.* (Known as the *Refuse Act.*) P.L. 33-407, Chapter 9. Washington, D.C.: Government Printing Office.

_____. 1894. *Rivers and Harbors Appropriation Act.* P.L. 33, Chapter 1, Section 1. Washington, D.C.: Government Printing Office.

_____. 1974. *Safe Drinking Water Act* (SDWA). P.L. 93–523. Washington, D.C.: Government Printing Office.

_____. 1986. *Safe Drinking Water Act Amendments.* P.L. 99-339. Washington, D.C.: Government Printing Office.

_____. 1996. *Safe Drinking Water Act Amendments.* P.L. 104–182. Washington, D.C.: Government Printing Office.

_____. 1956. *Water Pollution Control Act* (WPCA). (Known as the *Clean Water Act* (CWA)). P. L. 84-660. Washington, D.C.: Government Printing Office.

_____. 1987. *Water Quality Act.* P.L .100-4. Washington, D.C.: Government Printing Office.

APPENDIX A: ABBREVIATIONS

BAT: Best available technology economically achievable

BCT: Best control technology

BPT: Best practicable control technology currently available

BOD: Biological (or biochemical) oxygen demand

CERCLA: Comprehensive Environmental Response, Compensation and Liability Act of 1980, as amended by the Superfund Amendments and Reauthorization Act of 1986

COD: Chemical oxygen demand

CWA: Clean Water Act

FWPCA: Federal Water Pollution Control Act

IDHL: Immediately dangerous to life and Health

IU: Industrial user

MCL: Maximum contaminant levels

MCLG : Maximum contaminant level goals

mg/L: Milligrams per liter

NPDWR: National Primary Drinking Water Regulations

NPDES: National Pollution Discharge Elimination System

NTNCWS: Nontransient noncommunity water systems

PPB: Parts per billion

PPM: Parts per million

pH: The value of a chemical's acidity/alkalinity

POTW: Publicly owned treatment works

RQ: Reportable quantity

SARA: Superfund Amendments and Reauthorization Act

SDWA: Safe Drinking Water Act

SDWR: National Secondary Drinking Water Regulations

SPCC: Spill prevention, control and countermeasure plan

TDS: Total dissolved solids

TMDL: Total maximum daily load

TOC: Total organic carbon

TSS: Total suspended solids

TTO: Total toxic organics

μg/kg: Micrograms per kilogram

APPENDIX B: RECOMMENDED READINGS

Envirolink. *Environmental Resources*. www.envirolink. org/index.html

Environmental Protection Agency (EPA). 1996. 40 CFR 110. "Discharge of Oil." Washington, D.C.: EPA.

_____. 2002. 40 CFR 112. "Oil Pollution Prevention." Washington, D.C.: EPA.

_____. 2007. 40 CFR 122.41(i). "Conditions Applicable to All Permits; Inspections and Entry." Washington, D.C.: EPA.

_____. 2007. 40 CFR 122.41(j). "Conditions Applicable to All Permits; Monitoring and Records." Washington, D.C.: EPA.

_____. 2007. *Clean Water Act* (Sept). www.epa.gov/ r5water/cwa.html

_____. 2007. EPA 833-B-06-002, *Developing Your Stormwater Pollution Prevention Plan: A Guide for Industrial Operations* (accessed August 24, 2011). www.epa.gov/ npdes/pubs/industrial/swppp_guide.pdf

_____. 2007. EPA 833-B-06-002, *EPA Model Pretreatment Ordinance* (January). www.epa.gov/npdes/ pretreatment_model_suo.pdf

_____. 2008. *Clean Water Act—Analytical Test Methods*. www.epa.gov/waterscience/methods

_____. 2008. *Ground Water and Drinking Water*. www.epa. gov/safewater/index.html

_____. 2008. *Safe Drinking Water Act, Contaminants*. www.epa.gov/safewater/contaminants/index.html

_____. 2008. *Safe Drinking Water Act, Groundwater and Drinking Water*." www.epa.gov/safewater/public outreach/index.html

_____. 2002. *A Strategy for National Clean Water Industrial Regulations, Effluent Limitations, Guidelines, Pretreatment Standards, and New Source Performance Standards* (November). www.epa.gov/guide/strategy/304 mstrategy.pdf

_____. 2007. *Water Laws*. www.epa.gov/water/laws.html

_____. 2007. *Water Pollution Control Technologies*. www.epa.gov/waterscience/guide/p2/ch5.htm#1

_____. 2007. *Water Quality Standards*. www.epa.gov/ waterscience/standards

_____. 2007. *Wetlands; Laws, Regulations, Treaties*. www.epa.gov/owow/wetlands/laws

Farnan, J., General Superintendent, Metropolitan Water Reclamation District of Greater Chicago (MWRDGC). 2006. "Transmittal Letter for Board Meeting" (April 7). www.mwrdgc.dst.il.us

U.S. Army Corps of Engineers. 33 CFR 320-326. *Corps of Engineers, Department of the Army, Department of Defense*. www.wetlands.com/regs

U.S. Department of Agriculture (USDA). 2003. *Agricultural Impacts on Water Quality*. www.ers.usda.gov/ publications/arei/ah722/

U.S. Geological Survey (USGS). 2005. *Use of Water in the United States in 2000*. www.water.usgs.gov.circ/ 2004/circ1268

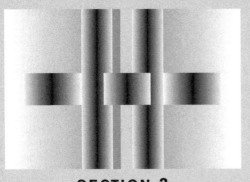

SECTION 3
ENVIRONMENTAL MANAGEMENT

LEARNING OBJECTIVES

- ▌ Analyze the fatality statistics of the solid waste industry as presented by the Bureau of Labor Statistics, indicating why this industry is one of the most dangerous in the United States.

- ▌ Become familiar with the basic introduction to solid waste regulations from the U.S. Environmental Protection Agency (EPA), including the definition of solid waste, and how these regulations apply to various types of solid waste landfills.

- ▌ Learn about historic waste-handling procedures and current solid waste definitions.

- ▌ Recognize which items are necessary in developing a landfill safety plan.

- ▌ Identify the safety and health issues to be considered at waste management and recycling facilities.

SOLID WASTE

William S. Fink

SOLID WASTE collection and waste treatment and disposal at solid waste landfills are dangerous occupations. The 2009 Census of Fatal Occupational Injuries (CFOI) provided by the U.S. Department of Labor, Bureau of Labor Statistics, indicates that "refuse and recyclable material collectors" work in occupations rated among the top six most dangerous in the United States.

The Bureau of Labor Statistics (BLS) reports fatality data in the Census of Fatal Occupational Injuries according to the North American Industrial Classification System (NAICS) Codes by (1) total fatalities, (2) transportation incidents, (3) assaults or acts of violence, (4) contact with objects and equipment, (5) falls, (6) exposure to harmful substances or environments, and (7) fire and explosions. Fatalities are measured per 100,000 workers (BLS 2010).

An analysis of the CFOI data for the occupations in solid waste collection (NAICS 562111) for the years 2003 through 2009 is presented in the following seven subsections. (BLS 2003, 2004, 2005, 2006, 2007, 2008, 2009).

Table 1 lists the highest-ranking occupations (excluding mining) by fatalities incurred in 2009.

Total Fatalities

In the seven-year period from 2003 through 2009 a total of 515 fatalities occurred in Waste Management and Remediation (NAICS 562). This code includes Waste Collection (Solid Waste), Waste Treatment and Disposal, Hazardous Waste Treatment and Disposal, Solid Waste Landfill and Other Nonhazardous Waste Treatment and Disposal.

Within the NAICS 562 code, Solid Waste Collection (NAICS 562111) indicated a total of 240 fatalities, which occurred during that same 7-year period. Solid waste collection activities accounted for 46 percent of the total number of NAICS 562 labor-classification fatalities.

A review of the NAICS 562 (Waste Management and Remediation) fatality data indicates that in 2003 a total of 91 fatalities occurred. During the subsequent five years (2004 through 2008), an average of 76 fatalities occurred each year. In 2009 a total of 43 fatalities occurred—a 43 percent decrease from the past 5-year average. The 2009 data is encouraging and has dropped this industry down from fifth to sixth in the ranking of most dangerous occupations in the United States.

A review of the NAICS 562111 (Solid Waste Collection) total fatality data indicates that, during the 6-year period from 2003 through 2008, an average of 26 fatalities occurred each year. The 2009 total fatalities' figure of 15 is well below the past 6-year average of 26. This drop in total fatalities is encouraging.

Transportation Fatalities

Transportation-related fatalities in the census include highway, nonhighway, air, water, rail, and fatalities resulting from being struck by a vehicle.

In the Waste Management and Remediation code, transportation fatalities accounted for 59 percent (302) of the total over the 7-year period from 2003 to 2009. The average fatality rate is 43 per year for the seven years. In 2009, 28 fatalities occurred due to transportation incidents—a 39 percent decrease from the preceding 6-year fatality rate of 46.

Solid Waste Collection (NAICS 562111) transportation fatalities accounted for 70 percent (169) of the total over the same 7-year period. The average fatality rate is 24 per year for the seven years. In 2009, 15 fatalities occurred due to transportation incidents—a 44 percent decrease from the preceding 6-year fatality rate of 27.

Assaults or Acts of Violence

Three fatalities related to this category were reported in 2007 for Waste Management and Remediation. No fatalities occurred in the other years evaluated (2003–2006 and 2008–2009). In addition, no fatalities occurred in this category for Solid Waste Collection (NAICS 562111) in the years 2003 through 2009.

TABLE 1

Selected Occupations with High Fatality Rates per 100,000 Employed, 2009

Occupation	Fatality Rate per 100,000 Employed	Total Worker Fatalities
Fishermen (and related) workers	128.9	50
Logging workers	115.7	82
Aircraft pilots and flight engineers	72.4	90
Structural iron and steel workers	46.4	36
Farmers and ranchers	39.5	317
Refuse and recyclable material workers	36.8	31
Roofers	34.4	69
Electrical power-line installers and repairers	29.8	35
Drivers/sales workers and truck drivers	22.8	815
Taxi drivers and chauffers	19.3	69

Total Fatalities = 5,701
All worker fatality rate = 6

NOTE: In 2008, CFOI implemented a new methodology, using hours worked for fatality rate calculations rather than employment. For additional information on the fatality rate methodology changes, please see www.bls.gov/iif/oshnotice 10.htm.
(*Source*: BLS 2009)

Contact with Objects and Equipment

Waste Management and Remediation reported a total of 120 fatalities (23%) in this category over the past seven years. The average fatality rate per year is 17. In 2009, 11 fatalities occurred due to contact with objects and equipment—a 39% decrease from the preceding 6-year fatality rate of 18.

Under the Solid Waste Collection code, a total of 51 fatalities (21%) was reported in this category over the past seven years. The average fatality rate per year is 7. In 2009, 5 fatalities occurred due to contact with objects and equipment—a figure slightly below the preceding 6-year fatality rate of 7.

Falls

Waste Management and Remediation reported a total of 21 fatalities (4%) in this category over the past seven years. The average fatality rate per year is 3.

Under the Solid Waste Collection code, no fatalities were reported in this category over the past seven years. Zero fatalities in this category is being achieved!

Exposure to Harmful Substance or Environments

Waste Management and Remediation reported a total of 41 fatalities (8%) in this category over the past seven years. The average fatality rate per year is 7. In 2009 no fatalities were reported in this category—the first year in the past seven in which zero fatalities in this category was achieved!

Under the Solid Waste Collection code, a total of 7 fatalities (3%) was reported in this category over the past seven years. The average fatality rate per year is 1. In the reporting years 2005 through 2009, no fatalities were reported in this category—zero fatalities in this category is being achieved!

Fires and Explosions

Waste Management and Remediation reported a total of 9 fatalities (2%) in this category over the past seven years. The average fatality rate per year is 1. From 2004 to 2007 and in 2009, no fatalities were reported in this category.

Solid Waste Collection reported no fatalities in this category over the past seven years. Zero fatalities in this category is being achieved!

INTRODUCTION TO SOLID WASTE REGULATIONS

The Solid Waste Disposal Act of 1965 (SWDA) was the first federal law that required environmentally sound methods for disposal of household, municipal, commercial, and industrial waste (SWDA 1965). This law was amended in 1970 by the Resource Conservation and Recovery Act of 1970 (RCRA 1976), which was the first nationwide recycling initiative. A definition of solid waste can be found in the Environmental Protection Agency (EPA) regulations (specifically, the RCRA statutes) that can be summarized as follows (RCRA 1985, amended 1987):

> A solid waste is any discarded material that is not excluded by 40 CFR 261.4(a), which addresses nineteen specific excluded materials, ranging from domestic sewage, industrial wastewater discharge, excluded scrap metals, mercury-free switches, shredded circuit boards, etc. Discarded materials may also be excluded by variance granted under 40 CFR 260.30 and 260.31.

Examples of solid wastes include discarded materials that are abandoned or recycled. Military munitions can be classified as solid wastes when meeting the criteria specified in 40 CFR 266.202. Materials are classified as solid waste if they are abandoned by being burned or incinerated; accumulated, stored, or treated (but not recycled) before or in lieu of being abandoned by disposal; or burned or incinerated. Materials are also solid wastes if they are recycled or accumulated, stored, or treated (before recycling) as specified in the regulations. The RCRA definitions are very complex and the regulations need to be studied closely to identify and classify particular waste streams (EPA 2000).

Methods for the management of solid wastes include landfilling, incineration, recycling, source reduction, and composting. Hazardous wastes and medical wastes must be managed separately from nonhazardous solid wastes. The EPA currently regulates the management of solid waste landfills (EPA 2006).

This rule is an important step in improving the safety of municipal landfills. It establishes comprehensive, protective standards for managing the nation's solid waste burden by specifying location provisions and design, operating, and closure requirements for municipal landfills.

By improving the safety of nearly 6000 municipal solid waste landfills, these regulations help to bolster public confidence in landfills as a component of a workable, integrated waste management system. In addition, the rule is an incentive for increasing source reduction and recycling nationwide.

The EPA establishes requirements for municipal solid waste landfills. It covers location restrictions, facility design and operations, groundwater monitoring, corrective action measures, and conditions for closing (including financial responsibility).

SOLID WASTE LANDFILLS

Modern landfills are well-engineered facilities that are located, designed, operated, and monitored in compliance with federal regulations. Solid waste landfills must be designed to protect the environment from contaminants that may be present in the solid waste stream. The landfill siting plan—which prevents the siting of landfills in environmentally sensitive areas—as well as on-site environmental monitoring systems that watch for any sign of groundwater contamination and for landfill off-gas provide additional safeguards. In addition, many new landfills collect potentially harmful landfill gas emissions and convert them into energy. Instead of allowing landfill gas (LFG) to escape into the air, it can be captured, converted, and used as an energy source. Using LFG helps to reduce odors and other hazards associated with LFG emissions and helps prevent methane from migrating into the atmosphere and contributing to local smog and global climate change. Landfill gas is extracted from landfills using a series of wells and a blower/flare (or vacuum) system. This system directs the collected gas to a central point where it can be processed and treated depending upon the ultimate use for the gas. From this point, the gas can be simply flared or used to generate electricity, replace fossil fuels in burned-off industrial and manufacturing operations, fuel greenhouse operations, or be upgraded to pipeline-quality gas (see Figure 1).

Landfill gas is the natural by-product of the decomposition of solid waste in landfills and is comprised primarily of carbon dioxide and methane. By preventing emissions of methane (a powerful greenhouse gas) through the development of landfill gas energy projects, the EPA Landfill Methane Outreach Program (LMOP) helps businesses, states, energy providers, and communities protect the environment and build a sustainable future (EPA 2008e). See Figure 2.

There are several types of solid waste landfills:

- municipal solid waste
- bioreactors
- construction and demolition debris
- industrial waste

Municipal Solid Waste Landfills

Municipal solid waste landfills (MSWLFs) receive household waste. MSWLFs can also receive nonhazardous sludge, industrial solid waste, and construction and demolition debris. All MSWLFs must comply with the federal regulations in 40 CFR Part 258 (Subtitle D of RCRA), or equivalent state regulations (EPA 2006). Federal MSWLF standards include:

- *Location restrictions*, ensuring that landfills are built in suitable geological areas away from faults, wetlands, flood plains, or other restricted areas.

   Suitable geological areas indicate areas meeting criteria acceptable to the EPA and state and local governments where the landfill will not adversely affect the surrounding environment because of depth to groundwater, stable soil conditions, and other relevant factors.

- *Composite liners requirements* that include a flexible membrane (geomembrane), overlaying two feet of compacted clay soil lining the bottom and sides of the landfill, protecting groundwater and the underlying soil from leachate releases.

- *Leachate collection and removal systems*, which sit on top of the composite liner, removing leachate from the landfill for treatment and disposal.

   Leachate is a liquid that has passed through or emerged from solid waste and contains soluble, suspended, or miscible materials removed from such waste. Leachate typically flows downward in the landfill but may also

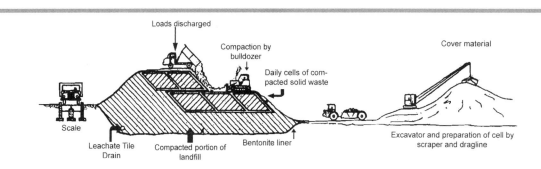

FIGURE 1. A modern municipal solid waste landfill (*Source:* EPA 2008e)

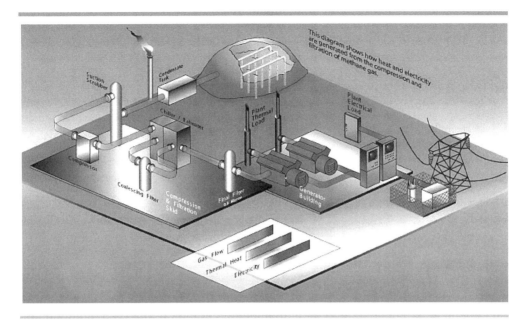

FIGURE 2. Example of a landfill gas-to-energy operation (*Source:* EPA 2008e)

flow laterally and escape through the side of the landfill.

A leachate collection system consists of pipes placed at the low areas of the landfill liner to collect leachate for storage and eventual treatment and discharge.

Leachate flow over the liner to the pipes is facilitated by placing a drainage blanket of soil or plastic netting over the liner. An alternative to collection pipes is a special configuration of geosynthetic materials that will hydraulically transmit leachate to collection points for removal.

Leachate will continue to be generated after the landfill is closed. The quantity should diminish if a good cover was placed over the landfill. Providing cover maintenance will also reduce leachate generation. The chemical composition will also change as the landfill becomes more biologically stabilized with pollutant concentrations slowly diminishing. Leachate collection and treatment generally will be necessary throughout the entire post-closure care period. Pumps and other leachate collection equipment must be operated and serviced. Every few years, leachate lines must be cleaned with sewer-cleaning equipment.

On-site leachate treatment facilities must be maintained and operated. Where leachate is transported off site, arrangements for trucking and treatment must be continued (EPA 1995).

- *Operating practices* include the following:
  - compacting and covering waste frequently (daily) with several inches of soil to help reduce odor
  - controlling disease vector populations (i.e., rodents, flies, mosquitoes)
  - controlling litter
  - protecting public health
  - controlling stormwater runoff and protecting surface water from pollutants
  - keeping out regulated hazardous waste
  - monitoring methane gas
  - restricting public access
  - keeping appropriate records
- *Groundwater monitoring requirements* require testing groundwater wells to determine whether waste materials have escaped from the landfill.
- *Closure and postclosure care requirements* include covering landfills and providing long-term care of closed landfills.
- *Corrective action provisions* control and clean up landfill releases to achieve groundwater protection standards.

• *Financial assurance* provides funding for environmental protection during and after landfill closure (i.e., closure and postclosure care).

Some materials may be banned from disposal in municipal solid waste landfills, including common household items such as paints, cleaners/chemicals, motor oil, batteries, and pesticides. Leftover portions of these products are called household hazardous waste (HHW). These products, if mishandled, can be dangerous to personal health and to the environment. Many municipal landfills have a household hazardous waste dropoff station for these materials. Homeowners may have options in local communities where municipalities set up HHW collection stations at fixed locations or have periodic HHW collection days. Services for collection may be contracted with licensed HW contractors. These HW contractors conduct collection from the public, segregate waste, test waste materials, and dispose of the waste (EPA 2008b).

Bioreactor Landfills

A bioreactor landfill operates to rapidly transform and degrade organic waste. The increase in waste degradation and stabilization is accomplished through the addition of liquid and air to enhance microbial processes. This bioreactor concept differs from the traditional *dry tomb* municipal landfill approach.

A bioreactor landfill is not just a single design and will correspond to the operational process invoked. There are three different general types of bioreactor landfill configurations:

1. *Aerobic:* In an aerobic bioreactor landfill, leachate is removed from the bottom layer, piped to liquid storage tanks, and recirculated into the landfill in a controlled manner. Air is injected into the waste mass using vertical or horizontal wells, promoting aerobic activity and accelerating waste stabilization.
2. *Anaerobic:* In an anaerobic bioreactor landfill, moisture is added to the waste mass in the form of recirculated leachate and other sources to obtain optimal moisture levels. Biodegradation occurs in the absence of oxy-

gen (anaerobically) and produces landfill gas. Landfill gas—chiefly methane—can be captured to minimize greenhouse gas emissions and for use in energy projects.
3. *Hybrid (Aerobic–Anaerobic):* The hybrid bioreactor landfill accelerates waste degradation by employing a sequential aerobic–anaerobic treatment to rapidly degrade organics in the upper sections of the landfill and collect gas from lower sections. Operation as a hybrid results in the earlier onset of methanogenesis in comparison to aerobic landfills

The Solid Waste Association of North America (SWANA) has defined a bioreactor landfill as "any permitted Subtitle D landfill or landfill cell where liquid or air is injected in a controlled fashion into the waste mass in order to accelerate or enhance biostabilization of the waste" (EPA 2008c).

The bioreactor accelerates the decomposition and stabilization of waste. At minimum, leachate is injected into the bioreactor to stimulate the natural biodegradation process. Bioreactors often need other liquids, such as stormwater, wastewater, and wastewater treatment plant sludges to supplement leachate and enhance the microbiological process by purposeful control of the moisture content. This differs from a conventional landfill, which simply recirculates leachate for liquid management. Landfills that simply recirculate leachate may not necessarily operate as optimized bioreactors.

Moisture content is the single most important factor promoting the accelerated decomposition. The bioreactor technology relies on maintaining optimal moisture content near field capacity (approximately 35–65%) and adds liquids when necessary to maintain that percentage. The moisture content, combined with the biological action of naturally occurring microbes, decomposes the waste. The microbes can be either aerobic (requiring the presence of oxygen) or anaerobic (requiring a lack of oxygen). A side effect of the bioreactor is that it produces landfill gas (LFG), such as methane, in an anaerobic unit at an earlier stage in the landfill's life and at an overall much higher rate of generation than traditional landfills. Another type is the hybrid bioreactor landfill, which accelerates waste degradation by employing a sequential aerobic–anaerobic treatment to rapidly degrade organics in the upper sections of the landfill and collect gas from the lower sections. Operation as a hybrid results in the earlier onset of methanogenesis (creation of landfill gas) in comparison to aerobic landfills.

Decomposition and biological stabilization of the waste in a bioreactor landfill can occur much sooner than in a traditional dry tomb landfill, providing a potential decrease in long-term environmental risks and landfill operating and postclosure costs. Potential advantages of bioreactors include (EPA 2008a):

- decomposition and biological stabilization in years (versus decades in dry tombs)
- lower waste toxicity and mobility because of both aerobic and anaerobic conditions
- reduced leachate disposal costs
- a 15–30 percent gain in landfill space because of an increase in the density of the waste mass
- significantly increased generation of LFG, which, when captured, can be used to provide energy on site, or sold
- reduced postclosure care

The EPA indicates that municipal solid waste can be rapidly degraded and made less hazardous (because of the degradation of organics and the sequestration of inorganics) by enhancing and controlling the moisture within the landfill under aerobic or anaerobic conditions. Leachate quality in a bioreactor rapidly improves, leading to reduced leachate disposal costs. Landfill volume may also decrease as airspace is recovered, extending the operating life of the landfill.

LFG emitted by a bioreactor landfill consists primarily of methane and carbon dioxide, as well as lesser amounts of volatile organic chemicals and hazardous air pollutants. The EPA indicates that the operation of a bioreactor may generate LFG earlier in the process and at a higher rate than a traditional landfill. The bioreactor LFG is also generated over a shorter period of time, because the LFG emissions decline as the accelerated decomposition process depletes the source waste faster than in a traditional landfill. The net result appears to be that the bioreactor produces more LFG overall than the traditional landfill does (EPA 2008a).

Construction and Demolition (C&D) Debris Landfills

These landfills accept only C&D debris, such as concrete, asphalt, brick, wood, drywall, asphalt roofing shingles, metals, and some types of plastics generated during the construction and demolition of homes, commercial buildings, and other structures. C&D landfills are subject to less stringent standards than municipal solid waste landfills because of the relatively inert nature of C&D debris.

Reducing C&D Debris

C&D debris consists of the materials generated during the construction, renovation, and demolition of buildings, roads, and bridges. C&D debris often contains bulky, heavy materials that include:

- concrete
- wood (from buildings)
- asphalt (from roads and roofing shingles)
- gypsum (the main component of drywall)
- metals
- bricks
- glass
- plastics
- salvaged building components (doors, windows, and plumbing fixtures)
- trees, stumps, earth, and rock from clearing sites

Reducing and recycling C&D debris conserves landfill space, reduces the environmental impact of producing new materials, creates jobs, and can reduce overall building project expenses by avoiding purchase/disposal costs.

C&D debris reduction can be achieved through *green building* techniques. The EPA's Office of Solid Waste (OSW) supports projects to reduce, reuse, and recycle waste generated from building construction, renovation, deconstruction, and demolition (EPA 2007g).

These techniques for demolition debris reduction and recycling involve setting demolition materials recycling goals and incentives for demolition contractors. Examples include recycling building brick for landscaping use or marine reef building; harvesting building wood products for resale to specialty-use contractors and carpentry shops; cutting up metal building components for scrap recycling; and stripping copper and aluminum wiring for recycling. All buildings slated for demolition must have hazardous and toxic materials removed or abated prior to demolition. These materials include, but are not limited to, PCBs found in ballasts and transformers, fluorescent light fixture tubes due to mercury content, and asbestos-containing building materials. Process piping and vessels must be pumped, decontaminated, and decommissioned in accordance with federal and state regulations. It is possible to achieve 80–90 percent recycling of C&D debris through aggressive *green demolition* programs, thereby vastly reducing the amount of solid waste going to the municipal landfill.

Reducing the amount of C&D debris disposed of in landfills or combustion facilities provides numerous benefits.

- Less waste can lead to fewer disposal facilities, potentially reducing associated environmental issues, including methane gas emissions that contribute to global climate change.
- Reducing, reusing, and recycling C&D debris offsets the need to extract and consume virgin resources, which also reduces greenhouse gas emissions.
- Deconstruction and selective demolition methods divert large amounts of materials from disposal and provide business opportunities within the local community.
- Recovered materials can be donated to qualified 501(c)(3) charities, resulting in a tax benefit.

Industrial Waste Landfills

These landfills are designed for the management of nonhazardous industrial process wastes. Industrial waste consists of a wide variety of nonhazardous materials that result from the production of various goods and products. Industrial waste landfills are subject to the federal requirements in 40 CFR Part 257, Subparts A and B, as well as any state-specific regulations (EPA 2008d).

In order to properly characterize a waste material as nonhazardous or hazardous, the waste generator can use the following:

- *Process knowledge.* The generator should obtain a thorough understanding of the process generating the waste material, enabling proper characterization of the waste. This includes information on process flow diagrams or plans and all inputs and outputs, as well as characteristics such as the physical states of the waste, the volume produced, and its general composition. Trade organizations can be contacted; many industries have already conducted thorough testing to characterize waste over time. This information may be beneficial in evaluating similar processes. Other resources to utilize include chemical engineering designs and plans showing process input chemicals, expected primary and secondary output chemicals and products, material safety data sheets (MSDSs), manufacturer's literature, previous waste analysis, and preliminary test results.
- *Leachate Testing.* The intent of leachate and extraction testing is to estimate the leaching potential of constituents of concern to water sources. Estimating leaching potential allows for the accurate estimation of the quantity of chemicals that could potentially reach groundwater or surface water resources. This includes drinking water supply wells and waters used for recreation. The toxicity characteristic and leachate procedure (TCLP) and elements of a sampling and analytical plan are discussed in detail in several EPA publications (EPA 1996e; EPA 1996b; EPA 1998a; EPA 1996a; EPA 2002).

Historical Waste-Handling Procedures and Current Solid Waste Definitions

Backyard Burning

Burning trash in the open produces many pollutants, including:

- dioxins
- particle pollution
- polycyclic aromatic hydrocarbons
- volatile organic compounds
- carbon monoxide
- hexachlorobenzene
- ash

Many dangerous health conditions can be caused by inhaling or ingesting even small amounts of these pollutants. Small children, the elderly, or people with preexisting respiratory conditions can be especially vulnerable to some of these pollutants. For details on these human health concerns, refer to the EPA Web site (EPA 2007b).

Batteries and Consumer Electronics

Batteries of all shapes and sizes supply power to everyday electronics like toys and power tools, but they affect our world in many more ways. During a power outage, phone lines still operate because they are equipped with lead-acid batteries. Batteries help control back-up power fluctuations, run commuter trains, and provide back-up power for critical needs like hospitals and military operations. The versatility of batteries is reflected in their different sizes and shapes, but all batteries have two common elements that combine to create power—an electrolyte and a heavy metal.

Batteries contain heavy metals such as mercury, lead, cadmium, and nickel, which can contaminate the environment when batteries are improperly disposed of. When incinerated, certain metals might be released into the air or can concentrate in the ash produced by the combustion process. For more details, refer to the EPA Web site (EPA 2007c).

The use of electronic products has grown substantially over the past two decades, changing the speed at which we communicate, and how we obtain information and entertainment. Our growing reliance on electronics (such as computers, cell phones, televisions, gaming systems, and printers) is illustrated by some remarkable figures. According to the Consumer Electronics Association (CEA), Americans own approximately 24 electronic products per household (CEA 2008).

The EPA is working to educate consumers and others on why it is important to reuse and recycle electronics and what the options are for safe reuse and recycling of these products.

Increasingly, state and local governments, manufacturers, and retailers are providing more opportunities to recycle and reuse this equipment. Many computer, TV, and cell-phone manufacturers, as well as electronics retailers, offer some kind of take-back program or sponsor recycling events.

More than twenty states have enacted legislation to manage end-of-life electronics, and more are expected to follow suit.

Recently, steps were taken to significantly increase safe reuse and recycling of electronic equipment. Recyclers can now become certified in responsible recycling standards by demonstrating to an accredited, independent third party that they can, and do, meet available standards. The EPA encourages all recyclers of electronics to become certified and all consumers to choose recyclers that are certified (EPA 2011a).

Composting

Yard trimmings and food residuals together constitute 23 percent of the U.S. municipal solid waste stream. This is a large percentage of waste going to landfills that could become useful, environmentally beneficial compost instead.

Composting offers the obvious benefits of resource efficiency and the creation of a useful product from organic waste that would otherwise have been dumped in a landfill.

Compost can:

- suppress plant diseases and pests.
- reduce or eliminate the need for chemical fertilizers.
- promote higher yields of agricultural crops.
- facilitate reforestation, wetlands restoration, and habitat revitalization efforts by amending contaminated, compacted, and marginal soils.
- cost effectively remediate soils contaminated by hazardous waste.
- remove solids, oils, greases, and heavy metals from stormwater runoff.

- capture and destroy 99.6 percent of industrial volatile organic chemicals (VOCs) in contaminated air.
- provide cost savings of at least 50 percent over conventional soil, water, and air pollution remediation technologies, where applicable.

For more details on composting, refer to the EPA Web site (EPA 2007d).

Household Hazardous Waste

Leftover household products that contain corrosive, toxic, ignitable, or reactive ingredients are considered to be household hazardous waste (HHW). Products that contain potentially hazardous ingredients, such as paints, cleaners, oils, batteries, and pesticides, require special care in disposal.

HHW FACTS AND FIGURES

- The American population generates 1.6 million tons of HHW per year.
- The average home can accumulate as much as 100 pounds of HHW in its basement, garage, and storage closets.

During the 1980s, many communities started special collection days or permanent collection sites for handling HHW. In 1997, there were more than 3000 HHW permanent programs and collection events throughout the United States.

Improper disposal of household hazardous wastes can include pouring them down the drain, onto the ground, into storm sewers, or in some cases putting them out with the trash. The dangers of such disposal methods might not be immediately obvious, but improper disposal of these wastes can pollute the environment and pose a threat to human health. Many communities in the United States offer a variety of options for conveniently and safely managing HHW. For more information on which wastes at home are hazardous refer to Figure 3, which identifies common household products containing potentially hazardous ingredients (EPA 2008g).

These items may be found in garages, basements, or other storage spaces around the home.

Cleaning Products
- Oven cleaners
- Drain cleaners
- Wood and metal cleaners and polishes
- Toilet cleaners
- Tub, tile, and shower cleaners
- Bleach (laundry)
- Pool chemicals

Indoor Pesticides
- Ant sprays and baits
- Cockroach sprays and baits
- Flea repellents and shampoos
- Bug sprays
- Houseplant insecticides
- Moth repellents
- Mouse and rat poisons and baits

Automotive Products
- Motor oil
- Fuel additives
- Carburetor and fuel injection cleaners
- Air-conditioning refrigerants
- Starter fluids
- Automotive batteries
- Transmission and brake fluid
- Antifreeze

Workshop/Painting Supplies
- Adhesives and glues
- Furniture strippers
- Oil or enamel based paint
- Stains and finishes
- Paint thinners and turpentine
- Paint strippers and removers
- Photographic chemicals
- Fixatives and other solvents

Lawn and Garden Products
- Herbicides
- Insecticides
- Fungicides/wood preservatives

Miscellaneous
- Batteries
- Mercury thermostats or thermometers
- Fluorescent light bulbs
- Driveway sealer

Other Flammable/Combustible Products
- Propane tanks and other compressed gas cylinders
- Kerosene
- Home heating oil
- Diesel fuel
- Gas/oil mix
- Lighter fluid

FIGURE 3. Common household items containing potentially hazardous ingredients (*Source:* EPA 2008g)

REGULATED MEDICAL WASTE

Medical and infectious waste or *regulated medical waste* is generally defined under state regulations. This waste stream is often described as any solid waste that is generated in the diagnosis, treatment, or immunization of human beings or animals, in research pertaining thereto, or in the production or testing of biologicals, including, but not limited to:

- blood-soaked bandages
- culture dishes and other glassware
- discarded surgical gloves (after surgery)
- discarded surgical instruments (scalpels)

- needles (used to give shots or draw blood)
- cultures, stocks, and swabs (used to inoculate cultures)
- removed body organs (tonsils, appendices, limbs, and so on)
- lancets (the little blades doctors use to prick fingers to get drops of blood)

For example, the state of Wisconsin defines medical waste as infectious waste and items that may be mixed with infectious waste, in order to call attention to the noninfectious items that should be recycled instead. Pharmaceuticals, mercury thermometers and medical supplies are not considered medical waste under this definition unless they are mixed with infectious waste (WisDNR 2011).

Medical wastes generally fall into one of four categories—infectious, hazardous, radioactive, and other general wastes from healthcare and medical facilities. Infectious, hazardous, and radioactive wastes represent only a small portion of all medical waste generated each year but garner the greatest amount of concern. The vast majority of medical waste is very similar to wastes generated in households and offices across the country.

The EPA defines infectious waste as a waste that contains pathogens with sufficient virulence and quantity that exposure to the waste by a suspectible host could result in an infectious disease (EPA 1995; EPA 2007f).

Currently, more than 90 percent of potentially infectious medical waste is incinerated (see Figure 4).

Treatment by incineration, and disposal of the resultant ash in a landfill, is an attractive option for managing medical waste. A major benefit of incineration is the destruction of pathogens (disease-causing agents) in the high temperatures of medical waste incinerators (MWIs).

Medical waste is burned in incineration units under controlled conditions to yield ash and combustion gases. The combustion process is a complex combination of chemical reactions that involve the rapid oxidation of organic substances in the waste and in auxiliary fuels. The goal of the process is to achieve complete combustion of the organic materials and destruction of pathogens in the waste while minimizing the formation and release of undesirable pollutants. How well the process approaches complete combustion is determined by temperature, time, turbulence, and mixture with oxygen.

Each organic substance in medical waste has a characteristic minimum ignition temperature that must be attained or exceeded, in the presence of oxygen, for combustion to occur. Above that ignition temperature, heat is generated at a sufficient rate to sustain combustion. Wastes containing high levels of moisture, however, require additional supplemental heat input. A waste constituent should stay in the high-temperature region of the MWI for a duration exceeding the time required for it to completely combust. Because the combustion reaction rate increases with increasing temperature, a shorter residence time is required for combustion at higher temperatures (assuming the presence of good combustion conditions). Adequate oxygen supplies and turbulence sufficient to promote the mixing of organic materials and oxygen are also essential for efficient combustion. Inadequate mixing of

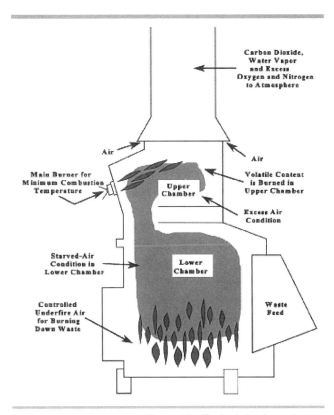

FIGURE 4. Example of a controlled-air incinerator (*Source:* EPA 1993)

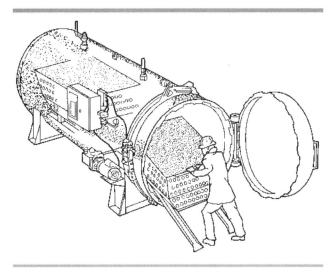

FIGURE 5. Example of an autoclave
(*Source:* OTA 1990)

combustible gases and air can result in emissions of incomplete combustion products. Turbulence within the primary chamber helps to break down the ash layer formed around burning particles of waste and expose the waste material to the high temperatures and combustion air. Bed turbulence is needed to maintain the combustion process and the elevated temperatures throughout the bed (EPA 1994).

The EPA promulgated regulations governing the emissions from medical waste incinerators (MWIs) (EPA 2007a). These regulations include:

- Stringent air emissions guidelines for states to use in developing plans to reduce air pollution from medical waste incinerators built on or before June 20, 1996.
- Final air emission standards for medical waste incinerators built after June 20, 1996.

These guidelines and standards will substantially reduce MWI emissions. The EPA estimates that mercury emission will decline by 94 percent, particulate matter by 90 percent, hydrogen chloride by 98 percent, and dioxin by 95 percent (EPA 2007f).

One anticipated result of the MWI standards and guidelines is the exploration of the use of alternative technologies for treating medical waste. Because of the high cost of compliance with the MWI standards, the EPA expects that few healthcare facilities will be likely to install new MWIs and that many facilities

are likely to discontinue use of existing MWIs. (The EPA expects that operation of 50 to 80 percent of the 2400 existing MWIs could be discontinued.) As an alternative to MWIs, facilities are likely to switch to other methods of waste disposal such as off-site commercial disposal or on-site disinfection technologies. Some potential alternative treatment technologies include thermal treatment (e.g., microwave technologies), steam sterilization (e.g., autoclaving; see Figure 5), electropyrolysis, and other chemical and mechanical systems (EPA 2007f).

MUNICIPAL SOLID WASTE (MSW)
Basic Facts

MSW—more commonly known as trash or garbage—consists of everyday items such as product packaging, grass clippings, furniture, clothing, bottles, food scraps, newspapers, appliances, paint, and batteries.

In 2009, U.S. residents, businesses, and institutions produced more than 243 million tons of MSW (before recycling), approximately 4.3 pounds of waste per person per day (EPA 2011b).

Figure 6 depicts the percentage by which different materials contribute to the municipal solid waste stream.

Several MSW management practices, such as source reduction, recycling, and composting, prevent or divert materials from the waste stream. Source reduction involves altering the design, manufacture, or use of products and materials to reduce the amount and toxicity of what gets thrown away. Recycling diverts

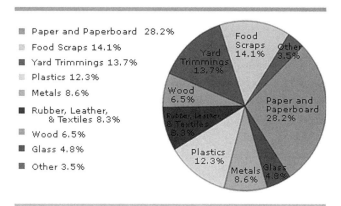

FIGURE 6. Total MSW generation (by material), **2009** (*Source:* EPA May 2011)

items, such as paper, glass, plastic, and metals, from the waste stream. These materials are sorted, collected, and processed and then manufactured, sold, and bought as new products. Composting decomposes organic waste, such as food scraps and yard trimmings, with microorganisms (mainly bacteria and fungi), producing a humus-like substance.

Other practices address those materials that require disposal. Landfills are engineered areas where waste is placed into the land. Landfills usually have liner systems and other safeguards to prevent groundwater contamination. Combustion is another MSW practice that has helped reduce the amount of landfill space needed. Combustion facilities burn MSW at a high temperature, reducing waste volume and generating electricity.

What to Compost

• Animal manure	• Eggshells	• Nut shells
• Cardboard rolls	• Fireplace ashes	• Sawdust
• Clean paper	• Fruits and	• Shredded
• Coffee grounds	vegetables	newspaper
and filters	• Grass clippings	• Tea bags
• Cotton rags	• Hair and fur	• Wood chips
• Dryer and	• Hay and straw	• Wool rags
vacuum	• Houseplants	• Yard trimmings
cleaner lint	• Leaves	

What Not to Compost

Black walnut tree leaves or twigs—release substances that might be harmful to plants.

Coal or charcoal ash—might contain substances harmful to plants.

Dairy products (e.g., butter, egg yolks, milk, sour cream, yogurt)—create odor problems and attract pests such as rodents and flies.

Diseased or insect-ridden plants—may transfer diseases or insects to healthy plants.

Fats, grease, lard, and oils—create odor problems and attract pests such as rodents and flies.

Meat or fish bones and scraps—create odor problems and attract pests such as rodents and flies.

Pet wastes (e.g., dog or cat feces, soiled cat litter)—might contain parasites, bacteria, germs, pathogens, and viruses harmful to humans.

Yard trimmings treated with chemical pesticides—might kill beneficial composting organisms.

FIGURE 7. Example of a type of source-reduction composting (*Source:* EPA 2007d)

Solid Waste Hierarchy

The EPA has ranked the most environmentally sound strategies for MSW. Source reduction (including reuse) is the most preferred method, followed by recycling and composting, and, lastly, disposal in combustion facilities and landfills.

Currently, in the United States, 30 percent of solid waste is recovered and recycled or composted, 14 percent is burned at combustion facilities, and the remaining 56 percent is disposed of in landfills.

Source Reduction (Waste Prevention)

Source reduction can be a successful method of reducing waste generation. Practices such as grass cycling, backyard composting (see Figure 7), two-sided copying of paper, and transport packaging reduction by industry have yielded substantial benefits through source reduction.

Source reduction has many environmental benefits. It prevents emissions of many greenhouse gases, reduces pollutants, saves energy, conserves resources, and reduces the need for new landfills and combustors.

Recycling

Recycling, including composting, diverted 72 million tons of material away from disposal in 2003, up from 15 million tons in 1980, when the recycle rate was just 10% and 90% of MSW was being recycled (EPA 2008f).

Typical materials that are recycled include batteries, recycled at a rate of 93 percent, paper and paperboard (48 percent), and yard trimmings (56 percent). These materials and others may be recycled through deposit systems, curbside programs, drop-off centers, and buy-back programs (EPA 2008f).

Recycling prevents the emission of many greenhouse gases and water pollutants, saves energy, supplies valuable raw materials to industry, creates jobs, stimulates the development of greener technologies, conserves resources for the future, and reduces the need for new landfills and combustors.

Recycling also helps reduce greenhouse gas emissions that affect the global climate. In 1996, solid waste recycling in the United States prevented the release of 33 million tons of carbon into the air—roughly the amount emitted annually by 25 million cars (EPA 2008f).

Combustion/Incineration

Burning MSW can generate energy while reducing the amount of waste by up to 90 percent in volume and 75 percent in weight.

The EPA's Office of Air and Radiation is primarily responsible for regulating combustors because air emissions as a result of combustion pose the greatest environmental concern.

In 2001, in the United States, there were 97 combustors with energy recovery with the capacity to burn up to 95,000 tons of MSW per day (EPA 2008f).

Landfills

Under the Resource Conservation and Recovery Act (RCRA), landfills that accept MSW are primarily regulated by state, tribal, and local governments. The EPA has established national standards that these landfills must meet in order to operate. Municipal landfills can, however, accept household hazardous waste.

The number of landfills in the United States is steadily decreasing—from 8000 in 1988 to 1767 in 2002. The capacity, however, has remained relatively constant. New landfills are much larger than those of the past (EPA 2008f).

Resource Conservation and Recovery Act of 1976 (RCRA)

The RCRA was enacted by Congress in 1976 and amended in 1984. The Act's primary goal is to protect human health and the environment from the potential hazards of waste disposal. In addition, RCRA is an integral source-reduction mechanism; the law calls for conservation of energy and natural resources, reduction in waste generated, and environmentally sound waste-management practices (EPA 1976).

Environmental Terms, Abbreviations, and Acronyms

The EPA provides a glossary that defines in nontechnical language some commonly used environmental terms appearing in EPA publications and materials. It also explains abbreviations and acronyms used throughout the EPA.

Recommended Sources for MSW Information

Municipal Solid Waste in the United States: 2005 Facts and Figures describes the national MSW stream based on data collected between 1960 and 2005. It includes information on MSW generation, recovery, and discard quantities; per capita generation and discard rates; and the residential and commercial portions of MSW generation (EPA 2008f).

The Decision-Maker's Guide to Solid Waste Management, Volume II, contains technical and economic information to assist solid waste management practitioners in planning, managing, and operating MSW programs and facilities. It also includes suggestions for best practices when planning or evaluating waste and recycling collection systems, landfill and combustion issues, source reduction and composting programs, and public education (EPA 1995).

Scrap Tires

There are at least 275 million scrap tires in stockpiles in the United States. In addition, approximately 290 million scrap tires were generated in 2003.

Markets now exist for about 80 percent of scrap tires—up from 17 percent in 1990. The states have played a major role in tackling this problem by regulating the hauling, processing, and storage of scrap tires and by working with industry to recycle and beneficially use scrap tires by developing markets for the collected scrap tires.

The three largest scrap-tire markets are tire-derived fuel, civil engineering applications, and ground-rubber applications/rubberized asphalt.

Several industries use tires as fuel, including the cement industry, the pulp and paper industry, electric utilities, industrial/institutional boilers, and dedicated tire-to-energy facilities.

Examples of civil engineering applications include: subgrade fill and embankments, backfill for walls and bridge abutments, subgrade insulation for roads, landfills, and septic system drain fields.

Examples of ground-rubber/rubberized asphalt applications include asphalt rubber and athletic and recreational applications, such as ground cover under playground equipment, running track material, and sports and playing fields. Other applications include molded rubber products (carpet underlay, flooring material, dock bumpers, patio decks, railroad-crossing blocks, livestock mats, roof walkway pads, rubber tiles and bricks, movable speed bumps), new tire manufacturing, brake pads and shoes, additives to injection-molded and injection-extruded plastics, automotive parts, agricultural and horticultural applications or soil amendments, and horse-arena flooring (EPA 2007e).

Oil

Oil keeps cars, lawnmowers, and many other machines running smoothly, but once it is used it must be discarded properly to keep from contaminating the environment. Recycling used oil is becoming the preferred way of handling it to protect the environment and conserve natural resources.

Used oils, such as engine lubrication oil, hydraulic fluids, and gear oils used in cars, bikes, or lawnmowers can pollute the environment if not disposed of properly. Used oil must be recycled or disposed of properly by local waste management authorities or automotive repair shops. Used oil filters pose similar waste concerns. If properly drained, they can be safely recycled or disposed of.

Benefits of Recycling Used Oil and Oil Filters

Recycling used oil keeps it from polluting soil and water.

Motor oil does not wear out—it just gets dirty—so recycling it saves a valuable resource.

Less energy is required to produce a gallon of re-refined base stock than a base stock from crude oil.

Used oil can be re-refined into lubricants, processed into fuel oils, and used as raw materials for the refining and petrochemical industries. Used oil filters contain reusable scrap metal that steel producers can use as scrap feed.

To recycle used oil, processors and refiners remove water, insolubles, dirt, heavy metals, nitrogen, chlorine, and oxygenated compounds from oil drained from automobiles or other machines. The resulting product, called *re-refined* oil, must meet the same stringent refining, compounding, and performance standards as

virgin oil for use in automotive, heavy-duty diesel, and other internal combustion engines, and hydraulic fluids and gear oils. Extensive laboratory testing and field studies conclude that re-refined oil is equivalent to virgin oil; it passes all prescribed tests and, in some situations, even outperforms virgin oil.

The same consumers and businesses that use regular oil also can use re-refined oil, because re-refining simply reconditions used oil into new, high-quality lubricating oil. Any vehicle maintenance facilities, automobile owners, and other machinery maintenance operations that use oil also can use re-refined oil. In some cases, fleet maintenance facilities that use large volumes of oil arrange to reuse the same oil that they send to be re-refined—a true closed recycling loop.

DEVELOPING A LANDFILL SAFETY PLAN

Compactors, bulldozers, and other heavy equipment pose many hazards. They require safety awareness on the part of operators and a planned approach to safety. Federal and state safety and health rules and regulations must be followed. Frequent safety training and frequent safety inspections of job-site materials and equipment are required.

The following items should be considered when developing a landfill safety plan:

- site-specific accident prevention procedures
- methods to limit exposure to disease and pollutants
- regular equipment and operations inspections
- list of safety rules for operations of site equipment
- personal protective equipment
- emergency notification procedures
- confined-space-entry procedures

The landfill safety plan should emphasize:

- identification of lines of responsibility and authority
- regular inspections and audits of health and safety operations
- becoming the basis for open safety discussions with all employees, chiefly through daily and weekly tailgate safety meetings

- a positive management attitude toward safety and health in order to instill a positive safety culture among employees

The landfill safety plan needs to address all safety and health issues that will arise in the facility-required solid waste program.

A special waste management plan must include procedures for special waste acceptance; record keeping; and waste characterization, handling, storage, and disposal.

The plan should contain:

- an analysis of special waste management alternatives
- a rationale for the proposed disposal alternative
- the physical and chemical characteristic of each waste
- the proposed (EPA- and state-approved) procedures for waste sampling, testing, and analysis
- an evaluation of whether the waste is compatible with the landfill (or other impoundment) liner and leachate management system
- procedures to document and record daily and annual waste quantities (weight or volume), waste sources, and generating processes
- potential hazards associated with some wastes that may require special handling for disposal (see Figure 8).

Potential Hazard	Example Waste
Personnel safety	Asbestos
Odor and vector problems	Large dead animals
Excessive leachate generation	Sewage sludge
Excessive settlement in landfill	Yard debris
Puncturing or tearing of landfill liner	Construction and demolition debris
Fire hazards	Tire chips
Increasing toxicity of landfill toxic materials	Clean-up materials contaminated with leachate

FIGURE 8. Special handling for toxic material disposal (*Source:* Oregon DEQ u.d.)

Special handling and training is required for asbestos waste materials. Consideration for specialized worker training, medical surveillance, state licensing, monitoring, postings, PPE, respiratory protection, and written safety plans that include spill response and emergency notification must be taken.

Sewage sludge also requires special handling and trained workers. Consideration for specialized worker training, monitoring, postings, PPE, respiratory protection, and written safety plans that include spill response and emergency notification must be taken.

An example of protective measures to safeguard against hazards presented by sewage exposure includes:

- the use of nitrile gloves to avoid hand contact with raw sewage and sewage-contaminated soils, piping, equipment and other materials
- the use of eye and or face protection to prevent splashes of sewage from contacting the open eye
- the use of respiratory protection as necessary
- the use of protective coveralls to prevent contamination of work clothing from gross sewage contamination
- the use of antibacterial soap and water for hand cleaning prior to breaks and at the end of work shifts
- the use of vigorous hand-cleaning practices to remove surface contamination from hands, fingernails, and face prior to eating, using tobacco products, applying cosmetics, using the restroom, and leaving the work site
- providing an eyewash station in the event of splash contamination of the eyes
- providing a full-body shower in the event of gross sewage contamination from a splash event on work clothes.

Toxic and hazardous contaminated materials require highly specialized handling and trained personnel. The Occupational Safety and Health Administration (OSHA) hazardous waste operations and emergency response (HAZWOPER) regulations found in 29 CFR 1910.120, require a training program, contingency plan, and provisions for preparedness and prevention.

WASTE MANAGEMENT AND RECYCLING FACILITIES— SAFETY AND HEALTH ISSUES

Waste transfer stations are facilities where municipal solid waste is unloaded from collection vehicles and briefly held while it is reloaded onto larger long-distance transport vehicles for shipment to landfills or other treatment or disposal facilities. By combining the loads of several individual waste collection trucks into a single shipment, communities can save money on the labor and operating costs of transporting the waste to a distant disposal site. They can also reduce the total number of vehicular trips to and from the disposal site. Although waste transfer stations help reduce the impacts of trucks traveling to and from the disposal site, they can cause an increase in traffic in the immediate area where they are located. If not properly sited, designed, and operated, they can cause problems for residents living near them (EPA 2001).

Facility Safety Considerations

Traffic: Important design and operating features:

- Select sites that have direct access to truck routes, highways, and rail or barge terminals.
- Provide adequate space within the facility so customers waiting to use the transfer station do not block public roadways or impact nearby residences or businesses.
- Designate haul routes to and from transfer stations that avoid congested areas, residential areas, business districts, schools, hospitals, and other sensitive areas.
- Designate safe intersections with public roads.

Noise: Heavy truck traffic and operating heavy-duty facility equipment (e.g., conveyors and front-end loaders) are primary sources of noise from transfer stations. Design and operating practices that reduce noise include:

- confining noisy activities within buildings or other enclosures as much as possible
- using landscaping, sound barriers, and earth berms to absorb exterior noise

- arranging site so traffic flows are not adjacent to properties that are sensitive to noise
- providing set-back distances, called buffer zones, to separate noisy activities from adjacent land uses
- conducting activities that generate maximum noise during the day
- providing hearing protection devices (HPDs) to operating staff

Odor: Garbage (food waste and grass) has a high potential for odor. Proper facility design can significantly reduce odor problems. Doorways should be carefully positioned, in consideration of neighbors. The waste transfer building can be equipped with filtered exhaust fans and rooftop exhaust vents.

Odor reduction operating procedures can include:

- "first-in/first-out" waste-handling practices that keep waste on site for short periods of time
- removing waste from the tipping floor or pit by the end of each day to allow for sweeping down and washing down
- "Good-housekeeping" measures that include regular cleaning and disinfecting of surfaces and equipment that comes into regular contact with waste
- water misting and deodorizing systems

Rodents and Birds: Rodents and birds can be a nuisance and a potential health concern at waste transfer stations. A few basic design and operational elements can control them.

- Good-housekeeping practices mean a simple and effective means of minimizing their presence and include:
  - removing all waste deliveries to the facility by the end of each day and cleaning the receiving floor daily
  - receiving waste only within an enclosed structure and otherwise preventing litter, to reduce the presence of birds
  - baiting and trapping rodents if problems persist in the vicinity

Litter: Stray pieces of waste may become litter in and around the waste transfer facility.

Measures to reduce litter include:

- positioning the main transfer building so that predominant winds are less likely to blow through the building and carry litter off site
- installing perimeter landscaping and fencing to reduce wind speeds and to trap litter
- ensuring that tarps on open-top trucks are secure
- providing skirting around loading chutes
- removing litter frequently to reduce the opportunity for it to travel off site
- patrolling nearby access roads to control litter from truck traffic

Exposure to Potentially Hazardous Equipment

Potentially hazardous equipment includes anything with moving parts, including conveyor belts, push blades, balers, and compactors. Facility operators need to develop an employee equipment-orientation program and establish safety programs to minimize the risk of injury from station equipment. A program to effectively control hazardous energy (lockout/tagout) that uses locks and tags to prevent equipment from operating while being serviced will aid in minimizing hazards in the transfer station. Transfer station operators must implement and strictly enforce rules that require children and pets to stay within vehicles at all times. Posting signs and applying bright-colored paint or tape to hazards will alert customers to potential dangers.

Personal Protective Equipment (PPE)

Transfer station workers coming in close contact with heavy equipment, machinery, and waste material should wear appropriate PPE. PPE should include hard hats, protective eyewear, dust masks, protective gloves, and steel-toed boots. When working in close proximity to loud machinery and heavy equipment, hearing protection devices must be used as well. Each facility must conduct a PPE hazard assessment, and all workers must be trained in the use, care, and limitations of assigned PPE.

Exposure to Extreme Temperatures

Facilities located in areas of extreme weather must account for potential impacts to employees from prolonged exposure to extreme heat or cold. Heat exhaustion and heat stroke are addressed with proper facility operations, including good ventilation inside buildings, access to water and shade, and periodic breaks. Cold stress is addressed by proper clothing, shelter from wind and precipitation, and access to warming areas. Extreme temperatures should not pose problems for customers, whose exposure times are much briefer than those of facility workers.

Traffic

Controlled, safe traffic flow in and around the facility is critical to ensuring customer and employee safety. Ideally, a transfer station is designed so that traffic from large waste-collecting vehicles is kept separate from self-haulers, who typically use cars and pickup trucks. Facility designers should consider:

- Traffic flow that may be directed in a one-way loop through the main transfer facility and around the entire site.
- Facilities with one-way traffic have buildings (and sometimes entire sites) with separate entrances and exits.
- Transfer trailers are difficult to maneuver, require gentle slopes and adequate turning radius. It is ideal that trailers need not back up.
- Building sites should be arranged to minimize road intersections and the need for vehicles to back up or make sharp turns.
- Space should be provided for incoming traffic to line up when tipping traffic is backed up. Sufficient space should be located after the scale house and before the tipping area to prevent backing up onto public roads.
- Easily understood and highly visible signs, pavement markings, and directions from transfer station staff should be set up to indicate proper traffic flow.
- Bright lighting, both artificial and natural, should be provided inside buildings. Using

light-colored interior finishes that are easy to keep clean is very helpful. When entering a building on a bright day, a driver's eyes need time to adjust to the darker interior. This adjustment period can be dangerous. Good interior lighting and light-colored surfaces can reduce the contrast and shorten adjustment time.

- An area for self-haulers should be provided to unload separately from large trucks. Typically, self-haulers must manually unload the back of a pickup truck, car, or trailer. This process takes longer than the automated dumping of commercial waste-collection vehicles and potentially exposes the driver to other traffic. It is often a good idea to have a staff member assist the public with unloading activities.

- Staff members should be required to wear brightly colored safety vests.

- Back-up alarms should be installed on all moving facility equipment and personnel trained in proper facility equipment operations safety. Back-up alarms must be maintained on moving facility equipment in working condition at all times. Cameras and monitors can be installed as an added precaution.

- Too much reliability should not be placed on reversing alarms. They may be a useful additional safeguard when segregating pedestrians from vehicle movements, but eliminating unnecessary reversing cannot adequately control risks. They cannot be heard by everyone, and on a busy, noisy site they can become part of the background noise or cause confusion when more than one vehicle is operating in reverse. The environmental impact of the noise and operating times may have to be considered.

- For good all-round vision when reversing, closed-circuit television (CCTV), or mirrors, or a mix of both, should be fitted to vehicles; the use of mirrors or CCTV alone may be insufficient. They should be checked at least daily and maintained in good working order. The reliability and quality of CCTV is now high and the costs of fitting and maintenance are low. CCTV can pay for itself within a few

months by reducing vehicle and property damage. All subsequent savings add to the company's profits.

Safe Vehicles

When attempting to make vehicles safer, the methods used must be evaluated in terms of their fitness for the purpose intended:

- Safety specifications of vehicles used on site are essential. Vehicle capabilities and site conditions have to be consistent with the tasks performed. A full risk assessment will be required to ensure that the task can be done safely. Stability and ground clearance of vehicles should be adequate for site conditions and tasks.

- Vehicles should be provided with suitable means of access and egress, including cab access for routine tasks.

- Reversing is a high-risk activity. The site should be laid out so as to eliminate or minimize the need to reverse wherever possible. Wherever reversing is required, all-around vision is essential wherever achievable. Closed circuit TV (CCTV), additional rear view mirrors and reversing (or back-up) alarms (or a combination of them) may be required as part of the controls in place to reduce the risks of reversing.

- Many operators are now purchasing new vehicles with CCTV fitted and are retrofitting existing vehicles based on risk assessments. They are also finding that the damage reduction and increased productivity achievable by fitting CCTV is a worthwhile return on investment.

- Roll-over protection (ROPs) should be provided to protect the driver in the event of vehicle rollover. This protection is also required for smaller mobile vehicles that may be used on site (e.g., dumpers, tractors, and so on).

- Falling-object protection (FOPs) should be consistent with the risks. Particular attention should be paid to loading tasks.

- For some tasks the vehicle cab may not be sufficient to protect a driver unless it has been specially reinforced. You should consider the adverse effects of providing extra reinforcement and the potential for obscuring rear vision, especially through rear windscreens. Examples include the loading/unloading of some metal scrap and demolition debris and the use of heavy prybars and shovels in the vicinity of the cab.

- Seatbelts save lives. Fitting seatbelts and enforcing their use can dramatically reduce injuries and fatalities in overturns and collisions. Brightly colored, high-visibility seatbelts can help ensure use.

- Seatbelt design is important in the avoidance of back and other musculoskeletal problems. Their correct adjustment should be part of operator training.

- Body props should be provided on tipper vehicles. Using body and door props should be part of site rules. Their use should be monitored and enforced.

- *Outside-of-cab* controls pose specific risks, potentially exposing drivers to other moving vehicles. External controls are not advised for tipping vehicles with a risk of fallover. Many vehicles with external controls are designed for one-person operation, with the operator in a safe position when at the controls. Others in the area may not be as well protected and should be kept clear.

- Other safety equipment may be required as determined by risk assessments, such as *impact grills* on plant windscreens, door props/clasps, and so on. They should be part of the risk-assessment and plant-specification process.

- Vehicle maintenance, regularly carried out to a good standard, is essential. It ensures that the safety features are working and can help in reducing noise and vibration.

- Many companies have instituted plans to ensure that
  - all new vehicles are fitted with auto-sheeting (or auto-tarping) equipment
  - existing vehicles are part of a retrofitting plan based on risk assessment.

- Some companies are revising their contracts with waste haulers to ensure that only auto-sheeted (or auto-tarped) vehicles will be permitted on site.

Containers

When considering containers for a facility, design and safety features are important:

- Container types and designs of door-locking mechanisms should be selected to be appropriate for the task. Violent door release has caused amputations and other serious injuries. Loads can move or settle and pressurize the door. Damage to containers can lead to doors being sprung, presenting the same risks.

- Use of ratchet and remote door-opening devices can reduce the risks associated with sprung and/or pressurized doors. Safe systems to work or deal with sprung or pressurized doors need to be in place. Containers should be of good construction, free from patent defect and constructed to appropriate standards.

- Containers' general integrity and the condition of their doors, hinges, opening mechanisms, lifting lugs, and other points are safety-critical. Drivers should visually inspect them regularly. A formal defect reporting system is expected for containers. Quarantine areas for defective containers at transport-operation sites will assist in ensuring that drivers do not use damaged containers by mistake.

Maintenance, Daily Checks, and Defect Reporting

Daily and weekly vehicle checks should be carried out for defects. They should include brakes, lights, tires, steering, and all-around vision. Keep a record of these checks. DOT-required inspections need to be programmed and carried out. They should include:

- Defect reporting, which is essential.
- Scheduled maintenance that should be carried out according to manufacturers' specifications.

• Keeping maintenance and legally required test records on site.

More regular maintenance schedules may be required, depending upon the activities carried out and the environment a vehicle may work in.

Visitors and Customer Vehicles

Customer vehicle design and condition is a valid safety concern for site operators. On landfill sites, vehicle design can affect the safety of tipping operations. Ultimately, site operators may choose not to allow unacceptable vehicle types on their sites. The risks posed by tipping vehicles (such as fallover) need to be controlled. All vehicles with obviously unsafe defects should be brought to the attention of the driver and the employer. Close cooperation and communication with customers on vehicle types can reduce the risks.

Spotters

Guiding vehicles through the use of spotters on the ground is a very high-risk activity. Actions to eliminate their use should be evaluated and implemented when reasonably practicable by improving site layout or traffic control and driver vision aids. In situations where spotters must be utilized:

• They should be adequately trained.
• They should wear ANSI Type-III reflective high-visibility vests (at minimum) and be visible at all times during vehicle movements.
• They must be provided with effective radio communication devices in order to communicate with one another and with drivers (as needed).
• Employees and visiting drivers must understand and obey their instructions.
• The system must be enforced to ensure compliance.

Falls

Accidental falls are another concern for facility employees and customers, especially in facilities with pits or direct-dump designs where the drop at the edge

of the tipping area might be 5 to 15 feet deep. Facilities with flat tipping areas offer greater safety in terms of reducing the height of falls, but they present their own hazards. These include standing and walking on loading floors that are slick from recent waste materials and being close to station operating equipment that removes waste materials after each load is dumped. A number of safety measures should be considered to reduce the risk of slips, trips, and falls:

• For direct gravity loading of containers by the public, a moderate grade separation will reduce the fall distance. For example, some facilities place roll-off boxes 8 feet below grade to facilitate easy loading of waste into the container (so the top of the roll-off box is even with the surrounding ground). This scenario, however, creates an 8-foot fall into an empty roll-off box. Alternatively, the roll-off box can be set about 5 feet below grade with the sides extending 3 feet above the floor. This height allows for relatively easy lifting over the box's edge yet is high enough to reduce the chance of accidental falls.
• For pit-type operations, the pit end can be tapered to accommodate commercial unloading at the deep end (typically 8–12 feet) and public unloading at the shallow end (3–6 feet).
• Safety barriers can be placed around the pit edges at the end of the day or during cleaning periods to prevent falls. The barriers can be removed during normal waste-loading operations.
• Substantial wheel stops can be placed to stop vehicles from backing into pits or bins.
• Locating wheel stops a good distance from the edge of the unloading zone keeps self-haul customers from finding themselves dangerously close to the edge of the bin pit during unloading or dangerously close to an operating zone for station equipment.
• To prevent falls caused by slipping, floors should be cleaned on a regular basis and treated with a nonskid flooring material.
• Designers need to provide a sufficient slope in floors and pavements so they drain readily and

eliminate standing water. This is especially crucial in cold climates where icing can cause an additional fall hazard. Because of transfer stations' large size and volume, and because of the constant flow of vehicles, it is impractical to design and operate them as heated facilities.

- Use of colored floor coatings (such as bright red or yellow) in special hazard zones (including the area immediately next to a pit) can give customers a strong visual cue.
- Designing unloading stalls for self-haul customers with a generous width (at least 12 feet when possible) maximizes the separation between unloading operations and reduces the likelihood of injury from activity in the next stall. For commercial customers, stall widths of at least 15 feet are needed to provide a similar safety cushion. This is particularly necessary where self-haul and commercial stalls are located side by side.
- If backing movements are required, design the facility so vehicles back in from the driver's side (i.e., left to right) to increase visibility.

Noise

Unloading areas can have high noise levels due to the stations operating equipment, the unloading operation and waste movement, and customers vehicles. Back-up safety alarms and beepers required on most commercial vehicles and operating equipment can also be particularly loud. The noise levels also might cause customers not to hear instructions or warnings or the noise from an unseen approaching hazard.

Designers have limited options for dealing with the noise problem. The principal way to reduce the effects of high-decibel noise in enclosed tipping areas is to apply a sound-absorbing finish over some ceiling and wall surface areas. Typically, spray-on acoustical coatings are used, but these finishes tend to collect dust, dirt, and grime and are hard to keep clean and bright. Using a rubber shoe on the bottom of waste-moving equipment buckets and blades and avoiding

use of track-type equipment that produces high mechanical noise can also limit noise exposure. These approaches, however, can affect the transfer system's operational efficiency. Regardless of which approaches are employed, transfer station employees exposed to high levels of noise for prolonged periods of time should use hearing protection devices such as earplugs or ear muffs to prevent hearing loss.

Air Quality

Tipping areas often have localized air-quality problems (dust and odor) that constitute a safety and health hazard. Dust in particular can be troublesome, especially where dry, dusty commercial loads (e.g., C&D wastes) are tipped. Prolonged exposure to air emissions from waste and motor-vehicle emissions in the building pose another potential health threat to facility employees. Facility air-quality issues can be addressed through a number of design and operational practices. These might include:

- Water-based dust-suppression (misting or spraying) systems used to knock down dust. Different types of systems are available that typically involve a piping system with an array of nozzles aimed to deliver a fine spray to the area where dust is likely to be generated (e.g., over the surge pit). These systems typically are actuated by the station staff on demand when dust is generated.
- Dust-suppression systems can operate using only water or they can have an injection system that mixes odor-neutralizing compounds (usually naturally occurring organic extracts) with the water. These dual-purpose systems effectively control both dust and odors. Water-based dust-suppression systems, however, can have adverse economic impacts. The additional moisture added to the waste increases the weight of the outbound loads, potentially reducing truck capacity and increasing costs.
- Hand-held hoses can be used to wet down waste where it is being moved or processed,

typically in a pit. Designers need to consider using conventional reel-mount hoses for this purpose.

- Ventilation systems can control air quality inside enclosed transfer buildings. Although the high roofs and large floor areas common in transfer stations put unique demands on ventilation systems, it is still possible through engineering techniques to create air velocities needed to entrain dust particles. One approach is to concentrate system fans and air-removal equipment above the dustiest and most odor-prone area, creating a positive air flow from cleaner areas. Often, the air-handling equipment is designed with multiple-speed fans and separate fan units that can be activated during high-dust or high-odor events. Filtering and scrubbing exhaust air from transfer stations is also possible.

- Respiratory protection may be necessary if employees' direct exposure to harmful emissions from vehicles and waste at the facility is not sufficiently minimized.

Hazardous Waste and Materials

Although MSW is generally nonhazardous, some potentially hazardous materials such as pesticides, bleach, and solvents could be delivered to transfer stations. Facility operators should ensure that employees are properly trained to identify and handle these materials. Some stations have a separate household hazardous waste (HHW) receiving and handling area. If the transfer station operates a program that manages HHW, the material is often collected by appointment only, during designated hours, or during special single- or multiple-day events.

All transfer stations must be equipped to handle the occasional occurrence of hazardous waste, real or suspected, mined with other wastes. Personal protective equipment (PPE), such as goggles, gloves, protective full-body coveralls, and respirators should be on hand and easily accessible to employees. Because staff or customers might inadvertently come into contact with a hazardous substance, it is also good practice and often required by code, to have dedicated emergency eyewash stations and deluge shower stations in the operating area. These stations must comply with the American National Standard Institute/International Safety Equipment Association (ANSI/ISEA) Standard Z358-1 2004, *Emergency Eyewash and Shower Equipment* (ANSI/ISEA 2004).

The transfer station's operating plan should outline detailed procedures to guide station personnel in identifying and managing these types of wastes. Many stations have a secure area with primary and secondary barriers near the main tipping area where suspect wastes can be placed for evaluation and analysis. Public education efforts can reduce the likelihood of hazardous materials showing up in the solid waste stream.

Ergonomics

Improper body position, repetitive motion, and repeated or continuous exertion of force contribute to injuries. Both employers and employees should receive ergonomics training to reduce the likelihood of injury. Such training provides guidance on minimizing repetitive motions and heavy lifting and using proper body motions to perform tasks. As of May 2011, there are no federal ergonomics standards. A few states have such standards under their job safety and health programs. The Occupational Safety and Health Administration (OSHA) lists states with such programs and provides links to a number of these states' Web sites (OSHA 2007).

Transport

Vehicle movements cause deaths and some of the most serious accidents in the waste industry. The aim is to ensure the following:

- safe sites
- safe vehicles
- safe working routines
- safe workers

	Yes	No
Site Safety		
Segregation of people, vehicles, and mobile plant to prevent collisions?		
Enforced speed limits?		
Clear site layout for visiting drivers?		
Adequate vehicle clearance of overhead power lines?		
Site roads designed and maintained for vehicle traffic (no potholes, no steep grades, no tight turns for large vehicles, and so on)?		
Blind corners eliminated at road intersections?		
Mirrors and warning signs placed at blind corners that cannot be eliminated?		
One-way traffic implemented as necessary to eliminate collisions and reversing of vehicles?		
Traffic safety, flagging, and other control systems in place at transfer stations and landfill access sites?		
Vehicle and Equipment Safety		
Vehicles equipped with driver visibility systems, such as mirrors and CCTV camera systems?		
100% enforcement of driver seat-belt use?		
Daily safety inspection by operators of all vehicles (documented and kept on file)?		
Daily safety inspections of forklifts, skidsteers, containers, doors, chains, hooks, lifting equipment, and so on (documented and kept on file)?		
System Safety		
Dumping/discharging restricted to specified areas?		
Dumping/discharging areas equipped with restraints to prevent vehicles and personnel from falling into pits?		
Adequate clearance provided from other vehicles and obstructions during dumping activities?		
Minimum of one vehicle length maintained between vehicles?		
No obstructions within swing radius of dump truck?		
Staging area for vehicles to allow safe tarping and untarping of loads?		
Safe access for work performed under waste containers?		
Safe Workers		
Drivers outside cabs and ground support personnel wearing ANSI Type-II reflective high-visibility vests?		
Traffic-control personnel and vehicle spotters wearing ANSI Type-III reflective high-visibility vests?		
Safety training and supervision provided for all workers on site?		
Safety Compliance Agreement form signed by workers, indicating that they understand the hazards and will comply with all elements safety and health rules part of the training?		
Safety enforcement procedures adequate for ensuring compliance with site safety and health rules?		

FIGURE 9. Site safety checklist for a waste transfer facility (*Source:* EPA 2001)

Figure 9 contains a brief checklist for sites. The list does not aim to cover everything, but it may help identify areas needing improvement at a particular site.

Major Causes of Slips and Trips

Figure 10 contains a brief checklist of some of the major causes of slips and trips at waste management sites. It does not aim to cover risks in refuse collection, where special and sometimes different risks arise.

CONCLUSION

The objective of this chapter on solid waste safety was not meant to be all-encompassing but to serve as an introduction to the history, regulatory background, and hazards of a complex and dangerous occupation that serves an important purpose in our society: solid waste management. The occupation of solid waste collection (specifically refuse and recyclable material efforts) sustains the fifth-highest fatality rate in the

Potential Safety and Health Hazard	Recommended Response and Controls
Dumping of wet and dry materials outside of designated areas	Implement spill response protocols
	Attempt to clear away materials as soon as practicable using spill response and clean-up materials, such as absorbents for liquids and grease.
	Cordon area off using barriers and signs to prevent vehicles and untrained personnel from interfering with activities.
	Determine how and why spill occurred through a root-cause analysis and enact a prevention plan to mitigate future events.
Waste piles on floors	Restrict access to these areas.
	Determine methods for preventing workers from walking over the waste piles.
Trailing water hoses and electrical cords	Electrical outlets and water sources may need to be relocated to minimize the need for trailing cords and hoses.
	Equipment must be positioned to avoid pedestrian routes.
	Restrict pedestrian access.
	Use suitable covers for pipes and cables.
Office rugs and mats, linoleum, tiles, other flooring surfaces	Ensure that flooring surfaces are secure and have no edges that can contribute to trips and falls.
	Select suitable flooring surfaces.
	Practice good maintenance.
Slippery surfaces	Minimize pedestrian traffic in these areas.
	Select suitable nonslip surface treatments to prevent slips, trips, and falls.
Transition areas from wet to dry floor surfaces	Provide door mats and foot scrapers as necessary to prevent water and mud from being tracked onto dry floors.
	Provide areas to change into clean, dry footwear.
	Post warning signs as appropriate.
Poor lighting	Improve lighting levels.
	Change bulbs as necessary.
	Keep bulbs clean.
Floor-level transition areas	Improve lighting levels.
	Add high-visibility tread and floor markings.
	Post warning signs as appropriate.
Unsafe footwear	ANSI-approved steel-toe footwear is recommended.

FIGURE 10. Major causes of slips and trips at waste management sites (*Source:* EPA 2001)

country, making it important for this occupation (and all solid waste management occupations) to become the subject of efforts to protect the safety and health of all workers within this industry. Lessons learned should be used to assist in the development and improvement of safety programs for these operations. After introducing the solid waste management regulations of the United States, the definitions surrounding landfill types, various waste-stream categories, and recycling and disposal methods, this chapter dealt with safety and health hazard identification at landfills; landfill safety plans; and identification of safety and health issues at waste management, waste transfer, and waste recycling facilities, attempting to pass on the insights necessary to improve safety and health in future solid waste management endeavors.

REFERENCES

American National Standards Institute and International Safety Equipment Association (ANSI/ISEA). 2004. ANSI Z358.1 2004, *Emergency Eyewash and Shower Equipment*. Arlington, VA: ISEA.

Bureau of Labor Statistics (BLS). 2003, 2004, 2005, 2006, 2007, 2008, 2009. *Census of Fatal Occupational Injuries (CFOI) – Current and Revised Data for 2003, 2004, 2005, 2006, 2007, 2008, 2009.* Table A-1. Fatal and Occupational Injuries by Industry and Event or Exposure.

Bureau of Labor Statistics, U.S. Department of Labor, Economic News Release, USDL 09-0979, National Census of Fatal Occupational Injuries in 2008 (retrieved September 02, 2010). www.bls.gov/news.release/archives/cfoi_08202009.htm

Consumer Electronics Association (CEA). 2008. *Market Research Report: Trends in CE Reuse, Recycle and Removal*. Arlington, VA: CEA.

Environmental Protection Agency (EPA). 1965. Solid Waste Disposal Act of 1965. P.L. 89-272, Title II. Washington, D.C: EPA.

_____. 1970. Resource Recovery Act of 1970. P.L. 91-512, 84 Stat. 1227. Washington, D.C.: EPA.

_____. 1976. Resource Recovery and Conservation Act of 1976. 42 USC 6901.6992k. Washington, D.C.: EPA.

_____. 1993. AP 42, *Air Pollutant Emission Factors*, Volume I: Stationary Point and Area Sources. Vol I. Emission Factors. Chapter 2, "Medical Waste Incineration" (July 1993; reformatted January 1995) (retrieved January 28, 2008). www.epa.gov/ttn/chief/ap42/ch02/final/c02s03.pdf

_____. 1994a. EPA-453/R-94-043a, *Medical Waste Incinerators—Background Information for Proposed Standards and Guidelines: Process Description Report for New and Existing Facilities* (July). Washington, D.C.: EPA

_____. 1994b. EPA QA/G4, *Guidance for the Data Quality Objectives Process*. Washington, D.C.: EPA.

_____. 1995. EPA 530-R-95-023, *Decision Maker's Guide to Solid Waste Management*, vol. II, chapter 9, "Land Disposal." Washington, D.C.: EPA.

_____. 1996a. EAP QA/G9, *Guidance for the Data Quality Assessment: Practical Methods for Data Analysis*. QA 96 Version. Washington, D.C: EPA

_____. 1996e. SW-846, *Test Methods for Evaluating Solid Waste, Physical/Chemical Methods* (retrieved January 28, 2008). www.epa.gov/sw-846/sw846.htm

_____. 2000. 40 CFR Part 261.2, *Definition of Solid Waste*. Washington, D.C.: EPA.

_____. 2001. EPA 530-D-005, *Waste Transfer Stations: A Manual for Decision-Making* (Draft) (February) (retrieved January 28, 2008). www.epa.gov/garbage/pubs/r02002.pdf

_____. 2002. EPA/240/R-02/009, *Guidance on Quality Assurance Project Plans*. Washington, D.C.: EPA.

_____. 2006. 40 CFR Part 258, *Criteria for Municipal Waste Landfills*. Washington, D.C.: EPA.

_____. 2007a. *Air and Radiation Regulations*. Mid-Atlantic Regulations and Plans. Hospital/Medical/Infectious Waste Incinerators. Undated (retrieved January 28, 2008). www.epa.gov/reg3artd/airregulations/ap22/incin2.htm

_____. 2007b. *Backyard Burning; Human Health* (retrieved January 28, 2008). www.epa.gov/garbage/backyard/health.htm

_____. 2007c. *Batteries* (retrieved January 28, 2008). www.epa.gov/epr/products/batteries.htm

_____. 2007d. *Composting* (retrieved January 28, 2008). www.epa.gov/epaoswer/non-hw/composting/index.htm

_____. 2007e. *Markets/Uses; Scrap Tires* (retrieved January 28, 2008). www.epa.gov/epaoswer/non-hw/muncpl/tires/markets.htm

_____. 2007f. *Medical Waste* (retrieved January 28, 2008). www.epa.gov/epaoswer/other/medical/#one

_____. 2007g. *Reducing C&D Materials* (retrieved January 28, 2007). www.epa.gov/epaoswer/non-hw/debris-new/reducing.htm

_____. 2008a. *Bioreactors* (retrieved January 28, 2008). www.epa.gov/epaoswer/non-hw/muncpl/landfill/bioreactors.htm#2

_____. 2008b. *Household Hazardous Waste* (retrieved January 28, 2007). www.epa.gov/msw/hhw.htm

_____. 2008c. *EPA Municipal Solid Waste; Bioreactors* (retrieved January 28, 2008). www.epa.gov/garbage/landfill/bioreactors.htm#1

_____. 2008d. *Landfills/Land Disposal* (retrieved January 28, 2008). www.epa.gov/epaoswer/non-hw/muncpl/landfill/landfills.htm

_____. 2008e. *Landfill Methane Outreach Program* (retrieved January 28, 2008). www.epa.gov/outreach/lmop/index.htm

_____. 2008f. *Municipal Solid Waste. Basic Information* (retrieved January 28, 2008). www.epa.gov/msw/facts.htm

_____. 2011a. *Wastes – Resource Conservation – Common Wastes & Materials – eCycling* (retrieved May 16, 2011). www.epa.gov/epawaste/conserve/materials/ecycling/index.htm

_____. 2011b. *Municipal Solid Waste: Basic Information* (retrieved May 16, 2011). www.epa.gov/msw/facts.htm

Occupational Health and Safety Administration (OSHA) 2007, *Safety and Health Topics: Ergonomics* (retrieved January 28, 2008). www.osha.gov/SLTC/ergonomics/index.html

Office of Technology Assessment (OTA). 1990. *Finding the Rx for Managing Medical Wastes*. Washington, D.C.: U.S. Government Printing Office.

Oregon Department of Environmental Quality (DEQ). Undated. *Land Quality – Solid Waste: Safe Disposal;*

Solid Waste Landfill Guidance Document; Section 9 – Landfill Operations. Salem, OR: Oregon DEQ (retrieved January 28, 2008). www.deq.state.or.us/lq/sw/disposal/landfillguidance.htm

Sales, John. 1986. EPA530-SW-86-014, *Guide for Infectious Waste Management*. Washington, D.C.: EPA.

Wisconsin Department of Natural Resources (WisDNR). 2009. *Medical and Infectious Waste; Material Description* (retrieved April 27, 2011). dnr.wi.gov/org/aw/wm/medinf/

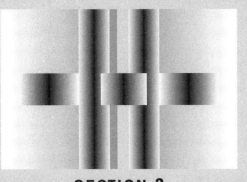

SECTION 3
ENVIRONMENTAL MANAGEMENT

LEARNING OBJECTIVES

- Recognize the criteria for identifying the characteristics of hazardous waste and for listing hazardous waste as defined in RCRA, Title 40 §261.

- Recognize and understand the definition of a solid waste as defined in §261.2.

- Recognize and understand the definition of a hazardous waste as defined in §261.3.

- Recognize the characteristic of ignitability as defined in §261.21.

- Recognize the characteristic of corrosivity as defined in §261.22.

- Recognize the characteristic of reactivity as defined in §261.23.

- Recognize the characteristic of toxicity as defined in §261.24.

- Recognize other regulations that require compliance when dealing with chemicals as discussed in Title 40 of the *Code of Federal Regulations*.

HAZARDOUS WASTE

Salvatore Caccavale, Barry R. Weissman, Thomas S. Butler, Jr., and Judy Freeman

THE ADVENT OF the Industrial Revolution in the late 1800s and early 1900s saw the birth of many innovative products that are now taken for granted in the twenty-first century. Cellular phones, new types of clothing, power tools, sports equipment, and new forms of transportation have all made our lives easier.

The flip side to these miraculous achievements is the increased generation of waste. Today, consumer product companies are trying to minimize waste by offering many different types of reusable packaging. Recycling has taken on a larger role in society, with many states and communities implementing mandatory programs to reduce the amount of solid waste placed in landfills.

In the early days of the Industrial Revolution there were no treatment, storage, or disposal facilities (TSDFs) to manage and/or destroy hazardous waste. Companies were not even required to determine if the waste generated at the end of the production line was categorized as hazardous. Typically a big hole was dug somewhere on the industrial site for the deposit of production waste. When that hole was filled, it was capped off and another hole was dug. Fortunately, some companies had the environmental insight to install liners, either natural (clay) or man-made (plastic or cloth), at their dumping grounds in an attempt to catch the leachate.

For years industries claimed they did not realize that what they were putting into the ground would have any effects on the environment. The growing influence of the environmental disciplines in the mid-1960s led society to realize what a mistake that approach was. Even today, abandoned industrial sites and misused landfills are still being cleaned up through the Environmental Protection Agency's (EPA's) "Superfund" program (SARA 1986).

Industry was not the only culprit, however; mom-and-pop shops, farmers, dry-cleaning operations, and other types of small businesses also played a role in polluting the environment.

The management of hazardous waste is a broad and complex subject. The purposes of this chapter are to present an overview of the hazardous waste regulatory system in the United States; to explain the process of hazardous waste determination, primarily through the application of the provisions of the Resource Conservation and Recovery Act (RCRA 1976); and to give a brief overview of other regulatory requirements applicable when dealing with chemicals. This chapter is not intended to be a definitive treatment of the U.S. hazardous waste regulatory system, but it should provide a reference for safety, health, and environmental professionals who may not have extensive background or experience in hazardous waste, allowing them to approach the topic and helping them obtain additional hazardous waste information.

It should be noted that under federal legislation, each state is permitted to establish its own regulatory system for hazardous waste as long as the state's regulatory system is at least as effective as the federal requirements (EPA 2009a). EHS professionals should review all applicable state and local hazardous waste regulations as appropriate (EPA 2010a-e).

In order to reflect this process, the following discussions of environmental laws are organized in chronological order rather than by subject matter. The balance of this chapter is organized by subject sections to facilitate their use as guidelines.

Resource Conservation and Recovery Act (RCRA)

In the early 1970s, Love Canal, a housing development built over a capped industrial dumpsite in suburban Niagara Falls, New York, was exposed by the media, and the story took the public by surprise. Concern that such a development could happen in "our backyard" led to public demand for legislation that would ensure the proper management of industrial wastes (for details, see Appendix C).

In 1965, Congress had passed the Solid Waste Disposal Act (SWDA 1965) for the purpose of improving solid waste disposal methods. SWDA has been amended several times, most significantly and largely as a result of the exposure of Love Canal, by the Resource Conservation and Recovery Act (RCRA 1976) and later by the Hazardous and Solid Waste Amendments (HSWA 1984). These acts collectively are known as RCRA.

RCRA was designed to establish a national program to protect the natural resources of the United States from the improper handling and storage of hazardous wastes. Congress gave the task of tracking this regulation to the Environmental Protection Agency (EPA). The codified RCRA regulations can be found in Title 40 of the *Code of Federal Regulations* (CFR), Parts 240 through 282.

The main components of RCRA include:

1. identification of hazardous waste
2. manifest tracking "cradle-to-grave"
3. operating standards for generators, transporters, and treatment, storage, and disposal facilities
4. a permit system for TSDFs
5. state authorization to assist in implementing the program

The current goals set forth by RCRA are to:

- protect human health and the environment from the potential hazards of waste disposal
- conserve energy and natural resources
- reduce the amount of hazardous waste generated
- ensure wastes are managed in an environmentally sound manner
- prevent future problems caused by irresponsible waste management
- clean up releases of hazardous waste in a timely, flexible, and protective manner

To achieve these goals three distinct yet interrelated sections (called subtitles) were created under RCRA. Other subtitles can be found in RCRA, but the three discussed in this chapter are the most significant (RCRA 1976).

- **Subtitle C:** Establishes a system for controlling hazardous waste from the time of generation until ultimate disposal.

- **Subtitle D:** Establishes a system for controlling solid (primarily nonhazardous) waste, such as household waste.
- **Subtitle I:** Established by HSWA, regulates toxic substances and petroleum products stored in underground tanks.

Another important section is the Land Disposal Restriction (LDR) (EPA 2010c). One of the major impacts HSWA had on the implementation of the RCRA program was the restriction of land disposal for certain wastes. These land disposal restrictions are commonly referred to as *land ban*, and the hazardous wastes affected are called *restricted wastes*. The EPA banned land disposal for certain hazardous wastes that can migrate through soil and pollute groundwater. Hazardous wastes covered by the land ban include: liquid metals; free cyanides; dioxin-containing wastes; and discarded chemical products, like xylene, formic acid, and methyl alcohol. The ban also prohibits land disposal of diesel fuel, hydrochloric acid, and used solvents without proper treatment or certification of limited recycling operations.

Although RCRA creates a framework for the proper management of hazardous and nonhazardous solid wastes, it does not address hazardous waste problems encountered at inactive or abandoned sites or those resulting from spills that require an emergency response. These issues are addressed by the Comprehensive Environmental Response, Compensation and Liability Act (CERCLA 1980), otherwise known as Superfund.

Subtitle C: Hazardous Waste Management

Subtitle C establishes a comprehensive "cradle-to-grave" program for regulating hazardous waste from generation through proper disposal or destruction. Generators of hazardous waste are the first link in this "cradle-to-grave" chain. Those creating more than 100 kilograms (220 lb) of hazardous waste, or 1 kilogram (2.2 lb) of acutely hazardous waste a month, must comply with all generator requirements under Subtitle C.

Subtitle D: State or Regional Solid Waste Plans

The SWDA established grant programs for the development of solid waste plans by states and/or interstate agencies (SWDA 1965). Subsequent amendments to the SWDA have substantially increased the EPA's involvement in solid waste management. However, the Subtitle D (EPA 2010a) program continues to be implemented by state and local governments.

The term *solid waste* used in Subtitle D refers almost exclusively to nonhazardous solid waste. The primary objectives of Subtitle D are to encourage environmentally sound solid waste management practices, maximize the reuse of valuable recoverable resources, and foster resource conservation.

Subtitle I: Regulation of Underground Storage Tanks

Congress enacted Subtitle I to control and prevent leaks from underground storage tanks (USTs). The UST program broke new ground for RCRA; for the first time, the RCRA program applied to products as well as wastes. Specifically, Subtitle I regulates underground tanks storing regulated substances, including petroleum products (e.g., gasoline and crude oil) and Superfund-defined hazardous substances (EPA 1994). Tanks storing hazardous waste, however, are regulated under Subtitle C.

Comprehensive Environmental Response, Compensation, and Liability ACT (CERCLA)

The Resource Conservation and Recovery Act (RCRA 1976) addresses the generation, handling and disposal of waste, but the Comprehensive Environmental Response, Compensation, and Liability Act (CERCLA 1980), also known as Superfund, addresses sites that have been contaminated by hazardous materials. The authority under CERCLA to respond directly to releases or threatened releases of hazardous substances that may endanger human health and the environment is held by the federal government and is not shared with the states. CERCLA established prohibitions and requirements concerning closed and abandoned hazardous waste sites, provided for liability of persons responsible for releases of hazardous waste at these sites, and established a trust fund to provide for clean up when no responsible party could be identified (EPA 2007b).

CERCLA was significantly amended by the Superfund Amendments and Reauthorization Act (SARA 1986) and again as the Small Business Liability Relief and Brownfields Revitalization Act (2001), both of which will be discussed later.

Used Oil Recycling Act

The Used Oil Recycling Act of 1980 was established to encourage the safe reuse of used oil and to discourage improper burning or disposal. Used oil not subject to the hazardous waste rules must be managed according to the requirements of 40 CFR 279 (EPA 2006d). There are also requirements pertaining to used oil processors, transporters, marketers, and burners for energy recovery. Some state environmental agencies (e.g., California, Massachusetts) classify used oils as hazardous wastes. Companies should check with their respective states to ensure compliance. Used oil must be sent to a reputable oil recycling company.

Used oil, if it is recycled or reclaimed, does not have to be managed as a hazardous waste if it meets specific conditions, such as:

- It includes any oil that has been refined from crude oil or any other synthetic oil that has been contaminated by physical or chemical impurities.
- It is not mixed with any listed hazardous waste.
- It contains less than 1000 ppm total halogens.
- It does not exhibit a hazardous waste characteristic (EPA 2006d).

Note: The proper federal terminology for labels and/or markings on containers and tanks is "Used Oil."

The Superfund Amendments and Reauthorization Act (SARA) Amendments

The Superfund Amendments and Reauthorization Act (SARA 1986) amended the Comprehensive Environmental Response, Compensation, and Liability Act (CERCLA) on October 17, 1986. SARA reflected the EPA's experience in administering the complex Superfund program during its first six years and made important changes and additions to the program.

SARA changes:

- stressed the importance of permanent remedies and innovative treatment technologies in cleaning up hazardous waste sites
- required Superfund actions to consider the standards and requirements found in other state and federal environmental laws and regulations
- provided new enforcement authorities and settlement tools
- increased state involvement in every phase of the Superfund program
- increased the focus on human health problems posed by hazardous waste sites
- encouraged greater citizen participation in making decisions on how sites should be cleaned up
- increased the size of the trust fund from $1.6 billion to $8.5 billion

SARA also required the EPA to revise the Hazard Ranking System (HRS) (EPA 2007c) to ensure that it accurately assessed the relative degree of risk to human health and the environment posed by uncontrolled hazardous waste sites that may be placed on the National Priorities List (NPL) (EPA 2007e).

Oil Pollution Act (OPA)

The purpose of the Oil Pollution Act (OPA 1990) was to consolidate oil-spill response systems and laws and to establish liability and financial responsibility requirements. It was enacted in response to rising public concern following the *Exxon Valdez* incident. "[O]n March 24, 1989, the Exxon Valdez oil tanker departed the Valdez oil terminal and struck Bligh Reef in Prince William Sound, spilling an estimated 10.8 million gallons of crude oil. . . . Only 7 of 26 monitored species and resources have recovered to prespill health and abundance" (Prince William Soundkeeper 1989).

Title III of SARA, Emergency Planning & Community Right to Know Act (EPCRA)

"In 1984 a deadly cloud of methyl isocyanate killed thousands of people in Bhopal, India. Shortly thereafter, there was a serious chemical release at a sister plant in West Virginia. These incidents underscored demands by industrial workers and communities in several states for information on hazardous materials. Public interest and environmental organizations around the country accelerated demands for information on toxic chemicals being released 'beyond the fence line'—outside of the facility" (EPA 2007i). EPCRA reporting provides vital information for emergency response personnel regarding chemical hazards in the community. EPCRA requires each state to appoint a State Emergency Response Commission (SERC) and Local Emergency Planning Committees (LEPCs) for each district; it is these entities who are responsible for compiling the information gleaned through this process and for planning for emergency eventualities.

Facilities required to maintain Material Safety Data Sheets (MSDSs) per OSHA's Hazard Communications Standard (OSHA 1994) must file with the SERC, LEPC, and local fire department and either provide copies or a list of their MSDSs.

To provide the necessary information to the various governmental agencies concerning those chemicals that a company releases into the environment (the air, land, and waters of the country), the company is required to complete an annual toxic release inventory (TRI) (EPA 2007i).

Inventory reporting is required for a specified list of chemicals (EPA 2011a).

Chemical releases exceeding specific threshold limits must also be reported. Lists of those chemicals may be found at the same Web site. The EPA has also compiled a list of all chemicals covered by name under these regulations into a single list and published them as the Title III List of Lists (EPA 2011a).

APPLIED SCIENTIFIC AND ENGINEERING PRINCIPLES IN ENVIRONMENTAL MANAGEMENT

Working within the framework of environmental law requires the diligent application of standards established within each regulation. The purpose of this section is to provide specific guidelines that the EHS manager can apply to operations that will assist in company compliance with these laws.

Waste Management

Those involved in the generation, handling, or disposal of hazardous wastes must comply with RCRA's "cradle-to-grave" control system. The first step in understanding how to comply with a regulation is to read not only the regulation but also the preamble to that regulation from the Final Federal Register Notice for that regulation. Unfortunately, RCRA was promulgated in 1976, before the Internet and the electronic publishing of the Federal Register.

There are many other guides that can also help generators sort through the system, including the EPA's *Managing Your Hazardous Waste: A Guide for Small Businesses* (EPA 2001a).

Registration

The initial step in beginning to determine what if any waste materials are hazardous begins with registering a facility as a hazardous waste generator. The EPA requires the completion of Form 8700-12 (EPA 2009).

Once the form has been completed and submitted, the EPA will issues an EPA Identification number consisting of three letters and nine digits. This number is unique to a particular property. If a location has never been a hazardous waste generator, it will be issued a new number. If, however, a property has already been registered, the EPA will reissue that number. This helps to preserve the history of waste generation on that site in the event of the site's abandonment and subsequent labeling as a superfund site.

Identification/Determination of Solid Waste

In order to determine regulatory requirements for disposal, wastes must first be classified as solid wastes. If they meet requirements for a solid waste, it must then be determined whether they are also a hazardous waste.

A waste classified as a solid waste nevertheless puts municipalities and waste management entities subject to a myriad of disposal regulations under RCRA. *Solid waste* is defined as any discarded material including garbage; refuse; sludge from a wastewater treatment plant, water supply treatment plant, or air pollution control facility; and other discarded material, including

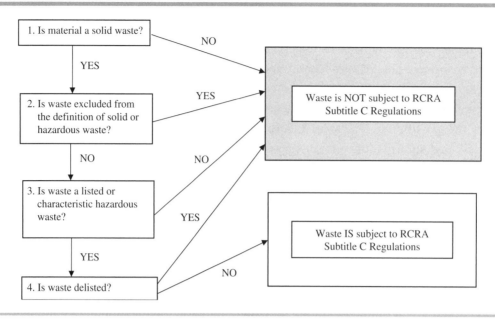

FIGURE 1. Hazardous waste identification process (*Source:* EPA 2006b)

solid, liquid, semisolid, or contained gaseous material resulting from industrial, commercial, mining, or agricultural operations or from community activities (40 CFR 261.2) (EPA 2010f).

Any discarded material is a solid waste, provided that no statutory exclusion applies. These exclusions include:

- domestic sewage or waste passing through a publicly owned treatment works (POTW)
- industrial discharges as defined under the Clean Water Act
- irrigation return flow
- nuclear material, nuclear source, or special nuclear or byproduct material, as defined under the Atomic Energy Act (1954)
- mining wastes that do not leave mines
- industrial scrap metal being recycled

A material is discarded if it is:

- abandoned
- recycled, including land applied, burned for energy, or reclaimed
- inherently waste-like
- military munitions

Hazardous Waste Determination

Once a material is determined to be a solid waste, it must then be determined whether it is also a hazard-

ous waste (see Figure 1). Certain materials are exempt by definition, including (40 CFR 261.4) (EPA 2010f):

- household waste, including that of hotels and other residential properties, but excluding incinerator ash
- agricultural wastes used as fertilizer
- arsenic-treated wood wastes generated by those who use such wood for its intended purpose
- petroleum-contaminated material failing the toxic characteristic leaching procedure (discussed elsewhere) and which may be subject to corrective action provisions for underground storage tanks (USTs) under RCRA
- used chlorofluorocarbons (CFCs) totally enclosed in heat transfer equipment and which may be reclaimed (40 CFR 260.20 and 260.22) (EPA 2009b)
- uranium wastes

Special Wastes

Some exempted wastes are classified as special wastes. At the time RCRA was written, those wastes designated as special wastes were considered of sufficient concern to warrant further investigation. Each of these special wastes has its own regulatory requirements, but none is considered hazardous under RCRA (EPA 2007h):

- mining wastes returned to the mine site
- utility wastes from fossil fuel combustion

- oil and natural gas exploration, or drilling mud and water
- wastes from the extraction, beneficiation, or processing of ores and minerals
- uranium wastes
- cement kiln dust wastes

Listed Wastes

If a waste is not excluded, exempted, or classified as a special waste, it could be a hazardous waste. Four series of hazardous waste codes list such materials (EPA 2010f):

- F-listed wastes come from general processes such as cleaning, degreasing, metal finishing, and manufacturing.
- K-listed wastes come from specific industrial processes and are grouped by industrial category, such as petroleum refining or metal manufacturing, and include wastewater treatment sludges (40 CFR 261.32).
- P-listed wastes include discarded commercial chemical products more toxic than U-listed wastes, include pesticides and pharmaceuticals, and are considered to be acute hazardous wastes (40 CFR 261.33(e)).
- U-listed wastes include old, off-specification, or discarded commercial products (40 CFR 261.33(f)).

Some of these wastes are considered "acutely hazardous" because of their inherently hazardous characteristics and will be discussed elsewhere.

Characteristic Wastes (40 CFR 261.3) (EPA 2010f)

Wastes can be hazardous if they exhibit (40 CFR 261.20–261.24):

- ignitability
- corrosivity
- reactivity
- toxicity

Ignitability (40 CFR 261.21)—D001 (EPA 2010f)

A waste is considered ignitable if it is:

- a liquid having a flashpoint of < 140°F (60°C) (ASTM closed-cup method)

- a nonliquid with the capacity for spontaneous combustion
- a DOT-listed ignitable compressed gas
- a DOT-listed oxidizer

Included in this classification are solvents, paints, and degreasers.

Corrosivity (40 CFR 261.22)—D002 (EPA 2010f)

A waste is considered corrosive if it is:

- aqueous, having a pH ≤ 2 or ≥ 12.5
- a liquid that corrodes steel at a rate greater than 6.35 mm yearly

Among other chemicals, this category includes rust removers, acid or alkaline cleaning fluids, and battery acid.

Reactivity (40 CFR 261.23)—D003 (EPA 2010f)

A waste is considered reactive if it:

- is unstable and readily undergoes violent change
- reacts violently with water
- forms potentially explosive mixtures with water
- generates toxic gases, vapors, or fumes when mixed with water
- is a cyanide- or sulfide-containing waste that can release toxic gases, vapors, or fumes between pHs of 2 and 12.5
- is capable of detonation or explosion when struck or heated
- is capable of detonation or explosive decomposition or reaction at standard temperature and pressure
- is a DOT-listed explosive

Cyanides and sulfide-bearing wastes are included in this classification.

Toxicity (40 CFR 261.24) (EPA 2010f)

A waste is considered toxic when the Toxic Characteristic Leaching Procedure (TCLP) produces leachate with one or more of the toxic constituents listed by the EPA in concentrations above permissible limits, as listed in Table 1 of 40 CFR 261.24 (EPA 2010f). To determine whether a waste is toxic, it is subjected to the Toxic Characteristic Leaching Procedure (TCLP). The TCLP is an analytical protocol simulating the leaching of toxic constituents in a landfill.

Land Disposal Restriction (LDR) (EPA 2010c)

Once it has been determined that a hazardous waste has been generated, the next question is, "Does the waste have a LDR?" The EPA has identified wastes that are prohibited from land disposal unless they meet specific treatment standards.

The LDR program has three main components: the disposal prohibition, the dilution prohibition, and the storage prohibition. This series of prohibitions restrict how wastes subject to LDR requirements are handled. According to 40 CFR 268.2, "Land disposal means placement in or on the land, except in a corrective action unit, and includes, but is not limited to, placement in a landfill, surface impoundment, waste pile, injection well, land treatment facility, salt dome foundation, salt bed formation, underground mine or cave, or placement in a concrete vault or bunker intended for disposal purposes" (EPA 2010c).

The *disposal prohibition* forbids the dumping of hazardous waste in land that has not been adequately treated to reduce the threat to human health and the environment. The criteria that hazardous wastes must meet before being disposed of are known as treatment standards. These treatment standards (EPA 2010c) can be either concentration levels for hazardous constituents that the waste must meet or treatment technologies that must be performed on the waste before its disposal is permitted.

The *dilution prohibition* bans the addition of soil or water to waste, for example, in order to reduce the concentrations of hazardous constituents and can prohibit ineffective or inappropriate treatment methods.

The *storage prohibition* prevents the indefinite storage of untreated wastes for reasons other than the accumulation of quantities necessary for effective treatment or disposal.

The full listing of wastes that are prohibited from land disposal can be found in 40 CFR 268.20 to 268.39 (EPA 2010c). Some waste examples that are restricted from land disposal include:

- solvent wastes, as specified in 40 CFR 261.31 (F001, F002, F003, F004 and F005) (EPA 2010f)
- dioxin-containing wastes, as specified in 40 CFR 261.31 (F020, F021, F022, F023, F026, F027 and F028) (EPA 2010f)

- the "California list" wastes, as specified in 40 CFR 268.32 (EPA 2010c)
- RCRA-listed wastes, as specified in 40 CFR 268.33–268.35 (EPA 2010c)

The initial generator of the hazardous waste is responsibile for determining whether the waste meets the applicable standards and for communicating the LDR status of the waste in writing to downstream treatment, storage, or disposal facilities. Specific LDR documentation and record-keeping requirements apply to generators and to treatment, storage, or disposal facilities.

The basic steps for generators to comply with LDRs are:

- Determine the significant LDR waste code(s) for the waste at the initial point of generation of the waste.
- Determine all treatment standards applicable to the waste, based on the significant waste code(s).
- Determine whether the waste meets the applicable standards.
- Notify the designated TSDF in writing if the waste does not meet the applicable standards, or certify if it does meet all applicable standards.
- Keep copies of all notifications, certifications, and any supporting documentation used to make any of the above determinations. Retain records for at least five years.

Most hazardous waste transporters and/or brokers have developed a standardized LDR certification form that must be reviewed, signed, and sent with the shipment. A copy should be retained in their files.

Determination of Generator Category

RCRA classifies hazardous waste handlers as generators, transporters, or disposal facilities. Transportation and disposal of hazardous waste is beyond the scope of this section, except as pertaining to generators.

The first step in the classification process is to audit the facility and develop a list of all wastes generated (hazardous and nonhazardous) and the approximate monthly and annual amounts from production areas, maintenance shops, laboratories, loading/unloading docks, and wastewater treatment plants. This list should be reviewed with the company or facility management team to obtain agreement with the inventory. This list can also be used in the company or facility pollution prevention program to reduce or eliminate these waste streams.

The next step is to meet with someone within the organization, such as the corporate RCRA specialist, or with a representative from the hazardous waste disposal company, to determine whether the identified wastes should be considered hazardous or not. Samples are taken and sent to a laboratory for analysis. Waste profiles are then developed to accurately describe each waste stream. According to Caccavale, most hazardous waste disposal companies have developed a standardized waste profile sheet, to gather as much information as possible on the waste from the generator prior to sending waste to its final destination. It is important that the information on the initial waste profile is accurate and that future shipments of the same waste stream remain within that range. The implications of sending incompatible wastes to an incinerator or fuel blender could be harmful to their personnel and equipment.

Developing a waste profile sheet is similar to developing a material safety data sheet (MSDS) for products. Information requested on the profile will include:

- general facility information
- waste description
- process or source that generates the waste
- physical properties, such as physical state; number of phases; viscosity; color; odor; boiling, flash, and melting points; pH; specific gravity; vapor pressure; total organic carbon; and btus per pound
- waste composition
- constituents
- regulatory status
- DOT information
- transportation requirements
- sample status
- special waste-handling instructions

Testing the waste to determine whether it is hazardous should be done by a certified laboratory that can handle the RCRA waste analytical methodologies (TCLP). EPA SW-846 outlines the testing methods for solid wastes (EPA 2008d). Someone in the organization should be familiar with these laboratory methodologies and conduct an audit of the lab facility. If this option is not available, other businesses in the area or trade associations should be contacted for referrals.

Once generators have determined whether wastes are excluded, listed, or hazardous by examining their characteristics (40 CFR 261) (EPA 2010f), they must then determine how they are regulated based upon the amount of waste generated each month. There are three classifications, between which a company can jump on a monthly basis. However, it is best practice for a company to determine what the highest volume of hazardous waste is that it may generate, preparing accordingly. If a company exceeds the threshold for the next largest classification, it must be in full compliance with the requirements of that classification on the day it enters that classification.

The classifications are as follows:

- Conditionally Exempt Small-Quantity Generators (CESQGs) produce less than 100 kg of total hazardous waste *and* less than 1 kg of acutely hazardous waste monthly.
- Small-Quantity Generators (SQGs) produce more than 100 kg but less than 1000 kg of total hazardous waste *and* less than 1 kg of acutely hazardous waste monthly.
- Large-Quantity Generators (LQGs) produce equal to or greater than 1000 kg of total hazardous waste or equal to or more than 1 kg of acutely hazardous waste monthly.

(Conversion: 2.2 lb = 1 kg)

Note: Acute hazardous wastes are defined in §261.5(e)(1) as wastes listed in §§261.30(d) or 261.33(e) (EPA 2010f).

The amount of all hazardous wastes that have accumulated on site, been sent off site for treatment, or been treated on site should be measured. A generator's classification can change month to month. These weights may be estimated as long as the estimation is conservative. When in doubt, the higher category should always be chosen.

TABLE 1

Summary of Requirements for Hazardous Waste Generators

	CESQG	SQG	LQG
Quantity Limits	≤100 kg/month ≤1 kg/month of acute hazardous waste ≤100 kg/month of acute spill residue or soil §§261.5(a) and (e)	Between 100–1000 kg/month §262.34(d)	≥1000 kg/month >1 kg/month of acute hazardous waste >100 kg/month of acute spill residue or soil Part 262 and §261.5(e)
EPA ID Number	Not required §261.5	Required §262.12	Required §262.12
On-Site Accumulation Quantity	≤1000 kg ≤1 kg acute ≤100 kg of acute spill residue or soil §§261.5(f)(2) and (g)(2)	≤6000 kg §262.34(d)(1)	No limit
Accumulation Time Limits	None §261.5	≤180 days or ≤270 days (if greater than 200 miles) §§262.34(d)(2) and (3)	≤ 90 days §262.34(a)
Storage Requirements	None §261.5	Basic requirements with technical standards for tanks or containers §§262.34(d)(2) and (3)	Full compliance for management of tanks, containers, drip pads, or containment buildings §262.34(a)
Sent To	State approved or RCRA permitted/interim status facility §§261.5(f)(3) and (g)(3)	RCRA permitted/interim status facility §262.20(b)	RCRA permitted/interim status facility §262.20(b)
Manifest	Not required §261.5	Required §262.20	Required §262.20
Biennial Report	Not required §261.5	Not required §262.44	Required §262.41
Personnel Training	Not required §261.5	Basic training required §262.34(d)(5)(iii)	Required §262.34(a)(4)
Contingency Plan	Not required §261.5	Basic plan §262.34(d)(5)(i)	Full plan required §262.34(a)(4)
Emergency Procedures	Not required §261.5	Required §262.34(d)(5)(iv)	Full plan required §262.34(a)(4)
DOT Transport Requirements	Yes (if required by DOT)	Yes §§262.30-262.33	Yes §§262.30-262.33

(*Source*: EPA 2005a)

Table 1 is a summary of the hazardous waste generator requirements.

Some states may require or recommend that a CESQG have an ID number.

Useful guides for measuring liquid wastes with a density approximately that of water follow:

- Slightly more than half of a 55-gallon drum (30 gallons) weighs about 220 pounds.
- Slightly less than 6 drums (300 gallons) weighs 2200 pounds.

- The number of gallons in a container × 8.34 × the density of the liquid waste = the number of pounds of waste in the container.

Requirements for Conditionally Exempt Small-Quantity Generators (CESQGs)

If waste is shipped off site and is not treated or recycled on site, it must be sent to a state- or federally regulated hazardous waste management treatment, storage, or disposal facility, or to a facility that will reuse, recycle, or treat it, and which is permitted, licensed, or registered by the state to handle that waste.

Use caution when adopting this category. Check whether the host state has more stringent requirements on this classification than the federal regulations. It is also important to make sure that all transporters and waste sites are properly permitted, and it is prudent to make a call to the state to verify permit status, as well as to document the call.

Unlike other hazardous waste generators, conditionally exempt small-quantity generators (CESQGs) are not required to notify the EPA of their activities and, as seen in Table 1, are not required to obtain an EPA ID number. However, some transporters will not accept any wastes without an ID number. Several states recommend that CESQGs obtain an ID number and will issue one in the same form as the EPA ID number (three letters and nine digits) so that CESQG wastes may be transported without problem.

Any company that feels it fits into the CESQG category should be very careful not to generate more than the various quantities of waste in a single month, moving it into a different category of generator where it is subject to additional requirements, as shown in Table 1 and as described below.

Requirements for Small-Quantity Generators (SQGs) and Large-Quantity Generators (LQGs)

EPA Identification Number

Form 8700-12 and its instructions can be downloaded from the EPA Web site (EPA 2009a).

Notification, Monitoring, and Tracking

Both small- and large-quantity generators must notify the EPA of their activities, as mentioned above, using Form 8700-12 (EPA 2009a). When the waste is shipped off site, the EPA ID number is required for the manifest.

Proper Packing, Packaging, Marking, Labeling, and Shipping

Generators are required to follow all Department of Transportation (DOT) regulations for the prepara-

tion and shipping of wastes. Vehicles used to ship wastes may need to be placarded in accordance with DOT regulations.

Selection of Shipping and Disposal Facilities

Waste generators are responsible to select an approved treatment, storage, and disposal facility (TSDF) that can properly handle the wastes shipped to it. The TSDF will have an EPA ID Number and sufficient insurance to handle all materials received for the life of the facility as well as for a period of time afterwards. The TSDF may recommend a transporter or may include a transportation division that is approved to move the wastes. All wastes must meet DOT requirements for shipping and must be manifested and tracked.

Chemical Analysis

Generators are responsible for properly identifying and classifying wastes. To ensure that this is correct, a TSDF may require that the analysis of the waste material be provided prior to shipment in order to safely handle the material.

A small-quantity generator (SQG) and a large-quantity generator (LQG) should develop a written general waste plan under 40 CFR 265.13 (EPA 2010b) to ensure that they can provide sufficient information about their wastes to any TSDF or governmental agency that may request it. The general waste analysis plan should follow the requirements in §265.13, and the generator may want to include, at a minimum, the eight points found in 40 CFR 264.13(b) (EPA 2010b).

Manifesting System

The *manifest* is the tracking document behind the entire RCRA "cradle-to-grave" concept. It is the official DOT shipping document, which tracks the hazardous waste shipment from the time it is loaded on the hazardous waste transporter's vehicle until the waste is disposed of (incinerated, fuel blended, made part of a landfill, recycled, and so on). The manifest carries with it legal liability for the person who signs the document from the facility.

Distribution of the manifest copies is important as well to ensure all applicable parties have received their respective copy in a timely fashion. The federal regulations were revised on September 5, 2006, so that the same Uniform Hazardous Waste Manifest form is now used for all shipments throughout the United States; individual states no longer have their own manifests. The manifest will consist of at least six copies, which will provide the generator, each transporter, and the owner or operator of the designated TSDF facility with one copy for their records. When the hazardous waste shipment has been accepted at the TSDF, one signed manifest copy is then returned to the generator, while another is sent to the state environmental agency (if applicable). Generators must check with individual state agencies to determine whether a copy of the completed manifest is required (EPA 2005c).

The generator must designate on the manifest one facility that is permitted to handle the waste described. The generator can also designate one alternate facility in the event that an emergency prevents delivery of the waste. If the transporter cannot deliver the waste to the primary or alternate facility, the generator should designate another facility or instruct the transporter to return the waste to the originating facility.

The generator must: (1) sign the manifest certification by hand, (2) obtain the handwritten signature of the initial transporter and date of acceptance on the manifest, and (3) retain three copies. The generator keeps one copy, one copy is forwarded to the generator's state agency, and one copy is forwarded to the hazardous waste destination state agency (only if applicable). The generator must then give the transporter the remaining copies of the signed manifest.

The dates next to the signatures are critical. There are limitations governing how long a waste can be in transit. If a generator does not receive a signed, completed manifest from the TSDF within 35 days of shipment, the generator must track the waste. If the waste is not found in 45 days for a large-quantity generator, or 60 days for a small quantity generator, an exception report must be provided to either the EPA or the state agency. Some states have more stringent requirements. As a rule of thumb, some type of file should be compiled that flags a waste shipment manifest not sent back to you within a certain timeframe (for example 20 days). This will enable the generator to call either the transporter or the TSDF to determine the delay.

Sometimes, TSDFs reject shipments because the manifest does not have the correct paperwork attached. For example, virtually all liquid hazardous wastes are banned from landfills until they are rendered nonhazardous. If such materials are being disposed of, a land ban certificate must be attached to the manifest.

A TSDF could reject a waste stream if a sample of the waste analyzed upon arrival at the TSDF does not meet the specifications of the waste profile agreed to prior to shipment of the waste. This can cause the TSDF treatment and/or catastrophic problems, such as fires or explosions.

The key to completing the manifest is understanding the DOT regulations for proper shipping names (DOT 2011). Most hazardous waste transportation company representatives can assist generators in filling out the manifest prior to shipment. This information is gathered from the waste profile already on record with the waste disposal company.

An important resource used in completing the manifest is the Pipeline and Hazardous Materials Safety Administration's *Emergency Response Guidebook* (ERG) (PHMSA 2008). Each hazardous material shipped across the highways and railroads in North America is affixed with a United Nations (UN) or North America (NA) number. These numbers are located on the DOT class placards on the sides of railcars and trucks (e.g., methyl ethyl ketone (MEK) is UN1193, sulfuric acid is UN1830).

On the manifest, the ERG guide number for each hazardous waste in the shipment can be referenced in Section 15, Special Handling Instructions, or a copy of each applicable ERG guide page may be attached to the manifest prior to shipment.

The manifest also requires the generator to provide a 24-hour emergency response number of a person knowledgeable about the waste. This means someone within the organization must be available to provide technical information in the event of an emergency scenario.

Accumulating Waste On Site

When discussing accumulation requirements at a facility, understanding which hazardous waste generator classification a facility falls into is very important. If your facility is classified as a CESQG [less than or equal to 100 kg (220 lb) of hazardous waste per month], there are no accumulation time requirements. If a facility is classified as a SQG [greater than 100 kg and less than or equal to 1000 kg (2200 lb) of hazardous waste per month], hazardous waste may be accumulated on site for 180 days or less without a permit, or up to 270 days if the hazardous waste must be transported, stored, or treated at a distance of 200 miles or more.

For an LQG, a generator may accumulate hazardous waste on site for 90 days or less without a permit or without having interim status, provided that:

- the waste is placed in containers and the generator complies with 40 CFR 265 Subpart I (Use and Management of Containers), or the waste is placed in tanks and the generator complies with Subpart J (Tank Systems) (EPA 2010b)
- the date upon which each period of accumulation begins is clearly marked and visible for inspection on each container
- while being accumulated on site, each container and tank is labeled or marked clearly with the words, *hazardous waste*
- the generator complies with the requirements for owners and operators in 40 CFR 265 Subparts C and D (Preparedness and Prevention, Contingency Plan and Emergency Procedures) and Part 265.16 (Personnel Training) (EPA 2010b).

An extension can be filed with the Regional EPA Administrator if the waste cannot be removed from a facility within 90 days for situations such as an unforeseen emergency or uncontrollable circumstances. However, these extensions (usually for 30 days) are judged on a case-by-case basis. A facility may have multiple less-than-90-day accumulation areas as long as it can maintain the areas and has the manpower to conduct inspections. The accumulation area(s) must be:

- located in an area with limited access
- clearly identified with posted signs and warning placards
- away from floor drains, furnaces, or open flames
- not be subject to extreme temperature changes

The regulations focus on ensuring that:

- containers are labeled properly
- incompatible wastes are separated
- the accumulation area has secondary containment
- the accumulation area is inspected
- written emergency procedures are up to date
- fire control and emergency response equipment is readily available
- site personnel involved in any aspect of handling the hazardous waste are trained
- arrangements for emergency response activities have been made with local authorities

Safe Handling of Hazardous Waste

If a facility is going to be handling hazardous waste, moving it is a high priority. Whether small containers of waste are transferred to larger containers, a large container is moved around a worksite and transferred to another location, or containers are moved to on-site storage, there are several things to consider.

The first consideration is personal protective equipment (PPE). What type of PPE is necessary depends on the potential danger from exposure to moving the hazardous waste. A company's respective safety and industrial hygiene personnel should be consulted to ensure proper PPE is selected. Personnel also need to be properly trained to wear the appropriate PPE.

Splashes are probably the most common form of hazardous waste exposure. When opening a drum, the small bung should always be opened first and unscrewed slowly. If there is any pressure in the drum, it should be vented while the cap is still partially threaded into the lid. A funnel should always be used when pouring from one container to another, and the containers must be grounded and/or bonded.

Two common types of containers used in hazardous waste storage are 55-gallon drums and five-gallon cans. Some of these cans are self-closing to prevent spills should they tip over and self-venting to prevent dangerous buildup of explosive vapors. Self-venting cans are required by law for certain flammable substances (EPA 2010b).

If small waste containers are being moved, a cart that has the capacity for secondary containment should be used. If one of the containers were to spill, the liquid would spill into the cart and not on the ground or onto a person.

Prior to moving a 55-gallon drum, both bung caps should be checked to make sure they are tight. The drum should always be checked for rust, dents, and/or leaks, especially if the drum has been sitting out in the elements for a period of time. If there is any evidence of damage to the drum, it should not be moved; the appropriate personnel within the company should be consulted to determine what needs to be done. To move a 55-gallon drum any distance, either a drum dolly with some type of restraint or a forklift should be used.

Falling drums are one of the most common causes of injuries. The drum might land on or pin an employee; if it ruptures, the employee can be exposed to the contents of the drum. If a drum starts to fall, the employee should let it go.

Vapor or particulate releases are another concern when handling hazardous waste. These releases can harm an employee in several ways. Inhalation of poisonous hazardous waste can irritate the eyes, nose, mouth, or lungs. Many vapors are flammable, so there is the potential of fire or explosion. Some vapors have the ability to corrode pipes, sprinkler heads, or equipment. The areas where people work with hazardous wastes, specifically transfers, should have adequate ventilation and/or an exhaust system that draws airborne contaminants away from workers and out of the area. For certain types of waste, respiratory protection may be required.

Another hazard is the mixture of incompatible wastes, which must not be done; this is called *segregation and separation*. A reaction could result if incompatible wastes are mixed. Some chemicals, such as acids, and any waste containing sulfide may become explosive when mixed together. Hazardous wastes should never be mixed together unless they are compatible. In addition, the container must be compatible with its contents.

Finally, the importance of grounding and bonding should be recognized. All stored metal containers should be properly grounded. The *storage* container is to be grounded while the *receiving* container (usually a 1– to 5-gallon container) is to be bonded to the storage container using bonding straps or cables to eliminate the potential generation of a static discharge. This concept also applies to the transfer of liquid waste materials between plastic containers to reduce the potential of static electricity.

Labeling and Marking (EPA 2010d)

Prior to transporting and offering hazardous waste for transportation off site, the generator must label each package (box, drum, and so on) in accordance with the applicable Department of Transportation regulations on packaging materials (DOT 2011). These labels reflect the DOT hazard classes (e.g., corrosive, flammable liquid, oxidizer, and organic peroxide).

Also prior to shipping, the generator must mark each container of 110 gallons or less with the following words and information displayed in accordance with the requirements of 49 CFR 172.304 (DOT 2011) or their state's labeling requirement:

> HAZARDOUS WASTE – Federal Law Prohibits Improper Disposal. If found contact the nearest police or public safety authority or the U.S. Environmental Protection Agency. Generator's name and address. Manifest document number.

These standardized hazardous waste labels (commonly yellow in color, although not required) can be purchased and even customized with the company's name, address, and telephone number.

Personnel Training Plan

Generators of hazardous wastes must ensure that all wastes are under the control of trained personnel. These regulations are found in multiple places, beginning with 40 CFR 262.34(a)(1)(i) (EPA 2010f), and then 40 CFR 265.16 (EPA 2010b), which states that the minimum training program will include:

1. Procedures for using, inspecting, repairing, and replacing facility emergency and monitoring equipment

2. Key parameters for automatic waste feed cut-off systems
3. Communications or alarm systems
4. Response to fires or explosions
5. Response to groundwater contamination incidents
6. Shutdown of operations

This training must be provided within six months of an employee's assignment to handle hazardous wastes, and such an employee must not work unsupervised if untrained. Employees must be retrained annually, and the training records of current employees must be kept for the life of the facility or for three years after the employees leave the company.

The company is required to maintain these training records along with:

1. The job title for each position at the facility related to hazardous waste management and the name of the employee filling each job.
2. A written job description for each hazardous waste position.
3. A written description of the type and amount of both introductory and continuing training that will be given to each hazardous waste employee.
4. Records documenting the training or job experience required of the hazardous waste employees of the company.

Preparedness and Prevention—Contingency Plan

LQGs are required to have a contingency plan describing preparations emergencies at the facility. The contingency plan must conform to the requirements listed at 40 CFR 265.50 (EPA 2010b). In addition, copies of the plan are to be submitted to local emergency agencies and to hospitals that could respond to or be affected by the activation of the plan.

SQGs are not required to have as complete a plan as are LQG facilities but should have trained personnel able to respond in an emergency. However, if the facility becomes a LQG because of excessive waste generation some month, it will need a complete plan. It is recommended that every generator, regardless of size, have a complete contingency plan.

CESQGs are not required to have a plan, but, again, it is recommended.

If the facility has an emergency plan as required under 29 CFR 1910.38 (OSHA 1980) or some other regulation, it only needs to include the additional information required by the hazardous waste regulations for a combination plan that covers all requirements. Having one coordinated plan will make it easier for plant personnel to understand their tasks when they respond to an emergency.

Waste Minimization

Every time a company representative signs a hazardous waste manifest, he or she certifies that, in addition to the hazardous wastes being properly packaged, packed, marked, and labeled according to the Department of Transportation regulations at 49 CFR, a program is in place to minimize the amount of wastes generated.

Waste minimization has been used successfully by industry for many years to reduce the volume and toxicity of waste streams, producing cost savings for materials and waste disposal. The EPA proposes incorporating a tiered approach to waste management (see Figure 2).

The EPA says that its waste minimization program has the following goals:

1. Complete elimination of, or substitution for, priority chemicals, wherever possible.
2. Minimizing the amount of priority chemicals used whenever elimination or substitution is not possible.
3. Maximizing recycling whenever elimination, substitution, or minimization is not possible, creating closed-loop materials management systems that eliminate or constrict release pathways.
4. Promoting cradle-to-cradle waste management instead of cradle-to-grave waste management.
5. Increasing cooperative efforts between the EPA, states, and regulated communities through partnership programs.

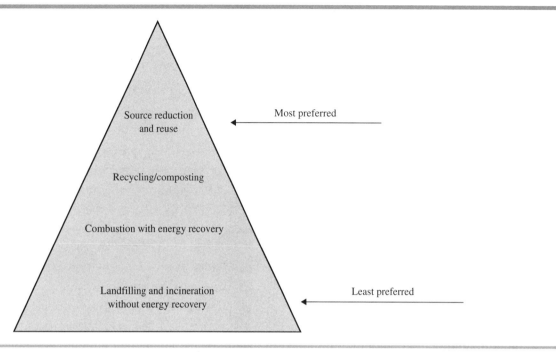

FIGURE 2. Solid waste management hierarchy (*Source*: EPA 2008b)

It thus makes very good sense for any company generating hazardous wastes to also adopt those goals, training its employees to work toward their implementation.

In addition, other simple waste minimization strategies that a company can implement include:

- segregating hazardous waste streams from nonhazardous waste streams
- recycling and reusing raw materials and extracting water and raw material from rinses, solvent tanks, and spent chemicals
- replacing toxic materials, products, or processes with less toxic alternatives
- controlling leaks and spills

Suppose, for example, that a company has been using methylene chloride as a paint stripper for the past thirty-five years, since the company's founding. Methylene chloride is an excellent paint stripper. However, it is now known that it is a human carcinogen, mutagen, and tumorigen. Because it is chlorinated, it has a low heat value (btus), which means that disposal costs are very high and that there are land ban restrictions upon its disposal. With a little research, the company finds and switches to one of several commercial paint strippers on the market that are both environ-

mentally friendly and either slightly toxic or nontoxic, a paint stripper so safe that employees may use it without wearing personal protective equipment. Thus the company has minimized its waste by eliminating a highly toxic material and replacing it with a less toxic material. The company's waste is now classified as industrial waste instead of hazardous waste, saving the company money.

Record Keeping

Hazardous waste generators are required to maintain records to identify the quantities, composition, and disposition of hazardous waste generated. Required reports include:

- a contingency plan—keep a current version
- emergency agreements with local authorities—keep a current version
- land disposal restrictions—keep for five years
- manifests—keep for three years
- manifest exception reports (40 CFR 262.40 (b))—keep for three years (EPA 2010f)
- personnel training documentation (40 CFR 262.34 (c) & (d))—keep for three years after employee termination or separation of employment (EPA 2010f)

• waste analyses/test results (or other bases used for hazardous waste determination) (40 CFR 262.34 (c))—keep until facility closure (EPA 2010d)

Requirements Specific to Large-Quantity Generators

Large-quantity generators (LQGs) may accumulate unlimited amounts of hazardous wastes on site, but they may store those wastes for no longer than 90 days from the date of initial storage, unless the LQG is a permitted storage facility. LQGs must abide by all other requirements listed above and must also submit a report on even-numbered years that includes:

• the generator's EPA ID number
• the EPA ID numbers for each transporter and designated facility used
• the quantity and nature of hazardous waste generated
• efforts to reduce volume and toxicity of waste
• changes in volume and toxicity of waste achieved

The biennial report is to be submitted on EPA Forms 8700-13 A/B (EPA 2007a).

Requirements Specific to Acutely Hazardous Waste

Acutely hazardous wastes are defined as wastes listed in §§261.31, 261.32, or 261.33(e); in §§262.34(c)(1) and other sections of the regulations, only those wastes in §§261.33(e) are considered acutely hazardous (40 CFR 261.5(e)(1)) (EPA 2010f). These wastes are considered acutely hazardous because of their inherently hazardous characteristics. Such waste contains chemicals dangerous enough to pose a threat to human health and the environment even when properly managed. These wastes are fatal to humans and animals even in low doses.

When any company generates more than 1 kg of acutely hazardous waste per calendar month, that company is a considered a large-quantity generator and must manage its wastes according to LQG requirements.

Medical Wastes

Medical wastes are generally managed by the states, but federal laws do exist that control emissions from incinerators and for treatment. Medical wastes were addressed in 42 U.S.C. 82, Subchapter X, as the Medical Waste Tracking Act of 1988, which was promulgated as a response to medical wastes that washed ashore (MWTA 1988). The Act, which expired after two years, called for demonstration projects for shipment and disposal of medical wastes in several east coast and Great Lakes states. After the demonstrations, the EPA made recommendations to Congress regarding additional steps needed for management of medical wastes. State laws and regulations should be referred to for specifics on the handling of medical wastes.

Universal Wastes

The category of universal wastes was finalized in the Federal Register in May 1995 by the EPA in order to encourage the recycling of certain potentially hazardous items generated in large quantities in the nonhazardous waste stream. Such wastes, including batteries, items containing mercury, certain pesticides, and certain light bulbs are found routinely in maintenance operations (40 CFR 273) (EPA 2005b).

Companies that generate universal wastes are broken down into two categories: small-quantity and large-quantity handlers of universal wastes. There are also universal waste transporters and universal waste destination facilities, but those are outside the scope of this chapter.

Small-Quantity Handler of Universal Waste (SQHUW)–Subpart B

Generators in the small-quantity category must stay below 5000 kg of all universal waste categories combined at their location at any time. They are required to manage their universal wastes in ways that prevent releases to the environment; in case of release, they must immediately respond and initiate clean up (RCRA 1976).

Large-Quantity Handler of Universal Waste (LQHUW)–Subpart C

LQHUWs are those companies that exceed the 5000 kg of all universal waste categories and will remain large-quantity handlers for the balance of the year. They must comply with all requirements that the SQHUW has to comply with, must have an EPA ID number, and must keep records of materials generated.

Requirements for All Handlers

Both large and small universal waste handlers must train their employees in basic waste handling and emergency response procedures.

Waste containers must be labeled in any one of the following ways (whichever makes sense) and with the date the material first became a waste or when it was received from another facility:

- Universal Waste *(name of material—lamps, batteries, oil, and so on)*
- Waste *(name of material—lamps, batteries, oil, and so on)*
- Used *(name of material—lamps, batteries, oil, and so on)*

Universal wastes may be allowed to accumulate for up to one year in order to collect sufficient volume for recycling and may be transported using any vehicle or transport company. If the SQHUW or LQHUW transports the universal wastes with a company vehicle, it becomes a Universal Waste Transporter and must comply with all regulations applying to transporters. SQHUWs may ship universal wastes off-site without manifests or recordkeeping. LQHUWs must develop a recordkeeping method, track all wastes shipped off-site and maintain those records for three years.

All items must be stored in containers and handled in such ways as to prevent release into the environment. In case of release, clean-up materials are considered a hazardous waste and must be stored and shipped as such.

Recycling of Hazardous Wastes (40 CFR 266, Subparts C & F)

The goal of these regulations is to ensure that hazardous wastes are handled properly for disposal. If wastes are recycled or reused instead of disposed of, the goal of these regulations is met.

However, there may be times when materials that could be recycled are "used in a manner that constitutes disposal" if applied to the land. The EPA is aware of those materials and the disposer must follow the generators regulations for the disposition of those materials (40 CFR 266, Subpart C). Certain precious metals, such as gold, silver, and platinum, are of significant value and not willingly discarded. The EPA recognizes this and allows those companies involved in the handling of these metals flexibility in doing so. These companies must have an EPA ID number and must follow the regulations concerning generators and transporters. They are required to use manifests and to note any discrepancies on manifests. If they store such materials on-site, records must be kept that show that the material is being recycled and not accumulated for speculation (40 CFR 266 Subpart F) (EPA 2010e). State environmental agencies should be consulted for any additional requirements for this type of recycling.

Achieving Excellence in Pollution Prevention

According to the Pollution Prevention Act of 1990, the following characteristics are repeatedly found in companies that achieve excellence in pollution prevention:

- *Top-level support and commitment:* A clear commitment to pollution prevention by senior management is exhibited through policy, communications, and resources.
- *Proactive management:* Management is proactive rather than reactive. Actions are taken in advance to prevent pollution.
- *Interdisciplinary management:* A wide variety of people in the company are exposed to the ideas and techniques of pollution prevention. Companies integrate the research, engineering, and production staffs into the pollution prevention programs, increasing understanding and commitment all the way from the design staff to the sales force.
- *Corporate policies that integrate environmental issues:* Specific statements regarding environmental issues are incorporated into the company's goals and policies. These are

often stated in a positive rather than a negative way (i.e., "Company policies should improve the environment," rather than "Company policies should not harm the environment").

- *Pollution prevention "champion":* Companies that excel in pollution prevention often have one or two key individuals who support and drive the programs. The champion believes in the program and pushes for its implementation.
- *High degree of employee awareness and training:* Thorough training of employees is essential in pollution prevention. Numerous examples exist where companies failed to prevent pollution simply because employees were not trained properly.
- *Strong environmental auditing program:* Frequent assessments of pollution prevention include: top-down, self-assessment, and third-party audits. These audits evaluate existing pollution prevention controls and measure pollution releases and reductions.

There are many examples of how a company can minimize its waste: equipment or technology modifications, reformulation or redesign of products, substitution of raw materials, improvements in housekeeping, and maintenance and inventory control systems. The best method should be chosen for each company; commitment should be obtained from management; and as many people as possible should be involved. Waste minimization, source reduction, pollution prevention—whatever the company uses to describe the reduction of hazardous and solid wastes—will not only benefit the company's bottom line, but also keep the environment healthy for generations to come.

Selecting a Hazardous Waste Transporter and a Treatment, Storage, and Disposal Facility (TSDF)

While reviewing the finer details of both good hazardous waste transporters and treatment, storage, and disposal facilities (TSDFs), the key word to remember is *liability*. Whether the waste generated is sitting on company property, in transit to the TSDF, sitting at a transfer station in the middle of nowhere or at the TSDF, the liability of the waste rests with the generator. Hazardous waste transporters will provide all kinds of guarantees, but the bottom line is that when an emergency response occurs involving a company's hazardous waste in the middle of the night in a rural area, someone in that organization must be ready to mitigate the situation, either with manpower or cash flow.

Transporters

Since hazardous waste transporters move regulated wastes on public roads and highways, rails and waterways, they are regulated not only by RCRA but also by the Department of Transportation (DOT). To avoid regulatory discrepancies, the hazardous waste transporter regulations were developed jointly by EPA and DOT. Although these regulations are integrated, they are not located in the same part of the CFR. DOT's Hazardous Materials Transportation Act regulations are found in the 49 CFR Parts 171–179 (EPA 2011b), while the RCRA Subtitle C transporter requirements are located in 40 CFR Part 263 (EPA 2010d).

Transporter regulations only apply to off-site transportation of hazardous waste. The regulations do not apply to on-site transportation of hazardous waste within a facility's property or boundary.

Prior to selecting a hazardous waste transporter, a waste-generating company must look for dependability, reliability, regulatory knowledge, and a good transportation track record.

The company can select either a TSDF with transportation capabilities or a waste broker who will subcontract transportation services. Such a determination should be based on the type and amount of waste streams the company generates.

Once the selection of hazardous waste transportation companies has been narrowed down to two or three that suit the company's needs, the state environmental agency should be contacted to confirm that the transporters are licensed in the state and to learn their compliance records, such as any filed or pending notices of violations (NOVs) in both EPA and DOT. The transporters' DOT numbers should be requested and each company's driving safety and inspection records should be reviewed online at the Comprehensive Safety Analysis 2010 System of the Federal

Motor Safety Analysis Administration (FMCSA) (DOT 2010).

Another avenue to pursue if the company is a multi-site organization, is to check with other facilities within the organization that may have used the transporter to determine if they are dependable. Finally, the company should always request and check the transporter's references.

Under the Superfund (CERCLA) regulation, if the transporter spills the hazardous waste in transit, the company that generated the waste will incur the financial responsibility toward the clean-up operation. The company is not released of any liability during the shipment phase, despite any statements the transporter may make (CERCLA 1980).

Information that a company should request from any transporter includes:

- EPA identification number
- DOT number
- TSDFs where the transporter is permitted to transport the waste streams
- waste destination, such as a transfer station (if so, where and for how long)
- waste pickup scheduling lead time
- regulatory background, such as assistance with completion of waste profiles, manifests, and land-ban forms
- on-site services, such as labeling, marking of containers, overpacking (if necessary), and lab-packing
- training competencies of on-site technicians and drivers
- emergency response capabilities
- pricing

Transfer Facilities

Transporters accepting hazardous waste from a generator or another transporter may need to hold waste temporarily during the normal course of transportation. A *transfer facility* is defined as any transportation-related facility, such as a loading dock, parking area, storage area, or other similar area where shipments are held during the normal course of transportation. A transporter may hold waste at a transfer facility for up to 10 days. Transfer facilities are usually used by transporters as a cost-saving measure to maximize trailer capacity on runs to different TSDFs.

TSDFs

Once the waste transporter has been selected, a decision must be made as to where to send the waste. The final disposition of the waste will determine the selection of a type of TSDF. Incineration, fuels blending, recycling, land-filling, and Class I injection wells are the most common options. Pricing will play a part in this decision, but liability must be factored into the decision. Some TSDFs have transportation services available, which make prices competitive. This may be the best option for a company that has consistent waste streams. If a company produces a variety of waste streams, they may need to go to different types of TSDFs, in which case a waste broker may be the best solution.

Waste minimization, or producing less waste, is the best way to protect the environment and reduce liability risk. However, once waste is produced, the EPA recommends recycling as the next best method for managing wastes. Recycling offers the advantages of avoiding disposal costs and protecting the environment. But if mismanaged, recycling can release hazardous waste into the environment. RCRA, therefore, exclusively regulates wastes destined for recycling.

Recycling includes burning wastes for energy, which must destroy at least 99.99 percent of the waste, which in turn minimizes the risk of future liability. The destruction efficiency is based on the type of incineration unit, temperature, and the type of waste burned. Recycling usually derives a useful product from wastes, plus recycling may preserve natural resources, such as coal and fossil fuels used in the incineration process. Depending upon the material, recycling may be less expensive (EPA 2010f).

Incineration and fuel blending have become popular disposal or treatment options as the EPA continues to tighten regulations governing landfills, and as future liabilities associated with buried wastes increase.

Land disposal of waste has the highest potential liability risk, and many consider it the method of last resort. The EPA's land disposal restriction (LDR) program prohibits placing untreated waste in land-based disposal or treatment units. Hazardous waste destined for land disposal must be pretreated to specified safe levels to reduce its risk to the environment.

The advantage of incineration and fuel blending is that both are forms of thermal destruction that break down hazardous components of the waste to an efficiency of 99.9999 percent. The volume and weight of the waste are reduced to a fraction of their original state (referred to as *ash content*).

The major advantage of these disposal methods is that many toxins are destroyed rather than merely contained; thus, the risk to the environment and the generator are limited. While thermal destruction generally costs more than disposal in a landfill, increasing costs and limited availability of landfills are closing the gap.

There is a difference between fuel blending and incineration. In the United States, there are approximately 80 to 90 cement kilns in operation, about 25 of which burn waste-derived fuel (or blended fuel). Fuel is fed into the lower hot end of the kiln where gas temperatures can reach 3500° F. As waste-derived fuels burn in the kiln, organic compounds are destroyed and inorganic compounds recombine with raw materials that are incorporated into gypsum used by ready-mix concrete makers.

Typically, *fuel blending* is the least expensive, most efficient form of incineration and has the least impact on the environment. Waste is converted into fuels with complete thermal destruction of organic waste. This waste-to-energy conversion preserves natural energy resources while destroying waste. *Incineration*, on the other hand, uses virgin fuels, such as coal, to fire the incinerator, which burns at temperatures ranging from 1000–2500° F. Because fuel blending uses wastes as energy, it is significantly less expensive than incineration.

Wastes that are high in btu (British thermal unit) value and have low residual ash content are prime candidates for fuel blending. These values are important in the incineration process because the higher the btu value, the more efficiently wastes will burn and convert to energy. For example, absorbents are most commonly used in daily maintenance to absorb oil leaks and spills; however, not all absorbents used

for this purpose are good candidates for fuel blending. Clay pellets, a low-grade absorbent frequently used in industry, are unacceptable for fuel blending because of their 100 percent ash-content remainder and low btu value.

Wastes sent for incineration and/or fuel blending operations used for btu value keep that unit operational. Thus, the higher the btu value of a hazardous waste stream, the more likely the incinerator or fuel blending facility will accept the waste.

Auditing the TSDF

Prior to sending waste to a TSDF, a company should develop a methodology for ensuring that the waste is in good hands for final disposal. Whether a TSDF facility audit is performed by someone within the waste-generating company or is contracted out, an audit of the TSDF is necessary for company liability purposes.

Most TSDFs are not that large and can usually be audited in a day or two. Much of the regulatory paper review can be done prior to the audit. Most TSDF facilities schedule audits certain days of the week and/or times of the month to maintain the least amount of interruption to their production schedule. The TSDF or waste broker representative can arrange an audit. With competition in the hazardous waste services field at its highest, most TSDFs have already developed a preliminary audit package for the auditor to review. The waste management facility evaluation document should include the following sections:

- *Facility history:* How many years in operation, EPA identification number
- *Processing capabilities:* Services available on site, waste types accepted and not accepted at the facility, hours of operation, weekly processing capacity
- *Storage practices and capacities:* Permitted waste storage capacity, truck unloading area, drum storage area, signs of leakage or deterioration, signs of growing backlog of wastes, air emission controls
- *Laboratory capabilities and waste stream qualifications:* On-site laboratory and capabilities, prequalification of waste streams

- *Receiving and loading practices:* Testing of waste deliveries prior to unloading each truck, notification to the generator or transporter of a rejection
- *Waste released by or shipment from the facility:* Any visible air emissions, detectable odors, control of storm water runoff from contained areas, wastes or by-products shipped from the facility for off-site disposal or use as a fuel (tank bottoms, leachate, and so on)
- *Regulatory compliance:* RCRA Part B permit in order; inspections from regulatory agencies (citations, corrective actions, compliance schedule met); employee training program; facility's financial capability to handle environmental impairment liability; security system; description of surrounding area (residential, industrial, wooded); groundwater monitoring and leachate control programs; record keeping
- *Other facilities:* Company-owned or -operated
- *Summary:* Concerns, comments, and observations

Although it is difficult and time-consuming to conduct an audit, it is probably in the best interest of the company to send an auditor familiar with both the environmental and safety regulations. The length of time between audits is determined by how well the audit goes; a three-year interval is a good rule of thumb; less than three years would be necessary in cases of regulatory intervention of the TSDF, or poor management practice.

Regulations Governing TSDFs

Any person who treats, stores, or disposes of hazardous waste is operating a TSDF. There are requirements established under the RCRA regulation for TSDFs (EPA 2010b and 2010f).

A TSDF needs to obtain approval to operate from the EPA or authorized state agency. There is a two-step approval process before a facility can be classified as a permitted TSDF. The "Part A" or *interim status permit* requires a facility to obtain an EPA ID number and submit summary information to the agency(s), which includes design, construction, operation, and maintenance of a facility. A TSDF may operate under a

"Part A" permit until the "Part B" application is either approved or denied.

The "Part B" permit allows a TSDF to accept, store, treat, and dispose of hazardous waste with the following requirements:

- waste analysis plan for incoming shipments
- security measures
- documented inspection program for malfunctions, operator errors, and discharges
- personnel training
- handling storage of ignitable, reactive, and incompatible wastes
- preparedness for and prevention of emergencies and releases
- written contingency plan and emergency procedures
- written operating records, manifest records, and biennial reports of facility activities
- groundwater protection for land disposal facilities
- closure plan and post-closure plan and use
- financial information regarding closure, post-closure, accidents, and bankruptcy

TSDFs must be built in locations away from natural disasters (floods, hurricanes, earthquakes, and so on). The facility must also be able to:

- accept wastes in accordance with manifest rules
- manage containers in accordance with container rules
- manage tanks in accordance with tank rules
- manage other units in accordance with applicable technical standards (surface impoundments, landfills, incinerators, and so on)
- control, monitor, and document volatile organic air emissions (fugitive emissions)
- comply with land disposal restrictions (where applicable)
- maintain adequate insurance during operating and adequate funding for closure and beyond (post-closure)

Some TSDFs provide their own transportation services; however, most do not and subcontract with licensed hazardous waste haulers. Even though the hazardous waste has shipped under the "cradle-to-grave" concept, the waste-generating company is liable for the hazardous waste shipment until official disposal of the waste. The transporter's terminal and TSDF should be audited by company personnel (including cement kilns), or by third-party auditor prior to sending waste off site. It is a worthwhile investment.

Companies or facilities do not have to apply for a RCRA permit if they fall under one of the following specific exemptions:

- generators that accumulate hazardous waste on site for less than 90 days
- generators that produce less than 100 kg (220 lb) of hazardous waste in a calendar month, which is treated, stored or disposed of accordingly
- owners or operators of totally enclosed treatment facilities; for example, a hazardous waste treatment facility directly connected to an industrial production process constructed and operated to prevent the release of hazardous waste into the environment during treatment (e.g., a pipe in which waste acid is neutralized)
- transporters that store manifested shipments of hazardous waste for 10 days or less in permitted containers at a transfer facility

These are the federal RCRA requirements; companies should check with their respective states for more stringent state requirements.

Hazardous Waste Combustion

Combustion in boilers, industrial furnaces, or incinerators can ultimately dispose of hazardous wastes. Thermal destruction is used to destroy not only toxic materials such as dioxins or polychlorinated biphenyls but also organics and nonhazardous trash or municipal wastes—but the methods differ significantly.

Hazardous waste combustors, such as boilers or industrial furnaces, use the waste as a fuel additive for such things as rotary kilns, blast furnaces, smelters, reactors, or calciners used in the manufacturing of cement or lime. The inclusion of the hazardous waste provides an increase in heat value (btus) thus lowering the amount of fuel required. To ensure that these units remain environmentally compliant, the waste gas mixture is put through precipitators, bag filters, and/or scrubbers to ensure that what's coming out of the stack is as clean as practical. The material going into these units is covered by 40 CFR 266 (EPA 2010e), and the materials coming out of the stacks are governed by air regulations at 40 CFR 60.

An incinerator is a special type of combustion unit that uses very high temperatures to completely destroy solids or liquids.

Hazardous waste incinerators must be permitted under regulations covered in 40 CFR 264 and 265 covering TSDFs. Wastes must be analyzed to ensure that they are allowable under the facility's permit. Strict performance, operating, monitoring, record keeping, and inspection requirements must be maintained.

Information on the EPA's research on combustion and incineration and diagrams of related equipment are available at the EPA Web site (EPA 2007d and 2006a).

Underground Storage Tanks (USTs)

The Solid Waste Disposal Act was amended in 1984 to regulate underground storage tanks (USTs). Specifically, the law covers USTs and related piping that have been used to store petroleum or hazardous materials, imposing minimum standards for performance and operation to minimize potential for leakage. The requirements include:

- spill protection, such as a catchment basin to contain spills from delivery hoses
- overfill protection, such as automatic shut-off valves when the tank is 95 percent full
- corrosion protection, such as tank construction with noncorrodible material, corrosion-resistant coating, or steel-clad with a thick layer of noncorrodible material
- financial requirements and the ability to pay for clean-up costs and environmental effects

Existing tanks can be brought into compliance by the addition of cathodic protection (such as the technology used in home water heaters in which a sacrificial anode attracts the electrical charge that causes corrosion), interior lining, or both. Piping, too, must meet standards requiring cathodic protection and a corrosion-resistant coating, or an encasement of noncorrodible material for piping systems.

Leak-detection requirements apply to new petroleum and hazardous substance UST systems. Because leaks from hazardous substances are more difficult to detect than are those from petroleum tanks, the resulting requirements are more stringent and mandate secondary containment systems and monitoring devices. Federal law does not cover heating oil tanks, although some state jurisdictions do.

Regulations can be found in 40 CFR 280–284 that address all UST systems. Existing systems installed before 1988 were required to meet standards for spill, overfill, and corrosion protection, or to be removed prior to December 22, 1998. Systems installed today must be in full compliance with 40 CFR 280.20—Performance Standards.

Proper closure and removal of a UST requires the following prior to removal:

- notification of the regulatory authority at least 30 days beforehand
- determination of releases from the UST and contamination of surrounding soils or groundwater
- emptying and proper disposal of tank contents in accordance with confined-space protocols

Some tanks can be filled with inert material (sand, stone, or concrete) rather than removed. However, local and state regulations vary in allowing this.

Regulatory Enforcement

The EPA or authorized state has three enforcement options under RCRA:

- administrative sanctions or penalties
- civil penalties
- criminal penalties

Administrative sanctions or penalties are nonjudicial enforcement actions taken by either the EPA or the state. There are two types: informal actions and administrative orders (i.e., compliance orders and corrective action orders). The maximum penalty is $25,000 per day of noncompliance for each violation.

Civil penalties involve a formal lawsuit against a person who has failed to comply with some statutory/regulatory requirement or administrative order. There are four types of civil penalties: compliance action, corrective action, monitoring and analysis, and imminent hazard. The maximum penalty is the same; $25,000 per day of noncompliance for each violation.

Criminal penalties are incurred by knowingly committing any of the following seven criminal acts under RCRA Section 3008:

1. Transporting waste to a nonpermitted facility.
2. Treating, storing, or disposing of waste without a permit.
3. Omitting information/false statement in any application, label, manifest, record, report, permit, or compliance document.
4. Not complying with record-keeping and reporting requirements.
5. Transporting without a manifest.
6. Exporting waste without the consent of receiving country.
7. Action resulting in imminent danger.

The maximum penalties are:

- $50,000 per day of violation and 2 years in prison
- $100,000 per day and 4 years in prison (for repeat offenses)
- $250,000 per day and 15 years in prison for an individual or $1 million for an organization (applicable to #7 only).

The seventh criminal act is the knowing transportation, treatment, storage, disposal, or export of any hazardous waste in such a way that another person is placed in imminent danger of death or serious bodily injury. This act carried a possible penalty of up to $250,000 or 15 years in prison for an individual or a $1 million fine for corporate entities (EPA 2008b).

Repeat offenses not only apply if a repeat offense has occurred in the same facility, but such offenses that occur in company facilities at different locations or states can be construed as repeat offenses, carrying the heavier fine and prison sentence. Therefore, if one facility in an organization is cited for a RCRA violation that carries a "fine and time," there should be a mechanism in place to communicate the violation to the rest of the company.

Property Transfers

CERCLA (Comprehensive Environmental Response, Compensation and Liability Act of 1980) establishes liability for clean up of sites that present a threat to human health and the environment because of the presence of hazardous substances and places the responsibility and liability for clean-up costs on those responsible for the contamination.

Liability and responsibility for clean up is established for a facility where a release or threatened release of a hazardous substance "causes the incurrence of response costs." The *potentially responsible party* (PRP) is either the current or prior owner/operator, the "arranger" (for disposal or treatment of hazardous substances at a facility), or the "transporter" (of hazardous substances to the facility). Liability can be transferred whether the property is acquired by land contract, deed, easement or lease of the property on which hazardous substances are placed.

The Superfund Amendments and Reauthorization Act (SARA 1986) established an innocent landowner defense by which a potentially responsible party (PRP) of a contaminated facility is not held liable if the PRP acquires ownership after disposal or placement of hazardous substances on the property, did not know and had no reason to know the property was contaminated, exercised due care, and took reasonable precautions.

Reasonable Precautions

A prospective purchaser of a commercial property should ensure that he or she is covered by the innocent landowner defense by performing or having performed an investigation of the history of the property. The history should show what chemicals were used on site, how they were disposed of (whether on site or off site), and what types of products and processes occurred on site. These reasonable precautions have been formalized by the American Society for Testing and Materials (now ASTM International) as published in its standard, E1527, "Environmental Site Assessments:

Phase I Environmental Site Assessment Process." This standard is the guide most consultants follow in performing a due diligence investigation on property to be acquired (ASTM 2005).

Phase I Environmental Site Assessment

The purpose of the Phase I Environmental Site Assessment is to provide "all appropriate inquiry" (AAI) into potential liabilities in the purchase of properties with potential environmental risks in order to qualify for an "innocent landowner defense" under SARA, under which "all appropriate inquiry" is not clearly defined (SARA 1986).

Industry standards were amended by the Small Business Liability Relief and Brownfields Revitalization Act (P.L. 107-118), which was enacted in January 2002 and took effect in November 2006. The purpose of the amendments was to relieve small businesses of the cost of environmental remediation and to encourage the development of Brownfield sites. Brownfield sites are defined by this law as "real property, the expansion, redevelopment, or reuse of which may be complicated by the presence or potential presence of a hazardous substance, pollutant, or contaminant." Certain legal exclusions apply.

The effects of these regulations on environmental professionals include changes in the due diligence process and new definitions of AAI. ASTM E1527 has also been revised to incorporate changes in the law, and ASTM E1527-05 is now considered the standard of care (ASTM 2005).

The EPA has developed several guidance documents regarding the amendments. Although there are many common elements between the 2000 and the 2005 ASTM standard that incorporates AAI, there are also significant changes.

For example, under the ASTM Standard, an *environmental professional* is defined as an individual with training and experience sufficient to conduct the assessment and provide the required opinion and conclusions. Note that some states require those doing site assessments to be licensed. Under the new amendments, specific qualifications of training and experience are for the first time delineated in describing environmental professionals (a minimum of five years' experience and a Bachelor's degree in a related program). Greater responsibility is also imposed upon environmental professionals in determining what to do with contamination once it is discovered. The uniqueness of each site is also recognized, and greater emphasis is placed upon judgment than upon standardization.

Under both protocols, the process of conducting a Phase I Environmental Site Assessment begins with a review of current and historical public records regarding the site. These may include building permits, Sanborn maps (described below), topographical maps, aerial photographs, and commercially available databases that map registered tanks, leaking underground storage tank incidents, RCRA generators, disposal facilities, and so forth. Sources of information may also include the federal EPA, state environmental offices, local or regional publicly owned treatment works (POTWs), offices of the States' Fire Marshalls, municipal water sources, commercial waste transporters, and local government (city and county) departments of buildings, public health, engineering and planning, fire protection, and waste. Histories and previous use records are also included for adjoining sites, which may have an environmental impact on the site in question.

Building permits often identify previous business uses, tank installation, or even the installation of monitoring wells, and so on. Often the exact dates of tank installation will be available from either local code officials or from state environmental offices.

Sanborn maps or other historical fire protection maps, used for insurance purposes, are a source of information regarding previous uses of the property. They are often particularly good sources of information regarding underground storage tanks. (Look for small circles initialed GT, which indicate gasoline tanks.) These maps are published about every decade and can reveal old tanks that may have been subsequently removed. According to copyright law, these maps must be purchased if they are to be included in a report.

Topological maps will help determine the direction of flow of a potential plume of contamination or whether a particular site is upstream from a source of drinking water.

Aerial photographs, also taken every decade, can show the use of a site. A site undeveloped 40 years ago might have been a gas station 30 years ago and a shopping center 20 years ago.

Research is followed by a site visit in which key personnel are interviewed and the site examined for signs of environmental issues that might not have surfaced in the research.

The final report contains observations and conclusions related to the apparent environmental conditions of the site and includes a description of the site conditions encountered, notations of records reviewed, and commentary regarding possible environmental effects.

A report written in accordance with generally accepted professional standards should not be construed as a guarantee or warranty of the potential liability associated with environmental conditions or effects on the site.

Please note that many companies offer Phase I assessments or provide historical information about environmental issues on site. Site-specific and customer-detailed Phase I assessments may be purchased from many vendors.

Should environmental or other issues be noted, a Phase II investigation may be recommended.

Phase II Environmental Site Investigations

The function of a Phase I investigation is to identify potential issues, but a Phase II investigation looks at a suspected site to verify the presence of environmental conditions that have negatively impacted a property. Specific geological and analytical chemistry data will be sought.

In the case of surface or subsurface soil contamination, soil borings are conducted around a tank or in the vicinity of a spill. The number of borings depends upon the size of the tank or the area of the spill.

A magnetic survey may be conducted to determine the presence or location of a tank. Samples are taken on the surface or every two feet until the desired depth is reached. A photoionization detector (PID) will screen the sample in the field for the presence of volatile organic contamination. After field screening, samples are collected.

Samples indicating the highest volatile contamination are then analyzed with gas chromatography/mass spectroscopy using the EPA Method 8260, volatile organics protocol, and the EPA Method 8270, semivolatile organics protocol, or are analyzed for specific constituents, such as RCRA metals, PCBs, and so on, using atomic absorption or inductively coupled plasma spectroscopy.

Monitoring wells may be installed if the contaminant zone is suspected of affecting groundwater. Suspect building materials may be analyzed for asbestos, lead, and mold.

Corrective Action to Clean Up Hazardous Waste Contamination

Where releases of hazardous wastes cause contamination of soil and groundwater, the EPA requires remediation to restore the land and water to acceptable limits. RCRA permits are withheld until such incidents have been adequately addressed. This process is sometimes known as Phase III.

Remediation

If contamination is found, a determination is made based on the impact of the contamination on the site. Risk-Based Corrective Action (RBCA) has been implemented in every state. This allows the state to establish limits of contamination for specific chemicals or for contamination that has a limited threat to human health and the environment (either because of naturally occurring geology or engineered barriers) to remain *in situ*.

Often, if a plume of contamination has spread, additional samples must be taken in order to determine how deep or how far contamination has spread. Recommendations are then made communicating whether the site requires remediation.

A remediation plan will be guided by state RBCA measures. Remediation may involve digging up contaminated soil and transporting it to a landfill. A "pump-and-treat" operation may be installed to remediate contaminated groundwater. More and more frequently, strategies involving biological oxidation or degradation are being employed. Levels of con-

tamination may be further mitigated by the use of engineering controls or administrative work practices.

Engineering Controls and Administrative Work Practices

In remedial activities, engineering controls might include the use of a cap on a site to discourage further attenuation of contamination. Administrative controls may be used, such as an agreement with the local authority to leave contamination under a street in such a way as to negligibly affect human health and the environment.

Construction Workplan

In cases in which hazardous waste must be remediated, the permit will require a construction workplan documenting the overall management strategy, construction quality-assurance procedures, and a schedule for constructing the corrective measure.

The elements required in a construction workplan using a project management approach must describe organization; lines of communication; qualifications of key personnel; the project schedule; the construction quality assurance/quality control program; waste management procedures; any sampling and monitoring activities that may be needed; a quality assurance project plan (QAPP) to ensure that all information, data, and resulting decisions are technically sound, statistically valid, and properly documented; construction contingency procedures for notification of the agency of unforeseen changes, problems, or emergencies; evaluation, documentation, and management procedures of analytical data and results; and a cost estimate and financial assurance section. Financial assurance mechanisms are used to assure the implementing agency that the project has adequate financial resources to implement and sustain the corrective measure.

The construction workplan must include a cost estimate describing construction, operation, and maintenance costs, and specifying the financial mechanism that will be used. The financial assurance mechanism is covered in 40 CFR 265.143 (EPA 2010b).

All monitoring procedures, sampling, field measurements, and sample analysis performed during these activities must be documented. Approved quality assurance, quality control, and chain-of-custody procedures must be used. Guidance may be found in the *EPA Requirements for Quality Assurance Project Plans* (EPA 2001b).

Construction safety procedures will be specified in a separate health and safety plan.

Construction Completion Report

A construction completion (CC) report documenting how the completed project is consistent with the final plans and specifications will include the synopsis of the corrective measure, design criteria, and certification that the corrective measure was constructed in accordance with the final plans and specifications; an explanation and description of any modifications to the final plans and specifications and why these were necessary; the results of any operational testing or monitoring, indicating how initial operation of the corrective measure compares to the design criteria; a summary of significant activities that occurred during construction, including a discussion of problems encountered and how they were addressed; a summary of any inspection findings (including copies of key inspection documents listed in appendices); "as built" drawings or photographs; and a schedule indicating when any treatment systems will begin full-scale operation (EPA 1994).

Monitoring Plans

Monitoring plans are covered in 40 CFR 268.6, and examples are given on the EPA Web site (EPA 2010c).

BENCHMARKS AND PERFORMANCE APPRAISAL CRITERIA IN ENVIRONMENTAL MANAGEMENT

With the myriad aspects of environmental management, operating within permitted limits is the critical benchmarking criteria.

Compliance Defines the Baseline

The movement away from traditional compliance models of environmental management to environmental management systems (EMS) does not change the requirements of management and staff to maintain operations within permitted limits. A model that measures, tracks, and encourages improvements in operations still holds compliance more important than all other elements.

ISO 14001 incorporates measuring and monitoring requirements, and not merely for permit compliance. The EMS extends to documenting such elements of an EHS program as what is tested, when it is tested, and how it is sampled and tested. Key to the EMS process is the establishment of performance tracking and monitoring for improvement. These monitoring criteria are also modeled in the EMS.

For some operations, benchmarking this compliance framework becomes very straightforward. If a waste does not meet certain threshold levels, it will not be disposed of in a designated landfill. Other environmental operations require more tweaking to stay compliant, such as wastewater treatment systems.

Benchmarking a UST Operation

More often than not, current UST operation requires routine monitoring activities, such as tightness testing and leak detection. Many times, monitoring test wells are installed alongside UST cavities to allow for routine groundwater testing.

Environmental Site Assessments

The environmental site assessment, investigation, and remediation process on contaminated properties involves benchmarking activities at every step. From identifying potential issues in Phase I to investigating the actual presence and perhaps extent of contamination in Phase II to the development of remedial strategies, the EHS professional is responding to available data from previous assessments to chart the course for each next step. In determining the impact of contamination, the EHS manager must determine what is contaminating the property and at what concentrations, where on the property the release occurred and how far and how deep it has migrated, whether it has impacted groundwater or nearby surface waters, and whether it has migrated to neighboring sites or public ways. Both field-screening measures [photoionization detectors (PIDs) or flame ionization detectors (FIDs)] and laboratory analyses are used.

Risk-Based Corrective Action (RBCA)

Risk-based corrective action is a streamlined approach in which exposure and risk-assessment practices are integrated with traditional components of the corrective action process to ensure that appropriate and cost-effective remedies are selected and that limited resources are properly allocated.

Risk-based corrective action measures allow contamination under certain threshold limits to remain *in situ*. Each state has its own rules, which may be more stringent than federal regulations. Sampling and analysis will extend into the remedial period. Where soil is taken, sampling assures that what is left is below the state's clean-up objectives. Soil removed must be tested to determine disposal criteria.

Where other clean-up strategies are used, the soil treated must be tested to ensure that it complies with the state's clean-up objectives.

Often, the state will allow contamination to remain with the imposition of engineering controls or administrative work practices. Among these may be ongoing sampling and monitoring activities. For example, there may be a requirement to monitor groundwater for a specified period of time to assure that no further contamination occurs.

Cost Analysis and Budgeting

Potential Areas of Loss from Hazardous Waste

The conventional economic wisdom associated with hazardous waste operations is that prevention of the generation and associated costs of collection, transportation, treatment, storage, and disposal of hazardous waste is the economically prudent as well as the environmentally sensitive course of action. In addition, the expensive potential financial and criminal penalties associated with infractions of hazardous waste laws

and regulations encourage a prudent course of action in compliance. This section examines the potential exposure to economic loss associated with the treatment, storage, and disposal of hazardous waste.

To fully determine the cost of waste disposal requires that a company determine both the fixed and variable cost of the product from inception to final delivery—or, in other words, the life-cycle cost of the product. Every product manufactured in any country of the world has a myriad of costs associated with its development, manufacture, storage prior to sale, and sales and delivery. Several countries (for example, Germany) have also imposed a cost of disposal of packaging materials and a cost of disposal of the product when it no longer serves it purpose. To undertake such a complete analysis is outside the scope of this chapter, but certain practices will be informative to discuss.

Initial design is where life-cycle cost savings begin. It is the designer who will determine what materials will be used in the product and how to best recycle either the product or its components once the product's life is spent.

Manufacturing can look at cost savings by ensuring that employees have the training and tools necessary to do their jobs properly and correctly the first time. Once materials have been found to be of no use in the process, they are a waste—either a nonregulated waste, a solid waste, or a hazardous waste. Regardless, there is a cost for disposal of such materials.

EHS is usually looked upon as a cost center. However, it can become a profit center by back-charging each department for the disposal of their waste materials. This provides a very important step. Rather than spread the cost of waste disposal over the fixed costs of the company, it places the costs of disposal where it should be—onto the product or the department that generated those wastes so that the actual cost of the product or of that department can be calculated.

Cost-Benefit Analysis

The application of cost-benefit analysis to hazardous waste operations can effectively identify economic solutions to the control of generation of hazardous waste and resulting costs of collection, transportation, treatment, storage, and disposal. The methodology of cost-benefit analysis is available from a number of sources: An excellent step-by-step explanation of the cost-benefit process is contained in the *Cost Analysis for Pollution Prevention* (Washington State 2005).

BEST PRACTICES IN ENVIRONMENTAL MANAGEMENT

The emphasis of environmental management is shifting from traditional "command and control" compliance to management systems. EMS are being implemented by corporations operating globally—often in multiple locations.

In the United States and in many other parts of the world, public pressure and regulatory requirements have given companies the incentive to implement pollution-prevention and sustainability measures.

As previously discussed, going beyond compliance, such as material substitutions and process changes, to achieve waste reduction and developing sustainability programs are measures that exceed the mandates of waste minimization under RCRA.

But beyond well-known and well-practiced strategies to achieve compliance in any given situation, EHS managers are being challenged to think strategically about their operations in order to meet the growing demand for a sustainable economy.

Green construction, using Leadership in Energy and Environmental Design (LEED) from the United States Green Building Council (www.usbgc.org), helps to maximize energy conservation and adaptive reuse, alternative energy from biofuels, and a myriad of other technologies that have moved beyond the demonstration phase to a level where viable models are being replicated worldwide. City governments are fostering this initiative as a way of reducing wastes and increasing renewable resources.

Waste Management

Waste management is a natural partner in such initiatives. For example, when the waste from one operation can be used as fuel for another and those operations colocated to minimize transportation, significant energy savings can be achieved.

The solid waste hierarchy represents baseline environmental management. It prioritizes waste management practices to encourage the use of source reduction, recycling, and reuse. These practices have less impact on the environment than incineration and landfilling. The waste disposal options that are chosen as best practices are those that maximize waste diversion into other processes, have lower harmful emissions, and have the best safety record. An incineration technology that produces energy would be considered preferable to one that does not.

Recent developments in gasification and digestion technologies show promise for producing energy with no emissions. Although landfilling and deep-well injection are generally considered less desirable than other forms of waste disposal, a landfill that collects methane is considered superior to one that does not.

Waste exchanges operate in virtually every state. They distribute catalogues of wastes that are available for use as raw materials by other companies. The Southern Waste Information eXchange (SWIX) (www.swix.ws) and the California Materials Exchange (CalMAX) (www.calrecycle.ca.gov/CalMax) are examples, or just do an internet search on the term "materials exchange."

Remediation Technology Development

Technologies continue to emerge that address contamination remaining on properties. *In situ flushing* is accomplished by injecting an aqueous solution into a contaminated soil or groundwater zone and then extracting and treating the elutriate. Phytotechnology uses various plants to extract contaminants from soil and water. Other treatment technologies, including activated carbon treatment, air stripping, bioremediation, oxidation, fracturing, natural attenuation, vapor extraction, air sparging, solvent extraction, and vitrification are addressed on the EPA's Web site (EPA 2008c).

SUMMARY/CONCLUSION

Hazardous waste management involves a complex legal structure and technical competence in many disciplines. An EHS manager must have knowledge and understanding of the waste streams generated by an operation, as well as of their permitting, monitoring, and reporting requirements, and the measures that must be taken in the event of release. Many guidelines are available, for which a number of references have been cited. When questions remain, remember that an entire industry is available to provide technical assistance on the management of hazardous waste or the clean up of sites where improper handling has occurred. Care should be taken in hiring hazardous waste consultants, brokers, laboratories, transporters, or disposal firms who must be verified to be properly permitted, licensed, and insured.

REFERENCES

American Society for Testing and Materials (ASTM). 2005. ASTM Standard E1527-05, *Environmental Site Assessments: Phase I Environmental Site Assessment Process*. West Conshohocken, PA: ASTM.

Atomic Energy Act of 1954. P.L. 83-703, 42 U.S.C. §2011 *et seq.* www.nrc.gov/reading-rm/doc-collections/nuregs/staff/sr0980/ml22200075-vol1.pdf#pagemode=bookmarks&page=14

Comprehensive Environmental Response, Compensation and Liability Act of 1980 (CERCLA or Superfund). 42 U.S.C. §9601 *et seq.* www.epa/gov/superfund/policy/remedy/pdfs/cercla/pdf

Department of Transportation (DOT). 2010. *Comprehensive Safety Analysis 2010* (retrieved July 28, 2010). www.csa2010.fmcsa.dot.gov

Environmental Protection Agency (EPA). 1994. OSWER Directive 9902.3-2A, "RCRA Corrective Action Plan (Final)" (May). www.epa.wastes/hazard/corrective action/resources/guidamce/gen_ca/rcracap/pdf

————. 1995. 40 CFR 280, "Technical Standards and Corrective Action Requirements for Owners and Operators of Underground Storage Tanks (UST)" (retrieved July 29, 2011). ecfr.gpoaccess.gov/cgi/t/text/text=idx?c=ecfr&sid=a91168e9620c9d76056cd1efaaa8cb&rgn=div5&view=text&node=40.27.0.1.1.10&idno+40

————. 2001a. EPA 530-K-01-005, *Managing Your Hazardous Waste: A Guide for Small Businesses* (December). www.epa.gov/wastes/hazard/generation/sgg/k01005.txt

————. 2001b. EPA QA/R-5. *Requirements for Quality Assurance Project Plans for Environmental Data Operations* (March). www.epa.gov/quality/qs-docs/r5-final.pdf

————. 2002. EPA-K-02-027, *25 Years of RCRA: Building on Our Past To Protect Our Future* (April). www.epa.gov/wastes/inforesources/pubs/k02027.pdf

————. 2005a. *RCRA, Superfund and EPCRA Call Center Training Module: Introduction to Generators*. (September). www.epa.gov/wastes/inforesources/pubs/hotline/training/trans.pdf

————. 2005b. 40 CFR 273. "Standards for Universal Waste Management." ecfr.gpoaccess.gov/cgi/t/text/text-idx?c=ecfr+3796b14b055e3c42d8adb6d1371f51b&rgn=div5&view=text&node=40:26.0.1.1.4&idno=40

————. 2005c. Form 8700-22, "Uniform Hazardous Waste Manifest" (June). www.epa.gov/wastes/hazard/transportation/manifest/pdf/manfst-cn.pdf

————. 2006a. *Hazardous Waste Incineration*. www.epa.gov/wastes/hazard/testmethods/sw846/pdfs/chap13/pdf

————. 2006b. *RCRA Orientation Manual, 2006*, www.epa.gov/epawaste/inforesources/pubs/orientat/rom.pdf

————. 2007a. "National Biennial RCRA Hazardous Waste Report." www.epa.gov/osw/inforesources/data/biennialreport/

————. 2007b. *CERCLA Overview*. www.epa.gov/superfund/policy/cercla.htm

————. 2007c. *Introduction to the Hazard Ranking System (HRS)*. www.epa.gov/superfund/programs/npl_hrs/hrsint.htm

————. 2007d. *Municipal Waste Combustion*. www.epa.gov/wastes/nonhaz/municipal/index.htm

————. 2007e. "National Priorities List (NPL)." www.epa.gov/superfund/sites/npl/index.htm

————. 2007f. *RCRA Online*. www.epa.gov/rcraonline

————. 2007g. 40 CFR 721, "Significant New Uses of Chemical Substances." ecfr.gpoaccess.gov/cgi/t/text/text-idx?c=ecfr&sid=ef220cad185d504c5471c4a11a9858cd&rgn=div5&view=text&node=40:30.0.1.1.10&idno=40

————. 2007h. *Special Wastes*. www.epa.gov/wastes/nonhaz/industrial/special/

————. 2007i. "*What is the Toxics Release Inventory (TRI) Program?* www.epa.gov/tri/whatis.htm

————. 2008a. 20 CFR 172, "Environmental Use Permits" (retrieved August 1, 2011). ecfr.gpoaccess.gov/cgi/t/text/text-idx?c=ecfr&sid=f4702581cd85b2176341a134acdf3b812&rgn=div&view=text&node=40.0.1.1.22&idno=40

————. 2008b. *Frequent Questions About Recycling and Waste Management*. www.epa.gov/epawaste/nonhaz/municipal/index.html#1

————. 2008c. *Remediation; Phytotechnology Project Profiles*. www.epa.gov/superfund/remedytech/remed.htm#tech

————. 2008d. SW-846, *Test Methods for Evaluating Solid Waste, Physical/Chemical Methods*. www.epa.gov/epawaste/hazard/testmethods/se846/index.htm

————. 2008e. *Orientation Manual*, Section III: RCRA Subtitle C--Managing Hazardous Waste, Chapter 10, "Engorcement of Hazardous Waste," III134-III135 (retrieved August 1, 2011). www.epa.gov/wastes/inforesources/pubs/orientat/rom310.pdf

————. 2009. Notification of RCRA Subtitle C Activity, Instruction and Form. EPA Form 8700-12, "Notification of Regulated Waste Activity" (July). www.epa.gov/wastes/inforesources/data/form8700/8700-12.pdf

_____. 2010a. 40 CFR 255, "Identification of Regions and Agencies for Solid Waste Management" (retrieved July 29, 2011). ecfr.gpraccess.cgi.t.text.text=if?c=ecfr&sid=a119b70g22c16a8ce1b48a1661919d19&rgn=div5&view=text& node=40.25.0.1.4.3&idno=40

_____. 2010b. 40 CFR 265, "Interim Standards for Owners and Operators of Hazardous Waste Treatment, Storage, and Disposal Facilities" (retrieved August 1, 2011). ecfr.gpoaccess.gov/cgi/t/text/text=idx?c=ecfr&sid=f470258cd85b176341acdf3b812&rgn=div5&view=text and node 40-26.0.1.1&idno=40

_____. 2010c. 40 CFR 268, "Land Disposal Restrictions." ecfr.gpoaccess.gov/cgi/t/text/text-idx?c=ecfr&sid=a91168e96200c6976065cd1ef4aaa8bc&rgn=div5&view=text&node=40:26.0.1.1.3&idno=40

_____. 2010d. 40 CFR 263, "Standards Applicable to Transportation of Hazardous Waste." ecfr.gpoaccess.gov/cgi/t/text/text-idx?c+ecfr&sid=379b614b055e3c42d8adb6d1371f51b&rgn=div5&view=text&node=40:26.0.1.1.4&idno=40

_____. 2010e. 40 CFR 266, "Standards for the Management of Specific Hazardous Wastes and Specific Types of Hazardous Waste Management Facilities" ecft.gpoaccess.gov/cgi/t/text/text=idx?sid=9f676a5375d650278f4362b9732e22&c=ecfr&pl=ecftbrowse/Title40cfrv27_20.tpl

_____. 2010f. 40 CFR 261, "Identification and Listing of Hazardous Waste" gpoaccess.gov/cgi/t/text/text_idx?c=ecfr&sid=a060ffb5c961de457c26bb1368f&rgn=div8&view=text&node=40:26.0.1.1.1&idno=40

_____. 2011. EPA 550-B-10-001, "List of Lists; Consolidated List of Chemicals Subject to the Emergency Planning and Community Right to Know Act (EPCRA) and Section 112(r) of the Clean Air Act" (July). (retrieved September 13, 2011) www.epa.gov/oem/docs/chem/list_of_lists_revised_7_26_11.pdf

Esty, Daniel C., Marc Levy, Tanja Srebotnjak, and Alexander de Sherbinin. 2005. *2005 Environmental Sustainability Index: Benchmarking National Environmental Stewardship*. New Haven, CT: Yale Center for Environmental Law & Policy. www.yale.edu/esi/ESI2005_Main_Report.pdf

Federal Facility Compliance Act of 1992. P. L. 102-386. www.epa.gov/fedfac/documents/ffc92.htm

Hazardous and Solid Waste Amendments of 1984 (HSWA), Pub. L. 98-616, 98 Stat. 3221 (November 8). www.cq.com/graphics/sal/98/sal98-616.pdf

Medical Waste Tracking Act of 1988 (MWTA). 42 U.S.C. 82, Subchapter X. www.epa.gov/epawaste/nonhaz/industrial/medical/tracking.htm

National Environmental Policy Act of 1969 (NEPA). P. L. 91-190, 42 U.S.C. 4321-4347. www.nepa.gov/nepa/regs/nepa/nepaeqia.htm

Occupational Health and Safety Administration (OSHA). 1978. 29 CFR 1910.1025, "Occupational Safety and Health Standards; Lead." ecfr.gpoaccess.gov/cgi/t/text/text-idx?c=ecfr&sid= 07658e28ffa5a495eae41c01c6ec0f2e&rgn=div5&view=text&node=29:6.1.1.1.1&idno=29#29:6.1.1.1.1.1.22

_____. 1980. 29 CFR 1910.38, "Emergency Action Plans." www.osha.gov/pls/oshweb/owadisp.show_document?table+STANDARDS&p_id=9726

_____. 1986. 29 CFR 1926.1101, "Toxic and Hazardous Substances; Asbestos." www.osha..gov/pls/oshaweb/owadisp.show_documents?p_tables+STANDARDS&p_id=10862

_____. 1993. 29 CFR 1926.62, "Health and Environmental Controls; Lead." www.osha,giv/SLTC/lead/construction.html

_____. 1994. 29 CFR 1910.1200, "Hazardous Communications." www.osha.gov/oshaweb/owadisp.show_document?p_table=STANDARDS&p_id=10099

_____. 1996. 29 CFR 1910.120, "Hazardous Waste Operations and Emergency Response (HAZWOPER)." www.osha.gov/pls/oshaweb/owadisp.show_document?p_table=STANDARD&p_id=9765

Peart, Karen & Dave DeFusco. 2005. "Finland Tops Environmental Scorecard at World Economic Forum in Davos." Yale Press Release (January 26). www.yale.edu/opa/newsr/05-01-26-02.all.html

Pipeline and Hazardous Materials Safety Administration. 2008. *Emergency Response Guide* (retrieved August 1, 2011). www.phmsa.dot.gov/statisfiles/PHMSA/DownloadableFile/Files/erg2008_eng.pdf

Prince William Soundkeeper. 1989. "*Exxon Valdez* Oil Spill." www.pws.wildapricot.org/Default.aspx?pageid+553853

Resource Conservation and Recovery Act (RCRA) of 1976. 42 U.S.C. §6901 *et seq.* frwebgate.access.gpo.gov/cgi-bin/usc.cgi?ACTION=BROWSE&TITLE=42USCC82

Small Business Liability Relief and Brownfields Revitalization Act. 2002. P.L. 107-118. www.osha.gov/fdsys/pkg/PLAW-107pub118/pdf/PLAW-107pub118.pdf

Solid Waste Disposal Act. 1965. P.L. 89 - 272, 79 Stat. 997, as added (October 20, 1965). epw.senate.gov/rcra.pdf

Superfund Amendments and Reauthorization Act of 1986 (SARA). frwebgate.access.gpo.gov/cgi/-bin/usc.cgi?ACTION=BROWSE&TITLE=42USCC103

Toxic Substances Control Act of 1976 (TSCA), P.L. 94-469, 15 U.S.C. §2601 *et seq.* www.epa.gov/lawsregs/laws/tsca.htm

Washington State Department of Ecology. 2005. Publication No 95-400, *Cost Analysis for Pollution Prevention* (Revised April). ecy.wa.gov/pubs/95400.pdf

APPENDIX A: ACRONYMS AND ABBREVIATIONS

ASTM: American Society for Testing and Materials

CAA: Clean Air Act

CAMU: Corrective Action Management Unit

CERCLA: Comprehensive Environmental Response, Compensation, and Liability Act

CERCLIS: Comprehensive Environmental Response, Compensation, and Liability Information System

CESQG: Conditionally Exempt Small Quantity Generator

CFC: Chlorofluorocarbon

CFR: *Code of Federal Regulations*

DOT: Department of Transportation

EPA ID number: Environmental Protection Agency Identification Number

EPCRA: Emergency Planning and Community Right-to-Know Act

HAZWOPER: Hazardous Waste Operations and Emergency Response Worker Protection Standard

HRS: Hazard Ranking System

HSWA: Hazardous and Solid Waste Amendments

kg: kilogram

lb: pound

LDR: Land Disposal Restrictions

LQG: Large-Quantity Generator

LUST: Leaking Underground Storage Tank

NCP: National Oil and Hazardous Substances Pollution Contingency Plan

NESHAP: National Emission Standards for Hazardous Air Pollutants

NPDES: National Pollutant Discharge Elimination System

NPL: National Priorities List

OPA: Oil Pollution Act

OSHA: Occupational Safety and Health Act

OSWER: Office of Solid Waste and Emergency Response

PCB: Polychlorinated Biphenyl

POTW: Publicly Owned Treatment Works

ppm: parts per million

PRP: Potentially Responsible Party

RBCA: Risk-Based Corrective Action

RBDM: Risk-Based Decision-Making

RCRA: Resource Conservation and Recovery Act

RCRIS: Resource Conservation and Recovery Act Information System

SARA: Superfund Amendments and Reauthorization Act

SPCC: Spill Prevention, Control, and Countermeasures

SQG: Small-Quantity Generator

SWDA: Solid Waste Disposal Act

SWMU: Solid Waste Management Unit

TCLP: Toxicity Characteristic Leaching Procedure

TSCA: Toxic Substances Control Act

TSDF: Treatment, Storage, and Disposal Facility

UST: Underground Storage Tank

APPENDIX B: RCRA AND SOLID WASTE RESOURCES

HOTLINES

Emergency Planning Community Right-to-Know Hotline CERCLA (SARA, Title III) 8:30 AM–7:30 PM ET	1-800-424-9346
EPA Hotline (Region V)	1-800-621-8431
EPA RCRA, Superfund, Hazardous Waste Hotline Office of Solid Waste and Emergency Response 8:30 AM–7:30 PM ET	1-800-424-9346
National Response Center/Coast Guard Command (Report spills, chemical releases, radiological incidents)	1-800-424-8802
Solid Waste Assistance Program	1-800-677-9424

ORGANIZATIONS

Environmental Protection Agency (EPA)
1200 Pennsylvania, NW
Washington, DC 20460   1-202-260-2090

EPA Web Site   www.epa.gov

EPA Region 1	(Boston, Massachusetts)	1-617-918-1111
EPA Region 2	(New York, New York)	1-212-637-3000
EPA Region 3	(Philadelphia, Pennsylvania)	1-215-814-5000
EPA Region 4	(Atlanta, Georgia)	1-404-562-9900

EPA Region 5   (Chicago, Illinois)   1-312-353-2000
EPA Region 6   (Dallas, Texas)   1-214-665-6444
EPA Region 7   (Kansas City, Kansas)   1-913-551-7003
EPA Region 8   (Denver, Colorado)   1-303-312-6312
EPA Region 9   (San Francisco, California)   1-415-947-8000
EPA Region 10   (Seattle, Washington)   1-206-553-1200

Public Information Center
401 M Street SW
Washington, DC 20460   1-202-260-7751

This EPA subsidiary maintains a wide selection of publications on major environmental topics. The materials distributed by PIC are nontechnical, and have been prepared as sources of general environmental information for the public.

RCRA Docket Information Center (RIC)
U.S. Environmental Protection Agency
RCRA Docket Information Center (5305W)
401 M Street, SW.
Washington, DC 20460   1-703-603-9230

Holds and provides public access to all regulatory materials on solid waste and distributes technical and nontechnical information on solid waste.

U.S. Government Printing Office
Superintendent of Documents
Post Office Box 371954
Pittsburgh, PA 15250-7954   1-202-512-1800

More than 15,000 books, pamphlets, posters, periodicals, subscription services, and other government publications are available for purchase from the Superintendent of Documents.

U.S. Department of Labor
Occupational Safety and Health Administration
200 Constitution Avenue, N.W.   1-202-693-2000
Washington, D.C. 20210   www.osha.gov

U.S. Department of Transportation
Hazardous Material Information Center   1-800-467-4922
Department of Energy – EH&S Home Page   www.tis.eh.doe.gov
Environmental Industry Web Site   www.enviroindustry.com

PROFESSIONAL SOCIETIES/ASSOCIATIONS and PRIVATE AGENCIES

Alliance of Hazardous Materials Professionals (AHMP)
Post Office Box 1216
Rockville, Maryland 20849   1-800-437-0137
Home Page   www.achmm.org

Established in 1985, the AHMP is a nonprofit membership organization dedicated to fostering professional development through continuing education, peer group interaction, the exchange of ideas, and information relating to hazardous materials management.

Air and Waste Management Association
1 Gateway Center, 3rd Floor
420 Fort Duquesne Boulevard
Pittsburgh, Pennsylvania 15222   1-412-232-3444
Home Page   www.awma.org

The Air and Waste Management Association is a nonprofit technical, scientific and educational organization with more than 14,000 members in 65 countries. Founded in 1907, the Association provides a forum where all viewpoints of an environmental issue (technical, scientific, economic, social, political, and risk assessment) receive consideration.

American Society of Safety Engineers
Environmental Practice Specialty
1800 East Oakton Street
Des Plaines, Illinois 60018-2187   1-847-699-2929
Home Page   www.ASSE.org

The ASSE Environmental Practice Specialty targets members with formal education and experience in safety management, engineering, chemistry, health, physics, toxicology, management, and training.

Environmental Document Service
Ben Franklin Station
Post Office Box 7167
Washington, DC 20044   1-800-424-9068

A document service providing copies of environmental legislation, legal decisions and court filings, EPA rules, Superfund plans, and policy statements and directives.

Environmental Hazards Management Institute
10 Newmarket Road
Post Office Box 932
Durham, North Carolina 03824   1-603-868-1496

A nonprofit environmental consulting corporation specializing in environmental and regulatory education and compliance assistance. Publishes the *Household Hazardous Waste Wheel*.

National Recycling Coalition, Inc.
1325 G Street NW, Ste. 1025
Washington, DC 20005   1-202-347-0450

Washington, DC-based association whose members distill, blend, recover, or recycle used chemicals and other hazardous and nonhazardous wastes.

APPENDIX C: LOVE CANAL–AN ENVIRONMENTAL TRAGEDY

Love Canal was originally meant to be a dream community. Instead, it is one of the most appalling U.S. environmental tragedies.

The vision of Love Canal belonged to the man for whom the three-block tract of the eastern edge of Niagara Falls, New York, was named: William T. Love. He thought that, by digging a short canal between the upper and lower Niagara River, inexpensive power could be generated to fuel the industry and homes there, and it would become a model city.

By 1910, the dream was shattered, and all that was left to commemorate Love's hope was a partial ditch where construction on the canal had begun. In the 1920s the canal was turned into a municipal and industrial dumpsite. In 1953, the Hooker Chemical Company, then owners and operators of the property, covered the canal with earth and sold it to the city for one dollar. It was a bad buy. In the late 1950s, about 100 homes and a school were built at the site. It wasn't Love's model city, but it was a solid working-class community, at least for a short while. On August 1, 1978, the lead paragraph of a story in the *New York Times* read:

> In an article prepared for the February 1978 EPA Journal, EPA Administrator for Region 2 Eckardt C. Beck wrote, regarding chemical dumpsites in general, that "even though some of these landfills have been closed down, they may stand like ticking time bombs." Just months later, Love Canal exploded. The explosion was triggered by a record amount of rainfall. Shortly thereafter the leaching began.

Twenty-five years after the Hooker Chemical Company stopped using the Love Canal as an industrial dump, 82 compounds, 11 of them suspected carcinogens, had been percolating upward through the soil and leached their contents into the backyards and basements of 100 homes and a public school built on the banks of the canal. Unusually high amounts of birth defects and miscarriages, as well as high white blood cell counts in the population, forced the New York State Health Department to respond and inquire about what was happening.

On August 7, 1978, then New York Governor Hugh Carey announced to the residents of the Canal that the state government would purchase the homes affected by the chemicals. State figures showed more than 200 homes were purchased, and all families were moved from the contaminated land.

On that same day, President Jimmy Carter approved emergency financial aid for the Love Canal area (the first emergency funds ever to be approved for a non-natural disaster).

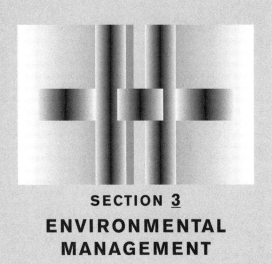

SECTION 3
ENVIRONMENTAL MANAGEMENT

LEARNING OBJECTIVES

▌ Identify the three federal agencies that regulate some aspect of hazardous material spills and releases and understand the basic roles of each.

▌ Gain an awareness of the various types of federal, public, private, and community sources of information and other assets.

▌ Know what types and sizes of spills or releases must be reported and to whom they must be reported.

▌ Gain a basic understanding of terms and concepts that relate to hazardous materials.

▌ Be able to perform a hazard assessment, and then develop and implement a site-specific emergency response plan.

▌ Understand federal hazardous materials training requirements.

▌ Learn the terms used in planning for and conducting responses to hazardous material spills or releases.

HAZARDOUS MATERIAL SPILLS AND RESPONSE

George and Cherie Walton

THE THREE PRIMARY agencies at the federal level that promulgate and enforce laws and regulations relating to spills and releases of hazardous materials are the U.S. Department of Transportation (DOT), the Environmental Protection Agency (EPA), and the Occupational Safety and Health Administration (OSHA). Because these regulations tend to intertwine and overlap, it is important to gain a general understanding of the role of each agency. The information that follows consists of significantly condensed overviews of the regulations. Complete information can be found in the appropriate section of the Code of Federal Regulations (CFR), published by the Government Printing Office.

Individual states have the right to promulgate and enforce standards that are stricter than the federal rules, except in the case of DOT regulations. According to 49 CFR 171.1(f), states may not impose provisions that are substantially different from any hazardous materials transportation law, regulation, or directive issued by the Secretary of Homeland Security.

In general, OSHA regulations apply to the safety and health of workers involved in spill clean up; EPA regulations apply to protection of the environment during and after the spill (including treatment and disposal of waste products and residues); and DOT regulations apply to the transportation of hazardous materials and waste resulting from the spill. As previously stated, agency regulations tend to overlap at times. For example, parts of DOT regulations are incorporated into EPA regulations and vice versa, and OSHA promulgated and enforces the *Hazardous Waste Operations and Emergency Response* (HAZWOPER) standard under a mandate from EPA. The resolution of any spill or release is likely to be governed by more than one federal agency as well as state and local agencies.

DEPARTMENT OF TRANSPORTATION

The mission of DOT as stated on its Web site at www.dot.gov/mission.htm is to "Serve the United States by ensuring a fast, safe, efficient, accessible and convenient transportation system that meets our vital national interests and enhances the quality of life of the American people, today and into the future."

DOT is composed of thirteen departments, nine of which are major modal, multimodal, and/or intermodal agencies. Of these agencies, the Pipeline and Hazardous Materials Safety Administration (PHMSA) provides many transportation-related safety and research services. Within PHMSA the Office of Hazardous Materials Safety is responsible for most of the regulations concerning the packaging and transportation of hazardous materials and hazardous waste in commerce.

DOT divides hazardous materials into hazard classes and divisions. A hazard class is a single-digit number—3 or 8, for example. Some hazard classes are further divided into divisions. Gases, for example, may be flammable, nonflammable, or toxic (poisonous, or pose an inhalation hazard). The general hazard class for all gases is 2. Specific hazards within the class are listed in specific divisions: flammable gases are in division 2.1; nonflammable gases are in division 2.2; and toxic, poisonous, or inhalation gases are in division 2.3.

Gases and liquids that pose an acute inhalation hazard are assigned to a Hazard Zone. In 49 CFR 171.8, "Definitions and Abbreviations," DOT defines "Hazard Zone" as one of four levels of hazard (Hazard Zones A through D) assigned to gases, as specified in 49 CFR 173.116(a), and one of two levels of hazards (Hazard Zones A and B) assigned to liquids that are poisonous by inhalation, outlined in 49 CFR 173.133(a). As specified in 49 CFR 173.133(a), the hazard zone is based on the LC_{50} value for acute inhalation toxicity of gases and vapors.

Federal Hazardous Materials Transportation Law

The hazardous materials transported in the United States are regulated by the U.S. Department of Transportation. The primary purposes of these regulations are to provide regulatory and enforcement authority to DOT to protect against the inherent risks during the transportation of hazardous materials in commerce. The Hazardous Materials Regulations (HMR) can be found in section 49 of the Code of Federal Regulations, Parts 171–178, which is generally written as 49 CFR 171–178.

The Hazardous Materials Transportation–Uniform Safety Act (HMT–USA) was enacted by Congress in 1990 to clarify conflicting state, local, and federal regulations. Additionally, this statute provides for the regulation of the transportation of radioactive materials and provides criteria for the issuance of federal permits to motor carriers of hazardous materials.

Transportation Security

Hazardous material shipments are very vulnerable when in transit. Without adequate security, tens of thousands of pounds of hazardous materials are accessible to unscrupulous individuals and groups. Some potential security risks include the theft or hijacking of vehicles carrying hazardous materials, tampering with valves on trucks or valves at tank farms, tampering with railroad equipment and cars, and tampering with other bulk transportation equipment. Additionally, forged shipping papers and fraudulent shipments of hazardous materials can put these materials in the wrong hands.

Written transportation security plans are required for organizations that offer or transport hazardous materials in commerce. The Department of Transportation's Pipeline and Hazardous Materials Safety Administration's *Hazardous Materials: Risk-Based Adjustment of Transportation Security Plan Requirements*, effective October 1, 2010, expands the requirement for shippers to prepare security plans. The current requirements for security plans include all placarded shipments as well as a "large bulk quantity" of hazardous materials. A *large bulk quantity* is any amount greater than 3000 kilograms (6614 pounds) of solids or 3000 liters (792 gallons) for liquids or gases in a single packaging, such as a cargo-tank motor vehicle, portable tank, tank car, or other bulk container.

DOT requires transportation security awareness training for all hazmat employees and in-depth security training for employees of an employer that is required to have a transportation security plan. General hazardous material training requirements are listed at 49 CFR 172.704. Detailed security training requirements are listed at 49 CFR 172.704 (a)(4) and (5) and 172.800.

DOT also requires that shippers of hazardous materials provide a 24-hour emergency telephone number on shipping papers (49 CFR 172.201(d)), so that in the event of an accident involving hazardous materials, 24-hour help is available. A helpful resource available from DOT is the *Emergency Response Guidebook*, which is designed to aid responders to hazardous material releases.

ENVIRONMENTAL PROTECTION AGENCY

The mission of the EPA, as shown at www.epa.gov, is to protect human health and the environment. EPA is a vast organization with many agencies that directly or indirectly oversee the management of hazardous material spills and releases. Of the federal agencies, EPA was the first to formalize emergency planning requirements. It is the controlling agency for most spills on land. Several branches of the EPA have separate spill prevention and reporting requirements for those facilities that manufacture or use certain chemicals. Some of the major laws and regulations are discussed below.

The Comprehensive Environmental Response, Compensation, and Liability Act (CERCLA)

CERCLA, commonly known as Superfund, was signed into law by Congress in 1980. This law imposed a tax on the petroleum and chemical industries that went into a trust fund for cleaning up abandoned or uncontrolled hazardous waste sites. CERCLA also gave the federal government authority to respond directly to releases or threatened releases of hazardous substances that may endanger human health or the environment and to provide for legal and financial liability of those responsible for releases of hazardous waste at these sites. In 1986, CERCLA was amended by the Superfund Amendments and Reauthorization Act (SARA). The most significant short-term effect of SARA was to increase the size of the clean-up trust fund to $8.5 billion.

EPA developed a list of chemicals, which, when released, could cause serious harm to human health and the environment. Facilities having any of these acutely toxic substances on site at any one time, above certain threshold levels, are subject to the emergency planning provisions of SARA Title III. SARA Title III is composed of four parts:

- Sections 301–303: These sections provide for the establishment of state emergency response commissions (SERCs) and local emergency planning committees (LEPCs).
- Section 304: This section states that facilities must notify the proper agencies if there is a release of a hazardous substance that exceeds the reportable quantity for that substance. The lists of chemicals are found at 40 CFR 355 and 40 CFR 302.4.
- Sections 311–312 (Community Right-to-Know) Reporting Requirements: This section requires that material safety data sheets (MSDSs) be submitted to the local emergency planning committee, state emergency response commission, and the local fire department. These reports are called Tier I and Tier II reports. Facilities do not have to submit reports if they have less than 500 pounds or the threshold planning quantity (whichever is less) of extremely hazardous substances—or have less than 10,000 pounds of hazardous chemicals, as defined by OSHA's *Hazard Communication Standard*.
- Section 313: This section provides for annual reporting requirements for companies that manufacture, process, or use a listed material in quantities greater than specific threshold quantities. Approximately 175 of the Section 313 toxic chemicals have been designated "Section 313 Water Priority Chemicals." Regulated facilities must meet the minimum pollution prevention plan requirements and must also comply with special provisions for areas where water priority chemicals are stored, processed, or otherwise handled. These provisions include standards for appropriate containment, drainage control, and diversionary structures.

The Resource Conservation and Recovery Act (RCRA)

RCRA was passed by Congress in 1976. Its primary goals are to ensure that all wastes are managed in a way that protects human health and the environment, to promote waste reduction and minimization, and to encourage recycling and recovery of energy and natural resources. RCRA regulations provide for cradle-to-grave management of hazardous wastes, imposing regulations on those who generate, transport, treat, store, dispose of, and recycle hazardous waste.

Clean Air Act (CAA)

The Clean Air Act of 1990, along with other EPA regulations, set minimum pollution guidelines. All states have developed and implemented EPA-approved state implementation plans (SIPs), which detail how each state administers CAA regulations. It is the CAA that requires "air" permits for those who discharge certain pollutants into the air.

Clean Water Act (CWA)

The CWA was originally called the Federal Water Pollution Control Act Amendments of 1972. After it was amended in 1977, it was more commonly called the Clean Water Act. The CWA sets standards for surface water quality and industrial wastewater discharges. The Spill Prevention, Control, and Countermeasures (SPCC) regulation (40 CFR 112) was created in 1973 under authority of the Clean Water Act. This regulation established spill prevention procedures, methods, and equipment requirements for nontransportation-related facilities with aboveground oil storage capacity greater than 1320 gallons (or greater than 660 gallons aboveground in a single tank) or underground oil storage capacity greater than 42,000 gallons. Facilities regulated by SPCC include those at which an accidental discharge could reasonably be expected to reach navigable waters. These accidents might include facilities where, in the event of a spill, rainwater could wash the spill into a stream or enter the groundwater.

The CWA also established the National Pollutant Discharge Elimination System (NPDES) permit (40 CFR 122), a nationwide program that regulates the sources of discharged pollutants into waters. Under the authority of the Clean Water Act, EPA requires facilities to develop and implement stormwater pollution prevention plans and conduct site inspections. Facilities subject to SARA Title III are also subject to additional NPDES requirements. Many individual states oversee implementation and administration of this program in their state.

Oil Pollution Act (OPA)

OPA contains provisions for facilities and vessels that have the potential to discharge oil. The significance of OPA is that it establishes civil, criminal, and financial liability to the responsible party of facilities and vessels from which oil is discharged (or which pose a substantial threat of oil discharge). Responsible parties must demonstrate evidence of financial responsibility and are liable for most costs resulting from a spill or discharge of oil. OPA also establishes requirements for contingency and emergency response plans.

OCCUPATIONAL SAFETY AND HEALTH ADMINISTRATION

OSHA's Web site states that its primary goal is to protect worker safety and health (www.osha.gov/oshinfo/mission.htm). To this end, OSHA has promulgated regulations concerning numerous specific occupational safety and health hazards. In the event that a particular hazard is not directly covered by a standard, the Occupational Safety and Health Act contains a General Duty Clause that requires all American employers to provide a workplace free of recognized hazards that cause, or are likely to cause, serious harm or death to employees. The two most relevant OSHA standards pertaining to spills and releases of hazardous materials are the *Hazard Communication Standard* (HCS) and *Hazardous Waste Operations and Emergency Response* (HAZWOPER).

The Hazard Communication Standard (HCS)

The primary goal of the HCS (29 CFR 1910.1200) is to reduce the number of chemically related occupational illnesses and injuries. Employers who use hazardous chemicals must have on hand a written program that provides information to employees who may be exposed to hazardous chemicals under normal conditions or in a foreseeable emergency. The program must include a determination of the hazards present in the workplace and discuss measures that employees must take to protect themselves against those hazards, thus reducing exposure to hazardous chemicals. The HCS also requires employers to maintain copies of material safety data sheets (MSDSs) on each chemical they use.

When a good hazard communication program has been developed and implemented in the workplace, workers will be able to protect themselves in the event of a small spill. They will know how to find, read, and interpret pertinent information on MSDSs. They will have been trained on labeling/hazard recognition and will know what kind of personal protective equipment they need to protect themselves from the chemical hazards presented by the spill.

As of early 2010, OSHA is proposing to change the requirements of the HCS to comply with the recommendations of the *Global Harmonization System* (GHS) proposed by the United Nations. The proposed changes include changing the name and format of MSDS, additional hazard categories and rankings, and new labels (pictograms). Additional information may be found on OSHA's Web site at www.osha.gov/dsg/hazcom/ghs.html.

Hazardous Waste Operations and Emergency Response

As the name implies, the HAZWOPER standard (29 CFR 1910.120) covers two major categories of workers: those whose primary function is to perform hazardous waste operations and those who perform emergency response. Emergency response includes work relating to actual or threatened releases of hazardous substances regardless of the location of the hazard. Hazardous waste operations include the following:

- hazardous substance clean-up operations required by a governmental body at uncontrolled hazardous waste sites, including initial hazard investigations at government-identified sites
- clean ups at RCRA sites

- voluntary clean up of uncontrolled hazardous waste sites
- hazardous waste operations that are conducted at RCRA treatment, storage, and disposal (TSD) facilities
- emergency responses without regard to location

An *uncontrolled hazardous waste site* is an area on either public or private land where the presence of hazardous substances creates a threat to people or the environment. To be considered an uncontrolled hazardous waste site, the site must be designated as such by a federal, state, or local government agency.

As used by OSHA, the term *emergency response* alludes to response efforts by employees or others (such as the local fire department) from outside the immediate release area to an emergency that results, or could result, in an uncontrolled release of a hazardous substance. Generally speaking, if the spill or other release is incidental and can be managed by employees in the immediate area or by maintenance personnel, the response effort is not covered under this standard, but it would still be covered under the HCS and perhaps under other standards, depending on the circumstances.

There are exceptions to the standards and regulations, so one must always read the full standard or regulation carefully to determine which parts apply to one's particular situation. For example, under certain conditions, conditionally exempt small-quantity generators do not have to comply with parts of the HAZWOPER standard.

The HAZWOPER standard specifies that an employer should have an emergency response plan in effect that would include pre-emergency planning; required training, personnel roles, all lines of authority, and communication; emergency recognition and prevention; designated safe distances and places of refuge; site security and control; evacuation routes and procedures; any decontamination procedures that are not covered by the employer's comprehensive site safety and health plan; provisions for emergency medical treatment and first aid; emergency alerting and response procedures; lists of personal protective and emergency equipment; and a critique of response and follow up.

In practical terms, the HCS mandates that employers have an MSDS for all hazardous materials used in the workplace, and that all employees must be trained on the nature of the hazards and how to protect themselves from those hazards. The HAZWOPER standard addresses pre-emergency planning, emergency equipment and procedures, and training for personnel. If all employers develop and implement the plans, programs, and training required by these two standards, spills and other releases—whether small or large—will likely be managed in a safe and efficient manner.

FEDERAL ASSETS AND SOURCES OF INFORMATION

Two essential requirements for any hazardous material spill response planner are: (1) technical details and properties of the materials for which the plan is being developed and (2) a sense of how the operation should be conducted—an operational definition of *good*. There are several federal government Web sites that provide information to meet both of these requirements.

These Web sites are useful for new planners who are looking for basic information as well as for personnel revising or updating existing plans. The list below is not intended to be exhaustive, but rather to provide entry onto the information superhighway.

Organization: Agency for Toxic Substances and Disease Registry

Web site: www.atsdr.cdc.gov
Typical information:
  –Hazardous substances
    • ToxFAQs: These are chemical-specific fact sheets that provide answers to frequently asked questions about exposures to hazardous substances found around hazardous waste sites and the effects of exposure on human health.
  –Information Sources
    • The HazDat database includes the hazardous substances release and health effects database.

–Emergency Response
  • This provides information on training recommendations and technical databases for hazardous substances.
–Publications
  • These are lists of publications available for downloading or in printed format.

Organization: Centers for Disease Control and Prevention

Web site: www.cdc.gov
Typical information:
  –Health and Safety Topics
    • These topics cover emergency preparedness and response, including preparation and planning information and chemical emergency information.
    • The focus is often on chemical emergencies, including an MSDS database from the Department of Energy.

Organization: Department of Justice

Web site: www.justnet.org
Typical information:
    The basic concepts in numerous publications are based on the needs of law enforcement and corrections, but the documents provide concise and useful information for planners and emergency responders.

  –Publications
    • *Draft NIJ CBRN Protective Ensembles for Law Enforcement*
    • *Comparative Evaluation of Protective Gloves for Law Enforcement and Correction Applications*
    • *Guidance on Emergency Responder Personal Protective Equipment (PPE) for Response to CBRN Terrorism Incidents*
    • *Guidance for the Selection of Chemical and Biological Decontamination Equipment for Emergency First Responders*

Organization: Department of Transportation

Web site: www.phmsa.dot.gov
Typical Information:

Emergency Response Guidebook (ERG). This emergency responders' guide is intended to assist in quickly identifying the specific or generic characterization of a hazardous material in an incident and to assist in protecting emergency responders during the initial response phases of an incident.

Organization: Federal Emergency Management Agency

Web site: www.fema.gov and www.usfa.fema.gov (U.S. Fire Administration)
Typical information:

–Typical information covered is incident management, including information on creating response management systems and coordinating plans with local and federal agencies.

Organization: National Institute of Occupational Safety and Health (NIOSH)

Web site: www.cdc.gov/niosh
Typical information:

NIOSH Pocket Guide to Chemical Hazards (NPG). This is a concise source of general industrial hygiene information for workers, employers, and occupational health professionals on 677 chemicals or substances commonly found in the work environment.

Organization: Occupational Safety and Health Administration (U.S. Department of Labor)

Web site: www.osha.gov/dep/etools
Typical information:

–Information covered is the Health and Safety Program, electronic format (e-HASP). An important message is that a safe response must be a planned response. This site shows than an excellent tool either for drafting new health and safety plans or for reviewing existing plans is the electronic health and safety plan. The following is a brief outline of the online plan. See the *E-Hasp₂ Software User's Manual* for complete information and details on each element.

- Organizational Structure: Documents how the authority, responsibility, and duties are divided among the various agencies and members of a response team.
- Job Hazard Analysis (JHA): This is a technique used to help identify, then reduce or eliminate, hazards. JHAs focus on the relationship between the worker, the task, the tools, and the work environment.
- Site Control: This plan shows how to define boundaries of contaminated zones and work areas. It also explains how to identify safe work practices, methods of routine and emergency communication, methods of controlling entry into contaminated areas, and methods of controlling the migration of site contaminants.
- Training Program: The training program identifies the jobs and tasks that require training, and how much and what type of training is needed for each. It describes how changing site-specific conditions or information will be communicated to employees and other site workers. It also tells where and how training documentation will be maintained.
- Medical Surveillance Requirements: This aspect describes various requirements and techniques, such as physical examinations, biological testing, the collection of workplace exposure data, and other needs that are mandated by various OSHA standards. A good resource for medical surveillance information is the Web site www.osha.gov/SLTC/medicalsurveillance/index.html.
- Personal Protective Equipment (PPE): What is described here is how PPE is selected, fit, used, stored, and maintained. This site tells how personnel will be trained for proper use and how one can ensure that workers are physically capable of using PPE under routine and extreme conditions, such as during emergencies or periods of extreme heat or cold.
- Exposure Monitoring: This part discusses how and when monitoring for hazardous

contaminants will be conducted. Included is a discussion of the monitoring instruments that will be used and how they will be calibrated and maintained. If an accredited analytical laboratory will be used, one can find how to describe sampling procedures and sample handling procedures.

- Thermal Stress: This describes measures to be taken to protect site workers from the effects of heat and cold stressors.
- Spill Containment Program: What is provided here is detailed information about the actions that will be taken in the event of a spill or a leak. Included is information about the equipment that is to be used to control and contain the released material; where tools and equipment are located; the personnel who are to respond; how and when to obtain off-site assistance; and other site-specific information.
- Decontamination Program: Described here are procedures to decontaminate personnel and equipment. Also explained is how disposable and reusable equipment will be managed and how to ensure decontamination is effective.
- Emergency Response Plan: This is a written plan that identifies the actions employees will take in the event of a chemical release, fire, accident, injury, or other type of emergency that may occur at the site.
- Standard Operating Procedures: Here, one can learn how to develop procedures to ensure safe, consistent, work practices that will minimize employee contact with hazardous substances and provide compliance with applicable standards and regulations.
- Confined Space Programs: If confined spaces are a potential site hazard, refer to 29 CFR 1910.146, Permit-Required Confined Spaces, to determine whether the circumstances necessitate the development and implementation of a written, confined-space-entry program.

- Hot Work: If welding, cutting, or other hot work is to be performed at the site, develop safety and operating procedures; list worker roles and responsibilities, and describe the location(s) where the hot work is to be conducted.
- Lockout/Tagout: If applicable, and based on site conditions, one can develop specific procedures that can be used to protect workers from the unexpected start up or energization of machinery and equipment and from the release of hazardous energy during equipment maintenance or other activities where energy could be suddenly released.

Organization: U.S. Coast Guard

Web site: www.uscg.mil/vrp

Typical information:

–Shipboard Oil Pollution Emergency Plans (SOPEP) and Shipboard Marine Pollution Emergency Plans (SMPEP).

- The Oil Pollution Act of 1990 (OPA-90) and the international treaty, MARPOL 73/78, require owners/operators of certain vessels to prepare a Vessel Response Plan (VRP) and/or Shipboard Oil Pollution Emergency Plans (SOPEP) approved by the U.S. Coast Guard. In addition, for certain vessels carrying noxious liquid substances, MARPOL 73/78 requires owner/operators to prepare and submit Shipboard Marine Pollution Emergency Plans (SMPEP), effective January 1, 2003. Access to information and key elements contained in those plans is available from the above Web site.
- These plans provide lists of the types of information and formats that good plans, even those not involving marine spills, should include.

PUBLIC AND COMMUNITY ASSETS

Many public and private community assets exist, both for providing assistance in emergency spill response situations and for providing help or guidance to facilities that want to ensure that they are doing everything possible to prevent spills and respond adequately in the event of a spill or release. The following assets are examples of the types of services that could be available in your area.

Public Service Agencies

In many cases, emergency responders to large spills or transportation spills will include some type of public service agency, such as the local police, fire, and/or emergency medical service (EMS) department. Local police departments generally do not participate directly in incident management, but may assist by securing the scene, managing traffic, routing emergency equipment, or notifying other local or state emergency response agencies. Approximately 65 percent of all fire departments provide EMS services and often have hazardous material teams whose members are trained and equipped to manage many types of emergency spills and releases (BLS, 2007).

Communication and preplanning with the local fire department are often required by state or local law, usually for facilities that have larger quantities of hazardous materials. Facilities of any size that use or store materials that pose unusual hazards during a fire should coordinate with the local fire department to discuss those hazards. For example, firefighters need to know if a material is water-reactive *before* they use water to try to extinguish it. Telling them after the ensuing explosion is useless. Likewise, local doctors, hospitals, and other medical facilities should be contacted prior to an emergency and made aware of the types of injuries and illnesses they can expect to see in the event of a spill or release so they are able to prepare adequately.

Industry-Related Assets

Responsible Care® (www.responsiblecare.org) is a voluntary initiative developed by the chemical industry. The Responsible Care initiative is a comprehensive environmental, health, and safety management system composed of ten key elements through which participating companies work together to improve their environmental, safety, health, and security performance.

Many chemical companies also participate in the Community Awareness and Emergency Response (CAER) program (described at www.caer-mp.org). Each CAER member-company has developed and implemented an emergency response program that enables it to respond quickly and effectively to emergencies at its facility. CAER members also have community outreach programs to address questions and concerns about any safety, health, and environmental issues concerning their product or process.

The International Organization for Standardization (ISO) (www.iso.org) developed a set of standards—a complete management system—that helps facilities adopt a proactive approach to managing environmental issues. By developing and implementing programs and best practices found in ISO 14000 and the Occupational Health and Safety Assessment Series (OSHAS) 18000, any type of facility or organization—large or small, public or private—can improve its safety and environmental programs. Sound environmental management results in cost savings such as reduced raw materials and energy consumption and less hazardous and non-hazardous waste generation and disposal. Sound safety and environmental management will reduce the likelihood of spills and releases and result in more efficient management of incidents if and when they occur.

Community Assets

Local emergency planning committees (LEPCs) are typically composed of emergency responders (both public and private), local industry, emergency management agencies, and the community. LEPCs take an active role in community emergency planning and are responsible for developing a community emergency plan for response to chemical emergencies. They often provide services such as the review of a facility's contingency plans, public education, industry outreach, and development and implementation of emergency drills and exercises. For more information about LEPCs, or to find out what services, if any, your LEPC offers, visit www.fema.gov/hazard/hazmat/hz_cres.shtm or search for your state's Web-site listing.

FEDERAL NOTIFICATION AND REPORTING REQUIREMENTS

The National Response Center (NRC)

The NRC is the sole federal point of contact for reporting regulated oil and chemical spills. The NRC maintains a 24-hour-per-day, 7-days-per-week, 365-days-per-year Operations Center, where all information is received via a toll-free number entered directly into an online database system, and electronically disseminated as part of the National Response System. Information such as the material involved, mode of transportation, injuries, damage, and fatalities will be disseminated to select federal agencies within 15 minutes of receipt. When any of the following incidents occur, the NRC should immediately be contacted by the responsible party via the toll-free number. Anyone who sees or discovers an oil spill or release of chemicals, even if he or she is not the responsible party, should immediately contact the NRC with whatever information is available.

- Oil spills in or along U.S. navigable waters: The definition of "navigable waters" found in 40 CFR 112.2 is rather broad and lengthy. Generally speaking, however, the term includes *all* waters that are currently used, were used in the past, or may be susceptible to use in interstate or foreign commerce, including territorial seas, rivers, ponds, streams, wetlands, wetlands adjacent to waters, lakes, impoundments, prairie potholes, wet meadows, and other areas in which the use, degradation, or destruction of which could affect interstate or foreign commerce.
- CERCLA requires that all releases of hazardous substances exceeding reportable quantities be reported by the responsible party to the NRC. Title 40 CFR Part 302 promulgates reportable quantities and reporting criteria. All the Extremely Hazardous Substances (EHS) that overlap with the CERCLA-listed chemicals table (40 CFR Part 302.4) should also be reported.
- Certain transportation accidents (see below under Department of Transportation).

- Others, including gas and liquid pipeline releases and discharges from a hazardous waste treatment or storage facility. Abandoned dump or waste sites should be reported by anyone having knowledge of such a site.

Department of Transportation

To comply with 49 CFR 171.15, incidents of the following types that occur during the loading, unloading, or storage of hazardous materials in commerce must be reported to the NRC by telephone by the person who has physical possession of the hazardous material(s) as soon as possible, but no later than 12 hours after the incident:

1. Incidents where, as a direct result of a hazardous material,
    - a person is killed
    - a person receives an injury requiring admittance to a hospital
    - the general public is evacuated for an hour or longer
    - a major transportation artery or facility is closed or shut down for at least an hour or the operational flight pattern or routine of an aircraft is altered
2. Incidents where breakage, spillage, or suspected radioactive contamination occurs involving a radioactive material
3. Incidents where breakage, spillage, or suspected contamination occurs involving an infectious substance other than a diagnostic specimen or regulated medical waste
4. Incidents where a release of a marine pollutant occurs in a quantity exceeding 119 gallons (450 L) for a liquid or 882 pounds (400 kg) for a solid
5. Incidents where a situation exists of such a nature that, in the judgment of the person in possession of the hazardous material, it should be reported to the National Response Center, even if it does not meet the above criteria

For incidents involving infectious substances, the report may instead be forwarded to the Centers for Disease Control and Prevention in Atlanta, Georgia, at (800)232-0124. Each report must include the following information:

- name of the reporter
- name and address of the person represented by the reporter
- telephone number where the reporter can be contacted
- date, time, and location of the incident
- extent of injury, if any
- if available, the proper shipping name, hazard class or division, and quantity of hazardous material involved
- type of incident and nature of hazardous material involvement and whether a continuing danger to life exists at the scene

Within 30 days of the incident, the person who makes the report must also file a written report on DOT Form F 5800.1.

DOT also requires that a written report be made when there has been an unintentional release of hazardous materials from a package (including a tank), or when any quantity of hazardous waste has been unintentionally discharged during transportation. Reports of hazardous waste discharges must include a copy of the hazardous waste manifest and other information, such as an estimate of the quantity of the waste removed from the scene, the name and address of the facility to which it was taken, and the manner of disposition of any removed waste. There are some exceptions to the reporting requirements, so refer to the full text of 49 CFR 171.16 for details.

Environmental Protection Agency

Under 40 CFR 302.6, EPA requires persons in charge of facilities (including transport vehicles, vessels, and aircraft) to report any release of a hazardous substance in a quantity equal to or greater than its reportable quantity, as soon as that person has knowledge of the release, to the National Response Center at (800)424-8802 or (202) 267-2675. The term *reportable quantity* (RQ) means the quantity, as set forth in 40 CFR 302, the release of which requires notification pursuant to the regulations contained in 40 CFR 302.

STATE REQUIREMENTS
Federal "States' Rights" Legislation

Some environmental laws are national in applicability. Deviations from these federal laws are not allowed. For example, transportation laws regulating hazardous materials may not be altered. All states must follow DOT regulations and standards because only Congress, as authorized by the U.S. Constitution, may regulate commerce between states. Bulk and nonbulk packages of hazardous materials must meet the manufacturing and quality assurance standards set by DOT at 49 CFR 178. Labels and placards must meet federal specifications set by DOT at 49 CFR 172. Some laws, however, allow states to add to, but not delete from, federal standards. For example, the document that must accompany shipments of hazardous waste—the Uniform Hazardous Waste Manifest (40 CFR 262)—was created by the Resource Conservation and Recovery Act (RCRA). All states must use the Uniform Hazardous Waste Manifest, but space is allotted on the form for state-specific waste codes. Lists of state-specific variations and additions are available at EPA regional offices or state environmental compliance agencies.

At the federal level, generators of hazardous waste may not store hazardous waste more than 90 days with a storage permit. Generators, at the federal level, may, however, use satellite accumulation areas, at or near the point of waste generation and under the control of the operator of the process generating the waste, to accumulate up to 55 gallons of waste without a time limit. Some states, however, do not allow satellite sites. In those jurisdictions, generators must ship all waste off site within 90 days or obtain a storage permit. This interplay of federal regulations and state-specific requirements tends to confound spill response plans and procedures because states and regional authorities within states may set specific standards that differ from federal requirements. Many state and federal regulations contain provisions for resolving conflicts between regulatory bodies. In the case of contradictory requirements, the more restrictive regulation generally applies. If in doubt, ask one or both of the agencies involved for a written, legal interpretation of the regulation(s) in question.

Personnel Licensing and Registration

Some states have established licensing and registration requirements for companies and individuals assessing the severity of a specific situation, conducting spill response operations, or determining the need for additional remediation efforts after the majority of the spilled material has been recovered or removed. For example, California's Environmental Protection Agency Department of Toxic Substances Control has published a *Preliminary Endangerment Assessment Guidance Manual*. Only individuals qualified as and recognized as a registered environmental assessor (REA) may complete a preliminary endangerment assessment (PEA) to determine if a spill or release site is *clean* or needs additional remediation. The Connecticut Department of Environmental Protection has established Remediation Standard Regulations. Connecticut also qualifies, tests, and recognizes environmental professionals. When organizations with only a single facility plan a spill response to include determining whether the spill or release has been remediated, contacting a single state environmental regulatory organization will be sufficient. For national organizations with facilities in numerous locations, spill response plans must include state and regional contacts, registration, and licensing requirements for specific operations and individuals. Check with your state's environmental agency to determine whether licensing or registration is required.

Notifications and Response Actions

Virtually all jurisdictions within the United States require notification of a spill or release based on the specific material(s) involved and the amount and location of the spill. The agency to which the notification is sent may be the local fire department, a state agency, or a statewide notification center. Generally, the emphasis is on responding quickly and safely to the spill or release. A spill response planner must be aware of the type(s) of notification(s) required, the organization(s) to which the notification should be sent, and the format of the notification(s), and should include this information in the spill response plan. Nationwide commercial organizations must include this information for specific facilities. Planners who write specific response plans

must contact the local fire department or state environmental agency to verify reporting and notification requirements.

POST-CLEAN-UP RESPONSE REQUIREMENTS

After the initial spill response actions have been completed, there is generally a requirement to assess, examine, or test the spill site to determine whether any harmful residual levels of the spilled materials or contaminants remain. As noted earlier, various states and regional authorities may have product-specific standards in certain areas of the United States. These authorities must be consulted, and their approval, if required, obtained before any long-term remediation work is initiated. In most jurisdictions, the sampling and analytical procedures in *Test Methods for Evaluating Solid Waste* (Physical/Chemical Methods) EPA Publication SW-846 (www.epa.gov/epaoswer/hazwaste/test/main.htm) must be followed. Because sampling involves specific procedures, methods, and sometimes health or safety hazards, only personnel with the appropriate knowledge should be permitted to obtain samples. Many environmental service companies and laboratories offer sampling services. Additionally, several good references are available. One is EPA publication EPA530-D-02-002, *RCRA Waste Sampling Draft Technical Guidance—Planning, Implementation, and Assessment* (August 2002). Another good resource is *ASTM Standards on Environmental Sampling*, now in its third edition (2006), which is published by ASTM International (www.astm.org).

For any post-clean-up issues concerning building safety or reoccupancy, consult local building codes or contact the local fire department for guidance.

Soil Decontamination

Soil decontamination is important for its own sake as well as to prevent cross-media contamination. Spill residues entrained in soil may volatilize and become airborne clouds of gases and vapors. On the other hand, contaminated soil may dry and be displaced by the wind, creating clouds of hazardous particulate matter. Soils highly contaminated by releases or spills may be removed during the emergency phase of the response, making decontamination a moot point. More likely, low levels of contamination will exist on the horizontal and vertical peripheries of the spill. Those are the soils that must be decontaminated. As in all phases of spill response, knowing the nature of the contaminant may indicate the type of decontamination that will be most efficient. Some heavy metals, such as arsenic, tend to be relatively soluble and migrate through the soil. Thus a 100-square-foot area of arsenic-contaminated soil after a spill may become a 1000-square-foot decontamination problem if not addressed quickly. Dense nonaqueous-phase liquids (DNAPLs) will migrate through soil, sink through the groundwater in the saturated soil zones, and cause both soil and groundwater decontamination problems.

A spill of elemental or white phosphorus results in extensive soil contamination. Because white phosphorus is a spontaneously combustible material, repeatedly tilling the contaminated area over a period of weeks forces the phosphorus to the surface, where it simply burns itself out. In a case like this, cross-media contamination (air contaminated by burning phosphorus) is determined to be less of a human and environmental health and safety concern than allowing the phosphorus to remain in place.

Groundwater

Groundwater decontamination is nearly always difficult. Especially in the case of sole-source aquifers, contamination must be reduced to extremely low levels. This reduction may be accomplished by pumping the contaminated groundwater to surface treatment units or, in some situations, by biological or chemical processes, using bacteria to degrade the contamination in place, or using chemicals to either oxidize or reduce the contamination. Depending on soil conditions, it may be necessary to inject the decontaminating chemicals directly into the groundwater. Or, it may be more efficient to build porous barriers in the soil, allowing contaminated groundwater to flow through the decontaminating barrier or reactive zone. The contaminants will be oxidized or reduced as they are carried by the water through these subsurface structures.

Building and Equipment

There are some specific clean-up standards in EPA regulations. The clean-up standard for polychlorinated biphenyls (PCBs), for example, is published at 40 CFR 761 and includes acceptable residual levels of PCBs. Experience often has shown, however, that there is no specific standard. Cleaning to background levels or method detection limits in SW-846 may be extremely expensive without providing any benefit to human health or the environment. OSHA standards may be used to provide some guidance for decontamination in industrial or commercial facilities. Recognizing human health and safety are the primary concerns; there will probably be requirements to clean processing equipment so that manufactured goods meet specifications and are not contaminated with spill residues.

APPLIED SCIENTIFIC AND ENGINEERING PRINCIPLES IN ENVIRONMENTAL MANAGEMENT
Chemical and Physical Properties of Hazardous Materials

The physical state of the material being dealt with will often determine the seriousness of a spill or release. Solids tend not to disperse as rapidly in the environment as liquids or vapors. Powdered solids, however, may become airborne quickly and create contaminated environments, both locally affecting spill response workers and, downwind from the release site, creating hazardous areas for people, the environment, and continuing operations.

When *water-insoluble liquids* that are lighter than water are spilled on water, they tend to spread over wide areas because these materials are dispersed by wind, current, or tidal flow. Water-insoluble liquids that are heavier than water tend to sink directly to the bottom and may form localized, concentrated, highly contaminated areas. The extent of the contamination depends to a large extent on bottom conditions and current characteristics.

Water-soluble liquids, when spilled on water, may be impossible to remove from the environment completely because the entire water column, from top to bottom, is contaminated. Water-soluble liquids, when spilled on soil, tend either to permeate the soil or to dissolve in precipitation and sink into the soil until groundwater is encountered. They tend to contaminate large areas.

Water-insoluble liquids spilled on soil tend to spread more slowly than water-soluble materials. These contaminated areas will be relatively small.

Water-soluble solids, when spilled on water, may be impossible to remove. As with water-soluble liquids, they contaminate the entire water column. Water-insoluble solids, when spilled on water, will either float or sink. Water-insoluble solids that are lighter than water tend to spread over wide areas because these materials are dispersed by wind, current, or tidal flow. Water-insoluble solids that are heavier than water tend to sink directly to the bottom and may form localized, concentrated, highly contaminated areas.

Spilled solid materials tend not to penetrate soils very deeply. However, water-soluble solid materials that are spilled on soil may dissolve in precipitation and act as a liquid, contaminating large areas.

The *boiling point* (BP) of a liquid is the temperature at which a liquid turns to vapor. Materials with a boiling point below ambient temperatures will evaporate rapidly, forming vapor clouds that may endanger both responders and people, operations, and the environment downwind from the spill or release (Bowling Green State University 2008).

The *lower explosive limit* (LEL) and the *upper explosive limit* (UEL) establish the range of flammability. The LEL is the minimum concentration of a material in air that will support combustion, given an ignition source. A synonym for LEL is LFL (*lower flammable limit*). Below the LEL, the material-to-air mixture is too lean to burn. The UEL is the highest concentration of a material in air that will support combustion, given an ignition source. Above the UEL, the material-to-air mixture is too rich to burn.

The instrument that measures the concentration of flammable vapors in air is called a combustible gas indicator (CGI). It is generally calibrated to either methane or pentane and displays contamination as a percentage of the LEL (%LEL). The highest level that OSHA has determined as safe for entry into confined or poorly ventilated spaces is 10% LEL. CGI readings are generally displayed as large numbers—percentages in air or tens of thousands of parts per million. Permissible exposure limits (PELs) and threshold limit values (TLVs) are generally small numbers—often only tens or hundreds of parts per million. It is critical that, after an atmosphere is tested for flammability with a CGI, it is tested for low levels of hazardous vapors with direct-reading organic vapor instruments to determine proper personal protective equipment. Because a CGI measures flammability, not toxicity, a toxic atmosphere may exist, but it might not be detected.

The *flash point* (Fl. P.) of a material is the temperature at which sufficient vapors are generated to support combustion, given an ignition source. Materials with flash points well below ambient temperatures pose extreme risk of fire and explosions to response workers. An extremely low flash point often determines both what and how emergency responders conduct operations, at least until the source of the flammable vapors is controlled.

The *ionization potential* (IP) of a material is the amount of energy, measured in electron volts (eV), that is required to form an ion. An instrument commonly used during spill responses to measure vapors in air is a photo ionization detector, or PID. A PID can detect many solvents, but only if the ionization lamp in the instrument produces more electron volts than are required by the molecule(s) of concern to form ions. Thus a PID with a low energy bulb may give very low readings when in high concentrations of vapor(s) with high ionization potential(s). PIDs are commonly calibrated to isobutylene in the low parts-per-million range. One should always refer to the manufacturer's instructions when interpreting instrument readings because a specific material may cause an instrument response that is significantly different from the actual levels of contamination. PIDs can be used to determine the need for, and type of, respiratory protection.

Specific gravity (Sp. Gr.) is the weight of a material relative to water (water being defined as having a specific gravity of 1). Materials with a Sp. Gr. of less than 1 will float on water and may spread significantly from the original release site. Such materials released onto soil tend to permeate or diffuse into the soil to the top of the water table, then float on underground water. This forms large pools of contaminated water that often require extensive and lengthy remediation efforts. Materials with a Sp. Gr. greater than 1 will sink in water. If such a material is released onto surface water, clean up or removal may be impossible without herculean efforts. Materials with a Sp. Gr. greater than 1 released onto soil may permeate into the ground, sinking through groundwater until a confining layer (a layer of geologic material such as clay, rock, or compressed silt that has little or no permeability) is encountered.

Vapor density (VD), sometimes expressed as the *relative vapor density* (Rel. VD), is a ratio of the density of the released gas(es) or vapor(s) compared to air, with the density of air equaling 1. Materials with a vapor density less than 1 will tend to rise and disperse. Materials with a density greater than 1 will tend to form pockets in low or poorly ventilated areas. Thus storm drains near a spill or release may contain hazardous concentrations of spilled, high-density gases and vapors. These drains may form dispersion pathways, allowing the spilled materials to contaminate large areas. Vapor density should always be used as a very general measure of the ability of a vapor to disperse. For example, mercury has a VD of 13.5, but air currents caused by personnel walking near a spill site will cause mercury vapors to rise and disperse in air (Bowling Green State University 2008).

Vapor pressure (VP) is the pressure, generally measured in millimeters of mercury (mm Hg) in equilibrium with the liquid or solid phase of the same material. VP will affect both on-site and off-site operations. Low vapor-pressure materials may produce relatively small contaminated areas with relatively low inhalation risks and small, if any, downwind hazard areas. On the other hand, high vapor-pressure materials may create large areas of high contamination, requiring the on-site use of respiratory protection equipment for long periods. In addition, high vapor-pressure materials may create large, long-lasting hazard areas downwind of the spill site.

Viscosity is the resistance of a liquid to flow or move. Highly viscous materials cling to surfaces—including personal protective equipment worn by response workers—the soil surface, and any equipment or structure in the spill or release site. High-viscosity fluids are typically difficult to decontaminate. Low-viscosity fluids may tend to disperse rapidly on soil or surface waters.

Miscibility is the ability of two liquids to form a uniform blend. For example, the DOT *Emergency Response Guidebook* (ERG) uses miscibility in lieu of solubility. The term may be used as a synonym for *solubility*. The water solubility, or miscibility, of a spilled material affects how the material will spread from the release site. A water-miscible material that is allowed to contact water will probably never be recovered. Surface waters will spread the material, creating huge areas with huge volumes of contaminated water. Controlling access to the contaminated water until natural forces dilute the spill to acceptable levels will probably be the remediation technique used. Groundwater aquifers contaminated with a water-soluble material may be abandoned, thus requiring new water supplies. It may not be possible, in some cases, to remediate the groundwater.

Water-immiscible materials may be either lighter than water (having a specific gravity less than 1) or heavier than water (having a specific gravity greater than 1). Water-immiscible, low-specific-gravity liquids will float on surface water until they degrade or meet a physical barrier. A gasoline spill on a river is an example of a water-immiscible material. If this type of material is allowed to soak into the ground and contaminate the aquifer, extensive decontamination will be required.

Water-immiscible, high-specific-gravity materials will sink to the bottom of any body of surface water. Removing these materials may be physically and financially impossible. Contaminated sediments and sludges in industrial harbors are examples of these materials. Water-immiscible, high-specific-gravity liquids are so difficult to remove from groundwater that they have been given a specific name: *DNAPLs, or dense nonaqueous-phase liquids*. Again, time is critical. Keeping these materials contained at or near the spill site can prevent major pollution events. Responding slowly, allowing these materials to seep into the soil, can create conditions that require decades to restore or remediate.

Nature of the Spilled Material—
Measures of Toxicity

Common measures of toxicity that affect an exposed population are called the lethal dose (LD) for a liquid or solid and the lethal concentration (LC) for a gas or vapor. The dose that kills 50 percent of the organisms in a test for skin contact or ingestion is called the LD_{50}. The concentration (in air) of a gas or vapor that kills 50 percent of the organisms in a test of respiratory exposure is shown as the LC_{50}. The proposed Global Harmonization System (GHS) expands the measure of toxicity to include target organ systemic toxicity (TOST) for either a single exposure or repeated exposures (UNECE 2005).

The *permissible exposure limit* (PEL) is the exposure ceiling set by OSHA that most workers can be exposed to based on 8-hour workdays and 40-hour work weeks. A PEL is measured as a *time-weighted average* (TWA). A TWA is the mathematical average value of a chemical exposure over the course of an 8-hour work shift. Longer exposure times—more than 8 hours per day or 40 hours per week—will cause an overexposure, even if the actual exposure is within permissible exposure limits.

The *threshold limit value* (TLV) is the exposure, measured as a TWA, set by the American Congress of Governmental Industrial Hygienists (ACGIH) and based on 8-hour workdays and 40-hour work weeks. Owing to differences in standard development, the TLV for a specific substance may vary significantly from the PEL. Both PELs and TLVs tend to be small numbers, measured in parts per million (ppm) or in milligrams per cubic meter (mg/m³).

The *short-term exposure limit* (STEL) is the exposure workers may safely be exposed to under the following conditions: (a) the exposure is limited to 15 minutes, (b) the exposure at this level may not occur more than four times within an 8-hour workday, and (c) exposures at the STEL level must be separated by at least one hour. STELs must be included in any calculations for the TLV® or PEL.

Chemical levels are considered to be *immediately dangerous to life or health* (IDLH) when they are present in the atmosphere in concentrations that pose an im-mediate threat to life, would cause irreversible adverse health effects, or would impair an individual's ability to escape from a dangerous atmosphere. Response workers should never be allowed to enter an IDLH atmosphere without adequate personal protective equipment or without proper rescue equipment and personnel on site, who are ready to provide support to injured or trapped workers immediately.

Nature of the Affected Area or Environment—
Geology and Hydrology

Near-surface soils affect the impact a spill has on the environment. Tight, nonporous, low-permeability soils tend to limit the diffusion or permeation of spills that migrate downward into the soil. Loose, porous, high-permeability soils offer little resistance to permeation or diffusion. A spill of a highly viscous material (a thick, tarlike substance) will tend to form puddles at or near the spill site on nonporous soils. Given a moderate surface slope, these materials will move slowly, if at all, down the slope or downward into the ground. On the other hand, a low-viscosity material (thin and watery, like fingernail polish remover) spilled on highly porous soil tends to move quickly down the slope and downward into the ground.

Saturated soils tend to retard the movement of water-insoluble materials into the ground. The water filling the spaces between soil particles acts like a dam, blocking the movement of spilled materials as they are pulled downward by gravity. On the other hand, saturated soils tend to accelerate the movement of water-soluble materials by acting as a dispersion pathway. The near-surface water may be connected to, and recharge, groundwater, forming a direct link between spilled materials on the surface and subsurface aquifers.

Basic soils, or soils derived from limestone, also influence how spilled materials affect the environment. Basic soils may assist in neutralizing spilled acids, minimizing the impact of the spill. Karst topography forms over limestone, dolomite, and gypsum and is characterized by sinkholes, caves, and underground drainage. This underground drainage actually allows spilled material to escape from the accident site in miles per hour in underground streams in caves.

Soils are rarely a uniform layer of a single material. Often there are lenses, beds, and other complex structures that may, in some instances, retard the movement of material away from a spill site and, in other instances, accelerate the movement of materials. Time is of the essence in spill response. A few hours' difference in response times can mean the difference between controlling a spill on or near the surface in one or two days or spending months attempting to remediate underground soils and water.

Nature of the Affected Area or Environment–Meteorology

As a general rule, the higher the ambient temperature, the faster spilled liquids tend to evaporate. Low temperatures may allow a spill response team adequate time to effectively contain spilled liquids, creating small downwind hazard areas. Higher temperatures tend to increase vapor pressure and evaporation, providing spill response teams very little time to contain and control liquid spills before a significant downwind hazard area is formed.

Some basic knowledge of atmospheric stability also can help predict the dispersion of contaminants in the atmosphere. A common classification of atmospheric stability is known as the Pasquill-Gifford (P-G) stability class system, which assigns a classification based on factors such as wind speed, solar radiation, and cloud cover. Seven classes are designated by letters: A (for unstable or turbulent conditions) through G (for very stable conditions). Sometimes the numbers 1 through 7 replace the letters. Neutral conditions are class D (or 4).

Very low winds (up to approximately 3 miles per hour) tend to limit the generation of a large downwind hazard area. High winds (above approximately 17 miles per hour) also limit the generation and spread of a large downwind hazard area. Wind speed and direction typically change after sunrise, during the warmest time of the day (approximately 10 AM to 4 PM), and after sunset.

The *Emergency Response Guidebook* (2008), available from the PHMSA Web site, uses a simplified, two-stage stability system to create protective action distances downwind from a spill site. This system consists of day (sunrise to sunset) and night. During the night, the air is generally calmer, corresponding to P-G class D to G (4 to 7) conditions. These conditions cause vapors to disperse less and therefore create a more toxic, but smaller, danger zone. During the day, P-G class A to D (1 to 4) conditions, vapors are generally dispersed by a more active atmosphere. The downwind danger zone will be larger, but generally have a lower toxicity level.

An atmospheric inversion, when warmer air aloft tends to trap cooler air near the surface, will cause large downwind hazard areas to be created quickly. Heavy cloud cover or other inversions will cause vapors or dust released from a spill to be carried miles downwind. This downwind hazard area may force the evacuation of large populations from large areas as well as posing environmental threats.

Nature of Response Operations

Ideally, a properly trained, equipped, and managed spill response team will respond instantaneously to any spill or release of a hazardous material. Unfortunately, time of day, weather conditions, spill location, and the characteristics of the material may prevent or delay response. Specific techniques and equipment used at a spill or release site must be based on actual conditions and the materials involved. In general, the following actions should be taken in any spill situation:

- Identify necessary emergency response equipment and supplies such as PPE, sorbents, hand and power tools, solvents, shovels, pumps, fire extinguishers, and any site-specific equipment or supplies and ensure that it is in good working order and readily accessible.
- Do not underestimate the seriousness of the situation. The first responders may need additional equipment, personnel, and expertise to safely and successfully respond to a situation.
- Control the leak or release as soon as possible. Small spills are always easier to clean up. Stopping the release of a material establishes safer working conditions and limits off-site effects.

- Contain spilled material. Material may escape from a spill site by numerous pathways. Contain vapor clouds, spilled liquids and solids as much as possible as soon as it is safely possible.
- Pump downhill, if possible, to increase efficiency. Working in personal protective equipment is difficult, especially in hot or cold conditions. Increased efficiency will benefit both personnel and the overall response effort.
- Keep hose lines as straight as possible. Again, the increased efficiency will significantly affect spill response operations. Curved or sharply bent hoses limit the efficiency of any pumping system.
- Do not make the situation worse. A spill is a complex situation. Stopping response operations to rescue improperly trained or equipped personnel increases risks to people, the environment, and operations. Using incompatible materials may cause additional spills or hazards such as fire, explosions, or the release of more toxic materials and spread contamination from the original spill site.

BENCHMARKS AND PERFORMANCE APPRAISAL CRITERIA

Several benchmarks exist against which various aspects of spill and release responses may be measured. The most commonly available benchmarks are for responder training, for development of response plans, and for measurements of effectiveness of the response effort.

Training Benchmarks–Sources of Information

For training, the most basic benchmark is set by OSHA in the form of regulatory minimums for response personnel (see the "Personnel Training" section later in this chapter). OSHA very clearly lists the minimum knowledge and skills required to participate in emergency response and hazardous waste operations. Lev-

els of training vary according to the employee's role in an emergency. To supplement these benchmarks, refer to National Fire Protection Association (NFPA) Publication 472, *Standard for Professional Competence of Responders to Hazardous Materials Incidents* (2008). NFPA 472 provides benchmarks for each level of responder, from the first responder at the awareness level up to incident commander, in several performance categories, including analyzing the incident, planning the response, implementing the planned response, evaluating progress, and terminating the incident. NFPA 472 also describes competencies for private-sector specialist employees, technicians for several types of tanks (e.g., tank cars, cargo tanks, and intermodal tanks), and others.

Plan Development Benchmarks–Sources of Information

There are several excellent resources that assist in developing new plans or evaluating existing plans. Many of these resources are available online.

First, the National Response Team has information at www.nrt.org. Of particular interest to planners are these guides:

- *Hazardous Materials Emergency Planning Guide* (NRT-1)
- *Criteria for Review of Hazardous Materials Emergency Plans* (NRT-1a)
- Update of the *Hazardous Materials Emergency Planning Guide*

Using these documents in the order listed provides a historical basis for benchmarking existing plans and illustrates how the planning process and the information sources have evolved. The documents provide a checklist to ensure that plans are comprehensive and complete.

Second, the Environmental Protection Agency's site (www.epa.gov/ceppo) provides significant, useful information, including the NRT-Integrated Contingency Plan Guidance ("One Plan"), which is intended to be used by facilities to prepare emergency response plans. Again, the information can be used as a checklist or benchmark to measure a facility's plan.

Also included on the EPA's Web site is information on local emergency planning committees (LEPC) created by the Superfund Amendment and Reauthorization Act (SARA). Larger facilities should have been coordinating plans with an LEPC since the 1990s. If plans have not been kept up to date, a new facility is being created, or an existing facility is being modified, using local emergency response organizations, as represented on an LEPC, is an excellent way to ensure that a facilities plan meets current standards and work.

Third, many insurance companies, as part of a risk assessment/risk management plan, work with specific facilities to design safe facilities and to develop (and keep current) emergency response plans. Also, many local cooperatives, commodity-specific organizations, and trade associations have prepared standards of good practice that are useful benchmarking tools.

Fourth, and finally, FEMA has developed an independent study course called "Exercise Design" (course number IS-139) that provides excellent information on exercise design, performance, and evaluation and that may be used as a benchmark for both the public and private sectors. This publication also may be used to assess performance and implementation of response drills and exercises.

Measures of Effectiveness

The effectiveness of spill and release response measures varies with the circumstances. For example, if a worker closes the leaking valve on a vat of acetone and the valve ceases to leak, the response is most likely a success. Other factors that could be considered in this example are the following:

- Was the worker or anyone else injured in the response?
- Was the material contained or prevented from spreading in accordance with the facility's emergency response plan?
- Was clean-up equipment readily accessible and in proper working condition?
- If the material leaked onto soil, was it completely removed, as demonstrated by sampling and analysis, or did it simply become an airborne

or waterborne spill (caused cross-media contamination)?

The most basic goal of most spill response plans is to safely stop, control, or contain the spill or release and clean up any spilled material (whenever possible). The details of how to accomplish the goal varies from facility to facility and often depends on the characteristics of the material and the quantity of spilled or released material. Benchmarks and performance appraisal criteria should be developed from those details and from any applicable regulatory requirements. In the example above, one very important benchmark of spill clean-up effectiveness is the sampling and analysis of contaminated soil. If analysis of a soil sample revealed contamination in excess of regulatory limits, the clean up was not completely successful—an indication that the spill response plan should be reevaluated.

Operational Readiness

Once plans are determined to be current, comprehensive, and complete, they should be tested. Table-top exercises and other small-group drills are a logical starting place. In preparation for exercises and drills, it may be useful to develop a site-specific checklist to help ensure operational readiness. Some of the following questions may prove helpful in checklist development:

- Do individual workers know how to safely detect and report a spill? Putting a pound of dry ice in a small puddle of vinegar creates a smoking, low pH spill simulation.
- Do workers walk by, or do they investigate? If shift supervisors are responsible for notifying the plant security force that a spill has occurred, are the supervisors capable of transmitting on the same frequency as the security radios? If shift supervisors use an in-plant telephone system, can they get from their normal workstation to the telephone quickly enough?
- Equipment should be inspected. Are self-contained breathing apparatuses (SCBAs) usable and equipped with filled cylinders?

Are pumps and hoses stored so they can be immediately used, or do they need to be reconfigured?

- Are high-dollar items such as direct-reading instruments (photo ionization detectors, chemical-specific detectors) and response suits immediately available? If they are kept in locked cabinets for physical security (a smart procedure), where are the keys to the locks?

- Are people ready to respond to emergencies? Can the in-plant response team be mobilized five minutes before the end of a shift on Friday or the day before a holiday? If off-shift personnel are equipped with pagers for rapid recall, will they answer their pagers and respond at night and on weekends? Can in-plant personnel operate safely until off-site emergency personnel respond?

- Is the facility's management prepared to implement an emergency response plan at 2:00 A.M.? Do they have the authority to incur the expense of mobilizing a commercial response team if that is part of the plan? Will they actually call the fire department and emergency medical service, or will they have to wait for authorization from senior personnel?

Once small teams have had the opportunity to practice, the entire plan should be implemented. Are the planned command-site locations realistic, given the nature and quantity of material likely to be involved in a spill? Does the plan assume that more personnel and equipment are available than actually exist? If forklifts are included as response equipment, who will operate them? Are a sufficient number of vehicles available, or will one function take priority? For example, if one in-plant vehicle is scheduled to move injured personnel to the first-aid clinic, one in-plant vehicle is scheduled to move the response team from their normal workstations to the spill site, and one in-plant vehicle is scheduled to move emergency response personnel and equipment, are three in-plant vehicles available, or will one function (e.g., moving the injured) take priority?

During table-top exercises, small group drills, and the first or second full-team exercise, no fault should be assessed for failure to implement the plan. Many failures at this level are due to simple lack of training or awareness of the implications of the training. Honest critiques, pointing out deficiencies in implementing the plan, should be conducted to ensure that all personnel know what their individual, specific roles are. A lab technician or part-time security guard may be the initial incident commander and should understand exactly what that means. Benchmarking, or measuring the success of implementing the emergency response safely and efficiently, means that everyone involved should be able to effectively perform their emergency response role, from reporting the spill on a radio to obtaining and donning the correct PPE and plugging leaking equipment.

Performance Appraisal Criteria

Performance appraisals are essential for the effective management of an incident and for the evaluation of worker effectiveness, techniques, and equipment and supplies used for emergency response. Appraisals both during and after the incident (whenever possible) and during and after exercises and drills help improve the effectiveness of the response and provide valuable information for future responses. Once specific goals or actions have been identified in the response plan, devise a simple way to measure their effectiveness, such as a checklist or any other convenient format (e.g., a narrative).

Performance appraisals conducted during exercises demonstrate the strengths and shortcomings of the emergency response plan—such as the use of inadequate equipment, the need for further employee training, or the need for improved communications during an incident. For example, the emergency response plan of a fictitious company directs a particular employee to close a particular valve to stop a release. On the day of the planned exercise, the employee was absent, so the valve was not closed. This fact would have been noted during a post-exercise performance evaluation and the corrective measures implemented.

COST ANALYSIS AND BUDGETING

Preparing for 24-hour spill response—personnel selection and training, medical surveillance, personal protective equipment, increased staffing for immediate, around-the-clock response—is a major expense. Before any resources are committed to spill response, a risk determination and a cost-benefit analysis should be performed. What is the likelihood that a spill or release will occur? Consuming thousands of dollars and hundreds of man-hours to prepare for an event that is unlikely to occur may not be justified. On the other hand, what are the consequences of a spill or release? Even in the unlikely event of a spill, severe consequences may require some type of immediate response.

The accidents at Three Mile Island, Pennsylvania, and Bhopal, India, demonstrate the disastrous consequences of improperly evaluating a seemingly small, unlikely event. Do the materials known to be present or likely to be involved in a spill or release require immediate response? If oil from a failing tank is contained within a dike, responders have some time before the oil is recovered. On the other hand, an oil spill from a ship or shore-based facility can result in tens of thousands of dollars in damages if an effective spill containment and control plan is not implemented within minutes. A small chemical reactor in a laboratory may release only a few liters of a spontaneously combustible catalyst. The ensuing fire may destroy thousands of dollars of equipment if it is not controlled immediately. Perhaps designing the plant to operate on a lower inventory of hazardous materials or using diluted, less hazardous materials may be a more efficient use of resources.

Assessment of Risk

There are numerous computer programs and planning processes that can assist in predicting the spread of a hazardous material and its effects on people, property, and the environment. The following discussion is not intended to replace these planning tools, but rather to present additional concepts that can valuable in determining the need for developing a spill or release response plan.

Damage to People

Human health and safety are the prime concerns before and during the response to any type of spill or release. Spectacular, world-scale events such as the incidents at Chernobyl, Ukraine, or Bhopal, India, cause direct, measurable loss of life and damage to human health. Even less-publicized events, such as transportation accidents in the United States that released chlorine or ammonia, have killed or injured people at the site and downwind from the spill or release site. Response workers have also been at risk. During the sarin (an extremely toxic chemical) attack in the subway in Tokyo in 1995, significant numbers of response workers were adversely affected while attempting to aid injured commuters. One spectacular event, a boiling liquid–expanding vapor explosion, or BLEVE, has killed responders minutes or hours after accidents involving railroad tank cars of propane.

Risk assessment during a chemical spill response must begin before the incident. Basic questions need to be asked and answered. What types of materials are present or likely to be present? What quantities of materials are involved or likely to be involved? Are responders trained to recognize the presence of these materials and amounts and the hazards involved in the response? Do the response workers have the equipment and training to work with these materials under poorly controlled situations that typically exist during the initial phases of a response? Do the response workers actually know how to use their equipment during adverse conditions?

Planning saves lives and protects health. Before materials are brought to a site, plans should be prepared and practiced for normal operations as well as spills or releases. Even if a facility is not required to comply with the provisions of section 112(r) of the Clean Air Act, using it and the implementing regulations at 40 CFR 68 (Risk Management Program) may indicate shortfalls in planning for the safe storage and use of a specific material. The off-site consequence analysis (OCA) in 40 CFR 68 is one way to plan for possible off-site or downwind consequences of a spill or release of material. Environmental laws and safety regulations such as the Superfund Amendment and Reauthorization Act (SARA) Title III, also known as the Emergency Planning and Community Right-to-Know Act (EPCRA), and the OSHA process safety management standard, 29 CFR 1910.119, should be studied not just for legal compliance but also from the respond-on-Sunday-afternoon-in-90°F-weather or the Friday-night-in-freezing-rain perspective.

Consider the materials expected to be present; are spills or releases likely to generate flammable atmospheres? How will response workers control the release and contain released materials if flammable vapor clouds are present? Are the materials, in the quantities likely to be involved in a spill, expected to generate vapor clouds above the permissible exposure level or threshold limit value? Will workers be expected to wear air-purifying respirators or air-supplying respirators (SCBA or air lines with escape bottles)? In addition to off-site consequence analysis, the on-site procedures and techniques to prevent a release and respond safely, efficiently, and quickly if a release occurs, should be closely examined to ensure that response workers have the tools, knowledge, and skills to complete their assigned tasks.

Damage to Property

Just as spills and releases pose risks to people, they also pose risks of damage to property. A spill of a reagent or raw material represents not only the loss of that product but also of adjacent materials in storage, awaiting processing or use. Concentrated acetic acid leaking from a feed line into a processing building was allowed to leak into the soil. The spill created not only a dangerous situation to people but also corroded through the fire main to the building, causing it to fail. The failure of the fire protection system forced the closing and evacuation of the processing building. The loss of the product was only a minor expense compared to the unplanned, forced shutdown; replacement of the fire main; and restart of the system. A spill of methyl ethyl ketone peroxide resulted in a fire. The fire destroyed thousands of dollars of spill response equipment that was stored in the hazardous materials warehouse, near where it was expected to be used. Planning and practicing the plan would have indicated the raw material and the response

equipment were too close to each other. Again, the loss of the product was only part of the total loss.

Spills and releases damage more than just raw materials. Loss of operating capability can greatly exceed the cost of the materials that were spilled—and this involves any type of material, not just hazardous materials. For example, heated sugar syrup was kept in insulated tanks in a manufacturing plant. Since sugar syrup is not a "hazardous material," there was no planning for any spills or responses. When a transfer line was ruptured by a forklift, the syrup immediately overflowed the poorly designed containment system and oozed from the warehouse into the manufacturing part of the plant. Because there were no provisions for containing this hot, viscous mass, it was allowed to cool before clean up began. Unfortunately for the plant, the only door between the warehouse and the manufacturing section was in the path of the spill. Even worse, that one door had been effectively sealed shut for three days. In the rush to restart manufacturing, forklifts moving raw materials from the warehouse were driven over the partially cleaned floor. The second clean up, removing crystallized sugar syrup from all parts of the plant, took longer and cost more than the initial, poor response and greatly exceeded the cost of the syrup. Even more severe consequences may result from the release of truly "hazardous" materials.

Finished materials may also be at risk. Solvents and building maintenance materials were spilled and spread over hundreds of thousands of dollars of finished aircraft parts during a fire. Unpacking the parts, cleaning and repackaging them, and disposing of the contaminated packaging not only closed the facility but cost more than the products and initial fire and hazardous materials response. Planning the storage of hazardous materials, in the amounts typically present in the plant or facility, makes spill response quicker, safer, more efficient, and saves money.

Critical infrastructures can also be damaged during spills or releases. Sewage treatment plants may be forced to close to prevent petroleum products, activated sludge-killing materials, and heavy metals from contaminating the plant, killing all the bacteria, and being released into the environment. Highways and railways may have to be closed during spill response work to protect workers and allow equipment to operate on site. A transportation spill or a release from a facility near a bridge may affect the community for extended periods. Again, there must be plans to safely, quickly, and efficiently respond to spills.

Damage to the Environment

Critical habitats can be severely damaged during hazardous material spills. Petroleum products spilled into or onto wetlands can destroy precious, nearly irreplaceable environmental assets, as well as consume thousands of dollars in clean up and remediation. Love Canal is one example of how releases of hazardous materials damaged the environment to such an extent that people could no longer safely live in their homes. Leaking underground storage tanks are another example of hazardous material releases damaging the environment—in this case groundwater—and requiring extensive and expensive remediation efforts.

Conclusion

There are a variety of commercial planning tools, laws, and regulations that can assist in estimating the damage to people, property, and the environment from hazardous material spills and releases. Spill response plans should address not just compliance with legal requirements and costs of response, but should also address safety concerns in a realistic, ethical manner.

BEST PRACTICES IN ENVIRONMENTAL MANAGEMENT—SPILL PREVENTION AND RESPONSE

Spill Prevention and Response Plans

Spill prevention, planning, and response programs or plans are required by several federal standards. In many cases, the development and implementation of one comprehensive plan will satisfy all of the applicable federal regulatory requirements. For example, if a facility has a contingency plan, as required by EPA regulations, and that plan addresses all elements required under the HAZWOPER standard, the contin-

gency plan may be used to satisfy the HAZWOPER emergency response plan requirement.

Employers who evacuate employees from the facility during an emergency and do not allow employees to help in managing the emergency do not have to have an emergency response plan, as required by the HAZWOPER standard, as long as they provide an emergency action plan that complies with the applicable regulation (e.g., 1910.120, 1926.35).

The following is a partial list of federal standards and regulations that require some type of emergency prevention, planning, or response plan or program. This list is not inclusive; however, it is intended to demonstrate the wide range of regulations that may require a plan.

- DOT (49 CFR): Part 130—Oil Spill Prevention and Response Plans
- EPA (40 CFR): Part 68—Chemical Accident Prevention Provisions
- OSHA (29 CFR): *General Industry:* 1910.38—Emergency Action Plans, 1910.119—Process Safety Management of Highly Hazardous Chemicals, 1910.120—Hazardous Waste Operations and Emergency Response, 1915.502—Fire Safety Plan, 1917.30—Emergency Action Plans, 1918.100—Emergency Action Plans *Construction:* 1926.35—Employee Emergency Action Plans, 1926.64—Process Safety Management of Highly Hazardous Chemicals, 1926.65—Hazardous Waste Operations and Emergency Response, 1926.150—Fire Protection

Nearly all industry-accepted best practices stress incident planning, written plans, and practice exercises as essential elements of a successful emergency response. Best practices include general concepts such as planning, PPE, mitigation, and decontamination, but these must always be adapted to provide for any site-specific conditions and contingencies.

Several references are available to assist organizations in the development of site-specific best practices. Some of these are listed here:

- NFPA 471 *Recommended Practice for Responding to Hazardous Materials Incidents*, 2002 edition

- NFPA 1600 *Standard on Disaster/Emergency Management and Business Continuity Programs*, 2010 edition
- National Response Team NRT-1 *Hazardous Materials Emergency Planning Guide*, 2001 edition
- OSHA *Best Practices for Hospital-Based First Receivers of Victims from Mass Casualty Incidents Involving the Release of Hazardous Substances*, 2005 edition

The basic steps in developing an effective spill prevention and response plan that incorporates industry-accepted best practices include performing a hazard assessment, identifying ways to eliminate or reduce the hazards, developing plans and procedures to be taken in the event of an emergency, and training personnel in their particular role in an emergency and in execution of the plan. To be effective, spill prevention and response plans should be site-specific. Because all facilities are not necessarily subject to all regulations, and because the regulations have varying requirements, it is not possible to provide one plan that fits all facilities and circumstances, but the plan elements discussed below will provide a good foundation for most facilities.

Hazard Prediction Model

General Behavior Model (GEBMO) is a hazard prediction model developed by Ludwig Brenner. Given a particular set of circumstances and conditions, predictable outcomes will result. GEBMO can be used to plan responses to virtually any situation: a broken syringe or vial in a biohazard lab, small-volume spills of low-hazard material, or large-volume spills of high-hazard material. As shown in Figure 1, GEBMO considers seven factors. GEBMO is a valuable tool for predicting outcomes when completing a hazard assessment.

Hazard Assessment

Hazards may be separated into three basic types: physical, chemical, and natural. Physical hazards are those that pose a threat to human physical well-being. Examples of physical hazards are fire, explosion, noise,

slips, falls, release of hazardous energy (e.g., electrical, steam, pressurized hydraulic or other fluids), entrapment, heat and cold, and others. Some physical hazards, such as fire or explosion, may cause a spill or release of hazardous materials or hinder response efforts.

Chemical hazards, radiation, and biological agents pose an external or internal physiological threat to one or more parts of the human body. Chemical hazards can cause short- and long-term health and physical effects, the severity of which depends on several factors, such as route of entry, toxicity, amount, and duration of exposure. Poisons, corrosive materials, anthrax, and asbestos are examples of chemical hazards. During emergency response and mitigation of a spill or release, personnel must take the appropriate precautions to protect themselves from the chemical hazards associated with all of the spilled or released material(s).

Natural hazards are those found in nature and that either affect such living things as animals and insects or are caused by or exacerbated by electrical storms, earthquakes, and wildfires. Natural hazards may cause or contribute to a spill or a release or may impede emergency response and clean-up efforts.

The hazard assessment should begin with a walk-through of the site or facility. Next, determine and

FIGURE 1. General Behavior Model (GEBMO)

document the actual or potential chemical hazards, including chemical names, locations, quantities, and packaging (e.g., bulk and nonbulk containers, underground and aboveground storage tanks, process vats, and compressed gas cylinders). In the event of an emergency, some scenarios to consider are:

- Will a spill or release harm people or the environment or both?
- If spilled, can the material reach a body of water?
- If the released materials commingle, what will the results be?
- Is it likely that a natural disaster, such as an earthquake or hurricane, will result in a release of material?
- Will response efforts be hindered by physical hazards such as confined spaces, fire, release of electrical or other hazardous energy, flooding, etc.?
- Will off-site significant structures, such as buildings, bridges, tunnels, water treatment plants, schools, houses, and the like, be affected by a release?
- Is there a downwind hazard, and if so, how far does it stretch?
- In the event of a major catastrophe, what is the likelihood that personnel evacuation would be hindered?
- What off-site resources (e.g., fire departments, hazmat teams, rescue squads, commercial response companies) are available that could respond in a timely manner?
- Which federal, state, and local agencies require notification during or after a spill or release?
- Does the facility have some response capability? If so, what types or sizes of spills or releases can personnel manage? Have personnel been properly trained? Is the correct equipment available?

After the hazard assessment has been performed, decide what procedures or actions can be used to reduce or eliminate the actual or potential hazards. The three most common hazard-reduction tools are engineering controls, administrative controls (including safe work practices), and the use of personal pro-

tective equipment (PPE). These tools are primarily aimed at increasing worker health and safety, but are very valuable in reducing the likelihood of an accidental spill or release because a safer workplace results in fewer accidents. The responsible party should try one or more of the following:

- Engineering Controls: Engineering controls are usually the most effective measures because they are used to control the hazard at its source. If possible, design the equipment or process so that it is less hazardous. This is sometimes accomplished by substituting a hazardous material with one that is less hazardous. Some engineering controls are quite simple. For example, enclosing a hazard may remove it completely. Barriers, spill containment, blast shields, automatic monitoring and shut-off equipment, and local ventilation are other ways to reduce or eliminate hazards.
- Administrative Controls: Administrative controls are measures that are designed to reduce employee exposure to hazards. Common measures include rotation of workers, exercise breaks, shorter shifts, heat/cold stress management, the use of additional relief workers, and others. Administrative controls are often used with other controls, such as PPE, that more directly prevent or control exposure to the hazard.

Safe work practices are often considered forms of administrative controls. These controls are generally presented as employer-specific and operation-specific rules, such as written operating procedures, the use of buddy systems, training, use of permits (e.g., hot work and confined space permits), warning signs, alarms, and the like.

- Personal Protective Equipment: PPE should be used as the last resort (after engineering controls and administrative controls) to protect personnel from hazards at the site or facility. The use of PPE requires its own hazard assessment to determine what kind of equipment is needed to protect against the hazards of the job. It is very important that employees are trained on the selection, use, and maintenance of PPE. They must understand that PPE does not eliminate the hazard. If the equipment is not the correct equipment for the job, or if it fails, exposure to the hazardous material(s) will occur. Again, keeping workers safe will help reduce accidents, including spills and other surprise releases.

It is very helpful to elicit worker input during this stage of emergency planning. Employees who actually work with the materials often have valuable suggestions that may greatly assist in developing hazard analysis and ways to mitigate those hazards.

Develop Written Plans and Procedures

Once the hazard analysis is complete and hazard reduction tools have been considered and implemented, as indicated, the written plan may be developed. The plan should be reviewed and evaluated every year and updated, as necessary. At minimum, the following plan elements should be addressed:

Facility or Site Description. This section should include the facility address and a general description of facility function. It should include topography (if applicable), the surrounding population, facility layout, off-site concerns (e.g., waterways, downwind hazard zones, significant structures), and a general description of the types and quantities of hazardous materials on site.

Personnel Roles and Communication. This section should describe the roles all personnel will play in the event of an emergency. Roles may be described by department (e.g., Maintenance Department or Radiation Department), job function (e.g., mechanic or administrative), title (e.g., vice president or safety manager), and/or by name. Lines of personnel authority and a description of how communication will take place should also be included.

Describe medical and security duties for those employees who are to perform them. The role of some personnel or departments may be simply to evacuate. If that is the case, clearly state that in the plan. List who will be responsible for ensuring all employees

have been safely evacuated and who will be responsible for federal, state, and local notifications. Also include in the plan the names or job titles of persons who can be contacted for an explanation of personnel roles and responsibilities or for questions about the plan.

Evacuation Routes and Procedures. Obtain a site map or diagram of the facility. On the map, mark evacuation routes, exits, locations of emergency supplies and equipment, locations of emergency shutoffs, floor drains, bodies of water, safe meeting places, hazardous locations, and any other information that would be pertinent in an emergency. Depending on the size and type of the facility, a lockbox located outside the facility, which contains MSDSs, a site map, emergency contact information, and facility keys, may be required by the local fire department. If such a lockbox is used, be sure to note its location on the map so that, if necessary, local responders may be directed to the box by the person reporting the emergency. Post the map in several locations throughout the facility, as appropriate.

Describe the conditions and procedures for reporting incidents to local, state, and federal governmental agencies. At some facilities, workers may be trained to respond to small spills and leaks, but also may depend on outside sources for help with management of larger spills. Because the meanings of *small* and *large* are relative, be sure to define those terms in the plan. Reporting procedures should include initial emergency reporting as well as any required written or follow-up post-incident reports.

Develop written procedures to be followed by employees who are to remain behind to operate or shut down critical plant operations or equipment before they evacuate. Develop procedures to account for all employees after an emergency evacuation has been completed and what to do if not all personnel can be accounted for.

Emergency Procedures. In this section, clearly describe, step by step, all procedures that should be used during a spill or other emergency involving hazardous materials. Each topic should be addressed in logical steps or bulleted lists so that during an emergency, when stress is likely to be high, the procedures are very clear and easy to follow. Some of the procedures may be redundant, but this section is meant to be clear, simple, and easy to follow during emergencies. For some facilities, the emergency procedures may consist only of two steps—evacuate all personnel and call 911—but for most facilities, the procedures will be more in depth. For very large facilities with multiple types of concurrent operations, a flow chart may be useful for showing how emergencies in one area do or do not affect other areas of the facility. These facilities may also benefit from having several smaller emergency response plans in various areas of the plant, with a master plan maintained by the administration or safety office.

Clearly describe the following, as applicable to the facility or site, as well as any other site-specific procedures that are needed:

- Emergency alerting and notification procedures: Outline how the emergency will be communicated to other facility personnel and to outside agencies, if necessary.
- Security: Spell out how to secure and control the spill or release site and how to secure and control the facility or any off-site locations.
- Evacuation/safe distances: Delineate where and by what route personnel are to go so they are a safe distance from the release.
- Outline facility, process, and equipment shutdown procedures.
- Lay out specific steps and methods to stop, contain, or confine the spill or release, including the necessary PPE and emergency equipment and supplies.
- List the monitoring frequency and methods.
- Emergency medical treatment and first-aid procedures: If medical treatment and first aid are to be administered only by trained outside professionals, state that; if injuries may be treated by facility personnel, this section may contain procedures for categories of injuries, such as burns, cuts, punctures, and others
- Decontamination procedures: Detail routine and emergency decontamination procedures.

Post-Response Actions. Once the spill or release emergency response and clean up is complete, it is very useful (and required by some regulations) to perform an incident investigation and to critique the response actions. This investigation is a tool that is useful for discovering hazards that were either inadequately addressed or completely missed in earlier stages of planning. The ultimate purpose of accident and incident investigation is to make the system better—to uncover and correct the root cause of the problem and to prevent future occurrences—not to place blame.

Another post-response action that may be required by federal or state regulations (e.g., the HAZWOPER standard and others) is a follow-up report. Consult the applicable agency or regulation(s) to ensure that the required information is submitted in a timely fashion.

Personnel Training

Before any spill response or other emergency plan is implemented, all affected personnel must receive training, the level of which depends on the employees' responsibilities during an emergency. For employees who are not likely to have contact with hazardous materials and who will have no responsibility other than to evacuate, minimal training is needed. These people need to be trained to understand the general contents of the plan and when and how to evacuate. Also, an appropriate number of people should be trained to help with the safe evacuation of employees during an emergency.

As the level of responsibility goes up, so does the amount and type of training. At a minimum, OSHA's *Hazard Communication Standard* training will apply, and depending on the type of site or facility, it is likely that training requirements of the HAZWOPER standard will also apply. Most hazardous waste site workers (including those who respond to emergencies at those sites) will need 40 hours of training plus an annual refresher, as detailed in 29 CFR 1910.120(e).

Employees who respond to hazardous material spills and releases at sites other than hazardous waste sites are required to have the appropriate level of training found in 29 CFR 1910.120(q). The five levels of training (which also require an annual refresher) and a brief description of duties found in this section include the following:

- First responder awareness level: These are workers who are likely to witness or discover a spill or release and whose only responsibility is to notify the proper authorities of the release.
- First responder operations level: These are workers who respond initially to help protect nearby people, property, and/or the environment from the effects of the release. They do not specifically try to stop the release, but instead try remotely to contain or stop the spread of the release.
- Hazardous material technician: This is a worker who more aggressively tries to stop the release by patching, plugging, or using some other method.
- Hazardous material specialist: This is a worker whose duties are similar to the hazardous material technician. The specialist has more of a specific knowledge of the material or process and provides support to hazardous material technicians. They also have the authority to act as the site liaison with federal, state, local, and other government authorities regarding site activities.
- On-scene incident commander: He or she assumes control of the incident scene and is able to implement the employer's emergency response plan and incident command system and local emergency response plan. The commander also has a thorough knowledge and understanding of the risks and hazards involved when employees are working in PPE (including decontamination procedures). In addition, the on-scene incident commander must have knowledge of the state emergency response plan and of the federal Regional Response Team.

At a minimum, personnel should be trained when the plan is first developed, whenever worker responsibilities or procedures change, and whenever the plan is changed or revised. For information on training benchmarks, see the "Training Benchmarks—Sources of Information" section earlier in this chapter.

Practice drills are recommended to familiarize workers with the procedures and to reinforce behav-

iors that are necessary during emergencies. Critiques of the drills can be used to discover and improve plan weaknesses.

Medical Surveillance

Medical screening and medical surveillance are two basic, distinct methods used to monitor and help protect worker health. The purpose of medical screening is the early detection, diagnosis, and treatment of an individual worker who has been exposed and adversely affected by an incident. As in pre-employment screening, the purpose of medical screening is to provide a baseline of the worker's current medical condition so that later changes resulting from workplace exposures can be detected. The main purposes of medical surveillance are to detect, then eliminate, the underlying causes of specific, work-related health problems and to detect exposure trends, often across groups of workers.

Numerous OSHA standards require some type of medical screening/surveillance. See OSHA's Web site (www.osha.gov) for more information and additional medical screening/surveillance resources. Personnel engaged in hazardous waste or emergency response operations must be covered under a medical surveillance program. Generally speaking, the employer must institute a medical surveillance program for any of the following employees:

- employees who are or may be exposed to hazardous substances or health hazards at or above the established permissible exposure limit, published exposure level (without regard to the use of respirators) for 30 or more days a year
- all employees who wear a respirator for 30 days or more a year
- all employees who are injured, become ill, or develop signs or symptoms as a result of an overexposure involving hazardous substances or health hazards from an emergency response or hazardous waste operation
- employees who work with specific substances (e.g., lead, arsenic, benzene, and many others)
- employees who are members of hazardous material teams

Personal Protective Equipment

The classic hierarchy of safety techniques is engineering controls, administrative controls, and personal protective equipment (PPE). Engineering controls are physical modifications of the work site to protect workers. During spill or release responses, engineering controls will be extremely difficult to establish. By the very nature of a spill or release, engineering controls have either failed or cannot be established until the response action is nearly complete. Similarly, administrative controls, although helpful in setting safe work conditions, will not provide adequate protection to response workers. Therefore, personal protective equipment, generally the last choice in protecting workers, becomes the prime, and sometimes the only, reliable way to protect workers during the initial phases of spill responses.

Table 1 lists the four levels of protection specified in the *Hazardous Waste Operations and Emergency Response* (HAZWOPER) standard, published at 29 CFR 1910.120, Appendix B. The table also lists selection criteria and some disadvantages for each level of protection. There are several factors that greatly enhance the safety provided by PPE. These include, but are not limited to, the following:

- Chemical compatibility: Any item of PPE—body protection, gloves, boots, accessories—must be resistant to the materials present or likely to be present in a spill. There are two measures of compatibility: breakthrough time and permeation rate. Breakthrough time, simply put, is the time it takes an item of PPE to leak. This time interval between first contact on the outside and detection of the material on the inside of the PPE is critical to proper selection. Some materials will cause virtually instantaneous failure of PPE. Obviously, this provides no protection to workers. The longer the breakthrough time, the better the PPE is suited for a particular response. The second measure of compatibility is the permeation rate. Again, simply put, this is the rate PPE leaks, once breakthrough has been achieved. The lower the permeation rate, the better the

protection provided to workers. Virtually all manufacturers provide breakthrough times and permeation rates for their particular brands and models of PPE. Do not use equipment without this information. Additional sources of information include NIOSH, the National Fire Protection Association (NFPA), and numerous commercial spill response manuals.

- All levels of PPE should be considered a complete ensemble. If the fabric of a Level A suit provides hours of breakthrough time when exposed to a specific chemical, but the facepiece fogs instantly when exposed to the same material, the ensemble fails. Outer gloves and boots or boot covers must provide the same breakthrough time and permeation resistance as the suit.

- Size: A 100-pound, 5-foot-tall worker cannot safely wear the same PPE that fits a 250-pound, 6-foot-tall responder. PPE selection is often based solely on chemical compatibility. Workers who cannot safely move on a spill site are not protected—they are just wearing a chemical resistant wrapping that creates slip, trip, and fall hazards.

- Suitability for the task: Full-facepiece respirators worn under a chemical protective suit with a hood and built-in facepiece provide excellent chemical protection but effectively destroy all peripheral vision. Most Level A suits, properly sized, will not allow the wearers to see their feet or what they are walking on. PPE must address all hazards on the spill site. Workers who need corrective lenses may not be able to achieve a proper fit with some half-mask respirators. Full-facepiece respirators with spectacle kits inside the mask may be required.

- Training: Life is different and difficult inside PPE—even something as simple as Level C splash suits and half-mask respirators. Breathing is more difficult and voice communications are limited. Workers must be comfortable enough and confident enough in PPE to work safely and efficiently. This comfort and

TABLE 1

Personal Protective Equipment				
Level	Selection Criteria	Respiratory Protection	Body Protection	Limitations
A	• The greatest level of eye, skin, and respiratory protection is required • Substances with a high degree of hazard to the skin are known or suspected to present, and skin contact is possible • Operations are being conducted in confined, poorly ventilated areas and the absence of conditions requiring Level A have not yet been determined	Pressure-demand, full-facepiece SCBA or pressure-demand supplied-air respirator with escape SCBA, NIOSH-approved	• Totally-encapsulating chemical protective-suit • Inner and outer chemical-resistant gloves • Chemical-resistant, steel-toe and shank boots Optional items: • Coveralls • Long underwear • Outer boots or boot covers • Hard hat (under suit)	• Fully-encapsulating suit material must be compatible with the substances involved • Movement is restricted • Induces heat stress
B	• The highest level of respiratory protection is necessary, but a lesser level of skin protection is needed. • The atmosphere contains less than 19.5% oxygen • The presence of incompletely identified gases are indicated by a direct-reading instrument, but they are not suspected of being harmful to the skin	Pressure-demand, full-facepiece SCBA or pressure-demand supplied-air respirator with escape SCBA, NIOSH-approved	• Hooded, chemical-resistant clothing (hooded one- or two-piece suit; disposable chemical-resistant overalls) • Inner and outer chemical-resistant gloves • Chemical-resistant steel toe and shank boots Optional items: • Coveralls • Long underwear • Outer boots or boot covers • Hard hat (under suit)	• Use only when exposure to materials will not adversely affect the skin • Suit, outer gloves, and boots must be chemically compatible with materials present • Induces heat stress
C	• The concentration(s) and type(s) of airborne substance(s) are known, and the criteria for using air-purifying respirators are met • Atmospheric contaminants, liquid splashes, or other direct contact will not adversely affect or be absorbed through the skin • The types of air contaminants have been identified, concentrations measured, and an air-purifying respirator is available that can remove the contaminants	Full-face or half-mask NIOSH-approved respirators	• Hooded, chemical-resistant clothing (hooded one- or two-piece suit; disposable chemical-resistant overalls) • Inner and outer chemical-resistant gloves • Chemical-resistant steel toe and shank boots Optional items: • Coveralls • Long underwear • Hard hat (under suit)	• Atmospheric concentrations of chemical must not exceed IDLH levels • The atmosphere must contain at least 19.5% oxygen • May not protect workers from sudden, drastic changes at the work site
D	• A work uniform providing minimal protection; used for nuisance contamination only • The atmosphere contains no known hazards • Work functions preclude splashes, immersion, or the potential for unexpected inhalation of, or contact with, hazardous levels of any chemicals	None required	• Coveralls • Chemical-resistant steel toe and shank boots Optional items: • Gloves • Hard hat • Safety glasses or chemical splash goggles • Face shield • Escape mask	• This level should not be worn in areas where chemical exposures are likely • The atmosphere must contain at least 19.5% oxygen • May not protect workers from sudden, drastic changes at the work site

(*Source*: National Institute for Occupational Safety and Health 1985)

The standard for personal protective equipment (PPE) is at 29 CFR 1910.120, Appendix B. It is important to note that this appendix includes the statement: ". . . Combinations or personal protective equipment other than those described for Levels A, B, C, and D protection may be more appropriate and may be used to provide the proper level of protection."

confidence comes only through repeated training exercises, under conditions likely to be encountered during spill responses. Training in the actual suits to be worn during a spill response may damage the suits. It may be necessary to dedicate specific suits to training use while saving other suits, of the same model, for actual responses.

- Disposable versus reusable: Reusable PPE may offer some long-term cost savings. But after exposure to specific materials, it may not be possible to completely decontaminate reusable PPE. Given that PPE is often stored for weeks or months between responses, small amounts of contaminants missed during decontamination may permeate through suits, gloves, etc., exposing responders as soon as they don the "protective" equipment.

Spill Kits

Spill kits can solve many problems in an emergency. While planning the response, two important questions to be answered are (a) Who will use the kits? and (b) How big is the potential spill? A 5-gallon bucket of sorbents will not control most spills from a rail car. An 85-gallon overpack drum full of rubber suits, goggles, shovels, and sorbents is useless in the hands of unskilled or untrained personnel.

Components of spill kits can be divided into two sections—PPE and containment and recovery tools. PPE should include head, body, hands, and feet protection. Relatively inexpensive coated and hooded Tyvek or PVC coveralls may be sufficient. Inner surgeon's gloves and long gauntlet outer gloves and boot covers, if resistant to the spilled chemicals, may complete the skin protection equipment. Respiratory equipment will range from half-mask disposable respirators to positive-pressure, full-facepiece SCBAs, depending on the vapor pressure of the spilled material, the toxicity of the spilled material, and the location of the spill. Other items include splash aprons, goggles, hard hats, and thermal protection, depending on the nature of the spill.

Containment and recovery tools are sorbents (absorbents and adsorbents), diking and patching materials, tools to deploy and recover them, and containers. Again, the type and amount of materials depends on the vapor pressure of the spilled material, the toxicity of the spilled material, the size of the anticipated spill, and the location of the spill. Materials generally useful on spills include the following:

- oil dry or some type of expanded clay (in 40- to 50-pound bags): used for general purpose diking and solidifying liquids
- granular activated carbon (in 40- to 50-pound bags): used to absorb and adsorb vapors and liquids from spill materials with high vapor pressure
- garden lime (in 50-pound bags): used to neutralize and solidify spilled liquid acids
- food-grade granular citric acid (in 50-pound bags): used to neutralize spilled liquid bases
- shovels, scoops, dust pans, and brooms to apply the material and to recover it once it has been used
- absorbent/adsorbent pads and pillows
- drums to hold everything ready for use and to contain used sorbents
- containment and sorbent boom if a spill is expected near water or if drains need to be blocked off
- plastic bags to contain used sorbent materials
- DOT-specification drums to contain and transport spill clean-up materials
- overpack drums if leaking drums are included in the plan
- warning barricades (tape, cones, portable barriers)
- documentation on transporting hazardous wastes—labels, manifests, and placards

The previous list is not exhaustive. Many products such as corn oil, vinegar, household hydrogen peroxide, liquid chlorine bleach, baking soda, soda ash, and sodium carbonate may be useful in certain cases. As mentioned previously, the components of the spill kit should be based on a realistic assessment of likely spill situations and the size and competence of the crew using the kit.

Site Layout

A spill or release site is typically divided into work zones to provide better control of the incident and to increase worker safety. In very general terms, a spill response contains three zones, as shown in Figure 2.

Hot Zone: Also called the work zone or the exclusion zone, it is the area of highest known or anticipated contamination. There may be areas of higher contamination or different types of contamination within the hot zone. For example, if a process building was damaged during a fire and explosion, each reactor vessel or broken pipe may be designated a separate high-risk area within the hot zone. Each drum or pallet of drums released from a truck or train may be designated a high-risk area, or there may be different risk areas (flammable, toxic, corrosive, oxidized) within the overall hot zone for a transportation accident. All personnel not wearing the proper personal protective equipment should be barred from entering the hot zone.

Warm Zone: Also called the contamination reduction zone or buffer zone, it is an area of reduced contamination or potential for worker exposure. Air monitoring to determine evacuation distances and soil and water sampling to determine the extent of contamination are significant activities conducted within the warm zone. As with the hot zone, only personnel wearing the proper personal protective equipment should be allowed to enter the warm zone.

Cold Zone: Also called the support zone or administrative zone, it is an area of no known contamination or no anticipated exposure to hazardous materials. The command post, first-aid station, equipment storage area, maintenance areas, media briefing area, and break areas are typically located within the cold zone. Keeping unwanted or unnecessary personnel from the cold zone can become a major activity if security is not maintained. Maintaining security on the site can be very difficult in urban areas, production facilities, and research laboratories.

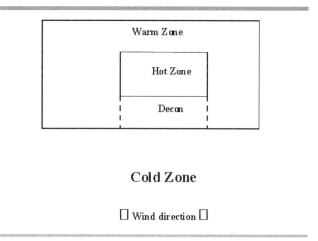

FIGURE 2. Spill response work zones (*Source*: NIOSH 1985)

Decon: Also known as the contamination reduction corridor or the personnel/equipment decontamination station, the decon area is where chemical contamination is removed from personnel, tools, instruments, and equipment before any person or any item is allowed to enter the cold zone. Decon, discussed elsewhere in detail, is a sizable subject. In general, the same level of personal protective equipment is used on decon and in the hot zone: Level A decons Level A, Level C decons Level C. Occasionally, it may be possible to step down one level: Level B decons Level A, Level C decons Level B. Decon personnel should always wear at least Level C. Improper or incomplete decon endangers personnel, property, and the environment by allowing contamination to escape into the general, uncontrolled environment. On multiple-day responses, every reasonable attempt should be made to keep decon uphill and upwind from the hot zone.

Wind Direction: If at all possible, the site should be established so that the wind blows from the command post in the cold zone, through decon, onto the hot zone. On the downwind side of the hot zone, the warm and cold zones should be large enough so that personnel outside the spill response site are not in risk of contact with either atmospheric (airborne) or physical (liquid, solid) contact with chemical contaminants.

It is important to realize that work zones are *never* uniformly shaped circles and rectangles. Rooms, hallways, buildings, roads, fences, streams, and other physical structures always make establishing work zones difficult. When establishing work zones, maximum use should be made of physical items. "Thirty feet" from the doorway is a meaningless expression in an emergency. Traffic cones, colored barricade tape, chairs laying on their sides, curbs—virtually any physical object—should be used to establish the work-zone boundaries.

Air Monitoring

When hazardous or toxic vapors are a concern at a spill or release site, the use of air-monitoring instruments is necessary to ensure the safety of both on-site and off-site personnel. To adequately sample the air at the site of a spill or release, air-monitoring instruments should be placed at various locations throughout the work site. In addition to semipermanent air samplers, area monitoring stations may also include direct-reading instruments (DRIs), such as photo ionization and flame ionization detectors, which are equipped with recorders and operated as continuous air monitors. Area monitoring stations should be placed in the following locations:

- *Upwind.* Many hazardous incidents occur near manufacturing facilities or highways that generate air pollutants. Air must be monitored upwind of the site, and wherever there are other potential sources of contaminants, to establish background levels of air contaminants.
- *Support or Cold Zone.* Air must be monitored near the command post or other support facilities to ensure that they are maintained in a clean area.
- *Contamination Reduction or Warm Zone.* Air should be monitored along the contamination control line to ensure that personnel are properly protected and the on-site workers are not removing their protective gear in a contaminated area.
- *Exclusion or Hot Zone.* The exclusion zone presents the greatest risk of exposure to chemicals and requires the most air sampling. The loca-

tion of an air-monitoring station should be based upon the hot spots or source areas detected by DRIs, types of substances present, and potential for airborne contaminants.

- *Fence Line/Downwind.* Air-monitoring stations should be placed downwind from the site to determine whether any air contaminants are migrating from the site. If there are indications of airborne hazards in populated areas, additional monitors should be placed downwind.
- *Periodic Monitoring.* Site conditions and atmospheric chemical conditions may change following the initial characterization. Periodic monitoring should be conducted when the possibility of a dangerous condition has developed or when there is reason to believe that exposures may have risen above PELs since prior monitoring was conducted. The possibility that exposures have risen should be seriously considered when any of the following occurs:

    1. work begins on a different portion of the site
    2. different contaminants are being handled
    3. a markedly different type of operation is initiated (e.g., drum opening, as opposed to exploratory well drilling)
    4. workers are handling leaking drums or working in areas with obvious liquid contamination (e.g., a spill or lagoon)

Personnel Monitoring

The selective monitoring of any high-risk workers (i.e., those who are closest to the source of contaminant generation) is required by 29CFR 1910.120(h). Because occupational exposures are linked closely with active material handling, personal air monitoring is not necessary until site operations have begun. If any employee is exposed to concentrations over PELs, monitoring must continue to ensure the safety of all employees likely to be exposed to concentrations above those limits.

Meteorological Considerations

As an integral part of any air-monitoring plan, data concerning wind speed and direction, temperature, barometric pressure, and humidity, or a combination of these, are needed for selecting air-sampling locations, calculating air dispersion, calibrating instruments, and determining population at risk of exposure from airborne contaminants.

Control and Clean Up

Spill Containment

Containment is the process of stopping a release or preventing its spread through mechanical means without adding chemical or biological agents. Containment methods may include patching and plugging the leaking container; building dikes, berms, or dams; reorientation of the leaking container; overpack drums; portable collection vessels; or others, as appropriate.

Containment devices or substitute containers may be useful in stopping a leak. Be sure the containment device is chemically compatible with the leaking substance. Build dikes, berms, or dams, using earth or sand. A container such as a plastic swimming pool or inflatable raft may be useful. Dig a pit or trench to stop the slow flow of liquids. Use sorbents to slow or stop the flow of material. Placing the leaking container in a larger container (overpack) and filling any space with absorbent materials is an effective means of containment.

Portable collection vessels are usually containers of a size that can be easily transported to the spill site. These may be used to catch the substance as it spills out. This method is often an interim measure used while the leak is being patched. Containment should be the first response considered when a spill occurs because it provides the following advantages:

- minimizes damage to the environment
- allows for on-site clean up
- prevents spilled material from flowing into the waterways or entering into sewers, streams, and subsurface water supplies

Sorbents

Sorbents are materials that physically remove liquid chemicals from surfaces (including the surface of other liquids, such as water). Generally, synthetic sorbents *adsorb* liquids, and natural sorbents *absorb* them. Absorption is the process of taking up a hazardous liquid material. Adsorption is the process in which materials adhere to the surface. Sorbents may be used to slow or stop the flow of material and are often also used as clean-up tools.

Patching and Plugging

If possible, attempt to patch or plug the leak to prevent further releases from occurring during the clean up. The degree of difficulty involved in patching or plugging a leaking container depends on the hazards of the substances involved and the size and location of the leak. For smaller containers, turn it so the leak is on top, then patch or plug with any suitable, chemically compatible material, such as wood plugs or golf tees, pieces of rubber (e.g., patches made from inner tubes), pieces of thin scrap metal, or commercially available kits and devices. Sometimes materials may be solidified or frozen to stop a leak. It may be possible to create an internal patch or barrier with matting or other material. Through proper planning, a plug and patch kit should be available and easily accessible.

Forklift Punctures

Because drums are heavy, they are frequently handled by forklifts. Consequently, many incidents are caused by the forks puncturing the drum about five inches from the bottom. If this occurs, the forklift should be withdrawn from the hole and the drum rotated so the hole is above the product level. The following sequence may be used to patch forklift or other holes:

- Use a wire brush to roughen the area over the hole, removing all paint down to bare metal. Be careful to consider flammability before creating friction and possibly sparks.
- Drive a wooden wedge into the hole with a hammer. Do not drive the wedge completely inside the drum. If lead wool is available, it

should be packed around the wedge to afford a tight seal. Cut the wedge flush with the drum.

- Put aluminum tape over the wedge.
- Put epoxy over the tape and smooth the surface even with the drum.
- Place the drum in a DOT specification overpack "salvage drum" before transporting.

Compressed Gases

Preparing for an emergency involving compressed gases is not possible without familiarity of the properties of the gases on site. After the hazards are identified, develop an emergency response plan that includes, at the minimum, procedures for managing leaks, first aid, and fire prevention. Positive-pressure SCBAs, PPE, fire extinguishers, and other emergency equipment should be readily available for use by trained personnel.

Fires

First, evacuate all personnel who are not actively involved in fire fighting. If a fire has started that is being fed by a flammable oxidizing gas, turn off the supply of gas *only* if it is safe to do so. If a flammable gas fire is extinguished when the valve is still open, explosive mixtures of flammable gas and air may be formed. Never enter an enclosed area unless it has been adequately ventilated and checked with an air monitor.

Once the fire is out, cool the cylinders and surrounding area with water spray (or other material, as indicated on the MSDS). Indiscriminate use of water on fires involving cryogenic liquids can produce icy surfaces. If the fire is coming from the cylinder, it is often best to let it burn itself out. Again, know the chemical and physical properties of the gases on site. Never put a cylinder that has been involved in a fire back in service.

Leaks

Do not attempt to control or repair a leak without the proper equipment and training. Never attempt to manage a leak without knowing the chemical and physical properties of the gas.

First, check the valve; it may not be fully closed. For flammable, inert, and oxidizing gases, notify the appropriate response personnel. Move the cylinder to an isolated area with adequate ventilation. Post warning signs that describe the hazard(s). For corrosive and toxic gases, notify the appropriate response personnel. Don the proper PPE and move the cylinder to an isolated area with adequate ventilation. If possible, direct the gas into an appropriate chemical neutralizer, such as a plastic drum filled with lime or a caustic soda solution. Post warning signs that describe the hazard(s).

Treatment

Depending on the type and amount of material released, one or more treatment or clean-up methods may be available. Spilled or released materials may be treated by chemical, biological, or physical means. Many times, acids and bases can be neutralized (chemical treatment) to make clean up safer and easier and to lessen disposal costs. Oxidation or reduction reactions are another example of chemical treatment. Biological treatment methods may include aerobic or anaerobic degradation, the use of specific fungi or bacteria, the use of abiotic technologies, and others. Coagulation, air stripping, clarification, and burning are examples of physical treatment methods.

DECONTAMINATION

Decontamination is the process of removing or neutralizing contaminants that have accumulated on personnel, PPE, tools, instruments, samples, vehicles, and all other equipment and supplies used on site. Proper decontamination protects all site personnel by minimizing the transfer of hazardous substances into clean areas, and it protects the community as a whole by preventing the transportation of contaminants from the site.

Everything—all personnel, clothing, equipment, samples, and so on—leaving the contaminated area of a site must be decontaminated to remove any contaminants that may have adhered to them. Decontamination methods either physically remove any contaminants, inactivate them, or remove contaminants by a combination of both physical and chemical means. Many factors, including availability, ease of use, site resources, and cost, influence the selection of decontamination equipment and methods. To be safe and effective, ensure that the selected decontamination methods are effective for the type of contamination present and that the decontamination methods do not pose additional health or safety hazards.

The best way to minimize the amount of necessary decontamination is to work as cleanly as possible. Here are seven ways to *work clean*:

- Minimize contact with contamination—do not walk through puddles, do not touch obviously contaminated surfaces.
- Use remote tools and equipment as much as possible. Be careful that you are not just contaminating equipment instead of people.
- Protect tools and equipment as much as possible by bagging or wrapping in disposable plastic.
- Wear disposable outer gloves, boot covers, head gear, and suits that are relatively quick and easy to change.
- Cover tools and equipment with strippable coatings that can easily be removed, taking any contamination with them.
- Contain the contamination—use overpacks, plastic sheeting, barrier foams, or thin layers of clean soil to cover contaminated ground.
- Whenever possible, use the least hazardous material/method when working (e.g., use water-based solvents; use a household neutralizer, such as vinegar, instead of a stronger acid).

Contaminants may be found on the surface of personal protective or other equipment or may have permeated the material. Surface contaminants are often easy to see and remove, but contaminants that have permeated a material are very often extremely difficult or impossible to detect and remove. Contaminants that have permeated a material such as gloves or coveralls, and remain undetected, can cause an unexpected, potentially serious exposure when the contaminant reaches the skin. The extent of permeation is determined by the following:

- *Contact time.* The longer the contact time, the greater the probability and extent of permeation. Minimizing contaminant contact time is one of the most important objectives of a decontamination program.
- *Concentration.* As concentrations of contaminants increase, the potential for permeation increases. One way to minimize this problem is to reduce worker contact time in areas of high contaminant concentration.
- *Temperature.* Generally, the permeation rate increases as temperatures increase.
- *Physical state of contaminants.* In general, gases, mists, vapors, and low-viscosity liquids tend to permeate more quickly and easily than high-viscosity liquids or solids, just as coffee (low viscosity) permeates your shirt faster than fudge sauce (high viscosity).
- *Molecule and pore space size.* As the size of the contaminant molecules decreases, the rate of permeation increases. Also, as the pore space of the material increases, the rate of permeation increases. Because flour has a relatively small particle size, it will pass easily through a flour sifter, but rice would not go through the same sifter as readily, if at all. But if you increase the size of the holes by using a spaghetti strainer, the rice will pass through much more easily.

Decontamination Plan

A decontamination plan should be developed and decontamination equipment should be staged before personnel enter areas where the potential for exposure exists. The decontamination plan should include at least the following information regarding:

- the types, amounts, and concentrations of expected contaminants
- ways to protect clean areas and prevent the spread of contamination both on and off site
- routine and emergency decontamination procedures, including personnel and equipment needed, the number and layout of decontamination stations, and methods that minimize personnel (both workers and decon personnel)

contact with hazardous substances during removal of PPE

- methods of disposal of contaminated clothing, equipment, and wash/rinse solutions

Decontamination Methods

Physical Removal. Removal of particles, vapors, and volatile liquids often may be accomplished by brushing, scrubbing, rinsing, wiping, or evaporating. Other physical removal methods, such as the use of pressurized air or steam jets, can spread contamination and cause injury and are generally not recommended, except under special circumstances.

Contaminants such as resins, adhesives, and other sticky materials are often more difficult to remove. Try scraping, brushing, or wiping. Some adhesive materials are easier to remove when frozen or melted. If the material is highly viscous, it may help to absorb or adsorb it into or onto a chemically compatible material before attempting removal.

Chemical Removal. After removing any gross contamination, follow with a wash and/or rinse, using an appropriate cleaning solution. Always use the least hazardous cleaner or solvent that will accomplish the task. In some cases, this may be merely ordinary household soap or detergent and water. Be sure the cleaning solvent is chemically compatible with the item being cleaned. Be especially careful when cleaning PPE because it can be damaged or destroyed by the use of an incompatible cleaning solvent.

Emergency Decontamination. It is essential to establish and train personnel on emergency decontamination procedures, including methods which will be used to protect emergency aid providers. Whenever possible, delay medical treatment until decontamination has been performed; otherwise, emergency aid providers may become contaminated, which could result in their being unable to perform their duties and result in more victims. In extreme situations where immediate medical treatment is necessary to save a life, delay decontamination until the victim has stabilized as long as it is safe for emergency aid providers to do so (NIOSH, 1985.) Never jeopardize the lives of several people unless absolutely necessary.

Disposable PPE. In order to save time, consider the use of disposable PPE. In this system, all outer wear (boot covers, gloves, suits) is cut or rolled away from personnel while going through the decontamination process. The used, disposable PPE is packed in DOT-authorized containers for transportation and disposal, generally as an RCRA-regulated hazardous waste. While this process consumes more PPE, total cost in terms of manpower for the decontamination system, containment structures for decontamination fluids, laboratory testing, and transportation and treatment of contaminated wash and rinse waters is often considerably more.

DISPOSAL

During the early stages of a spill response, three planning functions should occur simultaneously. Once the spilled materials are established, each of these functions should ensue:

1. Planning tactics to be used during the spill response should be developed. What are the best procedures and tools to be used to stop the release and control the released product?
2. Planning should begin on the type of personal protective equipment to be used and the material(s) that the equipment is made from. What level of protection is required by the response workers?
3. Planning should begin on how to manage—package, transport, and recycle or dispose of—the released material(s) and the sorbents or decontamination products.

The Resource Conservation and Recovery Act (RCRA) regulates the management of all hazardous wastes. There are three broad options under RCRA—storage, treatment, or disposal. Storage of a hazardous waste implies that the waste will be shipped at some future date. This is generally not a viable option for materials left after a spill response.

Treatment, at its simplest level, means the waste is going to be changed into a less hazardous or a nonhazardous material. One common form of treatment is wastewater treatment. If this is the planned waste disposal technique, keeping all spilled liquids in a liquid form, and not solidifying them, is the best tactic to be used. Planning on using pumps to transfer spilled material(s) to transportation containers (drums, vacuum trucks, tank trailers) will produce the desired results with the least handling and minimize risks to workers. If the treatment technique used will be incineration, keeping spilled liquids in a liquid form or adsorbing them on combustible sorbents will result in lower disposal costs. Because of air emission standards on hazardous waste incinerators some materials, such as mercury-containing wastes, must be packaged in relatively small containers. Planning, before the response begins, to place these free or solidified liquids in a container size accepted by incinerators will minimize repackaging after initial containment. Other forms of treatment, such as chemical oxidation, may be possible with either liquid or solid wastes. Again, planning for this option before the spill response begins will result in less waste-handling, minimizing risk to workers and lowering disposal costs.

The third option for hazardous waste management is land-based disposal, either land farming or land filling. Land farming is generally not a viable option for spill residues. Land filling hazardous wastes that have been solidified with nonbiodegradable sorbents is generally more acceptable than land filling wastes solidified with biodegradable materials. Because of land disposal restrictions (LDRs) (also called land bans), hazardous waste may require some type of treatment prior to land filling. As mentioned earlier, knowing the most effective and efficient way to manage the wastes generated by a spill response is vital for preparing response workers to conduct specific procedures and use specific types and sizes of containers. Failing to plan for disposal of spill residues often results in repackaging the waste, which can increase worker exposure and risk. Failing to plan for disposal may result in higher waste packaging, transportation, and management costs.

TRANSPORTATION SPILLS AND RELEASES

According to the U.S. Department of Transportation, there are more than 800,000 hazardous material shipments daily in the United States, of which about 315,000 are petroleum products. On the average, more than 3 billion tons of hazardous materials are shipped each year. In terms of the number of shipments, the vast majority are by truck. In any given year, with the exception of catastrophic air and rail disasters, truck incidents involving hazardous materials usually result in more deaths, injuries, and financial losses than all other modes of transportation combined.

The DOT's definition of *transport* and *transportation* is the movement of property and the loading, unloading, or storage incidental to that movement. It is clear, then, that transportation incidents happen at times other than when hazardous materials are actually being conveyed over the roadways. Improper loading, unloading, or transloading account for many transportation-related spills and releases of hazardous material. Examples of improper loading or unloading are dropped packages, loading incompatible materials together, incorrect packaging, punctured packages, improper bracing or blocking of the load, and so on. An example of *transloading* is transferring a hazardous material from a bulk packaging to a nonbulk packaging for the purpose of continuing the movement of the hazardous material in commerce. Since loading and unloading are literally in the hands of people, human error is most often the cause of these incidents. Luckily, people also have the ability to help prevent these types of incidents by ensuring that hazardous materials are properly loaded, segregated, and braced; vehicles are in sound working condition; and that drivers and equipment operators have the appropriate level of knowledge, skills, and experience to safely manage the load.

Operator Emergency Response Capabilities

The outcome of any hazardous material transportation incident is based, to a greater or lesser extent, depending on the circumstances, on the capabilities of the driver or equipment operator. In order to safely and successfully respond to a transportation incident, drivers and equipment operators must have adequate training, equipment, and other resources necessary to manage the spill or release.

DOT Training Requirements. Anyone who loads, unloads, handles, or otherwise prepares hazardous materials for transportation; operates a motor vehicle that transports hazardous materials in commerce; is responsible for the transportation safety of hazardous materials in commerce; or whose duties directly affect the safety of hazardous material transportation, is required to meet the DOT minimum training requirements found in 49 CFR 172.704. Motor vehicle operators must also comply with the training requirements of 177.816. Additionally, individual states may impose more stringent driver training requirements on those who live in that state as long as the requirements do not conflict with DOT training requirements.

DOT training includes four general areas: general awareness, specific functions, safety, and security awareness training. General awareness training familiarizes employees with DOT's training requirements and ensures that they are able to recognize and identify hazardous materials and know what measures to take to protect themselves from those hazards.

Function-specific training is just that: employees must be trained in their specific job functions. As an alternative, employees may be provided with mode-specific training, such as that required by the International Maritime Dangerous Goods (IMDG) Code (IMO, 2006) or the International Civil Aviation Organization (ICAO) (www.icao.int) Technical Instructions, as long as the training addresses the requirements of 49 CFR 171.12 (Import and Export Shipments) and 171.11 (Use of ICAO Technical Instructions).

Training may be provided by qualified in-house personnel or by outside companies or contractors. Many trade organizations, such as the American Petroleum Institute (www.api.org), the Association of Oil Pipelines (www.aopl.org), the American Chemical Society (www.acs.org), International Air Transport Association (www.iata.org), and International Institute of Ammonia Refrigeration (www.iiar.org) offer training programs or publications.

Equipment. The amount and type of available spill response equipment should be selected on the basis of the quantity, size, and type of container(s) being transported, the hazards posed by the materials, the training and experience level of the operator, and the mode of transportation. It is of little value in an emergency to include equipment the operator does not know how to properly and safely use or that is inappropriate for the potential spill or release.

The following list contains equipment and supplies that are useful for response to various types and sizes of transportation spills and releases. The first several items can be useful in nearly all transportation spill/release scenarios; the remaining items may be more useful for management of specific types and sizes of spills.

- personal protective equipment, including chemical-resistant and/or fire-resistant outer garments, gloves, boots, respiratory protection, safety glasses/goggles, and other chemical-specific equipment, as necessary
- first-aid kit
- reflective traffic vests
- fire extinguishers
- leak sealing/patching/plugging kit
- sorbent pads, rolls, or boom
- trash bags, rags and paper towels
- traffic cones, reflective warning devices
- caution tape
- communication devices such as cellular telephones, radios, and so on
- shovels, picks, rakes, brooms, squeegees, and so on
- flashlights or portable lights
- tape: duct and electrical tape have many potential uses at a spill scene
- camera, binoculars
- reference materials, such as material safety data sheets, DOT's *Emergency Response Guidebook*, and others, as applicable to the material(s)
- clean water, brushes, soap, and buckets for decontaminating small tools and equipment
- hand tools such as hammers, crescent and pipe wrenches, bolt cutters, pliers, saws, socket sets, drills, bung wrenches, utility knives, chisels, screwdrivers, vice grips, crow bars
- combustible gas indicator (or other air-monitoring instrument depending on the load) with spare batteries
- fall protection harness

- disinfectant, spray bottles, and biohazard bags
- hand and/or transfer pumps with any hoses, clamps, or necessary fittings
- spark-proof tools
- grounding cables
- dome clamps, hatch cones, valves, camlock adapters, and other specialized equipment and fittings
- plastic or metal pails
- rope
- overpack and salvage drums
- ladder

Other Resources. In some cases, other resources may be needed that are beyond the scope of what the driver or local fire or hazmat team can provide. Some spills or releases require specialized equipment such as cranes, vacuum trucks, compressed gas cylinder overpacks, specialized fire-extinguishing media, specialized valves, or leak-sealing equipment. For large spills and releases, it is likely that outside, contracted help will be needed. Some spills and releases require assistance from highly trained and specialized management teams. Are these resources available to the driver or operator? Does the driver or operator have a list with telephone numbers and points of contact that are available at various points along the route? Does the driver or operator have the authority to contract for emergency assistance? If not, can he or she reach the person with the appropriate authority at all times? Does the driver/operator have the authority to make statements or answer questions from the media? If not, to whom shall he or she refer them?

Driver/Operator Response Actions

If a spill or release of hazardous materials occurs during transport, a driver or operator must perform several tasks within the limitations of his or her training, experience, available equipment, and other resources. It is extremely important that drivers know and understand their personal limits in terms of response capabilities and the limitations of their equipment. Drivers and operators should only attempt control, containment, and other emergency spill response activities that they are fully trained and equipped to manage.

Begin the response action by analyzing the incident and planning the initial response, if it is safe to do so; otherwise, evacuate, call for help, then secure the scene to ensure that others are not injured. When evaluating the situation and gathering pertinent information, note product identification (chemical name), physical and health hazards associated with the product(s), type of container damage (e.g., puncture, crush, leak), extent of the spill or release (e.g., container size and type and the quantity of release), whether the spill or release is complete or ongoing, and whether there are factors that could change the nature or severity of the incident (e.g., the potential for fire, explosion, or the commingling of products).

If outside assistance is needed, notify local authorities, the owner, or other responsible party, and if applicable, the spill contractor or other response organizations. Provide information about the nature of the emergency, including location, product(s) involved, type of vehicle (if pertinent), approximate quantity of spilled or released material, any injuries, any special hazards (e.g., water reactive or radioactive), and any other relevant information.

If possible, provide responders with a method of contact, such as the driver's cellular telephone number or the availability of a citizen's band (CB) or other radio, to be used in the event responders need to contact the driver, which might be the case if the responders are delayed or have a difficult time finding the location of the spill or release.

For bulk containers, determine the safest method to off-load the product and where to position a vacuum or tank truck that will receive the off-loaded product. Possible bulk product removal methods include removal through vapor recovery lines, external or internal valves, unloading lines, or through the dome or hatch covers. Each method has both advantages and disadvantages, so this issue should be preplanned.

Next, secure the scene to ensure that other persons or vehicles are protected from inadvertently entering the area. Equipment and measures to secure the scene may include reflective warning devices, flares (if fire is not a potential hazard), barrier tape, traffic cones, signs, verbal warnings to bystanders or those in nearby dwellings, and so on. If fire is a hazard, turn off the vehicle and shut down other vehicle electrical systems (if so equipped), and remove all other possible sources of ignition.

Begin spill or release mitigation by donning the proper personal protective equipment. If relevant to the spill or release, set up air-monitoring instruments and a fire watch. For rail and tank cars carrying flammable materials, perform bonding and grounding to prevent buildup of static electricity. Perform spill or release control and/or containment procedures, which may include the following procedures, or others, in accordance with the company's spill response plan and procedures:

- Rotate the damaged container so the leak is at the top.
- Turn the container upright.
- Close valves and shut off all pumps.
- Seal storm sewers; dig containment ditches or construct earthen dikes; deploy sorbent pads, socks, or boom.
- Patch or seal leaks or holes.

It cannot be stressed enough that drivers and operators must recognize the limitations of themselves and their equipment. They must be able to recognize the need for more or advanced levels of personal protective and other equipment and the need for more response personnel or for those who are capable of managing more complex incidents. If drivers and operators do not recognize their limitations, it is very possible someone will be injured or, in the case of large or extremely hazardous substance releases, that the spill or release could escalate to the point of being catastrophic.

Incident Termination

When the emergency has passed and all hazardous materials are contained, contaminated equipment and supplies must be decontaminated. This may be accomplished at the scene if the driver/operator has the necessary supplies. If the necessary supplies are not available, contaminated items may be placed in drums or sealed in bags for later decontamination. If these items are contaminated with a hazardous waste, as defined by RCRA regulations, the wash and rinse water

from decontamination must be managed as hazardous waste along with the other hazardous waste produced at the scene.

The last step of an incident close-out is to file all required reports. These may include reports to the responsible party (DOT, state agencies, and others), depending on the type, quantity, and location of the spill or release. Refer to the "Federal Assets and Information Sources" section for more information on notifications and reporting.

ABBREVIATIONS

ATSDR	Agency for Toxic Substances and Disease Registry
BLEVE	Boiling Liquid–Expanding Vapor Explosion
CAER	Community Awareness and Emergency Response
CERCLA	Comprehensive Environmental Response, Compensation, and Liability Act
CFR	Code of Federal Regulations
DOT	Department of Transportation
EPA	Environmental Protection Agency
Fl. P.	flash point
HASP	health and safety plan
HCS	hazard communication standard
HAZWOPER	hazardous waste operations and emergency response
HMT–USA	Hazardous Materials Transportation–Uniform Safety Act
IP	ionization potential
ISO	International Standards Organization
LC_{50}	lethal concentration 50%
LD_{50}	lethal dose 50%
LEL	lower explosive limit
LEPC	local emergency planning committee
LFL	lower flammable limit
MSDS	Material Safety Data Sheet
NFPA	National Fire Protection Association
NRT	National Response Team
OPA 90	Oil Pollution Act of 1990
OSHA	Occupational Safety and Health Administration (U.S. Department of Labor)
PPE	personal protective equipment
PEL	permissible exposure limit
PHMSA	Pipeline and Hazardous Materials Safety Administration (U.S. Department of Transportation)
PID	photo ionization detector
RCRA	Resource Conservation and Recovery Act
RSPA	Research and Special Projects Administration (U.S. Department of Transportation) (now part of PHMSA)

SARA	Superfund Amendments and Reauthorization Act
STEL	short-term exposure limit
Sp. Gr.	specific gravity
TLV	threshold limit value
TWA	time-weighted average
UEL	upper explosive limit
UFL	upper flammable limit
VD	vapor density
VP	vapor pressure

REFERENCES

American Society for Testing and Materials (ASTM) International. 2005. *ASTM Standards on Environmental Sampling*. 3d ed. West Conshohocken, PA: ASTM International. www.astm.org

Bowling Green State University. 2008. *Mercury Vapor Experiment*. wbgustream.bgsu.edu/bgsu/epa/index-fl.html

Bureau of Labor Statistics (BLS). 2007. *Occupational Outlook Handbook*. 2006–2007 ed. Washington, DC: U.S. Department of Labor, Bureau of Labor Statistics. www.bls.gov/oco/

Environmental Protection Agency (EPA). 2002. EPA530-D-02-002, *RCRA Waste Sampling Draft Technical Guidance—Planning, Implementation, and Assessment*. Washington, D.C.: EPA. www.epa.gov

Fatah, Alim A., et. al. 2001. *Guide for the Selection of Chemical and Biological Decontamination Equipment for Emergency First Responders*. vol. 1. Washington, D.C.: U.S. Department of Justice, Office of Justice Program, National Institute of Justice. www.ncjrs.gov/pdffiles1/nij/189724.pdf

Federal Emergency Management Agency (FEMA). 2007. *FEMA Independent Study Program: IS-139 Exercise Design*. www.training.fema.gov/emiweb/IS/is139.asp

International Civil Aviation Organization. 2007. *Technical Instructions for the Safe Transport of Dangerous Goods by Air*. 2007–2008 ed. Montreal, Quebec. www.icao.int

International Maritime Organization. 2006. *International Maritime Dangerous Goods Code*. London: International Maritime Organization. www.imo.org

International Organization for Standardization (ISO). 2007. ISO 14000, *Environmental Management Systems: Requirements for Guidelines with Use* (retrieved 2007). www.iso.org

Investigation Process Research Resource Site. 2010. *The Story of GEBMO* (retrieved June 30, 2010). www.iprr.org/HazMatdocs/GEBMO/GEBMO.html

National Fire Protection Association (NFPA). 2002. *Hazardous Materials Response Handbook*. 4th ed. Quincy, MA: NFPA. www.nfpa.org

———. 2008. Standard 472, *Professional Competence of Responders to Hazardous Materials Incidents*. Quincy, MA: NFPA.

National Institute for Occupational Safety and Health (NIOSH). 1985. Publication No. 85-115, *Occupational Safety and Health Guidance Manual for Hazardous Waste Site Activities*. Washington, D.C.: Government Printing Office. www.cdc.gov/niosh/pdfs/85-115.pdf

Occupational Safety and Health Administration (OSHA). 1997. *Hazardous Waste Operations and Emergency Response* (Publication 3144). Washington, D.C.: U.S. Government Printing Office. www.osha.gov/Publications/OSHA3114/osha3114.html

———. 2007. *e-HASP₂ Software User's Manual*. www.osha.gov/dep/etools/ehasp/ehasp2_usermanual.pdf

Pipeline and Hazardous Materials Safety Administration (PHMSA). PHMSA 06-25885 (HM232F), *Hazardous Materials: Risk-Based Adjustment of Transportation Security Plans*. Washington, D.C.: PHMSA.

U.S. Congress. 1970. Occupational Safety and Health Act, Section 5(a), Public Law 91-596, codified at 29 U.S. Code 654. www.osha.gov/pls/oshaweb/owasrch.search_form?p_doc_type=oshact

———. 1976a. Resource Conservation and Recovery Act, Public Law 94-580, codified at 42 U.S. Code 6901. www.epa.gov/regulations/laws/rcra.html

———. 1976b. Toxic Substance Control Act, Public Law, 94-469, codified at 15 U.S. Code 2601. frwebgate.access.gpo.gov/cgi-bin/usc.cgi?ACTION=BROWSE&TITLE=15USCC53

———. 1977. Clean Air Act. Public Law 95-95, codified at 42 U.S. Code 7622. www.epa.gov/regulations/laws/caa.html

———. 1980. Comprehensive Environmental Response, Compensation, and Liability Act. Public Law 96-510, codified at 42 U.S. Code Section 9601. www.epa.gov/regulations/laws/cercla.html

———. 1986. Superfund Amendments and Reauthorization Act, Public Law 99-499, codified at 42 U.S. Code 9662. www.epa.gov/regulations/laws/cercla.html

———. 1987. Clean Water Act. Public Law 100-4, codified at 33 U.S. Code 1344. www.epa.gov/regulations/laws/cwa.html

———. 1990a. Hazardous Materials Transportation–Uniform Safety Act of 1990, Public Law 101-615, codified at 49 U.S. Code Chapter 51.

———. 1990b. Oil Pollution Act of 1990, Public Law 100-380, codified at 33 U.S. Code 2701. www.epa.gov/regulations/laws/opa.html

———. 1996. Federal Insecticide, Fungicide and Rodenticide Act, Public Act 108–199, codified at 7 U.S. Code 121. www.epa.gov/regulations/laws/fifra.html

United Nations Economic Commission for Europe (UNECE). 2005. *The Globally Harmonized System of Classification and Labelling of Chemicals (GHS)*. Blue Ridge Summit, PA: U.N. Publications.

U.S. Department of Transportation. 2002. *Hazardous Materials Transportation Enhanced Security Requirements* (Publication DHM50-0030-0903). hazmatonline. phmsa.dot.gov/services/Pub_Free.aspx

_____. 2004. *Emergency Response Guidebook*. www.phmsa. dot.gov/hazmat/library/erg

_____. 2006. Immediate Notice of Certain Hazardous Materials Incidents. 49 Code of Federal Regulations, 171.15. www.access.gpo.gov/cgi-bin/cfrassemble. cgi?title=201049

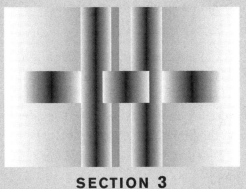

MANAGEMENT SYSTEMS

Robert R. Stewart

LEARNING OBJECTIVES

▌ Be able to explain the need for environmental compliance and the effects of noncompliance.

▌ Describe the basic components of an environmental management system (EMS).

▌ Discuss management theories that relate to EMSs.

▌ Outline the cultural and economic benefits of EMS implementation to an organization.

▌ List EMS cost factors and the reasons for higher or lower development costs within a particular type of organization.

▌ Describe several technologies available for processing, saving, and distributing EMS information across an organization.

ENVIRONMENTAL regulations, and their subsequent demands on the regulated community, have evolved steadily since their advent during the post–World War II years. One of the first environmental regulations in the United States addressed the need to prevent unauthorized excavation or filling operations that could interfere with water navigation (33 USC § 403). As the twentieth century progressed, increased public awareness of environmental issues led to the development of increasingly complex and stringent regulatory requirements. These regulations were designed by citizens, the regulated community, and government officials to assure a cleaner environment. For example, the Solid Waste Disposal Act (SWDA) of 1965 was amended by the passage of the Resource Conservation and Recovery Act (RCRA) in 1976. Additional waste management regulations were promulgated in 1984 (U.S. EPA 2007a).

Regulations are initiated as acts that are passed by Congress. Following the passage of an act, sets of regulations are designed specifically to implement the act for which they are written. Major environmental acts that are now law in the United States, in addition to the previously mentioned RCRA, include the Toxic Substances Control Act (TSCA 1976), Superfund Amendments and Reauthorization Act (SARA 1986), Resource Conservation and Recovery Act (RCRA 1980), Clean Water Act (CWA 1977), and Clean Air Act amendments (CAA 1990). All environmental requirements that a business or industrial entity must follow are derived to ensure compliance with an act.

The relatively rapid development of environmental acts and corresponding regulations has required industry and the regulated community to perform better environmentally (U.S. EPA 2005a). The need for a more organized approach rested with the regulated community to further ensure compliance with regulations and to better manage the economics of environmental affairs. A more efficient plan to preventing and mitigating environmentally damaging events, such as spills, accidents, and excess air-emission events, was clearly necessary.

Businesses are now expected by their surrounding communities to comply with environmental regulations. Communities have access to environmental performance information via the Internet (U.S. EPA 2002a). Internet resources, such as the U.S. Environmental Protection Agency's (U.S. EPA's) *My Environment* database, can provide up-to-date information on a facility's compliance status (U.S. EPA 2010). The Freedom of Information Act (FOIA) provides citizens with the right to access government environmental documents relating to a business, including inspection reports, monitoring and compliance assurance documents, and permits that are in control of the Agency (U.S. EPA 1992). However, FOIA access to many U.S. government technical documents was denied after the events of September 11, 2001 (Tien 2002). Permit applications and subsequent draft environmental permits for new pollution sources at industrial and commercial facilities are available for public review and comment before a final permit or authorization is issued. Draft permits are often available for review electronically, allowing a person to review a permit at any time from any location with Internet access.

Along with increased public scrutiny, many businesses are faced with the reality of high costs resulting from noncompliance with regulations. Such costs are in two forms, one financial, and the other through a potentially tarnished public image that can result in lost sales and increased liability through reduced public trust.

Noncompliance potentially carries high costs. For example, failure to notify the EPA before start-up of an air pollution source, a violation of the CAA, carries a potential fine of $27,500 per day (U.S. EPA 1999). In one case, the University of North Carolina was assessed a $19,633 penalty for several waste-handling violations, including failure to properly label waste containers (NCDENR 2006). Prosecutions of noncompliance with federal environmental laws involve businesses,

organizations, and local government, but can also be directed toward federal facilities (U. S. EPA 2010).

The 1989 Ashland Oil tank collapse in Floreffe, Pennsylvania, released an estimated 750,000 gallons of heating oil into the Monongahela River. As a result, Ashland paid a penalty of $1.25 million (*Pittsburgh Post Gazette* 1998).

As evidenced thus far, good environmental management, including sound environmental engineering practice, is critical to the economic success of a business. Management of environmental affairs can no longer be thought of as a secondary function left to subordinates. Senior corporate management is now both responsible and accountable for the environmental actions of a company's employees. Case law has shown this to be true, with senior corporate officials being held criminally liable for their company's alleged failures in environmental management. For example, in 2006 four officials of a New Jersey pipe manufacturing company were found guilty of environmental crimes, among them being the regular discharge of oil into the Delaware River in violation of the CWA. Each official was subsequently sentenced to federal prison for a term ranging from 6 to 70 months (U.S. EPA 2009a).

As regulations evolved and enforcement became a reality for the regulated community, a systematic approach to environmental management was needed. The first environmental management systems, or EMSs, were derived from popular management concepts linked to quality control, such as ISO 14001 (Dimond 1996) and total quality management (TQM) (U.S. EPA 2006b). These concepts will be discussed later in the chapter.

The U.S. EPA has long supported use of the EMS as a positive overall management tool not only to achieve compliance, but to achieve beyond-compliance results in environmental performance. The Agency stated its formal position in 1998, which was reinforced in 2002 with its memo "United States Environmental Protection Agency Position Statement on Environmental Management Systems (EMSs)," dated May 15, 2002 (U.S. EPA 2002b), and again in its "Statement of Principles" dated December 13, 2005 (see Figure 1) (U.S. EPA 2005c).

Statement of Principles

EPA's overall policy on EMSs, as with the EMS approach itself, will continue to be guided by the principles of continual improvement and learning, flexibility, and collaboration.

- EPA will encourage widespread use of EMSs across a range of organizations and settings, with particular emphasis on adoption of EMSs to achieve improved environmental performance and compliance, pollution prevention through source reduction, and continual improvement. The Agency will support EMSs that are appropriate to the needs and characteristics of specific sectors and facilities and encourage the use of EMSs as a means of integrating other facility management programs.

- EPA will promote the voluntary adoption of EMSs. To encourage voluntary adoption of EMSs, EPA will rely on public education and voluntary programs.

- EPA will encourage organizations that use EMSs to obtain stakeholder input on matters relevant to the development and implementation of an EMS and to demonstrate accountability for the performance outcomes of their EMSs through measurable objectives and targets. Additionally, the Agency will encourage organizations to share information on the performance of their EMSs with public and government agencies and facilitate this process where practicable.

- EPA will encourage the use of recognized environmental management frameworks, such as the ISO 14001 Standard, as a basis for designing and implementing EMSs that aim to achieve outcomes aligned with the nation's environmental policy goals and the principles of this Position Statement.

- EPA will collaborate with other key partners – including states, other federal agencies, tribes, local governments, industry, and non-governmental organizations – as it implements this policy. EPA will support international EMS initiatives that facilitate the increased use of EMSs in the United States. The Agency will ensure that as it implements this policy, its decisions and work are transparent to all interested parties.

- EPA will lead by example, by developing, implementing, and maintaining EMSs at appropriate EPA facilities.

- EPA will foster continual learning by supporting research and public dialogue on EMSs that help improve the Agency's understanding of circumstances where EMSs can advance the nation's environmental policy goals. EPA will continue to collect improved data on the application of EMSs as it becomes available, including the efficacy of EMSs in improving environmental performance and the costs and benefits of an EMS to an organization and the environment.

DATE: DEC 1 3 2005

Stephen L. Johnson
Administrator
U.S. Environmental Protection Agency

FIGURE 1. Statement of Principles on EMSs (*Source:* EPA, December 13, 2005)

The U.S. EPA has accepted the development and implementation of EMSs as a form of injunctive relief to facilitate remedial actions and ensure ongoing compliance (U.S. EPA 2003). An EMS component has been used to bring many facilities into compliance, including multifacility companies, colleges/universities, and federal facilities (U.S. EPA 2003). Complaints involving one violation and those involving thousands of violations have been settled through EMS development and implementation.

To qualify for injunctive relief (i.e., to assure ongoing compliance), the EMS needs to follow guidelines listed in the U.S. EPA's Office of Enforcement and Compliance Assurance (OECA)—National Enforcement Investigation Center (NEIC) Compliance-Focused Environmental Management Systems (CFEMS)—Enforcement Agreement Guidance. The Guidance details twelve necessary components ("Elements") and provides draft settlement agreement language for regulators. Along with its use in enforcement, the CFEMS model is often used as a guide for development and improvement of EMSs in many types of organizations (NEIC 2005).

The use of SEPs for settlement negotiations is further detailed in the U.S. EPA guidance document entitled "Guidance on the Use of Environmental Management Systems in Enforcement Settlements as Injunctive Relief and Supplemental Environmental Projects," dated June 12, 2003 (U.S. EPA 2003). Typically a violator will negotiate an agreement with the agency to implement an EMS as a beyond-compliance initiative in exchange for a reduced cash penalty assessment. Such agreements, called Supplemental Environmental Projects, or SEPs, are used by violators to negotiate for reduced cash penalties and by agencies to produce tangible environmental improvements outside of the original citation or penalty assessment. An EMS is just one form of SEP. Many other ideas can be found by contacting U.S. EPA or by reviewing the U.S. EPA's brochure "Beyond Compliance: Supplemental Environmental Projects" (U.S. EPA 2001a).

The federal government is actively involved in developing and employing EMSs at federal facilities. In 2007, President Bush issued Executive Order 13423, requiring federal agencies to implement EMSs as part of an overall policy of sustainability and environmental management at the federal level (Federal Register 2007). The order details specific resource reduction targets, including those involving water, greenhouse gases, energy, and petroleum products. Those looking for assistance in EMS development can now find and review a federal agency's EMS to obtain ideas and guidance.

Organizations that self-audit are shielded from excessive financial and legal liability, as evidenced by companies' success in applying for and receiving relief under the U.S. EPA audit policy. For example, in 2006, National Railroad Passenger Corporation (AMTRAK) had total penalties of $319,875 waived entirely by self-disclosing known violations and by complying with U.S. EPA's audit policy requirements (U.S. EPA 2006a). By continually checking and auditing its compliance status, an organization is able to protect itself from being cited during an inspection. Violations of environmental requirements are systematically eliminated or corrected in a properly functioning EMS, and are prevented from recurrence through training and follow-up auditing. Implementation of an EMS can aid in reduction of negative public perception through the systematic removal of violations and associated negative impacts.

APPLIED SCIENTIFIC AND ENGINEERING PRINCIPLES
Management Theory

Several management theories have had an effect on the development of EMSs in the United States and elsewhere throughout the world. Additionally, key individuals have played important roles in the development of popular management theory. In *The Handbook of Project-Based Management*, the author discusses Dr. Edwards Deming, who believed in continuous improvement in products and services, along with Philip Crosby, who developed the concept of *zero defects*, and the idea that doing a task correctly the first time was always the least expensive option (Turner 1993). Other influential leaders in quality-management theory include Joseph Juran, Shigeo Shingo, and Armand Feigenbaum (Certo 1999). The concept of *Gemba Kaizen®*, or continuous improvement, has been applied successfully in both manufacturing and the service sector.

Total Quality Management

After World War II, Japan experienced a period of tremendous industrial and economic growth (CIA 2007). Part of the reason for the Japanese success was their development and use of quality control systems. American manufacturers took notice of the Japanese success in industry and began to develop quality systems to compete better globally.

Total Quality Management, or TQM, is the concept of involving all members of an organization in a continuous improvement process that reduces defects and increases quality (Certo 1987). Although originally conceived in the United States, TQM was expanded upon and applied actively and aggressively by the Japanese (Certo 1999). The Japanese effort resulted in U.S. manufacturers becoming eager to increase quality and decrease defects and mistakes. Japanese manufacturers using TQM produced products similar to those built in the United States, but at a much lower cost and with fewer after-sale problems owing to manufacturing defects.

TQM principles are needed to build an effective EMS (U.S. EPA 2006b). Implementing TQM and an effective EMS involves the concrete and unmitigated commitment by senior management (U.S. EPA 2006b) and the development of teams of individuals who are intensively trained in the appropriate management principles. An experienced outside consultant hired by the company often facilitates initial training and coordination. The consultant is usually an expert who works for a company that has successfully implemented TQM or an EMS. Teams of self-taught individuals in-house can also learn and implement TQM, but it should be understood by management and employees that a learning curve will be needed for personnel to develop the necessary expertise.

TQM training involves coaching and motivating employees to continually look for ways to solve problems; consequently, they become more productive employees (Padhi 2007). Brainstorming sessions by trained quality-improvement teams identify and solve quality problems (Padhi 2007). The teams of supervisors, initially selected and trained by the company, then take their training onto the floor and train all other floor employees not only to identify mistakes, but also how to prevent mistakes from happening. Progress charts are developed for each process in a plant that show, for example, the number of defects per 100 parts manufactured. The goal of TQM is to find the cause of each defect and resolve it, under the principle that *zero defects* is not only achievable, but that eliminating defects saves money and reduces the cost to produce a product. The same TQM concept of zero defects applies to EMS implementation for organizations that want to proactively manage their environmental affairs.

Gemba Kaizen®

A management philosophy that effectively implements TQM is Gemba Kaizen®, a technique employed initially with tremendous success by Japanese manufacturers and currently implemented internationally both by manufacturers and the service sector.

The focus of Gemba Kaizen® is the workplace, or *Gemba* in Japanese (Imai 1997). The underlying theory of Gemba Kaizen® is that the focus of management should be on the manufacturing plant or area where products are made or services are actually delivered (Imai 1997). Virtually all problems in manufacturing, and their resultant solutions, are found in Gemba.

Senior management often finds itself physically detached from Gemba, in offices far away from the workplace. Corporate offices and corporate managers are often located in different towns or cities, isolated from Gemba. Managers sometimes may not enter an actual manufacturing plant for months or years. The theory of Gemba Kaizen® is that this management detachment restricts a company from being more effective at resolving workplace problems, cutting costs, eliminating waste, or producing products more efficiently (Imai 1997). Gemba Kaizen® encourages managers to enter Gemba and spend time in the workplace.

There are many examples of how managing from the workplace floor, instead of the office, has tangible benefit. An environmental manager who is regularly on the shop floor can readily recognize an unpermitted stormwater discharge, a diesel-fuel-powered electric generating system that may need an air permit to operate, a waste container that is not labeled properly, or other regulatory noncompliance issues. Plant operations personnel who are not trained or aware of the regulatory requirements a manufacturing facility must meet on a daily basis can overlook serious noncompliance items such as these. That same environmental manager, while on the shop floor, can ask questions of floor operators, maintenance personnel, and supervisors to gauge their knowledge base regarding environmental requirements and to learn about conditions that may not be apparent to the casual visitor to the plant. For example, a maintenance person may be able to explain how he disposes of fluorescent bulbs, at which point an environmental manager can assess whether the U.S. EPA universal waste-handling requirements (40 CFR, Part 273) are being followed.

Another key practice of Gemba Kaizen® is for a manager, in focusing on a problem, to ask *Why* five times. The purpose of asking *Why* five times is to get at the root cause of a problem (Imai 1997). Here is an example of how it works:

General Manager (GM): *Why* did our company receive a Notice of Violation?
Environmental Coordinator (EC): Because we did not collect our annual stormwater sample by the required date.
GM: *Why?*
EC: Because we forgot we had to take the sample.
GM: *Why?*
EC: Because we did not have it listed on our compliance calendar.
GM: *Why?*
EC: Because we did not update our compliance calendar when we received our new stormwater permit.
GM: *Why?*
EC: Because we didn't read the permit when it arrived at the plant and subsequently transfer all conditions and action items to our compliance calendar.

From this dialogue a serious management deficiency is uncovered—failure of the environmental manager to read the permit and record key compliance dates and requirements on the environmental

compliance calendar. Retraining in management skills would, in most cases, resolve this issue.

The Iowa Department of Management, Office of Lean Enterprise, a public-sector organization, has successfully employed the Gemba Kaizen® philosophy of eliminating waste and streamlining production processes throughout Iowa state government in the form of a *Lean*, or waste reduction, initiative. The organization's results show a significant improvement in government efficiency: collectively Iowa state agencies have completed over 100 Lean process improvements to reduce waste and to increase efficiency and customer satisfaction (lean.iowa.gov 2010). One example of the program's success is the Iowa Department of Natural Resources (DNR) Air Quality Program that reduced New Source Construction permit steps by 19 percent and handoffs by 33 percent (lean.iowa.gov 2010). Overall, the DNR has educated its permitting personnel to engage the regulated community in an immediate dialogue to ensure that applications can be administratively complete upon initial submittal, saving time in repeat submittals and technical reviews.

The use of Gemba Kaizen®, TQM, and related forms of management systems led to the creation of EMSs that could deliver the positive compliance results and company value that senior management, stockholders, and the public required. A look at EMSs follows; the first part will look at the ISO 14000 series of management systems, followed by overviews of similar systems.

STRUCTURE OF AN EMS

An EMS can be structured in many ways. Organizations often have EMS elements in place and desire additional structure to have a more complete system. The discussion below shows one suggested form of EMS. Because each organization has different needs, an EMS is bound to be completed and implemented in many ways. It is important to emphasize that any organization may deviate from the approach below to suit its individual needs.

An EMS is most often based on the Plan-Do-Check-Act principle (Figure 2), originated by Shewart and Deming (Stapleton, Glover, and Davis 2001).

The cyclical nature of this management system provides the user with steady improvement by continu-

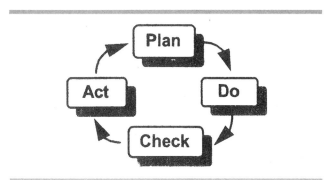

FIGURE 2. Plan-Do-Check-Act principle (*Source: EPA 2006*)

ally challenging the organization to review and revise its environmental objectives. Each step is described in detail below.

Step 1: Plan—Set goals and secure senior management commitment.

The ultimate success of any EMS is dependent on the organization's commitment to a realistic set of goals. This commitment must be demonstrated in a written form, so the company's environmental objectives will not be forgotten or misinterpreted. An implementation team is put together by the company's EMS "champion" (U.S. EPA 2006b) to define the organization's EMS goals and to review current compliance status.

After defining their organization's goals, most companies adopt the following protocol en route to publishing a written environmental policy statement, an example of which is shown in Figure 3.

Note the following characteristics, each of which is typical of a comprehensive environmental policy:

1. Endorsement by the company president or CEO, demonstrating senior management commitment
2. Compliance with all environmental standards, laws, and regulations as a primary objective
3. Promise of continuous improvement in environmental performance
4. Promise to engage in source reduction and recycling to the maximum extent possible

Depending on the level of commitment considered achievable by a company, it can expand the number of items in its policy statement. There is no standard format to an environmental policy statement; the only

requirements are that it be in writing and be communicated throughout the organization (U.S. EPA 2006b). The EMS can have, along with the four statements listed here, some that are focused more on a specific industry or work practice in which the company engages. For example, a company that uses large volumes of water may have, as part of its policy statement, the promise to reduce water consumption to the maximum extent possible. Companies using large volumes of electricity, natural gas, coal, stone, or other natural resources could implement similar statements.

Producing an environmental policy statement is a necessary step toward building a successful EMS (U.S. EPA 2006b). The policy assures that a company's employees are certain of how management views environmental affairs; therefore, a standard policy has been set for both senior management and all employees to follow. With such a standard in place, little question remains as to where the company stands on environmental issues. This actuality is extremely important when dealing with those affected by the company's operations, including customers, the public, and the regulatory community.

Although the policy statement demonstrates the level of management endorsement, management must also endorse the necessary budget (which includes time, money, equipment, and tools) if the organization is to implement the EMS (U.S. EPA 2006b).

Once the company has produced a working environmental policy statement, it must take the next step, which is to *do*—in other words, follow through on how the company intends to carry out its strategy to achieve the goals planned and listed in the policy statement.

Step 2: Do—Decide on how to ensure that the EMS is focused on (a) forming a committee composed of representatives from all operating sectors of the organization and (b) developing a comprehensive set of aspects and impacts that the organization has to address in its management of environmental issues.

Forming a Committee

Based on the company *organization chart*, representatives from each operating segment of the company need to be selected to represent their segment in EMS

HESS CORPORATION

ENVIRONMENT, HEALTH AND SAFETY POLICY

HESS CORPORATION AND ITS SUBSIDIARIES RECOGNIZE THAT EXCELLENCE IN ENVIRONMENTAL, HEALTH, AND SAFETY PERFORMANCE IS AN ESSENTIAL PART OF OUR GOAL TO BECOME THE LEADING GLOBAL INDEPENDENT ENERGY COMPANY. TO ACCOMPLISH THIS, WE WILL:

- IDENTIFY, ASSESS AND MANAGE THE ENVIRONMENTAL, HEALTH AND SAFETY RISKS AND IMPACTS OF OUR EXISTING AND PLANNED OPERATIONS.

- SET OBJECTIVES AND TARGETS THAT RESULT IN CONTINUOUS IMPROVEMENT OF OUR ENVIRONMENTAL, HEALTH AND SAFETY PERFORMANCE.

- PROVIDE THE LEADERSHIP AND RESOURCES THAT WILL ENABLE OUR WORKFORCE TO MEET IMPROVEMENT OBJECTIVES AND TARGETS.

- REQUIRE EVERY EMPLOYEE TO TAKE PERSONAL RESPONSIBILITY TOWARDS MEETING ENVIRONMENTAL, HEALTH AND SAFETY OBJECTIVES.

- INCLUDE ENVIRONMENTAL, HEALTH AND SAFETY PERFORMANCE WHEN EVALUATING MANAGERS, EMPLOYEES AND CONTRACTORS FOR COMPENSATION, REWARDS, AND RECOGNITION.

- COMPLY WITH APPLICABLE ENVIRONMENTAL, HEALTH AND SAFETY LAWS AND REGULATIONS.

- RECOGNIZE THAT NO TASK IS SO IMPORTANT THAT IT BE PERFORMED AT THE RISK OF HEALTH AND SAFETY.

- PROVIDE INTERNAL STANDARDS FOR OUR MANAGERS AND EMPLOYEES WHERE CONTROLLING LAWS AND REGULATIONS DO NOT EXIST OR ARE CONSIDERED INSUFFICIENT.

- COMMUNICATE REGULARLY WITH THE COMMUNITIES WHERE WE OPERATE TO DEVELOP AND MAINTAIN A MUTUAL UNDERSTANDING OF GOALS AND EXPECTATIONS.

- PROMOTE THE CONSERVATION OF ENERGY AND NATURAL RESOURCES AND REDUCE WASTE.

- ROUTINELY MONITOR, ASSESS AND REPORT ON THE COMPANY'S ENVIRONMENTAL, HEALTH AND SAFETY PERFORMANCE AND ON OUR CONFORMITY WITH THIS POLICY.

John B. Hess

John B. Hess
Chairman of the Board and Chief Executive Officer

May, 2006

lg-104

FIGURE 3. Sample environmental policy statement (_Source:_ Hess Corporation, May 2006)

Identifying Aspects and Impacts: Some Questions to Consider:

Identifying Aspects	Evaluating Impacts
❏ Which <u>operations and activities</u> interface with the environment in a way that could result (or has resulted) in environmental impacts?	❏ Are the impacts <u>actual or potential</u>?
❏ What <u>materials</u>, <u>energy</u> sources and other <u>resources</u> do we use in our work?	❏ Are the impacts <u>beneficial or damaging</u> to the environment?
❏ Do we have <u>emissions</u> to the air, water or land?	❏ What is the <u>magnitude or degree</u> of these impacts?
❏ Do we generate <u>wastes</u>, scrap or off-spec materials? If so, does the treatment of disposal of these materials have potential environmental impacts?	❏ What is the <u>frequency or likelihood</u> of these impacts?
	❏ What is the <u>duration and geographic area</u> of these impacts?
❏ Which characteristics or attributes of our <u>products or services</u> could result in impact the environment (through their intended use, end-of-life management, etc.)?	❏ Which <u>parts of the environment</u> might be affected (e.g., air, water, land, flora, fauna)?
	❏ Is the impact <u>regulated</u> in some manner?
❏ Does our <u>land or infrastructure</u> (e.g., buildings) interact with the environment?	❏ Have our <u>interested parties</u> expressed concerns about these impacts?
❏ Which activities (for example, chemical storage) might lead to <u>accidental releases</u>?	

FIGURE 4. Sample aspect and impact information (*Source:* Stapleton et al. 2001)

development to help develop a team concept within the organization (U.S. EPA 2006b). The person selected from each group must be willing to devote sufficient time and effort to identify the legal requirements as well as *aspects* and *impacts*. The time commitment by the members of this committee will be critical to the current and future success of the EMS.

Aspects and Impacts

Aspects are an organization's products or services and their interaction with the environment (Waters 1998). Some examples of aspects are a company's existing regulatory requirements, use of raw materials, and purchasing and disposal habits.

Impacts are the effects of aspects on the environment (Waters 1998). The effects can be either beneficial or deleterious. Examples of impacts are stormwater runoff, hazardous waste disposal to a permitted land-fill, air emissions from a baghouse, and recycling of

spent fluorescent light bulbs. Additional aspect and impact information is included in Figure 4.

Peer review is critical. All members of the committee should be given an opportunity to review the complete draft listing because each committee member will provide a unique perspective to any given aspect of the organization.

The committee members will be tasked with brainstorming ideas on how plant processes interact with air, water, or land; how their processes could potentially fail; and how emergency events could stop or impede operations. An example aspects identification checklist is included in Figure 5.

Checklists such as these can greatly simplify how an organization views its aspects and impacts.

Legal and regulatory requirements should be thoroughly reviewed, and the committee must assess the compliance or noncompliance of the organization with each regulatory requirement. Also, any promises or commitments made as part of a permit,

ENVIRONMENTAL ASPECTS IDENTIFICATION

Plant _____

Process/Activity: _____
Contracted? _____
Process/Activity Location: _____

RAW MATERIAL INPUTS

PARTS

CHEMICAL MATERIAL

ENERGY USE:

TYPE: USAGE

	High	Med	Low
Electricity			
Natural Gas			
Propane			
Steam			
Compressed Air			
Hydraulics			

OTHER INPUT

WATER USE:

TYPE: USAGE

	High	Med	Low

Provide brief description of
process/activity

Optional: Attach and circle
photo, schematic, sketch
drawing, detailed
description

PRODUCT OUTPUTS

AIR EMISSIONS
(include noise & odor)

WASTE (& BYPRODUCTS)
(SOLID & LIQUID)

Check if Recycled

☐
☐
☐
☐
☐
☐
☐
☐
☐

WATER

On site treatment (Type)

FIGURE 5. Aspects identification checklist (*Source:* Stapleton et al. 2001)

authorization, or agreement should be included in committee review. Review and listing of legal and regulatory requirements should be documented as a formal procedure within the EMS (Stapleton, Glover, and Davis 2001).

Training

All personnel in the organization should be trained in environmental affairs as they relate to each employee's specific area of operations and job tasks

(Stapleton, Glover, and Davis 2001). As such, operating procedures should be developed to ensure compliance with legal requirements (Stapleton, Glover, and Davis 2001). Employees involved in more than one area, or those in an emergency response role, must be trained further in multiple areas as well as in specific emergency response procedures.

A training matrix, such as the one in Figure 6, will become an integral part of an EMS because it helps the organization coordinate and ensure completion of all required and recommended training.

EMS Training Log (Sample)

Training Topic	Attendees*	Frequency	Course Length	Course Method	Comments	Date Completed
EMS Awareness						
Supervisor EHS Training						
Hazardous Waste Management						
Hazardous Waste Operations						
Spill Prevention & Response						
Chemical Management						
Emergency Response						
Accident Investigation						
Hazardous Materials Transport						
Hazard Communication						
Personal Protective Equipment						
Fire Safety						
Electrical Safety						
Hearing Conservation						
Confined Space Entry						
Lock-out/Tag-out						
Bloodborne Pathogens						
Job-Specific Training (list)						

Attendees Code
1: **All Employees**
2: **Supervisors / Managers**
3: **Operators**
4: **Maintenance**
5: **Material Handlers**
6: **Engineering**

FIGURE 6. Sample training matrix (*Source:* Stapleton et al. 2001)

Comparing Objectives and Targets - Some Examples

Objectives	Targets
Reduce energy usage	• Reduce electricity use by 10% in 2001 • Reduce natural gas use by 15% in 2001
Reduce usage of hazardous chemicals	• Eliminate use of CFCs by 2002 • Reduce use of high-VOC paints by 25%
Improve employee awareness of environmental issues	• Hold monthly awareness training courses • Train 100% of employees by end of year
Improve compliance with wastewater discharge permit limits	• Zero permit limit violations by the end of 2001

FIGURE 7. Sample objectives and targets (*Source:* Stapleton et al. 2001)

Objectives and Targets

Once the aspects and impacts of an organization have been drafted, reviewed, and finalized, the next step is to set objectives and targets, or clearly defined goals that demonstrate environmental commitment and reduction in environmental impact. For example, a company can commit to reducing dust emissions from its grinding operation by 10 percent in a 12-month period following implementation of the EMS, or installing fences around all of its aboveground storage tanks by the end of a specified year. Sample objectives and targets are shown in Figure 7.

A set of objectives and targets serves as the company "punch list" of specific goals for achieving and maintaining environmental compliance. The list must be reviewed periodically, at least annually, but preferably quarterly. Adhering to this review timetable will help ensure continuous improvement.

Documentation and Controls

How does an EMS get properly documented? The person in charge of managing the EMS must determine the most efficient and accurate way to complete and store all required documentation to validate the EMS. Documents include internal audit reports, inspection reports, analytical reports, and state or federal forms completed for a permit or authorization. Additional documents include standard operating procedures for environmental management, lists of objectives and targets, and emergency response procedures. An EMS manual can be a central location for compiling and storing documents that show the organization's EMS is working as planned (Stapleton, Glover, and Davis 2001).

A proven method of documenting responsibility is to create a responsibility matrix. A sample matrix is shown in Figure 8.

Each operating segment of the organization is listed, with associated duties in EMS development and implementation cross-referenced. Ideally, lead and supporting roles should be listed as well as the number of participants who are working in each area.

Current technology, such as spreadsheets and EMS software, can greatly reduce the time needed to organize an EMS and the ability of the organization to access EMS information. These concepts are discussed later in the chapter.

Environmental documents must be reviewed and updated periodically. Controls are written into EMS procedures to ensure that document updates and changes are standardized, apprehended by everyone, and easily located. Out-of-date or obsolete document management should be included in any document control procedure (Stapleton, Glover, and Davis 2001).

Emergency Preparedness

An organization must have a set of procedures to ensure life safety. Emergency response procedures are required by U.S. EPA Spill Prevention Control and

Responsibility Matrix

Legend:
L = Lead Role
S = Supporting Role

	Plant M'gr	EHS M'gr	HR M'gr	Maintenance	Purchasing / Materials	Engineering	Production Supervisor(s)	Finance	EMS Mg't Rep.	Employees
Communicate importance of environmental management	L	S					S			
Coordinate auditing efforts		L		S			S			
Track / analyze new regulations (and maintain library)		L								
Obtain permits and develop compliance plans		L				S				
Prepare reports required by regulations		L								
Coordinate communications with interested parties			L							
Train employees		S					L			
Integrate environmental into recruiting practices			L							
Integrate environmental into performance appraisal process			L							
Communicate with contractors on environmental expectations					L					
Comply with applicable regulatory requirements	L	L	S	S	S	S	S	S	S	S
Conform with organization's EMS requirements	L	L	S	S	S	S	S	S	S	S
Maintain equipment / tools to control environmental impact				L						
Monitor key processes		S					L			
Coordinate emergency response efforts	L	S								
Identify environmental aspects of products, activities, or services	S	L	S	S	S	S	S	S	S	
Establish environmental objectives and targets	L	S					S			
Develop budget for environmental management		S						L		
Maintain EMS records (training, etc.)		L								
Coordinate EMS document control efforts					S				L	

FIGURE 8. Sample Responsibility Matrix (*Source:* Stapleton et al. 2001)

Countermeasures (40 CFR, Part 112) regulations, Risk Management Plan (40 CFR, Part 68) regulations, and the Occupational Safety and Health Administration's (OSHA's) *Hazardous Waste Operations and Emergency Response* (29 CFR 1910.120) *and Process Safety Management Standard* (29 CFR 1910.119) regulations in applicable facilities (Federal Register1996). Because of similarities regarding emergency response aspects within these individual rules, the U.S. EPA has encouraged facilities covered by multiple emergency response requirements to use the Integrated Contingency Plan (ICP) format (Federal Register 1996). Emergency procedures should include: (a) assessments of the facility that has been designated for emergency potential, (b) roles and responsibilities of personnel, (c) existing levels of equipment and locations of emergency equipment, (d) levels of trained personnel within the plant, (e) evacuation measures, and (f) contact information for outside assistance. These procedures are an essential part of an EMS.

Spill prevention protects the environment, whereas fast and efficient emergency response minimizes damage to the environment; both save money and enhance third-party liability protection for the organization.

Step 3: Check—Continuous improvement of the EMS is necessary to meet the changing needs of an organization (Stapleton, Glover, and Davis 2001). Checking mechanisms should be included in an EMS to ensure this continuous improvement (see Figure 9).

Examples may include:

1. completion of plant environmental audits, with a corrective action checklist, follow-up responsibility, and target completion date
2. completion of routine (daily, weekly, monthly) environmental inspection reports

Plant audits should be completed at least annually (Stapleton, Glover, and Davis 2001). Auditors can be trained on the job or off site. Often an outside expert is used initially to help start the process. At least two trained plant auditors are recommended, if the company wishes to develop a team concept and provide continuity (Stapleton, Glover, and Davis 2001). Implementing a cycle of audit—review—corrective action within the EMS can ensure that the EMS is working

as planned by providing evidence of issues that need to be addressed, or of environmental stewardship, cost savings, and success.

Step 4: Act—As stated earlier, periodic management review of completed audits and other EMS parameters may reveal deficiencies in either the EMS or in how quickly and efficiently action items are being completed. This step is perhaps the most valuable to the organization because it brings the process full circle and back to Step 1—the Plan stage (Stapleton, Glover, and Davis 2001). Acting on deficiencies forces the organization to evaluate root causes and to develop a plan of action to eliminate them. Note that if the organization's evaluation of the root cause is incorrect or inaccurate, then the problem may not be able to be resolved and will have to go through the cycle once again until it is ultimately changed or eliminated.

Management reviews can include the following action items:

1. Periodic management reviews of EMS team recommendations and employee suggestions (A sample management review procedure is shown in Figure 10.)
2. Periodic EMS team reviews of objectives and targets for completed items and new items needing attention
3. Review of audit reports
4. Review of comments from the public or other stakeholders
5. Investigation into why a violation occurred that was outside the established aspects and impacts for the organization

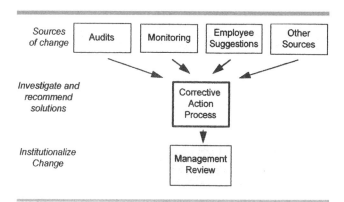

FIGURE 9. Checking mechanisms for continuous improvement (*Source:* Stapleton et al. 2001)

EMS PROCEDURE: MANAGEMENT REVIEW

I. Purpose

The purpose of this procedure is to document the process and primary agenda of issues to be included in the Management Review meetings for evaluating the status of the organization's environmental management system (EMS).

II. Scope

This procedure applies to all Management Review meetings conducted by the organization.

III. General

The Management Review process is intended to provide a forum for discussion and improvement of the EMS and to provide management with a vehicle for making any changes to the EMS necessary to achieve the organization's goals.

IV. Procedure

A. The ISO Management Representative is responsible for scheduling and conducting a minimum of two Management Review meetings during each 12-month period. The ISO Management Representative is also responsible for ensuring that the necessary data and other information are collected prior to the meeting.

B. At a minimum, each Management Review meeting will consider the following:

- suitability, adequacy and effectiveness of the environmental policy;

- suitability, adequacy and effectiveness of the environmental objectives (as well as the organization's current status in achieving these objectives);

- overall suitability, adequacy and effectiveness of the EMS;

- status of corrective and preventive actions;

- results of any EMS audits conducted since the last Management Review meeting;

- suitability, adequacy and effectiveness of training efforts; and,

- results of any action items from the previous Management Review meeting.

C. Minutes of the Management Reviews will be documented and will include, at a minimum the list of attendees, a summary of key issues discussed and any actions items arising from the meeting.

D. A copy of the meeting minutes will be distributed to attendees and any individuals assigned action items. A copy of the meeting minutes will also be retained on file.

FIGURE 10. Sample management review procedure (*Source:* Stapleton et al. 2001)

The frequency of management review meetings is best decided by the EMS team and the organization's senior management. To derive the best results, annual meetings are recommended (NSF 2001), although more frequent meetings may be needed early in the process. As the EMS becomes more familiar to the organization, fewer meetings should be needed.

Ultimately the process of Plan-Do-Check-Act will result in a highly efficient and sound EMS that will withstand repeated tests consisting of regulatory inspections, emergency events, and internal or external inquiries. In addition, as corrective action steps are taken, the organization should notice cost savings.

ISO 14001 EMS

The ISO 14001 *Environmental Management System* standard is a product of the International Organization for Standardization, a worldwide standards-setting body composed of standards-setting groups from each member organization (Waters 1998). The ISO 14001 standard is part of a family of ISO 14000 standards relating to environmental management. (The complete family of ISO 14000 standards is delineated in Figure 11.)

The ISO 14001 standard sets the framework for a company to develop and implement an environmental management system that is recognized internationally. Having an internationally recognized EMS is particularly advantageous to, and often required of, a company that operates both within the United States and globally. Overseas companies, as well as some U.S. companies, can require proof of ISO 14001 registration as a condition of doing business. Companies that fail to keep their registration can forfeit contracts and lose favored status with other companies. The U.S. automotive industry is a good example of an industry that has required ISO conformance of not only its own operating entities, but also of its suppliers. For example, Ford Motor Company required its preferred production suppliers' manufacturing facilities to acquire ISO 14001 certification by mid-2003 (Ford 2007). If a contract with an automaker is the primary income source for a parts supplier, achieving conformance with the ISO 14001 standard can be the difference between being profitable or going out of business.

Companies are not required to comply with ISO 14001 as part of any government regulatory requirement; however, agencies such as the U.S. EPA usually look at registration favorably as part of an overall regulatory compliance strategy. Additionally, although specific reductions in emissions of pollutants are not mandated, companies are required to set pollution reduction objectives and targets as part of an overall strategy of continuous improvement. In other words, a company's objectives, when met, should result in reductions in pollution.

Conformance to the ISO 14001 standard does not ensure environmental compliance. The standard is meant to set up the process of continuous improvement within an organization. Therefore, a company with a relatively poor environmental compliance record can, in fact, obtain ISO 14001 registration. By obtaining registration, the company can look forward to improved performance as the process of auditing and corrective actions required by the standard points out flaws and proposes solutions.

An ISO 14001 EMS contains the following five major elements: environmental policy, planning, implementation, checking and corrective action, and management review. Essentially, the organization is implementing its environmental policy through the actions carried out in the remaining four elements (Cascio et al. 1996).

Conformance with each element is demonstrated by publication of a company EMS manual. The manual describes each step that must be taken by the organization to establish and maintain compliance, along with personnel roles and responsibilities within the EMS, training requirements, objectives and targets, and audit requirements.

To acquire an ISO 14001 EMS, an organization must go through a rigorous registration process, usually assisted by the guidance of a registrar, who is an ISO-certified consultant with the credentials to award registration to successful applicants. The registration process involves showing the registrar the following:

- a corporate policy statement
- standard operating procedures
- a comprehensive set of objectives and targets
- a listing of personnel and their roles, along with responsibilities in environmental management

The registration process is completed once the registrar finishes interviewing key site personnel who will ultimately implement the EMS. The registrar will also review policies, procedures, and training records for any nonconforming issues (Cascio et al. 1996).

Registrars are often private consulting firms that specialize in providing ISO 14001 registration assistance to businesses and organizations. Such firms can help a company with all aspects, from initial consultation all the way through to final registration, and with each annual registration. Many private consulting firms offer ISO 14001 registration auditing and assistance. An Internet search under "ISO 14001" can

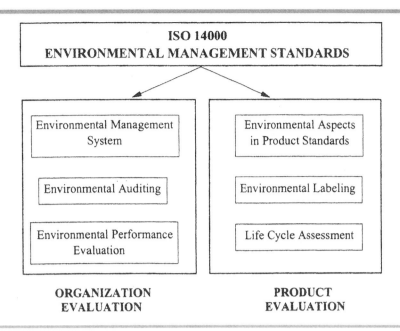

FIGURE 11. Complete family of ISO standards (*Source:* Cascio et al. 1996)

produce an extensive list of providers. A listing of public-based technical assistance providers that can help with EMS development and referrals to ISO 14001 registration providers can be found through the U.S. EPA's EMS Web site at www.peercenter.net (U.S. EPA 2007b).

STRATEGIC ENVIRONMENTAL MANAGEMENT

The idea of managing environmental affairs to produce minimum environmental impact is the basis for strategic environmental management (SEM) (Marcus 1998). Organizations that adopt SEM can reduce both regulatory liability and operating costs by converting environmental liabilities/costs into opportunities for competitive advantages in their businesses (Marcus 1998). SEM is summarized in Figure 12.

To properly implement SEM, an organization must actively work toward minimizing emissions and environmental impact. This often means an investment in new equipment or processes that produce less, or no, pollution; changing the company's public image to one of proactive environmental management; and compensating employees for environmental innovations (Marcus and Geffen 1998). An organization should be prepared to commit both capital and cultural invest-

ments to be successful at SEM. The results of successful SEM implementation can mean a more profitable business, an improved corporate public image, and a better corporate position for long-term success.

BENCHMARKS AND PERFORMANCE APPRAISAL CRITERIA

The effectiveness of an EMS can be measured by the results it provides to an organization. Such results can include fewer fines and penalties, reduced emissions, and lowered risk owing to increased auditing, checking, and corrective action implementation.

Current sustainability initiatives tie in well as measures of a functioning EMS. Sustainability measures such as tons of scrap recycled and energy use reduction targets show, when attained, that an EMS is serving its purpose by reducing impacts to the outside environment.

An ISO 14000 EMS registration is primarily reviewed annually, giving the organization an idea of how much improvement has been made. Sometimes, an EMS is reviewed more or less often, depending on the company and its auditor's recommendations.

Peer groups in the same industry can establish internal standards through their respective business associations to establish and promote best practices,

What Is SEM?

Strategic environmental management is the positioning of a business to take advantage of environmental challenges. It is the attempt to make these challenges into profit-making opportunities rather than threats that curtail business operations and prospects. Various companies have created value-adding programs in response to environmental issues. A list of some of the actions they have taken follows:

STRATEGY AND ORGANIZATION

- Cut back on environmentally unsafe operations.
- Carry out R&D on environmentally safe activities.
- Develop and expand environmental cleanup services.
- Compensate for environmentally risky endeavors.
- Purchase environmentally safe businesses.
- Change structure, compensation, and other systems.

PUBLIC AFFAIRS

- Try to avoid losses caused by appearing insensitive to environmental issues.
- Attempt to gain environmental legitimacy and credibility.
- Collaborate with environmentalists.

LEGAL

- Try to prevent confrontation with pollution control agencies.
- Comply early.
- Take advantage of innovative compliance programs.
- Rely on self-regulation rather than government requirements.

OPERATIONS

- Promote new manufacturing technologies.
- Encourage technological advances that reduce pollution from products and manufacturing processes.
- Modify production equipment and change manufacturing operations.
- Eliminate manufacturing wastes.
- Try to find alternative uses for wastes.
- Recycle wastes.

MARKETING

- Tell the truth, the whole truth, and nothing but the truth about your products' environmentally friendly features; avoid being attacked for unsubstantiated or inappropriate claims.
- Create consumer desire for environmentally friendly products as well as researching this market.

ACCOUNTING

- Demonstrate that anti-pollution programs pay.
- Show all affects of pollution reduction programs.

FINANCE

- Gain the respect of the environmentally concerned investment community.
- Recognize true liability.
- Recognize business opportunities.

Source: Buchholz, Rogene, Alfred Marcus, and James Post. *Managing Environmental Issues: A Casebook.* New York: Prentice-Hall, 1992.

FIGURE 12. Summary of strategic environmental management (*Source:* Marcus and Geffen 1998)

or benchmarks, throughout an industry. This method of benchmarking is beneficial because everyone in the group benefits. A primary example is the American Chemistry Council's Responsible Care® program, in which all American Chemistry Council member companies must participate (American Chemistry Council 2006).

Strategic environmental management (SEM) effectiveness will usually be measured by the amount of emissions reductions realized by the organization from year to year. Knowing that emissions reductions translate into reduced operating cost and regulatory liability makes SEM a reasonable add-on option for companies wishing to implement an EMS.

On June 26, 2000, the U.S. EPA established a public-private partnership called the National Environmental Performance Track that recognized companies that met predetermined performance goals with public recognition and low priority for routine inspection (U.S. EPA 2010). The program was terminated in 2009 with U.S. EPA working on new environmental leadership programs with both public and private stakeholders.

COST ANALYSIS AND BUDGETING
Budgeting for an EMS

Some organizations may have to develop an EMS out of necessity. A negative inspection report from a state or federal environmental agency can often provide enough impetus for corporate management to further refine their current environmental management strategy and enter into EMS development. Business associations voluntarily enter into EMS-like code programs, such as Responsible Care®, typically for two reasons:

1. To enhance public image
2. To show a clear difference between member and nonmember companies (NEETF 2000)

When entering into EMS development, a spending plan, or budget, should be developed to ensure that the organization is aware of and controlling costs. A budget for an EMS should include costs for the following items:

- staff time of site personnel, corporate personnel, and employees
- consulting expertise and assistance with program development and documentation
- training, including time spent on developing and delivering training

Costs can vary greatly, depending on the degree of personnel involvement, level of EMS detail, and desired level of registration. Internal labor accounts for the majority of costs for most organizations (U.S. EPA 2006a). However, an internally developed EMS can be accomplished at a relatively low cost. For example, an EMS developed by a Massachusetts Wastewater Utility produced significant cost savings and better customer service at a cost of $42,000. See Figure 13 for the EPA's comments regarding the City of Lowell Wastewater Utility EMS project.

The EMS focused on waste stream management, chemical use management, energy reduction, odor control, and industrial notification. Energy reduction alone resulted in a savings of $7000 over a 10-month period. Other benefits include improved communication at all levels of the organization, greater participation in decision making, more creative solutions, employee empowerment, as well as increased operation efficiencies and better service to customers (U.S. EPA 2006a).

Consultants will usually increase direct costs (Darnall and Edwards 2006), but will bring expertise to the process and free up internal staff time for their day-to-day work needs. Obtaining not-to-exceed cost and technical proposals from several consultants will give the company an idea of how much a consultant will cost versus how much is in the budget. A clearly defined scope of work will minimize additional charges as a company progresses with EMS development and implementation.

EMS adoption costs may be reduced by two means: having a good existing pollution-prevention program, and making use of government assistance. Additionally, those organizations with prior TQM experience usually have lower costs than those without (Darnall and Edwards 2006).

The type of company ownership may affect EMS cost. One study found that publicly traded organizations spent the least per employee ($268), whereas

---

The City of Lowell, Massachusetts, Lowell Wastewater Utility was selected as a project participant in the USEPA EMS Pilot Program for Local Government Entities. The Utility is an activated sludge wastewater treatment facility providing primary and secondary treatment to 170,000 users in five communities. The EMS focused on waste stream management, chemical use management, energy reduction, odor control, and industrial notification. Energy reduction alone resulted in a savings of $7,000 over a 10-month period. Other benefits include improved communication at all levels of the organization, greater participation in decision making, more creative solutions, employee empowerment, and increased operation efficiencies and better service to customers. These improvements resulted from a rather modest expenditure of about $42,000. For more information contact Mark Young, (978) 970-4248, e-mail: myoung@ci.lowell.ma.us.

FIGURE 13. A model cost-effective EMS

privately owned organizations ($531) and government spent more ($1,372). This cost variation may be attributed to the level of internal skill within the organization (Darnall and Edwards 2006).

COSTS FOR ISO 14001 REGISTRATION

Development and implementation costs for ISO 14001 registration include the following:

- registrar (consultant)
- internal staff time
- external consultant costs to train employees as internal auditors
- EMS development costs
- EMS registration costs

Design costs for an ISO 14001 EMS are usually less than $100,000 (Duke 2000). These costs are readily paid back in increased organization, decreased risk of fines and penalties, and positive public image for the company. Beyond design costs, initial registration fees are usually under $50,000 (Duke 2000). In one EPA study, a company reported an average cost of $89,000 per plant to achieve initial registration (Dimond 1996).

Given the broad range of expenses between an internally developed EMS and a fully registered ISO 14001 EMS, an organization must carefully plan on the basis of what level of management it desires. As mentioned previously, the decision may already have been made for the organization by a parent company, the board of directors, a member association, a customer, or the shareholders. In other cases, the organization will have to make the decision on which type of EMS to develop. In either case, a properly functioning EMS should provide a financial and social benefit to an organization.

EMS INFORMATION MANAGEMENT

Advances in technology have enabled environmental managers to streamline the many record-keeping and management requirements demanded by an EMS. Examples include:

- spreadsheet applications
- secure shared drives
- online communication systems

Each example is discussed below.

Spreadsheet Applications

Current spreadsheet applications are ideal for organizing a facility's environmental information. Spreadsheets can be used for the following:

- aspects and impacts
- legislative requirements
- training information
- objectives and targets
- responsibility matrix
- permit requirements

Spreadsheets allow the user to efficiently manage and save environmental information. Additionally, spreadsheet cells can be modified with formulas to automatically perform calculations or functions. Cells can also be linked to cells on another spreadsheet, allowing the user to potentially complete multiple tasks with a single action. For example, with a spreadsheet application a user can fill in the amount of product manufactured in a day. That spreadsheet cell can be linked to other cells that will calculate the facility's greenhouse gas emissions, fuel usage, and related parameters for the day. Daily data can be organized and summarized in a variety of ways to provide useful information, for example, annual emissions data, or annual fuel-usage data needed for air quality permit compliance reports. For example, a typical emissions calculation spreadsheet for a brick manufacturing plant is shown in Figure 14.

In addition, there are a number of commercially available, web-based online EMS applications. A discussion of these applications is beyond the scope of this chapter.

Secure Shared Drive

Many organizations offer their employees secure access to the company's computer system to conduct company business. In a typical application, an employee logs in (provides user identification and password) to the system, the system then grants access to a secure area where documents can be stored and information can be shared. The area, often called a shared drive, is accessible to all employees, but not to the public.

For EMS applications, a shared drive can offer many benefits. For example, the corporate Environmental Policy and EMS manual can be stored on the shared drive, and thus be available for instant access to any employee. Recent agency inspection reports can be posted to alert other facilities of any issues found at a particular location. Training presentations, policies, and standard operating procedures, when posted, can be used to provide consistency throughout the organization. The costs for providing a shared drive are low, as the needed systems are normally already in place at an organization.

Online Communication Systems

Online training and meetings can be conducted with an online communication system. A high-speed internet connection and telephone-conferencing capability

are usually necessary. Typically the meeting organizer sets up an account with a commercial provider. To hold a meeting, the organizer enters the provider's Web site, selects the date and time of the meeting, enters attendee e-mail addresses, and chooses a dial-in phone number to provide the meeting's audio component. The system then sends a Web link to all attendees with the meeting's date, time, and dial-in phone number.

The meeting begins with the organizer logging in to the meeting and signaling to the system to allow the organizer's computer screen to be seen by the attendees. When attendees log in to the Web site using the web link provided earlier, they will see the organizer's computer screen in live mode, meaning any actions taken by the organizer will be viewed by

Unit ID	Description	Control Device	Emission Limit		Control Device Required to Meet Limit?	Uncontrolled PTE > 100 ton/yr?	Subject to CAM?
101	Tunnel Kiln 1	N/A	PM:	0.04 gr/dscf	NO	NO	NO
		N/A	SO₂:	500 ppmdv	NO	NO	NO
		New: Dry Limestone Absorber (DLA)	HCl:	0.26 lb/ton b	YES	NO	NO[1]
		New: Dry Limestone Absorber (DLA)	HF:	1.2 lb/hr	YES	NO	NO[1]
102	Tunnel Kiln 2	N/A	PM:	0.04 gr/dscf	NO	NO	NO
		N/A	SO₂:	500 ppmdv	NO	NO	NO
		New: Dry Limestone Absorber (DLA)	HCl:	0.26 lb/ton b	YES	NO	NO[1]
		New: Dry Limestone Absorber (DLA)	HF:	1.2 lb/hr	YES	NO	NO[1]
104	Quarry Crusher	N/A	N/A		NO	NO	NO
105	Grinding/Screening/Manufacturing	C01: Sand Mixing Op. Fabric Collector	PM:	0.04 gr/dscf	YES	NO	NO
		C02: Shale Grdg Ln#2 Fabric Collector	PM:	0.04 gr/dscf	YES	NO	NO
		C03: Shale Grdg Ln#3 Fabric Collector	PM:	0.04 gr/dscf	YES	NO	NO
		C04: Fine Silo-Shale G Fabric Collector	PM:	0.04 gr/dscf	YES	NO	NO
		C05: Colonial Making Fabric Collector	PM:	0.04 gr/dscf	YES	NO	NO
		C08: Wirecut Sand B&S Fabric	PM:	0.04 gr/dscf	YES	NO	NO
		C10: Moldsander/Drysaw Fabric	PM:	0.04 gr/dscf	YES	NO	NO
106	Sand Dryer	C09: Sand Dryer Fabric Collector	PM:	0.04 gr/dscf	YES	NO	NO
		N/A	SO₂:	500 ppmdv	NO	NO	NO
107	Proctor Dryer	N/A	PM:	0.04 gr/dscf	NO	NO	NO
108	Space Heaters	N/A	N/A		NO	NO	NO
109	Shapes Dryer	N/A	PM:	0.04 gr/dscf	NO	NO	NO
		N/A	SO₂:	500 ppmdv	NO	NO	NO
110	Brick Shuttle Kiln	N/A	PM:	0.04 gr/dscf	NO	NO	NO
		N/A	SO₂:	500 ppmdv	NO	NO	NO
		N/A	HF:	0.91 tpy	NO	NO	NO
111	Emergency Generator No. 1	N/A	PM:	0.04 gr/dscf	NO	NO	NO
		N/A	SO₂:	500 ppmdv	NO	NO	NO
112	Emergency Generator No. 2	N/A	PM:	0.04 gr/dscf	NO	NO	NO
		N/A	SO₂:	500 ppmdv	NO	NO	NO

[1] Pursuant to §64.2(b)(1)(i), the emission limit is exempt from CAM requirements since it originates from the Brick MACT.
MACT standards proposed after 11/15/90 already contain sufficient monitoring to assure compliance with the limitation.

FIGURE 14. Typical emissions calculation spreadsheet for a brick manufacturing plant (*Source:* All4, Inc. 2010)

Association	Code name and year established

Chemical Manufacturers Association (CMA)
American Petroleum Institute (API)
National Association of Chemical Distributors (NACD)
American Textile Manufacturers Institute (ATMI)
National Association of Chemical Recyclers (NACR)
American Forest & Paper Association (AF&PA)
National Paint and Coatings Association (NPCA)
Responsible Care,® 1989
	Strategies for Today's Environmental Partnership (STEP), 1990
	Responsible Distribution Process℠ (RDP), 1991
	  • Encouraging Environmental Excellence (E3), 1992
	  • Quest for the Best, 1993
	Responsible Recycling, 1993
	  • Sustainable Forestry Initiative (SFI ℠), 1994
	  • Environmental, Health and Safety Principles, 1995
	Coatings Care,® 1996

FIGURE 15. Associations with codes of conduct (*Source:* NEETF 2000)

	ATMI's E3	CMA's Responsible Care®	NPCA's Coatings Care®	Responsible Distribution℠	SOCMA Responsible Care®	API's STEP	AFPA's SFI℠
Regulatory Compliance Required	Yes	No	No	Yes	No	No	Yes
Demonstrate Continuous Improvement	Yes	Yes	Yes	No	Yes	Yes	Yes
Community Involvement	Yes	Yes	Yes	Yes	Yes	Yes	Yes
Product Stewardship	Yes	Yes	Yes	Yes	Yes	Yes	Yes
Participation mandatory	No	Yes	Yes	Yes	Yes	Yes	Yes
3rd Party Verification	No	Voluntary	No	Yes	Voluntary	No	Voluntary

FIGURE 16. Certain aspects of codes of conduct (*Source:* NEETF, 2000)

the attendees. The corresponding dial-in number allows a conference call to take place along with the visual presentation.

The medium is ideal for holding update meetings or group discussions and can be used to rapidly and efficiently complete EMS training needs or information updates across an organization.

Subscriptions to the online service provider and telephone-conferencing service are required. At the same time, the savings in travel costs often translate into reduced overall costs for EMS implementation and ongoing training.

BEST PRACTICES

Best practices are commonly developed through the sharing of information between businesses through peer associations and business/government partnership (U.S. EPA 2007b). Peer associations with environmental best-practice codes of conduct are shown in Figure 15.

Member companies are often required to comply with association codes of conduct or have their membership revoked (NEETF 2000). Certain aspects of codes of conduct may also be voluntary, as shown in Figure 16.

There have been numerous business/government collaborations on EMS development and best-practice sharing. U.S. EPA grants have been used to fund best-practice initiatives for public use; these include the following:

- The Development of the 1998 document "Environmental Management Systems" by Jean S. Waters, Pollution Prevention Institute. This step-by-step EMS guidance document for small businesses was developed with help from a grant from the U.S. EPA to the Kansas Department of Health and Environment, under contract to the University of Kansas Center for Continuing Education (Waters 1998). It provides the user with a thorough discussion of EMS benefits, along with a review of each step in EMS development and implementation. Additional external information sources are included.
- The NSF International report titled "Environmental Management System Demonstration Project—Final Report," dated December 1996 (NSF 1996). This document summarizes the experiences of eighteen organizations in their quest for ISO 14001 EMS registration. The project was funded by a two-year grant from the U.S. EPA, which recognized the public need for information on EMS development. The participants included sixteen private companies, one government agency, and the U.S. Postal Service. Of the fifteen individual companies completing both the initial and final self-assessment, twelve reported positive progress toward EMS implementation over the course of the project (p. 18). The report can be of significant value to a company of similar size to any in the study.

Best practices on EMS implementation are shared on the U.S. EPA Web site, www.epa.gov/ems. Along with useful discussions, the Web page contains reference documents, case studies, policy statements, and other tools to assist virtually any organization in its EMS development and implementation.

Also, EMS best practices are being shared at industry association work groups, technical committee meetings, and local/state pollution prevention roundtables. Sample EMS documents, outlines, case histories, and spreadsheets can often be located through membership in these types of associations, or through government Web sites beyond EPA, such as the Public Entity EMS Resource (PEER) Center Web site (found online at www.peercenter.net) (U.S. EPA 2007b).

Typical best practices may include a detailed training matrix, an audit schedule, and a comprehensive aspects and impacts listing developed for a particular organization or line of business. Having this type of documentation allows an organization to take advantage of a time-tested format to develop a successful EMS implementation strategy.

Ongoing development of best practices is necessary to ensure the highest level of EMS performance, the greatest reduction in emissions, and the maximum cost savings. Technical committees and business associations will play a large part in development and implementation of best practices within their respective business sectors. Government will play a role in recognizing need and establishing funding mechanisms for best-practice development and sharing to assist the public.

The overall benefits of an EMS to an organization are obvious—improved environmental performance, better public image, and reduced costs (U.S. EPA 2007b). All organizations should have some form of EMS in place, not only to better manage their organization, but also to better compete in a global economy.

REFERENCES

A114, Inc. 2010. "Emissions Calculation Spreadsheet." Kimberton, PA: A114, Inc.

American Chemistry Council (ACC). 2006. *About Responsible Care and the American Chemistry Council.* www.responsiblecare-us.com/about.asp

Cascio, J., G. Woodside, and P. Mitchell. 1996. *ISO 14000 Guide: The New International Environmental Management Standards.* New York: McGraw-Hill.

Certo, Samuel C. "The Push for Quality." *Business Week*, June 8, 1987, p. 131.

_____. 1999. *Modern Management*. 8th ed. New York: Simon & Shuster.

Darnall, Nicole, and Daniel Edwards, Jr. 2006. "Predict ing the Cost of Environmental Management System Adoption: The Role of Capabilities, Resources, and Ownership Structure." *Strategic Management Journal*, January 2006, p. 305.

Delmas, Magali A. 2000. "Barriers and Incentives to the Adoption of ISO 14001 in the United States." *Duke Environmental Policy and Law Forum* 11(1):25.

Dimond, Craig D. 1996. "Environmental Management System Demonstration Project. NSF International. Environmental Management Systems." 2006. Michigan Department of Environmental Quality (MIDEQ) fact sheet no. 9838, Michigan Department of Environmental Quality.

Federal Register. Part II, The President, Executive Order 13423—Strengthening Federal Environmental, Energy, and Transportation Management. National Archives and Records Administration. Friday, January 26, 2007.

Ford Motor Company. 2007. *Sustainability Report 2005/6— Suppliers*. www.ford.com/en/company/about/sustainability/2005-06/relSuppliers.htm

Hess Corporation. 2006. *Environment, Health and Safety Policy*. www.hess.com/ehs/policies/ehspolicy.pdf

Imai, Masaaki. 1997. *Gemba Kaizen: A Commonsense, Low-Cost Approach to Management*. New York: McGraw-Hill. (Process Improvement—Standard Permits). www.iowadnr.com/air/prof/kaizen/kaizen03jun23.html

Iowa Department of Management, Office of Lean Enter-prise. 2010. *Lean Business Process Improvement in the Executive Branch of Iowa State Government*. www.lean.iowa.gov/results/index.html

Marcus, Alfred, and Donald Geffen. 1998. *Introduction to the Compendium on Strategic Environmental Manage-ment*. Ann Arbor, MI: National Pollution Prevention Center for Higher Education, University of Michigan.

North Carolina Department of Environment and Natural Resources. 2006. *Division of Waste Management, Haz-ardous Waste Section (civil penalty assessments, December 2006)*. www.wastenot.enr.state.nc.us/HWHOME/penalties/Dec06.html

Office of the Federal Register. 1996. "The National Re-sponse Team's Integrated Contingency Plan Guidance." Federal Register, 61 no. 109 (June 5): 28642.

Padhi, Nayantara. 2007. *The Eight Elements of TQM*. www.isixsigma.com/library/content/c021230a.asp

Pitz, Marylynne. "Fish Return after '88 Oil Spill, Study Says." *Pittsburgh Post-Gazette*, October 9, 1998. www.post-gazette.com/regionstate/19981009rivers5.asp

Public Entity Environmental Management System Resource Center. 2010. *About the Center*. www.peer center.net

Stapleton, Philip J., Margaret A. Glover, and S. Petie Davis. 2001. *Environmental Management Systems: An Implementation Guide for Small and Medium-Sized Organizations*. Ann Arbor, MI: NSF International.

The Institute for Corporate Environmental Mentoring. 2000. *The Emerging Role of Associations as Mentors, National Forum on Defining Environmental Excellence*. Washington, D.C.: The National Environmental Education and Training Foundation (NEETF).

Tien, Lee. "Access to Information after 9/11." Paper pre-sented at the Electronic Frontier Foundation's 12th Conference on Computers, Freedom and Privacy, San Francisco, April 16–19 2002.

Turner, J. Rodney. 1993. *The Handbook of Project-Based Management*. New York: McGraw-Hill.

U.S. Army Corps of Engineers. 1899. "Section 10 of the Rivers and Harbors Act of 1899," 33 U.S.C. 403. www.usace.army.mil/cw/cecwo/reg/rhsec10.htm

U.S. Central Intelligence Agency. 2007. *The World Factbook*. www.cia.gov/cia/publications/factbook/print/ja.html

United States Environmental Protection Agency (U.S. EPA). 1992. *EPA 1550—Freedom of Information Act Manual*. www.nepis.epa.gov

_____. 1996. *Companies Come Clean about Environmental Violations*. www.yosemite.epa.gov/opa/admpress.nsf/56d5d55f70218074852572a000657b5d/3902ba8165 18879085257212005225632563!OpenDocument

_____. 1998. "Memorandum: Issuance of Supplemental Environmental Projects Policy." Office of Enforcement and Compliance Assurance. www.epa.gov/safewater/wsg/wsg_119.pdf

_____. 1999. *Roto-Die Company cited for Clean Air Act violations at Micrometrics Systems plant in Virginia*. www.yosemite.epa.gov/opa/admpress.nsf/56d5d55f 70218074852572a000657b5d/78afaf2bf2cf7ef4852570d 60070fa56!OpenDocument

_____. 2001b. Office of Enforcement and Compliance Assurance. *Beyond Compliance: Supplemental Environmental Projects* (EPA 325-R-01-001).

_____. 2001a. *Environmental Management Systems and the Clean Water State Revolving Fund* (EPA 832-F-00-075). www.epa.gov/OW-OWM.html/cwfinance/cwsrf/emsfs.pdf

_____. 2002a. *Environmental Management Systems, Your Business Advantage* (EPA 240-F-02-002). www.epa.gov/EMS/docs/resources/ems_business.pdf

_____. 2002b. *Position Statement on Environmental Management Systems (EMSs)*. www.epa.gov/EPA-GENERAL/2006/February/Day-02/g1423.html

_____. 2003. *Guidance on the Use of Environmental Management Systems in Enforcement Settlements as Injunctive Relief and Supplemental Environmental Projects* (accessed June 11, 2010). www.epa.gov/ compliance/resources/policies/civil/seps/ems settlementguidance.pdf

_____. 2005a. *Compliance-Focused Environmental Management System—Enforcement Agreement Guidance* (EPA 330/9-97-002) (accessed June 11, 2010). www.epa.gov/ compliance/resources/publications/incentives/ emd/emd12elemr.pdf

_____. 2005b. *EPA Celebrates the Nation's Cleaner Environment on its 35th Anniversary."* www.yosemite.epa.gov/ opa/admpress.nsf

_____. 2005c. *United States Environmental Protection Agency Position Statement on Environmental Management Systems (EMSs).* www.epa.gov/ems/ position/position.htm

_____. 2006a. *EMS Costs and Benefits.* www.epa.gov/ ems/info/costben.htm

_____. 2006b. *Key Management Systems Concepts.* www.epa.gov/ems/info/keyconcepts.htm

_____. 2006c. *Laws and Regulations.* www.epa.gov/ epaoswer/osw/laws-reg.htm

_____. 2006d. *Plan, Do, Check, Act Model—Do.* www.epa. gov/ems/info/do.htm

_____. 2006e. *Plan, Do, Check, Act Model—Plan.* www.epa. gov/ems/info/plan.htm

_____. 2007a. *Envirofacts Data Warehouse—Overview.* www.epa.gov/enviro/html/ef_overview.html

_____. 2007b. *Gateway to International Best Practices & Innovations* (accessed June 11,2010). www.epa.gov/ innovation/international

_____. 2007c. *Summary of Criminal Prosecutions, Fiscal Year 1999.* www.cfpub.epa.gov/compliance/criminal_ prosecution/index.cfm

_____. 2009a. *Company and Four Senior Managers Sentenced for Environmental, Worker Safety Crimes After Longest Trial in Environmental Crimes History* (accessed June 11, 2010). admpress.nsf/www. yosemite.epa.gov/opa/d0cf6618525a9efb8525735 9003fb69d/41d5e11b5cc11a77852575a5005ed68f! OpenDocument

_____. 2009b. *National Environmental Performance Track.* www.epa.gov/performancetrack

_____. 2009c. *Next Steps for the National Environmental Performance Track Program and the Future of Environmental Leadership Programs* (accessed June 11, 2010). www.epa.gov/performancetrack/downloads/ PerformanceTrackNextStepsMemoExternal-text.pdf

_____. 2010. *My Environment* (accessed June 11, 2010). www.epa.gov/myenvironment

_____. 2011. *Civil Enforcement* (accessed November 8, 2011). www.epa.gov/compliance/civil

Waters, Jean S. 1998. *Environmental Management Systems, Prepared for the Small-Business Leadership Program under a Grant from USEPA.* Manhattan, KS: Pollution Prevention Institute.

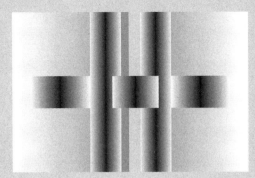

SECTION 4
SAFETY AND HEALTH TRAINING

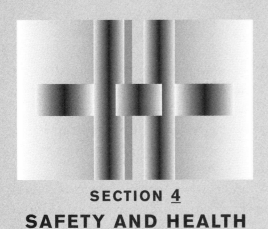

SECTION 4
SAFETY AND HEALTH TRAINING

LEARNING OBJECTIVES

▮ Be able to utilize three methods recommended by OSHA for prioritizing training needs.

▮ Be able to identify examples of both mandated and implied training requirements in OSHA standards.

▮ Learn how to use the OSHA Voluntary Training Guidelines to determine if training is needed.

▮ Be able to identify training needs and content, training goals and objectives, and develop learning activities. Conduct the training, evaluate its effectiveness, and develop recommendations to improve the training program.

▮ Learn to use a variety of OSHA resources available to develop and implement safety and health training, such as the OSHA Training Institute, the Resource Center Loan Program, Susan Harwood Grants Program, OSHA Web site and e-Tools, and the OSHA Outreach Training Program.

REGULATORY ISSUES: OSHA

Lon Ferguson

THE OCCUPATIONAL SAFETY AND HEALTH ACT of 1970 (OSH Act) does not directly address the responsibility of employers to provide health and safety information and instruction to employees. However, Section 2 of the OSH Act does encourage employers and employees to reduce workplace safety and health hazards through the institution of new and existing programs, and by specifically providing for training programs to increase the number and competence of personnel engaged in the field of occupational safety and health (OSHA 1970).

In terms of employer training responsibilities and duties, Section 5(a)(2) of the OSH Act requires each employer to "comply with occupational safety and health standards promulgated under this Act," and currently more than 100 of these standards contain training requirements (OSHA 1970). These training requirements reflect the Occupational Safety and Health Administration's (OSHA) belief that training is an essential part of every employer's safety and health program for protecting workers from injuries and illnesses (NIOSH 2004).

This is also reflected in OSHA enforcement activities in the construction industry: in 2008, two of the top ten most frequently cited violations [29 CFR Sections 1926.503, and 1926.454] were directly related to training (OSHA 1995 and 1996a).

In Title 29 of the *Code of Federal Regulations*, Section 1908.2, Consultation Agreements–Definitions, OSHA defines training as the planned and organized activity of a consultant to impart skills, techniques, and methodologies to employers and their employees to assist them in establishing and maintaining employment and a place of employment that is safe and healthful (OSHA 2000). While businesses sometimes object to the specific wording of an OSHA standard, there is little written in occupational safety and health literature stating that the OSHA-mandated training requirements are unnecessary or generally unreasonable (Saccaro 1994, 50–51).

From a legal perspective, the adequacy of employee training has become an issue in contested cases where the affirmative defense of unpreventable employee misconduct is pursued. Under case law well-established in the Occupational Safety and Health Review Commission, an employer may successfully defend itself against an otherwise valid citation by demonstrating that all feasible steps were taken to avoid the occurrence of the hazard, and that actions of the employee involved in the violation were a departure from a uniformly and effectively enforced work rule of which the employee had either actual or constructive knowledge. The adequacy of the training and education given to employees in connection with a specific hazard is a factual matter that can be decided only by considering all the facts and circumstances surrounding the alleged violation (OSHA 1998, 2).

Legally mandated training is an important component in a company's safety training program, but it should not be the foundation of the program. This legally mandated training should be viewed as minimal standards; training to merely avoid citations will not decrease the rate and severity of injuries, nor does it satisfy the spirit of the OSH Act (OSHA 1970). Companies can buy training programs that cover many of the OSHA training requirements. These programs are designed to meet the minimum training requirements established by OSHA. However, the programs do not address the specific company procedures, manufacturing processes, or hazards that are necessary for successful training. There are sure to be major gaps in a safety training program if the goal is merely compliance with government safety regulations, while company-specific safety hazards are left unaddressed (Saccaro 1994, 50–51).

THE ROLE OF TRAINING IN ACCIDENT PREVENTION

Current estimates identify that 80–90 percent of all accidents are caused in part by unsafe acts (Lawton and Parker 1998). Training, or the lack of training, may play a role in the occurrence of unsafe acts, and therefore play a role in accident prevention. There is very little disagreement in the role that training plays in reducing unsafe acts, but the more pressing problem for many employers is deciding which employees have the greatest need for training.

In OSHA's publication, *Training Requirements in OSHA Standards and Training Guidelines*, two methods for prioritizing training needs are discussed (OSHA 1998). The first method is to identify employee populations that are at higher levels of risk The nature of the work will provide an indication that such groups should receive priority for training on occupational safety and health risks. This risk can be influenced by conditions under which the work is performed, such as noise, heat or cold, or safety or health hazards in the surrounding area.

The second method of identifying employee populations at high levels of risk is to examine the incidence of accidents and injuries. Within the company, workers' compensation data and/or OSHA record-keeping logs (OSHA Form 300, Log of Work-Related Injuries and Illnesses) and reports (OSHA Form 301, Injury and Illness Incident Report) can be used to justify and define the role of training for targeting preventive follow-up action (OSHA 2004b). A thorough accident investigation can identify not only specific employees who could benefit from training, but also identify companywide training needs.

On a national level, federal as well as professional safety societies can be used to provide injury and illness data. Research from these data sources has identified several variables as being related to a disproportionate share of injuries and illnesses at the work site. These variables should be considered when identifying those with the greatest need for training (OSHA 1998, 7):

- the age of the employee—younger employees have higher incidence rates
- the length of time on the job—new employees have higher incidence rates
- the size of the firm—in general terms, medium-size firms have higher incidence rates than smaller or larger firms

- the type of work performed—incidence and severity rates vary significantly by the Standard Industrial Classification (SIC) Code
- the use of hazardous substances by SIC Code (OSHA 2010f)

Determining the content of training for employees at higher levels of risk is similar to determining what any employee needs to know. A job hazard analysis is a useful tool for determining training content from job requirements. This procedure examines each step of a job, identifies existing or potential hazards, and determines the best way to perform the job in order to reduce or eliminate the hazards (OSHA 1998, 7).

FUTURE OUTLOOK

In 1999, the National Institute for Occupational Safety and Health (NIOSH), the National Institute of Environmental Health Sciences (NIEHS), and OSHA sponsored a national conference to discuss emerging issues in the occupational safety and health field with a focus on training effectiveness. Specifically, this conference focused on the following (NIOSH 2004, 1):

- issues concerning the changing workplace and workforce
- methodologies for training
- evaluation of training
- systems of safety, including training
- policies and resources to meet projected training needs

What follows are some of the major findings from this conference related to training needs and challenges, and training policy and regulations.

Needs and Challenges

Although the reported number of workplace fatalities in the United States has decreased over the past decade, according to the Bureau of Labor Statistics (BLS), the number of reported fatalities is still substantial— 4547 fatalities in the United States in 2010 (BLS 2011). Therefore, improving training program quality and the effectiveness of training efforts, together with comply-

ing with the relevant OSHA training regulations, are important interventions aimed at workplace hazard prevention and control.

The acknowledged need for training is also being influenced by performance-based training, which is not mandated by law but is based on the need to improve job performance. In addition, workplace and workforce changes that are responding to advances in technology, demographic shifts, and global economic factors all act to complicate the task of training (NIOSH 2004, 2–4).

Examples of workplace changes in the United States include the shift from a manufacturing economy to one that is dominated by services and a reduced management-to-worker ratio. Since occupational hazards in the service sector tend to be more variable, training may have to change to incorporate alternative approaches to ensure learning of safe work practices. As an organization becomes flatter, the workers can be expected to play a greater role in OSH efforts. This implies that these same workers must receive appropriate training and information about hazards, control measures, and preventive actions commensurate with their safety and health program responsibilities (NIOSH 2004, 5–6).

Policy and Regulations

OSHA recognizes training as a critical action to take in further reducing workplace injuries and illnesses in the United States. This is especially true when training is combined with other workplace interventions, such as safety programs and procedures. However, OSHA also has found the effectiveness of OSH training as a sole intervention is less certain and more limited (NIOSH 2004, 11–13).

As a result of the 1999 NIOSH, NIEHS, and OSHA Training Conference, there were three major findings related to policy, regulation, and standards. The first was the need to prioritize training with a focus on directing OSH training at those conditions that represent the highest risk of work-related injury and illness. Three methods for prioritizing training were discussed earlier in this chapter. OSHA has also been gathering empirical evidence on the benefits of training (lives saved, injuries avoided, and reduced costs to business) through OSHA Consultation Safety and Health Program Evaluations completed at sites requesting consultation services. Data from these program evaluations support the premise that companies demonstrating a strong emphasis on worker training had the most effective occupational safety and health programs (NIOSH 2004, 11–13).

The second major finding was the need to set at least voluntary standards for acceptable OSH training program practices. This also included establishing competencies of those delivering OSH training. It was believed that these standards would help provide a certain level of quality control (NIOSH 2004, 12). OSHA has, in fact, developed Voluntary Training Guidelines, which are discussed later in this chapter.

The third major finding was the need to provide OSH training to all levels of the workforce to promote total staff knowledge of the training goals and to reinforce its objectives. As mentioned earlier, this is also important as organizations become flatter and additional safety and health responsibilities are placed on workers at all levels. To address this issue, OSHA is providing support for direct training and education of workers through grants to various nonprofit organizations, offering course s at OSHA Training Institute Educations Centers, and disseminating training products through distance learning technology, CD-ROMs, and the Internet (NIOSH 2004, 12).

OSHA TRAINING REQUIREMENTS

OSHA Revisions to the Voluntary Protection Programs to Provide Safe and Healthful Working Conditions

Section IV of the Revisions to the Voluntary Protection Programs to Provide Safe and Healthful Working Conditions outlines the requirements of a safety and health management system for all VPP participants. The four basic requirements are in line with the Voluntary Safety and Health Program Management Guidelines originally developed in 1989 (OSHA 1989). A summary of the four elements in the VPP Safety and Health Management System include (OSHA, 2009b):

- management leadership and employee involvement—integrating the OSH program

with the overall management system, clearly establishing policies with goals and objectives, responsibility/authority, and accountability for OSH activities, and involving workers in hazard recognition and control activities
- work-site analysis—analyzing the workplace conditions and work practices to identify hazards, policies, and procedures for the purpose of anticipating harmful occurrences (i.e., inspections and job hazard analysis)
- hazard prevention and control—eliminating or controlling hazards via engineering, administrative, work practices, or PPE
- safety and health training—addressing the responsibilities of all personnel at all levels of the organization

According to these guidelines, training is necessary to reinforce and complement management's commitment to prevent exposure to hazards. The guidelines do not suggest that elaborate or formal training programs solely related to safety and health are always needed. In fact, integrating safety and health protection into all organizational activities is the key to its effectiveness. Safety and health information and instruction is often most effective when incorporated into other training about performance requirements and job practices, such as management training on performance evaluation, problem solving, and employee training on the operation of a particular machine or the conduct of a specific task (OSHA 2009b).

A fundamental premise of the safety and health training included as part of the VPP Safety and Health Management System is that all employees must understand their safety and health responsibilities, the hazards to which they may be exposed, and how to prevent harm to themselves and others from such exposures. Without such an understanding, employees will not be able to perform their responsibilities for safety and health effectively. For this to happen, the training must ensure the following (OSHA 2009b):

- Managers and supervisors understand their safety and health responsibilities and are able to carry them out effectively. These responsibilities may include identifying unrecognized

potential hazards, maintaining physical safeguards in their work areas, and reinforcing
employee training on the nature of potential
hazards and on needed protective measures,
such as work practices and personal protective
equipment.

- All employees are made aware of hazards
  and are taught how to recognize hazardous
  conditions and the signs and symptoms of
  work-related illnesses. All employees are also
  provided with information and training in the
  safety and health program and the provision
  of applicable standards.
- All employees learn the safe work procedures
  to follow in order to protect themselves from
  hazards. This includes what is being done to
  control these hazards and the protective measures the employee must follow to eliminate
  or reduce exposure to these hazards.
- All employees and visitors on site understand
  what to do in emergency situations.
- All employees required to wear personal protective equipment must understand why it
  is required, its limitations, how to use it
  properly, and how to maintain it.

An important part of training is the need to evaluate employee understanding of the safety and health
information covered. It is a major mistake to assume
that the mere act of training ensures practical comprehension; there must be some means of verifying
comprehension. As part of the Construction Safety
and Health Outreach Program, the OSHA Office of
Training and Education publishes *Tools for a Safety
and Health Program Assessment*. This publication identifies three key components for assessing safety and
health training (OSHA 1996b, 10–11):

1. Ensuring that all employees understand
   hazards

   Documentation:

   - Does the written training program include
     training for all employees in emergency
     procedures and in all potential hazards to
     which the employees may be exposed?

   - Do training records show that all employees
     received the planned training?
   - Do the written evaluations, test results,
     and other forms of training indicate the
     training was successful in meeting training
     objectives?

   Interviews:

   - Can employees identify the hazards they
     are exposed to, why those hazards are a
     threat, and how they can help protect
     themselves and others?
   - If PPE is used, can employees explain why
     they use it and how to use and maintain it
     properly?
   - Do employees feel that health and safety
     training is adequate?

   Site conditions and root causes of hazards:

   - Have employees been injured or made ill by
     hazards of which they were unaware, or
     whose dangers they did not understand, or
     from which they did not know how to
     protect themselves?
   - Have employees or rescue workers ever
     been endangered by employees not know-
     ing what to do in a given emergency
     situation?
   - Are there hazards in the workplace that
     exist, at least in part, because one or more
     employees have not received adequate
     hazard control training?
   - Are there any instances of employees not
     wearing the required PPE properly because
     they have not received appropriate training?

2. Ensuring that supervisors understand their
   responsibilities

   Documentation:

   - Do training records indicate that all supervis-
     ors have been trained in their responsibilities
     to analyze work to idenitfy hazards, to
     maintain physical protections, and to reinforce
     employee training and work practices

through performance feedback and, where necessary, enforcement of safe work procedures and safety and health rules?

Interviews:

- Do supervisors know their safety and health responsibilities?
- Do employees confirm that supervisors are carrying out their safety and health responsibilities?

Site conditions and root causes of hazards:

- Has a supervisor's lack of understanding of safety and health responsibilities played a part in creating hazardous activities or conditions?

3. Ensuring that managers understand their safety and health responsibilities

Documentation:

- Do training plans for managers include training in safety and health responsibilities?
- Do records indicate that all line managers have received this training?

Interviews:

- Do employees confirm that managers know and carry out their safety and health responsibilities?

Site conditions and root causes of hazards:

- Has a manager's lack of understanding of safety and health responsibilities played a part in creating hazardous activities or conditions?

The documentation of safety and health training discussed above is a critical consideration in all safety and health training. At a minimum, this documentation should include the name of the worker, job title, personal identifier such as clock number, date, list of topics covered, length of training, and the trainer's name and signature. The documentation records can provide evidence of the employer's good faith and compliance with OSHA standards and also answer one of the first questions an accident investigator may ask: "Was the injured employee trained to do the job?" (Reese 2003, 238–239).

OSHA Voluntary Training Guidelines

In an attempt to assist employers with their occupational safety and health training activities, OSHA has developed a set of training guidelines. OSHA does not intend to make these guidelines mandatory and they are available for review in OSHA Publication 2254, *Training Requirements in OSHA Standards and Training Guidelines*. OSHA encourages a personalized approach to the training programs at individual work sites. Therefore, the guidelines are general enough to be used in any area of occupational safety and health training, and allow employers flexibility to determine for themselves the content and format of training (OSHA 1998).

The OSHA training guidelines recommend the following seven steps when developing safety and health training:

1. Determining if training is needed

Training is not a panacea for all safety and health problems. In general, training is most effective when addressing problems related to a lack of knowledge, unfamiliarity with equipment or processes, or incorrect execution of a task. However, training is less effective for problems arising from an employee's lack of motivation or lack of attention to the job, and training should not be used as a substitute for engineering or other administrative controls (OSHA 1998). Methods for addressing the unmotivated employee were discussed in an earlier chapter.

2. Identifying training needs

The first step in identifying training needs is to identify what the employee is expected to accomplish. The second step is to identify in what ways, if any, the employee's performance is deficient. To avoid unnecessary training and meet the needs of the employees, training must focus on those areas where improved performance is needed. A valuable tool available to the safety professional to identify deficiencies in employee performance is a job hazard analysis. The information obtained from the job hazard analysis can then be used as the content for the training activity.

Other means suggested by the guidelines for developing training content include (OSHA 1998):

a. Using company accident and injury records to identify how accidents occur and what can be done to prevent them from recurring.

b. Requesting employees to provide written descriptions of their jobs. These should include the tasks performed and the tools, materials, and equipment used.

c. Observing employees at the work site as they perform job tasks. Safety and health hazards can be identified through the employees' responses to such questions as, have they had any near-miss incidents, do they feel they are taking risks, or do they believe that their jobs involve hazardous operations, substances, and so forth.

d. Examining similar training programs offered by other companies in the same industry, or obtaining suggestions from such organizations as the National Safety Council, the American Society of Safety Engineers, or federal safety and health agencies such as OSHA and NIOSH.

e. Reviewing the specific federal or state safety, health, and environmental standards applicable to a business can also provide direction in developing training content.

3. Identifying training goals and objectives

Well-written instructional objectives will identify as precisely as possible what individuals will do to demonstrate that the objective has been reached. These objectives will be clear, measurable, and describe the important conditions under which the individual will demonstrate competence. The objectives will also define what constitutes acceptable performance (OSHA 1998).

4. Developing learning activities

Learning activities enable those being trained to demonstrate that they have acquired the desired skills and knowledge. To be effective, these activities should simulate the actual job as closely as possible. This is especially true if a specific process is to be learned, in which case the activities should be arranged in the same sequence in which the tasks are performed on the job. These training activities can include such things as lectures, role playing, self-paced instruction, and demonstrations. There are a few factors that will influence the type of learning activity selected. One of these factors is the training resources available to the employer. Another factor is the kind of skills or knowledge to be learned (OSHA 1998).

5. Conducting the training

A critical part of conducting the training is knowing your audience. This will be accomplished if the prior steps are done properly. The trainer must also get the audience to buy into the training. Specifically, the trainees must be convinced of the importance and relevance of the training material. When this is achieved, the audience is much more likely to pay attention and learn the material. When conducting the training, it should be presented so that its organization and meaning are clear to the employees. The OSHA training guidelines suggest one way to accomplish this is to do the following:

a. provide overviews of the material to be learned

b. relate the new information or skills to the employee's goals, interests, or experience

c. reinforce what the employees learned by summarizing the program's objectives and key points.

The training content, the nature of the workplace, federal and state regulations, and the resources available for training will help employers determine the frequency of training activities, the length of the sessions, the instructional techniques, and the individuals best qualified to complete the training (OSHA 1998).

6. Evaluating training program effectiveness

A critical component to a training program is the development of a method to measure the effectiveness of the training. The development of such a method should be considered at the same time the course content and objectives are being developed. As mentioned earlier, all good objectives are measurable, and the evaluation of the training will help determine how effective the trainer was in meeting the training objectives.

If done properly, this evaluation will also provide an indication on the trainees' improved performance on the job. The OSHA training guidelines provide the following examples of methods for evaluating training programs (OSHA 1998):

  a. student surveys (opinions/perceptions)
  b. supervisors' observations
  c. workplace improvements—the ultimate success of a training program may be changes throughout the workplace that result in reduced injury or accident rates.

A more specific discussion on evaluation of training as well as examples of the above evaluation tools will be included in the chapter titled, "Benchmarks and Performance Appraisal Criteria" in this section.

  7. Improving the training program

If the evaluation shows that the training did not meet its objectives, it may be necessary to revise the training program. One way to accomplish this is to repeat the steps in the training process by starting with the first step of determining if training is needed. The OSHA training guidelines suggest asking the following questions as part of improving the training program (OSHA 1998):

- If a job hazard analysis was conducted, was it accurate?
- Was any critical feature of the job overlooked?
- Were the important gaps in knowledge and skills included?
- Was material already known by the employees intentionally omitted?
- Were the instructional objectives presented clearly and concretely?
- Did the objectives state the level of acceptable performance that was expected of employees?
- Did the learning activity simulate the actual job?
- Was the learning activity appropriate for the kinds of knowledge and skills required on the job?
- When the training was presented, was the organization of the material and its meaning made clear?

- Were the employees motivated to learn?
- Were the employees allowed to participate actively in the training process?
- Was the employer's evaluation of the program thorough?

OSHA MANDATED AND IMPLICIT TRAINING REQUIREMENTS

Many of the standards promulgated by OSHA explicitly require the employer to train employees in the safety and health aspects of their jobs. An example of a standard that mandates training is 29 CFR 1910.178 (l)(1)(i), which states the following: "Prior to permitting an employee to operate a powered industrial truck (except for training purposes), the employer shall ensure that each operator has successfully completed the training required by this paragraph (l), except as permitted by paragraph (l)(5)" (OSHA 2006).

Other OSHA standards imply training by making it the employer's responsibility to limit certain job assignments to employees who are certified, competent, or qualified—meaning that they have had special previous training. An example of a standard that implies training is 29CFR 1926.1053(b)(15), which states that ladders shall be inspected by a competent person for visible defects on a periodic basis and after any occurrence that could affect their safe use (OSHA 1991).

A listing of all the mandatory and implicit training required by OSHA is available in OSHA 2254, *Training Requirements in OSHA Standards and Training Guidelines* (OSHA 1998). This is the most recent OSHA publication on training requirements in OSHA standards; some changes have been made in the regulations since 1998.

OSHA TRAINING RESOURCES
OSHA Directorate of Training and Education

The OSHA Directorate of Training and Education (DTE) is responsible for managing OSHA's national training and education policies and procedures. OSHA's DTE offers a variety of resources to help companies satisfy safety training requirements. The training guidelines developed by the DTE were discussed earlier

(OSHA 2009c). Other training resources provided by the DTE include the Resource Center Loan Program (OSHA 2008a), the Susan Harwood Grants Program (2009a), OSHA Training Institute, OSHA Training Institute Education Centers (OSHA 2009d), and the OSHA Outreach Training Program (OSHA 2010a). What follows is a brief discussion of these training resources and what they offer a safety and health professional.

Resource Center Loan Program

The Resource Center Loan Program was developed by the OSHA Directorate of Training and Education to respond to the many requests for safety and health training materials. The resource center has a collection of books and over 600 videos covering 100 occupational safety and health topics. Currently, these training materials are made available to the following: OSHA national, regional, and area office employees, employees of state plan states, Consultation Program employees, Voluntary Protection Program site employees, OSHA federal agency trainers, OSHA grantees, and OSHA outreach trainers within the United States. For those who are eligible to use these training materials, there are no direct fees charged by the center with the exception of paying the cost of return shipping. Those interested in using training material should make their requests at least fifteen days prior to the start of the training. The typical loan period used by the center is fourteen days, which includes days for shipping. *The Resource Center Loan Program Catalog*, which explains in detail the policies for borrowing training materials as well as a complete listing of subject titles, is available from the OSHA Web site (OSHA 2008a).

Susan Harwood Grants Program

OSHA offers grants to nonprofit organizations to train workers in the recognition, avoidance, and prevention of safety and health hazards in their workplaces through the Susan Harwood Grants Program. Each nonprofit organization awarded a grant is responsible for the following: developing a training program that addresses one of the safety and health topics identified by OSHA, recruiting individuals for the training, conducting the training, and following up

with trainees to find out what changes were made to reduce hazards in their workplaces as a result of the training. Additional information on the Susan Harwood Grants Program is available at OSHA's Web site.

In general, the grant program focuses on four areas:

1. Educating workers and employers in small businesses (250 or fewer employees).
2. Training workers about new OSHA standards.
3. Training at-risk workers and employer populations.
4. Training workers about high-risk activities or hazards identified by OSHA through the Department of Labor's Strategic Plan.

Examples of safety and health topics that have been funded through the grant program in recent years include crane safety, combustible dust, emergency preparedness and response, and the OSHA record-keeping process (OSHA 2009a).

OSHA Education Centers and Outreach Training Programs

Prior to 1992, the OSHA Training Institute (OTI) served as OSHA's primary training provider for federal and state compliance officers and state Consultation Program staff. The institute also offered training to private-sector employees on a space-available basis. However, during the 1980s, demand for training from private-sector employees increased substantially and the OTI did not have the capacity to handle this demand. As a result, in October of 1992, the OTI Education Center Program was established to meet the expanding need for OSHA training to private-sector employees. These Education Centers support OSHA's training and education mission by providing the following (Barnes 2003, 36–37):

- basic courses that teach students to recognize, avoid, and prevent unsafe and unhealthful working conditions
- enhance the agency's community outreach efforts, including Spanish-language courses and youth initiatives
- specialized local instruction tailored to specific regional industry needs

Initially, the OTI Education Center Program started with 4 education centers, but has now expanded to 27 centers, comprised of 45 member organizations, with at least one in each of OSHA's regions. This expansion allowed OSHA to nearly double its training capability to meet the increasing demand for OSHA training. In fact, in 2007 alone, more than 27,346 students were trained at education centers (OSHA, 2009c). The education centers offer numerous short courses, online training, on-site training for organizations, and training in Spanish, with a complete listing available from the OSHA Web site within the Office of Training and Education section (OSHA, 2009b). The courses available from the OTI range from 5 to 70 contact hours, while the Education Center courses typically range from 6 to 30 contact hours, with continuing education units (CEUs) available for all courses. Courses are both lecture-based and web-based, with a blended course being a combination of both.

Based on course enrollments, two of the most popular courses taught by the Education Centers are #500, "Trainer Course in Occupational Safety and Health Standards for the Construction Industry" and #501, "Trainer Course in Occupational Safety and Health Standards for General Industry." Students completing these courses and passing a test become authorized by OSHA to participate in the Outreach Training Program. The general industry outreach trainers are authorized to conduct 10- and 30-hour general industry outreach courses and receive OSHA course completion cards to issue to the participants.

To stay current on OSHA, general industry outreach trainers must attend #503, "Update for General Industry Outreach Trainers" every four years to maintain their status as authorized general industry outreach program trainers, or they may retake #501 to maintain their trainer status. Construction industry outreach trainers are authorized to conduct 10- and 30-hour construction industry outreach courses and receive OSHA course completion cards to issue to attendees. To stay current on OSHA, construction outreach trainers must attend #502, "Update for Construction Industry Outreach Trainers" every four years to maintain their status as authorized construction outreach program trainers, or they may retake #500

to maintain their trainer status (OSHA 2010a). More information on these outreach trainer courses is available on the OSHA Training Institute Education Centers Web site (OSHA, 2009d).

OSHA Outreach Training Program

Through OSHA's Outreach Training Program, individuals are permitted to obtain course completion cards verifying their participation in 10- and 30-hour general industry and construction courses. This outreach program has grown rapidly in recent years, with over 680,000 students trained and 43,000 classes offered in 2008. Over the past three years, 1.6 million students were trained with 80 percent working in the construction industry (OSHA 2011a). What follows is a brief overview of the 10- and 30-hour courses:

10-HOUR GENERAL INDUSTRY COURSE

The 10-hour general industry course is intended to provide a variety of training on safety and health to entry-level workers in general industry. This course emphasizes hazard identification, avoidance, control, and prevention. The program guidelines for the 10-hour course require a minimum of one hour in each of the following topics, except for the Introduction to OSHA, which must be two hours (OSHA 2011b):

- an introduction to OSHA (OSH Act; General Duty Clause, employer rights and responsibilities, whistleblower rights, record-keeping basics, inspections, citations, value of safety, OSHA Web site and 800 number)
- walking and working surfaces, including fall protection
- fire and emergency preparedness (exit routes, emergency action plans, fire prevention plans, and fire protection)
- electrical
- personal protective equipment
- hazard communication

In addition, the guidelines require two hours from at least two of the elective topic areas and two hours from any other general industry hazards or policies or from the elective list below, with a minimum of 30 minutes spent on topics covered:

- hazardous materials
- materials handling
- machine guarding
- ergonomics
- introduction to industrial hygiene
- bloodborne pathogens
- fall protection
- safety and health programs

30-HOUR GENERAL INDUSTRY COURSE

The 30-hour general industry course is intended to provide a variety of training on safety and health to those workers with at least some safety and health responsibilities within general industry. The course emphasizes hazard identification, avoidance, control, and prevention, as well as specific OSHA standards. The program guidelines for the 30-hour course require coverage of each of the following topics (OSHA 2011b):

- An introduction to OSHA (OSH Act; General Duty Clause, inspections, general safety and health provisions, citations and penalties, record keeping, value of safety, and OSHA Web site) – 2 hours
- Managing safety and health – 2 hours
- Walking and working surfaces, including fall protection – 1 hour
- Fire and emergency preparedness (exit routes, emergency action plans, fire prevention plans, and fire protection) – 2 hours
- Electrical – 2 hours
- Personal protective equipment – 1 hour
- Materials handling – 2 hours
- Hazard communication – 1 hour

The remaining time is spent on the coverage of a minimum of five elective topics (which must add up to at least ten hours, with a minimum of 30 minutes for any topic) from the list below, along with seven optional hours related to any general industry hazards or policies and/or expanding on the mandatory or elective topics:

- hazardous materials
- permit required confined space

- powered industrial vehicles
- lockout/tagout
- fall protection
- machine guarding
- welding, cutting, and brazing
- introduction to industrial hygiene
- bloodborne pathogens
- ergonomics
- safety and health programs

10-HOUR CONSTRUCTION INDUSTRY COURSE

The 10-hour construction industry course is intended to provide a variety of training on safety and health to entry-level workers in the construction industry. This course emphasizes hazard identification, avoidance, control, and prevention. The program guidelines for the 10-hour course require a minimum of the following (OSHA 2011a):

- An introduction to OSHA – 2 hours (OSH Act; General Duty Clause, record keeping, general safety and health provisions, citations, competent person, value of safety, and OSHA Web site)
- Four hours total in each of the OSHA Focus Four Hazards—falls (minimum of 1 hour and 15 minutes), electrocution (minimum of 30 minutes), struck-by (minimum of 30 minutes), and caught in/between (minimum of 30 minutes)
- Personal protective equipment – 30 minutes
- Health hazards in construction – 30 minutes

In addition, the guidelines require two hours of electives in at least two of the topics below with at least 30 minutes per topic, the remaining four optional hours can be spent on any other construction industry hazards or policies, or on the following electives:

- hand and power tools
- materials handling
- excavations
- cranes, derricks, hoists, elevators, and conveyors
- stairways and ladders
- scaffolds

30-HOUR CONSTRUCTION INDUSTRY COURSE

The 30-hour construction industry course is intended to provide a variety of training on safety and health to those workers with at least some safety and health responsibilities within the construction industry. The course emphasizes hazard identification, avoidance, control, and prevention, as well as specific OSHA standards. The program guidelines for the 30-hour course require coverage in the following topics (OSHA 2011a):

- An introduction to OSHA – 2 hours (OSH Act; General Duty Clause, record keeping, general safety and health provisions, citations, safety programs, value of safety, and OSHA Web site)
- Managing safety and health – 2 hours
- OSHA Focus Four Hazards – 6 hours—falls (minimum of 1 hour and 15 minutes), electrocution (minimum of 30 minutes), struck-by (minimum of 30 minutes), and caught in/between (minimum of 30 minutes)
- Personal protective equipment – 2 hours
- Health hazards in construction – 2 hours
- Stairways and ladders – 1 hour

The remaining time is spent on the coverage of a minimum of six elective topics (which must add up to at least twelve hours) from the list below, along with three hours of optional topics from any of the required areas or other construction industry standards or practices, with a minimum of 30 minutes per topic:

- ergonomics
- powered industrial vehicles
- excavations
- fire protection and prevention
- materials handling, storage, and disposal
- hand and power tools
- welding and cutting
- scaffolds
- cranes, derricks, hoists, elevators, and conveyors
- concrete and masonry
- steel erection
- safety and health programs
- confined space entry
- motor vehicles (roll-over protection, overhead protection, and signs, signals, and barricades)

OSHA Web Site and Web-Based Training (eTools)

OSHA recognizes the usefulness of distributing information through the Internet for accessing standards, directives, and other official documents with links to other agencies and private sources categorized by topic. Currently, the following electronic products are available from OSHA (OSHA 2010b):

- safety and health topics
- eTools
- PowerPoint presentations

A discussion follows of the web-based tools that are especially applicable to safety and health training.

Safety and Health Topics

The primary purpose of safety and health topics is to provide easy access to current technical information that will assist employees and safety and health professionals in reducing occupational injuries and illnesses. To maintain the quality of information on these topics, the references are selected by editors who are safety and health professionals. These editors are also assisted by editorial boards to keep the topic pages current (OSHA 2010c).

OSHA currently has more than 160 topics. Examples of topics include: accident investigation, alcohol, bioterrorism, combustible dust, dry cleaning, electricity, solvents, and teen workers. A complete listing of all topics is available at the OSHA Safety and Health Topics web page (www.osha.gov/SLTC/index.html). From a safety and health training aspect, the safety and health professional can use these topics to:

- review occupational safety and health information that is categorized on over 60 technical subjects
- identify ways to recognize, evaluate, and control general workplace hazards as well as hazards specific to an industry
- access a variety of reference materials such as OSHA and non-OSHA documents, standards, compliance guidance, training slides, course handouts, video clips, and links to other Internet sites.

eTools

Electronic Tools (eTools) are interactive web-based training tools on a variety of occupational safety and health topics. Highly illustrated and interactive, they allow users to answer questions and get reliable advice on how OSHA regulations apply to their work site. Many of the eTools can be downloaded using a supplied Microsoft Windows installer program for online use; some are also available in Spanish. Examples of eTool topics are anthrax, evacuation plans, lockout/tagout, machine guarding, nursing homes, and silica. A complete listing of available eTools is available on the OSHA eTools and Electronic Products for Compliance Assistance Web site (OSHA 2010d).

PowerPoint Presentations

OSHA has developed Microsoft PowerPoint presentations on a variety of occupational safety and health topics that are particularly useful for training courses. These PowerPoint presentations can be downloaded and used for safety and health training. Examples of topics where PowerPoint presentations are available include asbestos, crane, derrick, and hoist safety, ergonomics, eye and face protection, fall protection, powered industrial trucks, and radiation. A complete listing of available PowerPoint presentations is available at the OSHA Multimedia Web site and on the OSHA Training and Reference Library Web site (OSHA 2009c).

OSHA Publications

OSHA has numerous publications related to safety and health training that can be downloaded in either HTML or PDF formats from the OSHA Publications Web site (OSHA n.d.). These publications include booklets, fact sheets, guidance documents, pocket guides, posters, QuickCards, and QuickTakes. Two very useful training publications are OSHA 2019, *OSHA Publications and Audiovisual Programs* (OSHA 1998a) and OSHA 2254, *Training Requirements in OSHA Standards and Training Guidelines* (OSHA 1998b), which was discussed earlier in this chapter. A complete listing of available training aids and materials from OSHA is available from the OSHA Outreach Training Program Web site (OSHA 2010a).

CONCLUSION

Since the passage of the OSH Act in 1970, safety and health training has played a major role in both OSHA regulatory and enforcement activities. Currently there are more than 100 OSHA standards that contain training requirements and, in 2008, two of the top ten most frequently cited serious violations in the construction industry were directly related to training in fall hazards and scaffolding (OSHA 2010c). OSHA has also expanded the number of OTI Education Center Programs from four to twenty-seven centers over the past twenty years. This has resulted in a tremendous increase in the number of individuals being trained as part of the OSHA Outreach Training Program, from 305,000 cards being issued in 2003 to 680,000 cards issued in 2008 (OSHA 2009c).

Based on the above, it is the author's belief that the role of safety and health training within OSHA will continue to expand in the twenty-first century. Safety and health professionals must continue to stay abreast of these regulatory influences on safety and health program activities as well as on the profession as a whole.

REFERENCES

Barnes, Jim. 2003. "Focus on Education Centers." *Job Safety & Health Quarterly* (Summer/Fall) 14(4):36–37.

Bureau of Labor Statistics (BLS). 2011. *Census of Fatal Occupational Injuries Charts, 1992-2010 (Preliminary Data)* (accessed October 6, 2011). www.bls.gov/iif/oshwc/cfoi/cfch0009.pdf

Lawton, Rebecca, and Dianne Parker. 1998. "Individual Difference in Accident Liability: A Review and Integrative Approach." *Human Factors* 40(4):655–682.

National Institute for Occupational Safety and Health (NIOSH). 2004. Publication No. 2004-132, *Report from the 1999 Workplace Safety & Health Training: Putting the Pieces Together and Planning for the Challenges Ahead.* Cincinnati, OH: NIOSH.

National Safety Council (NSC). 2007. *OSHA's "Top 10" for 2007* (retrieved December 2007). www.nsc.org/plus

Occupational Safety and Health Administration (OSHA). 1970. *Occupational Safety and Health Act.* www.osha.gov/pls/oshaweb/owadisp.show_document?p_table+OSHACT&p_id=2743

———. 1989. *Safety and Health Program Management Guidelines; Issuance of Voluntary Guidelines.* www.osha.gov/pls/oshaweb/owadisp.show_document?p_id=12909&p_table=FEDERAL_REGISTER

_____. 1991. 29 CFR 1926.1053(b)(15), *Safety and Health Regulations for Construction; Stairways and Ladders; Ladders* (accessed June 16, 2011). gpoaccess.goc/cgi/text/text_rdx?c=ecfr&sid=70ba0712041e435f395b18f409e17308&rgn=div8&view=text&node=29:8.1.1.1.1.24.19.4&idno=29

_____. 1995. 29 CFR 1926.504, *Fall Protection; Training Requirements.*

_____. 1996a. 29 CFR 1926.454, *Scaffolds; Training Requirements.*

_____. 1996b. *Tools for a Safety and Health Program Assessment.* www.osha.gov/doc/outreachtraining/htmlfiles/evaltool.html

_____. 1998a. OSHA 2019. *OSHA Publications and Audiovisual Programs* (accessed June 16, 2011). www.osha.gov/Publications/osha2019.pdf

_____. 1998b. *OSHA 2254: Training Requirements in OSHA Standards and Training Guidelines.* www.osha.gov/Publications/osha2254.pdf

_____. 2000. 29 CFR 1908.2, *Consultation Agreements; Definitions.* www.osha.gov/pls/oshaweb/owadisp.show/document?p_table=STANDARDS&p_id=9686

_____. 2004a. *OSHA Forms for Recording Work-Related Injuries and Illnesses.* www.osha.gov/recordkeeping/new-osha300form1-1-04.pdf

_____. 2004b. 29 CFR 19001.1, *Draft Proposed Safety and Health Program Rule*, Docket No. S&H-0027. www.osha.gov/dsg/topics/safetyhealth/nshp.html

_____. 2006. 29 CFR 1910.178(l)(1)(ii), *Occupational Health and Safety Standards; Powered Industrial Trucks* (accessed June 16, 2011). www. gpoaccess.gov/cgi/text/text-idxc=ecfr&sid=64a653e603c51230209639b4c9629cb&rgn=div8&view=text&node=29:5.1.1.1.8.4.37&idno=29

_____. 2008a. *Resource Center Loan Program.* www.osha.gov/dcsp/ote/resource-center/loan.html

_____. 2008b. *29 CFR 1910, Occupational Safety and Health Standards.* www.osha.gov/pls/oshaweb/owadisp.show_document?p_table=STANDARDS&p_id=9686

_____. 2009a. *OSHA Susan Harwood Training Grant Program.* www.osha.gov/dte/sharwood/index.html.

_____. 2009b. *Revisions to the Voluntary Protection Programs to Provide Safe and Healthful Working Conditions.* www.osha.gov/pls/oshaweb/owadisp.show_document?p_id=18042&p_table=FEDERAL_REGISTER&p_id=21385

_____. 2009c. *OSHA Directorate of Training and Education.* www.osha.gov/dcsp/ote/index.html

_____. 2009d. *OSHA Training Institute Education Centers.* www.osha.gov/fso/ote/training/edcenters/background.html

_____. 2010a. *OSHA Outreach Training Program - How to Become an Authorized Trainer.* www.osha.gov/dte/outreach/construction_ generalindustry/authorized.html

_____. 2010b. *OSHA eTools and Electronic Products for Compliance Assistance.* www.osha.gov/dts/osta/oshasoft/

_____. 2010c. *Safety and Health Topics.* www.osha.gov/SLTC/index.html

_____. 2011a. *OSHA Outreach Training Program.* www.osha.gov/dte/outreach/construction_general industry/index.html

_____. 2011b. *OSHA Outreach Training Program-Program Guidelines.* www.osha.gov/dte/outreach/construction_generalindustry/guidelines.html

Reese, Charles D. 2003. *Occupational Health and Safety Management: A Practical Approach.* Boca Raton, FL: Lewis Publishers.

Saccaro, Joseph A. 1994. *Developing Safety Training Programs: Preventing Accidents and Improving Worker Performance Through Quality Training.* New York: Van Nostrand Reinhold.

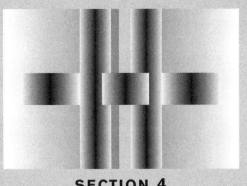

SECTION 4
SAFETY AND HEALTH TRAINING

LEARNING OBJECTIVES

▌ Become familiar with regulatory and nonregulatory environmental safety training issues.

▌ Learn about regulatory and non-regulatory training requirements and resources available to the safety professional.

▌ Gain an understanding of the interaction among OSHA, EPA, and other training requirements for environmental safety issues.

REGULATORY ISSUES: EPA

Charles Stanfill, Jr.

WHAT'S IN A NAME? Safety Department. Safety Compliance. Risk Management. Safety and Loss Control. Environmental, Health, and Safety. Regardless of the departmental name used within a company or public agency, or the title used by any manager, today's safety professional has increased responsibility for environmental issues. As far back as 1996, the *Accident Prevention Manual for Business and Industry, Administration and Programs* noted that, "managers responsible for occupational safety and health are increasingly affected by developments in environmental law" (Krieger and Montgomery 1996). As green building practices, and the green industry in general, gain acceptance in today's business world, and as companies raise their social consciousness, safety and health professionals "are often assigned environmental responsibilities as well as safety responsibilities" (Ayers 2010). For additional information on this issue, refer to the "Sustainability for the Safety, Health, and Environmental Professional" chapter in this Handbook.

When dealing with environmental regulations, it is sometimes difficult to ascertain the distinction between employee safety and the public's safety. Because environmental law calls for the protection of anyone coming in contact with certain products and hazardous substances, safety professionals benefit from having a basic understanding of environmental regulations that impact their business, products, and services.

Due to a memorandum of understanding (MOU) between the Occupational Safety and Health Administration (OSHA) and the U.S. Environmental Protection Agency (EPA) to coordinate environmental enforcement activities, several environmental activities have training requirements addressed in various OSHA standards. Those that involve hazardous waste, hazardous substances, and waste products tend to be the most prominent. This means that occupational safety, health, and environmental compliance issues are becoming even more intertwined. With Homeland Security issues such as chemical, biological, and biochemical threats getting increased attention from both the public and private sector, safety professionals are or will be tasked for greater involvement.

This chapter introduces the reader to a variety of environmental training issues and provides information regarding required and recommended training. Where available, references and resources for environmental training are provided.

To make this chapter as effective and user-friendly as possible, regulatory citations for promulgated EPA and OSHA standards will be provided so that readers can selectively choose to review those that apply to their workplace situation.

THE ENVIRONMENTAL PROTECTION AGENCY

The EPA was established in December 1970 in response to the growing public demand for cleaner water, air, and land. As new threats became known (hazardous and toxic spills, sewage, and wastewater spills), additional responsibilities were placed with the EPA to assist in those areas.

Following the terrorist attacks of September 11, 2001, the EPA was designated by a Presidential Decision Directive as the lead federal agency for reducing the vulnerability of the chemical industry and hazardous materials sector of our nation's infrastructure. The U.S. EPA maintains ten regional offices, each of which is responsible for several states and territories. Most states also have a regulatory agency that is responsible for environmental enforcement. (See Appendix A at the end of the chapter for a listing of the EPA regional offices.)

According to its history statement, "The U.S. Environmental Protection Agency was established in 1970 to consolidate in one agency a variety of federal research, monitoring, standard-setting and enforcement activities to ensure environmental protection. EPA's

mission is to protect human health and to safeguard the natural environment—air, water, and land—upon which life depends" (www.epa.gov/history/timeline/index.htm). Since the EPA's inception, environmental programs have expanded to include programs for:

- air quality
- effluents
- pesticides
- water
- noise abatement
- solid waste
- radiation
- toxic substances

By memorandums of agreement, regulations, and other avenues, several environmentally related training issues are found in the U.S. Energy Department, the Federal Emergency Management Agency (FEMA), the U.S. Nuclear Regulatory Commission (NRC), OSHA, and other agencies. The states also have state-managed environmental programs with varying degrees of training requirements, recommendations, and resources. State OSHA and environmental programs may also have unique training requirements. Check the state where the operations are conducted to become aware of all environmental training requirements that may impact that facility and operations. A listing of state agencies responsible for environmental enforcement is available at the EPA Web site.

If an employer has overseas operations, then familiarity with the environmental, safety, and health regulations of any country where the operation is domiciled is important.

EPA/OSHA REQUIRED TRAINING
Asbestos

During the late 1960s, asbestos became a safety and health issue in the United States as evidence emerged indicating that asbestos fibers were a dangerous health risk. In the 1970s, the U.S. government initiated action to address the risks associated with asbestos; in the 1980s, health concerns led to the new industry of asbestos abatement.

Training issues surrounding asbestos are dictated by the job functions performed while working with or around asbestos-containing material (ACM). The job functions are designated as Class I, II, III, or IV work, and they are further defined in 29 CFR 1926.1101. Accordingly, training issues became paramount for those employees who worked with or around ACM. The main areas and training needs for those working with ACM can be found at the citations listed below:

Asbestos Abatement

- Training for asbestos operations, including repair, removal, enclosing, or encapsulating ACM, is covered in 40 CFR Part 763, Subpart E, and 29 CFR Part 1926.1101.
- Appendix B of the *Inspection Procedures for Occupational Exposure to Asbestos*, OSHA Directive CPL 2-2.63 (REVISED) (1995), includes a summary and comparison of OSHA and EPA training requirements.

Asbestos Awareness

- Employee information and training is covered in 40 CFR 763.92(a)(1) and OSHA 29 CFR 1910.1001(j)(7)(i). This training must be provided according to OSHA standards, but only to "employees who are exposed to airborne concentrations of asbestos at or above the PEL and/or excursion limit." The employer must ensure employee participation in the program. An annual retraining requirement is included in the standard for those with exposure.
- OSHA 29 CFR 1910.1001(j)(7)(iv) requires that awareness training must be provided to housekeeping staff working near asbestos-containing material or presumed asbestos-containing material (PACM).

Asbestos-Competent Person

The training varies according to the type of asbestos work being performed (as defined in 29 CFR Part 1926.1101). For Class I and II work, personnel must have training in a special course that meets the criteria of EPA's Model Accreditation Plan (40 CFR 763) for

supervisor, or its equivalent. For Class III and IV work, the training must be provided in a manner consistent with EPA requirements for training of local education-agency maintenance and custodial staff as set forth in 40 CFR 763.92 (a)(2).

Asbestos Operations and Maintenance

Standards 40 CFR 763.92(a)(1), 40 CFR 763.92(a)(2), 29 CFR 1910.1101, and 29 CFR 1926.1101(k)(9) require asbestos training for the various types of asbestos operations and maintenance activities.

In addition, the employer shall maintain all employee training records for one year beyond the last date of employment of that employee.

Hazardous Waste Operations (HAZWOPER) and Emergency Response Standards

Found at 29 CFR 1910.120(a)(1)(i-v) and 29 CFR 1926.65 (a)(1)(i-v), HAZWOPER began as the Comprehensive Environmental Response, Compensation and Liability Act (CERCLA). This act was amended by the Superfund Amendments and Reauthorization Act (SARA) on October 17, 1986. SARA eventually became known as the HAZWOPER rule.

HAZWOPER training is required to ensure that employees are trained to perform the emergency response and clean-up activities associated with the release of hazardous materials expected of them in a safe manner. Employers must train their employees in accordance with paragraph 29 CFR 1910.120(e) and 1926.65. The training must occur during times that the employee is paid for work.

Training requirements are determined by the type of response activity an employee will be involved with during a spill. The various types of response categories covered in the OSHA requirements are listed below:

HAZWOPER Categories

- General Site Workers (40 hours of training). These are usually equipment operators, general laborers, and supervisory personnel who are engaged in hazardous substance removal or other activities that expose or potentially expose them to hazardous substances and health hazards.

- Occasional Site Workers (24 hours of training). These are workers who are occasionally on site for a specific, limited task such as, but not limited to, groundwater monitoring, land surveying, or geophysical surveying, and who are unlikely to be exposed over the permissible exposure limits and the minimum of one day actual field experience under the direct supervision of a trained, experienced supervisor.
- Supervisors (40 hours of training). On-site management and supervisors directly responsible for, or who supervise, employees engaged in hazardous waste operations. These individuals are also to receive 40 hours initial training and three days of supervised field experience. This particular training may be reduced to 24 hours and one day under certain circumstances. See 29 CFR 1910.120(e)(4).
- OSHA 29 CFR 1910.120(e)(8) states that employees specified in paragraph (e)(1) of this section, and managers and supervisors specified in paragraph (e)(4), shall receive 8 hours of refresher training annually.
- Treatment, storage, and disposal operations (24 hours of training). 29 CFR 1910.120(p)(7)(i) notes that "The employer shall develop and implement a training program which is part of the employer's safety and health program, for employees exposed to health hazards or hazardous substances at Treatment, Storage and Disposal (TSD) Facilities operations. . ." In addition to the initial training, for facility employees regulated under the Resource Conservation and Recovery Act (RCRA), refresher training shall be for 8 hours annually. A written certificate attesting that the employees have successfully completed the necessary training must be provided. It is the responsibility of the employer to develop this training, whether internally or through a third party.
- Hazmat Technicians (24 hours of training). These are individuals who respond to releases

or potential releases for the purpose of stopping the release. Employees with less aggressive responsibilities, such as performing defensive actions (First Responder Operations Level) or being able to recognize a spill and initiate the facility's Emergency Response Plan (First Responder Awareness Level), are required to receive 8 hours and "as necessary" initial training, respectively.

- Incident Command System (ICS) (16 hours of training). Due to the nature of spill response, where typically multiple agencies respond, such responding employees must have an understanding of the ICS. Additionally, it is possible for a first responder at the awareness level to be called upon to assume the duties of incident commander (IC) until a more senior and appropriately trained individual arrives at the response site. In that case, the IC shall have received at least 24 hours of training equal to the first responder operations level and additional competencies as listed in 29 CFR 1910.120(q)(6)(v)(A)-(F). FEMA has an online training course that is a good beginning to understanding the ICS (www.fema.gov/IS100b/index.htm).
- Hazardous Waste Refresher Training. Employees who have taken the 24- or 40-hour OSHA HAZWOPER course are required to maintain their certification by taking an 8-hour annual refresher course. Annual refresher courses are also required for First Responder Operations Level (4 hours) and Awareness Level (as needed) responders.
- The U.S. Department of Transportation in 49 CFR Part 172, Subpart H, requires employees who work with or transport hazardous materials be provided various types of training noted in 49 CFR Part 172.704. Training requirements include general awareness/familiarization training, function-specific training, safety training, security awareness training, and indepth security training. Some of the training can be satisfied through proper documentation

of related OSHA- or EPA-required training (29 CFR 1910.120).

Some useful resources for HAZWOPER, Haz Mat, and RCRA operations are also found in OSHA Directive CPL-02-02-071 (OSHA 2003). Additional guidance for HAZWOPER training is located in the following resources:

- Nonmandatory Appendix E for 1910.120 and 1926.65 (Training Curriculum Guidelines).
- Chapter 4, "Training," of the four-agency document, *Occupational Safety and Health Guidance Manual for Hazardous Waste Site Activities* (NIOSH 1985). It provides a chart listing the required training by job category.
- Chapter 4, "Training," in EPA publication 9285.1-03, *Standard Operating Safety Guides*, which provides a more detailed explanation of the various levels of training for workers at EPA-regulated sites (EPA 1992).

Hospital/Medical/Infectious Waste Incinerators

EPA 40 CFR 60.53(c) deals with operator training and qualification requirements for these incinerators.

In 1998, a MOU between EPA and the American Hospital Association (AHA) was signed to reduce the amount of pollution generated by the healthcare provider industry. The hospital safety practitioner should be aware of EPA 40 CFR 60 Subpart E—*Standards of Performance for Hospital/Medical/Infectious Waste Incinerators for Which Construction is Commenced After June 20, 1996.* The Texas Commission on Environmental Quality (TCEQ) has developed a useful flowchart in PDF format to assist in understanding the requirements (www.tceq.state.tx.us.assets.public/permitting/air/Rules/Federal/60/ec/f60ec.pdf).

Lastly, the Joint Commission on Accreditation of Healthcare Organizations is a resource the healthcare safety professional should use for areas of recommended training.

Lead

Employees who may be exposed to lead in the workplace, whether in general industry or construction, are required to maintain training depending upon tasks and exposure levels. These include:

- Awareness: OSHA 1910.1025(l) and 1926.62(l). Each employer who has a workplace in which there is a potential exposure to airborne lead at any level shall inform employees of the content of Appendices A and B of this regulation.
- Abatement: OSHA 1926.62(l) describes the training of employees who have a daily exposure to lead at or above the action level. EPA 40 CFR 745.225-226 describes the accreditation of training programs for lead-based paint in target housing and child-occupied facilities. Currently, contractors performing this type of work in child-occupied facilities and in pre-1978 housing must be certified as a lead-safe certified contractor and use lead-safe work practices. The certification includes an 8-hour training course from an accredited trainer. (A 4-hour refresher course may be substituted if an eligible renovation course has previously been completed.) The location of accredited trainers is available from the EPA Web site.

Oil Spills

EPA 40CFR 109.5(d)(1) specifies that an oil-discharge response operating team must consist of trained personnel. The response team can be from the public or private sector.

Training elements for oil storage facilities that must comply with the Spill Prevention, Control and Countermeasures regulation of the Clean Water Act are found at 40 CFR Subchapter D, Part 112.

Following the April 20, 2010, Gulf of Mexico oil spill and subsequent clean-up operations, training requirements were added for the different classes of responders, including volunteers. If a company allows employees to volunteer for such community service projects, the company's professional safety staff must

If you are:	You must receive:
Doing work that does NOT involve materials contaminated by the spill	45 minutes of site training [Module 2 or equivalent Site Health Safety and Environment (HSE) Orientation or equivalent]
Doing work picking up tar balls and other oil-contaminated debris on beaches and along the shoreline	4 hours of site training [Module 3 – Shoreline Spilled Oil Response] NOTE: These workers will be supervised by someone with 40 hours of hazardous waste operations training.
Doing work at decontamination areas, handling or cleaning oily boom and equipment, or using vacuum trucks and portable skimmers to clean up weathered oil along the shoreline	45 minutes of site training [Module 2 or equivalent Site Health Safety **and** Environment (HSE) Orientation] and 40 hours of hazardous waste operations training. NOTE: These workers will be supervised by someone with 40 hours of hazardous waste operations training. BP is not providing the 40-hour hazardous waste operations training.

FIGURE 1. Oil-spill training requirements (*Source:* www.osha.gov/oilspills/training.html)

ensure that volunteers are aware of the necessary training requirements. The relevant training categories and desired training requirements are shown in Figure 1.

Job-specific training requirements related to the various on-shore and off-shore job tasks for an oil-spill response can be found on the EPA Web site.

Pesticide Safety Training for Workers

All of the training issues surrounding the various types of duties and timelines for training an employee who applies or handles a pesticide regulated by the Federal Insecticide, Fungicide, and Rodenticide Act (FIFRA) are listed in 40 CFR 170.130, as well as the required content of the training program. The regulation addresses the requirements of the trainer and the content to be provided to workers who use and apply pesticides, as well as workers who are exposed to pesticides. Training requirements (initial and continuing education) are also imposed by different agencies within the various states. The National Pesticide Information Center (NPIC) is a respectable online resource one can use to identify training requirements for states and territories of the United States. The NPIC site provides links for each state's agency that regulates pesticide use and application for both individuals and corporations (npic.orst.edu/state_agencies.html#).

Risk Management Plan–40 CFR Part 68

With passage of the Clean Air Act Amendments of 1990, (Section 112r), the EPA was required to publish regulations and guidance for the prevention of accidental chemical releases at facilities using substances that pose a significant risk if released. The regulations are available at www.epa.gov/emergencies/lawsregs.htm#fraccident.

The regulations require companies, regardless of size, that use certain listed, regulated flammable and toxic substances to have a risk management program (RMP) in place. The RMP process is similar in scope to the OSHA process safety management process. Training requirements for the RMP are based on defined criteria and apply to companies meeting the Program Level 2 and Level 3 classifications. The various program levels and a decision tree can be found at www.epa.gov/emergencies/docs/chem/Chap-02-final.pdf.

Training requirements for the RMP Program 2 level are found in 40 CFR 68.54 (a)-(d) and 40 CFR 68.71 for the Program 3 level. Both program levels have requirements for refresher training at least every three years.

Radiation Protection

The U.S. Department of Energy governs the majority of training requirements associated with ionizing radiation.

The general training requirements for radiation workers are covered in 10 CFR 19. It requires that all individuals who, in the course of employment, are likely to receive an annual dose of radiation in excess of 100 millirems must receive adequate training to protect themselves.

Title 10 of the Code of Federal Regulations covers training requirements for various occupational areas using or involved with ionizing radiation. Some of the more common ones include:

- 10 CFR 34: Licenses for industrial radiography and radiation safety
- 10 CFR 35.900: Medical use of by-product material, including training requirements for:
  - the radiation safety officer
  - employees performing various laboratory processes and diagnostics using radioactive materials
  - employees using various diagnostic equipment, imaging and localization studies and procedures using radioactive devices
- 10 CFR 50.120: Training and qualification of nuclear power plant personnel
- 10 CFR 76.95: Training for employees who operate, maintain, or modify gas diffusion plants
- 10 CFR 835.901: Radiation safety training for Department of Energy employees
- 10 CFR 1046.12-DOE: Protective force personnel physical fitness training

OSHA 29 CFR 1926.53(b) indicates that individuals performing, "any activity that involves the use of radioactive materials or X-rays, whether or not under license from the Nuclear Regulatory Commission, shall be performed by competent persons specially trained in the proper and safe operation of such equipment."

Additional information regarding training for exposure to radioactive materials is found in the OSHA HAZWOPER standard.

Consideration should be given to the following training for employees working around or near ionizing or nonionizing radiation:

- training in principles of radiation protection
- training in shielding design
- training in shielding evaluation
- the specific type of machine application
- training in basic radiological health
- radiation instrument calibration

Resource Conservation and Recovery Act (RCRA)

RCRA has training requirements that cover both large- and small-quantity generators of waste, as regulated by the EPA in 40 CFR Part 265. Safety practitioners need to know if their company generates waste, and if so, in what quantities. Additional awareness of storage times and disposal locations may also be a factor in determining training requirements. This knowledge helps to establish the type of RCRA training needed. Topic areas to consider include:

- Large Quantity Generator (LQG): EPA 40CFR 262.34(a)(4)
- Small Quantity Generator (SQG): EPA 40CFR 262.34(d)(5)(iii)
- RCRA requirements for treatment, storage, and disposal facilities (TSDF): EPA 40CFR 264.16 and 265.16

Hazardous Waste Treatment, Storage, and Disposal Facilities—Solid Waste

Personnel training is covered by 40 CFR 264.16(a)(1). Facility personnel must successfully complete a program of classroom instruction or on-the-job training that teaches them to perform their duties in a way that ensures the facility's compliance with the requirements of this part. The owner or operator must ensure that this program includes all the elements described in the document required under paragraph (d)(3) of this section. *Note:* Part 270 of this chapter requires that owners and operators submit, with Part B of the RCRA permit application, an outline of the training program used (or to be used) at the facility and a brief description of how the training program is designed to meet actual job tasks.

Spill Management Facility Response Planning

EPA 40 CFR 112.21 describes the requirements for facility response training, along with and drills/exercises for facilities required to comply with the Spill Prevention, Control, and Countermeasures requirements in this section.

Universal Waste Handlers

EPA 40 CFR 273.16 states that the employer must inform all employees who handle or have responsibility for managing universal waste about the proper handling and emergency procedures appropriate to the type(s) of universal waste located at the facility.

Underground Storage Tank Training

EPA 40 CFR 280 TNRCC describes the requirements for contractors and supervisors who install and/or repair underground storage tanks.

RECOMMENDED TRAINING

Bioterrorism (Including Biological and Chemical Response) Training

The U.S. Department of Homeland Security Web site provides information on the following training:

- training resources, grants, and requirements (www.dhs.gov/files/training/prepresrecovery.htm)
- response and recovery (www.dhs.gov/xfrstresp/training)

- first responder training resources (www.dhs.gov/dhspublic/display?theme=63&content=3547)

Clandestine Methamphetamine Laboratories

This is a unique and growing area that has safety implications for all (i.e., law enforcement, emergency medical and fire department personnel, as well as those conducting regulatory environmental activities) who respond to the site of a clandestine methamphetamine ("meth") laboratory. Although this activity is not specifically referred to by name in the OSHA standard, the safety training information in the hazardous waste clean-up operations standard (OSHA 1010.120) is required to be followed for meth-lab responses and remediation. Training in the ICS is also recommended, as several agencies are involved in responding to meth labs. The U.S. Drug Enforcement Agency (DEA) offers a 40-hour training class to law-enforcement officers that is designed to certify attendees as Clandestine Laboratory Site Safety Officers. The DEA training meets the 40-hour OSHA HAZWOPER training requirement. Training in hazard assessment, PPE assessment and use, budgeting, clean up, and site security issues are good starting points.

Mold Assessment and Remediation

At the time of this writing, there are no specific OSHA or EPA training requirements for mold remediation. However, there are recommendations for PPE when working around known or suspected mold growth, and OSHA has indoor air-quality standards as well. Both OSHA and the EPA have resources available to assist in identifying training for mold-related issues.

The reader should refer to OSHA Safety and Health Information Bulletins on mold and EPA Office of Radiation and Indoor Air publications 402-F-93-005 and 402-K-01-001).

National Pollutant Discharge Elimination System (NPDES)

The NPDES program covers animal-feeding operations, combined sewer overflows, pretreatment, sanitary sewer overflows, and stormwater issues. Safety training for these areas is not located in a single resource, requiring the safety practitioner to be aware of the types of operations being conducted by the employer and to use OSHA training to ensure safe operations at NPDES sites. EPA provides NPDES training courses and workshops, but primarily for any administrative procedures surrounding the permitting process. Additionally, some states accept various OSHA-required training as fulfillment of the water/wastewater operator license/certification training requirements.

Regulatory Inspections and Assessments

State and private employers that conduct regulatory inspections need to ensure that hazard assessments are conducted and appropriate training is provided.

Green Building/Green Industry/ Environmental Sustainability

The need for safety training in the green industry is becoming increasingly apparent. In a January 2010 online science blog, NIOSH noted that: "Safety and health should be considered an essential component for all green job training, in addition to training on the skills workers need to complete job tasks" (NIOSH 2010b). NIOSH has also addressed this issue in an online publication, *Prevention through Design: Green, Safe and Healthy Jobs* (NIOSH 2010a).

As environmental sustainability issues move into the business world and stakeholders express a desire for corporate social responsibility, safety and health (S&H) professionals may find themselves with increased environmental responsibilities and will need to identify areas of training that address sustainability issues and environmental management systems (EMS). S&H professionals who have environmental management responsibilities will want to become familiar with the latest environmental management standard, ISO 14001. Employees of an ISO 14001-certified company that performs operations having the potential to create a negative environmental impact must be trained according to section 4.4.2 of the ISO 14001 standard.

ENVIRONMENTAL EDUCATIONAL TRAINING RESOURCES

While there are many companies and consultants that offer training and education on environmental issues, several links on the EPA Web site can assist in locating both private and government-supported environmental training topics. The EPA Web site also offers educational and informational resources and databases for environmental topics.

Examples of the training resources accessed from the EPA Web site include the following:

- CERCLA Education Center (Superfund Training). The CERCLA Education Center (CEC) is a unique training forum implemented by the EPA's Office of Solid Waste and Emergency Response (OSWER) Technology Innovation Office (TIO). It offers EPA on-scene coordinators (OSC), remedial project managers (RPM), site-assessment managers (SAM), and other environmental professionals' training courses on the many aspects of Superfund and the latest environmental technologies. The courses provide basic definitions and procedures, and detailed presentations on EPA's role with other federal agencies as well. CEC courses have been developed cooperatively by TIO, the Office of Emergency and Remedial Response, the Office of Acquisition Management, the Office of Enforcement and Compliance Assurance, and the Office of Research and Development. Site managers from many EPA regions also provided technical advice, comment, and support.

Environmental Response Training Program (ERTP) Courses

The Environmental Response Training Program is directed by the EPA's Environmental Response Team Center and derives its authority to develop and present various technical, health, and safety courses from CERCLA. The program is designed to train personnel from federal, tribal, state, and local government agencies in hazardous waste site investigation and remediation practices and procedures, as well as emergency response to hazardous chemical releases. Registration, required for taking the courses, can be accomplished on the Web site (www.ertpvu.org).

ADDITIONAL RESOURCES FOR EPA TRAINING

National Institute for Occupational Safety and Health (NIOSH)

Through university-based Education and Research Centers (ERCs), NIOSH supports academic degree programs and research-training opportunities in the core areas of industrial hygiene, occupational health nursing, occupational medicine, and occupational safety, plus specialized areas relevant to the occupational safety and health field. There are seventeen regional ERCs throughout the country. (NIOSH resources are more fully discussed in the next chapter.)

The Occupational Safety and Health Education and Research Centers were established by NIOSH to ensure an ample supply of well-trained professionals in the area of occupational safety and health.

In addition to the academic training programs, NIOSH supports ERC short-term continuing education (CE) programs for occupational safety and health professionals, and others with worker safety and health responsibilities. A current CE course schedule for all NIOSH Education and Research Centers can be found on the NIOSH ERC Web site (www.niosh-erc.org), or use the toll free number, 1-800-35-NIOSH (1-800-356-4674), or contact the NIOSH Publications Office. The reader should refer to the next chapter in this section for additional details and resources associated with NIOSH.

Trainex

Note: This information is for the convenience of the reader. Neither the author, the EPA, nor ASSE endorse any private-sector Web site, product, or service.

Trainex (www.trainex.org), in partnership with the Interstate Technology Regulatory Council and the EPA, is a provider that offers a range of training courses and information to the EPA, other federal agencies, and state, tribal, and local staff involved in hazardous waste management and remediation. Both classroom and Internet-based courses are available.

Many EPA and other federal offices provide training relevant to hazardous waste remediation, site characterization, risk assessment, emergency response, site/incident management, counterterrorism, and the community's role in site management and clean up. Some of the courses that have been provided by Trainex are listed in Appendix B at the end of the chapter. It provides insight to the reader into the varied array of environmental topics that are available beyond the basic Superfund courses.

Additional environmental training resources include:

- *Nonprofit course providers.* These include University of California, Berkeley; Georgia Tech; the University of Kansas; and the University of Utah.
- *Publications.* Various publications related to training requirements and resources for hazard communication, hazardous waste operations, RCRA, respiratory protection, and other topics are available from the OSHA Web site (www.osha.gov/pls/publications/pubindex.list).
- *EPA Education Center.* The EPA Education Center (www.epa.gov/teachers) is designed for teachers and educators. It has several useful resources that can be utilized by the environmental trainer. The resources are valuable training aids when the trainer needs to provide an overview of environmental issues to employees, management, and clients.
- *Miscellaneous Resources.* Appendix C at the end of this chapter lists EPA-hosted or EPA-sponsored Web sites that contain information related to a variety of environmental safety training. Some are at no cost for those who meet the criteria.

PROFESSIONAL ORGANIZATIONS FOR THE ENVIRONMENTAL SAFETY TRAINER

ASSE and ANSI collaborated on the consensus standard, ANSI/ASSE Z490.1-2001, *Criteria for Accepted Practices in Safety, Health, and Environmental Training* (ASSE 2001) to provide safety professionals with training methodologies they can use with assurance.

There are several accreditation and certification programs for trainers (Nilson 2001). There are also several corporate agencies that provide a safety training designation upon completion of their paid course.

Three environmental training certification programs related to occupational safety are listed here. Included for the reader's use is some brief information about the programs. Again, neither the author, the EPA, nor ASSE endorses any Web site, product, or service.

The National Environmental, Safety and Health Training Association

Founded in 1977 with support and assistance from the EPA, the National Environmental, Safety and Health Training Association is an international, nonprofit educational and professional society dedicated to promoting competency and excellence in education and training, with an emphasis on environmental, safety, and health training. The Certified Environmental Safety & Health Trainer designation (CET) is a voluntary credentialing system based on the certification guidelines published by the Council of Engineering and Scientific Specialty Board (CESB). Certification requires measuring instructional knowledge (as one competency indicator) and confirming technical knowledge in the following areas:

- emergency response
- management and transportation of hazardous materials and waste
- occupational safety and health
- radiation protection
- wastewater treatment
- water treatment

National Association of Safety Professionals

The National Association of Safety Professionals (www.naspweb.com) Board of Certification provides third-party validation of your specific safety training, planning, or inspection/auditing knowledge, based upon the qualifications recommended by ANSI, OSHA, and the Courts. It offers the Certified HAZWOPER Training Specialist (HTS) certification for environmental safety training.

Institute of Hazardous Materials Management

The Institute of Hazardous Materials Management (IHMM) (www.ihmm.org) was founded as a nonprofit organization in 1984, and launched the Certified Hazardous Materials Manager (CHMM) Program in June of that year. The Certified Hazardous Materials Manager Program is accredited by The Council of Engineering and Scientific Specialty Boards.

CONCLUSION

The key points in this chapter include the need for students and safety professionals to understand the interrelationship between OSHA training requirements and EPA training requirements. Several EPA training requirements are covered in the OSHA standard. The safety practitioner needs to be aware of the interconnectivity between the two agencies with regard to safety training issues.

REFERENCES

American Society of Safety Engineers (ASSE). 2001. *ANSI/ASSE Z490.1-2001. Criteria for Accepted Practices in Safety. Health, and Environmental Training*. Des Plaines, IL: ASSE.

Ayers, David, M.S., CSP, CHHM. "Environmental Aspects & Impacts." *Professional Safety Magazine*. February, 2010.

Environmental Protection Agency (EPA). 2006. *CFR Title 40: Protection of Environment* (retrieved August 2006). www.epa.gov/epahome/cfr40.htm

National Institute of Occupational Safety and Health (NIOSH). 1985 (October). *Occupational Safety and Health Guidance Manual for Hazardous Waste Site Activities* (Publication No. 85-115). Cincinnati, OH: NIOSH.

_____. 2010a. *Going Green: Safe and Healthy Jobs* (accessed October 20, 2011). www.cdc.gov/niosh/blog/nsb 010410_green.html

_____. 2010b. *Prevention through Design: Green, Safe and Healthy Jobs* (accessed February 19, 2010). www.cdc.gov/niosh/topics/PtD/greenjobs.html

National Safety Council (NSC). 1996. *Accident Prevention Manual for Business & Industry: Administration & Programs*. 10th ed. Gary R. Krieger and John F. Montgomery, eds. Itasca, IL: NSC.

Nilson, Carolyn, ed. 2001. *Training and Development Yearbook*. Paramus, NJ: Prentice Hall.

Occupational Safety and Health Administration (OSHA). 1995. *Guidance Manual for Hazardous Waste Site Activities* (accessed June 20, 2010). www.osha.gov/Publications/complinks/OSHG-HazWaste/4agency.html
_____. 2003. *OSHA Directive Number CPL 02-02-071. Technical Enforcement and Assistance Guidelines for Hazardous Waste Site and RCRA Corrective Action Clean-up Operations*. Washington, D.C.: Department of Labor.
Schroll, R. Craig. "Emergency Response Training—How to Plan, Conduct & Evaluate for Success." *Professional Safety Magazine*. December 2002.

APPENDIX A: EPA REGIONAL OFFICES

Region 1 (CT, MA, ME, NH, RI, VT)
Environmental Protection Agency
1 Congress St. Suite 1100
Boston, MA 02114-2023
www.epa.gov/region01/
Phone: (617) 918-1111
Fax: (617) 565-3660
Toll free within Region 1: (888) 372-7341

Region 2 (NJ, NY, PR, VI)
Environmental Protection Agency
290 Broadway
New York, NY 10007-1866
www.epa.gov/region02/
Phone: (212) 637-3000
Fax: (212) 637-3526

Region 3 (DC, DE, MD, PA, VA, WV)
Environmental Protection Agency
1650 Arch Street
Philadelphia, PA 19103-2029
www.epa.gov/region03/
Phone: (215) 814-5000
Fax: (215) 814-5103
Toll free: (800) 438-2474
Email: r3public@epa.gov

Region 4 (AL, FL, GA, KY, MS, NC, SC, TN)
Environmental Protection Agency
Atlanta Federal Center
61 Forsyth Street, SW
Atlanta, GA 30303-3104
www.epa.gov/region04/
Phone: (404) 562-9900
Fax: (404) 562-8174
Toll free: (800) 241-1754

Region 5 (IL, IN, MI, MN, OH, WI)
Environmental Protection Agency
77 West Jackson Boulevard
Chicago, IL 60604-3507
www.epa.gov/region5/
Phone: (312) 353-2000
Fax: (312) 353-4135
Toll free within Region 5: (800) 621-8431

Region 6 (AR, LA, NM, OK, TX)
Environmental Protection Agency
Fountain Place 12th Floor, Suite 1200
1445 Ross Avenue
Dallas, TX 75202-2733
www.epa.gov/region06/
Phone: (214) 665-2200
Fax: (214) 665-7113
Toll free within Region 6: (800) 887-6063

Region 7 (IA, KS, MO, NE)
Environmental Protection Agency
901 North 5th Street
Kansas City, KS 66101
www.epa.gov/region07/
Phone: (913) 551-7003
Toll free: (800) 223-0425

Region 8 (CO, MT, ND, SD, UT, WY)
Environmental Protection Agency
999 18th Street Suite 500
Denver, CO 80202-2466
www.epa.gov/region08/
Phone: (303) 312-6312
Fax: (303) 312-6339
Toll free: (800) 227-8917
Email: r8eisc@epa.gov

Region 9 (AZ, CA, HI, NV)
Environmental Protection Agency
75 Hawthorne Street
San Francisco, CA 94105
www.epa.gov/region09/
Phone: (415) 947-8000
(866) EPA-WEST (toll free in Region 9)
Fax: (415) 947-3553
Email: r9.info@epa.gov

Region 10 (AK, ID, OR, WA)
Environmental Protection Agency
1200 Sixth Avenue
Seattle, WA 98101
www.epa.gov/region10/
Phone: (206) 553-1200
Fax: (206) 553-0149
Toll free: (800) 424-4372

APPENDIX B: SAMPLING OF TRAINING COURSES OFFERED BY TRAINEX

2nd Civilian-Military Anthrax Response Technical Workshop

Application of Transport Optimization Codes to Groundwater Pump-and-Treat Systems

ASTM Phase I/Phase II Training

Bevill Amendment and Phase IV LDR Rule Workshop (U.S. EPA - Region 4)

Continuing Challenge Hazmat Workshop

Data Quality Objective Process Workshop

Data Validation Course

DOT Training for Offerers of Bulk and Non-bulk Hazmat Packages

Environmental Stability of Chemicals in Sediments

ESAT Project Officer Training

Hazard Ranking System

Identification of Regulated Hazardous Waste Course (U.S. EPA - Region 4)

Introduction to Environmental Management Systems

Management of Ordnance and Explosives at Closed, Transferred and Transferring Ranges (CTT) and Other Sites

Microbiology Workshop

Oilfield Production Facility Training

OSC Readiness Training

Permeable Reactive Barriers (In Situ): Application and Deployment

Pollution Prevention (P2) Training (U.S. EPA - Region 4)

Quality Assurance Project Plans (QAPPs) Workshop (U.S. EPA - Region 4)

Quickscore/Superscreen Training Course

RCRA Brownfields Prevention Initiative (U.S. EPA - Region 4)

RCRA Hotline Modules

RCRA Organic Air Standards Permitting and Compliance Training (U.S. EPA - Region 4)

RCRA Miscellaneous Units Permit And Compliance Training Course (U.S. EPA - Region 4)

RCRA Reforms Corrective Action Conference (U.S. EPA - Region 4)

RCRA Seminar (U.S. EPA - Region 4)

Risk Communication and Decision Making (U.S. EPA - Region 4)

Spill Prevention Control and Countermeasure

Temporary Relocation

Urban Rivers Forum Meeting

Achieving Data Quality - Developing & Review of Quality Assurance Project Plans (QAPPs)

Asthma Summit

Basic Inspector Training (BIT) (U.S. EPA - Region 10)

Community Involvement Outreach and Training Week (U.S. EPA - Region 4)

Customer Service/Communication Skills (U.S. EPA - Region 4)

Data Quality Objectives (DQO) Managing Uncertainty and Systematic Planning for Environmental Decision Making

Designing Your EMS: A Federal Facilities Workshop

Drum Job 101

EPA Region 10 Sponsored McCoy RCRA Seminar

EPA Region III Emergency Preparedness and Prevention Conference

Five Year Review Training (U.S. EPA - Region 4)

Hazardous Waste Operations and Emergency Response 8-Hour Refresher

In-situ Contaminated Sediment Capping Workshop

Leadership 2000 (U.S. EPA - Region 4)

Managing Conflict (U.S. EPA - Region 4)

Mobile 6 Modeling Course - Various Locations

National Superfund Radiation Meeting

On-Site Insight Training

Planning and Using Data for Site Assessment

PREscore Training Course

Quality Management Plan Workshop

Radiochemistry Workshop

RCRA Corrective Action Streamlined Orders (Internet-based seminar)

RCRA Corrective Action Workshop

RCRA Orientation/Permit Writers (U.S. EPA - Region 4)

Region 4 Brownfields Workshop

RevTech Conference - Cleaning Up Contaminated Properties for Reuse and Revitalization: Effection Technical Approaches and Tools

SPCC Inspector Training Short (8-Hour) Course

Superfund Hotline Training Modules

Triad Experts Training

Vapor Intrusion into Indoor Air: Introduction to OSWER Guidance (Internet-based seminar)

APPENDIX C: RESOURCES FOR ENVIRONMENTAL SAFETY TRAINING

Air Pollution Training Institute (APTI)	www.epa.gov/air/oaqps/eog
Alternative Dispute Resolution Training	www.epa.gov/adr/cprc_training.html
American Indian Environmental Office (AIEO)	www.epa.gov/aboutwpa/oia.html#aieo
Asbestos - National Directory of AHERA Accredited Courses (NDAAC)	www.epa.gov/asbestos/pubs/ncaac.html
CAMEO Training (Computer Aided Management of Environmental Operations)	www.epa.gov/emergencies/content/cameo/index.html
CERCLA Training Modules	www.epa.gov/wastes/inforesources/pubs/training/olaw.pfd
Chemical Information Exchange Newtork (CIEN) Project	jpl.estis.net/commuities/cien
CLU-IN Courses and Conferences	www.clu-in.org/courses
Drinking Water Academy	www.epa.gov/learn/training/dwatraining/
Evaluation Training	www.epa.gov/evaluate/training.htm
FIELDS Training–Region 5	www.epa.gov/region5fieldshtm/training.htm
Multi-Agency Radiation Surveys and Site Investigation Manual (MARSSIM) Training	www.epa.gov/radiation/marssim/training.html
National Association for Remedial Project Managers (NARPM) Training Program	www.epa.gov/oamsrpod.hcsc/NARPM
National Center for Environmental Assessment	cfpub2.epa.gov/ncea/basicinfo.htm
National Center for Environmental Economics (NCEE)	yosemite.epa.gov/ee/epa/eed.nsf/Webpages/homepage
National Enforcement Training Institute (NETI)	www.epa.gov/compliance/training/neti/index.html
Office of International Affairs	epa.gov/aboutepa/oia.html
Oil Spill Training	www.epa.gov/oem/content/learning/respmgmt.htm
On-Scene Coordinators	www.epa.gov/osweroe1/content/nrs/nrsosc.html
Pesticides: Safety Training	www.epa.gov/pesticides/health/worker.htm
Quality Assurance Training (Region 1)	www.epa.gov/region1/lab/qa/training.html
Quality System Training Program	www.epa.gov/quality/train.html
RCRA Compliance Assistance Training	www.epa.gov/compliance/assistance/bystature/rcra
RCRA Corrective Action Training Curriculum	www.epa.gov/epawaste/hazard/correctiveaction/curriculum/index.htm
RCRA Training Module–Solid Waste and Emergency Response	www.epa.gov/wastes/inforesources/pubs/training/hwid05.pdf
RCRA State Authorization Training Manuals	www.epa.gov/wastes/laws-regs/state/revision/training.htm
RCRA Training Modules	www.epa.gov/epawaste/inforesources/pubs/rmods.htm
Regional Environmental Justice (EJ) Training Contacts	www.epa.gov/compliance/neti/training/index.html
Regional Information Sensitivity (RIS) Training (Procedures for CBI) Region 4	www.epa.gov/region4/ris_training
Risk Assessment Training (NCEA)	cfpub.epa.gov/ncea/pdfs/ncea_brochure.pdf
Risk Management Workshops (ORD)	www.epa.gov/ttbnrmrl/index.htm
Science Advisory Board Ethics Training	www.epa.gov/sabproduct/nsf/Web/ethics?OpenDocument
Site Assessment: OnSite Tutorials	www.epa.gov/athens/learn2model/part-two/onsite/i_onsite.htm
Superfund Analytical Services Sample Documentation Training (FORMS II Lite)	www.epa.gov/superfund/programs/clp/f2ltrain.htm
Superfund Job Training Initiative (SuperJTI)	www.epa.gov/superfund/community/sfjti/
Superfund Training and Learning Center	www.epa.gov/superfund/training/index.html
Superfund Training Opportunities	www.epa.gov/superfund/training/index.htm
Superfund: Hazard Ranking System (HRS) Courses	www.epa.gov/training/hrstrain/hrstrain.htm
Superfund: Natural Resources Damages	www.epa.gov/superfund/programs/nrd/train/index.htm
Superfund, TRI, EPCRA, RMP and Oil Information Center	www.epa.gov/superfund/contacts/infocenter
Technology Innovation Program	www.epa.gov/etop/cont_tip.html
Toxics Release Inventory (TRI)	www.epa.gov/tri/report/training/index.htm
Toxics Release Inventory Training Modules	www.epa.gov/tri/training.2011
Waste, Pesticides and Toxics Training (Region 5)	www.epa.gov/region5/waste/training/
Water Program - National Pollutant Discharge Elimination System (NPDES) Training	cfpub.epa.gov/npdes/outreach.cfm?program_id=0&otype=1
Water Program - Training Opportunities	www.water.epa.gov/learn/training/index.cfm
Water Quality Standards Academy (WQSA)	www.epa.gov/learn/training/standardsacademy.didex.html
Watershed Academy	www.epa.gov/learn/training/standardsacademy.didex.html

SECTION 4
SAFETY AND HEALTH TRAINING

LEARNING OBJECTIVES

- Identify the occupational safety and health training available from NIOSH Education and Research Centers.

- Search the NIOSH Web site for further details on training available from the NIOSH Education and Research Centers.

- Be able to prepare state-of-the-art occupational safety and health training systems that will conform to the ANSI national consensus standard for accepted practices in safety, health, and environmental training.

REGULATORY ISSUES: NIOSH, ANSI Z490, AND OTHER STANDARDS

David Coble

ON DECEMBER 29, 1970, President Richard M. Nixon signed the Occupational Safety and Health (OSH) Act, passed by the 91st Congress. (The Occupational Safety and Health Act of 1970, along with the amendments made to it in 1998, can be accessed on the OSHA Web site (www.osha.gov) by clicking on the A-Z index link, then clicking on the letter "O" at the top of the page and scrolling down to OSH Act of 1970.) The law went into effect four months later, on April 28, 1971. The Occupational Safety and Health Act created five new federal government agencies:

1. The Occupational Safety and Health Administration (OSHA)
2. The Occupational Safety and Health Review Commission (OSHRC)
3. The National Advisory Committee for Occupational Safety and Health (NACOSH)
4. The Workers' Compensation Commission (WCC)
5. The National Institute for Occupational Safety and Health (NIOSH)

The purpose of the Occupational Safety and Health Act, as stated in Section 2(b) was "to assure so far as possible every working man and woman in the nation safe and healthful working conditions, and to preserve our human resources." One action intended by the writers of the OSH Act to continually assure safe and healthful workplaces was the creation of the National Institute for Occupational Safety and Health (NIOSH). NIOSH was established in Section 22 of the OSH Act and assigned its main goal, the prevention of injury and illness, in a three-pronged approach:

- identifying occupational hazards by conducting research and field studies of hazards

• conveying the results of that research and the field studies to OSHA and the Mine Safety and Health Administration (MSHA), as well as other federal agencies and safety and health professionals working in the field

• providing training programs based on the results of NIOSH's research and study

This last objective, which can be found at Section 21 of the Occupational Safety and Health Act, states that

> (a) The Secretary of Health and Human Services, after consultation with the Secretary [here meaning the Secretary of Labor] and with other appropriate Federal departments and agencies, shall conduct, directly or by grants or contracts (1) education programs to provide an adequate supply of qualified personnel to carry out the purposes of this Act, and (2) informational programs on the importance of and proper use of adequate safety and health equipment.
>
> (b) The Secretary [of Labor] is also authorized to conduct, directly or by grants or contracts, short-term training of personnel engaged in work related to his responsibilities under this Act.
>
> (c) The Secretary [of Labor], in consultation with the Secretary of Health and Human Services, shall (1) provide for the establishment and supervision of programs for the education and training of employers and employees in the recognition, avoidance, and prevention of unsafe or unhealthful working conditions in employments covered by this Act, and (2) consult with and advise employers and employees, and organizations representing employers and employees as to effective means of preventing occupational injuries and illnesses.

Primarily as a result of the OSH Act (but also in response to the high cost of injuries and illnesses), awareness of occupational hazards and interest in worker protection increased in both the public and private sectors. Because of studies conducted by NIOSH, it became apparent by the mid-1970s that there was a shortage of qualified specialists in industrial hygiene and safety qualified to achieve the goals of the OSH Act, which included:

• ensuring that employers were meeting OSHA's standards

• improving worker health and safety

TRAINING AND EDUCATION PROVIDED BY THE NATIONAL INSTITUTE FOR OCCUPATIONAL SAFETY AND HEALTH

In an effort to meet these challenges and to alleviate the manpower shortages in the safety, occupational health, and industrial hygiene fields, initially NIOSH established twelve Educational Resource Centers, now called Education and Research Centers, at selected universities across the country during the mid-1970s. [Information regarding NIOSH training and education can be found at the Centers for Disease Control (CDC) Web site at www.cdc.gov/niosh/training.] NIOSH gradually implemented and sponsored five broad areas of education and training:

• continuing education short courses

• training project grants

• academic degree programs in safety, industrial hygiene, occupational nursing, and medicine

• hazardous substance training programs

• emergency responder training programs

NIOSH also began sponsoring other, even more specific, training and education, including spirometry training programs and programs addressing safety and health in mining.

Education and Research Centers

At the outset, these twelve Education and Research Centers (ERCs), received five years of funding. NIOSH intended to provide seed money for academic institutions to develop or expand existing occupational health and safety degreed curricula and programs, as well as to provide continuing education courses for safety professionals, industrial hygiene professionals, nurses, physicians, and other specialists currently practicing in the occupational safety and health field. The ERCs are currently funded through monetary grants from NIOSH and by those who pay for the ERC's services (Buckheit 2010). Further information on the seventeen ERCs presently in operation, and their contact information as of May 19, 2010, can be found in the appendix to this chapter and at www.cdc.gov/niosh/oep/centers.html and niosh-erc.org.

ERCs are valuable resources to NIOSH in three of its five broad areas of training and educational activities.

Achieving Academic Degrees in Safety and Health

The first type of NIOSH training assists students in their pursuit of academic degrees in occupational safety and health. ERCs fund and otherwise support programs for students attempting to earn academic degrees in four core areas: industrial hygiene, occupational health nursing, occupational medicine, and occupational safety. ERCs also similarly assist students involved in specialized fields (called *component areas*) that are relevant to occupational safety and health, such as ergonomics, epidemiology, and toxicology. Each ERC is required to support two degree programs from the four core areas. Stipends and traineeships are made available to qualified applicants for advanced degrees in one of these academic areas. In addition to two degree programs, each ERC must sponsor an approved component area of education—epidemiology, toxicology, ergonomics, or some other related field of study.

DEGREE ACADEMIC PROGRAMS

The academic degree programs supported by each ERC sometimes change. The most current listing of ERC academic assistance is available at www.cdc.gov/niosh/oep/centers.html.

According to Kathleen Buckheit (2010b), Continuing Education Director of the ERC at the University of North Carolina, Chapel Hill, the most commonly offered degree program among ERCs are:

Industrial Hygiene: This degree teaches students to anticipate, recognize, evaluate, and control hazards related to employee health that arise in the workplace. It can also prepare experienced industrial hygienists

for research and teaching careers in occupational health and industrial hygiene. The typical curriculum includes sample collection, analysis, statistical modeling, and interpretation of exposure data for the purpose of identifying the relationship between exposure and disease.

Occupational Health Nursing: This degree encourages practice and research in nursing that relates to worker safety and health.

Occupational Epidemiology: This degree trains those who will develop and apply the theory, methods, and intent of epidemiology to promote and protect worker safety and health.

Occupational Safety: This degree educates those who will study, research, and apply the techniques for recognizing, evaluating, and controlling workplace hazards.

Ergonomics: This degree educates those who will study, research, and apply biomechanics, engineering, and the relationship workers have with their environments.

Occupational Medicine: This degree trains medical doctors who will specialize in the recognition, evaluation, and treatment of occupation-related injuries and illnesses.

The ERCs also offer other academic degrees, including industrial hygiene research, occupational epidemiology, toxicology, occupational injury prevention, agriculture health and safety, hazardous waste, and occupational health psychology. These degrees are offered through traineeships funded by NIOSH. Further information about the degrees promoted by ERCs can be obtained from the individual ERC (Buckheit interview 2010a).

Continuing Education (CE)

The second broad area of NIOSH training and education is continuing education. The NIOSH definition for continuing education is "[a] specific plan for preparing, distributing and conducting courses, seminars, and workshops to provide short-term continuing education courses for physicians, other industrial safety and health professionals, paraprofessionals and technicians, including personnel of labor-management health and safety committees." NIOSH supports ERC short-term continuing education courses for occupational safety and health professionals and others with worker safety and health responsibilities. A wide variety of personnel attend ERC continuing educational courses, including safety personnel, industrial hygienists, nurses, doctors, engineers, employees, union officials, union members, human resource specialists, production supervisors, managers, executives, quality-control specialists, environmental specialists and professionals, ergonomists, and others. A current continuing education course schedule for all NIOSH Education and Research Centers can be accessed at the NIOSH ERC Web site (www.niosh-erc.org/), by contacting NIOSH toll free at 1-800-35-NIOSH (1-800-356-4674), or by contacting the NIOSH Publications Office. Many of the seventeen ERCs sponsor a variety of safety and health courses customized for particular companies, employers, or industries. ERCs also hold courses that are open to the public. Not all ERCs offer all topics, but new topics continue to be added throughout the year. Among the many subjects included in continuing education are:

- OSHA's 10-hour and 30-hour courses for General Industry and Construction
- Fundamentals of Safety
- Fundamentals of Industrial Hygiene
- Industrial Hygiene Sampling Techniques
- Occupational Health Nursing
- Occupational Medicine
- Asbestos
- Lead Abatement
- Contractor Safety Management
- Safety and Health Auditing
- OSHA Injury and Illness Recordkeeping
- Toxicology
- Electrical Safety
- Machine Guarding and Lockout/Tagout
- Safety and Health Management Systems

Another important aspect of continuing education is interdisciplinary education, a hallmark of each ERC and required of them all. Because of the expanding roles of occupational safety and health practition-

ers, many safety and health professionals are receiving training in other disciplines so that they can function adequately while meeting new job responsibilities. The crossover has become extensive—occupational physicians and nurses take safety-related courses, safety professionals study ergonomics, and industrial hygienists learn about safety and health management. The ERCs' continuing education programs have been charged with providing the continuing education needed for professionals to upgrade their skills and knowledge in other program areas and disciplines (Buckheit interview 2010a).

Hazardous Substance Training Programs

The third area of NIOSH training and education deals with hazardous substances. Although NIOSH ERCs are not required to offer this program, it is available. In 1988, NIOSH entered into an Interagency Agreement with the National Institute of Environmental Health Sciences (NIEHS). The purpose of the agreement was to develop and conduct a continuing education program for hazardous substances. The authority for this agreement and the resulting training was established in Section 311 (a)(1)(B) of the Comprehensive Environmental Response, Compensation and Liability Act (CERCLA) of 1980, as amended by Section 209 of the Superfund Amendments and Reauthorization Act (SARA) of 1986. Furthermore, in 1993, in response to urging by professional personnel, the hazardous substance training program was expanded to include graduate-level academic training. The NIEHS Superfund Basic Research Program (www.niehs.nih.gov/research/supported/srp) provides financial support for this training through additional grants to the NIOSH Education and Research Centers.

According to the Superfund Amendments and Reauthorization Act, enacted on August 17, 1986, as well as the NIOSH Web site at www.cdc.gov/niosh/oep/training.html#erc (scroll down to ERC Hazardous Substance Training Programs Target Audience), this training targets primarily:

- health and environmental agency personnel at the state and local levels

- any other professional personnel involved in the management and control of hazardous substances

According to the same Web page, this training is intended to assist employees of state and local agencies, and other professionals in this field, in meeting certain requirements of laws and codes such as OSHA 29 CFR 1910.120 (*Hazardous Waste Operations and Emergency Response*), CERCLA, SARA, and National Fire Protection Codes concerned with a response to emergencies involving hazardous substances. These professionals respond to incidents involving hazardous substances, including releases of hazardous substances, and they travel to hazardous waste sites around the country that must be monitored, controlled, and, sometimes, cleaned up and remediated. These personnel are in continual need of training through both brief courses and degree programs.

There are two types of hazardous substance training programs.

HAZARDOUS SUBSTANCE CONTINUING EDUCATION PROGRAM

The hazardous substance training (HST) program includes the following elements:

- training activities coordinated with the agencies responsible for training of personnel, for enforcement, and for clean up, as dictated by CERCLA and SARA requirements, as well as with other related groups
- specific plans of instruction developed and implemented to assist in adequately training personnel throughout the duration of approved clean-up or remediation projects
- a project director who is expected to demonstrate leadership and competence in conducting training concerning the handling, managing, and evaluation of hazardous substances. This person should have a level of education and experience in the hazardous substance field adequate for the project.
- a project staff able to demonstrate proper experience and technical expertise in the area

of hazardous substances, as well as to develop the necessary curricula while providing quality training
- short courses and continuing education courses developed for state and local health and environmental professionals, among others, who are involved in evaluating, managing, controlling, and handling hazardous substances
- a thorough evaluation of the hazardous substances training program, including a determination of whether the needs of these professionals are being met

HAZARDOUS SUBSTANCE ACADEMIC TRAINING PROGRAM (HSAT)

The purpose of the hazardous substance academic program is to prepare occupational safety and health professionals who specialize in hazardous substances for the responsibilities they accept in responding to hazardous substance spills and releases, as well as in managing, controlling, cleaning up and remediating areas affected by incidents involving hazardous substances. This program is intended to be a specialty area within the existing ERC industrial hygiene core programs.

The key program elements of the HSAT include:

- an assessment of the needs of government and private professionals who practice in the area of hazardous substances
- a training plan developed to satisfy the needs of these individuals
- a formal curriculum that includes a minimum level of coursework that must be met before receiving a degree
- a program director and staff whose experience makes them competent to manage the program
- a formal plan for evaluating the overall effectiveness of the training

A listing of hazardous substance training program directors can be found at www.cdc.gov/niosh/oep/hstcontacts.html.

Two Other Broad Areas of NIOSH-Sponsored Training

Two other broad areas of NIOSH-sponsored training are not administered by the Education and Research Centers, but rather by other universities or associations: training project grants (TPGs) and emergency responder training programs.

Training-Project Grants

Training-project grants are awarded by NIOSH at academic institutions primarily providing single-discipline graduate training in the industrial hygiene, marine safety, occupational health psychology, occupational health nursing, occupational medicine, and occupational safety fields, as well as in closely related occupational safety and health fields. Typically these grants are awarded to colleges and universities wishing to provide a single degree in a safety- and health-related field. They are usually awarded for three to five years and are renewable. A current list of training-project grants is available at www.cdc.gov/niosh.oep/trngrnt.html.

Any public or private institution of higher learning located in a state, in the District of Columbia, or in a U.S. territory that is able to demonstrate its competency in the field of occupational safety and health education is eligible to apply for a training-project grant.

Each April an announcement of available training funds is published in the *Federal Register*. More information on the training grants can be obtained from:

> Grants Management Officer,
> Procurement and Grants Office
> Centers for Disease Control and Prevention
> Acquisitions and Assistance Field Branch
> 626 Cochrans Mill Road
> PO Box 1870
> Pittsburgh, PA 15236
> 412-386-6428

Emergency Responder Training Program

The last broad area of NIOSH-sponsored training involves emergency responders. Primarily in response to the terrorist attacks of September 11, 2001, NIOSH began, in the 2002 fiscal year, to support training for emergency responders through a cooperative agreement with the International Association of Fire Fighters (IAFF). The IAFF has implemented a comprehensive nationwide Emergency Responder Training Program for firefighters, paramedics, and other first responders employed in over 30,100 fire departments throughout the United States. National Fire Protection Association data for the year 2008 indicated that 77,900 firefighters were injured while on duty. In 2009, the NFPA reported that 82 firefighters died while on duty (NFPA 2010). Thousands of other first responders are exposed to hazardous toxic materials that increase their long-term risk of cancer, respiratory ailments, leukemia, and other diseases.

A primary emphasis of the Emergency Responder Training Program is the health and safety of first responders. Chief among the training efforts is the recruit training initiative (RTI), an initiative intended to provide training to new first-responder recruits nationwide, as well as in the New York City and Washington metro regions in response to the terrorist attacks. Each year, in approximately 165 courses, the IAFF trains over 5000 first-responder firefighters.

The objectives of this training program include:

- conducting hazardous materials training at the first-responder level to ensure that first responders have the knowledge, skills, equipment, and materials to adequately and safely respond to emergency situations
- providing workshops to help current emergency responder instructors maintain their skills, and to train new instructors, ensuring an adequate supply of instructors for the future
- conducting analysis intended to identify the risks of hazardous materials at the local level, with the goal of assessing the level of training needed
- continually updating the first-responder training program to meet local needs
- initiating marketing and outreach efforts that use a variety of media to ensure that training reaches its intended audience
- implementing a thorough quality-assurance effort in order to maintain the program at a high level of quality

Contact Information:

> International Association of Fire Fighters
> 1750 New York Avenue, NW
> Washington, DC 20006
> IAFF Web site: www.iaff.org
> IAFF HazMat Training Department
> 1750 New York Avenue, NW
> Washington, DC 20006

Conclusion

NIOSH offers a wide variety of training and education, including continuing education courses, academic degree programs at selected universities, training project grants, and specific programs, including training about hazardous materials and emergency response. This section summarizes these offerings. To inquire about current training and education available, visit the NIOSH Office of Extramural Programs Web site at www.cdc.gov/niosh/oep/training.html#erc.

A Summary of American National Standard ANSI/ASSE Z490.1-2009–Criteria for Accepted Practices in Safety, Health, and Environmental Training

Safety and health professionals generally agree upon a few basic elements that must be incorporated into any effective safety and health management system. Those basic elements include:

- management support, commitment, leadership, and action
- employee involvement and acceptance
- hazard recognition, evaluation, and control
- training and education

On September 19, 1997, the charter was accredited by ANSI for the preparation of the American National Standard ANSI/ASSE Z490.1, *Criteria for Accepted Practices in Safety, Health, and Environmental Training*. A need was recognized by the safety, health, and environmental (SH&E) profession to improve training regarding safety, health, and environmental management. To be effective, such training must provide man-agement, workers, and SH&E professionals with the knowledge, skills, perspective, and abilities to recognize, evaluate, and control hazards in order to protect themselves and others while in the workplace.

Development of the standard began in April 1996, when the ASSE conducted focus-group meetings in Houston, Chicago, and Gaithersburg, Maryland. More than 100 training experts, representing businesses, industry associations, professional societies, providers of training, and organizations both large and small, participated. ASSE needed to know whether there was a need for a national training standard. ANSI/ASSE Z390.1-1995, *Accepted Practices for H2S Training*, was approved just before these focus groups began meeting, demonstrating the industry's support for the development of training standards.

After three years of development, approximately 48 organizations and a number of individuals developed ANSI/ASSE Z490.1-2001. During the standard's process of enactment, each ASSE chapter president and governmental affairs chairperson was asked to review the drafts and comment upon them. ASSE's practice specialty administrators also reviewed the drafts and added their comments. Finally, nearly 1500 copies of the draft standard were made available for public review, resulting in a dramatic response and a much higher quality standard.

The ANSI/ASSE Z490.1-2001 standard was developed in order to improve the consistency and quality of training development, delivery, evaluation, and management. Members of the ANSI/ASSE Z490.1-2001 committee had as their goal the combination of accepted practices from the training and education industry with accepted practices of professionals involved in safety, health, and environmental management.

In May 2009, an updated ANSI/ASSE Z490.1 standard was issued. Numerous changes that were primarily intended to improve readability and understanding were made in the explanatory section of the standard. A comparison of the changes from 2001 to 2009 is available from the American Society of Safety Engineers in the *Comparison Document of Z490.1 American National Standard Criteria for Accepted Practices in Safety, Health and Environmental Training* published in November 2009 (ANSI/ASSE 2009).

The purpose and scope of Z490.1-2009 is established in Paragraph 1 of the standard: "the establishment of criteria for effective development, delivery, evaluation, and management of training in safety, health, and environmental management, and the description of accepted practices in such training."

Please note that there are other chapters in this book that address the "how-tos" of training, including training course design, delivery of training, evaluation of training, and numerous others. Please refer to those chapters for more specific information.

Management and Administration of SH&E Training

Section 3 of Z490.1-2009 lists the criteria necessary for effective management of SH&E training, recognizing that training and education are a part of the SH&E management system and must be integrated into it. Effective management of SH&E training and education includes:

- responsibility for the training program
- accountability for proper administration of the program
- resources adequate for trainers and trainees to complete training and education
- personnel qualified to design, develop, and deliver training and education by use of appropriate techniques
- strategies for meeting learning goals
- evaluation sufficient to assure the effectiveness of training and education
- oversight of the training process sufficient to assure its consistency, quality, and constant improvement

SH&E training historically has been most effective when integrated into organizational goals and objectives rather than as a stand-alone training event. Any organization can enroll its employees in the course "Control of Hazard Energy during Servicing and Maintenance of Equipment, Processes and Machinery" (popularly known as "Lock, Tag and Try"), but this training is most effective when integrated into overall goals and policies for machine guarding, electrical safety, production strategies, quality systems, and cost control.

In paragraph 3.2, the Z490.1-2009 standard describes proper management of a SH&E training system as beginning with a needs assessment, the establishment of learning objectives, and a written plan that documents methods of training and education.

Other key criteria that must be managed properly are:

- training development
- course content and format
- resource materials
- indicators of satisfactory completion of training and education
- evaluation of training and education effectiveness
- submission of documentation of training and education

Management at any organization providing SH&E training must report adequate numbers and expertise of personnel who administer and support training and education, as well as adequate budgets for training and education, supporting technologies (including presentation equipment and practice equipment), adequate time investment, and suitable facilities and materials, including classrooms, handouts, and lesson plans.

Training Development

Training must be developed to meet and improve the organization's safety, health, and environmental goals. The knowledge, skills, and abilities of employees should be enhanced so that workers will be able to identify and understand the hazards of their jobs while using proper control measures. In order to accomplish this, Z490.1-2009 recommends a systematic process of training development that includes:

1. *An Assessment of the Need for Training.*
   Training may not be the correct response to an organization's needs. In some cases, improved equipment design, new tools, personal protective equipment, or other physical change (or merely greater accountability) may be a more appropriate response.

The training needs assessment should inquire into:

- the nature of the audience to be trained

- the things trainees are expected to know and do as a result of their training
- job procedures and job hazard analyses
- the communication abilities of trainees, including their native language and their ability to see or hear
- the nature of any prior training given to the trainees
- regulations, laws, and standards concerned with the training

2. *Learning Objectives and Their Prerequisites.* Goals and objectives should be in written form and should describe:

- the target audience
- the knowledge, abilities, and skills that employees must learn
- the knowledge, abilities, and skills that training will impart
- how to ascertain whether training has had its desired effect

The results of the training should be demonstrable and measurable. If an employer wishes to train a small group of maintenance employees how to use ladders safely, the goals of the training should specify whether it will include both portable and fixed ladders, as well as special ladders such as those used in the maritime industry or rolling ladder stands. The goals should specify whether training will deal simply with the proper use of ladders or whether it will also include proper inspection of ladders. They should specify whether the effectiveness of the training will be measured by a written test, an oral test, or by direct observation of the newly trained employees' use of ladders—or by a combination of the three.

Prerequisites should include prior formal training, certifications or licenses, level and length of experience, knowledge of equipment, tools and processes, and so on.

3. *Design of Training Course.* When designing the course, consider delivery methods, course content, instructional materials, trainer materials, the physical environment of the training, the time needed, the qualifications necessary

for the trainers, and methods by which to evaluate the effectiveness of the training.

Delivery methods might include classroom time, on-the-job training, formal lecturing, computer-based simulation, peer discussion, multimedia demonstrations, hands-on practice, distance learning, and much more. Usually, a variety of methods work best to keep trainees' attention; and some delivery methods work better than others during instruction about certain types of material. All methods must include plans for collecting adequate, timely feedback; for answering questions and concerns; and for assessing the receptivity of trainees to the training. Various methods could include techniques that develop attendees' interest, such as trivia questions, history lessons, competitive knowledge-based games, and use of the facilities for real observations related to the subject at hand. If an instructor is presenting a course on electrical safety, attendees could be asked to identify electrical hazards in the classroom and to explain how any potential electrical hazards are being controlled.

Course content should consist of the information needed by the trainees and should be based on such elements as:

- organizational policies
- procedures and practices
- current and state-of-the-art peer-reviewed literature
- recognized scientific and professional principles
- knowledge and judgment of experts in the subject
- site-specific issues and concerns
- regulatory requirements

Instructional materials should be pertinent to the targeted audience, to the method of delivery, and to the learning objectives. These materials might include a trainer's guide; attendee handouts; multimedia aids such as video, PowerPoint, flip charts, or whiteboards; "show and tell" devices; tools and equipment able to give trainees hands-on practice and experience; copies of regulatory standards; and the organization's written policies and procedures.

A trainer's lesson plan, guidebook, or outline should be developed and should include:

- an agenda
- training goals
- prerequisites
- a schedule for presentation, breaks, meals, and so on
- a list of training aids
- copies of handouts
- requirements for the physical environment, such as classroom size, style of seats, lighting level (including individual lamps for students if required), computer access, available equipment, and any other physical necessities
- methods for evaluating the effectiveness of training, such as critique sheets, tests, or demonstration requirements
- a list of accessible reference documents

Be sure to include the date the trainer's guide was prepared or revised, and by whom.

The physical environment must take into account the number of trainees per class; whether interactive discussion will be encouraged (which affects classroom seating arrangements); any necessity for watching or using machines, equipment, tools, or similar items; and any multimedia needs.

The design of the course is also based on the time allocated for delivering the information. In some cases, government regulations or certifying organizations specify a minimum time. Training classes may be spread over days and weeks or can be delivered in one time block. Human resource requirements for staffing and running the organization must be taken into account. In addition, some topics will generate more questions and the need for individual tutoring than will others. Decide whether time for questions and tutoring should be reserved beforehand or taken as necessary after the training. Methods and times of testing must also be considered.

With more qualified trainers comes better training. Indicate any necessary requirements of trainers, such as certifications, licenses, degrees, experience, background, expected delivery techniques, and anything else required to abide by regulations.

4. *A Strategy for Evaluation.* Determining how well course attendees understood, accepted, and are prepared to apply their training is difficult at best. Adult trainees do not comprehend oral presentations as well as they do hands-on practice. Methods of evaluation might include written tests, oral tests, demonstrations by course attendees, observations by supervisors while in the field, written reports in which attendees describe what they learned, or other such methods. Multiple evaluation techniques may be needed.

5. *Completion Criteria.* The development of the training must include a minimum level of accomplishment below which training is not considered complete, and the training plan must specify procedures to follow when an attendee does not successfully complete the course. Satisfactory completion of a training curriculum should include, as applicable

- minimum attendance requirements, such as attendance during a certain number of hours or a percentage of the entire course
- minimum passing test scores
- certain mandatory times of attendance
- any requirements for demonstration of proper tool or equipment usage
- any required exercises, drills, or role-playing

6. *Continuous Improvement.* The final parameter for development discussed in Z490.1-2009 is continuous improvement. All training must be revised and upgraded periodically. The best way to learn what needs upgrading is to scrutinize the contents of attendee course evaluations. Develop an evaluation form and allow attendees adequate time to fill it out—preferably as the course progresses, but certainly by the end of the course—and review the evaluations. Qualified personnel should review all training courses annually or even more frequently.

Training Delivery

This section of Z490.1-2009 describes requirements for acceptable trainers and delivery of training content. The minimum qualifications of the trainers must be specified during the training development plan and should include:

Trainers' Expertise in the Subject Matter. At a minimum, establish any certifications, licenses, degrees, continuing education, length of experience, skills, abilities, and technical knowledge needed by trainers.

Trainers' Delivery Skills and Abilities. Trainers should have a thorough knowledge of adult learning methods as well as of delivery techniques. This is usually best evaluated by references who are able to give feedback about previously conducted training.

Trainers' Current Status of Required Skills and Knowledge. All those involved in training must stay current in their profession and its subject matter. This can be evaluated by discovering how often trainers deliver courses on the subject matter, to whom training has been delivered, and how competency is maintained (whether by attending continuing education seminars, by publishing articles and books, by speaking at conferences and meetings, by teaching higher education courses, or by consulting with organizations), as well as by reviewing references from those who have attended previous training courses.

Documentation of Trainers' Abilities. Z490.1-2009 specifies that documentation of trainers' abilities is necessary, but it does not specify any particular method of documentation. Documentation may include curriculum vitae; biographical experience sheets; résumés; continuing education transcripts; a written biography; or copies of certifications, registrations, or licenses.

Delivery of the training itself must be carefully planned and managed. Trainers must be evaluated to assure that they understand course learning objectives, are familiar with specific course materials, display necessary expertise, use appropriate delivery techniques (those suitable for the audience—neither offensive nor distasteful), and are familiar with the principles of adult learning. Ensure that the trainer has customized the training to the audience receiving it.

To facilitate acceptable delivery of training, the training environment and location should be free of obvious hazardous conditions and should have access to potable water and restrooms while maintaining a suitable climate (including temperature and air qual-

ity) with sufficient lighting, seating, and work space, as well as planned emergency evacuation routes and procedures. Also consider the necessity for snacks and meals and whether all phones and pagers should be turned off or placed on silent mode, as well as the timing and length of any breaks. Ensure an adequate supply of training materials; handouts; back-up multimedia equipment, such as spare projector bulbs and extension cords; adequate electrical power; furniture, such as tables and chairs; and computers, along with telephone lines or Internet connections, if needed.

The room or training area must be arranged so that all attendees can see and hear the instructor. Trainees with special needs must be considered.

Most adult attendees will want to learn and have a successful training experience. In return, the trainer must treat trainees with respect and fairness; recognize and respond appropriately to each individual's learning styles and abilities; and exercise good professional judgment when responding to difficult, unexpected situations or individuals. The pace of the training should match the audience's ability to internalize the training. In most cases, attendee participation should be encouraged and welcomed. Trainers should answer *all* questions and answer them respectfully, even when it means searching out answers later and conveying them to questioners by other means.

Training Evaluation

The tools and techniques for training evaluation should apply equally to trainers, trainees, training, and the training management system. Trainers' abilities to effectively impart and transfer knowledge, skills, and abilities to trainees must be evaluated. Trainees' understanding and use of the training content must be evaluated—perhaps by having attendees perform tasks correctly. The training and its environment must be evaluated. The system that manages the needs assessment, planning, delivery, and evaluation must also be evaluated periodically. The key question to be answered is: Are the organization's goals being met?

Each training event should include evaluation tools, which must be prepared during the training development. Tools should be reliable and act as valid measures, and they must be based on accepted practices. Reliable, valid measures are those that give consistent feedback over time, reflecting the knowledge, skills, and abilities that are the goals of the training.

The selection of the evaluation approach is based on the training audience, the expected outcomes of the training, and the established learning objectives. Evaluation approaches might include:

Reaction Surveys. Sometimes called critique sheets or course evaluations, these are questionnaires that attendees can fill out to subjectively evaluate the trainer's abilities, the training location, the trainer's delivery technique, the training environment, the pace of the training, the course's content, and all other aspects of the training.

Evaluation of Knowledge, Skills, and Abilities. This might include a written test, an oral test, the completion of an assigned project (such as a written paper), the design of a tool or device, demonstration of a new skill in the real or simulated work setting, observation over time by a supervisor or auditor, a decrease in the number of unwanted events, or an increase in the number and quality of proactive metrics for safety, health, and environmental management activities.

Quantitative Measurements. These can include a pre-test and a post-test to measure improvement, linking performance to training. In many cases, this helps identify gaps that impede the value and application of training, such as the availability of appropriate equipment, conflicting direction from a supervisor, or the lack of management support, leadership, and accountability.

Organizational Results. Another evaluative technique compares the results of those trained with those who have not yet been trained. To accomplish this, a control group of workers who have not yet been trained is compared with the trained group. Measurements to compare the trained group with the control group can include:

- increasingly safe behaviors (also called actions) or decreases in unsafe behaviors
- increasing use of preventative measures, controls, and devices

- fewer near hits, injuries, illnesses, and other unwanted events
- diminishing costs and workers' compensation claims
- higher returns on investment
- fewer observable regulatory noncompliance findings

Overall, the evaluation must be used to continuously improve the content of the training course and its delivery methods, materials, and environment.

Documentation and Record Keeping

A favorite expression of many SH&E professionals is, "What has not been documented has not been done." The final paragraph of Z490.1-2009 provides guidance for documenting training. Some regulatory standards, such as OSHA's standard for personal protective equipment [29 CFR 1910.132(f)(4)], require that training be documented. Best practice is for all training to be documented. The most effective method of managing evidence of completed training is documenting the who, when, what, and so on, of all training.

The record-keeping management system for documentation of training should, according to Z490.1-2009, ensure that records are:

- readily retrievable, identifiable, and orderly
- current, accurate, legible, and dated
- retained for a reasonable time specified by a "record retention policy" developed with the assistance of legal counsel, ensuring that records are properly controlled
- in compliance with all regulatory and legislative requirements

The most important uses of the training records include:

- allowing management to assess the extent of the training system requirements and allowing auditors to discover who is being trained, whether the training is timely, whether training make-up sessions will adequately allow everyone opportunity to attend training,

and whether regulatory requirements are being met
- safeguarding against governmental regulatory actions or other liability claims

Development Records

Records documenting training development should identify the targeted audience, the learning goals and objectives, the personnel and organization used to develop the training curriculum and materials, and the qualifications of those who designed and developed the training curriculum and materials, as well as including copies of the actual materials used and plans for evaluating the effectiveness of the training course.

Delivery Records

When training courses are being delivered, several pieces of information should be documented, including the date, location, and duration of the training, the name and description of the course, the names and qualifications of those delivering the course, copies of the materials used and of handouts provided to attendees, the names (preferably the signatures) of the attendees, and some indication of which attendees successfully completed the training. Z490.1-2009 also recommends a unique identifying number for each attendee.

Evaluation Records

The forms used by attendees to evaluate the training should be retained for use in evaluating the training management system as well as for regular evaluation of continuing improvement of a particular course.

Records Confidentiality and Availability

Regulations that require records to be kept should be met. Regulatory requirements might stipulate that the records be readily available for a government inspector while remaining confidential and protecting trade secrets. Some sort of statement should be made in the written management training system document about to whom the records may be disclosed.

Certificates

Certificates for training completion, while not always required, should be provided to attendees as documentation. However, should they be issued, best practice is for certificates to include trainees' names; the course name; the date; the total number of hours of instruction; a statement that attendees successfully completed the course; the names and addresses of those who provided training; some indication of whether a refresher course is required or suggested, and at what time interval; the training's expiration date, if applicable; trainees' individual identification numbers; the level of training attended or the type of certification achieved, if applicable; any other information required by government regulations; and the number of continuing education credits or units (often called CEUs) earned. CEUs are required by many professions to indicate that professionals who hold certifications, licenses, and other designations are maintaining their professional knowledge and skills at an acceptable level. Some certifying or licensing bodies require that a minimum number of CEUs be acquired during a set period.

If continuing education credits or units are earned, credits must be in accordance with the certifying body's requirements and should be filed with the certifying body.

Annexes

There are three annexes (or appendices) to the Z490.1-2009 standard, as well as a checklist designed to assist on the day of training.

Annex A provides fourteen references for further information. These include ISO standards, such as 9001 and 14001; other ANSI standards, such as Z1.11; two NIOSH documents; one OSHA document (OSHA Publication 2254); one ASTD (American Society for Training and Development) document; and two books.

Annex B provides guidance for training course development, reiterating the Z490.1-2009 standard in a more step-by-step, "how-to" approach.

Annex C provides training delivery guidelines to assist trainers in delivering effective training. It also provides advice and guidance for traditional learning techniques, advanced technology training, and on-the-job training.

Day of Training Checklist

The last page of Z490.1-2009 is a two-page checklist of issues to manage on the day of training, including the training location's seating, lighting, temperature, and level of comfort; audiovisual equipment; training devices, materials, and supplies; what to do before attendees arrive; trainers' opening remarks; how to encourage participation; how to effectively present training material; proper documentation; and thanking the participants in such a way as to give a lasting impression.

CONCLUSION

ANSI Z490.1-2009, *Criteria for Accepted Practices in Safety, Health, and Environmental Training*, was prepared by a group of safety, health, and environmental management professionals whose intent was to cover all aspects of training, including development, delivery, evaluation, and management. To ensure quality training, review other chapters in this handbook that address training and education.

References

American National Standard Institute (ANSI). 2009. *ANSI Z490.1-2009 Criteria for Accepted Practices in Safety, Health and Environmental Training*. Des Plaines, IL: American Society of Safety Engineers.

American Society of Safety Engineers (ASSE). 2001. "ANSI Z490.1—2001 Approved." *The Advisor* (Fall) 1(1).

_____. November 2009. *Comparison Document of Z490.1 American National Standard Criteria for Accepted Practices in Safety, Health and Environmental Training*.

Buckheit, Kathleen. 2007. Personal Interview with Kathleen Buckheit, MPH, COHN-S/CM, FAAOHN, Director, Continuing Education, North Carolina Occupational Safety and Health Education and Research Center (January 30, 2007).

_____. 2010a. Email Correspondence with Kathleen Buckheit, MPH, COHN-S/CM, FAAOHN, Director, Continuing Education, North Carolina Occupational Safety and Health Education and Research Center (May 17, 2010).

_____. 2010b. Email correspondence with Kathleen Buckheit, November 29, 2010.

Centers for Disease Control & Prevention (CDC), National Institute for Occupational Safety & Health (NIOSH), *Education and Research Centers for Occupational Safety and Health*. www.niosh-erc.org

_____. NIOSH Office of Extramural Programs. *Training Programs*. www.cdc.gov/niosh/oep/training. html#erc

_____. NIOSH Office of Extramural Programs. *Hazardous Substance Training (HST) Program and Hazardous Substance Academic Training (HSAT) Program Grantees*. www.cdc.gov/niosh/oep/hstcontacts.html

_____. *Training*. www.cdc.gov/niosh/training

Kane, Steven F. *Use of the Z490 Voluntary National Consensus Standard to Improve Safety, Health, and Environmental (SH&E) Training*. Presentation by Steven F. Kane, CSP, PE, Chair, Z490 Committee at the ASSE Professional Development Conference. June 12, 2002. Nashville, TN.

National Fire Protection Association (NFPA). "Fire Service Statistics." www.nfpa.org/itemDetail.asp? categoryID=417&itemID=18246&URL=Research %20&%20Reports/Fire%20reports/Fire%20service %20statistics

National Institute for Occupational Safety and Health. 2010. *Education and Research Centers for Occupational Safety and Health 2010* (retrieved October 4, 2011). www.niosh-erc.org.

National Institutes of Health (NIH), National Institute of Environmental Health Sciences, Superfund Research Program. www-apps.niehs.nih.gov/sbrp

Occupational Safety and Health Administration (OSHA). www.osha.gov

Occupational Safety and Health Act of 1970, Public Law 91-596, 91st Congress, S.2193, December 29, 1970. www.osha.gov

Rogers, Bonnie. Telephone Interview with Bonnie Rogers, DrPH, COHN-S, LNCC, FAAN, Director of the University of North Carolina Occupational Safety and Health Education and Research Center. January 4, 2005.

APPENDIX

The following list of sixteen NIOSH Education and Research Centers is current as of May 19, 2010. For the most current information, go to www.cdc.gov/niosh/oep/centers.html.

Alabama Education and Research Center

University of Alabama at Birmingham
School of Public Health
1665 University Blvd.
Birmingham, AL 35294-0022
(205) 934-6208
Fax: (205) 975-6341
R. Kent Oestenstad, PhD, Director
Email: oestk@uab.edu

California Education and Research Center–Northern

University of California, Berkeley
School of Public Health
140 Warren
Berkeley, CA 94720-7360
(510) 643-4702
Fax: (510) 642-5815
John R. Balmes, MD, Director
Email: john.balmes@ucsf.edu

California Education and Research Center–Southern

University of California, Los Angeles
School of Public Health
650 Charles Young Drive South
Los Angeles, CA 90095-1772
(310) 206-6141
Fax: (310) 206-9903
John R. Froines PhD, Interim Director
Email: jfroines@ucla.edu

Cincinnati Education and Research Center

University of Cincinnati
Department of Environmental Health ML. Box 670056
3223 Eden Avenue
Cincinnati, Ohio 45267-0056
(513) 558-1751
Fax: (513) 558-2772
Carol Rice, Ph.D., CIH, Director
Email: alerdilr@ucmail.uc.edu

Colorado Education and Research Center

University of Colorado at Denver and Health
Sciences Center
4200 E. Ninth Ave.
Denver, CO 80262
(303) 315-0880
Fax: (303) 315-7642
Lee S. Newman, MD, MA, FCCP, FACOEM, Director
Email: lee.newman@uchsc.edu

Harvard Education and Research Center

Harvard School of Public Health
Department of Environmental Health
665 Huntington Avenue
Bldg. 1, Rm. 1407
Boston, MA 02115
(617) 432-3323
Fax: (617) 432-3441
David C. Christiani, MD, Director
Email: dchris@hohp.harvard.edu

Illinois Education and Research Center

University of Illinois at Chicago
School of Public Health
2121 West Taylor St.
Chicago, IL 60612
(312) 996-7469
Fax: (312) 413-9898
Lorraine M. Conroy, ScD, CIH, Director
Email: lconroy@uic.edu

Iowa Education and Research Center

University of Iowa
College of Public Health
Department of Occupational and Environmental
    Health
100 Oakdale Campus - 126 IREH
Iowa City, IA 52242-5000
(319) 335-4428
Fax: (319) 335-4225
Craig Zwerling, MD, PhD, MPH, Director
Email: craig-zwerling@uiowa.edu

Johns Hopkins Education and Research Center

Johns Hopkins University
Bloomberg School of Public Health
615 North Wolfe Street Rm 7503
Baltimore, MD 21205
(410) 955-4037
Fax: (410) 614-4986
Jacqueline Agnew, PhD, Director
Email: jagnew@jhsph.edu

Michigan Education and Research Center

University of Michigan
School of Public Health
1420 Washington Heights
Ann Arbor, MI 48109-2029
(734) 936-0757
Fax: (734) 763-8095
Thomas G. Robins, MD, Director
Email: trobins@umich.edu

Minnesota Education and Research Center

University of Minnesota
School of Public Health
420 Delaware Street, S.E.
Minneapolis, MN 55455
(612) 625-5934
Fax: (612) 626-4837
Susan G. Gerberich, Ph.D., Director
Email: gerbe001@umn.edu

New York/New Jersey Education and Research Center

Mount Sinai School of Medicine
Department of Community and Preventive Medicine
P.O. Box 1057
One Gustave L. Levy Pl.
New York, NY 10029-6574
(212) 824-7018
Fax: (212) 996-0407
Philip J. Landrigan, MD, MSc, Interim Director
Email: phil.landrigan@mssm.edu

North Carolina Education and Research Center

University of North Carolina at Chapel Hill
School of Public Health
1700 Airport Rd., CB 7502
Chapel Hill, NC 27599-7502
(919) 966-1765

Fax: (919) 966-8999
Bonnie Rogers, DrPH, COHN-S, FAAN, LNCC,
   Director
Email: rogersb@email.unc.edu

South Florida Education and Research Center

University of South Florida
College of Public Health
13201 Bruce B. Downs Blvd., MDC Box 56
Tampa, FL 33612-3805
(813) 974-6629
Fax: (813) 974-4718
Thomas E. Bernard, Ph.D., Director
Email: tbernard@ health.usf.edu

Texas Education and Research Center

University of Texas Health Science Center at Houston
School of Public Health
P.O. Box 20186
Houston, TX 77225-0186
(713) 500-9464
Fax: (713) 500-9442
Sarah A. Felknor, PhD, Director
Email: sarah.a.felknor@uth.tmc.edu

Utah Education and Research Center

University of Utah
Rocky Mountain Center for Occupational and
   Environmental Health
391 Chipeta Way, Suite C
Salt Lake City, UT 84108
(801) 581-4800
Fax: (801) 581-7224
Kurt Hegmann, MD, MPH, Director
Email: kurt.hegmann@hsc.utah.edu

Washington Education and Research Center

University of Washington
Department of Environmental Health and
   Occupational Health Sciences
P. O. Box 354695
Seattle, WA 98105
(206) 685-7189
Fax: (206) 616-6240
Noah S. Seixas, PhD, Director
Email: nseixas@u.washington.edu

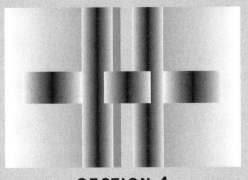

SECTION 4
SAFETY AND HEALTH TRAINING

LEARNING OBJECTIVES

▮ Be able to apply a knowledge of learning theories to select or develop appropriate training programs.

▮ Learn about factors that affect memory.

▮ Recognize the different categories of learning needed to teach problem-solving skills to beginning, intermediate, and advanced learners.

▮ Be able to identify motivational problems and implement strategies that will increase learners' interest in safety training.

▮ Learn how to conduct a performance and training needs assessment.

▮ Be able to analyze a target audience and develop training strategies based on audience characteristics.

▮ Master the terms goals and objectives, and be able to write course objectives.

APPLIED SCIENCE AND ENGINEERING: SAFETY TRAINING THEORIES

Phyllis Simmons

MARIA IS A human resources manager for a law firm that employs 50 employees at one location. She is responsible for safety training in addition to her other responsibilities. Workers at her company are college-educated and computer-literate English speakers. Hazards at the firm consist of typical office hazards and those related to computer use. John, on the other hand, is a safety officer for a manufacturing company with 2000 employees who work at eight different geographic locations. Workers in his company speak four different languages, and their education levels range from seventh grade to college (the company also employs teenage workers during the summer). Hazards at the company include office hazards, chemical hazards, and hazards related to moving machinery. Each profile of the above-mentioned officials and their work environments reflects the diverse world in which today's trainers work. Even though Maria and John work in two different worlds, they have one thing in common—the need to understand how people learn best. Regardless of where trainers work, the fundamental philosophy stays the same: "If you know your audience, you will know what learners need and what motivates them."

IMPORTANCE OF LEARNING THEORIES AND TRAINING DEVELOPMENT

The first section describes learning theories, specifically cognitive, behavioral, and motivation theories that give trainers information about the learning process so they have a sound rationale for selecting training activities and materials. Many safety trainers purchase off-the-shelf training materials, and they may not be aware why certain learning activities have been selected by the

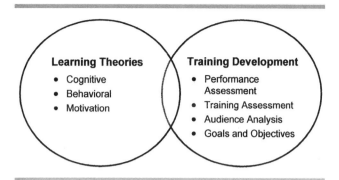

FIGURE 1. Chapter overview

designer. Theoretical principles are derived from the science behind how information is organized and presented. Once principles are learned, they can be applied to any type of work environment, especially those like Maria's and John's. Even though all workplaces are different, the principles about how people learn are the same.

In the second section, trainers will learn the mechanics of the training development process—performance assessment, training assessment, audience analysis, setting of goals and objectives—how to implement them. As Smith and Ragan (1999, 2) point out, "development is the systematic process of translating learning theories into plans for training materials, activities and evaluation." Although the two systems are different, they are dependent on each other. Theories are the foundation for training, and safety trainers are somewhat like architects in that, just as architects design houses based on sound engineering principles, trainers develop training based on established learning theories.

LEARNING THEORIES

This section will focus on three learning theories: *cognitive*, *behavioral*, and *motivational*. Each theory will help instructors create effective training programs regardless of whether they deliver training in the classroom or via technology. Learning theories are the foundation from which training is derived, and they have shaped learning as we know it today. Learning theories help trainers understand why certain

concepts are important and provide rationale as to why specific training activities are used.

Cognitive theories describe how people process and remember information. This area is where one can find answers to questions like How do people learn? and Why do workers sometimes forget information? Behavioral theory is especially important because it describes why it is important to reinforce principles after training. Behavior-based principles are used in companies to create a safety culture, and these principles have direct application to training. Equally important is motivation theory because it describes ways trainers can make safety training interesting and relevant to learners.

Cognitive Theory

In cognitive theory, the primary focus is on understanding the learner, specifically, (a) how people process information, (b) what affects memory, and (c) what type of strategies trainers should use to help employees learn safety information.

How the Brain Processes Information

Many theorists believe that memory has three components: sensory register, short-term memory, and long-term memory. Atkinson and Shiffrin (1968) designed an information-processing model describing how each system works and how those systems affect learning and the ability to recall information (see Figure 2).

A person's brain constantly receives information from the five senses and the environment, information that is transmitted to the first memory system called the *sensory register*. Information in this area is only held for a few seconds and is lost if the trainee does not actively pay attention to it. If the person pays attention to the information, then it is transmitted to the second part of the memory system called the *short-term memory*, or *working memory*.

Working memory holds information that is currently being used and is where most thinking and mental processing occurs (Woolfolk 1998). According to Bernstein et al. (2000), information is held in short-term memory—which has limited storage capacity—

for no more than 30 seconds. The best way to retain training information longer in short-term memory is through repetition (saying it over and over) or rehearsal (having the person mentally thinking about it). "Rehearsal is important because the longer an item remains in short-term memory, the greater the chance it will be transferred to long-term memory" (Slavin 2000, 178). Short-term memory is believed to have a limited storage capacity (5 to 9 bits of information), which is why people may feel overwhelmed or forget what was taught when they are given a large amount of information at one time, such as during new employee orientation. If large amounts of information must be presented all at once, it needs to be well organized and connected to information already in the trainee's long-term memory (Slavin 2000). Woolfolk (1998) recommends grouping individual ideas into meaningful categories (also called *chunking*) when people have to learn about several topics. When information is unorganized, the situation can cause confusion and frustration and negatively affect learner motivation. To better understand the power of chunking, read the following list of safety items new employees have to learn at John's manufacturing company—then, without looking, try to recall the safety items.

Safety orientation items (before chunking):

- gloves
- respirator
- keyboard tray
- fire extinguisher
- eyewash station
- glare screen
- safety glasses
- back belt
- wrist rest

Try the exercise again using the chunked list.

Safety items (after chunking):

Computer Safety Equipment

- glare screen
- keyboard tray
- wrist rest

Personal Protective Equipment

- back belt
- gloves
- respirator
- safety glasses

Safety Equipment

- eyewash station
- fire extinguisher

Notice how the information is now alphabetized and categorized by type of equipment, making it easier for people to process and remember. Chunking can also be done in visual form using symbols or pictures to convey messages, like the commonly used symbols

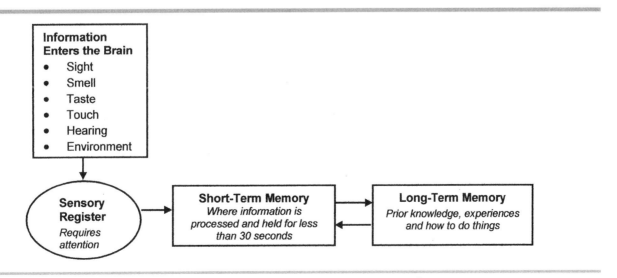

FIGURE 2. Information-processing model (Based on the Atkinson-Shiffrin model.)

in safety warning signs that are displayed in many companies. The brain processes mental images better than large amounts of text. The saying "A picture is worth a thousand words" holds true for learning and assimilating knowledge.

The third and most important memory system is called *long-term memory*. Theorists believe this memory system can hold an unlimited amount of information. It is the permanent storage system of the brain where prior knowledge is stored. In Figure 2 the arrows go in both directions between short-term and long-term memory, because to store new information in long-term memory, a person must draw on prior knowledge stored in this area (Ormrod 1998). Accessing prior knowledge is an important factor in learning and retention for both the trainer and trainee. Trainers, when they are aware of what learners already know, can use that information to help make the training more meaningful for the audience. Similarly, during the learning process, trainees will mentally search for prior knowledge to connect it to something familiar and meaningful to them. Long-term information is encoded in memory in three different ways, through *personal experiences*, *general knowledge*, and *procedural knowledge*, formally also known as episodic, semantic, and procedural memory systems, respectively. McCown, Driscoll, and Roop (1996) recommend training strategies for each area.

PERSONAL EXPERIENCES (EPISODIC MEMORY)

Personal experiences are usually stored in the form of mental images, including memorable events involving the five senses. For example, many people can recall the taste of their favorite childhood treat.

Training strategies: Because of the way personal experiences are stored in the brain, trainers should strive to make training sessions interesting and interactive. Instead of a lecture-only format, learners should be taught according to learning styles that involve the senses, such as discussions, hands-on activities, and visual-aids learning that facilitates long-term memory processing (James and Galbraith 1985). Slavin (2000) suggests using training activities that can create memorable events in the trainee's mind like visual aids, role playing, videos, and other forms of active learning.

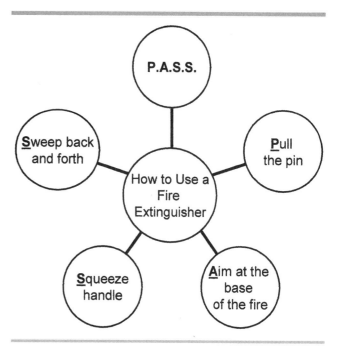

FIGURE 3. Mental network map

GENERAL KNOWLEDGE AND CONCEPTS (SEMANTIC MEMORY)

Many cognitive psychologists have hypothesized that general knowledge and concepts are organized in the brain like a network map (see Figure 3), and that people mentally connect similar concepts to each other. How people mentally organize information influences how they learn and retrieve information.

Training strategies: Find out what people already know and use that information to connect it to newer information. To access prior knowledge, trainers can use activities such as pre-tests, discussions, and asking questions during training.

PROCEDURAL KNOWLEDGE (PROCEDURAL MEMORY)

Procedural knowledge (how to do things) is acquired through practice, and if practiced enough, this knowledge can be retrieved automatically without conscious effort—like riding a bike, for instance. "When procedural knowledge becomes automatic it can also build problem solving skills because basic principles are embedded in long term memory" (McCown, Driscoll, and Roop 1996, 221).

Training strategies: Give participants time to practice procedural skills, especially when teaching important safety topics such as emergency response, first aid, and machine safety. Because of storage-space limitations in short-term memory, people can only learn so much at one time. Trainees need time to process the concepts that are being taught. Trainers can help by introducing redundancy into training sessions; they can, for example, present the ideas several times but in different ways. "Information encoded in different ways is more easily retrieved from long-term memory than just one way" (Ormrod 1998, 591). Another technique Ormrod recommends is pacing, in which the trainer pauses at 10-minute intervals to discuss the concepts that will activate mental processing.

Putting Theory into Practice: How to Help People Better Process and Retain Information

Based on the principles of information processing, here are more cognitive training strategies that can be used to help trainees better process and retain information.

Present information in an organized manner. According to cognitive principles, the brain seeks to arrange incoming information and put it in some type of order to help learners process materials more efficiently. Well-organized materials make it easier for a person to learn and recall information. Methods that trainers can use to organize instruction include the following (Ormrod 1998, Mayer 1989, Schunk 2004):

- Equipment and objects can be used as visual aids.
- Graphic organizers such as pictures, diagrams, and charts can also provide visual aids.
- Outlines or organization charts provide a framework for the training.
- Grouping concepts into modules (or sections) establishes links between concepts.
- Using paragraph headings with written material helps the learning process.
- Provide a chapter overview—Figure 1 was designed not only to help the reader understand the organization of this chapter, but also to provide him or her with a mental roadmap.

- Summarizing information at the end of instruction will help learners review and pull concepts together.
- Use acronyms—this is an abbreviation technique used to help learners remember names, concepts, and procedures. The acronym is the first letter of a word that, in aggregate, forms a familiar phrase; for example, the acronym PASS is used to help people remember how to use a fire extinguisher.
- Mayer (1989) found that supplementing verbal instruction with simple visual aids promotes greater long-term-memory storage and retrieval.

Integrate concepts into prior knowledge. One of the most important points stressed in cognitive theory is the use of prior knowledge. Information is better learned and retained if it can be integrated into existing knowledge and taught in a meaningful way. One way to do this is by using a technique called anchoring—linking new concepts to something familiar to the learner. For instance, when teaching employees how to read a material safety data sheet (MSDS), relate the process to something that is familiar, such as the labels on household cleaning products. MSDSs contain warnings and safety precautions similar to consumer labels, except they provide more extensive information. Connecting training content to learners' prior knowledge and familiar experiences is an effective way to help them learn and make the information more meaningful.

Another method a trainer can use to help workers access prior knowledge is through an *advanced organizer* (Ausubel 1977). The purposes of an organizer are (1) to connect new material to prior knowledge, (2) to remind learners of relevant information they already have, and (3) to direct the learners' attention to what is important in the upcoming material (Schunk 2004, Woolfolk 1990). Usually an advanced organizer is presented at the beginning of the instruction to provide the learner with a mental framework to facilitate encoding information into long-term memory. The following techniques are considered advanced organizers (Gredler 1997):

- Chapter overviews lay out a mental roadmap.
- Course outlines or knowledge maps (also called mind maps) graphically show concepts that will be discussed. (Figure 3 is an example of a knowledge map). To access prior knowledge, the trainer can leave the areas of the knowledge map blank and fill them in by asking participants what they already know about the subject. These maps can also be used to visually summarize information at the end of a training session.
- Analogies are images and concepts that compare new information to what trainees already know (Slavin 2000, 209). When using analogies, use examples that are familiar to the audience.
- Define concepts and terms early. For example, when training on ergonomics, trainers should define the term at the beginning of instruction and relate it to the daily, familiar activities of the workers.
- Pre-tests can be good learning motivators. Asking learners a few quiz questions at the beginning of the training will activate prior knowledge and catch their attention.

Make training interactive. Researchers have found that the more individuals pay attention to and interact with materials in a meaningful way, the more they remember and learn (Slavin 2000, Smith and Ragan 1999). Gaining the attention of learners is a necessary step in helping them enter information into their sensory registers. Active learning focuses on the learner and is more effective than passive teaching methods, such as lecture-only sessions. Active learning is a cognitive teaching method designed to help learners better process, store, and remember information. Learning activities that promote this process have one key ingredient—the learner is actively involved in the training. Activities such as discussions, problem solving, scenarios, quizzes, role playing, drills, hands-on training, case studies, and educational games promote learner participation. Workers generally find active learning more interesting and motivating as long as the activities have a point and are firmly connected to course objectives (Silberman 1995). Active learning makes training more meaningful, promotes deeper

cognitive thinking, and builds on prior knowledge. Silberman found active learning has at least seven characteristics.

1. Active learning concentrates on teaching learners critical items using real-world problems.
2. Active learning includes a balance of cognitive, behavioral, and motivational elements.
3. The active-learning principle influences the design of courses, including in them a variety of learning activities to peak interest and accommodate different learning styles.
4. Active learning provides opportunities for trainees to share their knowledge and experiences.
5. Active learning builds on prior knowledge by reintroducing concepts previously learned.
6. Active learning focuses on helping participants solve their problems.
7. Active learning in technology-based training contains interactive elements, such as quizzes, to promote cognitive processing. Live discussion on a subject, especially during a safety meeting, is a good way to make technology-based training more interactive.

Why Do People Forget Information?

As noted earlier in this section, memory is important for learning, and some information is naturally lost due to inattention. As a result, no one can remember everything. Researchers (Loftus and Loftus 1980, Schunk 2004) found several reasons why people forget:

- time (information decay)
- interference
- memory loss due to biological factors
- lack of motivation and the information not being meaningful to the learner
- the person has trouble accessing information from long-term memory
- the trainer presents too much information at one time—a situation known as information overload
- information is presented in an unorganized manner

Time is a critical factor when it comes to memory because some theorists believe that information can slowly dissipate and be forgotten if not used on a regular basis (Anderson 1990, Elliott et al. 2000). Decay can be lessened through effective presentation of the material and the amount of practice included during and after the training. Conducting interactive training, practice sessions, and refresher training is thus very important in fighting this decay of information.

Interference occurs when material that is being taught is very similar to another subject or gets mixed up with other information (Anderson 1995). New information cannot be stored because it conflicts with prior knowledge. For example, say a person receiving training on a new machine is familiar with the controls on an older machine. The person may experience interference in this situation (or move the controls incorrectly), because the controls, even though they may look familiar, could operate with different outcomes.

Putting Theory into Practice: How to Help People Remember Information

To help learners overcome these memory barriers, researchers (Slavin 2000, Driscoll 2000, Bernstein et al. 2000) suggest trainers use the following strategies:

- Try to connect the material to existing knowledge or something familiar to the learner.
- Integrate the practice of learned knowledge and skills into training sessions. People need to use the information or they may lose it.
- Make sure people understand the fundamentals before teaching them more complex subjects.
- Group similar ideas together or categorize the information. Build on themes and concepts. Chunking information (noted in the short-term memory section) into categories helps clarify thinking and aids memory. Use visual aids, pictures, and charts to organize information for learners.
- On critical safety topics, such as equipment lockout, spill response, and first aid/CPR (cardiopulmonary resuscitation), provide periodic reviews and drills so recall becomes automatic, especially during an emergency.

- When teaching concepts that interfere with each other, point out major differences and provide a checklist or job aid (such as a poster) if necessary.
- Make training interesting. Theorists suggest there is an area of the brain called the limbic system. It monitors incoming information, and when people experience pleasant emotions and feel relaxed during training, the brain is more receptive to retaining the material and transferring it to long-term memory (Lawlor and Handley 1996).

Teaching Higher-Level Problem Solving

So far this section has focused on basic cognitive principles and has provided training strategies for many safety topics. However, some safety topics require a higher level of cognitive thinking—topics such as ergonomic assessments, accident investigation, and emergency response. What is common to these types of classes is that learners need to activate a variety of information stored in their memory networks, to know how to apply it in different situations, and to be able to problem solve. Teaching these types of subjects can be challenging because there may be several possible solutions and ways to address a problem. When teaching more advanced and complex subjects, trainers can use the following strategies that are designed to promote higher-level thinking.

Putting Theory into Practice: Helping Learners Deal with Complex Problems

Knowing how to apply concepts from training to a variety of situations is called transfer learning. Some learners may have difficulty applying information if it is not taught in the context of their job. Transfer-of-learning problems can also be caused by motivational issues, language barriers, and target-audience appropriate training. To promote transfer of learning, researchers (Ormrod 1998, Smith and Ragan 1999, Bernstein et al. 2000) suggest that trainers practice the following:

- Create learning conditions that correspond to the workplace. Use real-life examples, equipment, and situations that trainees will likely encounter in the workplace.

- For learners who speak English as a second language, training may need to be provided in their native language to avoid misunderstandings and transfer-of-learning problems.
- Provide many opportunities for practice and problem solving. Encourage learners to bring up their own scenarios or case studies.
- Use a variety of examples, including challenging situations learners are likely to encounter and show them different ways to solve safety problems.

Teaching Beginner, Intermediate, and Advanced Courses

A worker's day is filled with many situations that call for complex decision making and problem solving. Many safety subjects involve the use of different cognitive skills, ranging from recalling basic facts (for example, what is an MSDS?) to making critical or emergency judgments (for example, rescuing a worker trapped in a confined space). Benjamin Bloom (1956) developed a six-level classification model that can be used to establish the course difficulty level as well as to teach problem-solving skills. His model is designed in hierarchal order, from skill building with knowledge, which is the first level, also called the beginner level, to the highest level, which is the evaluation level (advanced).

Each level of the hierarchy is defined in terms of learner comprehension (Gagne 1988, Cantonwine 1999):

> *Level 1: Basic knowledge.* Learners understand basic principles.
> *Level 2: Comprehension.* Learners understand information and can use it.
> *Level 3: Application.* Learners know how to use information in different situations.
> *Level 4: Analysis.* Learners can break a problem into smaller parts and use the principles to solve that problem.
> *Level 5: Synthesis.* Learners can put together different concepts to solve a problem.
> *Level 6: Evaluation.* Learners can use the principles to evaluate a situation and make the

appropriate decisions. At this level, learners are highly knowledgeable and can usually teach others.

This model has important training implications. Instructors can use the model to design different levels of training (basic to advanced). If training is to help prevent life-threatening injuries, it needs to be designed at a different level than training for basics. The class difficulty level can also affect learner motivation. For example, if most of the participants are highly knowledgeable in a subject area and the trainer makes the course too basic, then the participants will be bored and may not pay attention. Remember that attention is needed to activate short-term (working) memory. On the other hand, if many of the participants are novices and the course is taught at a high level, then the learners may become frustrated and be less motivated to learn. Figure 4 describes teaching strategies trainers can use to help learners actively process information in a way that involves a deeper level of problem-solving skills that can be used in a variety of situations.

Behavioral Theory

Whereas cognitive theory mainly focuses on the internal learning processes of a person, behaviorism studies how external factors influence human behavior and learning. The two behavioral theorists most relevant to safety training are B. F. Skinner and Albert Bandura. Skinner's work focused on understanding how learning and behavior can be influenced by external factors, such as positive reinforcement, and the how the environment can serve as a reinforcer. *Positive reinforcement* occurs when a reward follows a particular behavior, resulting in the increased likelihood of that behavior being repeated (Bernstein et al. 2000). Bandura's work (1986) focused on the influence of *modeling* (learning from observing others) and how it can shape and encourage similar behavior.

Putting Theory into Practice: Behaviorism and Safety Training

Skinner's principles of positive reinforcement (i.e., praise, rewards, and constructive feedback) are especially

LEVELS OF THINKING	COGNITIVE TEACHING STRATEGIES
Beginner Level	
1. Basic knowledge	**Teach fundamental principles.** Ask questions about the information presented.
2. Comprehension	**Test competency** and learners' understanding of the fundamentals before moving to higher levels. Ask them to explain the information in their own words: for example, Describe . . . Explain . . . Show me how . . .
Intermediate Level	
3. Application	**Teach learners how to apply the principles to their job.** Ask learners to explain how the information can be used. Introduce more complex principles.
4. Analysis	**Present basic problems for learners to solve.** At this level, trainers could present different scenarios to help trainees learn how to apply the principles. Introduce potential problems. Use scenarios, what-if exercises, or case studies.
Advanced Level	
5. Synthesis	**Increase the level of complexity** of problems presented in the intermediate level. Learners should be able to trouble shoot as well as make assessments and recommendations. Use more complex scenarios, what-if exercises, or case studies.
6. Evaluation	**Set up complex teaching situations.** At this level, learners should possess a strong grasp of the subject to be able to teach it to others or solve very complex problems. Train-the-trainer courses should be designed at this level. Ask learners to present challenging cases and show how they would solve the problem.

FIGURE 4. Higher-level teaching strategies (Adapted from Cantonwine 1999 and Bullard et al. 1994)

applicable to safety training. Praise, rather than threats, and constructive feedback are powerful reinforcers and motivators for longer-lasting behavior changes. Skinner's work also shows that, to be effective, positive praise (reinforcement) should be gien over different intervals, not just during the day of training (Elliott et al. 2000). When reinforcement is scheduled over periods of time and integrated into day-to-day operations, it has more sustainability. It is not enough to train workers once and hope they will use the principles taught. Rather than waiting until an accident happens to reapply reinforcement, positive reinforcement should continue on an ongoing basis—for example, during job observations, inspections, and safety meetings. Incentive programs and recognition are other examples of positive reinforcement that can be tied to training performance.

Skinner's research also demonstrated how the *environment* can act to either reinforce or hinder behaviors learned in training. In the case of safety, the environment can include the workplace, people, and job design. For example, Maria needs to train her employees on proper lifting techniques, but because heavy boxes are stored on shelves above shoulder level, the company's storage practices (the job design) will most likely promote unsafe lifting practices. To minimize these kinds of environmental barriers, instructors need to consider the impact of the environment on training performance and determine if the problem can be addressed during training or through the company's hazard-correction process. In Maria's case, because the hazard cannot be corrected immediately, she should incorporate interim solutions in her upcoming training and submit a hazard-correction recommendation to the department supervisor.

Bandura's concept of *modeling* is another behavioral technique that can be used to support safe work practices and principles learned during training. To use this method, trainers should model proper techniques during instruction and give participants adequate time to practice the skill themselves. Most importantly, trainers should elicit the help of supervisors and encourage them to consistently model safe work practices in their department during and after training, reminding them that they are in a position of influence and can be powerful role models for safety.

Motivation Theory

At some point during the training process, trainers will ask themselves, how can I motivate workers to want to learn about safety? To answer this question, instructors must first understand what motivation is, and that motivated people can often be recognized by their outward behavior. Researchers have defined motivation as:

- A person's tendency to find learning activities meaningful (Wlodkowski 1999).
- "An internal state that arouses action and keeps us engaged in certain activities" (Elliott et al. 2000, 332).

Motivation is so powerful that it influences how much people remember and the extent to which workers will participate in learning activities. Here lies one of the most challenging issues for trainers; if learners are not motivated, learning cannot occur, and injuries can result. For these reasons motivational strategies must be included in the instructional design process and not be left to chance.

It is important to recognize that motivation exists in everyone in varying degrees. The degree of effort learners will exert is influenced by a variety of *intrinsic* and *extrinsic* factors (Keller 1983).

Intrinsic Motivation

Intrinsic motivation comes from within the person, meaning the student wants to learn because of personal reasons, without external motivational influences such as praise and rewards (Elliott et al. 2000). Among the many factors that can greatly influence intrinsic motivation are the following: people's beliefs, attitudes, self-worth, and feelings about their job and health (Wlodkowski 1999). If, as a trainer, one can affect one or more of these dimensions, half the motivational battle has been won.

People's attitudes and beliefs can greatly influence their level of interest in safety. Some may believe safety is the company's responsibility, while others could believe that they have a role in safety and thus embrace training to avoid injury. To promote personal responsibility, a trainer should actively involve the employees in the training process.

Self-worth is how people feel about themselves and their abilities. When people feel confident, their desire to learn increases. Confidence can be negatively affected if people have experienced learning difficulties in the past or were in situations where they felt incompetent or embarrassed. One way trainers can promote self-worth is to help learners feel emotionally safe as well as confident in learning activities (e.g., create an environment where the participants are not worried about being embarrassed in front of a group).

The last intrinsic motivational factor of importance is how learners feel about their job and personal health. When people like their job (and supervisor) and they feel respected, their motivation to learn can be high. Furthermore, if well-being is a priority for learners, they will be receptive to injury-prevention information. Because intrinsic motivation factors vary from person to person, it is important for trainers to understand learners' motives. Even though these factors are primarily controlled by each individual, instructors can learn how to use extrinsic methods (those outside of the individual) to enhance intrinsic motivation.

Extrinsic Motivation

Whereas intrinsic motivation comes from within, extrinsic motivation comes from sources outside the individual. External factors that can enhance training motivation include the following (Wlodkowski 1999, ASTD 1997, Pike 1994):

- feedback and praise
- meaningful learning activities
- a comfortable learning environment
- free refreshments
- recognition and awards

An instructor can act as an external motivator and increase someone's desire to learn. Most people can recall an energetic teacher who sparked their curiosity for learning. Trainers can inspire by showing enthusiasm and creating pleasurable learning experiences.

Putting Theory into Practice: Motivation and Learning

The specific types of motivational strategies instructors should use will depend on both the characteristics and needs of the target audience. Therefore, it is important for trainers to know their audience and to identify and address potential motivational barriers.

Assessing Motivational Problems

Driscoll (2000) recommends that instructors take time before training to think about potential motivational problems. According to Keller (1987), motivational problems can be generated by the learner, the instructor, or the method of instruction. Trainers can identify and implement strategies to solve motivational problems using the ARCS model developed by Keller. The initials for this acronym stand for four conditions that must exist for learners to be motivated:

1. **A**ttention
2. **R**elevance
3. **C**onfidence (self-worth)
4. **S**atisfaction

ATTENTION

As discussed earlier in the cognitive section, the learner must pay attention in order for learning and mental processing to occur. In the ARCS model, attention refers to strategies trainers can use to gain the learners' interest and keep them motivated. Some trainers use an attention-gaining activity only at the beginning of instruction and then later notice a decline in learner interest and motivation. The important point to consider is that in order to sustain attention, varied strategies must be deployed throughout the training. In other words, trainers should vary the way the information is presented by changing the tone of voice, method of instruction, and learning activities (Smith and Ragan 1999). Other ways to sustain attention is to incorporate different modes of learning in a session, such as using interesting stories, visual aids, scenarios, discussions, and problem-solving activities that capitalize on students' interest.

RELEVANCE

Relevance strategies help learners see that what they are learning is meaningful and useful. This is often referred to as customized training. People are motivated when they feel training applies to their lives and their jobs, or that training can help them achieve a goal. If learners feel the training is a waste of time, they will not be motivated to learn. Researchers (McCown, Driscoll, and Roop 1996; Smith and Ragan 1999) suggest that trainers use the following techniques to establish relevance:

- Inform participants at the beginning of instruction how the information is useful and applies to them (e.g., state the course objectives).
- Give experienced workers an opportunity to be a co-trainer and share their knowledge with others.
- Use real examples, equipment, and challenges workers encounter in their job.
- If employees learn better in their native language, use a translator and provide materials in their language.
- Give employees a choice in the methods of instruction that matches their learning style; some may prefer Web-based learning, while others may like hands-on classroom training.
- Provide interesting, easy-to-read training materials that include color and familiar graphics.

CONFIDENCE

Confidence builds self-worth, and learners are motivated when they believe they can be successful or achieve a goal. Trainers can help build confidence in several ways (Gagne 1988):

- Provide learning opportunities where participants can experience success.
- Make sure the course difficulty level matches the students' abilities. Add challenging (not overwhelming) situations as trainees master basic concepts.
- Provide helpful feedback both during and after training and point out ways the trainees can further excel.

SATISFACTION

The last element required for motivation is learner satisfaction—meeting the learner's expectations. When people attend training, they usually have varied expectations. However, there are some needs participants have in common, which are to learn useful information, to have a pleasurable learning experience, and to have a comfortable learning environment. The following are examples of satisfaction strategies (ASTD 1997, Gagne 1988):

- Ask learners at the beginning of the course what they want to get out of the class.
- Survey employees to find out the best times to hold training. For example, having a class on a Friday at 3 P.M. may be demotivating to many employees because it is the end of the work week. Class length is also a motivating factor—find out the participants' preferred class length. Attending a class for a few hours versus all day can impact a person's satisfaction level.
- Inform learners when expected goals are achieved, such as providing answers to quizzes so learners can evaluate their performance; giving prizes or verbal praises for correct responses; or providing certificates of achievement for course completion.

Using the ARCS Model

John plans on conducting a one-hour refresher class on MSDS to teach employees about hazardous chemicals. Normally, he would only show a video and the employees would fall asleep. Figure 5 contains a list of strategies John can use to sustain employee motivation and attention throughout the session using the ARCS model.

Motivation Summary

To answer the question posed at the beginning of the chapter (How can I motivate workers to want to learn about safety?), instructors must first learn who their students are and understand what factors inspire or demotivate them. Because there is no definitive answer, Keller designed the ARCS model to help trainers iden-

tify barriers that could negatively affect both intrinsic and extrinsic motivation. Strategies to address many motivational problems can be developed by answering the following ARCS questions before teaching or developing any safety-training class.

What strategies will I use to:

1. Gain students' attention and maintain it throughout the session?
2. Make training relevant to the learners?
3. Build learner confidence?
4. Ensure learner satisfaction and promote positive feelings about learners' successes?

Although the model does not cover all possible factors, it can help trainers reduce a number of potential barriers so employees are motivated to learn about safety.

ACTIVITY LENGTH	MOTIVATIONAL STRATEGIES
20 minutes	• First, explain how the training will help them prevent injuries. Also, ask employees if they encountered any challenges in reading an MSDS. Address their challenges during the lecture. These are examples of **relevance** and **satisfaction**.
	• To gain their **attention**, begin the session with a mock chemical accident that requires learners to find information using an actual MSDS, and then discuss their findings.
20 minutes	• Next, to make the training **relevant**, use real-life props, such as chemical containers and personal protective equipment, to lecture on how to read an MSDS of a commonly used chemical.
	• If possible, ask a knowledgeable employee to help give the lecture to build **confidence**.
15 minutes	• Then summarize what was learned by giving a group quiz where the participants use a different MSDS and work together to find the answers. This will also give employees additional practice on how to read an MSDS and help build confidence.
5 minutes	• Provide the answers to the quiz so employees can evaluate their performance. Give verbal praise for satisfactory performance on the quiz and for class participation. This is an example of a **satisfaction** strategy.

FIGURE 5. Motivational strategies

DEVELOPING TRAINING PROGRAMS

The goal of the first section was to provide insight on several learner-centered theories that affect learning: cognition, behavior, and motivation. Section two will focus on the actual training development process, which includes performance assessment, training assessment, audience analysis, learning styles, and setting goals and objectives. Each step builds upon theoretical principles discussed in section one and helps trainers gain a deeper understanding of learners' characteristics and needs.

The development process normally begins with an assessment. There are two types of assessments trainers need to become familiar with—a performance assessment and a training needs assessment. A *performance assessment* is designed to help trainers determine if training is needed to solve problems related to unsafe work practices and accidents. The information is used to improve workers' safety performance or prevent an accident from reoccurring. Conversely, a *training assessment* is used for curriculum development to determine which subjects should be taught. Each assessment produces different results, yet both are equally valuable in the development process.

Performance Assessment: Is Training the Solution?

When an unsafe work practice or accident is discovered, a common reaction is to immediately provide more training. This is like a doctor treating a patient without knowing the patient's symptoms. Before spending valuable time and money on training, managers and other decision makers, with help from the trainer, need to stop and assess the situation. *Finding out the cause of the problem should be the first course of action.* Assessing a performance problem is similar to investigating an accident. Both require problem-solving skills, identification of the root cause, and recommendation of corrective action.

Executing a Performance Assessment

According to Mager and Pipe (1997), trainers should first ask "Did the incident occur because of a knowledge or skill deficiency?" and "Are there other factors that might be involved?" Other reasons could be related to motivation, lack of supervision, and job or equipment design. The problem could be the result of one or several of these factors. When a safety-performance problem occurs, the first step is to investigate its nature to determine if lack of knowledge was the cause or a contributing factor. To accomplish this investigation, interview supervisors and employees involved in the situation. If the incident was documented, review the report. During the interview, ask open-ended questions (described below) to promote two-way dialog, as opposed to questions that only require a yes-or-no response (Leshin, Pollock, and Reigeluth 1992).

Interview questions for supervisors. What type of feedback or coaching has the employee received and how often? How often does the problem occur? What task was the person trying to complete when the unsafe act occurred? What are the consequences of not solving the problem?

Interview questions for workers. Why was the job performed that way? Can you demonstrate how to . . . ? Can you describe how to . . . ? Why do people . . . (state the unsafe act)?

After collecting the facts, determine if training alone can solve the problem. If other problems are discovered or more information is needed, continue collecting information by observing employees and interviewing other workers if necessary (Gupta 1999).

Determining Solutions

Once the causes are identified, develop possible solutions that may or may not include training. When considering solutions, think about feasibility, cost factors, and the impact the solutions may have on other areas. Solutions to some common performance problems are described in Figure 6.

Training Needs Assessment

Determining What Should Be Taught

Whether a performance assessment calls for training that can solve the problem or is needed to fulfill

PERFORMANCE PROBLEMS	POSSIBLE SOLUTIONS
1. Lack of knowledge or a training design problem The worker does not know the information or forgets critical information when explaining safety procedures, such as how to lock out a machine.	• Provide training if there is a knowledge deficiency. • If someone cannot remember critical safety procedures that involve multiple steps, place job aids or posters in the work area. • Trainers may also need to look at the way training information is organized or use visual aids or other techniques that do not rely on memory.
2. Lack of motivation Workers feel training information is not practical and are not motivated to use it. Workers disregard company safety policies. The person feels safety is not his or her responsibility and wants to take short cuts.	• Ask employees to suggest ways training can be improved. • To make training relevant, complete an audience analysis. • In cases where policies are disregarded, ask the supervisor to conduct job-performance counseling. Make sure safety policies and enforcement standards are in writing and are clearly communicated to employees.
3. Lack of reinforcement Workers feel they are too busy and often forget to follow the safety procedures.	• Talk to the supervisor to see if there is work overload or a scheduling problem. • Ask supervisors to reinforce procedures on a daily basis.
4. Lack of leadership The organization or supervisor places greater emphasis on productivity, and safety is not a high priority.	• Safety should be addressed on a senior-management level. Accountability and responsibility standards should be developed and tied to performance evaluations for supervisors and employees. Incentive programs could be considered.
5. The way a job or equipment is designed Because the way a job is designed, an employee may bypass safety procedures to complete the task.	• Observe the job to see if something in the job process or the equipment is causing employees to work unsafely. For example, workers may bypass safety instructions to reduce defects, to achieve production quota, or to complete a deadline. • Talk openly with supervisors and employees to see what needs to be changed to make the job safer, or to make the environment more supportive of safe choices.
6. Language and cultural barriers Workers may perform an unsafe act because of cultural belief. Language barriers are discovered.	• Address cultural beliefs by explaining why safety procedures must be followed and the consequences if they are not. Supervisors may need to consider enforcement and feedback practices. • To overcome language barriers, provide training in languages that are understandable to employees. Check the accuracy of information being delivered by translators.

FIGURE 6. Solutions to performance problems (*Source:* Mager and Pipe 1997, Geller 1996)

regulatory requirements, instructors should complete a training assessment. According to Smith and Ragan (1999), an assessment can help trainers in any of the following ways:

- Identify the knowledge and skills that learners need to perform their job safely.
- Determine what subjects should be taught and aid in selecting appropriate learning activities.
- Find out what participants already know about the subject.
- Learn what to avoid.
- Plan reinforcement strategies to promote transfer of learning.
- Assess how much practice and training time is needed.

- Establish the level of difficulty for a course.

Once information is collected, it is accepted practice to use the results to develop companywide training programs, orientations, and single courses.

Executing a Training Assessment

Identifying potential hazards and reviewing past injuries are the most important elements of this particular assessment. The time needed to complete this process depends on the nature of the job and the types of hazards involved. A training needs assessment consists of three basic steps (Gupta 1999):

Step 1: Define the purpose of the assessment.
Step 2: Get prepared.

Step 3: Gather data and determine which subjects will be taught.

DEFINING THE PURPOSE

Having a purpose will make the process more efficient and help trainers determine what type of information is needed. For example, the purpose of the assessment is to design a safety-orientation training program, or to tailor a safety-training program for office employees.

GETTING PREPARED

The next step is to prepare a list of areas to review; this step will guide the data-collection process. Valuable information in developing training programs includes the following:

- specific knowledge and skills workers need to prevent injuries (obtain from job descriptions and supervisors)
- potential hazards of the job and the work environment
- types of personal protective equipment used or needed
- injuries related to the department
- OSHA-required topics and training frequency
- special department information, such as hours of operation, number of shifts, preferred training length, and days and times
- budget and record-keeping considerations
- existing safety documentation, such as accident reports, OSHA log of work-related injuries and illnesses, and current safety policies and training programs

GATHERING DATA AND DETERMINING THE SUBJECTS TO BE TAUGHT

Gathering data can involve several methods, such as interviews (with supervisors), job observations (if logistically possible), and safety documentation review. In cases where companies have different geographic locations, trainers may need to rely on telephone interviews in lieu of face-to-face discussions. One of the most useful documents for assessing training needs is a job safety analysis (JSA). This traditional tool is used to identify job hazards to help practitioners develop company safety policies. The methodology used to conduct a JSA is applicable to instructional design. Often, department supervisors and human resource managers can help trainers complete this task. To complete an assessment, use the following steps (National Safety Council 2009). An assessment worksheet can be found in Appendix A.

1. Identify potential job hazards using interviews, job observations, and information from safety documents.
2. Use the information in step 1 to identify the knowledge and skills needed.
3. Once the knowledge, skills, and hazards are known, the trainer can then identify the required safety-training topics for a particular department or job.

Figure 7 shows an example of a training needs assessment completed for Maria's office administration department, an assessment she can use to set up a training program.

LIST POTENTIAL HAZARDS

Identify potential hazards or possible accidents that could occur.

Office Example:

1. Back injuries from lifting supplies
2. Repetitive-motion injuries using computers
3. Trips and falls
4. Workplace emergencies

IDENTIFY THE KNOWLEDGE AND SKILLS NEEDED

Using the information in the first column, decide what knowledge and skills are needed to prevent injuries and also to fulfill OSHA training requirements.

Office Example:

1. How to lift objects and use lifting equipment
2. How to prevent repetitive-motion injuries
3. General office safety
4. What to do in emergency situations

LIST THE TRAINING TOPICS

Using the information in the second column, list the recommended safety-training topics.

Office Example:

1. Back-injury prevention and how to use lifting equipment
2. Office ergonomics
3. General office safety
4. Emergency action plan

FIGURE 7. Training assessment for office employees (Adapted from National Safety Council 2009)

Audience Analysis

An audience analysis is performed after the completion of a training assessment to specifically gather detailed information about learners; this process helps customize training according to the characteristics of learners. Skipping this step can result in wasted time and money; it can also lead to ineffective instruction, which can demotivate learners and create negative perceptions about future training sessions. Ultimately, the analysis can mean the difference between a poorly designed program and an effective one. Its importance cannot be overemphasized.

When completing an audience analysis, sensitive information should be kept confidential and used only by the trainer for course-development purposes. An audience description can vary in length from a few paragraphs to several pages, depending on how much detail the trainer needs. Information can be compiled in a number of ways (Gupta 1999, Mager 1988):

- Interview a representative sample of the audience in person or by telephone. This technique will also increase learner motivation because people feel valued when their opinions are considered and when they are shown a level of caring. Let people know how the information will be used and why it is needed.
- Observe the audience performing the job related to the subject.
- For a day, walk in their shoes. Shadow a person for a few hours to observe how to make the training relevant—when shadowing, follow the company's safety policies to avoid injury.
- Interview people who work with the target audience. Human Resources can be very helpful in providing audience information.
- Review past training evaluations and job descriptions.

Most importantly, when analyzing culturally and linguistically diverse audiences, avoid stereotyping—remember that no group is homogenous. Even though ethnic groups may share common experiences, there are differences within each ethnic group. Talk to different people within a cultural group to get broader viewpoints.

There are certain learner characteristics (e.g., learning styles and education level) that are important to know when developing programs. The information gathered will help the instructor develop course content that motivates participants. Trainers should spend a good portion of their development time on this step. The following five categories represent the critical characteristics to consider when assessing an audience: background information, general characteristics, education/prior knowledge, attitudes/interests, and preferred learning methods (Smith and Ragan 1999, Mager 1988). See Figure 8 for examples of important information that can be gathered for each category.

Depending on the subject that needs to be taught, certain information may be more critical. For example, physical characteristics such as height can be significant when training on proper lifting techniques because body dimensions are an integral part of the subject matter. Likewise, in chemical training, knowing the education range is valuable because the trainer may need to alter the vocabulary level accordingly.

IMPORTANCE OF LEARNING STYLES

Of the five characteristics just described, learning styles is being highlighted because it directly correlates to motivation and information processing. When learning activities are congruent with people's learning style, they are better able to cognitively process information and retain it in long-term memory (Sarasin 1999).

Everyone has a preference in how information is presented to him or her. Researchers (James and Galbraith 1985, Sarasin 1999) found that people learn best through one of the senses or a combination of senses. Some people process information *visually* (e.g., videos), others process it through *auditory means* (e.g., discussions), and still others process information *kinesthetically* (e.g., hands-on activities). Some researchers (Kolb 1981; Harb, Durrant, and Terry 1993) categorize learning styles by other modalities: concrete, reflective, abstract, or active. A *concrete learner* likes to learn through feelings and prefers activities that include other people. They also need concrete, real-life examples—as opposed to abstract concepts—to better understand things. *Reflective learners* like to learn by observing others, and they need time to ponder information. *Abstract*

CATEGORIES	EXAMPLES OF IMPORTANT INFORMATION
1. Background information	• Number of trainees • Tools and equipment used by the audience • Safety, operations, or supervisory barriers that might prevent the audience from successfully using the information on the job • Learning or physical disabilities that can impact training • Any injury information related to the audience • Think about ways the audience is similar and different
2. General characteristics	• Physical characteristics and cultural beliefs relating to safety and the subject matter • Age ranges • Job experience • Languages and dialects spoken
3. Education and prior knowledge	• Education levels, prior training experience, knowledge, and literacy levels
4. Attitudes and interests	• Attitude toward safety • Motivation to learn • Likes and dislikes about training • Hobbies and outside interests
5. Preferred learning styles	• Demonstrations, discussions, videos, scenarios, lectures, role playing, etc.

FIGURE 8. Target audience characteristics (*Source:* Smith and Ragan 1999)

learners, who are usually analytical thinkers, like information presented in a logical and organized manner. *Active learners* prefer action-oriented activities; they, like kinesthetic learners, learn through action.

What is important to know is that no one learning style is better than another. Both theories depict diverse ways people process and understand information.

Training an audience using the trainer's preferred learning style or only one learning style are common mistakes trainers make. Focusing on one learning style, for example, is a reason participants may become bored or demotivated during training—this approach lacks variety and relevance. As discussed earlier in the motivational theory section, variety and relevance are two required conditions in the ARCS model to gain attention and stimulate motivation. Because audiences have diverse learning styles, trainers should survey or interview employees not only to identify and incorporate different learning activities into the training, but also to ensure that each trainee's needs are met. Figure 9 provides a graphic overview of both learning theories to help trainers choose appropriate learning activities (Lawson 1997, Cantonwine 1999).

ADULT LEARNING STYLES	APPROPRIATE LEARNING ACTIVITIES
Visual Learners • Learn best by seeing the information	Diagrams, pictures, videos, handouts, charts, colorful visual aids
Auditory Learners • Learn best by hearing the information	Videos, lectures, discussions
Kinesthetic and Active Learners • Learn best through active participation	Demonstrations, role play, simulations, games, discussions
Reflective Learners • Like to assess their own knowledge and skills	Quizzes, tests, self-assessment exercises, what-if scenarios
Concrete Learners • Learn best by observing and when activities simulate their job	Real-life examples, scenarios, role play, simulations, use of actual job props when possible
Abstract Learners • Learn best when information is organized and requires mental processing	What-if scenarios, charts, statistical information, facts, problem-solving exercises

FIGURE 9. Learning styles and activities
(Adapted from Lawson 1997 and Cantonwine 1999)

Putting Theory into Practice:
An Audience Analysis

The following example uses the audience-analysis principles described in this section to show how they would apply to a training situation at John's manufacturing company. It also includes a wide range of challenges that trainers may encounter, along with recommended training solutions. It is important to note that in this real-world example, the company employs minors (under the age of eighteen) during the summer. Every state has child labor laws that prohibit the use of dangerous equipment and machinery (U.S. Department of Labor 2006, NIOSH 2003, OSHA 2006). Trainers should become familiar with the child labor laws when minors are involved.

DESCRIPTION OF MANUFACTURING AUDIENCE CHARACTERISTICS

Course Title: Back-Injury–Prevention Training

Course Background Information
- Conduct a lifting training program for 50 employees in the Receiving Department.
- There are two shifts: 9 A.M.–5 P.M. and 5 P.M.–1 A.M.
- This is an initial training class for the audience.
- Manual lifting represents approximately 50% of the job (this information can be obtained from the job description or the supervisor).

- The audience also uses lifting devices such as dollies and carts.
- Back injury rates are low.
- Training is mandatory for all employees of the company.

General Characteristics of the Target Audience
- The audience is 90% male and 10% female.
- The audience age ranges from 15 to 40 (obtain from Human Resources).
- There is one worker who is hearing impaired but can read lips.
- Heights range from five to six feet.
- Lifting strength varies by person and gender.
- The languages needed for training are: English, Chinese, Spanish, and Tagalog; bilingual supervisors can assist in translation.

Education and Prior Knowledge
- Most of the audience completed high school and some completed community college.
- Even though this is a new training course, all participants have lifted objects in prior jobs or in their personal lives.
- Some are new employees while others have worked for fifteen years.
- Minors are employed during the summer (child labor laws apply).

Attitudes and Interests
- Attitudes toward using the correct techniques is fair because some feel they are strong enough

COMMON CHARACTERISTICS	TRAINING STRATEGIES TO USE
• Employees lift the same types of objects and use the same material-handling equipment.	• Use actual objects or equipment that employees use to establish relevance. Discuss the importance of using the material-handling equipment.
• All have some type of lifting experience. Employees either lift at home or work (prior knowledge).	• Ask the audience to share their prior lifting experience and have them discuss their lifting challenges at home and work.
• Everyone is from the same department.	• Use lifting examples that pertain to the department.
• Outside interests are similar in that they relate to physical activity.	• Discuss how the information benefits their personal activities, such as sports and fitness.
• Learning methods are similar; the audience likes active and visual learning activities.	• Use demonstrations with video feedback to provoke discussion on current techniques and props.
• Everyone has to complete the course.	• Bring refreshments.
	• Use relevant examples and ask knowledgeable workers to share their expertise with others; this process helps create a pleasurable learning experience.

FIGURE 10. Common audience characteristics and possible training strategies

to lift heavy objects rather than ask for help or use the carts—some feel asking for help is a sign of weaknesses.

- General audience interests include physical fitness, sports, and music.
- Supervisors have a positive attitude toward providing feedback after the training.

Preferred Learning Styles

- The audience prefers visual aids and active learning, that is, demonstrations and video with some discussion.

STEP 1: ANALYZE INFORMATION—LOOK FOR COMMON TRENDS

Once the audience description is completed, look for common audience characteristics to help make the training relevant to the participants (Smith and Ragan 1999, Jonassen and Grabowski 1993). Once the common characteristics are identified, list training strategies for each one using cognitive, behavioral, and motivational principles described in section one. Figure 10 describes the common characteristics and training strategies for John's audience analysis.

STEP 2: IDENTIFY AND ADDRESS POTENTIAL BARRIERS

It is not enough to simply identify commonalities; attention also needs to be given to addressing and finding solutions for potential barriers or unique challenges that can negatively affect motivation and learning. Figure 11 highlights potential training challenges for John and describes solutions that could be used to overcome each barrier.

STEP 3: HOW TO USE THE INFORMATION

Once the audience analysis is completed, the trainer should have enough knowledge about the participants to customize the training and make it relevant. Next, the trainer's job turns to developing goals and objectives before conducting the training.

Goals and Learning Objectives

Goals and objectives are developed after the needs assessment and audience analysis. In these two steps trainers will have determined what subjects should be taught, and what knowledge and skills trainees need in order to work safely. Next, through the writing of

BARRIERS OR CHALLENGES	SOLUTIONS TO BARRIERS AND CHALLENGES
• There are two work shifts.	• Conduct a class for each shift.
• The gender make-up of employees is mixed.	• Let the participants know that, regardless of gender, everyone needs to use proper lifting techniques.
• There is a gender and cultural stigma associated with asking for help or using a cart (actions perceived as signs of weakness).	• Discuss the perceived sign of weakness in an employee asking for help. Reinforce the company's policy on lifting. Use real-life cases of how back injuries have affected people's lives.
• The height of participants may affect lifting techniques.	• During demonstration exercises, use examples for taller and shorter people.
• One person is hearing impaired.	• Find out how the hearing-impaired person learns best. He or she can tell you about the special needs involved.
• Four training languages are needed.	• For multilingual training needs, find out how many workers need to have the class in their native language. Use bilingual supervisors or trainers.
• The length of employment varies from new to fifteen years.	• To address employment variations, include a review of basic principles for new employees and add demonstrations and problem-solving scenarios for more experienced workers.
• Minors sometimes work in the department.	• Review the state's child labor laws for prohibited equipment. During the training, reiterate to minors that they are not allowed to use forklifts or other prohibited equipment.

FIGURE 11. Training barriers and solutions at the manufacturing company

goals and objectives, trainers will learn how to describe the capacity of the trainees after training. *Goals* describe the overall intent of a course. They are broad statements describing the overall scope of the training and are generally not measurable (Mager 1988). For example, the goal of a workshop may be to teach supervisors how to conduct workstation evaluations for computer users. Notice that this statement does not describe how the trainer will accomplish the goal, nor does it describe the specific skills trainees will acquire. When developing goals, trainers should ask, what is the purpose of the course? Overall, what do I want learners to achieve? Once the goals are developed, the next step is to write the objectives, which are the key actions that are necessary to achieve the goals.

An objective is different from a goal. *Objectives* are statements that specifically describe what trainees will be able to do after training, the learning conditions under which they will be able to perform, and how learners will demonstrate competency (Dowling and McKinnon 2002). Objectives should not refer to the trainer. For example, an objective for an office ergonomics course reads as follows: provided with the tools and furniture, the trainee will be able to correctly set up computer workstations using the neutral-posture guidelines. Another distinct difference between a goal and an objective is that the latter, unlike the former, must be measurable, observable, and attainable (Lawson 1997). The office ergonomics example meets all three criteria. A trainer can see if a workstation is set up correctly (observable), and measure if a worker is sitting in neutral postures by using the ergonomics guidelines (measurable). And because all the necessary training tools would be provided to the learner, the objective is considered attainable. Courses can have more than one goal and usually have many objec-

tives; the number will depend on what a trainer wants learners to achieve—notice the number of objectives listed at the beginning of this chapter.

HOW OBJECTIVES ARE USED BY TRAINERS

Learning objectives are used for several purposes (Leshin, Pollock, and Reigeluth 1992):

1. To guide the instructor on what content, learning activities, and test items to include in the training. The information can serve as a reminder of items to include in a lesson plan.
2. To assess learners' knowledge and skills during and after instruction.
3. To help trainers plan how students will demonstrate competency.
4. To communicate to trainees what they will learn and the performance expectations.

The familiar phrase most frequently used to communicate course objectives is, "after the training, you will be able to . . . (*list what the trainees will be able to do—use action verbs*)." Objectives are also stated at the beginning of training sessions to initiate cognitive processing and stimulate learner motivation. By doing this, the audience will know what will be covered and what to expect.

WRITING OBJECTIVES

Keep in mind that objectives describe the trainee, not the instructor or course content. An effective objective has three components: condition(s), skill, and performance standard. A helpful way to remember the three components is through the acronym CSP. The following is an example of a learning objective that is typically worded in the order of that acronym (Mager 1988):

KNOWLEDGE, SKILLS, AND ATTITUDES NEEDED	CONDITIONS OR TOOLS TRAINEES NEED	SKILLS	PERFORMANCE STANDARDS
Knowledge needed:	• Ergonomics policy	Trainees will be able to	According to the neutral-posture guidelines
• Ergonomics principles	• Ergonomics principles	set up a workstation	
• How to evaluate a workstation	• \Workstation		
	• Neutral-posture checklist		

FIGURE 12. Developing learning objectives (*Source:* Mager 1988)

Condition: Given the ergonomics policy, a discussion on ergonomics principles, an actual computer workstation, and the neutral-posture checklist. . . .

Skill (action verb): The supervisors will be able to correctly set up workstations that promote neutral postures.

Performance Standards: The employee must be able to sit in neutral positions according to guidelines.

An easy way to write an objective is to break it down into four categories as shown in the ergonomics example (Figure 12). A goals-and-objectives worksheet is included in Appendix B.

Begin by writing down each knowledge, skill, or attitude trainees would need in order to work safely (column 1). Next, for each knowledge, skill, or attitude listed, describe the learning *conditions* (such as the tools, materials, activities, or equipment) that will be used to help learners achieve the desired performance (column 2). The condition part of an objective is typically worded as, given . . . (*then describe the learning conditions*)—for example, given the ergonomics policy, an actual computer workstation, and the neutral-posture checklist.

The third step describes the *skill* (column 3), which is the desired knowledge or abilities learners should possess after the training. An action verb is used to describe the skill. Some of the most common verbs used to describe safety skills are listed in Figure 13. For example, the supervisors will be able to correctly set up (*action verb*) the workstation.

Finally, *performance standards* (column 4) describe the acceptable levels of performance (meaning, when someone is determined to be proficient) and how competency will be measured. Standards can be stated in terms of speed, accuracy, quantity, quality, time, and frequency (Lawson 1997). After completing the work-sheet, there should be one objective for each skill, knowledge, or attitude listed.

TESTING OBJECTIVES

Finally, to determine if an objective is effectively written, Mager (1988) suggests that trainers ask the following questions:

1. Does it say what the worker will be able to do after the training?
2. Does it describe testing conditions or real-world situations under which the desired performance would be achieved?
3. Does it explain how to recognize satisfactory performance?

It is important to remember that goals represent the overall desired result for a course and are stated in general terms; objectives, on the other hand, focus specifically on the learners' performance. Both goals and objectives are considered important elements in the training development process.

CONCLUSION

The focus of this chapter has been on learners: who they are, how they learn, and what motivates them. The goal of the first section was to stress the importance of learning theories and how they are the basis for instruction. In the second section, the emphasis was geared toward providing practical tools and strategies trainers could use to develop training programs. Although the principles in each section are different, the intent was to show that one cannot exist without the other. Throughout this chapter the stories of Maria and John were used to show the diverse worlds of safety training and how to apply the principles to real-life situations. And finally (as stated at the beginning of the chapter), if you know your audience, you will know what learners need and how to provide effective training to them, regardless of the work environment.

Analyze	Discuss	Practice
Approve	Instruct	List
Demonstrate	Conduct	Select
Describe	Investigate	Set up
Determine	Recommend	Solve

FIGURE 13. Common Verbs for Learning Objectives
(*Source:* Cantonwine 1999)

REFERENCES

American National Standards Institute (ANSI). Z490.1-2009. *Criteria for Accepted Practices in Safety, Health, and Environmental Training*. Des Plaines, IL: American Society of Safety Engineers.

American Society for Training and Development (ASTD). 1997. *How to Motivate Employees*. Info-line series. Alexandria, VA: ASTD.

Anderson, J. R. 1990. *Cognitive Psychology and Its Implications*. New York: W. H. Freeman.

———. 1995. *Learning and Memory: An Integrated Approach*. New York: Wiley.

Atkinson, R. C., and R. M. Shiffrin. 1968. "Human Memory: A Proposed System and Its Control Processes." In K. Spence and J. Spence, eds., *The Psychology of Learning and Motivation*, vol. 2. New York: Academic Press.

Ausubel, D. P. 1977. "The Facilitation of Meaningful Verbal Learning in the Classroom." *Educational Psychologist* 12:162–178.

Bandura, A. 1986. *Social Foundations of Thought and Action: A Social-Cognitive Theory*. Englewood, NJ: Prentice Hall.

Bernstein, D. A., A. Clarke-Stewart, L. A. Penner, E. J. Roy, and C. D. Wickens. 2000. *Psychology*. Boston: Houghton Mifflin Company.

Bloom, B. S., M. B. Englehart, E. J. Furst, W. H. Hill, and O. R. Krathwohl. 1956. *Taxonomy of Educational Objectives: The Classification of Educational Goals. Handbook 1: The Cognitive Domain*. New York: Longman.

Bonner, J. 1988. "Implications of Cognitive Theory for Instructional Design: Revisited." *Educational Communication and Technology Journal* 36:3–14.

Bullard, R., M. J. Brewer, N. Gaubas, A. Gibson, K. Hyland, and E. Sample. 1994. *The Occasional Trainer's Handbook*. Englewood Cliffs, NJ: Educational Technology Publications.

Cantonwine, S. C. 1999. Safety *Training that Delivers: How to Design and Present Better Technical Training*. Des Plaines, IL: American Society of Safety Engineers.

Di Vista, F. J., and L. P. Rieber. 1987. "Characteristics of Cognitive Engineering: The Next Generation of Instructional Systems." *Educational Communications and Technology Journal* 35:213–230.

Dowling, N. L., and S. H. McKinnon. 2002. "Instructional Objectives: Improving the Success of Safety Training." *Professional Safety*, Journal of the American Society of Safety Engineers (47)9:41–44.

Driscoll, M. P. 2000. *Psychology of Learning for Instruction*. Needham Heights, MA: Allyn and Bacon.

Elliott, S., T. Kratochwill, J. Littlefield, and J. F. Travers. 2000. *Educational Psychology*. Boston: McGraw-Hill.

Gagne, E. D., C. W. Yekovich, and F. R. Yekovich. 1993. *The Cognitive Psychology School of Learning*. New York: Harper Collins.

Gagne, R. M. 1988. *Essentials of Learning Instruction*. Englewood Cliffs, NJ: Prentice Hall.

Geller, E. S. 1996. *The Psychology of Safety: How to Improve Behaviors and Attitudes on the Job*. Radnor, PA: Chilton Book Company.

Gredler, M. E. 1997. *Learning and Instruction: Theory into Practice*. Upper Saddle River, NJ: Merrill.

Gupta, K. 1999. *A Practical Guide to Needs Assessment*. San Francisco: Jossey-Bass Pfeiffer.

Harb, J. N., S. O. Durrant, and R. E. Terry. 1993. "Use of Kolb Learning Cycle and the 4MAT System in Engineering Education." *Journal of Engineering Education* (April) 82(2):70–77.

James, W. B., and M. W. Galbraith. 1985. "Perceptual Learning Styles, Implications and Techniques for the Practitioner." *Lifelong Learning* (January), pp. 20–23.

Jonassen, D. H., and B. L. Grabowski. 1993. *Handbook of Individual Differences*. Hillsdale, NJ: Erlbaum.

Keller, J. M. 1983. "Motivational Design of Instruction" in C. M. Reigeluth, ed., *Instructional-Design Theories and Models*, pp. 383–434. Hillsdale, NJ: Erlbaum.

———. 1987. "Development and Use of the ARCS Model of Motivational Design." *Journal of Instructional Development* 10(3):2–11.

Knowles, M. 1988. *The Modern Practice of Adult Education: From Pedagogy to Andragogy*. Revised and updated. Englewood Cliffs NJ: Cambridge Books.

Kolb, D. 1981. *Learning Style Inventory*. Boston: McBer and Company.

Labor Occupational Health Program (LOHP). 2005. University of California, Berkeley. *Facts for Employers: Safer Jobs for Teens* (retrieved June 12, 2006). www.lohp.org

Lawlor, M., and P. Handley. 1996. *The Creative Trainer: Holistic Facilitation Skills for Accelerated Learning*. Berkshire: McGraw-Hill.

Lawson, K. 1997. *Improving On-the-Job Training and Coaching*. Alexandria, VA: American Society of Training and Development.

Leshin, C. B., J. Pollock, and C. M. Reigeluth. 1992. *Instructional Design Strategies and Tactics*. Englewood Cliffs, NJ: Educational Technology Publications.

Loftus, E. F., and G. R. Loftus. 1980. "On the Permanence of Stored Information in the Human Brain." *American Psychologist* 35:409–420.

Low, W. C. 1981. "Changes in Instructional Development: The Aftermath of an Information Process Takeover in Psychology." *Journal of Instructional Development* 4:10–18.

Mager, R. F. 1988. *Making Instruction Work*. Belmont, CA: Lake Publishing Company.

Mager R. F., and P. Pipe. 1997. *Analyzing Performance Problems*. Atlanta: CEP Press.

Maslow, A. 1987. *Motivation and Personality*. New York: Harper and Row.

Mayer, R. E. 1989. "Models for Understanding." *Review of Educational Research* 59:43–64.

McCown, R., M. Driscoll, and P. G. Roop. 1996. *Educational Psychology*. Boston: Allyn and Bacon.

Meier, D. 2000. *The Accelerated Learning Handbook*. New York: McGraw-Hill.

National Institute for Occupational Safety and Health (NIOSH Alert). 2003. Publication No. 2003-128. *Preventing Deaths, Injuries, and Illnesses of Young Workers* (retrieved October 22, 2006). www.cdc.gov/niosh/topics/youth

National Safety Council (NSC). 2009. *Supervisors' Safety Manual*. 10th ed. Itasca, IL: NSC.

Occupational Safety and Health Administration (OSHA). *Teen Worker Website* (retrieved October 22, 2006). www.osha.gov/SLTC/teenworkers

Ormrod, J. E. 1998. *Educational Psychology: Developing Learners*. Upper Saddle River, NJ: Merrill.

Pike, R. W. 1994. *Creative Training Techniques Handbook*. Minneapolis, MN: Lakewood Books.

Sarasin, L. C. 1999. *Learning Style Perspectives: Impact in the Classroom*. Madison, WI: Atwood Publishing.

Schunk, D. H. 2004. *Learning Theories: An Educational Perspective*. Upper Saddle River, NJ: Merrill.

Silberman, M. 1995. *Active Training: A Handbook of Techniques, Designs and Case Examples, and Tips*. Lexington, MA: Lexington Books.

Slavin, R. E. 2000. *Educational Psychology*. Boston: Allyn and Bacon.

Smith, P. L., and T. J. Ragan. 1999. *Instructional Design*. Upper Saddle River, NJ: Merrill.

U.S. Department of Labor. *Youth Rules Website!* (retrieved October 22, 2006). www.youthrules.dol.gov

Wildman, T. M. 1981. "Cognitive Theory and the Design of Instruction." *Educational Technology* 23:14–20.

Wlodkowski, R. J. 1999. *Enhancing Adult Motivation to Learn*. San Francisco: Jossey-Bass Publishers.

Woolfolk, A. E. 1998. *Educational Psychology*. Boston: Allyn and Bacon.

APPENDIX A: TRAINING ASSESSMENT WORKSHEET

Department / Job	Supervisor's Name	Date
Type of Training		
Best Days and Times to Train	Number of Employees	
Required Personal Protective Equipment		
Accident Trends (if any)		

List Potential Hazards	**Identify the Knowledge and Skills Needed**	**List Training Topics**

Source: National Safety Council 2009

APPENDIX B: GOALS AND OBJECTIVES WORKSHEET

Trainer: _____   **Date:** _____

Course Title: _____

Goals:

_____

_____

Guide to Developing Course Objectives

Knowledge, Skills & Attitudes Needed	Conditions (Tools, Materials, Activities, or Equipment Needed)	Skills	Performance Standards
List the knowledge, skills or attitudes trainees need to work safely.	Describe the learning conditions. Given a . . .	List the skills trainees will be able to do after the training (use action verbs). Trainees will be able to . . .	Describe when performance is good enough.

Write the Course Objective(s) in the CSP Format

_____

_____

_____

_____

Source: Mager 1988

SECTION 4
SAFETY AND HEALTH TRAINING

LEARNING OBJECTIVES

▌ Become familiar with the basic applications of training in order to conduct safety training within an organization.

▌ Learn about various models and applications of training to make informed decisions about the best ways to present safety training.

▌ Learn how to document training to meet government standards and, in the process, gain ready access and understanding of the history of safety training conducted by an organization.

APPLIED SCIENCE AND ENGINEERING: SAFETY TRAINING AND DOCUMENTATION PRINCIPLES

Fred Fanning

As PEOPLE MOVE through life and interact with others, they assume roles as trainers and educators. People teach others through their words, actions, and deeds. That means that readers come to this chapter with real-life experience, and the key for them is to build on what they already know or perhaps change it into something that works better. If done right, this will allow employees and management to know what their roles and responsibilities are in preventing accidents. This is a skill that every safety, health, and environmental professional needs to have.

CONDUCTING THE TRAINING

This chapter is about adult learning, which is different from child or adolescent learning. The goal in providing safety training is to form an environment where adults want to learn, using hands-on learning techniques when possible.

Moran provides us with a model to follow prior to conducting training. He writes, "OSHA's training guidelines follow a model that consists of: determining if training is needed, identifying training needs, identifying goals and objectives, developing learning activities, conducting the training, evaluating program effectiveness, and improving the program" (Moran 2003, 151). This chapter will address the identification of training needs. Prior to developing a lesson plan, goals and objectives should have been established. "Instructional objectives, if clearly stated, will tell employers what they want their employees to do, to do better, or to stop doing" (Moran 2003, 153).

WRITING A LESSON PLAN

There are three documents that facilitate the transfer of learning from the instructor to the student: the syllabus, the course outline, and the lesson plan. The syllabus is a large, formal document. It is normally used in a school environment and is often approved by faculty administrators. The outline is also a formal document that breaks down the course of instruction into a list of elements. Instructor supervisors may also approve this document. The lesson plan is the deliberate process of documenting the breakdown of a course of instruction. The lesson plan is normally printed out and used to prepare for and conduct the lesson. This document is prepared by the instructor and does not require anyone's approval for use.

The lesson plan outlines the training and is used to break down a course of instruction into bite-size subjects or lessons that a student could learn in a concise and effective manner. The purpose of training "is to create change in learners that they consistently reproduce without variance" (Stolovich and Keeps 2002, 10). In this chapter training is further defined to include various formats that can be used in conducting training on the job through computers, through the Internet, in a workshop on equipment, or in groups located almost anywhere. The reason for this expansion of the definition is that "Learning, by contrast, is a much larger umbrella that covers all our efforts to absorb, understand, and respond to the world around us" (HRDC 1997, 11).

"The lesson plan is a must for all teachers because it acts as a reference and guide for each class meeting" (Grieve 2005, 67). There may be as many as eight lessons in a one-day course. For a course that requires several days to complete, the lesson plan may cover the extensive matter one day at a time. The flexibility and its use lie with the instructor. Foremost, the lesson plan provides instructors with a tool to develop the training based on the outcome of learning they want to achieve. Within the lesson plan the instructors identify points they want to stress. "The plan contains important questions and quotes from supplemental material" (Grieve 2005, 67).

An instructor will want to prepare for a lesson by going over the learning objectives, major points of learning, times for conducting training, and ways to conduct the training. The lesson plan provides him or her with all of that information. "An effective method of planning a course is to construct a plan

for each class meeting, number the lessons, place them in a loose leaf binder, and maintain them as a record and guide for activities" (Grieve 1996, 16). This method may be used to instruct everything from a one-day class to an eight-week college course. It is a very simple and effective way to provide an instructor with a plan for each lesson, a plan that is easy to follow and keeps the instructor on task.

Most instructors cannot keep an entire lesson in their heads. Instructors also need a way to document what was taught. Using a lesson plan allows them to document the content of the lesson. The material to be covered is placed in the lesson plan in a logical manner that will allow the instructor to provide a consistent and yet inclusive lesson to each class. The goal is to put pen to paper and develop a complete plan of how to conduct the lesson and then to use that document to present the training.

Once the goals and objectives of the training have been established, research will need to be conducted on the topic. In the past, instructors used the regulatory codes and standards, consensus standards, as well as books and periodicals from the local library, to research the topic. Notes were taken, and that information was integrated into the lesson plans and student handouts. Today instructors have the ability to conduct large amounts of research using the World Wide Web, where almost any subject for developing and conducting training can be found. Even some of the books and periodicals in the library can be accessed from a home computer. Identifying goals and objectives for the training and then conducting research to gather information needed for lesson plans and handouts will lead the instructor to identify an instructional method.

There are a number of methods that can be used to help an employee to learn. "Job rotations, special assignments, reflecting on experience, coaching and counseling, mentoring, manager as teacher, learning teams and self-development, and individual development plans are just a few available methods" (HRDC 1997, 16). Each of these methods has benefits and drawbacks. The most obvious method is to provide instruction in a classroom. However, it may not be the most effective method. Choose the method that best provides the environment for learning and then proceed with a format for the lesson plan.

There are a number of formats for the lesson plan. The instructor should choose one that is right for him or her. This normally includes identifying the course number and name, the date or dates of the presentation, and student and instructor activities that should take place during the lesson (Fanning, 2006).

The best way to organize the lesson plan is to put it in a format that allows for ease of instruction. This usually means laying out the plan in a linear fashion that focuses on the timeline of the class. This process allows the instructor to teach according to the plan and the timeline. The lesson plan should highlight major activities and identify videos, slide shows, and exercises to be used in class. Special instructions should be added for areas that require a unique activity or piece of equipment so that the instructor need not search for this information. It is also helpful to include notes that tell the instructor where to find the material. For example, the lesson plan may say the following (Fanning 2006):

> Play video "Fall Protection" using video number 5115-0987 (NOTE: video is located at the factory engineering office. Video must be picked up and played forward to the starting point of video. After use, the tape must be rewound and returned to the engineering office.)

This type of instruction makes the training effective for students and easy for the instructor. The lesson plan should also periodically reference the timeline for conducting the course. For example, the lesson plan might say the following (Fanning 2006):

0900–0950: Brief slide show on "Slips, Trips, and Falls"

0950–1000: Break

This kind of detail will allow the instructor to remain on time and complete the lesson plan, covering all the material outlined for the student.

Supporting material comes in many forms. The task is to identify all the material available and then to determine which material will enhance learning. Supporting material might include articles in trade journals that demonstrate a teaching point or provide the student with an opportunity to think about a real-life application of the issue. Exercises also provide situations in which an individual or a group of students can think through real-world problems or issues and determine solutions to them. There are also talking points, information papers, OSHA guidelines, informational material from trade organizations, questionnaires, and newspaper articles, just to name a few. All this support material is used to emphasize points in class by bringing real-world application to the learning process.

Every lesson plan must have a beginning and an end. That sounds rather obvious, yet it is very easy to jump right into the middle of the teaching material or cut off the plan when time runs out. The beginning of the lesson plan helps identify the learning objectives and outcomes. It introduces the content of material and gives the student a reason to stay for the training. Like the beginning of a story, it sets the stage for the entire lesson plan. The beginning can include ice-breaking exercises to let the students relax and get to know each other. It can be used to set the stage for the class by checking the class materials and briefly telling the participants how each one contributes to learning. It is also a good time to refer to the timeline of the course and inform the students if videos, slide shows, or group exercises will be offered, or if analysis of articles will be conducted. In contrast, the ending provides a completion to the learning session and the lesson plan. The instructor can restate the learning objectives and outcomes and ask students if the objectives and outcomes were met. Instructors can allow students to wrap up what they have learned. The whole point is to bring the learning to a discrete close. The student may read articles, attend additional classes, read books, or attend lectures on the subject in the future, so the learning will probably go on, but each learning session must be brought to proper closure.

The final outline of a lesson plan is the result of simply putting the information into a format that identifies major points, supporting points, and general information. The outline allows the instructor to adjust for a better flow of information. The outline puts all the information into a neat package from which the instructor can develop the plan. Without a good and understandable outline, the lesson plan will not be effective or useful. The outline will help identify holes or weaknesses in the training material and provide research guidance to alleviate those problems; it will also help complete the process.

UNDERSTANDING GROUP DYNAMICS

Members of a class, course, or training program form teams. The same dynamics and development stages that affect teams in work situations also affect groups in training. The theory is that groups that are put together go through stages of development to form a team. Issues, hazards, and productive outcomes depend on the time and experience of group members. It is believed that all groups go through these stages. The amount of time and struggle a group has with each stage is dependent on the group. Some groups can go through the stages rather quickly, while others could get stuck at some point. The standard stages of group development taught in most, if not all, courses are commonly referred to as forming, storming, norming, and performing. Gardenswartz and Rowe developed a parallel theory for the stages of team development; their theory works along the same lines and is referred to as infancy, adolescence, middle age, and maturity (Gardenswartz and Rowe 2003, 194–195). Blanchard, Carew, and Parisis-Carew, authors of the *One Minute Manager Builds High Performing Teams*, tell us group interactions are broken down into two paths, which are content and process (Blanchard et al. 2009, 20). This theory was developed along with two branches of development. The content branch is made up of the *what* and the tasks, and the process branch consists of the *how* and the team functions (Blanchard et al. 2009, 20). These stages are important to an instructor because, as one can imagine, in several of the stages, learning will be difficult, if not impossible. The instructor can facilitate the development of the group through the various stages to the performing stage, where high-impact learning can take place with great retention.

People coming together, with all of the unknowns that surround the experience, represent the first stage. Gardenswartz and Rowe refer to the first part of their four-part stages of development as infancy. They tell us this stage focuses on the team members not knowing much. They state the basic unknowns are: "we keep asking what we are doing and why, team members don't know enough about each other, and are unclear about what we are supposed to do" (Gardenswartz and Rowe 2003, 195). During this stage the instructor can use ice-breaking techniques to end some of those unknowns.

Gardenswartz and Rowe tell us that their second developmental stage is known as adolescence. They tell us this stage focuses on the team members. "We're having trouble getting along, members are jockeying for power" (Gardenswartz and Rowe 2003, 195). Instructors, to facilitate an effective transition through this stage, can help students identify class norms or acceptable classroom behavior. They can also use group exercises to allow students to work with each other and become more familiar with each other's needs.

Gardenswartz and Rowe, on the other hand, inform us that the third part of their developmental stages is middle age. They tell us this stage focuses on the team members. "We're seeing the progress of work, team members are open and honest in asking questions and giving feedback, and as we get to know each other better, we are working more smoothly together" (Gardenswartz and Rowe 2003, 195). The instructor can facilitate this stage by again using group exercises when possible to get the students to work together.

Gardenswartz and Rowe inform us that the last part of their four-part stages of development is maturing. "We feel pride in our accomplishment, we're really cooking, and we all do what it takes to get the job done" (Gardenswartz and Rowe 2003, 195). The instructor takes advantage of this stage by challenging students with materials that stimulate learning and by allowing them to learn from each other.

Students, as members of a group, have distinct personalities, and they bring to class, for good or bad, their abilities to influence those around them. The instructor must identify each student's sphere of influence and use that to the class's advantage. For example, everyone remembers the class clowns, who acted out their skits in spite of the needs of the rest of the class. Often these class clowns influenced students through their antics. There are also other students who possess experience or knowledge that others look to for answers or ideas. In either case, the instructor should identify the influence of these members and determine the best way to use that influence for the good of the class and to further their learning.

Beside *influential* students, one also encounters over-achievers. These students excel and often arrive at the answers and solutions before other students. These overachievers can help others learn the lesson or see further applications of the knowledge. Unfortunately they can also short-circuit learning by ending a lesson before the others have had an opportunity to learn the material. The instructor should thus use the strength of such overachievers to further group learning to the point where each student is ready to move forward.

There are many exercises that an instructor can use to open a presentation. The main goal of these is to prepare students to learn. Let us begin with the easiest method, introductions, which calls for each person to stand and tell the group about himself or herself. Normally people state their names, where they work, why they are taking this course, what they hope to get out of the course; they usually also share something personal with the group. Another way to use the introduction is to have the group split up into pairs. Each person in a pair should interview the other person. Questions that are asked during such interviews include the person's name, where they work, why they are taking this course, what they hope to get out of the course, and one thing personal to share with the group. When everyone is done, both people in a pair stand, and they introduce and tell the class a little about the other person. A third way to do the introductions is to give people 3-by-5-inch cards and have them write down their names, where they work, why they are taking this course, what they hope to get out of the course, and one thing personal to share with the group. Put all the 3-by-5-inch cards into a hat or box and have each person come forward and pull out a card. Each participant then stands and asks the person whose name is on the card to stand as well before introducing him or her. This provides some time for group members to relax, get to know each other, and begin to fit in with the group.

Group norms are rules that help maintain harmony and balance in the group. It is essential to identify these group norms and for each student to agree to abide by them. The instructor can help the group members to identify the norms or rules they feel are appropriate, and then also help them reach full agreement through a show of hands. This does not have to take a long time. The norms in a class are usually fairly straightforward and often include letting everyone speak, not interrupting one another, raising hands and waiting to be called on to speak, being on time, turning off cell phones, agreeing to disagree, and so on. The instructor can expedite the process by providing the students with a standard set of norms to pick from. With this additional information, the process can take as little as ten minutes, but save hours of conflict in the long run.

Students in a class setting learn individual as well as group lessons. The group develops alternatives to the learning process, and through discussion and analysis determines solutions and their proper applications. This process is also used in the work environment where an organization or a team learns together. The group learning adds to the individual learning process; it may even provide individuals with applicable knowledge that the individual may not have otherwise received. The instructor can increase the possibility of group learning through group activities such as exercises, discussions, projects, presentations, and even group examinations.

COMPARING POPULAR TRAINING METHODS

In today's environment there is no one best way to learn material needed to be a productive and safe worker. For this reason, there are several ways in which an organization may want to provide training. Each method has its own positive and negative points. The primary means of providing training are the traditional classroom method, on-the-job training, and online training. Actually, the traditional method of training has been on the job. In the early years of our country, academic learning was restricted to the elite. Later, various movements obtained the right to a general education for everyone, and, at that stage, the country moved to the traditional classroom environment where a teacher told students what they needed to know and how best to interpret it. The method used by an organization depends on the organization, and there is no right or wrong choice.

The personnel of an organization need to look at the learning they want as an outcome and determine the best, most cost-effective, and supportable way to provide that learning. No organization should provide the traditional classroom method as the sole method. Instead, organizations should adopt a holistic approach to learning. It is beneficial to compare the above-mentioned primary methods of training.

When deciding on the training technique, an instructor could investigate whether on-the-job or classroom training will be a better fit for the lesson plan. At least three categories of on-the-job-training (OJT) expenses exist. Then there are costs associated with company equipment, which, because they are used for training, become *nonproductive*.

Of the many issues involved in the comparison between classroom-based training and on-the-job training, the two primary ones are cost and availability of actual learning. Other issues that one might consider are the cost of potential waste produced during on-the-job training or the cost of injury due to unsafe practices of workers. On-the-job training can produce variations in what is taught and learned because it requires more instructors and because of the variations that occur each day on the job. In addition, on-the-job training could pose a concern to the company insurance underwriter. A suitable classroom for training must also be located, a classroom in which audio-visual equipment could be required as part of the traditional classroom method.

Peer learning is essential if an employer is to get the most from a training opportunity. Each worker has information about the way work is done in the organization, information that could increase productivity were it known by all workers. In this age, where employers are asking their workers to think and improve their work processes, the natural extension of such a process is for workers to share their knowledge with their colleagues. This can happen in the classroom. However, because the instructor drives the learning process and the lesson, the amount of peer learning is small. However, in on-the-job training, the

student is out among his or her peers and will normally be privy to information about how things work, short cuts, and lessons learned at work. The main concern at this stage is making sure that peers are not teaching the new employee bad habits. However, if the organization is open to workers having ideas and expressing ways of doing their jobs better, the bad effects of peer sharing can be greatly reduced.

It is much cheaper to put workers in a classroom and tell them what they need to know. In addition, learning on the job, because it keeps employees from *productive* work, can be quite expensive. This learning process requires the supervisor or trainer to focus on teaching instead of *working*. In a classroom, the instructor can deal with 25 to 30 students effectively. However, for on-the-job training, the ratio of trainer to students needs to be closer to 1 to 1 or 1 to 3 trainers to students, thereby significantly increasing its cost. However, that is but one measurement available. The actual learning should also be measured. Putting those 25 to 30 students in a classroom may yield a 25 to 50 percent knowledge retention rate. On-the-job training, on the other hand, may provide a 45 to 70 percent retention rate of the work students practice each day. That would make on-the-job training the most effective.

The second comparison that can be made is between classroom and online training. When comparing classroom training with online training, one should first consider the hardware and software they have or need, as well as the need for fast internet connections and perhaps even a company intranet setup. When considering classroom training, the company must have access to a classroom and the automation equipment needed to run slide shows, videos, and audio presentations.

Most online training comes *canned*, which means that it is produced with a specific topic in mind, and thus is primarily able to teach that particular topic. An organization can purchase a customized course, but that will normally cost more money. In most cases the canned presentation will meet the organization's needs and can be purchased on a per-student basis or for a period of time. Courses of instruction may also be purchased for downloading onto company intranets and used at the company's convenience. The automation that the company is currently using is also a major consideration. The automation required for online training is fairly sophisticated and requires the most modern software with the newest hardware. If the organization does not meet this format, it may have to purchase computer hardware and software and even install an intranet.

As noted above, peer learning is essential if an employer is to get the most from a training opportunity. Peer learning can happen in the classroom, but the drawback is that the instructor drives the lessons and the learning process, potentially stifling peer learning. However, online peer learning is high if the learning is connected to chat rooms or online conferences; if it is not, then there is virtually no peer learning.

Let us return to some of the beneficial points of classroom training. It is much cheaper to put workers in a classroom and tell them what they need to know than to provide computers, modems, and other automated equipment for online training. However, if a company already has access to the automated equipment needed for online training, a large classroom or audiovisual equipment would be unnecessary. In a classroom the instructor can deal with 25 to 30 students, with little time spent on each of them. However, in online training, the student-trainer ratio is normally 15 students to 1 trainer, and the training provides the student with a self-contained training package. The actual learning should also be measured. Putting those 25 to 30 students in a classroom may yield a 25 to 50 percent retention rate on the training provided. Online training may provide 85 to 90 percent retention because students can work at their own pace and even go back to previous lessons. These reasons make online training the most effective. "Classroom training, although normally more expensive because of the classroom, provides a better learning environment that supports the student and allows for the security to ensure the student actually takes the training" (Fanning 2009, 1).

The third and final comparison is between on-the-job training and online training. This is a more modern comparison that completely eliminates classroom training. Online training has a student ratio closer to 1 to 15 and provides the students with the ability to move through the training at a variety of locations. This training ratio is a little misleading because each student receives one-on-one time with the instructor. This method of training is online, with the contact between instructor and student over an internet connection. The class can be active, with an instructor and additional students, or it can be passive, with a computer program conducting the class, with the student responding to the computer replaying information. An active online class is conducted at specific periods of time that accommodate a variety of time zones and locations. Work is completed and submitted online. Instructors use e-mail, blogs, and social networking accounts to create a common environment where students can discuss the issues presented in the course. The passive classes are built and launched on a Web site. The student can register, review, and complete online examinations, interacting with the online program. Companies must consider the need for hardware and software as well as the need for fast modem connection and perhaps even a company intranet setup.

The issue of canned online training has already been addressed, but the topic is worth raising here because on-the-job training is the most tailored way to provide training. What can be more tailored than a person learning to do the job by actually doing it? However, an organization can purchase a customized course that meets the organization's needs; the purchase can be made on a per-student basis or for a period of time. Courses of instruction may also be purchased for downloading onto company intranets and used at the company's convenience. The automation that the organization is currently using is also a major consideration. The automation required for online training is fairly sophisticated and requires the most modern software with the newest hardware. Of the many issues involved in this comparison, the primary two are cost and availability of actual learning. Other issues or costs that one might consider are waste produced during on-the-job training or unsafe acts leading to worker injuries. On-the-job training can produce variations in what is taught and, obviously, what is learned, due to the limited instructor-to-student ratio; it can also produce variations that occur each day on the job. In addition, the company insurance underwriter might voice concerns were training provided on the job. With on-the-job learning, the student normally has ready access to a live mentor in the form of his or her supervisor. This situation not only facilitates the learning process for the present course of instruction, but also for all training in the future.

In contrast, the online courses can connect the student to an online instructor who can provide mentoring similar to that of the on-location supervisor. So even though the course may be without an instructor, there are ways instructors can be part of the process.

A value judgment is hard to make in this comparison because of the variables involved in both training methods. On-the-job training can be quite costly because the supervisor or trainer is not doing *work* while training, and because waste is produced by the student and there is a potential for student accidents. However, learning by doing has been an effective method of training through the ages. There are a lot of benefits to this type of training. The students learn hands-on in the environment where they will work. They actually do the work, which allows them to form a connection between the learning and the work. This method works best for training needed on machinery or processes. However, if the work involves automated equipment or decision-making or thinking skills, the use of online training can be just as effective because the actual use of automation is built into the course. Retention is also greater with online courses because the students can repeat the training again or access information they might have forgotten.

MEDIA AND TECHNIQUES

"Engagement is what it's all about today in education, and technology promises unique ways to engage students in learning. In particular, educational technology enthusiasts tout Web 2.0 as the silver bullet for motivating even recalcitrant students to get with the program" (Simkins and Schultz 2010).

Web 2.0 refers to the wide range of easy-to-use online tools that foster interaction, collaboration, and group productivity. Examples include (Simkins and Schultz 2010):

- social and professional networking sites
- blogs
- wikis

- file-sharing and collaboration sites
- collaborative resource tagging
- user-submitted reviews and ratings

One Web 2.0 application is the digital music player. The more famous of these players is the iPod® and the MP3 player. These players have significantly changed the way we listen to music in this country, and have the potential to do the same for the way we give and receive training.

The iPod® is a small media player from Apple Computer. There are other products on the market, but the name iPod® is most recognizable, and many people use this name to refer to MP3 players from other companies. From this device comes the term PodCast. This is short for iPod® Broadcast, which is an audio broadcast that can be played on the iPod® or similar small device. The PodCast is becoming commonplace when listening to lectures. Today's instructor can record and send PodCasts via email to students with assignments or lectures to be listened to before class starts. This can level the playing field by providing students with basic information. This allows the instructor to get the students to the same level of knowledge before starting class.

There is a great deal of written material that workers can read to learn the information they need. The primary sources are books, periodicals, and workbooks. Many students have used these sources and have a great deal of experience with them. In some cases, students may have already formed opinions about the usefulness of printed material; these opinions, depending on whether they are positive or negative, may support or hinder the learning process.

Books are something we are familiar with. They are the mainstay of public education in this country and are used by many to enjoy free time. However, books have their pros and cons. "Pros are that they are cheap, the reader can access worldwide experts, there is more opportunity to go into depth, the reader does not have to be certain of the application, it is self paced, they can be read practically anywhere, and serve as a constant reminder" (Clegg 2000, 91–92). Cons include ". . . the reader can't learn from a book, they won't actually read it, there isn't a book that meets our specific needs, it's the instructor shooting him or herself in the foot, we've got a library, and the student gets to keep something we've paid for" (Clegg 2000, 92–93). Books are a great way to disseminate information to the workforce that can read and be counted on to read the book. Literacy is a great concern in this country and must be considered when providing reading assignments to workers. An adjunct to that issue is the large numbers of workers who speak English as a second language. This situation leaves the company with the possibility of having to purchase books in more than one language, if that is possible, or not purchasing books at all. Books can be used as lessons in themselves, or they can be used to supplement a course as source material. Books can be reread by the student and even kept as a resource for future use, should questions arise.

Periodicals are known as magazines or newsletters that are printed periodically. They have some of the pros and cons of books. Many Americans enjoy reading magazines and spend a great deal of money on them each year. However, they normally do not purchase educational periodicals. There is a distinct difference in the quality of periodicals. A safety article in a magazine such as *Professional Safety* has more credibility than a safety article in *Time*. The former is an industry periodical that focuses on safety and peer reviews its articles, while the second is an entertainment magazine that uses reporters to develop stories. Periodicals are a great source of training if the suitable ones are identified and used properly; some research may be needed to identify a peer-reviewed academic or industry periodical. Periodicals are normally not used alone to teach a subject, but rather they are used as source material to develop the lesson plans and for group exercises on a specific topic.

Workbooks are another throwback to public education and a great source of information. They have many of the shortcomings as books and periodicals that must be overcome before they are used. Workbooks enable students to apply lessons learned through application. An instructor can even grade this work. As with other materials, workbooks can be kept for future reference by the student or serve as proof of course completion.

In addition to printed material, there is also nonprinted material. This is material that is not normally provided in hard copy in a readable format, or it supplements a hard copy in an alternate format. The newer-generation workers are familiar with these nonprint applications and prefer them to books.

The first example of the nonprint material is the e-book, which is in an electronic format and can be used on a personal computer, laptop, or a personal digital assistant. The e-book is normally read from the electronic device in much the same way that the book is read. The electronic book can also add hot links to Web sites for further information and allows the user to bookmark special sections for rereading or to mark one's place. The e-book saves physical space. Because the books are electronic, they reside in cyberspace and not on a bookshelf. They do have to be read and, in that sense, they have a great deal in common with the printed book. Some e-books are simply the electronic versions of printed books; in other cases, an e-book can be unique in that there is no printed version.

Distance learning replaces the old method of teleconferencing where students in a classroom listen to lectures from a trainer over the telephone while viewing slides operated by a facilitator:

> Distance learning, also known as interactive videoconferencing (IVC), occurs when two or more people at different locations see and hear each other at the same time (two way interactive video). Participants can see the remote instructor on the monitor, which can be projected for larger classes. (*Media and Methods Magazine* 2010)

> Video streaming technology allows schools that do not have videoconferencing capabilities to participate in these educational experiences and ask questions via email, instead of face-to-face interaction like a point-to-point call. (*Media and Methods Magazine* 2010)

> Cisco is delivering its own take on videoconferencing over 3G/4G networks with the Cisco Cius tablet. (*The Buzz* 2010)

This tablet is a small, hand-held device, about the size of a book, using the cell phone network for access. In addition,

> AVI-SPL [Audio Visual Innovations (AVI)] and Signal Perfection Ltd [(SPL)] announced the launch of Caméléon, a first-of-its-kind multifunction telepresence

solution designed to adapt to a customer's environment while providing the highest quality meeting experience. (*The Buzz* 2010)

The Caméléon is an interactive system of devices, PCs, and monitors that create the telepresence. These new tools are designed to enhance the usefulness of videoconferencing, making it available to almost anyone anywhere.

Video is normally operated through a digital videodisk. Most organizations have the equipment necessary to play this form of material. In most cases, employees have the same ability to play the material. Video is a popular teacher at small firms.

Digital recordings can be a useful way to train the target audience, and they can also be reused to train a wider group of employees.

Today students are open to experience-sharing. This method allows students to share lessons they have learned or ways to apply those lessons. This method is especially important for adult students who have a great deal of life experiences. They can share these life experiences with others to prove a point, share learning, or adapt learning to new situations.

Every individual has life experiences, which are normally unique and forged through trial and error. This makes each person an instructor. If there were a way they could share all that information, it would benefit the entire organization. Experience-sharing is how an employee can communicate that information. Lesson plans should facilitate this type of learning through opportunities to share. Instructors should allow and encourage students to speak about their experiences and demonstrate how those experiences apply to the subject under study. This can be done through group exercises, individual presentations, individual papers, debates, or through open discussions between pairs of students. The key is to get the valuable experience of each person out in the open for all to share and learn from. Individual sharing can be used to supplement an ongoing training program such as classroom, on-the-job, or online training.

Roundtable discussions are also a good way for students to get together and share information. The instructor acts as a group facilitator, keeping the discussion going and on track. The students take turns adding information to the discussion, analyzing the points made, determining the validity of the points, and discussing ways in which the material discussed could be used to solve a problem in the workplace. These discussions can be formal or informal. An instructor who keeps the discussion on track usually facilitates formal roundtable discussions. The process is in the format of a lesson plan and is intended to develop solutions to problems or to share information to facilitate learning. However, the roundtable discussion can be informal and run by students. They determine the structure or lack of it to be used and take the discussion where they want. They can use the session to supplement class learning or just to share experiences with each other. Roundtable discussions can be used to supplement a class or training program.

There is a great deal of publicity about the chat room these days. It is considered by many to be a bad thing that distracts people from their work, lives, and, in some cases, reality. However, the cyberspace chat rooms and discussion boards can be a great place for students to share information, discuss alternatives, opine about each other's information, analyze the data, and develop solutions for problems. The chat room and discussion board are basically the same thing. They occupy a site in cyberspace where e-mail or live messages are posted for all to see and comment on. Some sites are live while others have some delay. The cyberspace discussion can be considered the same as a roundtable discussion in the way it is applied. One occurs in cyberspace and the other in physical space and time. This method can be a stand-alone learning device or used to supplement an on-going training program, such as classroom or on-the-job training.

The value of experience-sharing lies in its importance to the student. The student can share and receive information, learning for free. In most cases there is not even a personal cost of embarrassment, fear, or reprisal connected to the learning process. Experience-sharing can add to any training program and offers the instructor another approach to provide information to students from other students. With the exception of connecting to cyberspace, there is little cost involved in experience-sharing. However, many homes are now connected to cyberspace and most people know how to use it and feel comfortable with it. The cyberspace option also provides anonymity if students need to pursue a thought or idea that otherwise might embarrass them. Students retain a great deal of information learned through experience-sharing because it is done at the student level. They often find more meaning in it and thus more of a reason to re-member it. Some of the material learned through this method is not usable and a little may even be coun-terproductive to the learning objectives. However, these normally do not detract from the ease and the low-cost option of using experience-sharing.

There is a large audience across the nation for self-improvement. Millions of dollars are spent each year on books to help one diet, speak another language, live a stress-free life, love one's children or spouse more, make more money, or handle personal problems better. "Self-development is a collection of techniques and approaches for an individual to manage their own process of learning. These include self-analysis of com-petencies and interests, personal development plans, learning contracts, learning logs, reading lists, involve-ment in professional organizations, networks, attending demonstrations at other organizations, and partici-pating on interagency committees" (HRDC 1997, 17). Because of the popularity of this method, students are probably more open to using it. Instructors can use the self-improvement approach to develop lesson plans and identify methods of instruction that help employees improve. Instructors can point out to the worker the benefits of training and also encourage students to apply themselves in learning to improve themselves.

COLLABORATIVE AND ACTIVE LEARNING

Today more than ever society is moving away from telling people what to think and allowing them to think for themselves. This is causing a major shift in how we learn. Many organizations are adapting to this new style of collaborative or active learning. The Motorcycle Safety Foundation has made a giant leap in providing training to motorcycle riders that uses the instructor as a coach rather than as a teacher and requires the students to lead their own learning through

classroom discussions and hands-on riding of the motorcycle. It is a shift to think that an instructor—who provides the conditions for students to learn and the material to learn—can stand back and coach the students through learning the objectives of the lesson. It may seem even harder when one realizes it takes this organization sixteen hours to turn a person who has never ridden a motorcycle into one who can ride a motorcycle with basic proficiency and complete a skills test.

Students taking responsibility for their own learn-ing have obvious links to other students as members of the class or perhaps as employees of the same orga-nization. There are also deeper links that each stu-dent may have to the other students. One student may share previous learning experiences or work experi-ences with one or more students, giving that student links to the class as a whole. Some students may also share beliefs and values with other students, which will link them to those students and the group as a whole. The instructor should identify links and make use of them to facilitate learning within the group. Students accept ideas more easily when they share links with other members of the group who accept those ideas.

"In reality, teachers are on a stage; they are actors or actresses whether or not they recognize and admit it" (Grieve 2005, 17). One role that instructors play is that of facilitating. This role is difficult for instructors because it puts them in a position of not directing the learning but establishing the conditions under which it occurs among the students—with the materials pro-vided or from completely new sources identified and provided by students. To do this effectively, instructors must be able to consider that adult students know a great deal about the world, and perhaps even the subject being taught. With a little help, the students might be able to figure the material out on their own with more retention and better understanding than an instructor could ever provide.

Groups might use interactive videoconferencing, video-streaming, interactive systems such as Caméléon, or tablets that achieve access via cell phone networks. *Peer-to-peer networking* is another way to actively engage in the learning process.

The evolution of the World Wide Web from Web 1.0 to Web 2.0 is creating subtle but profound changes in the ways human beings locate and access information, communicate with, and learn from each other. The paradigms for learning have already evolved beyond traditional classroom models to synchronous and asynchronous, interactive, and collaborative learning, which is further extended by Web 2.0 tools and social networking approaches (Gunawardena, et al. 2009).

As Burgess (2003) points out:

By incorporating social networking into the online course curriculum, instructors help women increase their social capital. . . . Instructors can include a number of activities to introduce learners to a social networking framework (Burgess, 2009).

She recommends that trainers do the following to encourage students to participate in social networking to improve learning (Burgess 2009):

- Create a profile, and encourage students to follow.
- Define community early in the course.
- Create a class network.
- Blog to reflect.

The group has a lot of work to do in a collaborative or active learning environment. This is due to the group ownership of the learning environment. In this method of learning, the students cannot just sit back and expect the instructor to spoon-feed them the information they need. In this method each student is hungry and ready to learn because of the environment and freedom to take the learning as it comes and move it in any direction to further explore thoughts and concepts. There are three types of roles that students take: task roles, maintenance roles, and blocker roles. Task roles include initiator, contributor, information seeker, information giver, evaluator, and summarizer. Maintenance roles include harmonizer, encourager, gatekeeper, and compromiser. Finally there are blocking roles, including dominator, blocker, aggressor, and disrupter.

Students can also serve as instructors in almost all methods of training. In collaborative learning the student may lead a discussion on the subject or ways to implement the subject. The student may serve as a facilitator of a session used by other students to discuss, analyze, and implement ideas. Students may also be

called upon to develop and conduct lessons for the entire class as part of the grade for completing the course. In general, all students bring life lessons to the training. Each student can provide feedback to class activities, relating lessons learned to life experiences they have had. This way each student is an instructor and a student for the group. Each student can learn from his or her fellow students if the group is open to learning from each other.

In collaborative or active learning students take responsibility for their learning. They identify themselves with thoughts and ideas they want to know. They put forth the effort necessary to expand those thoughts and ideas while sharing them with fellow students to explore new ways of learning and applying what they learn. This puts the student squarely in charge of his or her learning. Instructors must facilitate this role and make sure they do not take it from the students or allow the students to give it to them.

In a collaborative or active learning environment, fellow students may record the proceedings of a learning session in the role of recorder. The recording is also used as minutes of the proceedings for each student to use in the future and to provide applied lessons for grading by the instructor. Each student who documented his or her own work traditionally played this role. Today, with learning in groups, there is often a group product that is documented and graded rather than individual products. This role also allows the student to learn from the process. The role is not one of passively taking notes but of actively viewing and trying to make sense of the process and how others participate in it.

If possible each student should step back from the proceedings and watch the process, rather than work on the problem, in the role of observer. This rare experience can teach a student more about process than a lecture or book on the subject. The student stands back from the group, listening to, watching, and feeling what is taking place. He or she notes the body language used as well as the words; determines if group norms are followed or changed; and is prepared to brief the group on what he or she observed. This provides a learning experience not just for the observing student but also for all the students who participated.

Great insights can be gained from the information shared by the observer. Instructors should include the use of observers whenever they engage in group work where the process is as important as the product.

When conducting safety training, one is normally providing training for adults who are in the workforce. These adults learn differently than children do; they should be given credit for the life experiences they bring to the training. The instructor must take advantage of the adult's experience by providing them opportunities to engage in the learning process. This can be done through group exercises, presentations, hands-on exercises, student-led training, or allowing students to determine answers or solutions to problems rather than being told the textbook answer. By engaging learners, the instructor can increase retention and understanding of the material.

Active learning is a buzz word for many. Some instructors use it to describe almost any kind of learning. This is unfortunate because it tends to confuse students about what active learning really is. Most of us can remember sitting in an auditorium or classroom and listening to someone speak about a particular topic. In this situation there is no effort given by the learner to participate in the learning. Lecturing is often done because it is the easiest way to teach or instruct for the person doing the speaking, it has been modeled for years so it must work, and it is the fastest way to put out a lot of information (Bowman 2003, 11). However, Sharon Bowman, in *Preventing Death by Lecture*, tells us that people normally remember only 20 percent of what they hear (Bowman 2003, 2). To increase how much a student remembers, the trainer must provide learning opportunities for more than one sense. By providing material for the student to see and hear, retention is improved.

Passive learners are *not* active in the learning process. Their role in a passive learning environment does not require them to perform any action. Many learners become bored and tired, begin to daydream, or let their minds drift to other subjects. When learners are active in the learning process, they are more awake, focused, and interested in the learning that is taking place. Learners should also be interacting with each other, the environment, the instructor, and training

materials. Learning environments should be interactive and not passive. Interactive learning environments facilitate the learning process for the opposite reasons that passive environments degrade learning. "*Interactive* means that listeners are talking to each other, participating in activities with each other, and learning from each other" (Bowman 2003, 14).

Now it is important to take a look at what active learning is. Students have always sat in classrooms listening to others speak and learning information from that speaking. This is the model of teaching that has been used for centuries. This model, on occasion, required the student to write notes, work problems, speak to the group, and do homework in an effort to increase the learning that took place—all of which added to the learning. "The best way to make sure our listeners learn, remember, and use what we teach them is to involve them in the learning" (Bowman 2003, 82).

"Hands-on means that listeners are doing something, as opposed to just sitting and listening" (Bowman 2003, 14). This can be anything that includes movement and action. Things like reading, writing, standing, moving parts of the body, and asking or answering questions are just a few examples. This takes a little more work on the part of the instructor because activities must be planned and prepared for. It also takes more time than standing in front of the class and lecturing.

We have all done the obligatory reading of endless paragraphs for homework throughout our school years. That type of reading is important, but reading can also be done as the class is in session. Reading a short passage can add to most students' retention of the material. This reading can be done aloud by an individual learner to the group from a page or slide. It may also be done as a group reading aloud. The option also exists that each student reads a passage to him or herself, followed by group discussion.

In addition to reading, we have all done the necessary written homework assignments. That type of writing is as important as reading for homework. However, writing can also be done as the class is in session. Writing a bullet, sentence, or even a short passage can add to most students' retention of the material. This writing can be done on butcher paper, white boards, or even chalkboards by an individual learner in front of the group. It may also be done as a group telling a recorder what to write. The option also exists that each student writes a passage to him or herself then shares that writing with a group of students.

Each person is accustomed to speaking in small, informal groups. Instructors should take advantage of this experience and put students into small groups that facilitate a discussion of the class topics. This discussion allows each student to share with his or her fellow students experiences that relate to the learning objective, and then the other members of the group can discuss the relevance and applicability of each other's ideas. New ideas are thus shared and evaluated. In most instances a group can generate more ideas than a single instructor, making the small group method more productive.

Work in the classroom should require students to work through to solutions, not just to learn ideas and concepts. This focus on problem solving will teach work skills that employees can use for preventing accidents as well as performing other job duties. By focusing training on problem solving, the instructor ties classroom lessons to real-world life experiences.

Higher-order thinking involves taking a problem apart, looking at the pieces, determining what allowed it to occur, seeing how the environment affected it, and then putting it all back together in a new form that can be understood and to which a solution can be applied. The real difference lies in the application of synthesis, or putting the pieces back together to determine a usable solution.

"We must first assume we are educating adults who have had years of experience that brings richness to the learning situation—both for themselves and for their students in the classroom" (Ryder 2002, 1). The employees in the workplace are capable of taking problems apart and putting pieces back together to identify solutions. Listing pieces and steps or reciting directions will not help an employee to think for himself or herself. Building higher-order thinking skills into training provides employees with the experience of thinking for themselves to determine the best course of action. Employees who can think for themselves usually have a better understanding of hazards in the workplace and are better able to translate the information about that hazard into a solution to reduce or eliminate the hazard and are able to decide which solutions will produce the best results. Linda Ryder tells us that synthesis looks like "proposing a plan for an experiment" or "formulating a new scheme for classifying objects, events, or ideas" (2002, 5). According to Ryder (2002), a person using higher-order thinking also uses evaluation skills such as reasonableness, validity, reliability, appropriateness, and correctness.

To determine if the solution to a problem works, the individual or group that develops the solution must simultaneously develop a method of evaluation. As the instructor develops lesson objectives, a way to evaluate the learning is also developed. This evaluation should be short and long term. The evaluation plan must contain a methodology to check the learning when the student returns to work.

The instructor must work to bring meaning to the learning. If meaning can be found, then the students will retain more of the information and want to use the information in their work. The topic of using discussion to facilitate learning has already been addressed. However, there is another aspect to this that helps a student develop meaning. Each student has self-talk going on in his or her head at all times. This talk can support or detract from the meaning of the learning. The thoughts and ideas that a student thinks must integrate the learning to bring meaning to the subject. Students also speak to each other about ideas and concepts that may at first seem unrelated to the subject being taught. However, in hindsight the ideas and concepts being discussed may directly relate to each other, and the dialogue between students may bring meaning to the learning. The instructor can identify what students say in the form of questions and comments in class and determine what those statements and questions mean to the learning. Students also find meaning in watching what other students and instructors do. Their actions may identify a meaning to the learning that the student alone does not identify, yet can share once he or she sees action to support the learning. Finally, students find meaning in doing. Students can be told how to carry out a particular duty and may know the material, but if students actually perform the duty, they not only learn through hearing, but also through seeing, feeling, and smelling. Through these additional attachments to the learning, the student finds meaning.

A good example of active learning is to teach a student the process of speaking to a coworker about an unsafe practice. To make that learning point interactive, the instructor lets a student pretend to perform an unsafe act and then lets a second student speak to the first about the hazards and potential outcomes. The students get more out of the interactive nature of the method. This method also applies to computer and automated training. Many organizations like the idea of buying videotapes and playing them to teach their workers about safety. The video could, to promote active learning, have areas where it is stopped while students perform a task. The same method may be used for computer-based training: requiring a student to do something to react to points made by the software provides the basis for interaction for the student. There are many ways an instructor can use interactive learning, and each time it is used, the learning is reinforced.

Case studies and role-playing are effective methods that allow a student to look at a real-world situation and determine the facts that occurred, identify relevant causes and contributing factors, and then determine courses of action that could eliminate or control the problem. The fact that these learning situations are born of real-world cases provides the students with applicable learning that they can find meaningful.

The first step to any successful learning from the case-study method is to design a case that provides for the learning of the material identified for the class. There are canned studies that can be used. However, they are less effective than studies that are directly tied to a particular learning point. The case study must also be interesting to the student. A boring case study, no matter how effectively written, will not make the student want to participate with passion.

After the case study has been written, it must be conducted. The instructor must make sure that all material necessary for the study is provided. This includes physical material as well as time. A great case study that is executed badly disrupts the learning process, and the students may lose interest and not learn the lesson. The students in the class must analyze the evidence contained in the case study carefully and with an eye for detail. This will allow them to see the pattern of events that occurred and how each point was related to the next. A careful and detailed examination or analysis of the evidence is followed by a synthesis of the information, and from that synthesis the students form conclusions, recommendations, and implications for courses of action.

There are many things a case study offers the instructor. Case studies teach integrated ideas to the students that directly apply to the way life works.

The case study provides the students with an opportunity to work through an organized problem. This facilitates the learning process and allows learning points to be raised as the students moves through the case study. This helps the students not only to learn the material but also to place the learning in perspective with the problems they will face in real work. This leads the students to an opportunity to demonstrate what they have learned to the instructor, as well as to themselves. Demonstrating the learning to themselves is the more important of the two. By demonstrating learning, a student has the opportunity to participate in the lessons and learn from the practice as well as the lesson that is intentionally designed into the class.

Role-playing is another very powerful technique. Role-playing can be spontaneous. Everyone should be given a role, even it is only to observe.

All learners are assigned a role, and the validity and effectiveness of the learning is based on their enthusiasm in playing their role. The real learning is based on the believability of the role-play and how that role-play forces the other participants to respond in their roles. Another strength of role-play is that it simulates complex interpersonal interaction that in itself creates a valuable lesson, not just about the topic, but about how it can be used and how others will respond to it.

In addition to the identified learning objectives, the students who participate in role-playing learn some valuable life skills that will help them to use the learning objectives in the workplace. Role players will learn and practice subtle interpersonal skills as they work through the role and interact with other role players. The students will also learn that there are hidden complexities to each situation that may not be clear or taught in the lesson. This ancillary learning helps the students to use the learning in their lives. This provides a great deal of benefit to the employer.

DOCUMENTING SAFETY AND HEALTH TRAINING

Many training requirements state or imply that the employer shall document that training.

Employers should maintain an office file on each employee. This file, which should include a record of training completed by the employee, provides a historical document that shows what training the employee has received and the frequency of training.

As the leader of an organization, the employer must determine the minimum qualifications of the trainers they will use. An evaluation of the instructor's academic training, background, and experiences can provide the employer with the information needed to determine if an instructor is qualified and competent to present the courses needed by the employees. If the trainer is from outside the organization, the employer should locate and speak to others who can provide the employer with adequate information from which to make an informed decision as to the qualifications and competencies of a trainer. An employer who has identified trainers should develop a list of the trainers and the courses they are qualified and competent to present.

Documenting training provides both a means for the employer to document employee training and provide employees with a document that not only shows their completion of training but also allows them to take pride in their accomplishment. A certificate, letter, memorandum, or other written document can do this. The length of the training, what the employees desire, and reasonable cost should determine the method the employer uses. Obviously, a certificate can be expensive, whereas a short letter or card could be much cheaper. However, what do they mean to the workers? If one provides them with a document they do not value, they may not experience pride in their accomplishment.

The format for documenting training must include the full name of the person receiving the training. The title of the training should be included along with the date the training was conducted. The length of training should also be included. The method used to conduct the training should be included so that it is clear which version was used and what that version included. Some choices discussed in this chapter include the use of classroom with lectures, computer-based Web training, and on-the-job training. The employer will also want to include the method of evaluation used to test the knowledge or skill learned by the employee. The choices that are most commonly used are written examinations, including quizzes and tests, oral examinations, and hands-on examinations. The name of the person or company conducting the training should be noted on the record. It is also very important to note whether the training is a refresher or initial training. The next logical question is how long to keep the record. The Occupational Safety and Health Administration requires that training records for the *Hazard Communication Standard* be kept for the length of employment plus 30 years. For most purposes, five years is long enough to keep training records. This will allow the training records to be kept for the same period of time as some OSHA forms (Fanning 2003, 50). However, the employer must meet any specific requirements in OSHA standards that require they be kept longer.

SUMMARY

The organization cannot expect employees to perform their jobs safely if they have never been trained to do so. The amount of training and its corresponding cost determine what an organization can afford. However, even 5-minute toolbox talks can provide training if a company is strapped for money. This chapter has addressed the methods and procedures of presenting and documenting training. There are a variety of methods that can be used by organization personnel. The key is to identify the training need and the best method to deliver it, develop a lesson plan for what will be presented, present it, and finally document it properly to make sure there is an adequate record. Training must be built into the organization's processes. The tragedy is that, if it is not, it becomes an add-on, and little thought is given to it.

REFERENCES

Alexander, Brian. 2006. "Web 2.0: a new wave of innovation for teaching and learning?" *Educause*, March/April 2006.

Bixby, Daniel W. 2010. "To Be Continued: Using Social Media for Training Conversations." *T+D, American Society of Training and Development*.

Bises, Stephen D., and Daniel J. Fabian. 2004."Sophomore Men: The Forgotten Class, the Forgotten Gender, Recruitment and Retention in Higher Education." *Magna Publications*, Volume 20 Number 3.

Blanchard, Kenneth, Donald Carew, and Eunice Parisis-Carew. 2009. *The One Minute Manager Builds High Performing Teams*. 3rd ed. New York: William Morrow.

Bowman, Sharon. 2003. *Preventing Death by Lecture*. Glenbrook, NV: Bowperson Publishing Company.

Bradley, Paul. 2009. "Special Report: Distance Learning, Whither Twitter." *Community College Week*.

Burgess, Kimberly R. 2009. "Social Networking Technologies as Vehicles of Support for Women in Learning Communities." *New Directions for Adult and Continuing Education*, Issue 122, pp. 63–71.

Clegg, Brian. 2000. *Training Plus: Revitalizing Your Training*. Sterling, VA: Kogan Page.

Fanning, Fred. 2003. *Basic Safety Administration: A Handbook for the Safety Professional*. Des Plaines, IL: American Society of Safety Engineers.

_____. 2009."Classroom vs. Computer Based Training." *The Communicator*, volume 2, number 2, Winter 2009. American Society of Safety Engineers.

Gardenswartz, Lee, and Anita Rowe. 2003. *Diverse Teams at Work: Capitalizing on the Power of Diversity*. Alexandria, VA: Society for Human Resources Management.

Grieve, Donald. 2005. *A Handbook for Adjunct/Part-Time Faculty and Teachers of Adults*. 6th ed. Ann Arbor, MI: Adjunct Advocate Inc.

Gunawardena, Charlotte N., Mary Beth Hermans, Damien Sanchez, Carol Richmond, Maribeth Bohley, and Rebekah Tuttle. "A Theoretical Framework for Building Online Communities of Practice with Social Networking Tools." *Educational Media International*, Volume 46, Number 1, pp. 3–16.

Miner, Zach. 2009. "Twitter Takes a Trip to College." *U.S. News & World Report*, Vol. 146, Issue 8, pp. 56–57.

Moran, Mark. 2003. *Construction Safety Handbook*. 2d ed. Rockville, MD: Government Institutes Inc.

Ryder, Linda B. 2002. *Higher-Order Thinking Skills* (retrieved August 1, 2002). www.amsc.belvoir.army.mil/ecampus/sblmp-nr/readings/Higher-level_thinking_skills/Higher_Order_Thinking/html

Schneier, Craig, Craig Russell, Richard Beatty, and Lloyd Baird. 1994. *The Training Development Source Book* 2d ed. Amherst, MA: Human Resource Development Press.

Simkins, Michael, and Randy Schultz. 2010. "Using Web 2.0 Tools at School." *Leadership Association of California School Administrators*, Jan/Feb 2010, Volume 39.

Stolovich, Harold, and Erica Keeps. 2002. *Telling Ain't Training*. Alexandria, VA: ASTD Press.

"Video Conferencing." *The Buzz*. Service Online, 09/2010 (retrieved October 20, 2011). blog.svconline.com/thebuzz/2010/09/17/videoconferencing-watch-avi-spl-cameleon/

"Video Conferencing and Video Streaming." 2010. *Media and Methods Magazine*, January/February 2010.

Young, Jeffrey. 2009. "Teaching with Twitter Not for the Faint of Heart." *The Chronicle of Higher Education*, Volume A1, Number 10.

APPENDIX: ADDITIONAL READING

Cantonwine, Sheila Cullen. 1999. *Safety Training That Delivers*. Des Plaines, IL: American Society of Safety Engineers.

Fanning, Fred. 2003. *Basic Safety Administration: A Handbook for the New Safety Specialist*. Des Plaines, IL: American Society of Safety Engineers.

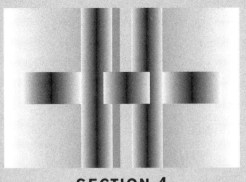

SECTION 4
SAFETY AND HEALTH TRAINING

LEARNING OBJECTIVES

■ Understand the factors that contribute to the costs and financial benefits of safety, health, and environmental (SH&E) training.

■ Perform a comparison of the costs and benefits of training alternatives.

■ Be able to estimate the return on investment (ROI) and break-even point for a training class or program.

■ Acquire the tools to plan a training budget.

COST ANALYSIS AND BUDGETING

Brent Altemose

IN MOST ORGANIZATIONS, particularly large organizations, significant resources are dedicated to training. Nearly $60 billion is spent each year in the United States on workplace training programs (Phillips 2002). Despite this large sum, the true cost of training programs is often not evaluated or recognized (Phillips 2003). Furthermore, safety risks are typically not adequately incorporated into economic planning and decision making (Asche 2004). Safety, Health, and Environmental (SH&E) and training professionals may be intimidated by financial concepts, or, worse yet, they may be worried that their programs or jobs may be jeopardized depending on the outcome of the analysis. But it would be difficult to imagine making a large capital expenditure, such as a new ventilation system, without considering the costs and benefits, or the most cost-effective way to implement the system. Careful utilization of cost analysis and budgeting techniques is just as important for a training program.

This chapter discusses how to leverage training dollars through effective budgeting, accurate cost estimates, and utilization of cost-benefit analysis techniques. Proper application of these techniques will not only identify where training money is being spent, but it will also aid in projecting the costs of proposed programs and comparing the costs of alternatives. Furthermore, business and accounting terms, besides being more credible to management, are better understood by them than is safety jargon (Bird, 1996).

The advent of computer-based training and other technology-driven training techniques has made cost analysis more critical, because the cost of such programs varies widely (Devaney 2001). These technologies have resulted in great savings in some cases; for example, where training has been provided to large numbers of people in a cost- and time-effective manner. In other cases, however, instructor-led training may actually be more cost effective, particularly when the total number of people to be trained is relatively small, and they can easily be brought together in one location.

COSTS OF TRAINING

An accurate estimate of the cost of training depends on an evaluation of many factors, but one should not be intimidated by the scope of information that needs to be collected. Even though detailed and thorough data lead to more accurate estimates, in many cases precise estimates are not available. If the estimate is reasonable, and it is based on experience and the best available data, then it will have great value in making training-program decisions. Sometimes, industry benchmarks are the best data available. The American Society for Training and Development (ASTD) Benchmarking Forum is one source of training-cost data (Waagen 2000, 4).

The method for collecting data is described in detail in this section and supplemented by the following realistic example that will be revisited throughout this chapter. Say, a mid-size telecommunication company, XYZ Telecom, is considering a new computer-based training program for hazard communication (HazCom). The program will be used to provide both initial and refresher training to employees located in three states at twenty different locations. Approximately 500 employees will complete the 2-hour initial training for new and transferred employees. Every year about 4000 employees will take an hour-long, mandatory refresher training. An *off-the-shelf* program, with some customized company-specific designs, will be purchased for the above purposes.

Table 1 shows a worksheet for collecting data to estimate the cost of safety training, including data filled in for the XYZ Telecom example. The cost data, as well as the expected timing of the expenditure, which is important for both budgeting and cost-benefit analysis purposes, are recorded. *Note:* This example is not intended to demonstrate the entire breadth and depth of costs that may need to be considered. It is not feasible to describe all of the possible costs of training with a single example. However, this section and the accompanying example will demonstrate the types of costs that will need to be considered.

Development Costs

A significant contributor to the cost of a training program, particularly a new program, is the cost to develop the program. Development costs include the time spent by subject-matter experts, training professionals, computer programmers, or others, depending on the course. It is worth noting that even off-the-shelf programs may present development costs for reviewing their content, customizing them to the organization's needs, or even simply integrating them into the existing training program. When estimating the time required to develop a traditional, instructor-led course, it is best to assume twenty hours of development time for each hour of class time; for self-instructional print media such as workbooks, the development time is typically 80 hours per hour of class time; for computer-based training, the time varies widely, but may reach or exceed 300 hours per hour of class time, depending on the level of complexity of the training (Head 1994, 64). The addition of video and audio to computer-based training can be particularly time-consuming. However, as the example will show, if the cost of this time is amortized across a large number of students, it very well may be the most cost-effective option.

Either internal personnel or external consultants could be involved in course development. For internal personnel, the cost of development time is based on the *loaded cost* of the internal salaries. The loaded cost includes base salary, fringe benefits, and, in some cases, opportunity costs, which are discussed later (Phillips 2003, Nathan 2009). Fringe benefits generally amount to 25–75 percent above the employee's base salary, and include costs to the organization such as health benefits, matching retirement contributions, vacation pay, bonuses, and so on. (Head 1994, 35). To calculate the total cost to the organization, multiply the average loaded-salary rate by the number of hours worked specific to the project. For external consultants, multiply the expected hourly rate by the number of hours worked. Do not forget to include any travel costs associated with the course development.

Not all courses are customized; there are also many off-the-shelf safety training programs available. For these programs, be sure to include the cost to review the content to ensure applicability and suitability for the target audience and target workplace.

The cost of materials during course development might include money spent on presentation materials such as videos. For computer-based training, evaluate whether upgrades to technology infrastructure will be necessary. Also be sure to factor in the cost of computer workstations if new workstations will be required to deliver the training for a particular group. For instance, if the target audience is a group of manufacturing employees who do not have their own computer workstations, computer labs, shared computers, or kiosks may need to be provided. Of course, the cost to purchase software must also be included. Other types of equipment may need to be purchased as well, such as disposable gloves and suits for a course on emergency response.

For XYZ Telecom's computer-based HazCom program, it was estimated that 150 hours would be spent by internal personnel to learn the software and to customize the course content. The average salary of these personnel is $45 per hour, and the estimated loaded-salary rate, including fringe benefits, is $70 per hour. Multiplying 150 hours by the loaded-salary rate of $70 per hour, the total organizational cost is $10,500. External consultants and travel were not needed because the vendor included training in the cost to purchase the software, which was $8000. No other significant development costs were expected.

Implementation Costs

When internal personnel are used as instructors, their salary cost should be computed as a loaded cost in the manner previously described (average loaded-salary rate times the number of hours worked). In addition, if training is not their primary job function, there may be an additional cost to the organization, which can be recorded in the table as "Other business impacts." Other business impacts are described in more detail in the student-costs discussion. For external consultants, again use the going rate for their services. Fin-

ally, include expenses the instructor will incur while traveling to and from the training sessions, expenses such as the cost of their time, their meals and lodging, the airfare, and so on.

The cost of time spent by employees attending training cannot be ignored in training-cost analysis. In fact, student costs often represent more than 80 percent of the overall cost of a training program (Head 1994, 36). *Student costs* include the loaded salaries paid to employees for their time in training, incidental expenses (such as travel costs, if applicable), and *lost-opportunity costs*, which are described later. Due to the significance of these costs, the choice between two equally effective programs—one which is appreciably shorter in duration—quickly becomes apparent, because the shorter program dramatically reduces salary and lost-opportunity costs.

Considering salaries and lost-opportunity costs also can highlight the importance of offering training at a time and place that is most convenient to the employees and the organization. For instance, offering computer-based training (CBT) or a training class near the employees' work site can eliminate significant time lost travelling to and from training. Offering training outside of normal business hours can reduce lost production time; however, the cost analysis must also consider overtime pay for off hours. In order to accurately assess all of these costs, the SHE professional should actively engage knowledgeable individuals from the organization, such as production management and human resources professionals.

To compute the cost of student salaries, multiply the average loaded-salary rate by the number of hours of training (including travel time) and by the total number of students. Also include their incidental expenses. Finally, it may be important to consider the other business impacts such as lost-opportunity costs. In this context, lost-opportunity costs refer to productivity that may be lost in manufacturing, or sales opportunities that may be missed while employees are attending training. In a more generic sense, opportunity costs refer to an engineering economics concept that says whenever funds (or time) are invested elsewhere, the opportunity to obtain a return on investment is lost (Grant et al. 1990).

TABLE 1

Training Cost Data Worksheet—Computer-Based Training Example

TYPE OF COST	Estimated Unit Cost	Unit Multipliers	Total Cost	Timing of Expense
DEVELOPMENT COSTS				
Curriculum Development				
Internal salaries—loaded cost	$70/hour	150 hours	$10,500	Year 1
External consultants				
Meals, travel, and incidentals				
Materials				
Presentation materials (videos, etc.)				
Computer hardware				
Computer software	$8000	n/a	$8000	Year 1
Equipment purchases				
Marketing materials (flyers, etc.)				
IMPLEMENTATION COSTS				
Instructor Cost				
Internal salaries—loaded cost	$35/hour/ coach	20 × 24 hrs. 20 × 5 hrs.	$16,800 $3,500/yr.	Year 1 Year 2 to 5
External consultants				
Meals, travel, and incidentals	$100/coach	20 coaches	$2000	Year 1
Other business impacts				
Student cost				
Internal salaries—loaded cost	$35/hour/ employee	500 × 2 hrs. 4000 × 1 hr.	$35,000 + $140,000 = $175,000/yr.	Year 1 to 5
Meals, travel, and incidentals				
Other business impacts	$20/hour/ employee	50 × 2 hrs 500 × 1 hr	$2000 + $10,000 = $12,000/yr.	Year 1 to 5
Materials				
Student materials (manuals, etc.)				
Equipment rental				
Facilities cost				
Lease or rental of facilities				
Catering				
Cost of new construction				
Telecommunication charges				
Facilities overhead				
OTHER LIFE CYCLE COSTS				
Recordkeeping, evaluation of training,	$35/hour/	3 × 20 hrs.	$2100	Year 1
revisions to training	employee	3 × 15 hrs.	$1575	Year 2 to 5
Software licensing or maintenance fees	$1000/yr.	n/a	$1000/yr.	Year 1 to 5
Information technology support—	$52.50/hr.	100 hours	$5250	Year 1
internal salaries—loaded cost		40 hours	$2100	Year 2 to 5
		YEAR 1 COST	$232,650	
		YEARLY COST, YEARS 2 TO 5	$194,175	
		TOTAL PROGRAM COST, 5 YEARS	$1,009,350	

To obtain these lost-opportunity costs, SHE professionals typically need to rely on production or sales departments to estimate them. It is important to understand the basis for these estimates, so that there is no double-counting of certain costs and benefits (for in-stance, employee salaries will likely already be factored into the cost of producing a product).

Sometimes, the costs of temporary or reassigned personnel are included in a training-cost analysis. This is not necessary, however, when the internal salaries of those involved with the training are included in the cost analysis, because the inclusion presumes that employees will be away from their standard job and, therefore, not involved in productive work. If replacements fill in for these employees, it is reasonable to assume that the cost would be similar to the loaded-salary cost of the absent employees. Even though temporary personnel are typically paid less, they may also be less productive. If the costs of lost productivity, decreased work quality, or lost sales are above and beyond the loaded-salary cost of the absent employee, those costs should be included in the analysis. If someone does not fill in for employees while they are attending training, their salary should still be included in the cost analysis because of their reduced total productive hours for the week, month, or year.

A discussion of the cost entries in Table 1 will produce a better understanding of the reasons for including them in the overall cost analysis. In Table 1, under "Materials" in the section on "Implementation Costs," the costs of all materials provided to students should be included, such as handbooks, binders, training aids, and so on. This is also the place to include the cost of equipment rented for the training, such as audio-visual or training-aid equipment (if purchased, they should be included in development costs). A driving simulator for a defensive driving course or entry equipment for a confined space course are examples of training-aid equipment that might be rented.

Overhead costs for training may include the cost of corporate management, office space, conference rooms, and utilities. These costs are typically low or insignificant (2 percent or less of the total cost) if existing, suitable training facilities are available within the organization (Phillips 2003, Phillips et al. 2007). However, if these fixed overhead costs are actually increased—for instance, if facilities must be obtained, refurnished, or remodeled to accommodate training, then these associated costs should be identified and included in the analysis. If necessary, assistance from accounting, operations, or engineering departments may be required for an accurate estimate of these costs.

For technology-driven training, such as computer-based training, employees may need coaching on the use of the technology. Also, be sure to account for the cost of ongoing information-management support, whether internal or external.

The cost of compiling and tracking training records is another consideration. In some organizations, a validated tracking system may be required. Such a system could increase both the time and cost of the tracking system.

Finally, include the cost of at least one cycle to review, test, and revise the training program. This might include having a pilot program with a small class, for instance, or sending a selected group of employees through a computer-based program.

The estimated implementation costs for XYZ Telecom's HazCom training are shown in Table 1. Because the program is completely computer-based, one might expect instructor costs to be zero. However, in this example, a "coach" was to be trained at each of the company's twenty locations to provide instruction for employees who needed extra help getting started, a need created by the fact that many employees do not spend significant time on a computer. The coaches were expected to spend four hours being trained (including travel time) and twenty hours coaching employees the first year, followed by five hours for every subsequent year thereafter (program life was estimated to be five years). The loaded average salary rate used in the table for both coaches and students was $35 per hour, which was obtained from the human resources department, which indicated that the average company salary was $20 per hour and the cost of fringe benefits an additional $15 per hour. For the sake of simplicity, salary increases over the 5-year life of the program were neglected. However, this may be an important consideration, because average salaries typically increase every year, due to factors such as cost-of-living increases and general inflation. An assumption about the rate of inflation can be applied to estimate the amount of salary increases. The student costs in the example include the time employees spend in training, at $35 per hour, with 500 employees per year taking the initial 2-hour training and 4000 employees per year taking the 1-hour refresher. Because the training is delivered on computers at each employee's work site, the travel time and the incidental expenses are zero.

For one group of critical employees, additional lost-opportunity costs were identified. This group was the service department, whose employees, because of their level of training, could not be replaced by temporary personnel or reassigned internal personnel. When someone in this department is absent, a lesser volume of work is completed, including fewer installations of equipment for new customers. The absence of these employees also increases the average amount of out-of-service time for existing customers when problems arise. Previous estimates have shown the cost to the company to be at least $20 per hour when service department personnel are absent; the cost is due not only to lost business in the form of customers who are not charged for the days the services are out of order, but also due to customers who decide to use another service provider because the time required for repair or for establishing new service is unacceptable. The additional $20-per-hour cost for service department personnel is included. Approximately 50 new service department personnel will be required to take the initial 2-hour HazCom training, and 500 personnel will be required to take the 1-hour refresher course. Note that the above is, of course, a fictional example. These costs are difficult to estimate, but they should be kept in mind because they may be significant.

In the above example, all necessary instruction and student materials were electronic, so no cost was included. Also, all facilities and equipment necessary for the training were already available.

Other Life-Cycle Costs

Costs for the entire anticipated life cycle for a training class or program should be considered. Life-cycle costs may include costs for record keeping, for training evaluation, for reviewing and revising training content, and so on. Life-cycle assessment methods are discussed further in the introductory chapter, "Basic Economic Analysis and Engineering Economics."

In our example, the cost of record keeping is minimized due to the electronic nature of the training records. However, three human resources employees will each spend approximately fifteen hours per year running reports, at a loaded salary rate of $35 per hour. In the first year, each of these employees will spend an additional five hours being trained to run the reports.

All costs of revisions and updates to the software were included in a 5-year service contract with the software vendor. For $1000 per year, the vendor provides technical support and any necessary updates to the material based on changes and regulations. However, additional internal information-technology support was expected for networking issues and for calls to a centralized help desk. It was estimated, based on past experience with similar software, that 100 hours of support would be necessary in the first year, and 40 hours each year thereafter. The loaded salary rate for information-technology support personnel is $52.50 per hour ($30-per-hour base salary plus $22.50 fringe benefits).

Based on these estimates, the total cost to implement this program at XYZ Telecom for five years is over $1,000,000! Why even go through all this analysis! Is it not easier just to sell the $8000 software purchase to management than it is to explain why the total cost of the program is over a million dollars? Well, if this is where the analysis stopped, it would mostly likely be better to avoid presenting these intimidating numbers to management. But understanding the true cost of training is the first and most critical step to an effective cost-benefit analysis, which is the best way to reveal cost-saving opportunities within the organization.

COST-BENEFIT ANALYSIS IN SH&E TRAINING

At first glance, a cost-benefit analysis for SH&E training may appear bleak. As discussed in the introductory chapter, "Basic Economic Analysis and Engineering Economics," SH&E investments are not generally seen as making money for the organization. Worse yet, SH&E training often may have a lower benefit-to-cost ratio than other SH&E investments, such as hazard prevention and control or management leadership and employee involvement (Jervis and Collins 2001). However, recent studies have demonstrated that SH&E training can reduce injury rates, which consequently has financial benefits. In one study, safety-trained construction laborers were 12 percent less likely to file for workers' compensation, and this percentage increased to 42 percent for construction workers between 16 to 24 years old (Dong et al. 2004). In another study of workers in the plumbing and pipefitting industries, 3.4 percent of workers who received safety orientation were injured, compared to 11 percent of workers who did not receive the orientation (Kinn et al. 2000). Effectiveness of the training is a key consideration. Typically, only 10 to 15 percent of training is retained after one year, making training-program design for effective knowledge transfer critical (Machles 2002). Furthermore, we know that simply transferring knowledge will not change behaviors (Geller 2005), making frequent on-the-job reinforcement of SH&E training objectives even more critical than the training content.

Many of the benefits of training are intangible and difficult to quantify, making cost optimization and justification all the more critical. When an effective SH&E training program is implemented, and all of the benefits of the training are carefully considered, including the financial ones, the case for training becomes much stronger.

A well-executed cost-benefit analysis is the best tool available to both secure and manage available training funds. This type of analysis not only demonstrates the value of training to the organization, but it also identifies opportunities to improve the training process and to modify or eliminate ineffective programs. Furthermore, credibility with management is gained by using financial language that they are familiar with; this practice helps demonstrate to them the need to fund training initiatives (Phillips et al. 2007).

Unfortunately, such an analysis is rarely performed, at least on a formal basis. Too often, alternatives such as computer-based training or outsourcing of training are ruled out-of-hand as being too expensive, even though they might actually save the organization money. Worse yet, expensive, trendy programs are often implemented without an adequate analysis of their true benefit.

It is also important to recognize that cost-benefit analyses can be time-consuming. However, although the task may appear daunting, cost-benefit analysis of training has been successfully applied even at small- and medium-sized businesses (Devaney 2001). Be sure to identify in advance how the data will be used. Make sure the organization's management is willing to consider alternatives to existing training programs. If improvements will not even be considered, the cost-benefit analysis will be a waste of time.

Eventually, in order to secure funds for a new training initiative (or even to continue the existing budget), the costs must be justified. Whether this justification is a formal proposal to the board of directors or an informal presentation to the boss, it must be well thought out.

Benefits of an Effective SH&E Training Program

While reduced costs of training certainly may be one of the benefits of a new program, other benefits of training also must be evaluated and included, particularly for new programs or to justify programs that do not address regulatory requirements. For SH&E professionals, the benefits of training are typically cost-avoidance benefits, such as reduced injuries or fines that have been averted. However, some training may have other benefits, both tangible and intangible, such as increased productivity or improved organizational reputation. Some of the benefits to consider are:

- reduced workers' compensation costs
- reduced absenteeism and/or time away from work due to injury
- avoiding indirect costs of injuries and accidents (e.g., investigation costs, retraining of personnel, decreased productivity)
- avoiding fines due to regulatory noncompliance
- decreased legal liabilities (lawsuit settlements, etc.)
- avoiding property damage caused by incidents and accidents
- improved attendance and increased productivity
- improved public image as a responsible organization
- increased job satisfaction of employees

As discussed earlier, many of the benefits shown in the list above are intangible or are difficult to estimate. Still, it is appropriate and often necessary to include estimates of these benefits in a complete cost-benefit analysis. The estimates used should be realistic and conservative (i.e., not overstated) so that valid, credible conclusions are reached. Uncertainty in the data is best dealt with through a sensitivity analysis, as described later in this chapter. It is also reasonable to include in the analysis arguments such as "If we avoid one lost-time injury as a result of this training, it will pay for itself," as long as this outcome is a realistic possibility if employees are not trained. Some of these variables can also be analyzed after the fact; for instance, by comparing workers' compensation costs before and after training. Note that analyzing injury costs is a complex task, and further discussion of the costs of accidents is provided in other sections of this handbook, including the "Cost Analysis and Budgeting" chapter by Michael Toole in Section 1, "Management of Safety Engineering Work." When analyzing injury costs, it is particularly important to include indirect costs, which can range anywhere from 2 to 20 times the direct medical costs of an injury (Brady et al. 1997, Brandt 1999, Hinze 2000, Kinn et al. 2000, Miller 1995, OSHA 2010). The wide range of indirect costs cited in these references depends largely on what type of indirect costs are included and whether only costs to the employer are included, or whether societal costs are also considered. When deciding which factor to apply, it is important to consider the objectives of the analysis and the assumptions made in the reference used.

Investment Analysis Methods

As discussed in the introductory chapter, "Basic Economic Analysis and Engineering Economics," by James Ramsey and Anthony Veltri and the "Cost Analysis and Budgeting" chapter by Michael Toole in Section 1, there are many different ways to analyze and express cost data. Three concepts are used in this chapter to illustrate how to apply engineering economics to an SH&E training program: the return on investment (ROI), the break-even point, and net present worth (NPW). The ROI concept is particularly useful in communicating the costs and benefits of training to the organization because it is a simple but powerful concept, and it is a term that is frequently used and easily understood by management. However, the SH&E department should work with the finance department of the organization to learn and understand the terminology used there.

ROI and the break-even point are closely related terms. ROI is expressed as a percentage, and is equal to the net program benefits (savings and profits minus costs) divided by the total program cost (Phillips 2002, 17). The break-even point is the time required to recoup the initial or incremental investment and is equal to the program cost divided by the yearly benefits (Grant et al. 1990). For instance, consider a request to spend $20,000 to implement a new training program that will save the company $10,000 per year. In this simple example, the ROI per year is 50 percent ($10,000 ÷ $20,000) and the break-even point is two years ($20,000 ÷ $10,000 per year).

There are several ways financial planners use ROI information. First, alternatives may be compared, with the greatest percent return or shortest break-even point being, of course, the preferred choice from a financial perspective. A second way to use ROI is to determine whether to initiate a program at all. For instance, if the $20,000 investment example was for an office safety-training program that is not required by regulation, the organization would need to decide if a 50 percent ROI or a 2-year break-even point is acceptable. The ROI a given organization expects varies greatly, and depends on many factors, including the availability of capital, the company's profit margin, and so on. The finance department of an organization should be able to help determine how to present cost-benefit analysis information and also to determine what management might typically be looking for in terms of a return on investment.

As also discussed in the "Cost Analysis and Budgeting" chapter in Section 1, the ROI and break-even point, while powerful and easily understood, are both limited since they ignore the time value of money as well as all cash flows after the return on investment or break-even point is reached. Therefore, an even more powerful concept is net present worth. The power of this concept lies in its explication that all cash flows can be converted to one value and therefore accurately compared. Unfortunately, it is less widely understood and therefore not as commonly used in training cost analysis. However, if it is difficult to express the cost-benefit analysis in terms of ROI, or if it is necessary to compare many different options or more complex patterns of cash flow, one should consider using this or similar techniques, such as equivalent annual cost. An example of both techniques is presented at the end of this cost-benefit analysis discussion.

Now consider the example of XYZ Telecom's new HazCom training program. As seen in Table 1, the estimated cost to the organization is $232,650 in the first year, and $194,175 each year thereafter. Additional information is needed for the cost-benefit analysis. It is important to first analyze whether this option is preferable to others. In this example, only one alternative is considered. A separate cost analysis of the existing stand-up training revealed an estimated cost to the organization of $215,000 per year. So, in the first year, the additional cost to the organization to implement the program is $17,650 ($232,650 – $215,000). In subsequent years, $20,825 per year will be saved ($215,000 – $194,175). So the ROI = $20,825 per year ÷ $17,650 = 118 percent per year. The break-even point (beginning at the end of the first year) = $17,650 ÷ $20,825 = 0.85 years, or about ten months. In the view of most organizations, this is a relatively short period to recoup the investment. Please note that these calculations are simplified for demonstration purposes, and therefore assume linear and constant cost and benefit streams over time, and do not amortize the costs of benefits over a period of time. A more precise consideration of cash flow is described in a forthcoming example using the NPW concept.

In comparing the two training alternatives, consider what happens if a new piece of information is presented. XYZ Telecom instituted the new instructor-led HazCom training program two years ago. The cost to develop the new program and train the instructors via train-the-trainer courses was over $100,000. Should the fact that this cost will now be wasted deter the organization from pursuing the computer-based training program? The answer is no, it should not. The money spent previously cannot be recovered, and therefore the cost analysis

TABLE 2

Example Analysis of Two Training Alternatives Using Net Present Worth

Conversion of Yearly Costs (A) to Net Present Worth (NPW) at Year 1		
	Computer-based training	Instructor-led training
Year 1	NPW = $232,650	NPW = $215,000
Year 2–Year 5	A = $194,175; NPW = $643,360	A = $215,000; NPW = $712,360
NPW	NPW = $876,010	NPW = $927,360

A = Yearly Cost; NPW = Net Present Worth = A $\{[(1 + i)^n - 1] \div [i^*(1 + i)^n]\}$; n = number of years; i = rate of return = 8% or 0.08 for this example.

Assumes costs incurred at the beginning of each year. Equation for Net Present Worth based on Future Costs (NPW = $F(1 + i)^{-n}$) for Years 2–5 could also be used and is the appropriate choice if the annual yearly costs are not equal.

is not affected by this information; the new computer-based program is still more cost effective. One way to look at it is that there is only one past, and it affects all future alternatives equally. It is the difference between alternatives that is relevant in the comparison (Grant et al. 1990). Of course, depending on the objectives of the analysis, the sunk costs (money that has already been spent) may be relevant. For instance, if the objective is to retrospectively perform a cost-benefit analysis on a training program, the historical costs must be included. Furthermore, sunk costs may bias the organization's view of past choices, for better or for worse.

Another way to compare two alternatives is by using net present worth (also known as net present value in economics textbooks). The calculations of the NPW for the two alternatives in the XYZ Telecom example are shown in Table 2.

As shown in Table 2, the NPW (i.e., cost, in this case) of the computer-based training alternative is less than the NPW (cost) of the instructor-led training, and therefore the computer-based training should be chosen. A critical value in this analysis is the rate of return (*i*) chosen for the calculation, which should be based on the norms of the organization. In this example, a rate of return of 8 percent per year was used. Notably, organizations that expect high rates of return are not willing to accept long periods of time to achieve a return on investment.

Because HazCom training is required in the United States, as is similar training in many other countries, there is no alternative for XYZ Telecom but to provide and complete this training. However, if the training were not required, it would still be reasonable for management to request a cost-benefit analysis to determine if the training should be held, in which case the cost-benefit comparison is conducted between the training program and a *do-nothing* alternative. For the sake of argument, what if HazCom training were not a regulatory requirement? The cost-benefit analysis would need to compare the program costs ($232,650 in the first year and $194,175 each year thereafter) to the benefits and savings realized by the organization. Assume that HazCom training reduces costs for XYZ Telecom by $200,000 per year, in the form of reduced injury or accident rates. Based on this, during the first year, the organization incurs a net cost of $32,650 but has a net gain of $5825 per year thereafter. This translates to an ROI = $5825 per year ÷ $32,650 = 18 percent per year. The break-even point = $32,650 ÷ $5825 = 5.6 years. Although an 18 percent ROI may sound attractive, five years is a long waiting period for most organizations to reach the break-even point for an investment.

Sensitivity Analysis

One problem with many cost-benefit analyses is that they omit uncertainty as a consideration (Myers et al. 2008, Phillips et al. 2007). As discussed in the "Cost Analysis and Budgeting" chapter in Section 1, if a different set of assumptions were made in the cost-benefit analysis, a different conclusion might be drawn. Using techniques discussed in that chapter, a range of values should be considered for each variable, and the impact on the analysis should be considered. Spreadsheets and even more sophisticated software that utilize Monte Carlo analysis techniques may be necessary; however, even a simple substitution and recalculation, changing a few critical variables, can be very revealing.

For instance, as presented in the example in Table 1, consider the impact on the cost-benefit analysis if the number of hours spent by employees in training was 10 percent higher (internal salaries–loaded cost), or $192,500 instead of $175,000. Then, the annual cost (A)

shown in Table 2 would be $211,675 for computer-based training, with a total NPW of $933,993. This is more than the NPW for instructor-led training, and, unlike the first case, leads us to the conclusion that instructor-led training is the more cost-effective option—or, more accurately, that the true outcome is more uncertain than our initial analysis might imply.

More advanced techniques, such as a *Monte Carlo analysis*, may be necessary if there is a fairly wide range of uncertainty for multiple cost and benefit estimates in the analysis. In these cases, a random variable can be assigned to each cost and benefit across the expected possible range of outcomes. Then, a large number of iterations (100, 1000, or more) to calculate the ROI, NPW, or other outcome variable would be applied by using a random number generated for each cost and benefit.

Selling SH&E Training to Management

An SH&E training program is only one aspect of a comprehensive injury- or accident-prevention program. Furthermore, in the real world, organizations do not have unlimited funds and usually do not have sufficient funds for all of their desired programs. Theoretically, an optimal equilibrium point exists where total prevention and detection costs of SH&E programs equal the potential failure costs, including injuries and accidents (Behm et al. 2004, 23). Therefore, it is necessary to prioritize and optimize training programs based on the overall impact each program has on the organization's training goals and, of course, on the bottom line. Still, it is important to recognize that a more cost-efficient alternative is not always the best choice either, because training effectiveness must also be considered. An in-depth cost-benefit analysis should consider training effectiveness as a variable as well. As previously discussed, more effective training may provide greater benefits in terms of injury avoidance.

Sometimes, when the cost-benefit analysis of an existing training program reveals little or no ROI, those who implemented the program may feel threatened or insulted. Despite this situation, it is important to take an impartial view and to see the results of the analysis as an opportunity to make positive changes that management could ultimately view as a victory.

There are many reasons why a program may not have an attractive ROI. Sometimes, these reasons are due to suboptimal program design and are thus avoidable. For instance, an inadequate needs assessment may have been performed, and therefore injury rates were not impacted as expected. Or, perhaps a popular trend in the training industry was chosen, such as computer-based training, but it was not appropriate for the situation or application.

On the other hand, SH&E training will not always be financially beneficial. Even the likelihood and magnitude of potential fines by regulatory agencies and the potential costs of injuries and illnesses may not outweigh the costs of training. Less scrupulous organizations might use a cost-benefit analysis to justify discontinuing a training course, even if regulations require it. However, often the legal and moral obligations to provide training are paramount to the financial analysis. For instance, even if the potential for an injury due to the unexpected energization of machinery is extremely low in a particular organization, lockout/tagout training should be provided to employees, where applicable, because the potential severity of an injury is so great, and because there are regulations requiring such a program.

If a cost-benefit analysis is performed, at some point a presentation of the findings will likely be necessary. When preparing a presentation, first examine the cost-benefit analysis and establish a position. Identify the goals of the presentation. Is the goal to secure a budget? Or is it to gain management's support for the goals of the training program? Focus the message specifically to achieve these goals.

Be prepared to make specific requests or recommendations and be able to back them up. Also be sure to consider how and whether the recommendations fall in line with the organization's overall culture, strategies, goals, and metrics; be sure to highlight any areas where there is a direct, positive impact. This might include not only organizational goals around SH&E, such as incident rates, but also organizational financial goals, such as profitability through reduced operating costs.

Assess the attitudes that the target audience is likely to have. Will they be supportive? Resentful? Threatened? Tailor the message accordingly. For instance, if the audience is likely to be skeptical of the findings, devote a little extra time to providing background on the evaluation process; this step should help build credibility for the results.

The exact message depends on the culture of the organization and the anticipated level of support by management. In a highly regulated industry, such as pharmaceuticals, making the case based on regulatory obligations may be very effective. In other organizations, an appeal based on humanitarian values (saving lives and avoiding injuries) may be the best approach. However, management will pay more attention to the message when it is expressed in financial terms (Bird 1996). In general, the most effective way to convince management to invest in SH&E is first to convince them of the inherent worth in reducing the risk of harm (i.e., tug at their heart strings) and then to clinch the argument with the supportive economic analysis (i.e., appeal to their purse strings) (Myers et al. 2008). If the SH&E program recommendation is based on legal or moral issues, but the cost-benefit analysis is not overly supportive of the recommendation, the presentation obviously should not focus on the financials.

Finally, if the cost-benefit analysis reflects negatively on an existing training program, be sure to present a plan for improvement. Do not be afraid to suggest *cutting your losses* and scrapping a program in favor of a new approach.

MANAGING A TRAINING BUDGET
Getting the Most Out of the Training Dollars

As professionals, SH&E practitioners are asked to perform a function that many of them are ill prepared for: managing a budget. Even though this section is not intended to provide a comprehensive discussion of the subject, it does provide some helpful tips for training budget management as well as some time- and cost-saving ideas for a training program. For more information on budgeting for SH&E, see both the introductory chapter, "Basic Economic Analysis and Engineering Economics," and the "Cost Analysis and Budgeting" chapter in Section 1.

A needs analysis is critical to establishing the scope of the training program. First, determine what courses will be offered, including regulatory requirements (e.g., HazCom), courses aimed at addressing a specific hazard or source of injuries (e.g., ergonomics), and courses that are situation- or process-specific (e.g., training on grounding and bonding for employees who work with flammable liquids). In order to facilitate the rest of the budgeting process, consider prioritizing courses based on whether they are "must haves," such as regulatory requirements, or whether they are expected to have a significant impact, or whether they are "nice to haves," which might include classes that are not required by any regulation or have more uncertain and less significant benefits. Also consider conducting a cost-benefit analysis of each course before prioritizing.

Note that when working within an existing budget or with limited resources, it may be necessary to cut some courses from the budget, or to offer certain courses in a more cost-effective manner. If a larger budget is required, though, do not be afraid to request an increase if justified.

Table 3 shows an example of a budget-planning worksheet. Internal costs, such as the cost of employee time, while important when performing a cost-benefit analysis, are not considered in this budget. Examples of both capital (assets that can depreciate over time) and expense items (ongoing costs) are included.

One word of caution—do not assume an organization's existing list of training courses to accurately reflect what is really needed. Often, training is conducted year after year without adequate consideration to its relevance and, in fact, its appropriateness; furthermore, the frequency of the required refresher courses may not have been adequately considered when the class was established. So define the scope of the training program based not on what currently exists, but rather on a careful needs analysis. Section I of this volume provides more detail on regulatory issues in SH&E training. At times, tough decisions will need to be made. For some courses, new training materials may have to wait until another year. Other courses may need to be cut out completely.

Consider the example presented in Table 3. After submitting this request, the SH&E manager was told that she had to trim $18,000 from the expense budget. What courses should she cut? One approach is to jus-

TABLE 3

Sample SH&E Training Budget–Planning Worksheet

Budget Line Item	Capital	Expense
New Employee Orientation		
Materials		$1000
Hazard Communication		
New computer-based program	$8000	
Excavation Safety		
External consultants		$12,000
Employee meals, travel, etc.		$24,000
Lockout/Tagout		
Employee meals, travel, etc.		$3000
Electrical Safety		
External train-the-trainer course		$3000
Employee meals, travel, etc.		$4000
Emergency Response Teams		
External consultants		$3000
Course materials (suits, gloves, etc.)		$500
Employee meals, travel, etc.		$1000
Emergency Action Plan		
Course materials		$500
Laboratory Safety		
Annual fee, existing software		$1000
Ergonomics		
External consultants		$15,000
Office Safety		
Course materials		$500
Defensive Driving		
External train-the-trainer course		$2000
Employee meals, travel, etc.		$5000
Fire Safety		
External consultants		$6500
Fall Protection		
External consultants		$10,000
Other		
New electronic records database	$18,000	
TOTALS	$26,000	$92,000

TOTAL ANNUAL TRAINING BUDGET = $118,000

tify why funds cannot be cut from the budget, and this may work, given the right data or persuasive arguments. Those arguments may not suffice in every situation, though. So which courses can be sacrificed?

Cutting ergonomics training might be a tempting choice if regulations do not require it, but in this case the SH&E manager was expecting the program to reap great benefits in terms of injury reduction. So she looked elsewhere. The excavation safety course was contracted with a reputable national firm and included hands-on demonstrations using backhoes to slope the sides of a trench and to construct shoring.

Employees were brought in from multiple locations to attend the training. Utilizing a cost-benefit analysis, a much more cost-effective alternative was indentified: to purchase the training materials and deliver the course in-house, forgoing the hands-on demonstration. The SH&E manager was concerned, though, that the course may not have the same impact without the hands-on practice. But she realized this: the target audience digs trenches and constructs shoring nearly every day. The training objective at this point was really to influence behavior, because all but the newest employees were familiar with the regulations and techniques of excavation safety. So, in the end, the organization was able to save most of the requested $18,000 budget cut by using the new approach to this training class.

When making a request to spend capital or expense money from the budget, consider what policies or thresholds the organization has for these requests. For instance, capital expenditures for items such as new computer equipment may have a different process than an expense expenditure, which might include items such as paying for an instructor or training materials. Also, the number and level of approvals necessary often depends on the total dollars spent.

When submitting a yearly budget request, carefully consider how budgets are managed in the organization. Some common budgeting techniques are zero-based budgeting and baseline budgeting (Shim 2009). If an organization uses baseline budgeting, it needs to look at the previous year's budget and justify why maintaining or increasing the budget is necessary, or, more commonly, where costs can be cut. On the other hand, with zero-based budgeting, the entire budget must be justified *from the ground up* each year, in which case the concepts in this chapter are even more critical.

Another important concept in budgeting is opportunity costs. When money is budgeted for a certain program or purpose and left unspent, there is a cost to the organization in terms of missed opportunity (Shim 2009). For instance, the money could have been invested elsewhere to grow a business or to earn interest. Thus, one must not fall into the trap of requesting more money than one really needs or can spend.

Effective budget execution includes continuous record keeping, tracking, and monitoring. And even though the actual tracking and record keeping may be performed by the accounting or finance departments, do not rely solely on these departments to accurately reflect where the budget stands. Lag time in debiting accounts may cause financial reports to overestimate the amount of funds that is truly still available. Therefore, use a log to track expenses as they occur, similar to using a check register for personal expenses.

Continuous Improvement

All training programs and courses are candidates for continuous improvement. Some ideas for saving time and money for SH&E training are as follows:

- Shorten training times by focusing course content on the training objectives.
- Provide training materials, such as bulky handouts, electronically to save printing costs.
- For geographically dispersed audiences, save on travel costs by using computer-based training, teleconferences, or a train-the-trainer approach.
- Do not use highly experienced, highly paid trainers to teach basic topics if other qualified trainers are available (or could be trained to deliver the material).
- Save on development costs by purchasing off-the-shelf training programs.
- Where travel time is not an issue, consider providing long courses in shorter segments. It may be possible to offer shorter segments at more convenient times or outside of core business hours.
- When multiple topics are covered in one course, switching to several modules may allow more flexibility for employees in terms of attending only the specific segments they need.

Consider coaching, on-the-job training, or other alternatives to traditional training that may save significantly on the cost of instructors, development, materials, and travel.

Another source of ideas for continuous improvement of training costs may come from course attendees. If feedback consistently indicates that the course is too long, a shorter class might accomplish the same learning goals in a more efficient manner. Or, if many employees indicate that they would prefer computer-based training over the current instructor-led course, then perhaps computer-based training would allow for easier scheduling and impact less on employee productivity.

Cost-benefit analyses must be periodically reviewed or redone to determine if the current program is still the most cost efficient (Grant et al. 1990). If, ten years ago, computer-based training was considered too expensive, it may be that technological developments in the ensuing years have made that alternative more attractive for the present. Furthermore, assumptions made in the original analysis may no longer be valid, or they may have been proved wrong through experience. Perhaps the initial cost-benefit analysis for outsourcing respiratory-protection training and fit-testing was based on a much smaller number of employees than are currently in the program. Outsourcing may now be justified, so it may be time to crunch the numbers again. The frequency with which the analysis should be redone depends on how rapidly the content and available delivery alternatives are changing. At least once per year, when reviewing the SH&E training program, ask the following questions:

1. Are improved alternatives available?
2. Are substantial changes to the content required?
3. Is the program no longer meeting its objectives?

If the answer to any of these questions is yes, a cost-benefit analysis to compare alternatives should be considered.

In conclusion, the concepts described in this chapter, including cost accounting, cost-benefit analysis, and budgeting, are all critical tools in the ongoing efforts to improve training. By employing these concepts, SH&E professionals are likely to not only save their organizations time and money, but also to improve their own status and image with management.

REFERENCES

Asche, F., and Terje Aven. 2004. "On the Economic Value of Safety." *Risk, Decision and Policy* 9(3):263–367.

Behm, M., A. Veltri, and I. K. Kleinsorge. 2004. "The Cost of Safety." *Professional Safety* (April) 49:22–29.

Bird, F. E. 1996. *Safety and the Bottom Line*. Logansville, GA: Febco.

Brady, W., J. Bass, R. Moser, Jr., G. W. Anstadt, R. R. Loeppke, and R. Leopold. 1997. "Defining Total Corporate Health and Safety Costs—Significance and Impact." *Journal of Occupational and Environmental Medicine* 39(3):224–231.

Brandt, J. 1999. "Hitting the Injury Iceberg." *Ergonomics Supplement*, pp. 160–165.

Devaney, M. 2001. "Measuring ROI of Computer Training in a Small- to Medium-Sized Enterprise." In *In Action: Measuring Return on Investment*, vol. 3, pp. 185–196. Edited by J. Phillips. Alexandria, VA: American Society for Training and Development.

Dong, X., P. Entzel, Y. Men, R. Chowdhury, and S. Schneider. 2004. "Effects of Safety and Health Training on Work-Related Injury Among Construction Laborers." *Journal of Occupational & Environmental Medicine* 46(12):1222–1228.

Geller E. S. 2005. *People-Based Safety: The Source*. Virginia Beach, VA: Coastal Training Technologies Corp.

Grant, E. L., W. G. Ireson, and R. Leavenworth. 1990. *Principles of Engineering Economy*. 8th ed. New York: John Wiley & Sons.

Head, G. E. 1994. *Training Cost Analysis: A How-To Guide for Trainers and Managers*. Alexandria, VA: American Society for Training and Development.

Hinze, J. 2000. "Incurring the Costs of Injuries Versus Investing in Safety." In *Construction Safety and Health Management*. Edited by R. J. Coble et al. New York: Prentice-Hall.

Jervis, S., and T. R. Collins. 2001. "Measuring Safety's Return on Investment." *Professional Safety* 46(9):18–23.

Kinn, S., S. A. Khuder, M. S. Besesi, and S. Woolley. 2000. "Evaluation of Safety Orientation and Training Programs for Reducing Injuries in the Plumbing and Pipefitting Industries. *Journal of Occupational and Environmental Medicine* 42:1142–1147.

Machles, D. 2002. "Training Transfer Strategies for the Safety Professional." *Professional Safety*, February 2002.

Miller, T. R., and M. Galbraith. 1995. "Estimating the Costs of Occupational Injury in the United States." *Accident Analysis and Prevention* 27(6):741–747.

Myers, M., H. Cole, J. Mazur, and S. Isaacs. 2008. "Economics & Safety: Understanding the Cost of Injuries and Their Prevention." *Professional Safety*, April 2008.

Nathan, E. P. "Determining the ROI of an Online English as a Second Language Program." *Performance Improvement* 48(6):39–48.

Occupational Safety and Health Adminstration (OSHA). 2010. *OSHA $afety Pays Program* (retrieved October 2, 2010). www.osha.gov/ dcsp/ smallbusiness/safety pays/index.html

Phillips, J. 2003. *Return on Investment in Training and Performance Improvement Programs*. 2d ed. Burlington, MA: Butterworth-Heinemann.

Phillips, P. P. 2002. *The Bottom Line on ROI; Basics, Benefits and Barriers to Measuring Training and Performance Improvement*. Atlanta, GA: CEP Press.

Phillips, P., J. Phillips, R. Stone, and H. Burkett. 2007. *The ROI Field Book: Strategies for Implementing ROI in HR and Training*. Burlington, MA: Butterworth-Heinemann.

Shim, J. K., and J. G. Siegel. 2009. *Budgeting Basics and Beyond*. Hoboken, NJ: John Wiley & Sons Inc.

Waagen, Alice K. 2000. *How to Budget Training*. Alexandria, VA: American Society for Training and Development.

ADDITIONAL RESOURCES

Adams, S. 2003. "Costs Drive Safety Training Needs." *HR Magazine*, January 2003.

Kilgore, C., and P .L. Clemens. 2008. "Economy-Based Countermeasure Decisions: A Tutorial for SH&E Professionals." *Professional Safety*, April 2008.

Purcell, A. 2000. "20/20 ROI." *Training & Development*, July 2000.

Snyder, M. 2004. "The Time-Cost-Quality Triangle." *Training & Development*, April 2004.

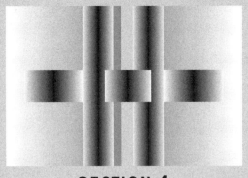

LEARNING OBJECTIVES

- Understand the concepts of assessment for safety and health training.

- Be able to discuss the benefits of assessment and their use in improving safety and health training.

- Apply the concepts of assessment to safety and health training.

- Be able to discuss the assessment criteria provided in ANSI Z490.1.

- Understand benchmarking basics and be able to apply them to safety and health training.

BENCHMARKING AND PERFORMANCE CRITERIA

Richard A. Stempniak and Linda Tapp

ANY COMPANY THAT regularly provides safety and health training for its employees is making a considerable investment of money and staff time. A good investment will yield a good return on investment (ROI). Because the principal value of employee safety and health training is in what employees *learn*, evaluation or assessment of a program's value should concentrate on "doing assessment as if learning matters most" (Angelo 1999).

Assessment is the process of collecting "the best possible data about . . . learning and the factors that affect it" (Walvoord 2004).

Breaking the definition down, "best possible data" are generally those indicators available to the person(s) doing the assessment during and after instruction. These indicators can include:

- questions answered by employees about the subject being taught during the instruction session
- instructors' judgment on whether the employees they are training understand and retain the information presented to them
- questions answered by employees after a training session regarding their perception of the effectiveness of the instruction
- employee performance on the job after training
- formal grades or quiz results
- impact on company operations

KIRKPATRICK'S FOUR LEVELS OF EVALUATION

Donald Kirkpatrick set the standards for training effectiveness metrics when he identified four distinct categories of measurement. These are commonly known as the four levels of evaluation. These four levels are:

- Level 1: The nature of employees' reactions

- Level 2: The extent of employees' learning
- Level 3: The extent to which employees' learning is reflected in their on-the-job behavior
- Level 4: The extent to which employees' changed behavior affects the organization (Kirkpatrick 1998)

The first two levels are relatively simple to evaluate. Employees' reactions to a training class can be determined by means of a simple questionnaire or by what is often known in the training industry as a "smile sheet," which usually asks participants to rank the instructor and instruction on a scale of 1–5. One way to measure the extent of employees' learning is by using both pre-test and post-test evaluations. The improvement, evident in increasing percentages of correct responses, helps to demonstrate how much trainees have learned as a result of their training. Levels 3 and 4, however, are much harder to evaluate, because the data involved can require either subjective or objective measurement (Cheney 2001). If employees have been trained in the safe handling of chemicals, it may be difficult to measure how they apply this knowledge once back on the job. Who should do the observations depends on the particular program in place. It could be the supervisor but it could also be a safety trainer or line worker trained in observation techniques. One method that can be used is making workplace observations that are then recorded and tracked—but, again, it is important to have taken baseline measurements by making pre-training observations. Even when results of the training are known, fully understanding their effects on an organization can be even more difficult. Training may affect many unknown areas within the organization—or even have external effects. Decreases in worker compensation costs or reduced employee turnover can provide partial methods of measurement, but any such forms of evaluation should insist on tying the data as directly as possible to the training given. Still other effects may never be known—an employee may use safe chemical handling techniques at home as well as at work because of the training presented, thereby avoiding a serious chemical burn at home.

WHY ASSESS?

Assessment has several purposes:

- determining the ROI the program yields the company because of lower accident and injury rates.
- continuously improving employee safety and health training (We are assuming this is one of the company's regular business goals. If not, and the company has set no goals whatsoever for its safety and health program, it will be nearly impossible to complete a valid assessment. As the saying goes, "If you don't know where you're going, how will you know when you get there?")
- continuously locating and evaluating factors affecting safety and health training (whether positively or negatively), including the physical environment during training, the trainer's knowledge of the subject and ability to teach, class size, individual employees' ability to learn (particularly as affected by interest in learning the subject), the training's format and content, including length of class, and the existence of language barriers
- discovering what employees are learning from the program and what their reactions to it are: for example, are employees applying their training on the job; is such application achieving results—a better safety record with fewer accidents and injuries, less lost work time, increased productivity, and more employees taking personal responsibility for following safety procedures (Kirkpatrick 1998)
- identifying topics or themes that are missing in the training (Are expected improvements in behavior or knowledge not seen after the training has concluded? A topic or tangential topic may have been subconsciously excluded from the class content.)

Assessment is intended to have a local, fairly rapid (evident within months) effect on the safety and health training program in order to help the company more rapidly attain its goals. Assessment focuses on continuous improvement by following a cycle of evaluation, planning, and implementation of change as necessary. To be as effective as possible, assessment results should take their appropriate place in the company's annual planning and budgeting process. A review of incidents and accident investigations that have occurred at the facility can also be used to identify gaps in existing training.

The Benefits of Assessment

The greatest benefit assessment can give a company is in its role as a catalyst for change. Done properly, assessment can provide a basis for wiser planning, budgeting, and revision of procedures, preventing the wasting of resources in response to vague notions about what might (or should) be effective (Walvoord 2004).

Continuously assessing safety training effectiveness and rapidly instituting changes in that training can save lives and reduce levels of injury and property damage, allowing the company to redirect funds from insurance and compensation budget lines to even more productive uses.

Types of Assessment: Summative, Formative, and Systematic

The Occupational Safety and Health Administration (OSHA) includes three methods of evaluating training effectiveness in its informational booklet on training requirements (OSHA Pub. 2254). These include student opinion, supervisor observations, and workplace improvements, which can be further divided into five commonly accepted types of training evaluation: participant satisfaction, learning outcomes, attitude changes, behavior/job performance changes, and productivity/accomplishment of goals (Dinardi 2003). These five areas of evaluation can be considered formative assessments, summative assessments, systemic assessments, or some combination of them.

Summative assessment occurs after training has been completed and is used to evaluate the overall effectiveness of a fully developed training course, informing decisions about whether to continue, expand, modify, or drop particular training in response to its results. Summative assessment measures outcomes. In its simplest

form it answers the question: Did the training cause the company to achieve its stated goal? The primary audience of summative assessment is management.

Assume that the company has established "the elimination of all preventable motor-vehicle accidents" as a goal for a safety training course it commissioned. The course is to be taught over six weeks, and classes will be held every Monday morning from 10:00 A.M. to noon. A summative assessment of that course would issue a report containing the number of preventable motor-vehicle accidents during the quarter *prior* to the completion of the training course and the number of preventable motor accidents in the quarter *after* the completion of the course. If the second number dropped to zero, the course would be judged a success.

A more complex summative assessment would not only answer the above question but also document the course's processes, including how the selection of students for this course was made and what measurements of their learning were taken during the course. The assessment would also report on any unplanned outcomes, such as the reduction in miles driven by employees in company vehicles during the quarter (the assessment process would have to continue to discover the cause of such an occurrence; perhaps the employees stopped driving company vehicles for personal errands). A summative assessment would help to determine actions and conditions that affected training outcomes such as these.

Formative assessment takes place while the training program is under development. Though the trainer may be using a particular training outline or manual, it is not written in stone and may be changed in response to the formative assessment conducted. The conclusions drawn from formative assessment are used to modify and improve the processes of the training while the course is still being developed or is underway.

When assessing the training during the development phase, it is important to ask three things: (1) Is the training understandable? Can the trainees easily understand the material being presented and the instructions for interactive activities? (2) Is the training content accurate—for example, is the material that is presented indeed correct? (3) Is the training functional—do all parts work? Do the handouts match the slides?

Do prepared quizzes adequately cover the content of the class? Does the training match the current course objectives? It is essential to consider understandability, accuracy, and functionality during the development phase (Carliner 2003).

Formative assessment observes training activities, anticipates potential problems, and monitors employees' current job conduct for positive or negative changes that may have been brought about by training (Boulmetis and Dutwin 2000).

In the example above, the formative assessor may monitor the job performance of those being trained. Here are some typical questions: Did the accident reports of one employee, or certain employees, suddenly increase or decrease as a result of training? Did those whose preventable accident count increased misunderstand something the trainer said? Did the awareness level of an employee or employees increase regarding a particular situation or activity? What about those employees whose preventable accident count decreased? Did a particular point made by the trainer hit home? Should that particular point be repeated and emphasized again in training? Are most of the employees consistently late to class or late in returning to work?

The formative assessor should report these data to the trainer, allowing him or her to make changes in the course that will eliminate misunderstandings, place more emphasis on key concepts or ideas, and (if necessary) adjust training dates and times to increase employee attendance.

This type of assessment is detailed, diagnostic, and informal. It asks why negative results suddenly occurred and what trainers can do right now—before the next class session, even—to prevent those results from occurring again.

Systematic assessment examines a training program systematically by studying the input, throughput, and output associated with it. *Input* includes the trainer, the employees, the location of instruction, the outlines of topics or subjects the trainer will cover at each training session, and training materials and equipment such as printed handouts, projectors, and viewing screens. The room where the training will take place should be large enough for each trainee to feel comfortable and able to comfortably participate in class activities and see all visual aids, such as slides

or flipcharts. The benefits of good training will be diminished if overcrowding distracts students (Dinardi 2003). In addition to supplying adequate space, the training location should also be climate controlled, well lit and ventilated, and free of outside distractions. Unfavorable physical factors can make it difficult for trainees to pay attention to instruction (Hutchinson 2003). All elements of input, including the trainer and the employees in training, should be planned for before the first training session. *Throughput* refers to those events or actions that occur as the training is conducted, as well as to the adequacy of resources, including teaching aids, handouts, and facilities. *Output* is the results of the training and includes the number of employees trained, the total cost of the training both in dollars and staff time, and (of course) the safety performance of the employees after training. The efficiency of the training process is assessed in this state (Boulmetis and Dutwin 2000).

Systematic assessment is essential to understanding whether an organization met its goals and what amount of measurable improvement followed the training. These improvements are not limited to improvements in safety records, but also include an organization's overall increase in performance and productivity.

Systematic assessment is a *before, during, and after* progression. Before training, define the goals of the training. During training, collect and organize evidence about the employees' learning process. After training, ask, "Did the training help meet the training goals?" All three steps must be performed to complete a systematic assessment.

WHO ASSESSES, AND WHEN?

Assessment may be carried out internally or externally—that is, by an employee or by an outside consultant. Whoever assesses should ideally be part of the planning process that organizes the training and should stay involved, participating in the formative assessment process while the training is developed and conducted, and perform the summative assessment after the training is completed.

Ideally, the assessor involves all the stakeholders in assessment, just as all of them should be involved in planning. The *stakeholders* are everyone involved in the training program, including the management; external sources of funding, if they exist; training staff; employees to be trained; and the supervisors of those employees. Frequently these last two groups of stakeholders are left out of both planning and assessment during and after the completion of training—especially when the training is driven by an urgent need (such as when management perceives a need for training because accident frequency and associated costs have recently increased dramatically). In a case like this, management orders the training of employees. The company's training staff (or a person who is designated) sets up training through an internal employee or external consultant, and training is then conducted. The accident record may improve, but it may not. Lack of improvement after training may be caused by the exclusion of the recipients of the training—the employees and their supervisors—from the assessment process (Boulmetis and Dutwin 2000).

Except in cases where there is an emergency need to train employees about a particular hazard that has just injured another employee, a company should use of a formal training planning cycle that includes a standing committee, a formal group of employees, or a training department that makes recommendations to management about the nature of the company's training needs: What subjects should be taught, and by whom? Who should receive the training? What assessment process should be used? This group may even be able to suggest possible external sources of funding to underwrite the cost of training.

Methods of Assessment and Data Collection

Within the several types of assessment discussed above are two methods by which data can be collected; one is direct and the other is indirect.

Direct assessment attempts to evaluate trainees by examining empirical data such as that provided by exams, quizzes, projects, and future on-the-job behaviors and attitudes. The *one-minute paper* technique elicits prompt but (because of its brevity) limited employee answers to one or two specific questions about the course in general or a specific class session. Cross and Angelo (1998) explain the technique by stating that a trainer should stop the class session a

few minutes early, posing one or two questions to which trainees are asked to react. The trainees write their answers anonymously on half-sheets of paper. The instructor simply tabulates the answers and makes note of any useful comments.

Pros: This method can provide valuable self-correcting feedback, enabling more effective teaching and learning. It allows a quick response to the trainees and demonstrates respect for and interest in student reactions, encouraging active engagement in the class process. It also allows individual students to compare their responses with the class as a whole.

Cons: If one-minute papers are overused or poorly used, the technique can degenerate into a gimmick or an exercise in polling, obtaining feedback that neither the trainer nor the rest of the class want to hear or act upon. Preparing a question that can be immediately and clearly comprehended and quickly answered can be harder than it sounds (Cross and Angelo 1998).

The most direct method of assessment is collecting data on the accident records of trainees after they return to the job (if the intent of the training was to change behaviors that caused accidents or to provide new safety information to be used in the prevention of accidents). This is part of summative assessment and is probably the major piece of data at which management will look. Similarly, direct observations of behavior can be made. If safe forklift-driving training was given, the safe forklift-driving skills of the trainees could be observed and evaluated. If training was provided on company-specific energy control procedures, the correct applications of these procedures can be observed and recorded.

Indirect assessment measures include asking employees (and their supervisors) how well they thought they learned. This is qualitative (rather than quantitative) evidence, but if employees are asked a week or two after the training has been completed, they will have a better perspective on their own retention of the training material, and their supervisors will have had a better opportunity to observe their employees' on-the-job behavior (Walvoord 2004).

Cohen and Colligan, in their study *Assessing Occupational Safety and Health Training* (1998), cited numerous examples of successful training programs that were designed to reduce specific accidents or injuries (see

Table 1). Table 2 provides extracts from the Bureau of Labor Statistics's work-injury reports that indicate real or possible gaps in job safety and health training. This study is an example of a systematic assessment.

As the above examples demonstrate, health and safety training requires continual assessment conducted as if *learning matters most*. By monitoring, and by using feedback indicators, instructors can continue to improve the quality of training by changing and adjusting the training course outline and instructional methods.

BENCHMARKING

Benchmarking is about comparing and measuring performance against other similar organizations and then using lessons learned from the best ones to introduce breakthrough improvements (Koskela 1992). Benchmarking can and should be used in goal-setting, especially if the organization's goals are to perform at the highest level. One example can be found in the United States' attempt to lower traffic fatalities by comparing the U.S. rates to other nations and then using this data to set goals (TRB 2010).

Benchmarking is a type of assessment based on comparison to external activities and sources. These external activities and sources can be external to the department being benchmarked (such as another department conducting safety and health training), external to the company, or even external to the industry. The idea of benchmarking started in 1979 when the Xerox Corporation decided to be a leader in their industry. Businesses have used benchmarking to improve in all areas, from financial controls to employee compensation packages. Benchmarking can also be applied to health and safety training—with dramatic results. Benchmarking is easier to implement in areas involving easily measurable outputs, such as production. In areas that are more difficult to measure—such as training—it proves to be more of a challenge.

Benchmarking is best treated as a continuous process whereby the effectiveness of the safety training is continuously monitored and measured so that the quality and desired outcomes continue to increase.

What is benchmarking in relation to safety and health training? Benchmarking is the process of learning from the best in order to make a program or process stronger. Its three steps are (1) evaluation of the training program intended to be improved, enabling the (2) identification of weaknesses or other areas for improvement, and, finally, (3) identification of other companies with strong safety and health training programs to look at for best practices and leadership.

One of the main benefits of benchmarking is its ability to rapidly help a program improve. Without benchmarking, changes to a training process or program may occur only by trial-and-error. Needed improvements may take longer to identify and make as issues are more clearly seen. Benchmarking can help identify what has already been proven to work at other companies by comparing safety and health training programs, allowing personnel to make the changes necessary to bring their programs closer to the *benchmark* or the level of excellence set by the identified leader. This can rapidly improve the quality of a safety and health training program.

Types of Benchmarking

Benchmarking can be either internal or external. External benchmarking can further be broken down into three types: competitive, cooperative, and collaborative.

Internal benchmarking occurs when different parts of a company are compared to each other, or when one part is compared to itself over time. The number of hours employees attend training from year to year is one type of safety training benchmark used by some companies. *External benchmarking* involves looking outside the company. *Competitive* benchmarking looks at what competitors are doing; although this information may be difficult to discover, informal research can help. *Cooperative* benchmarking targets an unrelated industry against which to benchmark, so long as the other industry has the same practices in the area of safety and health training. *Collaborative* benchmarking occurs when similar companies voluntarily share information (sometimes anonymously) for the purpose of benchmarking.

TABLE 1

Training Intervention Studies as Found in the Literature Addressing Various Types of Occupational Hazards

| | | | | Safety/Injury Hazard Control | | |
Work Setting Operation (Ref)	Training Objective	Training Plan	Evaluation Method	Extra-Training Factors	Results	Comments
96 operators of industrial lift trucks at two warehouse sites. (Cohen & Jensen 1984).	To promote operator awareness and adoption of 14 specific actions critical to safer operator/vehicle use.	Focus was on 14 worker behaviors that could be observed, measured, and related to accident occurrences as defined by a task-hazard analysis, 5 training sessions (20–45 minutes long) were given on 5 successive days; 1 introductory, 3 instructional, and 1 practice/exercises. Slides were used to show incorrect/correct behaviors; Practice sessions had group grade performance of each trainee on a practice run.	3 observers counted frequencies of the correct/incorrect 14 behaviors as noted at 8 locations at each warehouse on a daily basis. At Warehouse 1, operators were divided in 3 groups: training only, training + feedback, and a control group that was trained only after 1st post-training evaluation. Study plan had monthly pre-training and post-training 1 & 2 phases, plus a retention phase that was 3 months after post-training 2. At Warehouse 2, all workers trained at same time and all received feedback.	All levels of management had input into the program and supported its development. Feedback supplied daily through verbal and posted summaries of group performance. All groups subjected to training set at 80% goal attainment level.	For Warehouse 1, at end of retention phase and after all workers trained, overall decrease in incorrect acts was 44%. Training + feedback group showed best scores in post-training 1. At Warehouse 2, overall improvement in 14 behaviors was 70%. 12 of 12 target behaviors indicated clear improvements; 2 were resisted because they involved an uncomfortable posture, and exposure to exhaust fumes.	The effect of training to achieve safer work behaviors is clear. Question: Will it reduce accident/injury rate in lift truck operations?
55 workers in 4 sections of the vehicle maintenance division of a city public works department showing one of the highest injury rates as compared with other divisions (Komaki, Heinzman & Lawson 1980).	To effect changes in worker behavior with regards to proper equipment/tool use, wearing personal protective/safety equipment, improving housekeeping procedures, and other actions aimed at upgrading general safety performance.	Accident logs for past 5 years reviewed and weaknesses in current safety program used to frame behavioral targets specific to each of the 4 sections. After baseline observations directed to existent behaviors, workers attended session to view/discuss slides of unsafe acts and ways to prevent them, which became formulated into safety rules. Copies of these rules issued to workers.	Checklist of prescribed safety behaviors was used by trained observers who monitored workers' actions in each section 3–5 times per week. Study plan had 5 phases where these observations were taken to show the effects of training alone, training plus feedback, withdrawing and then reinstituting feedback as compared with baseline data. Total study span was 45 weeks; phases varied from 5–11 weeks.	Upon completion of training phase, supervisors of each section indicated goals to be met in complying with safety rules and observed and provided feedback on level of adherence through graphic displays. In subsequent phases, this graphic feedback was withdrawn and then reinstituted to define its effect in enhancing safe behaviors as prescribed in the original training.	Comparing % safe acts against the pre-training baseline data for the various phases showed the following gains: Training alone = 9%; Training + feedback = 26%; Feedback withdrawn = 17% (reduced the previous gain by 9%); Reinstituting feedback = 21% (regained 4% of the previous loss). During the 8 month period of the program, lost-time injuries dropped to 0.4 per month; before program the rate was 3.0/month; after program the rate was 1.8/month.	Results show feedback as important motivator in realizing benefits of workers training and increased worker knowledge. Authors comment that management gave verbal support to program but was inconsistent in actions such as attending safety sessions or recognizing persons for their program efforts. Frequency of feedback notices by supervisors also dropped off in the last phase, which could account for less than the full recovery of the earlier gain.

(*Source*: Cohen and Colligan 1998)

TABLE 2

Extracts from Bureau of Labor Statistics (BLS) Work Injury Report or Discerning Real/Possible Gaps in Job Safety/Health Training

Database Sample Surveyed (period of survey)	Limitations in Extent/Nature of Training					Follow-up Actions/Needs
	Form/Source of Training	Training Content	Workforce Coverage	Date of Last Training	Age/Job Experience	
1400 respondents to survey of 2000 workers with reportable injuries from ladder mishaps (Winter 1978).	73% not provided written instructions on safe use of ladders. 78% trained on-the-job.	66% lacked training in how to inspect ladders.	59% lacked training of use of ladders.	Of those noting training, 50% indicated it took place over 1 year ago.	Most injuries in 25–34 year old group (25%).	
803 respondents to survey of 1230 workers with reportable injuries from scaffold mishaps. (July– November 1978).	On-the-job training noted by 62%–71% in learning different safety requirements; over 50% by just watching others.	Safety requirements covered for scaffold assembly, planking, inspection, weight limits, guard rails; no more than 71% noted training in any topic.	26%–35% of respondents indicated no training in any of the topics noted in the content column.	71% indicated training received more than 1 year ago (71% from other than the current employer).	Highest % of injured in 25–34 year old group (24%); next was 20–24 year olds group (18%).	
1364 respondents to survey of 2300 workers with injures from welding/cutting operations (July–November 1978).	Both on-the-job and classroom training noted but not more than 37% received either form of such training.	81% believed subject coverage adequate but coverage of different topics ranged from 40% to 83%.	30% indicated they learned welding/cutting safety on their own through job experience. 11% never had any safety training.	69% of those receiving training noted the date of more than 1 year ago.	26% had less than 1 year of work experience; 16% less than 6 months. 2–34 year old group had greatest % of injuries (32%).	
1746 respondents to survey of 2300 workers with reportable injuries from power saw use. (September– November 1978).	On-the-job and classroom instruction were main forms of training but each noted for no more than 39% of the worker respondents.	For those receiving training, coverage of various topics drew response rates varying from 32% to 59%.	89% learned power-saw safety through their own job experience. 17% never had any safety training.		44% working with saw less than 1 year, 19% less than 1 month. 20–24 year old group and 25–34 year old group tied for highest % of injuries (25%).	
1033 respondents to survey of 1881 workers with reportable head injuries at work (July–September 1979).	Information on "hard hat" protection mainly from supervisor or safety officer (81%), but co-worker (19%) and printed material (25%) also noted.	Instruction emphasized when and where to use (61%); Other topics such as how to adjust, maintain and types available drew less than a 35% response.	32% received no information or instruction on "hard hats".		20–24 year old group had highest % of head injuries (32%).	In head injury cases 41% of the respondents did not know of any action employers took to prevent recurrence. Where noted, accident investigation and issuance of warnings were main (33%) follow-up actions, training noted at 1%.

(Continued)

TABLE 2

Database Sample Surveyed (period of survey)	Limitations in Extent/Nature of Training					
	Form/Source of Training	Training Content	Workforce Coverage	Date of Last Training	Age/Job Experience	Follow-up Actions/Needs
1251 respondents to survey of 2005 workers with reportable foot injuries at work (July–August 1979).	Given information on safety shoes from supervisor or safety officer (92%).	Information stresses where/when to wear (41%); coverage of features available, maintenance, and advantages ranged from 6% to 17%.			Most foot injuries in 25–34 year old group (25%) followed by 20–24 year old group (23%).	Fewer than 25% wearing safety shoes at time of accident though 72% aware of company policy on wearing shoes in specific areas and jobs. 21% indicated employer took no follow-up actions after injury. 28% did not know of any.
1052 respondents to survey of 2118 workers with reportable eye injuries at work (July–.August 1979)	Main instruction on eye protection from supervisor or safety officer (91%); co-workers (15%0 and classroom session (14%) also noted.	Subjects of where and when to wear drew a 72% response; followed by type to wear (39%). Care and limitations had a 16% response.	20% of respondents had no instruction in use of protective eye wear.		25–34 year old group had highest % of eye injuries (32%). Next was 20–24 year old group (25%).	Though over 70% of workers indicated company policy on wearing eye protection, more than 20% noted enforcement came after injury. Common response to nonuse was impractical or not required.

* The shaded entries in the tables are meant to suggest major training deficits for sizeable percentages of the afflicted workers.

(*Source*: Cohen and Colligan 1998)

Benchmarking can be broken down into ten steps (Camp 1989). When benchmarking any area, the first step is to determine specifically what you want to benchmark. When deciding what to measure as part of a benchmarking project, first establish what the key performance measures are and what activities are going to improve the overall safety program. Benchmarking efforts will not be effective without the right metrics. In areas of health and safety training, it might be a good idea to benchmark how many hours employees attend training in comparison to employees of other companies—as well as the type of training delivered and the nature of the delivery method itself, whether classroom, on-the-job, or online. A little more difficult, though still useful, is benchmarking the ROI of health and safety training.

The second step of benchmarking is to identify certain leaders in the areas against which the company will be benchmarking. This will likely be the most difficult step.

The third step is to collect data that can be used to benchmark against the top performer, collecting data from industry leaders as well as the company to be benchmarked. Steps two and three both require the identification of industry leaders and the collection of their best practices, information that can be found in many places, including the following, which were included in the *Department of the Navy Benchmarking Handbook* (Kraft n.d.):

- newspaper articles
- internal publications
- magazine articles
- trade and industry publications
- journals
- seminars
- professional associations
- industry experts
- press releases
- software and hardware vendors
- literature searches
- consulting firms
- plant tours
- newsletters

- interviews
- focus groups
- commercial services

Company safety and health data is continuously updated on the Internet by many organizations and is freely available. Government Web sites, such as those provided by the Occupational Safety and Health Administration (OSHA) and the Bureau of Labor Statistics (BLS), can be relied on to provide free and accurate information. Accident and injury statistics provided by these groups can be one asset in benchmarking efforts.

It is important only to evaluate and collect information that relates specifically to the health and safety benchmarking project in question. How much better or more successful are their best practices than the procedures and programs currently in place?

The fourth step is to identify gaps between the company's performance and that of the leaders. What do they do that is successful that can be emulated? The size of the gap should also be considered both at the current time and in the future. The size of the gap could have implications for the safety and health training program.

The fifth step is to extrapolate the data from the leaders, evaluating where they will be in 3–5 years. That should be the benchmark for the company's health and safety training program.

The sixth step is communicating the findings of benchmarking efforts to gain support for improvement plans from every level in the company. This step cannot be overlooked. Improvement plans often require additional funding. Thorough explanation and excellent communications are often necessary to achieve this.

The seventh step is to develop goals to present to senior management. Based on the results of benchmarking, goals can be set that are aligned with where the leaders will be in 3–5 years (the goals identified in step 5). The goals should be in the form of operational statements that will enable specific action plans to be developed.

The eighth step is to develop action plans based on the goals submitted to senior management. A goal to increase the percentage of employees attending safety training on a particular topic needs a step-by-step plan to ensure that the goal in this area is met.

The ninth step is to put the action plans into place and monitor and report on progress. If the goal is to provide eight hours of safety awareness training to all new hires—and two hours are currently provided— a detailed plan to expand the current class needs to be in place that has measurable goals and a timeline.

Finally, the tenth step is to recalibrate the benchmarks. Benchmark levels change over time, making benchmarking like aiming at a moving target. Set a schedule for recalibrating benchmarks and *follow through.*

Considerations When Benchmarking Safety and Health Training

Benchmarking safety and health training can be an important tool in emphasizing the impact of a sound safety and health program to senior management (and throughout the organization). The information collected during a benchmarking study will help provide objective data about the results of safety and health training. The return on investment for safety training can be difficult to measure, but benchmarking can help to determine this. Benchmarking also serves to improve safety and health training programs and, in doing so, improves the safety program as a whole. The financial benefits of a successful safety and health program were discussed in the chapter, "Cost Analysis and Budgeting" by Brent Altemose in this section of the Handbook.

Benchmarking is most valuable when results, not just activities, are measured. Measuring training results can be the most difficult task of all. In safety training, the real measures of training effectiveness are whether or not trainees have gained new skills and whether or not they apply these skills in the workplace in ways that support the overall safety program.

In any safety program's benchmarking efforts, the existence of various methods of computing metrics may affect the benchmark. Some companies calculate injury rates by different methods, according to where they are located or using parent companies' guidelines. When collecting benchmarking data, make sure to compare like with like.

There are common difficulties in carrying out benchmarking. These include: (1) a lack of suitable partners for comparing data; (2) constraints on resources

SIDEBAR

ANSI Z490.1-2009 Criteria for Accepted Practices in Safety, Health and Environmental Training

Training Program Management

When ASSE developed this Standard, the right-hand column, designated "Explanatory Information" (*not* a part of the ANSI Z490.1-2009 Standard), suggested that "[w]hen evaluating training program management, some of the functions to review include, but are not limited to: accountability, responsibility, development, delivery and evaluation processes." ASSE also went on to state: "When evaluating the training organization and administration, some of the elements to review include, but are not limited to: staffing, budgets, facilities, equipment, documentation and record keeping."

In terms of safety training program evaluation, ANSI Z490.1-2009 states (ANSI Z490.1-2009 [9–10]):

3.4.1 The training provider shall periodically evaluate the training program.

3.4.2 The elements to be evaluated shall, at a minimum, include:

- training program management
- training process
- training results

Training Process

ASSE explained in ANSI Z490.1-2009 (10), "When evaluating the training process, some elements to review include, but are not limited to, the:

- clarity and appropriateness of training goals;
- relevance of training goals to trainees;
- learning objectives;
- content and methods that support the learning objectives;
- adequacy of learning environment
- training effectiveness."

Training Results

In addition, as part of ANSI Z490.1-2009, ASSE suggests the following: "Training results should be used to improve the training program. When analyzing training results, some of the elements to review include, but are not limited to: a definite plan of action for training employees; a plan for conducting regular needs assessments; support for lifelong learning; adequate funding; program manager competence; links among training program elements; the provision for training program long-term and strategic planning; a system for identifying competing demands, and the ability to set priorities."

such as time, money, and expertise; (3) staff resistance; and (4) confidentiality of data (Holloway 1997).

In addition to what has already been reviewed from the ASSE interpretation of ANSI Z490.1-2001, Section 6, which deals with training evaluation, will now be discussed.

6. TRAINING EVALUATION IN ACCORDANCE WITH ANSI Z490.1-2009

Training evaluation tools may measure performance of trainees, trainers, training events, or training programs. Training providers must incorporate appropriate evaluation tools into each training event. This section provides acceptable criteria for the different evaluation approaches.

"There are a wide range of outcomes that can be evaluated such as: the trainee's possession of some knowledge, skill ability, and/or attitude; the trainer's ability to effectively transfer knowledge, skills, abilities, or attitudes to the trainees; the trainee's satisfaction with the training experience; the ability of the training to contribute to the organizational goals." (ANSI Z490.1-2009 [15])

6.1 GENERAL CRITERIA

6.1.1 The evaluation approaches for each training event and the tools for implementing them shall be established during training development.

ASSE states: "Different evaluation approaches may be selected to evaluate each specific outcome mentioned above."

6.1.2 An evaluation shall be made of the trainee's achievement of each learning objective, considering the performance, conditions, and criteria specified in the learning objective.

ASSE states: "In some instances, trainees may be allowed to *test out*: i.e., demonstrate achievement of the learning objective(s) without attending or participating in the training event. The criteria for *testing out* should be specified during training development. Special care should be taken to ensure regulatory compliance."

6.1.2.1 The evaluation tools used shall be reliable and valid measures of the trainee's achievement of the learning objective.

ASSE states: "A *reliable measure* is one that gives consistent results over time. A *valid measure* is one that reflects the knowledge, skills, abilities, or attitudes specified in the learning objective."

6.1.2.2 Successful completion of each evaluation shall be specified during training development.

ASSE states: "Successful completion of an evaluation will depend on a number of factors, including the evaluation approach and the importance of the learning objective(s). For example: successful completion of a test may be specified in terms of percent correct; successful completion of an observation may require the trainee [to] perform the steps of a task in the proper sequence; successful completion of a project may require that all key elements be included as per instructions."

6.1.2.3 Training providers shall furnish trainees with the results of any test or task observation included as part of the evaluation.

ASSE states: "The trainees may use feedback for seeking more information or practice, and to contribute to a plan for future training. Supervisors, managers, and trainees may use the information for individual performance support, for job design issues, or other job-related issues."

6.1.2.4 Training development shall include procedures for assisting or retraining trainees who do not achieve the learning objective(s).

6.1.3 Each trainee or trainer being evaluated shall be properly identified.

6.1.4 Evaluation shall comply with all applicable regulations.

ASSE states: "Regulatory requirements often reflect the minimum acceptable level of training. The training may exceed required regulatory levels."

6.1.5 The training program shall include periodic evaluation of trainees in relation to learning objectives and determining the effectiveness of the program.

ASSE states: "Periodic reevaluation should also be part of training development and general requirements, including regulations mandating refresher training to occur at certain and specific cycle times."

6.2 EVALUATION APPROACHES

An evaluation shall be conducted using one or more of the following techniques.

ASSE states: "The selection of the type of evaluation is based on the particular learning objective(s), audience, and desired outcome(s). The training program should attempt to incorporate all four types of evaluation as appropriate."

6.2.1 Reaction Survey

A reaction survey shall be designed to be easily administered, tabulated, and summarized, with space for written comments.

ASSE states: "A reaction survey is a subjective evaluation of the training course by the trainees. Questions about trainer presentation skills, accommodations, pace, and difficulty and usefulness of content may be included in a reaction survey. Results from a reaction survey may be used by trainees to assess and report their learning, or by trainers to assess and improve the course design and delivery."

6.2.2 Evaluation of Knowledge, Skills, and Abilities

An evaluation of knowledge, skills, and abilities shall take place while the trainee is in the learning environment.

ASSE states: "Tools used to evaluate knowledge, skills and abilities may take many forms, depending on the focus of the learning objective(s). These include: written test; oral examination; completion of an assigned project; demonstration of the skill in a simulated work setting; on-the-job demonstration of the skill in the trainer's presence.

Note—Evaluation of knowledge, skills, or abilities may be administered as pre- and post-tests only, or self-administered evaluations. They may be automated, as technology permits."

6.2.3 Observation of Performance

Observation of performance shall be used when it is necessary to verify that the trainee can demonstrate the targeted skills or abilities under actual work conditions.

ASSE states: "This approach may include pre- and post-test measurement to link performance of training. Performance information may be collected from supervisors, coworkers, or customers, or from indirect measurement such as those found in production records or safety reports.

When observation of performance reveals a gap between the desired performance and actual performance, the factors that prevented the desired performance should be identified. These may include nontraining issues, such as the availability of equipment on the job, conflicting information from a supervisor, or other indication of lack of organizational support for implementing the targeted skills."

6.2.4 Organizational Results

Measures of organizational results shall be used to link training to overall organization performance.

ASSE states: "To measure organizational results, training factors must be isolated from nontraining factors. To do this, there is often a control group of workers who have not received the training.

"Fundamental to this type of evaluation is an agreement on key business measures before the training takes place. These may include, but are not limited to: increase in safe behavior(s) by all trainees; increase in implemented preventive measures and controls; reduction in near hits, injuries and illnesses; reduction in worker's compensation claims; improved environmental compliance; or higher return on investment (ROI)."

6.2.5 Rubrics

Rubrics are a set of criteria used for the assessment of a trainee's achievement. Rubrics judge the quality of services, products, or performances (Popham 2003). In addition, rubrics are "descriptive scoring schemes" used for analysis (Moskal, 2000). Rubrics have been widely used in the K–12 education communities for years; however, rubrics are now being introduced into the world of industrial (safety) training programs as a means of plotting the trainee's success rate. Generally, rubrics are performance-based, leading to the evaluation of the trainee's performance to a given set of tasks. It is therefore the responsibility of the trainer to specify the criteria that he/she will use to evaluate the trainee. Figure 1 shows a sample evaluation form. According to the Web site, TeAch-nology.com (rubrics), "Rating scales can be either holistic or analytical. Holistic scales offer several dimensions together while analytical scales offer a separate scale for various dimensions."

How do we develop a rubric?

According to TeAch-nology.com, there is a four-step process for developing a rubric:

1. Define the learning outcome/objective that students (trainees) are expected to achieve.
2. Determine how to describe each level of the activity.
3. Define scores (numerical or qualitative) that can be assigned for each activity.
4. Once the level is determined with rating scales assigned, share the description with the students (trainees) and ask for feedback, so that each level is clearly understood by the students (trainees).

6.3 COMMITMENT TO CONTINUOUS IMPROVEMENT

6.3.1 The information from training evaluations shall be used for continuous improvement of the course content, delivery methods, collateral materials, and learning environment.

ASSE states: "Management may use the information to assess the effectiveness of the training program

Subject	0 No Understanding	1 Minimal Understanding	2 Majority Understanding	3 Full Understanding
X				
Y				
Z				
Notes				

FIGURE 1. A typical rating scale

in meeting organizational goals and to determine the level of investment in training."

CONCLUSION

In any good organizational safety environment, assessment is essential for the continuing improvement of the organization's safety program. Without a valid assessment program in place (and the tools to do it), the organization's long-term goal of an improved safety program is merely a dream. Return on investment cannot be measured with respect to the success of an organization's safety program unless an assessment program is in place. Benchmarking is one way to continuously strive to improve health and safety training, and thus the entire safety and health program. Continuous improvement of the organization's safety and health program (training) is paramount in today's health and safety environment and is truly vital to its success.

REFERENCES

Ahmed, Ishfaq et al. 2010. "How Organizations Evaluate their Trainings? An Evidence from Pakistani Organizations." *Interdisciplinary Journal of Contemporary Research In Business* 2(5) (accessed August 29, 2011). ijcrb.webs.com

American National Standards Institute (ANSI), Committee Z490 on Criteria for Accepted Practices in Safety, Health and Environmental Training. 2009. *American National Standard Z490.1-2009.* Des Plaines, IL: American Society of Safety Engineers.

Angelo, Thomas A. 1999. "Doing Assessment as if Learning Matters Most." *AAHE Bulletin* 51(9):3–6.

Boulmetis, John, and Phyllis Dutwin. 2000. *The ABCs of Evaluation: Timeless Techniques for Program and Project Managers.* San Francisco: Jossey-Bass.

Boxwell, Jr., Robert J. 1994. *Benchmarking for Competitive Advantage.* New York: McGraw-Hill.

Burke, Lisa, and Holly Hutchins. 2008. "A Study of Best Practices in Training Transfer and Proposed Model of Transfer." *Human Resource Development Quarterly* 19(2):107–128.

Camp, Robert C. 1989. *Benchmarking: The Search for Industry Best Practices that Lead to Superior Performance.* Milwaukee: Quality Press.

_____. 1995. *Business Process Benchmarking: Finding and Implementing Best Practices.* Milwaukee: Quality Press.

Carliner, Saul. 2003. *Training Design Basics.* Alexandria, VA: ASTD Press.

Cheney, Scott. 2001. "Benchmarking: Evaluation and Research." *American Society for Training and Development, Info-line* 9801.

Cohen, Alexander, and Michael J. Colligan. 1998. *Assessing Occupational Safety and Health Training: A Literature Review.* Cincinnati: National Institute for Occupational Safety and Health.

Cole, Nina 2008. "How Long Should a Training Program Be? A Field Study of 'Rules-of-Thumb'." *Journal of Workplace Learning* 20(1):54–70.

Cross, K. Patricia, and Thomas A. Angelo. 1998. *Classroom Assessment Techniques: A Handbook for Faculty.* Ann Arbor, MI: National Center for Research to Improve Postsecondary Teaching and Learning.

Dinardi, Salvatore (ed.). 2003. "Worker Education and Training." In *The Occupational Environment: Its Evaluation, Control, and Measurement,* 2d ed. Des Plaines, IL: American Society of Safety Engineers.

Galbraith, Diane, and Sandra E. Fouch. 2007. "Principles of Adult Learning Application to Safety Training." *Professional Safety* 52:(9):35–40.

Herman, Aguinis, and Kurt Kraiger. 2009. "Benefits of Training and Development for Individuals and Teams, Organizations, and Society." *Annual Review of Psychology* 60:451–474.

Holloway, J. A., C. M. Hinton, D. T. Mayle, and G. A. J. Francis.1997. "Why benchmark? Understanding the processes of best practice benchmarking." Proceedings of Business Track, British Academy of Management Conference, London, pp. 271–291.

Hutchinson, Linda. 2003. "ABC of learning and teaching: Educational environment." *BMJ* 326:810–812.

Kirkpatrick, Donald L. 1998. *Evaluating Training Programs: The Four Levels,* 2d ed. San Francisco: Berrett-Koehler Publishers.

Koskela, L. 1992. *CIFE Technical Report: 72.* "Application of the New Production Philosophy to Construction." Palo Alto, CA: Stanford University.

Kraft, Joan. n.d. *The Department of the Navy Benchmarking Handbook: A Systems View.* unpan1.un.org/intradoc/groups/public/documents/aspa/unpan002509.pdf

Moskal, B. M. 2000. "Scoring Rubrics: What When, and How?" *Practical Assessment, Research and Evaluation,* 7(3).

Occupational Safety and Health Administration (OSHA). 1998. *OSHA Standards and Training Guidelines, OSHA 2254.* www.osha.gov/Publications/2254.html

Popham, J. W. 2003. *Test Better, Teach Better: The Instructional Role of Assessment.* Alexandria, VA: Virginia Association for Supervision and Curriculum Development.

Transportation Research Board (TRB). 2010. *Special Report 300: Achieving Traffic Safety Goals in the United States:*

Lessons from Other Nations (accessed August 29, 2011). www.onlinw.trb.org/onlinepubs/sr/sr300.pdf

Walvoord, Barbara E. 2004. *Assessment Clear and Simple: A Practical Guide for Institutions, Departments, and General Education.* San Francisco: Jossey-Bass.

Ya Hui Lien, Richard Bella, Yu Yuan Hung, and Gary N. McLean. 2007. "Training evaluation based on cases of Taiwanese benchmarked high-tech companies." *International Journal of Training Development* 11(1): 35–48.

Appendix: Recommended Readings

Boston, Carol. 2002. "The Concept of Formative Assessment." *Practical Assessment, Research & Evaluation* 8(9) (retrieved October 30, 2004). PAREonline.net/getvn.asp?v=8&*n*=9

Diamond, Robert M. 1998. *Designing and Assessing Courses and Curricula: A Practical Guide,* rev. ed. San Francisco: Jossey-Bass.

Fitz-Gibbons, Carol Taylor, and Lynn Lyons Morris. 1987. *How to Design a Program Evaluation.* Newbury Park, CA: SAGE Publications.

Hill, Daryl C. (ed.). 2004. *Construction Safety Management and Engineering.* Des Plaines, IL: American Society of Safety Engineers.

Maki, Peggy L. 2002. "Moving from Paperwork to Pedagogy: 'Channeling Intellectual Curiosity into a Commitment to Assessment.'" *American Association for Higher Education, AAHE Bulletin* May: 3–5.

Massachusetts Institute of Technology Teaching and Learning Laboratory Staff. 2004. *Assessment and Evaluation Electronic Forum* (retrieved October 30, 2004). www.mit.edu/tll/assessment.htm

Stark, Joan S., and Alice Thomas (eds.). 1994. *Assessment and Program Evaluation.* New York: Simon and Schuster.

LEARNING OBJECTIVES

▌ Specify indicators of an effective safety and health training program.

▌ Explain the limitations of training as a solution in OHS problem solving.

▌ Explain the role training plays in a company's overall safety and health program.

▌ Describe the six key principles when designing and delivering training to adult learners.

▌ Describe the training requirements of widely used safety and health standards, including ISO 14000, ANSI Z-10, and OHSAS 18000.

▌ Explain the difference between education and training.

▌ Define the desirable characteristics of a safety and health trainer.

▌ Identify several organizations that are involved with safety and health training research.

BEST PRACTICES

Michael Behm and C. Keith Stalnaker

IN READING THE CHAPTERS from this section of the handbook, several safety and health training best practices clearly emerge. The purpose of this chapter is to offer additional considerations for strategy development in the area of occupational safety and health training.

A goal of most companies is for employees and managers to have the required aptitude, skill, and knowledge to successfully and safely carry out their jobs. Training is one means that leads to a skilled, knowledgeable, and collaborative workforce. When effectively integrated with personnel resources, management development, and technical procedures, training can help provide a workforce that achieves reliable operations and drives performance improvement.

Training should *not* be utilized as the primary method for solving occupational health and safety issues. It is one of the simplest solutions, but is usually the most ineffective (Petersen 1999). Too often, an organization will seek to train employees if it views occupational health and safety (OHS) solely as a people problem rather than as a systems problem. As this handbook demonstrates, the hierarchy of controls should be followed in solving OHS problems, and training falls into the category of administrative controls. Elimination, substation, and engineering controls should be considered *before* training and other administrative controls. While training does not remove hazardous conditions, it can help people recognize hazardous conditions so they can be removed or controlled (Brauer 2006). Moreover, effective training will usually supplement the higher-order controls to ensure they are and remain effective. An adequately designed employee training and education program can assist the organization in considering and utilizing higher-order controls to solve OHS problems. Workers typically have excellent process knowledge. Combining this knowledge with OHS education can drive organizational creative thinking in OHS. Of course, the organization needs adequate communication channels and a high level of trust within its culture for this to occur freely.

Training is a challenge in even the most diligent organizations. When the difficulties of designing and implementing an effective training program are overcome, the challenge then becomes keeping the program that way. The Institute of Nuclear Power Operations (INPO 2002) analyzed the twenty most significant events in nuclear power since 1974 to identify common event causes. Operator knowledge and training weaknesses were identified as causes in seven (35 percent) and were contributors to most others. Training-related deficiencies included improper operator responses to abnormal conditions and making erroneous assumptions during operations. The National Academy for Nuclear Training (NANT 2003) cited examples of training-related problems in the nuclear industry that are likely to exist in many industries. The problems NANT identified include the following:

- field work being performed by unqualified persons
- knowledge and skill weaknesses that lead to field performance issues
- deficient training content
- inadequate evaluation of trainees

Examining the training practices of others and learning from their successes and failures are ways for the safety professional to improve safety training. The materials presented in this section are intended to help the safety professional identify training methods that add value and contribute to safety performance. The practices described may not be appropriate for every training situation. Establishing the appropriate training practice for a specific situation requires careful analysis and evaluation that may reflect competing objectives and priorities.

ADULT LEARNERS

Safety and health professionals design and deliver training to adult learners. This presents challenges but also opportunities to enhance overall organizational learning. Milano and Ullius (1998, pp. 24–27) devised six key principles for designing and delivering training to adults. They are highlighted below.

1. *Personal experience is the key learning tool.* Adults come to training with vast personal experiences that they want to use and share. They learn quickly when things fit well into their experience and need more time to process those that do not. They want to be involved in the learning process.

2. *Motivation for learning is driven by needs, problem solving or personal satisfaction.* Adults are most driven to learn about things that directly relate to their needs. This assumes the learners recognize the need for safety training. A needs assessment is important not only for the trainer and the organization, but the learners must also recognize the need for training.

3. *Adults are independent learners.* While adult learners may value the trainer's opinions and message, the ultimate test of the training is whether they apply it in their work lives. The applicability will depend on whether they judge the training to be valuable. This reinforces the importance of assessing the training, as discussed in other chapters.

4. *Protecting the learners' self-esteem is critical.* Adult learners need to feel that they can question what is being taught and discuss their personal experiences without threat. Safety management systems, safety culture, and organizational trust are essential foundations for this environment and are critical components of effective safety training. Effective safety training hinges on many other aspects of the safety system.

5. *Adults have clear expectations about training.* Adult learners will bring a variety of expectations and assumptions with them to the training session. These will largely be based on their previous training experiences. The designer has the task of planning what can be done early in the training to clarify

expectations and to meet or modify them as appropriate.

6. *Adults learn in a variety of different ways and have preferences in learning styles.* Adult learners have a variety of preferences that affect the way they learn. The challenge for training designers is to appeal to and engage a variety of different learning styles so that participants can learn in ways that are best for them. This is, or course, a bit easier if the trainer knows the audience. However, in discussing expectations about training early in the session, adjustments can be made if a variety of methods are planned and organized that meet the objectives developed.

TRAINING OR EDUCATING?

Training and education are very closely bound and often used interchangeably. However, there are distinctions that are important to best practices in OHS. Milano and Ullius (1998) explain the distinction between education and training as follows: "Education focuses on learning about; training focuses on learning how." In OHS, do companies desire trained or educated employees? Perhaps, they want both. Organizations often focus on giving employees OHS skills or traditional training. *Training* in hazard communication typically might focus on how to read MSDSs and labels, handle common chemicals in one's work area, and recognize upset situations within the process. *Education* in hazard communication could focus on a historical perspective, and on examining case studies of OSHA fines on hazard communication in similar industries. For an example of historical perspective, an educator could utilize the 1984 Bhopal disaster as a case study to highlight current needs in hazard communication. Poor communication about the released methyl isocyanate resulted in medical intervention problems and distrust in the community. Training is more immediate, skills-oriented, and focused on application as compared to education, which is the process of building a knowledge base (Milano & Ullius 1998).

Educating employees and managers about OHS management systems, historical events, and current

trends can assist the overall organization to mature in OHS thinking. Consider Appendix B in the ANSI Z-10 standard, where roles and responsibilities are set forth. For the system to work, each person within the organization needs to understand his/her roles and responsibilities (AIHA 2005). The standard lists roles and responsibilities for the President, CEO, or owner; executive officers, VPs, or senior leadership; directors, managers, and department heads; supervisors; employees; and the OHS department. Since most other professionals do not have a formal background in OHS, by default it becomes the OHS professionals' responsibility to educate the rest of the organization on how to properly manage and carry out their OHS roles and responsibilities. Therefore, it is important for OSH professionals to stay current on issues through continuing education, personal research, and the quest for lifelong learning. In order to educate, safety professionals must first know what they are talking about. OHS professionals must ensure they are qualified to educate others within the organization—that means staying current and being humble. When engaging with adult learners, trainers/educators should reflect upon their own lifelong learning and open-mindedness. Safety professionals and readers of this book come from very diverse backgrounds. In their careers, they will be called upon to train and educate on a wide and diverse range of topics. There is no way they can be experts on all of them. Consider how many professionals still quote Heinrich and talk about safety as purely a people problem. Individuals are encouraged to reflect on their own career, their expertise, and where they need to learn more as a best practice. The actions and philosophies of lifelong learning and staying humble will translate into becoming a better educator and trainer.

ORGANIZING AND MANAGING THE TRAINING PROCESS
Strategic Planning

Senior management's commitment to strategic planning is critical to business success and long-term viability. Proactively committing an organization to a carefully planned course prevents organizational drift, competitive mediocrity, and lackluster results. A strategic plan helps mold the decisions and actions of various divisions within the organization into a coordinated, compatible whole (Thompson and Strickland 2001). The International Safety Equipment Association (ISEA) is an example of how an organization can use a strategic plan to chart a growth path and target priorities. The ISEA identified and used the major trends and issues affecting the safety equipment industry as background for developing its strategic plan. The ISEA has committed to making regular plan updates to reflect changing conditions, past performance, and its mission (ISEA 2004):

> ISEA has published a Strategic Plan every year since 1985. The plan establishes a broad set of strategic priorities, generated by the membership, that provides ISEA its guiding principles. Each year a planning task force consisting of the ISEA Board of Trustees and Planning Committee meets to discuss and refine the Strategic Plan. This meeting is an organized and wide-ranging examination of the economic and public policy environments, the effects of globalization and industry consolidation, and market issues unique to safety equipment. The task force looks at the core competencies of the association, how well it's performing, and what it can do to return value to its member companies.

Crafting a business strategy to achieve corporate objectives is one element of strategic planning. Properly completed, a safety and health strategy establishes the managerial plan for running the safety and health program in support of the company's overall business strategy. The safety and health strategy shows how activities will be managed to achieve the company's safety and health objectives and missions.

A safety and health plan often identifies how training is integrated into the overall safety and health strategy. An example is the annual safety and health plan of Canadian Pacific Railway (CPR). In addition to stating its long-term goal of being recognized as the safest railway by its customers and stakeholders, the CPR plan includes specific measures of success, how these strategies will be accomplished, and how CPR management supports the health and safety plan. One of the ten strategies in the plan includes safety and health training. In 2003, nine specific safety and health training tactics were established for integration into day-to-day operations, including providing management safety training to all levels of management and supervision, ensuring employees and managers receive the training necessary to perform their jobs safely, and conducting accident investigation training (CPR 2003). Lower-level or local health and safety plans can be prepared to reflect implementation of the training tactics; for example, identifying the categories of supervisors to be trained on specific health and safety topics, and when that training will occur during the year.

TYPE OF TRAINING	DESCRIPTION	SPECIFIC RECOMMENDATIONS
Team coordination training	Includes an awareness phase (classroom training), a practice and feedback phase, and a continual reinforcement phase (refresher training).	• Effective even with teams that do not have a fixed set of personnel • The training addresses a particular set of nontechnical skills
Cross-training	Each team member is trained in his or her duties and those of their teammates.	• Team has a high level of interdependence between members • There is a lack of knowledge about the roles of other team members
Team self-correction training	This type works on the premise that effective teams review events, correct errors, discuss strategies, and plan for future events.	• Team has a high level of interdependence between members • Low staff turnover
Event-based training	This approach systemically structures training by tightly linking learning objectives, exercise design, performance measurement, and feedback.	• Useful when there are problems with a particular subset of tasks, and the tasks can be simulated.
Team facilitation training	This approach is designed to help leaders stimulate learning by creating on effective learning environment, supporting more formal training, and encouraging team discussions.	•There are limitations in training resources

FIGURE 1. Approaches to training (Flin et al. 2008)

In this section, Fanning (2012) provides excellent information for comparing various training models. For a best-practice training strategy regarding training techniques to be utilized, the OHS professional will need to assess the issues to be addressed, the resources available, and the makeup of the team to be trained (Flin et al 2008, p. 250). Flin offers recommended approaches based on the types of training shown here in Figure 1. OHS professionals should consider these approaches.

ANSI Z10:2005 Occupational Health and Safety Management Systems

The American National Standard Institute's (ANSI) *Standard for Occupational Health and Safety Management Systems* (OSHMS) recognizes education, training, and awareness as a key component of the implementation and operation of OHSMS. The standard requires organizations to (AIHA 2005):

1. Define and assess the OHSMS competence needed for employees and contractors.
2. Ensure, through appropriate education, training, or other methods, that employees and contractors are aware of applicable OHSMS requirements and are competent to carry out their responsibilities as defined in the OHSMS. The standard provides examples, such as training for engineers in safe design, incident investigation training that includes identifying underlying OHSMS deficiencies, and training for procurement personnel on how their decisions impact OHSMS.
3. Ensure effective access to, and remove barriers from, participation in education and training as defined in the organization's OHSMS. Barriers include disability issues, training on uncompensated time, scheduling, the training environment, and literacy and language issues.
4. Ensure training is provided in a language that trainees understand.
5. Ensure that trainers are competent to train employees. Competency is achieved through

one or more of the following: education, training, mentoring, experience, certification, licensing, and performance assessment.

The ANSI Z10:2005 standard provides training resources, including those from the American Petroleum Institute (API), the International Association of Oil and Gas Producers (OGP), ANSI Z490.1-2009, and OSHA. The latter two are described in other chapters of this section.

Occupational Safety and Health Management System Standards

The Occupational Safety and Health Administration (OSHA) developed the 18000 family of standards known as the Occupational Health and Safety Assessment Series (OHSAS), which include OHSAS 18001:2007, *Occupational Health and Safety (OHS) Management Systems Specification*, and OHSAS 18002, *Guidelines for the Implementation of OHSAS 18001*. OHSAS 18001 was created from the *British Standard for Occupational Health and Safety Management Systems*, BS 8800:1996, and other documents from international standards bodies (BS8800 OHSAS and OHSAS Project Group 2007). The 18001 standard was designed to enable companies to control their OHS risks and to demonstrate their commitment to providing a safe working environment, protecting their employees, and improving their performance. OHSAS 18001 was developed to be compatible with the ISO 9001 and 14001 management system standards. To allow for easy integration into a company's quality and environmental management systems, many OHSAS sections and subclauses are similar, such as management review, document control, and corrective and preventive actions.

OHSAS 18001 Section 4.4.2 addresses training, awareness, and competence (OHSAS Project Group, 2007):

> The organization shall ensure that any person(s) under its control performing tasks that can impact on OH&S is (are) competent on the basis of appropriate education, training or experience, and shall retain associated records. The organization shall identify training needs associated with its OH&S risks and its OH&S management system. It shall provide training or take other action to meet these needs,

evaluate the effectiveness of the training or action taken, and retain associated records. The organization shall establish, implement and maintain a procedure(s) to make persons working under its control aware of:

a) the OH&S consequences, actual or potential, of their work activities, their behavior, and the OH&S benefits of improved personal performance;

b) their roles and responsibilities and importance in achieving conformity to the OH&S policy and procedures and to the requirements of the OH&S management system, including emergency preparedness and response requirements;

c) the potential consequences of departure from specified procedures.

Training procedures shall take into account differing levels of:

a) responsibility, ability, language skills, and literacy;

b) risk.

Selecting the Training Staff

Finding health and safety trainers who can provide the training results desired requires the definition of selection criteria and careful evaluation of trainer candidates against those criteria. Selection criteria need to be specific to the training technique being used and the training results desired. Needed attributes of a trainer providing traditional style training will differ from those for role playing or case-study training styles, but will always include the ability to make the training relevant to students. Having the ability to encourage adult learning is another needed attribute, and trainers should be required to demonstrate proficiency with the adult education technique to be used (NIEHS 1998).

Trainers should be considered professionals who, like all professionals, need specialized skills and education. This may dictate the use of subject-matter experts like firefighters to conduct fire extinguisher training, the use of electricians to conduct lockout/tagout training, and the use of a chemist to provide chemical safety training. Safety and health training does not need to be restricted to professional trainers or safety practitioners, but should always be performed by persons with appropriate training skills. Furthermore, subject matter experts also need to be good communicators and teachers. If trainers have poor interpersonal rapport or communication skills, they will not be effective trainers.

While many companies use safety experts or other subject-matter experts to deliver safety and health compliance training, some have had success using worker-trainers. A worker-trainer is defined as a trainer who has a common work background and/or experience with those being trained (NIEHS 1998). Trainees typically view the trainer as a peer. Such persons may be employed as full-time or part-time trainers, and methods range from the classroom to on-the-job training. One of the best worker-trainer examples is in the delivery of hazardous materials training (40-hour Hazwoper). More than 1000 worker-trainers provide Hazwoper training under the NIEHS-supported hazardous worker training programs. NIEHS reports that employers have found that the use of hazardous materials workers

---

Questions about the trainer's qualifications and experience

- What experience do you have in training adults in the workplace?
- What experience of workplace health and safety issues in this industry do you have?
- What experience do you have of training adults who come from non–English-speaking backgrounds?
- What qualifications in health and safety do you have?
- What qualifications in training/ teaching do you have?
- How long have you been a consultant in health and safety?
- How do you keep your knowledge up to date?
- What other businesses or organizations have you provided health and safety training to and could they give me a reference?
- What are your areas of expertise/specialization?

Questions about how the trainer will train and assess people in the organization

- What will I or my employees be able to do as a result of this training program? (What new skills and knowledge will we be able to put into practice in the workplace?)
- Where and when would you provide the training?
- How do you plan to assess whether the people doing the training have achieved the outcomes of the program ?
- How will the training contribute to the management of health and safety in this organization?
- As a small organization, we do not want to be totally dependent on health and safety consultants to provide us with the information and training we need. In the training you provide, how will you ensure that we gradually take control of our health and safety training?
- As an employer, I am keen to be involved in the health and safety training that takes place. How will you involve me in the process?
- What sort of training material and records do you supply to employers to keep for future reference?

FIGURE 2. Questions to ask when selecting a health and safety trainer (*Source:* Commonwealth of Australia 1996, p. 20)

as trainers increases the quality of the training since it allows for the application of practical knowledge and direct experience. Worker-trainers have the ability to use personal experiences to illustrate the training, making recipients more receptive to the message.

The Commonwealth of Australia (1996) suggests the following knowledge and experience attributes should be expected of health and safety trainers:

- applicable health and safety codes
- hazard identification, risk assessment, and risk-control approaches to health and safety training
- principles of safety management
- health and safety issues specific to the work assignments and industry of those being trained
- student competency evaluation skills
- adult training skills

Questions to ask when selecting a health and safety trainer are presented in Figure 2. The questions relate to qualification and experience, the conduct of training and training assessment, and related business practices.

Suggested guidelines for worker-trainers have been identified by NIEHS (1998) and include an understanding of adult education training methods and techniques. NIEHS (1994) identifies three principles that need to be addressed to meet the needs of adult learners:

1. Physical environment
   - How are the chairs, tables, and other learning stations arranged in the classroom?
   - How does this arrangement encourage or inhibit participation and interaction?
   - Can the arrangement be changed easily to allow different kinds of interaction?
2. Social environment
   - Are warm-up activities or "ice breakers" used to put people at ease?
   - Do trainers allow participants to say things in their own words, or do they translate what is said into other words or jargon?
   - Are participants encouraged to listen carefully to each other?
   - Are they encouraged to respect different points of view?
   - Are they encouraged to use humor?

3. Differing learning styles, backgrounds, and experiences
   - Do the learning activities in the training program provide participants with an opportunity to listen, look at visuals, ask questions, read, write, practice with equipment, discuss critical issues, identify problems, plan actions, and try out strategies in participatory ways?
   - Is the program sensitive to literacy differences?
   - Do the trainers check privately with anyone having reading and writing difficulties?
   - Is reading aloud or writing in front of the group only voluntary and never mandatory?
   - Are all instructions and other required material read aloud?
   - Do the materials incorporate enough visual aids and props?
   - Do the trainers repeat out loud anything they write on a board or flip chart?

Goetsch (2005) suggests that safety and health trainers understand the principles that explain how people learn. Based on those principles, he suggests that trainers can do a better job of facilitating learning if they have the capability to incorporate the following practices:

- Trainers need to spend time motivating learners, including letting them know how they will benefit from the training.
- Start each learning activity with a brief review of the preceding activity.
- Train in a step-by-step manner that proceeds from the simple to the complex, and from the known to the unknown.
- Classroom presentations are most effective when followed by application activities that require the student to demonstrate understanding by doing something.
- The more often students use what they are learning, the better they will remember and understand it. Infrequent tasks may require more frequent training to maintain skill levels.
- Organize training into segments that are long enough to allow learners to see progress, but not so long as to be boring.

• Give students immediate and continual feedback on learning performance.

The subject of trainer qualifications can become contentious. For example, the workers' bargaining unit represented by the Ontario Public Service (OPS) has suggested that health and safety training be delivered only by workers who have faced actual workplace hazards and who, it claims, better understand workplace health and safety challenges. The OPS Employees Union (OPSEU) Health and Safety policy prohibits its local unions from agreeing to have workers trained by employer-based trainers, has suggested its members file grievances when training is provided by employers, and directs local unions to remove employer-trained workers. It is clearly in the interest of employers and their employees to develop and deliver appropriate health and safety training. Sometimes, the delivery of such training must be managed within the constraints of collective bargaining agreements (OPSEU 2001). The goal, however, should always be the delivery of accurate and effective training.

Petersen (1999) proposes that the supervisor should be responsible for training workers, and that this is particularly important at the front-line supervisory level. If the supervisor is held accountable for safety training, along with other OHS responsibilities, this can be more effective than giving the new employee to an experienced employee. The National Safety Council (NSC) (2010) developed the Supervisor's Safety course that teaches supervisors how to integrate OHS aspects into their daily management process. If supervisors are to be involved in safety training and have other safety responsibilities, it is the organization's OHS professional who will need to educate and train the supervisors, deliver to them the tools necessary to be successful, and develop proper accountability systems.

TRAINING RESEARCH

National Institute for Occupational Safety and Health (NIOSH)

The NIOSH Centers for Disease Control and Prevention (CDC) and participating Institutes and Centers and the National Institutes of Health (NIH) accept grant applications for research related to occupational safety and health. NIOSH research programs support priority areas identified in the National Occupational Research Agenda (NORA) and other significant programs related to occupational safety and health.

NORA represents a research agenda for occupational safety and health in the United States. Using an industry-sector-based approach to develop research agendas, NIOSH is the steward of the NORA program for the nation. There are ten sectors:

1. Mining (except oil and gas extraction)
2. Oil and gas extraction
3. Manufacturing
4. Healthcare and social assistance
5. Wholesale and retail
6. Transportation, warehousing, and utilities
7. Public safety
8. Services
9. Agriculture, forestry, and fishing
10. Construction

OSH training and education is a separate construction-sector strategic goal, and training is included in all other sectors as intermediate and activity goals. Noteworthy is that, in addition to worker training, management and supervisor training is listed frequently within the sector's agenda. NORA has also granted awards for training-effectiveness research. Examples include the effectiveness of computer-based training for vineyard workers carried out at the Oregon Health Sciences University (OHSU) and training and reinforcement in the use of hearing-protection devices done at the University of Washington (NIOSH 2006). In the OHSU study (Anger et al. 2009), workers' knowledge significantly increased after the training. They found that retention in the long term is an issue, and training must be frequently updated.

CONCLUSION

This chapter offered additional strategies in developing best practices in occupational safety and health training, while supplementing previous chapters in this section. Readers are encouraged to benchmark within their own industries and professional circles, and to learn more beyond the field of occupational safety and health training. One can generalize from other disciplines. For example, in engineering education, Richard Felder provides interesting insight on learning styles and student preferences in his model. He categorizes student learning styles and preferences in one of four dimensions (Felder and Silverman 1988, Felder 1993):

1. sensing or intuitive
2. visual or verbal
3. active or reflective
4. sequential or global

Training is just one method for problem solving in the safety and health professional's toolbox. Proper utilization of the hierarchy of controls in problem solving should be thoroughly investigated. Training can be utilized in conjunction with other controls to enhance their effectiveness. Organizations need to understand their population and the population's learning style.

REFERENCES

American Industrial Hygiene Association (AIHA). 2005. *American National Standard for Occupational Health and Safety Management Systems.* ANSI / AIHA Z10-2005. www.aiha.org/ansicommittees/html/z10committee. html

Anger, K., L. Patterson, M. Fuchs, L. Will, and D. Rohlman. 2009. " Learning and Recall of Worker Protection Standard (WPS) Training in Vineyard Workers." *Journal of Agromedicine* 14(3):336–344.

Brauer, R. 2006. *Safety and Health for Engineers.* 2d ed. Hoboken, NJ: John Wiley and Sons.

BS8800 OHSAS and OSHA Health and Safety Management Group. 2002. *OHSAS 18001 Made Easy.* www.osha-bs8800-ohsas-18001-health-and-safety.com/ohsas-18001.html

Canadian Pacific Railway (CPR). 2003. *2003 Health and Safety Plan.* Calgary: CPR Safety and Health Management Committee, pp. 1–24.

Centers for Disease Control and Prevention (CDC). 2000. *Healthy People 2010.* www.healthypeople.gov

Commonwealth of Australia. 1996. *Organising Health and Safety Training For Your Workplace.* Canberra, ACT: Commonwealth Information Services.

European Agency for Safety and Health at Work. 2000. *Facts 7: Future Occupational Safety and Health Research Needs and Priorities in the Member States of the European Union.* www.agency.osha.eu.int/publications/factsheets/7/en/facts7_en.pdf

Felder, R. 1993. "Reaching the Second Tier: Learning and Teaching Styles in College Science Education." *Journal of College Science Teaching* 23(5):286–290.

Felder, R., and L. Silverman. 1988. "Learning and Teaching Styles in Engineering Education." *Engineering Education* 78(7):674–681.

Flin, R., P. O'Connor, and M. Crichton. 2008. *Safety at the Sharp End: A Guide to Non-Technical Skills.* Burlington, VT: Ashgate Publishing Company.

Goetsch, D. 2005. *Occupational Safety and Health for Technologists, Engineers, and Managers.* Upper Saddle River, NJ: Pearson Prentice Hall.

Institute of Nuclear Power Operations (INPO). 2002. *Analysis of Significant Events* (INPO 02-005). Atlanta: INPO.

International Safety Equipment Association (ISEA). 2004. *2004 Strategic Plan.* www.safetyequipment.org/plan2004.pdf)

Milano, M., & D. Ullius. 1998. *Designing Powerful Training: The Sequential-Iterative Model.* San Francisco: Jossey-Bass/Pfeiffer, A Wiley Company.

National Academy for Nuclear Training (NANT). 2003. *The Objectives and Criteria for Accreditation of Training in the Nuclear Power Industry* (ACAD 02-001). Washington, DC: NANT.

National Institute of Environmental Health Sciences (NIEHS). 1994. *Interpretive Guidance to the Minimum Criteria for Worker Health and Safety Training for Hazardous Waste Operations and Emergency Response.* Research Triangle Park, NC: NIEHS.

_____. 1998. *NIEHS Worker-Trainer Programs: Suggested Guidelines for Success.* Research Triangle Park, NC: NIEHS.

National Institute of Occupational Safety and Health (NIOSH). 2006. *Office of Extramural Programs Annual Report, Fiscal Year 2005.* www.cdc.gov/niosh/oep/pdfs/Annual-Report-2005.pdf

_____. 2001. *National Occupational Research Agenda (NORA)*, Publication No. 2001-147 Cincinnati: NIOSH.

National Institute on Deafness and Other Communication Disorders. 2004. *Research.* www.nidcd.nih.gov/research

_____. 2006. Office of Extramural Programs. "Annual Report, Fiscal Year 2005" (retrieved May 16, 2006). www.cdc.gov/niosh/oep/pdfs/Annual-Report-2005.pdf

National Safety Council (NSC). 2010. "Supervisor Safety Training" (retrieved June 16, 2010). www.nsc.org/PRODUCTS_TRAINING/TRAINING/WORKPLACE SAFETY/Pages/SupervisorSafetyTraining.aspx

OHSAS Project Group. 2007. "Occupational Health and Safety Assessment Series, Occupational Health and Safety Management Systems – Requirements." ICS 03.100.01; 13.100. July 2007. London, UK.

Ontario Public Service Employees Union. 2001. *Update on Workplace-Specific Hazard Training.* www.opseu.org/hands/certificationupdate1.htm

Petersen, D. 1999. *Safety Supervision.* 2d ed. Des Plaines, IL : ASSE.

SECTION **5**
WORKERS' COMPENSATION

Regulatory Issues

Benchmarking and Performance Criteria

Best Practices

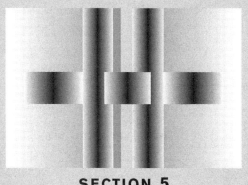

LEARNING OBJECTIVES

▌ Understand the history and purpose of workers' compensation systems.

▌ Understand employee rights and employer responsibilities.

▌ Understand the interaction between workers' compensation systems and federal and state labor laws.

▌ Understand the distinct compensation schemes applying to unique categories of workers.

▌ Develop a proactive system for evaluating and managing workers' compensation claims, identifying affirmative defenses, and implementing legally effective return-to-work programs.

REGULATORY ISSUES

Adele L. Abrams

IN 1902, MARYLAND became the birthplace of workers' compensation benefits when State Senator David J. Lewis introduced legislation that would be the precursor to today's workers' comp statutes (IWIF 2007b). The basic premise of the workers' compensation system is that insurance coverage for workers—addressing both medical expenses and the offsetting of lost wages—is available regardless of fault (with limited exceptions) in exchange for injured workers' abdication of the right to sue employers in tort litigation (with limited exceptions). The employer who provides the injured worker with workers' compensation coverage is also immune from liability to a third party for contribution or indemnity arising from the workplace incident.

Before the enactment of workers' compensation laws, employee wage payments were at the discretion of employers, and medical treatment was the workers' responsibility. Workers often went uncompensated by their employers. Although tort litigation was an option, in practice, many workers did not sue their employers for fear of retaliation, and others found recovery barred by contributory negligence laws. On the other hand, employers who were successfully sued faced both punitive and compensatory damage awards that could threaten their ability to remain in business (MD WCC 2010).

Since 1911, every state has adopted a workers' compensation law. Virtually all states make insurance coverage mandatory. However, the Texas State Workers' Compensation Act also allows employers to opt out of the system (Tweed 1994). New Jersey, which in the past was listed as an exempt jurisdiction in terms of mandatory insurance requirements, covers all workers, whether under its statutes governing workers' compensation or through the uninsured employers' fund. Table 1 lists by state the types of laws and insurance requirements.

TABLE 1

	Type of Law and Insurance Requirements—Private Employment					
State	**Type of Law (Compulsory or Elective)**	**Waivers Permitted?**	**Employer Insures Through State Fund?**	**Employer Insures Through Private Carrier?**	**Individual Employer Self-Insure?**	**Group of Employers Self-Insure?**
AL	C	No	No	Yes	Yes	Yes
AK	C	Yes	No	Yes	Yes	No
AZ	C	Yes	Competitive	Yes	Yes	Yes
AR	C	Yes	No	Yes	Yes	Yes
CA	C	No	Competitive	Yes	Yes	Yes
CO	C	No	Competitive	Yes	Yes	Yes
CT	C	Yes	No	Yes	Yes	Yes
DE	C	No	No	Yes	Yes	Yes
DC	C	No	No	Yes	Yes	No
FL	C	Yes	No	Yes	Yes	Yes
GA	C	Yes	No	Yes	Yes	Yes
HI	C	No	Competitive	Yes	Yes	Yes
ID	C	No	Competitive	Yes	Yes	No
IL	C	No	No	Yes	Yes	Yes
IN	C	No	No	Yes	Yes	No
IA	C	Yes	No	Yes	Yes	Yes
KS	C	No	No	Yes	Yes	Yes
KY	C	Yes	Competitive	Yes	Yes	Yes
LA	C	Yes	Competitive	Yes	Yes	Yes
ME	C	Yes	Competitive	Yes	Yes	Yes
MD	C	Yes	Competitive	Yes	Yes	Yes
MA	C	No	No	Yes	Yes	Yes
MI	C	Yes	No	Yes	Yes	Yes
MN	C	No	Competitive	Yes	Yes	Yes
MS	C	No	No	Yes	Yes	Yes
MO	C	Yes	Competitive	Yes	Yes	Yes
NE	C	No	No	Yes	Yes	No
NV	C	No	No	Yes	Yes	Yes
NH	C	No	No	Yes	Yes	Yes
NJ	E	No	No	Yes	Yes	No
NM	C	Yes	Competitive	Yes	Yes	Yes
NY	C	No	Competitive	Yes	Yes	Yes
NC	C	No	No	Yes	Yes	Yes
ND	C	No	Exclusive	No	No	No
OH	C	Yes	Exclusive	No	Yes	No
OK	C	No	Competitive	Yes	Yes	Yes
OR	C	No	Competitive	Yes	Yes	Yes
PA	C	No	Competitive	Yes	Yes	Yes
PR	C	No	Exclusive	No	No	No
RI	C	Yes	Competitive	Yes	Yes	Yes
SC	C	Yes	No	Yes	Yes	Yes
SD	C	Yes	No	Yes	Yes	Yes
TN	C	Yes	No	Yes	Yes	Yes
TX	E	No	Competitive	Yes	Yes	Yes
UT	C	No	Competitive	Yes	Yes	Yes
VT	C	Yes	No	Yes	Yes	No
VI	C	No	Exclusive	No	No	No
WA	C	No	Exclusive	No	Yes	Yes
WV	C	No	Exclusive	No	Yes	No
WI	C	No	No	Yes	Yes	No
WY	C	No	Exclusive	No	No	No
US						
FECA	C	No	Exclusive	No	Yes	No
HWCA	C	No	No	Yes	Yes	Yes

(*Source*: DOL 2006b)

State laws may permit various methods of insuring liability. In Virginia, where employers with three or more full-time or part-time employees must maintain workers' compensation insurance, the state offers four options:

1. Purchase and maintain a workers' compensation policy from a company licensed in Virginia.
2. Apply to the Virginia Workers' Compensation Commission for approval as an independent self-insurer.
3. Become a member of a group self-insurance association licensed by the state.
4. Enter into an agreement with a professional employer organization as provided in Section 65.2-801.A.4 of the Virginia Code.

In general, workers' compensation programs provide either full or partial payment for medical treatment—including diagnostic procedures, medical supplies and equipment, rehabilitation costs, travel associated with medical treatment, and prescription medicines (DOL 2006a). The insurance generally provides the injured or ill employee with a partial salary while he or she is recovering from a temporary injury or illness arising from working conditions or a work-related accident, or in cases in which workers have suffered permanent disabilities as a result of workplace injury or illness.

Payments are made without regard to an employer's liability, and the system is designed to bar employees from suing employers for injuries arising from the accident (under tort law). This is an employer-financed system, which means that workers cannot be required to contribute toward the cost of workers' compensation insurance.

However, the exclusive remedy provisions of many states' workers' compensation laws have been eroded in recent years by court decisions in which injuries or illnesses relate to intentional or gross misconduct by agents of the employer.

In *Trahan v. Trans Louisiana Gas Company,*[1] the court held that the employer committed an intentional act by repeatedly exposing an employee to chemicals when the employer knew the employee had become ill on prior occasions after being exposed to the same chemicals. In such situations, the exclusive remedy doctrine was found not to apply.

In the case of *Errand v. Cascade Steel Rolling Mills,*[2] the plaintiff was unable to collect workers' compensation benefits for a preexisting condition because the state law required the work to be a "major contributing cause" of the injury. Upon failing to secure workers' compensation benefits, the employee sued his employer. In holding for the injured employee, the Oregon Supreme Court held that the exclusive remedy provision protected an employer from liability only when the employer owed benefits under the act.

There may also be exceptions to the exclusive remedy provisions where injury is caused by a co-worker, and it can be demonstrated that the co-worker acted in an intentional effort to cause injury, for a personal motive. In such instances, the injured worker may be able to bring suit against the aggressor co-worker. Some states, however, address this through statute, such as the Connecticut law that bars actions against fellow employees unless the wrongful action was malicious or arose from the fellow employee's negligence in operation of a motor vehicle.[3]

Louisiana recognizes an "intentional act" exception to the exclusive remedy, and holds that an employer can be liable for a co-worker's action that causes injury to an employee, based upon whether the act was primarily employment-rooted, the violence was reasonably incidental to the performance of the employee's duties, the act occurred on the employer's premises, and whether it occurred during hours of employment.[4] Other exceptions may include instances where injuries result from sexual assault, libel, slander, intentional infliction of emotional distress, false imprisonment or arrest, sexual harassment, and professional negligence.

Moreover, workers' compensation insurance carriers are more frequently denying benefits to workers whose own misconduct (such as violation of corporate safety procedures or mandatory safety standards promulgated by the Occupational Safety and Health Administration, the Mine Safety and Health Administration, or state analogs) was the proximate cause of the injury or illness. If a workers' compensation claim is successfully controverted by the employer, or is denied by the insurance carrier, the injured employee can pursue a tort action against the company but may be thwarted by the application of contributory or comparative negligence laws.

Because each workers' compensation system is state-specific, this chapter can address only general principles commonly found in such statutes. Users of this handbook are advised to consult the specific state agencies that administer each unique workers' compensation statute for more details on compliance responsibilities, filing procedures, attorney fee provisions, payment systems, medical review board provisions, and other related issues, such as vocational rehabilitation services.

In general, all employees are covered by workers' compensation programs, with the exception of part-time domestic help, family members, and babysitters. Other potentially excluded individuals include business owners, independent contractors, commissioned salespeople, railroad workers, seamen, professional athletes, and operators of leased taxicabs. In some state programs, temporary workers are covered, and many states recognize doctrines such as *statutory employers* and *borrowed employees* in order to minimize tort litigation. This requires a state-by-state analysis, and employers should be familiar with prevailing trends in the locations where they have facilities.

Separate workers' compensation systems apply to federal employees and to workers in unique industries covered by other laws (such as the Longshore and Harbor Workers' Compensation Act of 1927). These are addressed elsewhere in this chapter. In addition, compensable work-related injuries or illnesses may give rise to additional employee protections under federal statutes such as the Americans with Disabilities Act (ADA),[5] the Rehabilitation Act,[6] and the Family and Medical Leave Act (FMLA),[7] as well as analogous state-specific human rights laws. These issues are discussed more fully below.

OVERVIEW OF THE WORKERS' COMPENSATION SYSTEM
Key Definitions

Although each state's workers' compensation system has its own statutory definitions, the following is an introduction to common definitions of terms and concepts often employed in state statutes governing the workers' compensation programs (IWIF 2007a):[8]

i. *Workers' Compensation.* A state-run system that pays benefits on behalf of an insured employer, should one of its employees become injured on the job; a schedule of benefits payable to an employee by that employee's employer without regard to liability; required by state law in the case of injury, disability, or death as a result of occupational hazards.

ii. *Temporary Partial Disability.* A condition in which an injured party's capacity to work is temporarily impaired, but the worker is able to continue working in a reduced manner and is expected to fully recover.

iii. *Temporary Total Disability.* A condition in which an injured party is expected to recover but is unable to work at all during recovery.

iv. *Permanent Partial Disability.* A condition in which the injured party's earning capacity is impaired for life, but the worker is able to work at any gainful employment for his remaining lifetime.

v. *Permanent Total Disability.* A condition in which the injured party is permanently and totally disabled and is not able to earn wages in the same capacity or in other employment.

vi. *Average Weekly Wage.* A term generally used in workers' compensation laws. It is often the basis for determining weekly benefits under the law.

vii. *Compromise and Release Agreement.* A settlement practice under which an injured worker agrees to a liability amount (usually a lump sum) in exchange for releasing the employer from further liability.

viii. *Accident.* An unexpected or unforeseen event, happening suddenly and violently, with or without human fault.

ix. *Accidental Injury.* An injury sustained accidentally; only the result need be accidental. Injury must arise out of, and occur in the course of, employment.

x. ***Occupational Disease.*** Sickness or disease occurring from employment. State compensation laws provide coverage for this type of loss.

General Principles

Not all injuries are covered by most workers' compensation laws, even if the injury happened *on the job*. In some states, in order for an injury to be covered, the harm suffered by the employee must have been caused by an *accidental personal injury arising out of and in the course of employment*. In other words, even though workers are hurt "while working," "on the job," or "at work," this may not suffice to provide them with workers' compensation coverage. If the conditions under which the work is required to be performed by the employer cause a worker's injury, it is said to "arise out of" the employment, and the first prong of the analysis is thus satisfied. The emphasis is on the exposure of the employee to some risk or danger *because of* the job's requirements.

The second prong that must be satisfied under most workers' compensation systems is that the injury must be *in the course of employment*. The emphasis on this factor is on the time, place, and circumstances of the injury. If the injury occurs during the period of time when an employee was at work, was at the employer's place of business or such other location as may have been designated by the employer, and was performing job duties or something related to them, the injury is said to have arisen in the course of that person's employment.

Some claims become complicated, as when an injury occurs in the employer's parking lot,[9] the employee is off site on business at a hotel or conference,[10] or the worker is at the work site of a third-party employer who may seek to claim the worker as a "borrowed employee" in order to prevent tort litigation exposure.

There is a trend toward covering *quasi-work* activities, such as injuries occurring during company picnics, barbecues, and receptions, while playing on company sports teams, while participating in charitable events at the behest of the employer, and even while commuting as a member of a company-managed car pool. Some states, such as Texas, apply a multipronged analysis. For example, in *Mersch v. Zurich Insurance Company*,[11] the test inquired whether the claimant's participation in a social or recreational activity was within the course and scope of employment, whether the injury occurred at or near the place of employment, whether the employee's participation in the social or recreational activity was expressly or impliedly required by the employer, or whether the participation furthered the affairs of the employer other than in terms of morale.

There is an increasing trend toward company-sponsored *wellness programs* of various types, some of which are subsidized by the employer. These can range from company sports events to health-club privileges, weight-loss contests, and on-site exercise programs. Some of these are voluntary, while others may be mandated by the employer or conducted while workers are on-the-clock. Many states tend to follow the legal analysis conducted in 2009 by a New York court.

This New York case addressed the issue of a company wellness program where an employee suffered a spinal cord injury while off duty, but participating in athletic activity at a health club. The court examined whether the employee was encouraged, required, or compensated for participating in the activity, or whether the employer otherwise sponsored the activity. In *Torre v. Logic Technology, Inc. et al.*,[12] the worker met his burden of showing that the employer sponsored the activity, through "an affirmative act or overt encouragement . . . to participate." Here, the claimant was encouraged by his employer to have a gym membership, and the employer offered partial reimbursement for fees; the employee's position required him to develop client contacts, and participating in the gym's classes furthered that function. Consequently, the trier of fact was able to find that the injuries incurred at the gym were work-related and compensable.

Some states also recognize compensable claims arising from work at home in *telework* situations, as long as the employee was on duty (performing tasks for the employer) at the time the injury occurred—and it is *not* required that employer-provided equipment be a causative factor!

Combination workers' compensation and employers' liability insurance policies are becoming more prevalent, according to the author's research and observation. These are policies that provide coverage for an employer's two key exposures arising out of injuries sustained by employees. Part one of the policy covers the employer's statutory liabilities under workers' compensation laws, and part two of the policy covers liability arising out of employees' work-related injuries that do not fall under the workers' compensation statute. In most states, the standard workers' compensation and employers' liability policy published by the National Council on Compensation Insurance (NCCI) is the required policy form.[13]

Occupational illnesses are also covered, if the statutory criteria are satisfied, but such claims often have different filing deadlines because of the latency periods associated with some conditions that relate to chemical exposures in the workplace (such as silicosis, asbestosis, lung disease caused by diesel particulate exposure, or poisoning by chemicals in solvents). Conditions such as these may result in an employee's coverage by workers' compensation, even though no specific acute accident occurred. Such conditions (which may result from chronic or long-term exposure to a toxic chemical) are covered as *occupational diseases*.

There are also emerging occupational illness claim categories that some states are recognizing as compensable. The most commonly compensable occupational illnesses arise from workplace exposure to toxic substances such as asbestos, lead, arsenic, cadmium, crystalline silica, diesel particulate, and benzene. However, workers' compensation courts are increasingly awarding benefits for *ergonomic conditions* (carpal tunnel syndrome and other musculoskeletal disorders), psychological injuries linked to on-the-job harassment (often coupled with a Civil Rights Act[14] claim), sick building syndrome (as in cases of mold contamination), chemical exposures, post-traumatic stress arising from violent workplace incidents, and HIV/AIDS resulting from exposure to bloodborne pathogens in the workplace (Frankenmuth Mutual Insurance Company 2007).[15]

For example, in 2010, twelve teachers from Minnesota filed suit seeking workers' compensation for the treatment of post traumatic stress disorder that stemmed from a 2005 school shooting they were involved in. On March 21, 2005, a student gunman took Red Lake High School hostage. Ten people, including the student gunman, died on the Red Lake Indian Reservation that day (Minnesota Public Radio 2010).

Generally, to establish that a compensable psychiatric injury arose out of employment, the employee must prove the mental injury was caused by an identifiable, stressful, work-related event producing sudden mental stimulus, such as fright, shock, or excessive unexpected anxiety.[16] However, "the stress produced may not be usual stress, but must be extraordinary and unusual in comparison to the stress ordinarily experienced by an employee in the same type duty."[17]

Poor indoor air quality can cause myriad illnesses, including Legionnaire's Disease and Hypersensitivity Pneumonitis. Causes include exposure to dust, airborne fungi, allergens, bacteria, and other microscopic material delivered by the ventilation system of an office building (Sullivan 1992, 672).

In *Mead v. American Smelting and Refining Co.*, the Arizona Supreme Court held that medical evidence established the causal relationship between the conditions of work and the illness, despite the fact that medical testimony indicated that the inhalation of dust from the employment was a minor factor in producing the illness. The concept of gradual injury has also been applied to inhalation illnesses held compensable under workers' compensation.[18]

Occupational illness claims are often more difficult to sustain when challenged by an employer because of the infeasibility of preserving evidence, and gathering workplace air or wiping samples *after the fact*— that is, once an employee discovers an illness. Doctors may classify such illnesses as *idiopathic* in origin if no direct cause/effect link is immediately apparent, if the condition arises long after the employment relationship ended, or if the worker has been employed by a series of companies at any of which exposures to the harmful substance could have occurred.

The employee bears the burden of proving that a compensable event has occurred. If an employee can prove that an occupational injury or disease qualifies under the statutory definition, the worker will be entitled to workers' compensation benefits including the payment of some lost wages and costs of medical treatment, devices, and prostheses, and vocational rehabilitation services. Injuries that do not fit into this category may still be covered by general health insurance, but will not be compensable under the state workers' compensation laws.

In some states, if an employer controverts a worker's compensation claim and the worker prevails in further litigation, the employer must pay the worker's attorney fees and costs;[19] however, in many systems, the fees come out of the worker's award instead, lowering the effective benefit that the injured or ill worker receives over the course of disability.

In determining whether an injury falls under the coverage of workers' compensation, the first thing to understand is that this law protects only employees, although some contract or temporary workers may be able to levy claims under the prime employer's policy if the *statutory employer* or *borrowed employee* tests are satisfied. These issues are discussed in more detail below. Generally, each state's workers' compensation statutes provide legal guidance on who qualifies as a covered employee, and who is deemed the *employer*, under that state's system.

Once a claimant's eligibility for coverage is determined, there may be other components which are common to workers' compensation systems. These include:

- *Calculation of the employee's lost wages.*
  Most systems base this on an *average weekly wage* determination, which can be the average of only a few weeks—or even 26 weeks or more—of the worker's last compensation. Shorter periods can result in either a windfall or a deprivation, because overtime and bonuses may be included in the computation, as well as periods of schedule cutbacks or leave without pay taken prior to the accident. Most states establish, by statute, 66.67 percent of the worker's average weekly wage (gross earnings) as the maximum benefit for permanent total disability, although some states go as high as 80 percent of the worker's spendable earnings.[20]

- *Waiting period.* This is also state-specific, with the norm being three days away from work to one week. Some systems waive the disqualification period if the employee is hospitalized—or, if the injury results in a lengthy absence from work, payment for the first few lost days is made retroactively.

- *Durational period.* All systems appear to place a cap on weekly wage benefits for temporary disabilities and it is common to have a payout program for certain categories of injuries (such as amputation of specific body members) and a specified lump sum in the event of death. Benefits for permanent total disability are normally payable for life, but some states cut off benefits at a certain number of weeks or after a certain dollar amount, stop payments once the claimant qualifies for Social Security by reaching a certain age (typically age 65 or 67), or link a cap on benefits to the claimant's marital status and dependents.

- *Awards to surviving spouse and children.* All programs provide that the surviving spouse and children will collect death benefits. However, it is important to note that some states will not award benefits to common law spouses or to stepchildren or illegitimate children. Thus, it is critical to ensure the legal status of any purported beneficiaries before making payment under workers' compensation insurance. Too often, employers discover after the fact that a deceased worker had a spouse in another state from whom they were never divorced, resulting in multiple payouts.

- *Medical benefits.* All medical costs associated with the work-related injury or illness are normally covered; however, in some states the employer can designate a medical review panel to evaluate the worker's condition and to determine the course of treatment.

Many employers purchase workers' compensation insurance from one of the major companies offering these products. However, companies in high-risk categories, as well as those with poor safety records, may find themselves ineligible for such policies and will be forced to purchase their coverage through state insurance pools at much higher rates. There is an increasing trend, especially among larger employers, toward self-insuring their workers' compensation programs, although some states prohibit this. Smaller employers may, in some states, have the option of joining a self-insurance pool through trade associations. Self-insurance can be a less expensive alternative and can provide employers with more control of the claims process. In some states, a statutory discount exists on workers' compensation insurance premiums for companies that have a written, implemented safety and health management program.

Third-Party Considerations

Although injured workers will normally receive benefits from their direct employers, if the injury was caused by the negligent or intentional wrongful action of a third party, tort actions may be initiated against the individual or company that caused the harm. In such situations, the negligence of a third party may allow an employer or insurer to recover monies paid to the employee as part of workers' compensation. Thus, from the direct employer's perspective, it is critical to investigate workplace accidents with an eye toward establishing third-party liability—such as of contractors, members of the public, or products open to liability claims against their manufacturers or suppliers.

On multiemployer work sites (in all industry sectors), more than one employer may be cited for a hazardous condition that violates an OSHA or MSHA standard.[21] If the violation attributed to a third party was a direct or indirect cause of the worker's injury, the worker may be able to claim workers' compensation from one employer while simultaneously suing the other employer, because OSHA citations can be used to establish "negligence per se," and an OSHA citation of "willfulness" can constitute evidence of misconduct that can justify punitive damage awards. The injured worker's direct employer may also seek reimbursement for any workers' compensation benefits that it has paid on behalf of the worker through

subrogation of its claims to the third-party employer's general liability insurance.

From the prime employer's viewpoint, contractual documents are pivotal, and indemnification language must be explicit in order to permit the employer to recoup workers' compensation outlays through tort litigation. Contractual language can also include "duty to defend" provisions in the event that the employer seeks to controvert an employee's compensation claim.

Third-party suits also may be brought in cases where:

- manufacturers provide faulty equipment (*product liability* claims)
- subcontractors cause injury to the employer's worker
- landlords or building owners allow defects to exist that cause injury (*premises liability*)
- insurance companies show *bad faith* in handling a workers' compensation claim
- medical providers negligently or intentionally cause injury during treatment of work-related injuries

Statutory Employer and Borrowed Worker Doctrines

Under certain state laws, as defined by various court rulings, in some situations a third party can invoke the workers' compensation shield against tort litigation by claiming that it is the *statutory employer* of the injured worker, or that the individual is a *borrowed worker*. States tend to encourage this, because it provides quicker payment to injured individuals instead of drawn-out litigation, and because it may provide protection in cases in which the individual's actual employer lacks worker's compensation insurance or the injured individual was an independent contractor or the sole proprietor of a business.

Employer status is defined in several distinct ways:

- as a primary/direct or *de facto* employer
- as a statutory/*de jure* employer
- as a *special employer*

Direct employment is traditionally the most common type of relationship, and it is normally created by either a formal written contract or an understood contract of hire. Significantly, direct employers are those with the ability to hire and fire any employee (subject to applicable state and federal laws). Direct employers pay remuneration to workers and are the source of employee benefits. They also withhold applicable taxes from workers' paychecks, and their employees are entitled to unemployment benefits if employment ends. These *de facto* employers are also required to provide workers' compensation benefits to their employees.

Where *de facto* employers seek to skirt federal or state employment laws or workers' compensation mandates by misclassifying employees as independent contractors, the consequences can be harsh. For example, the Maryland Workplace Fraud Act of 2009 is intended to prevent construction industry employers from misclassifying workers as contractors to avoid payment of payroll taxes and related costs, such as unemployment taxes and workers' compensation premiums. The law gives Maryland's Department of Labor, Licensing, and Regulation broad investigatory and enforcement powers, and imposes financial penalties of up to $5000 per misclassified worker (with doubled penalties for companies with a history of violations), and up to a $20,000 penalty for conspiring with, or assisting an employer in, violating the Act. In addition, the employer can be required to pay restitution to improperly classified workers up to three times the actual losses.

Statutory, or *de jure*, employers are created by force of law, and while not the direct employer (and sometimes not related to the statutory employee), this company may become the employer of record through legal or legislative proceedings. In 44 states, general contractors (GCs) that hire uninsured subcontractors may become the *de jure* employer, responsible for providing workers' compensation benefits in the event of an injury. Hold harmless agreements between the GC and the subcontractor may require endorsement to the workers' compensation policy.

Special employers are those involved in a borrowed servant arrangement: one who has been loaned a worker by another employer.

The Internal Revenue Service (IRS) explains the analysis for determining whether an individual should be classified as an employee or an independent contractor. It advises that common-law analysis of evidence concerning the degree of control and independence falls into three categories:

1. *Behavioral*: Does the company control or have the right to control what the worker does and how the worker does his or her job?
2. *Financial*: Are the business aspects of the worker's job controlled by the payer? (These include things like how the worker is paid, whether expenses are reimbursed, and who provides tools/supplies.)
3. *Type of relationship*: Are there written contracts or employee-type benefits (such as a pension plan, insurance, and vacation pay)? Will the relationship continue, and is the work performed a key aspect of the business?

Businesses must weigh all these factors when determining whether a worker is an employee or an independent contractor. Some factors may indicate that the worker is an employee, while other factors may indicate that the worker is an independent contractor. There is no magic or set number of factors that makes the worker an employee or an independent contractor, and no one factor stands alone in making this determination. Also, factors that are relevant in one situation may not be relevant in another.

The key is to look at the entire relationship, consider the degree or extent of the right to direct and control, and finally, to document each of the factors used in coming up with the determination (IRS 2010).

State law may also be implicated. For example, the Vermont Workers' Compensation Act utilizes two tests to determine if a worker is an independent contractor or an employee for purposes of requiring workers' compensation coverage. First is the *right to control test*, which does not require an employer to actually exercise control; it is sufficient that the employer *could* exercise control, if it chose to do so. If that test is not satisfied, the state will look at the *nature of the business test*, which is used to determine if the work being performed equates with the business, trade, or occupation of the employer. If either test is met, an employer-employee relationship is deemed to exist.[22]

Some courts apply what is known as the Internal Revenue Service *20-factor test* (TimeLegal 2007), with an emphasis on those factors dealing with the *right to control* the work. The four main factors considered are:

1. Direct evidence of the right to control, or its exercise
2. Methods of payment
3. Furnishing of equipment
4. The right to fire (IRS 2005)

Some courts find that a general contractor is the statutory employer in cases in which the subcontractor who actually employs an injured worker lacks compensation insurance. The U.S. Court of Appeals, Fifth Circuit,[23] held that an appropriate test is to examine whether a worker is engaged in:

1. Work that is a subcontracted portion of a larger project
2. Work that is normally conducted by the employer's own employees rather than by independent contractors (the *integral relationship* test)

Other factors considered in assigning statutory employer status include whether the work undertaken by the general contractor is part of its trade, business, or occupation; whether there is an antecedent contract under which the principal contractor was to perform the work; and whether the contractor has subcontracted the work (and whether this was motivated by a desire to evade obligations under the workers' compensation laws). Once the statutory employer relationship is established, that employer assumes all obligations of a normal employer under the relevant workers' compensation statute and becomes a guarantor of the benefits in the event that the subcontractor is uninsured. The trade-off is that the principal contractor is granted immunity from tort liability to the subcontractor's employees.[24]

In *Matthews v. United States*,[25] a private-sector worker who was providing services to a federal agency under contract received injuries when she fell on a sidewalk maintained by the federal General Services Administration. The contract between her direct employer, Calculon Corporation, and the U.S. Department of Energy provided that Calculon would carry

workers' compensation insurance, but the United States paid for the insurance indirectly, under a cost plus contract. The United States asserted a statutory employer defense to the personal injury action filed under the Federal Tort Claims Act [28 U.S.C.A. Sec. 1346(b)].

The Circuit Court of Appeals looked to Maryland's Workers' Compensation Act, which provided:

> When any person as a principal contractor, undertakes to execute any work which is a part of his trade, business or occupation which he has contracted to perform and contracts with any other person as subcontractor, for the execution by or under the subcontractor, of the whole or any part of the work undertaken by the principal contractor, the principal contractor shall be liable to pay to any workman employed in the execution of the work any compensation under this article which he would have been liable to pay if that workman had been immediately employed by him. . . .[26]

Under that state law, once the statutory requirements above are met, the principal contractor may involve the same immunity from common-law tort actions available to the injured worker's actual employer. In *Matthews*, however, the appeals court stressed that such immunity requires two contracts to exist: the first contract is between the original contractor and a third party, in which it is agreed that the principal contractor will execute certain work for the third party; the second contract is between the principal contractor and a subcontractor, whereby the subcontractor agrees to do the work that the principal contractor agreed to do for the third party, in whole or in part. Both prongs were not satisfied by the federal government, and so the tort action was allowed to proceed.

In a state case, a manufacturer was found to be the statutory employer for workers' compensation purposes, where the injured worker was hired through a temporary agency, but the manufacturer owned the premises and carried on the business where the worker worked, as well as supervising the work and having the ability to replace the worker if his work was not satisfactory.[27] Not all jurisdictions would hold in the same way on similar fact patterns because the precise mandates of workers' compensation statutes vary from state to state.[28]

The *borrowed employee* theory holds that when one employer borrows the worker of another employer, the employer responsible for compensating any injuries is identified by analyzing

1. Who had control over the worker and the worker's duties
2. Whether the employee acquiesced in the work situation
3. Who furnished the tools and the place for performance
4. Who had the right to discharge the worker
5. Who had the obligation of paying the worker
6. Whether the original employer terminated his or her relationship with the employee
7. Whose work was being performed
8. Whether an agreement or meeting of the minds existed between the original employer and the *borrowing* employer
9. Whether the new employment took place over a considerable period of time[29]

Miscellaneous Legal Issues

Affirmative Defenses

Although the workers' compensation system is designed to be *no fault*, employers can, in certain cases, raise affirmative defenses to injury or illness claims that occur as a result of incidents in the workplace (Fargason and Price 1994). The main affirmative defenses, because of which compensation is excluded under many compensation systems, are set forth below:

- *Intentional Employee Wrongdoing.* An employee who intentionally injures himself will not be compensated. This can include injuries sustained as the result of horseplay and suicide attempts. One example of an intentional "unsafe act" is an employee who wanted to see what would happen if a chemical used in the processing plant was mixed with water while in a confined container (two-liter soda bottle with the cap). When the container exploded and burned the employee, the workers' compensation carrier denied the claim under "we don't pay for stupid." The employee was

left solely responsible for all medical costs; loss of hourly wages for missing work; loss of spouse's wages (because the spouse had to miss work to address the emergency); and all of the follow-up appointments. These expenses also resulted in the couple losing their home (DeVaul 2010). As a rule of thumb, if an employer can successfully sustain a defense in OSHA enforcement based on unforeseeable employee misconduct, it is possible that the related workers' compensation claim will also be defensible.[30]

- *Fighting.* Workers who are the aggressors in workplace fights may not receive compensation. Workers who are the *victims* in such altercations may still be eligible for compensation.[31]
- *Intoxication.* Workers who are under the influence of alcohol or illegal drugs may be barred from recovery of workers' compensation benefits under many state workers' compensation programs.
- *Statute of Limitations/Lack of Timely Notice.* Employers may successfully defend against claims where workers failed to follow notice requirements, or to satisfy deadlines of filing claims under applicable statutes of limitation.
- *Refusal to Cooperate/Failure to Mitigate Damages.* Under many workers' compensation laws, employees can be disqualified from receiving benefits if they fail to cooperate with treatment plans, fail to show up for evaluation by independent medical examiners, fail to attend hearings, or refuse to participate in vocational rehabilitation programs. In addition, workers who reject jobs for which they are qualified, and which are commensurate with their prior compensation rates, can have benefits cut off or diminished for failure to mitigate damages.

Exceptions to Exclusive Remedy Provisions

Although one of the primary purposes of the workers' compensation system is to help employers avoid tort liability exposure by agreeing to provide insurance through the compensation program, workers can penetrate the *shield* in certain situations, which include:

i. ***Willful violations of OSHA, MSHA, or other regulatory standards.*** Willful violations of mandatory safety standards set by the Occupational Safety and Health Administration (OSHA) or findings of "aggravated conduct" for violations of the Mine Safety and Health Administration that constitute an "unwarrantable failure" under Section 104(D) of the Mine Act may be sufficient to establish a level of gross negligence warranting circumvention of the workers' compensation shield in a number of states. Others use a *multiplier* factor that permits workers to receive a heightened benefit under the workers' compensation system for injuries resulting from an employer's *high negligence* violation of mandatory laws.

ii. ***Intentional torts.*** Actions taken by the employer or its agents, officers, or directors intended to injure workers or cause disease may permit tort actions in lieu of workers' compensation claims.[32] Such situations may also subject employers and management personnel to criminal prosecution by OSHA or MSHA, or assault, battery, manslaughter, and murder by states. If the employer has committed another tort arising from the accident, such as false arrest or defamation, this can be separately pursued by the employee even if he or she has exercised rights to workers' compensation coverage.[33] Moreover, a co-employee is viewed as a *person other than the employer* and therefore may be sued in tort, in most states, for the co-employee's tortuous actions.[34]

iii. ***Infliction of emotional distress.*** Employers may have tort exposure or bear enhanced financial responsibility if discrimination-based harassment of an employee causes emotional distress (often coupled with an EEOC action under Title VII of the Civil Rights Act or the Americans with Disabilities Act). Although many such claims are already cognizable under workers' compensation laws, intentional infliction of emotional distress remains a separate tort action in some states and includes claims for punitive damages. Workers who are severely traumatized by workplace violence incidents that occurred despite the employer's prior knowledge of the potential for such danger, and because the employer failed to take reasonable precautionary measures, may also have a basis for a tort lawsuit in lieu of a workers' compensation claim.

Undocumented Workers

An evolving area of law involves the issue of whether undocumented workers (also known as illegal aliens) are entitled to workers' compensation benefits for work-related injuries. The federal Immigration Reform and Control Act of 1986 (IRCA) and the U.S. Supreme Court's decision in *Hoffman Plastic Compounds v. NLRB*[35] have established that plaintiffs' status as undocumented aliens will bar or limit recovery for lost wages and that the IRCA preempts state tort laws, but the application under distinct state workers' compensation statutes has not been even-handed.

A recent ruling by the Supreme Court of Michigan addressed this issue and considered related matters such as whether the worker would be disqualified because performance of work without valid papers was a criminal act and, since the worker could not return to his job, whether an employer could raise this as an affirmative defense in terms of mitigation of damages. On July 23, 2004, the Michigan Supreme Court, in the consolidated case of *Sanchez et al. v Eagle Alloy, Inc.*,[36] allowed the lower court's ruling to stand. This provides, at least in Michigan, that undocumented aliens are entitled to benefits until such time as the employer actually learns of the employees' illegal status. From the date the employer learns of the employee's status, benefits are not to be paid based on the worker's "commission of a crime."

In the 2005 decision of *Design Kitchen and Baths v. Lagos*,[37] the Maryland Court of Appeals held that exclusion of this class of persons from the state workers' compensation law's coverage would retard the goals of workers' compensation and leave such individuals with only two options: receive no relief for work-related injuries or sue in tort. Moreover, the court said, without statutory protections, unscrupulous employers could take advantage of this class of persons and engage in unsafe practices without fear of retribution. Society would end up bearing the cost for the injuries of the undocumented workers under this scenario.

Other states have also taken an activist approach. In New York, the state workers' compensation law specifically provides that "Compensation under this chapter to aliens not residents or about to become nonresidents of the United States or Canada, shall be the same in amount as provided for residents . . . ."[38] However, two decisions rendered in 2004 held that although undocumented workers can seek damages as a result of injuries incurred at work, such "lost wages" will be based on the prevailing wage in their home countries, rather than being based on their U.S. earnings.[39] It remains to be seen how these decisions will affect New York workers' compensation claims by undocumented aliens in the future.

In 2000, the Commonwealth Court of Pennsylvania considered the IRCA as applied to the Pennsylvania Workers' Compensation Act and held that an illegal alien was not precluded from receiving workers' compensation benefits simply because of his immigration status.[40] In recent decisions, Louisiana, Oklahoma, Florida, and New Jersey appear to adhere to this approach, but Virginia has disqualified an illegal alien from receiving workers' compensation benefits.[41]

Florida's law expressly disqualifies claimants from receiving compensation based on fraud, and it defines "obtaining employment under false pretenses" (such as proffering fake identification in order to be initially hired) to fall within the disqualifying criteria.[42] Wyoming's law provides that the definition of "employee" includes "legally employed minors and aliens authorized to work by the United States department of justice, immigration and naturalization service."[43] In short, only legal aliens need apply for workers' compensation benefits.

Undocumented workers were held to be entitled to benefits under the Longshore and Harbor Workers' Compensation Act. In *Bollinger Shipyards v. Director, Office of Workers' Compensation Programs*, the U.S. Court of Appeals, Fifth Circuit held:

> [T]he LHWCA provides workers' compensation benefits to "employees" who are injured "upon the navigable waters of the United States. . . ." We also find persuasive the section of the LHWCA which states that "[c]ompensation under [the Act] to aliens not residents . . . shall be the same in amount as provided for residents. Although the statute does not expressly define the term "alien" and makes no reference to "illegal" or "undocumented" immigrants, its coverage of nonresident "aliens" is significant. . . . we are convinced beyond cavil that [the plaintiff] was an employee within the intendment of the statute and is thus eligible for workers' compensation benefits.[44]

Clearly, employers need to consult local rulings to determine whether federal and/or state courts are following these trends or whether a worker's illegal status will constitute a total bar on recovery of damages. However, even if an illegal worker is barred from compensation claims, this is not an automatic disqualification from bringing a tort action against the employer, so provision of workers' compensation coverage may ultimately be the least expensive option.

OTHER STATUTES AFFECTING WORKERS' COMPENSATION CLAIMS

Human resources and safety professionals are often confused by the interaction between applicable statutes that may bestow rights upon workers who are injured or who become ill because of a work-related event, in addition to those rights conferred by states' workers' compensation schemes. The two primary statutes implicated in such situations are the Family and Medical Leave Act (FMLA) and the Americans with Disabilities Act (ADA). In addition, states and (in some instances) municipalities may have enacted analogous statutes to the FMLA and ADA that go further than the federal laws to confer rights upon injured or ill employees. It is imperative to review the locally applicable laws when developing corporate leave policies and when handling workers' compensation claims—especially companies that may have operations in multiple jurisdictions—to ensure that no relevant laws are violated.

It is significant to note that workers' compensation statutes, as well as these other employment laws, have antiretaliation provisions.

For example, Florida's workers' compensation statute prohibits employers from discharging, threatening to discharge, intimidating, or coercing any employee because of the employee's valid claim for compensation or his attempt to claim compensation under the workers' compensation laws of the state.[45]

In *Humphrey v. Sears Roebuck & Co.*,[46] the court applied the same antiretaliation analysis as that used under Title VII of the Civil Rights Act of 1964: "an injured employee must show: (1) she engaged in a statutorily protected activity; (2) she suffered an adverse employment action; and (3) the adverse action was in some way related to the protected activity." The court looks at evidence, including whether the employer was aware of the protected conduct, and whether there was a close temporal proximity between that awareness and the subsequent adverse employment action.

In light of such rulings, the issue of how to handle termination of an employee who is currently receiving workers' compensation benefits may arise. Although filing a workers' compensation claim does not prevent an employer from justifiably terminating a worker for a legitimate, nonretaliatory reason, courts often view discharge of claimant employees through the lens of whether the discharge was "for cause" and whether such a discharge violates some public policy. In general, an injured worker's entitlement to disability benefits is treated as a separate issue and may not be conditioned upon the propriety of the employee's discharge. For example, in *Interstate Scaffolding, Inc. v. Illinois Workers' Compensation Comm'n et al.*,[47] the Illinois Supreme Court held that an employer's obligation to pay disability benefits to an injured worker did not cease because the employee had been discharged, regardless of the cause. The critical question remained whether the claimant's condition had stabilized. If the employee was still disabled and could not work as the result of a job-related injury, the employee would continue to be entitled to benefits.

The following summarizes the main federal law provisions and their interrelationship with workers' compensation claims. Violations may subject an employer to prosecution for a single offense by multiple agencies (workers' compensation board, Equal Employment Opportunity Commission, and the Department of Labor's Employment Standards Administration, as well as by state human rights commissions).

The ADA, the Rehabilitation Act, and the FMLA

The interface between state workers' compensation programs and employment laws such as the Americans with Disabilities Act (ADA), Rehabilitation Act, and the Family and Medical Leave Act (FMLA) is confusing at best and has been recognized as the "treacherous triangle" of human relations law (Thompson 2000). These statutes most often collide when an employee becomes sick or injured, and the level of interaction largely depends on the severity, duration, and permanence of the worker's condition.

In some cases, the statutory requirements may conflict with each other. The ADA prohibits differential treatment because of a worker's status as a recovering addict or alcoholic but does not require an employer to accommodate active drug addicts (Batiste 2005). FMLA leave may be available to alcoholics and addicts seeking leave to undergo rehabilitation treatment. However, workers' compensation laws in some states may deny benefits if post-accident tests show the worker was impaired by alcohol or drugs at the time of the accident and was deemed at fault in causing the accident.

In addition, some states have expanded upon the federal protections through enactment of analogous statutes that can *trump* the requirements of the federal laws. Safety and human relations professionals should be familiar with all requirements and consult counsel where appropriate when considering requests for disability accommodation, workers' compensation, leave associated with medical treatment, reinstatement following an absence due to illness or injury, or when the employer is developing a light- or restricted-duty job program for injured workers.

All of these laws require the employee to notify the employer before the statutory protections apply. The disabled worker must act for a reasonable accommodation under ADA, request FMLA leave (specifying the leave as such), and report the work-related injury or illness to the company promptly. State laws carry specific provisions for filing workers' compensation reports and claims with both the employer and the workers' compensation commission, and these should be examined with respect to the employer's obligation to file reports and to understand when compensation must be paid to workers, because brief leave periods (for example, less than four consecutive days) may not be compensable under some workers' compensation systems.

There can be *no retaliation* against employees for exercising rights under the ADA/Rehabilitation Act, the FMLA, or state or federal workers' compensation laws. The statutory provisions of the ADA and FMLA specifically prohibit reprisal, and any such retaliation can provide a separate count in litigation in addition to the underlying claim. Most state workers' compensation laws also have no-retaliation provisions, and even where specific provisions are absent, firing or discriminating against an employee who has sought or received workers' compensation can form the basis for a common-law tort action (wrongful discharge in violation of public policy) even where an "at will" employment relationship exists.[48]

In summary, employers must offer employees the maximum amount of benefits available when a conflict exists between statutes—whether under federal or state law—to avoid potential legal liability. Early medical certification from the employee's healthcare provider can help the employer determine if ADA, FMLA or workers' compensation issues are present. Because protections can vary, and because each law has different reporting requirements and enforcement provisions, both employees and employers must carefully evaluate the applicability of *all* relevant statutes in processing work-related injury or illness claims. Although a detailed explanation of each statute is outside the scope of this chapter, the following discussion provides a summary of the relevant laws and their key provisions.

Americans with Disabilities Act (ADA)

The purpose of the ADA is to protect qualified disabled individuals against discrimination in employment. No minimum duration of employment is required, and applicants are also protected. Covered disabilities are limited to conditions that "substantially limit a major

life activity" (EEOC 2007). Generally, the ADA does not cover temporary conditions (such as a broken leg) but can confer protections upon individuals who are permanently disabled, whether partially or totally, provided a major life activity is affected (such as caring for one's self, walking, seeing, hearing, speaking, breathing, working, performing manual tasks, and learning). Thus, an individual left with a permanent, significant limp, loss of a body member, or a permanent loss of hearing following an industrial accident could be protected under the ADA for the remainder of his or her working life. Complaints of discrimination under the ADA are investigated and may be prosecuted by the U. S. Equal Employment Opportunity Commission (EEOC) or its counterparts at the state level, human rights or human relations commissions.

Rehabilitation Act of 1973

Section 504[49] of the Rehabilitation Act protects qualified individuals from discrimination in employment, programs, or services, based on their disability. The nondiscrimination requirements of the law apply to federal government agencies, as well as to employers and organizations that receive financial assistance from any federal department or agency. These organizations and employers may include hospitals, nursing homes, mental health centers and human service programs. It is generally enforced by the Department of Health and Human Services (HHS); however, complaints alleging employment discrimination on the basis of disability against a single individual will be referred to the EEOC for processing after initial notice is given to the HHS.

As with the ADA, *individuals with disabilities* are defined as persons with a physical or mental impairment that substantially limits one or more major life activities. People are also covered who have a history of, or who are regarded as having, a physical or mental impairment that substantially limits one or more major life activities. Some examples of impairments that may substantially limit major life activities, even with the help of medication or aids and devices, are AIDS, alcoholism, blindness or visual impairment, cancer, deafness or hearing impairment, diabetes, drug addiction, heart disease, and mental illness.

TABLE 2

Comparison of Federal Americans with Disabilities Act (ADA) and Family and Medical Leave Act (FMLA) Statutory Provisions to General State Workers' Compensation Statutory Coverage Provisions

ADA	FMLA	Workers' Compensation
15 or more employees	50 or more employees	Minimum number of employees varies from 1–5 (by state law)
No eligibility requirements other than being a qualified person with disability or an individual "regarded as" disabled.	1. 50 or more employees at worksite or within 75 miles 2. Employee employed a total of 12 months (need not be consecutive) 3. Employee has 1,250 hours of service in 12 months before leave	No eligibility requirements other than work-related injury or illness (definition of work-relatedness varies according to state law).
Leave may be required as "reasonable accommodation" for the disability. Leave may have to be paid.	Leave required up to 12 weeks but may be unpaid. State laws may offer more liberal benefits (e.g., District of Columbia provides 16 weeks). However, employee does not get BOTH state and federal leave, only the maximum provided under the most generous applicable law.	Leave may be required if employee is unable to work. Worker who is injured gets percentage of normal wages as workers' compensation benefit (varies under state law and federal employee workers' compensation system).

Family and Medical Leave Act (FMLA)

The purpose of the FMLA is to provide leave and to preserve a worker's job for up to 12 weeks while the employee obtains treatment or recovers from a serious health condition, or while the worker cares for a child, spouse, or parent who has a serious health condition, or while the worker cares for a newborn or a newly adopted child.[50] To qualify for FMLA leave, the employee normally must have been employed for at least a year working at least 1250 hours during that period. There are exceptions for "key employees" in terms of eligibility with respect to preservation of the job position during the leave period. The leave may be unpaid under the FMLA, although many employers permit workers to use accrued sick time or vacation time, or to use leave donated through a *leave bank*.

The FMLA covers all serious health conditions that require in-patient care or continuing treatment by healthcare providers, regardless of the permanency of the condition. Also, unlike the ADA, the health condition does not have to affect a major life activity in order to qualify for the FMLA leave. Violations of the FMLA are investigated by the U.S. Department of Labor's Employment Standards Administration. Table 2 compares the federal Americans with Disabilities Act and Family and Medical Leave Act Statutory Provisions to general state workers' compensation statutory coverage provisions.

OTHER WORKERS' COMPENSATION SYSTEMS

The Department of Labor administers several additional programs that provide monetary benefits and medical coverage to certain classes of workers in unique industries, as well as to those who are employed by the federal government (DOL 2007b).

Longshore and Harbor Workers' Compensation Act (LHWCA)[51]

The LHWCA is administered by ESA's Office of Workers' Compensation Programs (OWCP). This program provides for compensation and medical care to certain maritime employees (including a longshore worker or other person in longshore operations, and any harbor worker, including a ship repairer, shipbuilder, and shipbreaker) and to qualified dependent survivors of such employees who are disabled by or die because of injuries that occur on the navigable waters of the United States, or in adjoining areas customarily used in loading, unloading, repairing, or building a vessel (DOL 2007c).

Energy Employees Occupational Illness Compensation Program Act[52]

This is a relatively new compensation program designed to provide compensatory benefits to workers at certain federal facilities whose work involves exposure to radiation, beryllium, and crystalline silica. As former President William J. Clinton noted in his Executive Order on this issue, "Existing workers' compensation programs have failed to provide for the needs of these workers and their families. Federal workers' compensation programs have generally not included these workers. Further, because of long latency periods, the uniqueness of the hazards to which they were exposed, and inadequate exposure data, many of these individuals have been unable to obtain State workers' compensation benefits. This problem has been exacerbated by the past policy of the Department of Energy (DOE) and its predecessors of encouraging and assisting DOE contractors in opposing the claims of workers who sought those benefits. This policy has recently been reversed" (Department of Labor 2000).

The law provides a lump-sum payment of $150,000 and prospective medical benefits to employees (or certain of their survivors) of the Department of Energy and its contractors and subcontractors as a result of cancer caused by exposure to radiation, or certain illnesses caused by exposure to beryllium or silica incurred in the performance of duty, as well as for payment of a lump-sum of $50,000 and prospective medical benefits to individuals (or certain of their survivors) determined by the Department of Justice to be eligible for compensation as uranium workers under section 5 of the Radiation Exposure Compensation Act.[53]

Federal Employees' Compensation Act (FECA)[54]

FECA establishes a comprehensive and exclusive workers' compensation program to pay compensation for the disability or death of a federal employee resulting from personal injury sustained while in the performance of duty. The FECA, administered by OWCP, provides benefits for wage-loss compensation for total or partial disability, schedules awards for permanent loss, or loss of use, of specified members of the body, related medical costs, and vocational rehabilitation.

Black Lung Benefits Act[55]

This system provides monthly cash payments and medical benefits to coal miners totally disabled from pneumoconiosis (black lung disease) arising from their employment in the nation's coal mines. The statute also provides monthly benefits to a deceased miner's survivors if the miner's death was caused by black lung disease.

Each coal mine operator is required to pay an excise tax based on the tonnage and the price of its coal sold to support payment of benefits to miners under the Act, and to cover the costs of administering the Act. Operators must provide for the payment of benefits to miners, either directly or through insurance, when they are the responsible employer of the miners. For purposes of determining responsibility for paying benefits, a coal mine operator includes (1) any owner, lessee, or other person who operates, controls, or supervises a coal mine or preparation plant, or (2) any independent contractor performing services or construction at a mine, or (3) companies transporting coal from mines to preparation plants (DOL 2007a).[56]

Railroad Workers and Seamen

Workers in these industries obtain redress outside the workers' compensation system and file suit under specialized statutes. For railroad workers, the Federal Employers' Liability Act[57] mandates the common-law principle of comparative negligence, with modifications favorable to the employee. For seamen, the Merchant Marine Act of 1920[58] (also known as the Jones Act) provides comparable protections.

HEALTH INSURANCE PORTABILITY AND ACCOUNTABILITY ACT (HIPAA) PRIVACY RULES

The Health Insurance Portability and Accountability Act of 1996 (HIPAA)[59] has raised concerns among employers that their management and disclosure of workers' compensation information may subject them to the administrative and privacy provisions of this law and possible prosecution for disclosures made without worker consent. The main sections of HIPAA affecting workers' compensation are the privacy rule provisions.

The Privacy Rule protects all *individually identifiable health information* held or transmitted by a covered entity or its business associate, in any form or media, whether electronic, paper, or oral. The Privacy Rule calls this information *protected health information* (PHI).[60] Individually identifiable health information is information, including demographic data, that relates to

- the individual's past, present, or future physical or mental health or condition
- the provision of healthcare to the individual
- the past, present, or future payment for the provision of healthcare to the individual, and that identifies the individual, or for which there is a reasonable basis to believe can be used to identify the individual[61]

A covered entity is permitted, but not required, to use and disclose protected health information, without an individual's authorization, for the following purposes or situations:

1. To the individual (unless required for access or accounting of disclosures)
2. Treatment, payment, and healthcare operations
3. Opportunity to agree or object
4. Incident to an otherwise permitted use and disclosure
5. Public interest and benefit activities
6. Limited data set for the purposes of research, public health, or healthcare operations[62]

Covered entities may rely on professional ethics and best judgments in deciding which of these permissive uses and disclosures to make. Although the legislation specifically excludes most matters related to workers' compensation,[63] all other applicable federal and state privacy rules must be followed. In addition, because employers may qualify as "covered entities" for purposes other than workers' compensation, it is beneficial to understand generally the requirements of HIPAA.

Disclosures under HIPAA relative to workers' compensation are permitted generally. This situation is addressed by regulations codified at 45 CFR 164.512(l). Individuals' privacy rights are addressed at 45 CFR 164.522. The U.S. Department of Health and Human Services (HHS), which is charged with managing HIPAA compliance, has issued policy guidance on the subject of HIPAA and workers' compensation. It states, in the relevant part:

> [T]he HIPAA Privacy Rule does not apply to entities that are workers' compensation insurers, workers' compensation administrative agencies, or employers, except to the extent they may otherwise be covered entities. However, these entities need access to the health information of individuals who are injured on the job or who have a work-related illness to process or adjudicate claims, or to coordinate care under workers' compensation systems. Generally, this health information is obtained from health care providers who treat these individuals and who may be covered by the Privacy Rule. The Privacy Rule recognizes the legitimate need of insurers and other entities involved in the workers' compensation systems to have access to individuals' health information as authorized by state or other law. Due to the significant variability among such laws, the Privacy Rule permits disclosures of health information for workers' compensation purposes in a number of different ways" (HHS 2003).[64]

In summary, HIPAA permits covered entities to disclose otherwise protected health information to workers' compensation insurers, state administrative agencies, employers, and others involved in workers' compensation systems without the injured workers' permission. Disclosure is permitted, without regard to fault, to the extent necessary to comply with the workers' compensation laws and similar systems (such as black lung benefits and energy workers' compensation programs). The disclosures are permitted for the purpose of obtaining payment for any health care provided to injured and ill workers. Additional information may be disclosed with the affected worker's authorization, as long as the requirements of 45 CFR 164.508 are followed. Any disclosures should be limited to the minimum information needed to accomplish the purpose, but the disclosed information can be shared to the full extent authorized by state or other laws. The HHS intends to monitor the effects of HIPAA and the interaction with workers' compensation programs to ensure that there are not negative impacts on workers' privacy.

HHS is actively providing technical assistance to help covered entities voluntarily comply with HIPAA.

The statute and its implementing regulations provide processes for persons to file complaints with HHS, describe the responsibilities of covered entities to provide records and compliance reports, and cooperate with (and permit access to information for) investigations and compliance reviews. HHS may impose civil money penalties on a covered entity of $100 per failure to comply with a privacy rule requirement. That penalty may not exceed $25,000 per year for multiple violations of the identical privacy rule requirement in a calendar year. HHS may not impose a civil money penalty under specific circumstances, such as when a violation is due to reasonable cause, did not involve willful neglect, and was corrected by the covered entity within 30 days of when it discovered, or should have discovered, the violation.

CONCLUSION

Although the workers' compensation system remains a "crazy quilt" of state laws that often conflict substantively in their procedures and coverage provisions, creating compliance problems for companies who conduct business at a national level or who move workers between different work sites in multiple states, prudent companies will adhere to certain principles:

- Train management and other employees about workers' compensation procedures, rights, and responsibilities.
- Enforce a policy preventing retaliation against workers who file claims (and create a solid paper trail, if necessary, to discipline a worker who has engaged in protected activity by filing a compensation claim).
- Ensure proper coordination of the various statutes that protect workers' rights.
- Conduct thorough accident investigations.
- Use a medical review panel or independent medical examiners, where permitted, to vet the veracity of claims and the proposed course of treatment.
- Thoroughly scrutinize claims in order to prevent workers' compensation fraud and controvert bogus claims, thus minimizing insurance costs.
- Oversee payments to avoid fraudulent billing practices arising from overuse, phantom billing, upcoding, and other common categories of fraud committed by healthcare providers.
- Make use of vocational rehabilitation services.
- Implement vigorous return-to-work programs.

Most importantly, employers should adopt strong safety and health management programs, which will help prevent accidents in the first place, foster a culture of safety among the workers, and help the company qualify for preferential workers' compensation insurance rates.

ENDNOTES

[1] *Trahan v. Trans Louisiana Gas Company*, 618 So. 2d 30 (La. App. 3 Cir. 1993).

[2] *Errand v. Cascade Steel Rolling Mills*, 888 P. 2d 544 (Ore. S. Ct., 1995).

[3] Sec. 31-293a of the Connecticut Workers' Compensation Act, as amended to Jan. 1, 2009.

[4] Louisiana Workers' Compensation Act, LSA- R.S. 23:1021 et seq.

[5] 42 U.S.C. 12101 et seq. As discussed below, federal employees, some state workers, and employees at organizations receiving federal monies are covered instead by the Rehabilitation Act, which contains equivalent protections.

[6] 29 U.S.C. 721 et seq. Regulations implementing the Rehabilitation Act are codified at 45 CFR Part 84.

[7] Family and Medical Leave Act of 1993, 29 U.S.C. 2654 et seq. The implementing regulations are codified at 29 CFR Part 825.

[8] These definitions are drawn from the Injured Workers' Insurance Fund (IWIF) as well as from other consistent statutory sources.

[9] In *Turner v. B Sew Inn*, 18 P.3d 1070 (Okla. 2000), the Oklahoma Supreme Court held that a worker who was injured while falling in the parking lot as she arrived at work was entitled to workers' compensation benefits. Moreover, in *Bitar v. Wakim*, 572 N.W. 2d 191 (Mich. 1998), the Michigan Supreme Court held that receipt of workers' compensation benefits did not bar an injured worker's later tort action against the employer's sole corporate stockholder and property owner.

[10] A Florida appeals court wrote, "A traveling employee is deemed to be in the continuous conduct of his

employer's business including those times when he is not actually at work but is engaged in . . . normal and necessary activities. Thus, so long as a traveling employee's injury arises out of a risk which is reasonably incidental to the conditions of employment, the injury will be compensable." *Thompson v. Keller Foundations, Inc.*, 29 Fla. L. Weekly D2159a (Fla. 1st DCA Sept. 27, 2004).

[11]781 S.W. 2D 447 (Tex. App.—Fort Worth 1989).

[12]*Torre v. Logic Technology, Inc. et al.*, 881 N.Y.S. 2d 675 (S. Ct. NY App. Div. 2009).

[13]International Risk Management Institute, Inc. (IRMI), Insurance Glossary (retrieved DATE),www.irmi.com/online/insurance-glossary/terms/w/workers-compensation-and-employers-liability-policy.aspx

[14]42 U.S.C. 2000e et seq.

[15]See "Tech Bulletin: Mold and Worker's Comp," Frankenmuth Mutual Insurance Company (www.fmins.com/pdf/safety_SERVICES/Safety_Tech_Bulletin_Mold_&_WC.pdf). Also, in *Barren River Dist. Health Dept v. Husey*, SW 3d No. 1998-CA-001387-WC, 2000 WL 377497 (Ky. App. Apr. 14, 2000), the Kentucky Supreme Court held, in an incident in which a nurse contracted AIDS from a needlestick incident on the job, that for purposes of the state workers' compensation statute, AIDS is an occupational disease rather than an injury. A federal appeals court in Mississippi recently held that workers injured or killed in a 2003 shooting at a Lockheed Martin plant were limited to workers' compensation remedies. *Tank v. Lockheed Martin et al.*, No. 05-60028 (5th Cir, 7/18/05).

[16]*Goodloe v. State*, 36 S.W. 3d 62, 65–66 (Tenn. 2001).

[17]Gatlin v. City of Knoxville, 822 S.W. 2d 587, 592 (Tenn. 1991).

[18]*Mead v. American Smelting and Refining Co.*, 399 P. 2d 694 (1965).

[19]For example, under D.C. Code § 32-1530(b), an employer can be ordered to pay a claimant's attorney's fees when an informal conference is held in an attempt to resolve the controversy, a Memorandum of Informal Conference is issued, the employer rejects the Memorandum and does not pay benefits in accordance with the recommendation, and the claimant resorts to the use of an attorney; the compensation subsequently awarded is greater than the amount tendered by the employer.

[20]According to the U.S. Department of Labor, the "spendable" earnings approach, rather than gross wages, has been adopted in Alaska, Connecticut, Iowa, Maine, Michigan, and Rhode Island. Texas has the highest percentage of gross average weekly wage (75 percent) while New Hampshire has the lowest percentage award (60 percent). Federal workers, under the FECA system, receive 75 percent of gross average weekly wage as their disability benefit.

[21]See Occupational Safety and Health Administration (OSHA) *Field Operations Manual*, CPL 02-00-148, November 9, 2009 (www.osha.gov/OshDoc/Directive_pdf/CPL_02-00-148.pdf); OSHA's *Multi-Employer Citation Policy*, CPL 2-0.124, December 10, 1999; and Mine Safety and Health Administration (MSHA). *Program Policy Manual*, Vol. 111, Part 45-1 (www.msha.gov/REGS/COMPLIAN/PPM/PMVOL3A.HTM#5).

[22]See, generally, Vermont Department of Labor. 2010. *Independent Contractor Fact Sheet*, www.labor.vermont.gov/businesses.

[23]*Chavers v. Exxon Corp.*, 716 F.2d 315 (5th Cir. 1983). See also *Para v. Richards Group of Wash. Ltd. P'ship*, 661 A. 2d 737 (Md. 1995).

[24]See *Kelly v. Eclipse Motor Line*, 305 F. Supp. 191(D.Md. 1969), *aff'd*, 432 F. 2d 1009 (4th Cir. 1970).

[25]*Matthews v. United States*, 825 F. 2d 35 (4th Cir. 1987).

[26]Md. Ann. Code art. 101, Sec. 62. Virginia, a neighboring state, has a similar definition of statutory employer. See Va. Code Sec. 65.2-302.

[27]*Candido v. Polymers, Inc.*, 166 Vt. 15 (1996).

[28]See, e.g., *Bozeman v. McCarty Corp.*, 428 So. 2d 1159 (La. App. 5 Cir. 1983); *Fugunt v. Tennesse Valley Authority*, 545 F. Supp. 977 (E.D. Tenn. 1982). In Louisiana, courts have held that to be immune from tort liability under this theory, there must be a written contract between the two companies identifying the prime contractor as the "statutory employer." *Berthelot v. Murphy Oil, Inc.*, 2010 U.S. Dist. LEXIS 1140 (E.D. La. 2010).

[29]*Total Marine Services, Inc. v. Director, OWCP*, 87 F. 3d 774 (5th Cir. 1996).

[30]*Nance v. State Indus., Inc.*, 33 S.W. 3d 22 (Tenn. 2000) (worker's willful violation of safety rules barred workers' compensation claim).

[31]See *Smith v. Raytheon*, 9 Mass. Workers' Comp. Rep. 477, 480–481 (1995) (worker barred from receiving benefits when he provoked a co-worker into fighting with him).

[32]See, e.g., *Federated Dept. Stores, Inc. v. Lee*, 595 A. 2d 1067 (Md. 1991).

[33]*Tynes v. Shoney's Inc.*, 86 F. Supp. 330 (D. Md. 1994).

[34]See, e.g., *Powell v. Erb*, 709 A. 2d 1294 (Md. 1998).

[35]The decision is published at 535 U.S. 137 (2002).

[36]658 NW 2d 510 (Mich App 2003), leave to appeal denied 684 NW2d 342 (2004).

[37]*Design Kitchen and Bath v. Lagos*, 378 Md. 176, 835 A. 2d 1103 (2003).

[38]This traditional approach to nonresident aliens is consistent with the New York statutory framework of awarding compensation "regardless of any question of wrongdoing of any kind." *Testa v. Sorrento Restaurant Inc.*, 10 A.D.2d 133, *appeal denied* 8 N.Y. 2d 705 (1960).

[39]*Sanango v. 200 East 16th Street Housing Corp.*, NY App. Div., No. 2571 (2004); *Balbuena v. IDR Realty*, N.Y. App. Div. No. 2191 (2004). In both cases, the men were working illegally in the United States and were seriously injured while working on construction sites. The *Sanango* case was brought as an indemnification cross-claim by the tort defendant against Sanango's employer. In *Balbuena*, the injured worker sued a number of entities under NY labor laws.

[40]*Reinforced Earth Co. v. WCAB*, 749 A. 2d 1036 (Pa. 2000).

[41]*Jose Granados v. Windson Development Corp.*, 257 Va. 509(1999).

[42]Florida Statutes 440.105(4)(b)(9).

[43]Wyoming Statutes Ann. 27-14-102(a)(vii). See also, *Felix v. Wyoming Workers' Safety & Compensation Div.*, 986 P. 2d 161 (Wy. 1999).

[44]*Bollinger Shipyards v. Director, Office of Workers' Compensation Programs*, (5th Cir. 4/22/2010, Lawyers USA No. 993-1824).

[45]Florida Statutes Sec. 440-205.

[46]*Humphrey v. Sears Roebuck & Co.*, 192 F. Supp. 2d 1371 (S.D. Fla. 2002).

[47]*Interstate Scaffolding, Inc. v. Illinois Workers' Compensation Comm'n et al.*, 923 N.E. 2d 26 (Ill. 2010).

[48]See, e.g., *Shick v. Shirley*, 716 A. 2d 283 (Pa. 2000).

[49]29 U.S.C. 794.

[50]29 U.S.C. 2654; Secretary's Order 1-93 (58 FR 21190). See also 29 CFR Part 825.

[51]33 U.S.C. 901 et seq. The implementing regulations are codified at 20 CFR 701 et seq. Compliance guidance is posted by the U.S. Department of Labor at www.dol.gov/esa/owcp/dlhwc/lstable.htm.

[52]42 U.S.C. 7384 et seq. Both the U.S. Department of Labor and the HHS's Centers for Disease Control are involved in managing claims under this statute. Implementing regulations can be found at 42 CFR Part 81 and at 20 CFR Parts 1 and 30.

[53]42 U.S.C. 2210 et seq. The RECA was passed in 1990 to compensate workers who suffered injuries due to atmospheric testing of nuclear weapons in the Western United States, including civilian government and contractor workers (if employed and present at the atomic test site), civilians injured by fallout (who were downstream of fallout between 1951 and 1958); and mining and milling workers who produced uranium for weapons between 1947 and 1971. Proof of causation is not required under this statute, as long as potential exposure is demonstrated and the claimant has developed one of the specified types of cancer. This program is carried out by the U.S. Department of Justice, and claimants receive lump sum payments ranging from $50,000 to $150,000, depending upon their category.

[54]5 U.S.C. 8101 et seq.

[55]*See* black lung provisions of the Coal Mine Health & Safety Act of 1969, 30 USC 901 et seq.; *see also* 20 CFR Parts 718, 722, 725,726, and 727.

[56]This law does not cover metal/nonmetal miners who suffer occupational illnesses associated with asbestos, silica, or other toxic exposures in the mining environment. Such claims are handled under applicable state workers' compensation laws. Additional information on black lung benefits can be obtained at www.dol.gov/asp/programs/guide/blklung.htm.

[57]45 U.S.C. 51–60.

[58]46 U.S.C. 688 et seq.

[59]42 USC 1301 et seq.

[60]PHI excludes identifiable information that must be maintained, such as OSHA 300 logs and First Report of Injury forms. See 45 CFR 164.501.

[61]45 C.F.R. § 160.103. Individually identifiable health information includes many common identifiers (such as name, address, birth date, and Social Security Number).

[62]45 C.F.R. § 164.502(a)(1).

[63]Psychotherapy notes are not exempted under the workers' compensation exclusion and, because of the increasing number of workers' compensation claims associated with stress and psychological disorders, a patient authorization should be obtained for disclosure of those records.

[64]In addition, many state governments have established Internet sites providing specific information on this subject for regulated employers.

REFERENCES

Batiste, Linda Carter. 2005. *Employees with Alcoholism.* www.jan.wvu.edu/media/alcohol.html

Department of Health and Human Services (HHS). 2003. *OCR HIPAA Privacy: Disclosures for Workers' Compensation Purposes.* www.hhs.gov/ocr/hipaa/guidelines/workerscompensation.pdf

Department of Labor (DOL). 2000. *Executive Order 13179, Providing Compensation to America's Nuclear Weapons Workers.* www.dol.gov/esa/regs/compliance/owcp/eeoicp/law/eo13179.htm

_____. 2006a. *Medical Benefits Provided by Workers' Compensation Statutes.* www.dol.gov/esa/regs/statutes/owcp/stwclaw/tables-pdf/table5.pdf

_____. 2006b. *Type of Law and Insurance Requirements for Private Employment.* www.dol.gov/esa/regs/statutes/owcp/stwclaw/tables-pdf/table1.pdf

_____. 2007a. *Black Lung Compensation.* www.dol.gov/asp/programs/guide/blklung.htm

_____. 2007b. *Compliance Assistance by Major Law.* www.dol.gov/dol/compliance/compliance-major-law.htm

_____. 2007c. *Longshore and Harbor Workers' Compensation Program.* www.dol.gov/esa/owcp/dlhwc/lstable.htm

DeVaul, Randy. 2010. "Taking Shortcuts: Why Do Employees Risk It All?" (retrieved March 7, 2011). www.precast.org/precast-magazines/2010/12/taking-shortcuts

Equal Employment Opportunity Commission (EEOC). 2007. *Americans with Disabilities Act.* www.eeoc.gov/types/ada.html

Fargason, James, and John J. Price. 1994. "Workers Compensation." *Internal Auditor* (June). www.findarticles.com/p/articles/mi_m4153/is_n3_v51/ai_15536323

Frankenmuth Mutual Insurance Company. 2007. *Tech Bulletin: Mold and Worker's Comp.* www.fmins.com/pdf/safety_SERVICES/Safety_Tech_Bulletin_Mold_&_WC.pdf

Injured Workers Insurance Fund (IWIF). 2007a. *Glossary of Terms.* www.iwif.com/html/comp/06_04.shtml

_____. 2007b. *Workers Compensation History.* www.iwif.com/html/comp/06_01.shtml

Internal Revenue Service (IRS). 2005. *Publication 1779, Independent Contractor or Employee.* www.irs.gov/pub/irs-pdf/p1779.pdf

_____. 2010. *Independent Contractor (Self-Employed) or Employee* (retrieved September 28, 2010). www.irs.gov/business/small/art0,,id=99921,00.html

Maryland Workers' Compensation Commission (MD WCC). 2007. *Maryland Workers' Compensation Law: Available Benefits, Who Files the Claim? and the Commission Process.* www.wcc.state.md.us/Gen_Info/WCC_Benefits.html

Sullivan, J., M. Van Ert, and G. Krieger. 1992. Chapter 59, "Indoor Air Quality and Human Health." *Hazardous Materials Toxicology.* J. Sullivan and G. Krieger, eds., p. 672. Baltimore, MD: Williams and Wilkins.

Thompson, Brenda B. 2000. *FMLA, ADA & Workers' Comp: Navigating the Treacherous Triangle.* Brentwood, NJ: M. Lee Smith Publishers.

TimeLegal. 2007. *IRS 20 Factor Test on Employment Status.* www.timelegal.com/employee.pdf

Tweed, Vera. 1994. "Moving Toward 24-hour Care—Integrating Claims Management for Health Insurance and Workers' Compensation Could Decrease Costs." *Business and Health* (September). www.findarticles.com/p/articles/mi_m0903/is_n9_v12/ai_15860586/

APPENDIX: OTHER RESOURCES

Case Law

Balbuena v. IDR Realty, N.Y. App. Div. No. 2191 (2004).

Barren River Dist. Health Dept v. Husey, S.W. 3d No. 1998-CA-001387-WC, 2000 WL 377497 (Ky. App. Apr. 14, 2000).

Berthelot v. Murphy Oil, Inc., 2010 U.S. Dist. Lexis 1140 (E.D. La. 2010).

Bitar v. Wakim, 572 N.W. 2d 191 (Mich. 1998).

Bollinger Shipyards v. Director, Office of Workers' Compensation Programs, 5th Circuit 4/22/2010. Lawyers USA No 993-1824.

Bozeman v. McCarty Corp., 428 So. 2d 1159 (La. App, 5th Cir, 1983).

Candido v. Polymers, Inc., 166 Vt. 15 (1996).

Chavers v. Exxon Corp., 716 F. 3d 315 (5th Cir. 1983).

Design Kitchen and Bath v. Lagos, 378 Md. 176, 835 A. 2d 1103 (2003).

Errand v. Trans Louisiana Gas Company, 618 So. 2d 30 (La. App. 3 Cir. 1993).

Federated Dept. Stores, Inc. v. Le, 595 A. 2d 1067 (Md. 1991).

Felix v. Wyoming Workers' Safety & Compensation Div., 986 P. 2d 161 (Wy 1999).

Fugunt v. Tennessee Valley Authority, 545 F. Supp. 977 (E.D. Tenn 1982).

Gatlin v. City of Knoxville, 822 S.W. 2d 587, 592 (Tenn. 1991).

Goodloe v. State, 36 S.W. 3d 62, 65–66 (Tenn. 2001).

Hoffman Plastic Compounds, Inc., v. National Labor Relations Board (NLRB), 535 U.S. 137 (2002).

Humphrey v. Sears Roebuck & Co., 192 F. Supp. 1371 (S.D. Fla. 2002).

Interstate Scaffolding, Inc. v. Illinois Workers' Compensation Comm'n et al., 923 N.E. 2d 26 (Ill.2010).

Jose Granados v. Windson Development Corp., 257 Va. 509 (1999).

Kelly v. Eclipse Motor Line, 305 F. Supp. 191 (D.Md. 1969), aff'd, 432 F. 2d 1009 (4th Cir. 1970).

Matthews v. United States, 825 F. 2d 35 (4th Cir 1987).

Mead v. American Smelting and Refining Co., 399 P. 2d 694 (1965).

Mersch v. Zurich Insurance Company, 781 S.W. 2d 447 (Tex. App.-Fort Worth 1989, writ denied).

Nance v. State Indus., Inc., 33 S.W. 3d 22 (Tenn. 2000).

Para v. Richards Group of Wash. Ltd. P'ship, 661 A. 2d 737 (Md. 1995).

Powell v. Erb, 709 A. 2d 1294 (Md. 1998).

Reinforced Earth Co. v. WCAB, 749 A. 2d 1036 (Pa. 2000).

Sanango v. 200 East 16th Street Housing Corp., NY App. Div., No. 2571 (2004).

Sanchez, et al. v. Eagle Alloy, Inc, 658 N.W. 2d 510 (Mich App 2003), leave to appeal denied, 684 N.W. 2d 342 (2004).

Shick v. Shirley, 716 A. 2d 283 (Pa. 2000).

Smith v. Raytheon, 9 Mass. Workers' Comp. Rep. 477, 480–481 (1995).

Tank v. Lockheed Martin et al., No. 05-60028 (5th Cir, 7/18/05).

Testa v. Sorrento Restaurant Inc., 10 A.D. 2d 133, appeal denied 8 N.Y. 2d 705 (1960).

Thompson v. Keller Foundations, Inc., 29 Fla. L. Weekly D2159a (Fla. 1st DCA Sept. 27, 2004).

Torre v. Logic Technology, Inc., et al., 881 N.Y. S. 2d 675 (S. Ct. NY App Div 2009).

Total Marine Services, Inc. v. Director, OWCP, 87 F. 3d 774 (5th Cir. 1996).

Trahan v. Trans Louisiana Gas Company, 618 So. 2d (La. App. 3 Cir 1993).

Turner v. B Sew Inn, 18 P. 3d 1070 (Okla. 2000).

Tynes v. Shoney's Inc., 86 F. Supp. 330 (D. Md. 1994).

Code of Federal Regulations

Department of Labor, Employment Standards Administration. 20 CFR 701 et seq. *Longshore and Harbor Workers' Compensation Act (LHWCA) and Related Statutes*

Department of Labor, Office of Workers' Compensation Programs. 20 CFR Part 1, *Performance of Functions.*

Department of Labor, Office of Workers' Compensation Programs. 20 CFR Part 30, *Claims for Compensation Under Energy Employees Occupational Illness Compensation Program Act of 2000, as amended.*

Department of Labor, Employment Standards Administration. 20 CFR Parts 718–726. *Federal Coal Mine Health and Safety Act of 1969.* [and 727.]

Department of Labor, Wage and Hour Division. 29 CFR Part 825, *Family and Medical Leave Act.*

Department of Labor, Occupational Safety and Health Administration (OSHA). 29 CFR Part 1910, *Occupational Safety and Health Standards.*

Department of Labor, Occupational Safety and Health Administration (OSHA). 29 CFR Part 1915, *Occupational Safety and Health Standards for Shipyard Employment.*

Department of Labor, Occupational Safety and Health Administration (OSHA). 29 CFR Part 1918, *Safety and Health Regulations for Longshoring.*

Department of Labor, Occupational Safety and Health Administration (OSHA). 29 CFR Part 1926, *Safety and Health Regulations for Construction.*

Department of Labor (DOL), Mine Safety and Health Administration (MSHA). 30 CFR Parts 1–100, *Mine Safety and Health Administration.*

Department of Energy (DOE). 42 CFR Part 81, *Guidelines for Determining Probability of Causation Under Energy Employees Occupational Illness Compensation Program Act of 2000.*

Department of Health and Human Resources (HHR). 45 CFR Part 84, *Nondiscrimination on the Basis of Handicap in Programs or Activities Receiving Federal Financial Assistance.*

Department of Health and Human Resources (HHR), Social Security Administration (SSA). 45 CFR § 160.103, *General Administration Requirements; Definitions.*

Department of Health and Human Resources (HHR), Social Security Administration (SSA). Subpart E, 45 CFR §164.501, *Privacy of Individual Identifiable Health Information; Definitions.*

Department of Health and Human Resources (HHR), Social Security Administration (SSA). 45 CFR §164.502(a)(1), *Uses and Disclosure of Protected Health Information; General Rules.*

Federal Statutes

Americans with Disabilities Act (ADA). 1993. 42 USC 12101 et seq.

Civil Rights Act of 1964. 1964. 42 USC 2000e.

Coal Mine Health and Safety Act. 1969. 30 USC 901.

Energy Employees Occupational Illness and Compensation Act, 42 USC 7384 et seq.

Family Medical Leave Act (FMLA). 1993. 29 USC 2601 et seq.

Federal Employees' Compensation Act (FECA). 1958. 5 USC 8101.

Federal Employers' Liability Act (FELA). 1908. 45 USC 51–60.

Health Insurance Portability and Accountability Act (HIPAA). 1996. 42 USC 1301.

Immigration Reform and Control Act of 1986 (IRCA). 1986. 8 USC 1101 note.

Longshore and Harbor Workers' Compensation Act (LHWCA). 1927. 33 USC 901.

Merchant Marine Act of 1920. 1920. 46 USC 688.

Radiation Exposure Compensation Act (RECA). 1990. 42 USC 2210.

Rehabilitation Act. 1973. 29 USC 721 et seq.

State Statutes

District of Columbia Code (DC Code). 2001. *Chapter 15, Workers' Compensation. § 32-1530(b), Attorney's fees.*

New Jersey Workers' Compensation Commission (NJ WCC). 2007. N.J.S.A. 34:15-1, *Employees' right to recover for negligent injury, willful negligence as a defense; jury questions.* (Rev. Jan 31).

Orders

Secretary's Order 1-93 (58 FR 21190).

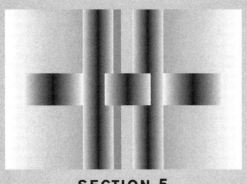

SECTION 5
WORKERS' COMPENSATION

LEARNING OBJECTIVES

▌ Be able to identify basic statistical mechanisms for reporting data.

▌ Understand the basic data required for budgeting for a workers' compensation program.

▌ Be able to identify sources of comparison data for benchmarking a program to other similar programs.

▌ Recognize key factors impacting budgets for workers' compensation programs for a given timeframe.

▌ Understand and identify factors impacting the cost of workers' compensation for a given organization.

BENCHMARKING AND PERFORMANCE CRITERIA

James Bradshaw

MODERN MANAGEMENT SYSTEMS allow for and require the collecting and analysis of substantial amounts of data. This, coupled with relatively inexpensive computing power, can drive data and the multiple mechanisms for presenting a bewildering flow of material that can be difficult to comprehend and that at times can be meaningless. As part of such analysis, data and statistics are important, however, without considering the reasons that a particular set of data is collected and to what use the analysis will be put, the exercise of counting simply doesn't count.

Any usable discussion of cost analysis will necessarily begin with consideration of which data elements are important and how that data (once analyzed) may be useful for explaining or improving the program in question. To borrow from the Six Sigma methodology for process improvement as envisioned by Bill Smith (1929–1993) while an engineer at Motorola (Chadwick 2003), there is a five-step approach that can be applied to any project, including analyzing budgeting of workers' compensation data (define, measure, analyze, implement, control). As with any project, the foundation is to define not only the process or problem, but also the data available and the metrics by which it will be collected, categorized, and (hopefully) used to improve the process.

Within the worker's compensation setting, some data is readily available. It is precise, clear, detailed, but meaningless without the selection of appropriate and meaningful metrics. For example, annual premium (or total expenditure) is of little value without further comparison or definition.

Although each risk management professional will rely on measures particular to his/her own organization, the author has found the following to be some usable measures:

- total cost versus peer group (by industry, region, size, and so on)
- incidents or costs by location/group/work shift/function
- cost per claim
- cost by body part injured
- age/experience/tenure of claimant

As metrics are selected, a clear focus on data needs is required—not only on what, but for whom, and, particularly, why.

- management wants/needs to know (to drive competitiveness/profitability)
- for budgeting
- training/safety/compliance with regulations
- best practices

SOURCES OF DATA

Who cares about data from a workers' compensation program? Anyone and everyone with a financial stake in its success or its impact on the organization's success should care. Each one of those parties may well be a source of or a requester of both raw data and the related analysis.

Analysis of workers' compensation data begins well before any claim or even internal policy development. Even startup operations should review sources of data from established operations in the same or similar industry, trade journals, and best-practice reports (engineering and ergonomic analysis of similar activities provide a wealth of information for guidance in design and policy creation). New programs may also find data from each state's Insurance Commissioner to be useful for benchmark data. These data sets derive from a variety of sources (for example, experience of insurance companies licensed to conduct business in that state as well as various organizations insured by those insurers).

The law of large numbers is a mathematical principle which states that when the number of similar independent exposure units increases, the relative accuracy of predictions about future outcomes based on those exposures also increases (Berthelsen, Elliot, and Harrison 2006). Use of that experience data lends greater validity to assumptions drawn, particularly for comparisons to proposals for insurance and when cross-checking cost projections.

In the author's experience, many risk management professionals do not have the luxury of predesigned planning. Often the assignment is to improve a program, reduce cost, lower incidents, and so on, based on an existing set of circumstances. For these situations, both the sources and types of data present different challenges and opportunities. For a program with significant history, reports from insurers, third-party administrators, or internal staff will drive the collection and analysis of data. However, regardless of the source, data collection whose purpose is unclear or whose analysis does not meet the needs of the stakeholders is a waste.

Specific Data Sources

Specific sources from which data may be collected include:

- reports/loss runs from insurers or third-party administrators (if not provided regularly, these should be requested from the insurance agent, broker, or other assigned representative)
- third-party reports [for example, State Workers' Compensation Commission Reports such as annual Summary Loss Data Reports (required by all workers' compensation programs in some states) as well as State Insurance Commissioner data on performance of insurance companies licensed to provide policies in the state]. *Note:* Developing a relationship with key individuals within the State Workers' Compensation Commission is an absolute necessity, especially for a new program or risk management professional needing to compare data across a large number of programs. Persons in those positions have ready access to data analysis from many workers' compensation programs that may prove beneficial for

comparison purposes. The author has also found that these individuals may also be able to provide anecdotal information related to success or failure of other similarly situated programs.

- professional associations such as the American Society of Safety Engineers (ASSE), the Risk and Insurance Management Society (RIMS), and local/statewide self-insurer associations
- rating services such as the National Council on Compensation Insurance, Inc. (NCCI)
- specialty insurer reports (for example, stop-loss insurer benchmark analysis)
- actuarial valuation.

Actuarial Valuation

One organization defines this item as "A valuation carried out by an actuary on a regular basis, in particular, to test future funding or current solvency or the value of the pension fund's assets with its liabilities" (OECD 2005). Substituting "workers' compensation program" for the term "pension fund" allows this definition to apply to the current discussion.

An example of this type of actuarial valuation report was developed by Midwest Employers Casualty Company (MECC 2005) for the self-insured workers' compensation program operated by the city of Little Rock, Arkansas, for the periods shown in Table 1. The major class codes included in Little Rock's payroll over the policy periods analyzed include:

8810 – Clerical   9102 – Parks
7704 – Fire Fighters   9403 – Garbage
7720 – Police Officers 9410 – Municipal Township

Midwest's analysis focuses on the following three statistical components:

- total losses
- number of claims (frequency)
- average cost per claim (severity)

Each of these components is actuarially projected to an ultimate basis. Ultimate losses and claim counts are estimates of the final cost for all claims incurred during a specific period of time. Actuarially projected losses and claim counts include amounts paid to date plus the following unpaid amounts:

- case reserves—costs of known claims as estimated by the third-party administrator (or internally if self-administered)
- adverse development—costs of increasing reserves in known claims
- costs of claims that have been incurred but not reported (IBNR)

Adverse development (increase in the cost of a claim over time) and IBNR costs are estimated using actuarial projection techniques.

MECC analyzed the city of Little Rock's historical performance for the period from January 1, 2000 through June 30, 2004. Using data valued as of June 8, 2005 (for the policy year ending June 30, 2004), expected results for the number of injuries incurred are as follows:

Frequency: Little Rock's expected number of claims incurred is 24 percent fewer claims than their composite benchmark (average performance) during the historical period analyzed (see Table 1).

TABLE 1

Comparison of Actual Claims Data for Little Rock, Arkansas, Versus Benchmark (Average) Claims and Projected Outcomes for Organization Following Best Practices

	Ultimate Number of Claims						Total	Avg.	Diff.
Little Rock	275	245	130	237	263	257	1407	235	
Benchmark	428	371	167	321	285	291	1863	310	−24%
Best Practices	342	297	133	257	228	233	1490	248	−6%
Policy Period	01/00	01/01	01/02	07/02	07/03	07/04	Historical Period		

Note: The initial data for years 2000–2002 was based on a calender year start date, but was cut off to match a policy year (which begins 1 July). "Historical period" means the timeframe covered by the data.

(*Source*: Midwest Employers Casualty Company 2005)

Severity: Little Rock's average cost per claim results is 48 percent less than their composite benchmark (average performance) during the historical period analyzed.

Total Cost: Little Rock's total direct losses are $5,270,000 *lower* than their composite benchmark (average performance), and $1,800,000 better than the best-practice benchmark for the historical period analyzed.

As the data in Table 1 shows, Little Rock has performed 24 percent better than benchmark over the entire historical period and has achieved best-practice performance. Little Rock is expected to incur 456 fewer claims than benchmark over the entire historical period. This is a yearly average of 75 fewer claims than expected.

INTERNAL PAYROLL

A starting point for virtually all comparisons within the workers' compensation area is that of total payroll for each workers' compensation category for an annual time frame. Since the "manual premium" (the sum of payroll times assigned rate for each category) in effect gives a comparable risk profile for the covered group (and/or a projection of premium rate), it may serve as a starting point for those peer comparisons. This will only be true as long the numbers themselves are accurate, and each organization has accurately assigned positions to the appropriate workers' compensation categories. This will be one particular area in which the relationship with analysis from the workers' compensation commission can prove particularly useful. Reviewing those category assignments by workers' compensation specialists helps to ensure that risk will be appropriately assigned and that comparisons between programs and employers will be valid.

COST COMPARISON PROJECTION ISSUES

Before plugging numbers into a budget model, one must consider what could/should/might happen within the program or system. Data collected is simply a snapshot or series of snapshot conditions as they existed at a point in time. To be useful, particularly since a budget is a prediction of the future, there will need to be some additional prediction of the change in the conditions of the system represented by those numbers over that upcoming budget period. Various factors impacting the system or trends must be considered as projections and predictions are made.

Some internal factors that exhibit as salary (payroll) changes include:

- increase or decrease in number of employees
- increase in average wage
- expansion or reduction in production in one state versus some other state with different worker's compensation rules
- technological change and the impact on types of positions, safety, average wage, and so on
- addition or deletion of entire operations
- claim trends (numbers of incidents, average costs per claim)
- planned changes in workers' compensation programs with projection of the impact (for example, modified duty/return to work program, enhanced on-time reporting, changes in union agreements)

Some of the external market factors include:

- *Medical cost trends.* Numerous sources track these and have shown them in excess of double-digit growth for each of several years prior to this printing. Some organizations that regularly track these cost trends are Milliman, USA and Aon. Aon's Spring 2007 Health Care Trend Survey shows rates across various health insurance vehicles to average from 10.5–18.3 percent for the period of 2002–2006 (AON 2007).
- *Insurance markets.* Aggressive competition for premium dollars during soft-market versus hard-market conditions, when capacity is not available or catastrophic conditions have restricted surplus and tightened underwriting requirements, is a factor.

- *Random variations.* Even relatively large, stable programs will show variations over the course of time, both in numbers of incidents and in relative severity. Beyond the budgeting process, any analysis will require comparisons to some standard to be useful for cost analysis and program adjustment. This standard of comparison may be to:
  - peers (organization of similar size and complexity or industry)
  - benchmarks (a set of standards such as average of peer group)
  - world-class organizations (as good as anyone in the world)
  - ISO (International Organization for Standardization, an organization headquartered in Geneva, Switzerland that has developed several programs for use by organizations to ensure standardization of processes across organizational lines and internationally)
  - similar certifications
  - best practices (which may be precise descriptions or anecdotal descriptions of methods used by organizations to accomplish successful outcomes)

This comparison to peers or benchmarks allows the cost comparison to become meaningful from the standpoint of measurement and analysis of program functions to determine where improvement may be undertaken. It may also be important for setting relative values for budget projections based on how the program compares to the peer or benchmark.

At this level of analysis, descriptive statistics will provide a straightforward approach. Although these statistics are straightforward and simple to compute, caution is urged because, even though the expression's origin is obscure and it has perhaps become trite, "figures don't lie, but liars do figure." Therefore, these statistics may be a beginning point but cannot be relied upon to draw conclusions regarding the health of the workers' compensation program.

Some of the basic statistics that will provide a beginning point for comparison include:

- *Mean:* the simple arithmetic average of the data.
- *Median:* the value of the term that is greater than or equal to half of the other terms and equal to or less than half of the other terms.
- *Mode:* the value appearing most often in the population.
- *Standard deviation:* a measure of a variation of data points around the mean (Weinberg and Schumaker 1974).
- *Correlation:* the measure of how closely two sets of data track each other. It ranges from +1 (perfect correlation, meaning that a change in one of the factors being reviewed shows an identical change in the other factors) through 0 (no relationship between the factors) to −1 (absolute inverse relationship, meaning that changing one factor generates a completely opposite observation in the other factor).

STRATEGIC PLANNING

The budget is necessarily a part of a broader planning process, as well as a tool to be used in ensuring execution of those plans. Unfortunately, in many organizations little real planning (particularly of a strategic nature) is accomplished. This seems particularly true in many public-sector settings where balanced budgets are legally required and where the struggle to balance income to outflow overshadows most real long-term strategy. With Workers' Compensation generally falling into that "legal requirement" category, there can be a tendency to simply plug in as small a number as possible and hope for the best.

Strategic planning must be a broad-based, thorough review that focuses on the long-term existence of the organization and the programs in particular. Planning must consider the strengths, weaknesses, opportunities, and threats relevant to the program and the organization. A model of the strategic planning process is displayed in Figure 1.

Planning specifically for the operations of the workers' compensation program and its connection to organizational goals not only helps ensure cooperation and

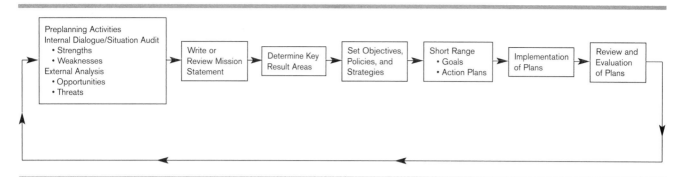

FIGURE 1. Model of strategic planning process (*Source:* Credit Union National Association 1995)

coordination of those goals, but also provides another set of benchmarks for cost analysis. Some questions for the planning process may include:

- Where are we now? What are the statistics and benchmarks?
- What could we do better? How? At what cost? For what benefit?
- What do management/membership/employees expect?
- What environmental factors will have an impact (positive or negative)? Do we expect changes in those factors?
- When and how do we evaluate the progress or goals?
- What if we do not do anything?

Throughout the planning process, communication with all levels of management is crucial. This does not mean that all conclusions or goals should start with the executive level. Indeed, having all conclusions dictated from that level renders subordinate planning impotent, as described quite eloquently by Professor Harry Levinson (1973).

> All of the problems with objectives and appraisals outlined in the example discussed in the foregoing section indicate that management by objectives (MBO), a system of performance evaluation/process review in which overall objectives are set by a higher level of management and each succeeding level appraised according to success in reaching goal derived from those objectives, does not work well despite what some companies think about their programs. The underlying reason is that MBO misses the whole human point.

To see how the point is being missed, let us follow an MBO process. Characteristically, top management sets its corporate goal for the coming year. This may be in terms of return on investment, sales, production, growth, or other measurable factors.

Within this frame of reference, reporting managers may then be asked how much their units intend to contribute toward meeting that goal or they may be asked to set their own goals relatively independent of the corporate goal. If they are left free to set their own goals, these in any case are expected to be higher than those they had the previous year. Usually, each reporting manager's range of choices is limited to his option for a piece of the organizational action or to improvement of specific statistics. In some cases, it may also include obtaining specific training or skills.

Once a reporting manager decides on his unit's goals and has them approved by his superior, those become the manager's goals. Presumably, he has committed himself to what he wants to do. He has said it and he is responsible for it. He is thereafter subject to being hoisted with his own petard.

Now, let us reexamine the process closely; the whole method is based on a short-term, egocentrically oriented perspective and an underlying reward-punishment psychology. The typical MBO process puts the reporting manager in much the same position as a rat in a maze who has choices between only two alternatives. The experimenter who puts the rat in the maze assumes that the rat wants the food reward; if he cannot presume that, he starves the rat to make sure he wants the food.

Management by objectives differs only in that it permits the man himself to choose his own bait from a limited range of choices. Having done so, the MBO process assumes that he will (1) work hard to get it, (2) be pushed internally by reason of his commitment, and (3) make himself responsible to his organization for doing so.

In fairness to most managers, they certainly try, but not without increasing resentment and complaint for feeling like rats in a maze, guilt for not paying attention to those parts of the job not in their objectives, and passive resistance to the mounting pressure for ever higher goals.

The exchange of information and commitment of all related programs to overall organizational objectives are absolute necessities. Tied to the planning function in general, and management's goals in particular, is a determination of the impact a change in operations will have on the workers' compensation program. It will be important to review what happens to workers' compensation-related costs with a significant increase or decrease in the number of personnel in the particular area, a significant change in the average tenure/age of assigned employees, or with the addition of a completely new program.

Since the program costs will (probably) change, and since that change will likely be disproportionate to the size of the program or the number of personnel involved, additional tools for analyzing the probable costs are needed. Some of these may include:

- *Expert estimate/analysis.* Although deemed the "least mathematically sophisticated approach," estimates from parties deemed to be experts lend credibility to the planning process (Ivancevich 2004).
- *Inferential statistical techniques.* There are numerous statistical techniques far beyond the scope of this chapter that may be useful in projecting specific organization needs based on analysis of existing or historical data. These include regression analysis, various probability analyses, and analyses of variants. Regardless of their usefulness, many whose opinion should be swayed by these materials may adopt the opinion of Mark Twain that there are "three types of lies: lies, damned lies, and statistics."
- *Intuition or gut instinct.* Although these cannot serve as the authoritative measures, a best guess from those directly involved in the workers' compensation program for a particular organization probably form a reasonable

basis for initial review. As an example, one benefit-plan CEO who had been involved in all aspects of that particular plan for many years (including marketing and underwriting) included a "local credibility factor" in renewal calculations. Over a period of many years, almost invariably the calculations that included this factor were closer to the actual utilization than the calculations without it.

OTHER SPECIAL BUDGET OR COST ANALYSIS CONSIDERATIONS

There are a number of items whose impact on workers' compensation cost and budget projections must be considered, or which of themselves require additional analysis, for recommendation to management. One of those considerations is the determination of the proper mechanism for funding a workers' compensation program. The two obvious choices are to purchase insurance or to self-insure. For those organizations that operate simple insured programs, much of the budget process may be simply asking "how much?" Analysis of program costs could be as simple as comparing two or more insurance carrier proposals or requesting a best price quote.

Those programs that are self-funded, and particularly those whose circumstances dictate a review of the best approach for funding the program, will find various other analyses are required. To make that determination and to further establish appropriate funding levels within a self-insured program, a number of items must be defined for consideration. Those items include:

- *Claims paid:* Total of all expenditures related to a claim (or all claims for a period of time) including administrative, medical, legal, and so on.
- *Expected claims:* Projected claims for a period of time based on historical claim data plus an inflation factor.
- *Claim lag:* The period of time between the claim occurrence and payment of costs related to that claim.

- *Claim development:* Change in the total cost of a claim due to additional activities over a period of time.
- *Incurred but not reported (IBNR):* Claims that have occurred but of which the program management is not yet aware.
- *Incurred but not paid (IBNP):* Claims that have occurred but for which no expenditure has yet been made.
- *Outstanding reserve:* Estimated future costs related to an incident.
- *Total incurred cost:* All paid and estimated total cost of an incident.

Determining which approach is most beneficial to the organization for arriving at a target budget projection for a self-funded program seems simple enough intuitively. However, in practice, several of the factors noted above will impact that determination.

In a simple form, the starting point can be the calculation of expected claims, which can then be modified by those complicating factors.

Upon the initial startup of a self-funded program, the claim lag between the occurrence of the earliest occurring incidents and when the actual claim payments are made results in some savings, and potentially investment income, on the cash allocated to the plan. The projected funding level must take into consideration the expected claims (including the inflation trend) plus the additional expected cost (administration, legal interventions, investigation, and reinsurance plus a factor for incurred but not reported claims).

PRESENTATION OF MATERIALS

Although not specifically related to the analysis of cost within the workers' compensation program, or development of a budget for such a program, a key issue for workers' compensation professionals to consider is the mechanism for presenting the related materials. As Dr. Joseph Juran described this process related to quality, a key issue for presentation is to "communicate to executives in the language they understand. Learn to show the benefits of quality—and the worth of your expertise in cold, hard dollars." (Phillips-Donaldson 2004). Unless organization executives understand the impact of changes within the workers' compensation

program and budget appropriately (not only for current costs, but also for outstanding reserve, IBNR, and other future costs), the likelihood of appropriate funding diminishes.

Precise, well-defined analyses based on the expertise of trusted professionals can serve as an anchor to help executives understand the value that should be assigned to an area within the workers' compensation program. Because many executives do not have specific workers' compensation-related experience, various cognitive biases may cause decisions to be based on inappropriate staffing. An example of such cognitive bias is anchoring and adjustment. Behaviorists Daniel Kahneman and Amos Tversky (Teach 2004) suggest "that people frequently form estimates by starting with a given easily available reference value—which could be arbitrary—in adjusting from that value. An estimate, therefore, would be 'anchored' to that value."

Regardless of precision, the analysis and the skill applied to the budgeting process, failure to present it clearly and precisely and overcome these confounding factors will lead to an unsatisfactory result.

SUMMARY

Perhaps, unfortunately, the correct answer to the question of how to best analyze cost and project budget for a worker's compensation program is, "it depends." The critical activities for the risk manager or analyst involved in those considerations is the type of data available, peer comparisons, the needs of the appropriate stakeholders, and the critical need of management at a given point in time. Tools provided by this guide will lay the groundwork for establishing a baseline appropriate to the organization reviewing its program. Precise data collection, coupled with appropriate benchmark comparisons, will provide a starting point for analyzing and determining program effectiveness. It is indeed unfortunate that the key tools for determining the effectiveness of a worker's compensation program are those of total cost or projected cost savings. There simply does not exist a mechanism for tracking or analyzing "pain savings" (the employee agony component of an on-the-job injury) until those exist. The exercise of data precision and benchmark comparison, coupled with total cost, will be the most useful measures.

CASE STUDY

The XYZ Company

The XYZ Company has 20 years of history operating a qualified self-funded workers' compensation program. Components of the program are routinely audited by the State Workers' Compensation Commissioner's Self-Insurer Group to ensure that reported payroll figures are assigned to the correct workers' compensation category codes and that the payroll figures reported match the figures reported though other agencies. Audited figures show a total payroll in excess of $95,000,000 for calendar year 2006, with a risk profile that translated that payroll into a manual premium amount of $2,985,000.

XYZ operates on a calendar-year budget cycle. Self-insurer premium tax is due on April 1 each year, and is usually 3 percent of the manual premium. Both the third-party administrator (TPA) contract and the stop-loss insurance policy renew on July 1. During its 20-year history of self-funding, XYZ has seen the market for that coverage represent several complete cycles, from soft (excess capacity with significant competition for premium dollars) to hard (limited availability of capacity and reduced competition between carriers for placing individual policies). Current stop-loss coverage provides XYZ with protection for specific losses only (all costs above $400,000 for a single incident are paid by the stop-loss insurer) with no additional coverage for aggregate annual losses for the plan.

On a three-year rolling average, XYZ has experienced an average of 360 reported claims (with random variation of approximately plus or minus 10 percent in a given year) and total costs for the program averaging $927,000. This total includes average annual costs of:

- $90,000 for self-insurer premium tax
- $103,000 for TPA and related services
- $190,000 for stop-loss insurance (717-794-3800)
- $514,000 for claims costs (current year and run-out).

There is an unfunded liability outstanding for those prior years' open claims.

This amount changes regularly as new claims are added and old ones are closed. The unfunded amount has averaged $650,000. Despite spreading costs over multiple years, an average cost projected by using the total expenditure and the average number of claims per year will provide a reasonable estimate of the per-claim cost ($514,000/360 = $1,428).

NOTE: An alternate method is to set aside an actuarially-determined amount projected to cover costs of open claims from prior years and pay only the current year claims from this budget. For budgeting purposes, there is still a need to project current year costs and compute an amount needed for those prior claims.

The XYZ Board of Directors approves the annual budget no later than December (prior to any of the contract renewals and data collection for the tax payment calculation noted).

For the past five years, inflation (as measured by the Consumer Price Index for Urban Consumers, or CPI-U) has averaged 2.75 percent, but healthcare inflation has averaged 9 percent. However, the state agency that oversees workers' compensation establishes maximum amounts that physicians and other healthcare providers are allowed to charge for treating work-related incidents. Through regular contact with various members of the Workers' Compensation Agency, the risk management professional charged with operating this program has found that the factors used to develop manual premiums are expected to remain close to the current (2006) figures for the foreseeable future.

About 70 percent of the XYZ employees are represented by three unions, two of which have multi-year agreements at 4 percent and 4.25percent across-the-board increases set for 2007. The third union and the nonrepresented employees are thought to be scheduled for an increase amount of about 4 percent. No major additions to or reductions in the employee base are planned. However, additional safety training programs are scheduled to be implemented.

By September 10, 2006, the risk management professional must submit a projected total 2007 budget amount for the worker's compensation program.

To estimate the approximate costs for 2007, the following may be useful:

- Self-insurer tax – assuming that the rates for each category will remain unchanged but that the total payroll will increase about 4 percent: $90,000 × 1.04 = $93,600
- TPA and related services – assuming these will change at about the rate of inflation: $103,000 × 1.0275 = $105,800
- Stop-loss insurance – assuming no significant change and the positive experience of the program, plus possible renewal credits (may or may not be available from an individual carrier): $190,000 × 0.95 (5 percent reduction) = $180,500
- Claims – given medical inflation moderated by state workers' compensation limits on charges, and considering new safety-related training programs, cost per claim could remain static. However, since the projection requires preplanning by several months, using the 9 percent inflation rate is prudent. That leaves a concern for the number of claims that might occur. With this reported average and variation, the risk management professional projects that claims could be as few as 324 (10 percent below average) or as high as 390 (10 percent above average). To ensure that the budgeted amount is sufficient, the worse case of higher-than-average claims plus the full extent of medical inflation should be selected. This produces a claim cost projection of 390 × $1428 × 1.09 = $607,043

The total projected for budget year 2007 thus becomes $90,300 + $105,800 + $180,500 + $607,043 = $983,643.

As physicist Niels Bohr has stated, "Prediction is very difficult, especially about the future." We can only be sure that this number is probably not exact, and perhaps not even close to the actual results. It does at least give a reasoned guide to what may occur in this program.

REFERENCES

Berthelsen, Richard G., Michael W. Elliot, and Connor M. Harrison. 2006. *Risk Financing*. 4th ed. Malvern, PA: American Institute for Chartered Underwriters (AICPCU)/Insurance Institute of America (AII).

Credit Union National Association, Inc. 1995. *Strategic Planning Volunteer Achievement Program Module*. 3d ed. Madison, WI: Kendall/Hunt Publishing Company.

Ivancevich, John. 2004. *Human Resource Management*. 9th ed. New York: McGraw Hill/Irwin.

Levinson, Harry. 1973. *The Great Jackass Fallacy*. Cambridge, MA: Harvard University Press.

Midwest Employers Casualty Company (MECC). "Understanding the Total Cost of Your Workers' Compensation Program: A Management View Report." June 2005. Chesterfield MO: MECC.

Phillips-Donaldson, Debbie. 2004. "100 Years of Juran." *Quality Progress* (May) 37(5):6.

Teach, Edward. 2004. "Avoiding Decision Traps." *CFO Magazine* (June), p. 97.

Weinberg, George H., and John A. Schumaker. 1974. *Statistics: An Intuitive Approach*. 3d ed. Belmont, CA: Wadsworth Publishing Company.

APPENDIX: RECOMMENDED READING

Brown, Mark. 1996. *Keeping Score; Using the Right Metrics to Drive World-Class Performance*. New York: AMACOM/American Management Association.

Chadwick, Gail C. 2003. *Remembering Bill Smith, Father of Six Sigma*. www.isixsigma.com/library/content/c030915a.asp

Ivancevich, John M. 2005. *Organizational Behavior and Management*. 7th ed. New York: McGraw-Hill/Irwin.

National Alliance for Insurance Education and Research. 2007. *Society of Certified Insurance Counselor Certification: Agency Management Institute*. (retrieved December 3, 2007). www.scic.com/OnLineEducation.main.htm

Organization for Economic Co-operation and Development. 2005. *Private Pensions: OECD Classification and Glossary*. Paris: OECD Publishing. www.oecd.org/dataoecd/0/49/38356329.pdf

Popovich, Mark, ed. 1998. *Creating High Performance Government Organizations: A Practical Guide for Public Managers*. San Francisco, CA: Jossey-Bass.

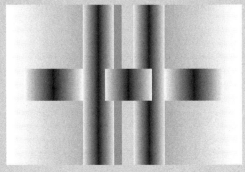

LEARNING OBJECTIVES

▌ Be aware of the evaluation criteria for medical clinics.

▌ Explain functional capacity testing.

▌ Realize the benefits of an early return to work (ERW) program.

▌ List the essential elements for successful accident investigations.

▌ Understand the services an insurance carrier should provide.

▌ Learn about the questions internal claims administrators should consider in periodic claims reviews.

▌ Explain how claims fraud differs from claims abuse.

▌ Understand how the psychosocial climate affects claims.

BEST PRACTICES

Fred Drennan and Katina Drennan

WORKERS' COMPENSATION (commonly referred to as "workers' comp") is the third largest American social insurance after Social Security and Medicare. Workers' compensation provides income and medical benefits to the 9000 workers injured each day and the families of the 15 workers who die as a result of work-related injuries. It also covers the 135 workers and retirees that die each day from work-related illnesses. The total annual economic impact is estimated at $171 billion (NIOSH 2010, p. 7). The purpose of best practices in workers' compensation is to reduce employer costs to acceptable levels while delivering optimum benefits to injured workers and surviving family members.

Over the years, employers and labor have both been dissatisfied with certain aspects of workers' compensation (LRA Online 2003). Labor attacks the system for inadequate benefits, coverage limitations, and exclusion of many injuries, illnesses, and disabilities that it considers job related. Employers criticize the system for covering some injuries and diseases they do not consider job related and for the high cost relative to apparent benefits (NSC 2006).

For the most part, the system works. Injured workers are paid benefits until they have recovered and return to work. Employers get acceptable service from their workers' compensation carriers. However, cost- and service-effective management take dedicated effort. This chapter identifies those best practices proven to effectively manage claims; provide benefits to injured workers; and avoid excessive cost, fraud, and abuse. These practices are widely used in organizations that consistently maintain the highest safety performance records in their industry. (References to data or laws from individual states are included as examples only and may not be representative of other states.)

CHALLENGES TO IDENTIFYING BEST PRACTICES

Today's safety practitioners face some significant challenges in managing workers' compensation. Outside of the insurance industry, little independent research exists that validates best practices in handling workers' compensation claims. Most literature on the topic is published by major insurance companies in the form of Web-site data and in-house brochures and booklets. Their intent is to reduce the cost to the employer for workers' compensation and ultimately reduce the cost to the insurance company, which is contractually obligated to pay the claims. While this information is helpful, other sources should be available to practitioners seeking an unbiased opinion.

Because no standardization of workers' compensation laws and applications exists among the fifty states and the District of Columbia, it is difficult to compile a comprehensive list of best practices that could be used across the nation. Best practices appropriate in one state may not be allowed in another. This lack of standardization makes it difficult for multistate employers to consistently apply cost-control measures and to administer claims within their own organizations. For example, in one state injured workers may be required to go to the "designated medical clinic," while in another state they are free to see their family physician. Therefore, an organization must make adjustments to its policy for how injured workers will receive medical treatment in different states.

Another challenge is the amount of litigation in the workers' compensation system. In many states, advertisements by law offices encourage employees to obtain a lawyer if injured on the job. This practice has falsely led employees to distrust their employers and the workers' compensation system and to create excessive litigation. In California, claimants' attorneys (representing injured workers) were paid $276 million in legal fees during 2008. Employer defense attorneys were paid $607 million. That means that in one year alone California employers paid a total of $883 million in legal fees (out of $7.1 billion in paid losses) for a "no-fault" legal system! Of course, in some states, the claimant's attorney fees are paid from the injured worker's award.

In organizations that tend to incur an excessive number of litigated claims, additional control measures may be needed. Conducting training classes to educate employees about the workers' compensation system and how this "no-fault" system provides benefits without the need of an attorney may help to rectify this situation. Another strategy may be to conduct climate or culture surveys to determine whether other causes may be generating litigated claims.

To be covered by worker's compensation insurance, injuries must "arise out of and in the course of employment" referred to as AOE/COE. When litigation develops, it is often the result of a dispute regarding where an injury occurred. For example, on a Monday morning, an employee reports a back strain while bending over to pick up a box. But during the investigation, the employee honestly admits to rearranging furniture at home over the weekend. Even best practices may not stop the accusations or possible litigation arising from such a case.

Safety professionals should never lose sight of the major drivers of workers' compensation. According to the National Safety Council (NSC 2010), 38 percent of all lost-time cases were due to "bodily reaction or exertion," with the back being the part of the body most affected. Even though an injured employee might state that lifting the box hurt his or her back, most experts believe these types of injuries are *cumulative trauma disorders* (CTDs). CTDs are injuries or disorders to the soft tissues (such as muscles, nerves, and tendons) that occur over time due to daily stresses (on and off the job), the aging process, and a general lack of fitness.

One of the greatest challenges in workers' compensation for the near future is the growth of an aging workforce, which is at high risk for musculoskeletal disorders (MSDs). According to the National Institute of Occupational Safety and Health, 29 percent of all workplace injuries requiring days away from work resulted from an MSD (NIOSH 2009). Even though a comprehensive ergonomics program can help to reduce these injuries, the aging workforce is often overlooked as a contributing factor to the rise in incidence and severity of MSDs (NIOSH 1997). As people age, the body's resilience to chronic wear-and-tear injuries (CTDs) is reduced (Putz-Anderson 1997).

Add to this the fact that most Americans are overweight, out of shape, and do not exercise enough to maintain basic health. The protuberant bellies so prevalent in the overweight workforce add stress to the lumbar spine and are one of the biggest risk factors for back injuries (Cable 2006). Studies show that workers who have low isometric strength to perform their jobs have three times the incidence and severity of MSDs (Chaffin et al., 1999).

The following sections describe programs widely used in many work environments before, during, and after a claim. Each has demonstrated effective cost control, medical care, and injury prevention (Chaffin et al., 1999).

ESSENTIAL ELEMENTS FOR COST CONTAINMENT

Although workers' compensation laws vary from state to state, the principles behind the system and employers' ability to influence their own premiums remain consistent (California Chamber of Commerce 2006). Effective management of workers' compensation requires specific policies and procedures are in place before an injury occurs. These elements—from choosing a clinic to managing case files—must be continuously monitored just like any other management process. Common themes found in publications to help employers run an efficient workers' compensation program are described in the next few sections. By gaining a thorough understanding of these principles and implementing the proven cost-control strategies described, organizations can realize substantial savings while providing injured workers with adequate, equitable, and prompt medical and income benefits.

Designated Occupational Health Clinic

Every state's laws require employers to provide benefits for medical care to injured workers. For many years, medical disbursements composed about one-third of the total losses for workers' compensation. Now, medical disbursements account for half of the nation's spending on workers' compensation; medical benefits have risen to 51 percent of the total losses (NASI 2009). Just as providing health care is important, controlling medical costs should also be a high priority in managing workers' compensation costs.

Almost half the states give employers the right to designate physicians and place limits on medical benefits. Having a high-quality occupational health clinic treat injured workers is the first step in curtailing excessive medical costs.

Patient satisfaction has a direct correlation with optimal workers' compensation outcomes. Numerous studies indicate that satisfied patients often recover from treatment faster and better than unsatisfied patients (Press 2002). Patient satisfaction communicated via word-of-mouth promotes employee goodwill toward an organization. Choosing the right clinic will make the difference in both quality of care for injured workers and effective medical control for the organization.

Not all industrial medical clinics are alike. Some are doctor owned and operated, while others are part of nationally owned chains. Some are small, with limited services, while others are part of a large hospital. It is important to periodically evaluate the clinic. Ownership changes, doctors come and go, and the quality of service may change. One of the first red flags indicating a change for the worse is rumors or complaints from injured workers.

What should be included in evaluation criteria for medical clinics? In a formal survey in the authors' geographical area, employers were asked what qualities they valued most in their occupational health clinic. The most consistently reported qualities were competence of the treating physician, convenience, communication, patient satisfaction, services offered, and efficiencies in administrative procedures and billing practices. Whether evaluating the present clinic or seeking a new one, it is important to consider these qualities.

Competence of the Treating Physician

In workers' compensation cases, it is important to ensure that the injured worker is treated by a physician trained in occupational medicine and workers' compensation practice rather than a family physician, who may not be familiar with the system. A physician who is knowledgeable in workers' compensation practice is an employer's partner when it comes to getting workers back on the job.

Treating physicians play a pivotal role by

- deciding what type of medical care to prescribe for an injury or illness
- determining when workers can return to work
- prescribing the kinds of activities workers can do safely while recovering
- referring workers to other specialists if necessary
- writing medical reports that affect the outcome of the case

The treating physicians' reports and subsequent treatment can make the difference between getting injured workers back to work with effective, appropriate treatment and incurring expensive lost-time injuries.

Convenience

Choose a clinic that is easily accessible to the workforce. If the work takes place in different locations, contact clinics nearest each work site. Some clinics are members of large clinic groups. These are especially helpful because billing and records are readily transferable between locations or are maintained in a centralized database.

Communicating with the Treating Physician

In surveys conducted by author-interviewed service providers, employers highly value medical clinics where the treating physician is accessible and willing to communicate with the employer. This two-way communication can greatly improve the outcome for all parties involved, especially the injured worker. It should be noted that the Health Insurance Portability and Accountability Act (HIPAA) prohibits "covered entities" from releasing "protected health information" (PHI) without patient authorization.

Patient Satisfaction

Patient satisfaction is key to the successful resolution of workers' compensation claims. It is important to remember that when workers are injured, they are in pain, and maybe they are worrying about discipline or even job security and future earnings. A satisfied patient is more likely to return to work quickly than a dissatisfied patient (Press 2002). A patient who is dissatisfied may become disgruntled and seek medical care elsewhere and may be more likely to seek legal action in a workers' compensation case. The process of getting patients back to work—satisfied, pain free, and in a timely manner—begins the minute they walk through the clinic door.

The clinic should have sufficient staff to provide prompt, thorough treatment so that patients feel they are getting the best possible care. It is important for organizations to periodically interview injured workers about the services they received at the clinic. Were they promptly greeted when they arrived at the clinic? Did someone there understand and speak their language? Was there a long wait before they were seen by a physician? Were the waiting and treatment rooms healthful and clean? Did the treating physician spend an appropriate amount of time with them? Were all their questions and concerns answered? Finally, employers should ask themselves whether they would trust their own treatment and recovery to this clinic. If there is any doubt, it may be time to look for a new clinic.

Services Offered

In the authors' experience, the clinic should be a one-stop shop. Does it have X-ray facilities, a pharmacy, and physical therapists on site? Does it have staff certified to conduct DOT testing if employees' work requires a drug and alcohol testing program? If the clinic doesn't provide the services typically needed by workers, injured workers will often spend excessive hours traveling from one location to another to obtain these services.

Administrative Procedures

Employers should choose a clinic that will accommodate their policies and procedures. For example, if a *Doctor's First Report of Injury* is required within 24 hours of the first visit, ensure that the clinic can consistently produce it within 24 hours. These forms should be available to clinics through their state organization. For example, California provides a specific form for this purpose—State of California, Division of Labor Statistics and Research, Form 5021.

Also, a business will want to know that the treating physician will call the employer immediately to report injuries that require restricted or modified/light duty?

Additional procedures to discuss with the clinic are routine post-accident drug and alcohol testing and use of the employer's ADA-compliant job descriptions (which include physical activity requirements) to prescribe the appropriate modified duty. Whatever procedures are established, it is up to employers to monitor the clinic and ensure that standards are maintained.

Billing Practices

Almost all states now have a workers' compensation medical fee schedule that delineates the maximum amount medical providers can charge for a service. For example, in May 2006, the state of Illinois enacted the Illinois Workers' Compensation Act, which includes a workers' compensation fee schedule. Employers should check with their workers' compensation insurance carrier to see whether their state has created a fee schedule.

Doctors or clinics may charge more than what is shown on the schedule, but the employer's insurance carrier is obligated to pay only the allowed expense. Employers should ask whether the clinic abides by this fee schedule and should periodically review billing statements to ensure that they do.

To help control medical expenses, some states have passed new legislation to allow the use of *healthcare organizations, medical provider networks,* and *pharmacy benefits managers.* Employers should check with a claims adjuster or insurance broker to see what options are available in their state.

To summarize, if a clinic's services do not measure up to an organization's expectations, it is likely that they will not meet injured workers' expectations either. Employers should thoroughly research and select the best service provider. Workers deserve the best possible clinical services available in the area, and employers will benefit from better management of workers' compensation claims.

Job Descriptions with Physical Requirements

Job descriptions have long been an essential part of the hiring and promotion process. Most include the salary, grade, scope of responsibility, educational and experience requirements, and certifications required. The Americans with Disabilities Act (ADA) (United States Code 1990) introduced the element of physical requirements to the job description. As defined by the ADA, a qualified individual must be able to perform the "essential functions" of the job. ADA-compliant job descriptions that accurately define the physical demands of a job are useful not only for the hiring process, but also as a physician's reference when a worker is injured.

A well-developed job description includes such physical demands as how much standing, stooping, lifting, sitting, and forceful gripping will be performed, what hand and power tools will be used, and what environmental conditions the employee will be exposed to, such as heat, vibration, noise, and cold.

Developing ADA-compliant job descriptions should be a team effort. The safety department, department supervisors, and the human resources department should work together to ensure that all of the physical and mental demands of the job are included. Once job descriptions are completed, organizations have a legal basis for screening new-hires and accommodating current injured or disabled workers. Most medical clinics will not conduct a *functional capacity testing program* unless they are provided with this level of job description.

Functional Capacity Testing

Is the organization *hiring* its workers' compensation claims? Many state laws compensate employees for illnesses resulting from preexisting conditions such as bad backs, bad knees, or other MSDs that are aggravated by their current employment.

An effective method of screening potential new-hires with preexisting conditions is to conduct *functional capacity testing*. While this type of testing cannot predict an actual injury, it is a good predictor of risk for injury.

Functional capacity testing should not be confused with the common preemployment physical. In the authors' experience, a typical preemployment physical may include measuring blood pressure, performing an eye test, taking a back X-ray, and doing a medical interview to screen out extreme cases. Functional capacity testing expands on the preemployment physical to include tests of lifting, bending, stooping, and other movements that mimic tasks performed at the work site. Additional evaluations include a visual scan of the back, wrists, neck, and knees to detect surgical or injury scars. This type of testing presents a more accurate picture of the prospective employee's true physical strengths and limitations than does the typical preemployment physical.

Functional capacity testing is not a new concept. In the authors' practice, it was learned that the California Fire Department had been testing new recruits in this way for the last 25 years because it needed to determine whether job applicants were truly capable of performing the strenuous work fire fighting requires. Obstacle courses were created that tested candidates' ability to perform using fire-fighting equipment such as ladders, heavy hoses, and large wrenches. Following the fire department's example, many organizations have found value in such programs and have adopted similar testing protocols.

Many industrial medical clinics and physical therapy organizations provide customized functional capacity testing as part of their services. In the authors' experience, functional capacity testing is generally more expensive than a standard preemployment physical; however, screening out a major back injury or carpal tunnel disorder will recover employers' costs many times over. For example, the average lost-time carpal tunnel syndrome injury in California for 2008 cost $37,500 (WCIRB 2008). This cost is only for direct benefits to the injured worker; it does not include administrative, legal (if litigated), and uninsured costs borne by the employer.

Early Return to Work

Workers' compensation carriers agree that getting injured workers back on the job as soon as possible is a major cost-saver. According to the New York State Insurance Fund, employers that implement early return to work (ERW) programs can save from 20 to 40 percent in workers' compensation costs (NYSIF 2007). In 2004, the state of California recognized this fact by including employer incentives to develop and maintain ERW programs in its landmark Workers' Compensation Reform Act (SB 899 2004). This change increases or decreases permanent disability payments by 15 percent based on whether the employer can offer modified or transitional assignments.

ERW programs may be known by many names—transitional work, light duty, modified work, and restricted duty. Many large insurers, such as the California Compensation Insurance Fund (State of California State Compensation Insurance Fund 2006), and National Insurance Company (Zenith National Insurance Corporation n.d.a and b) have created easy-to-understand online training programs to help employers develop and implement effective ERW programs. The carriers list the following benefits:

- reduced temporary disability costs
- reduced claim reserves
- continued worker productivity
- reduced litigation expenses
- fewer fraudulent claims
- avoidance of the replacement and training costs of hiring new employees
- identification of cross-training opportunities that enhance employees' abilities in their regular jobs

Developing an ERW Program

Commitment and support from management is essential in developing an ERW program. Managers and supervisors are responsible for administering the plan and will ultimately determine its success or failure. However, organizations should not be surprised if management has some objections. There may be some resistance to implementing an ERW program for a number of reasons:

- administrative time required
- payroll cost
- close supervision needed to keep employee activity within limits
- morale problems affecting both injured and noninjured workers
- employees preferring the modified assignment

Organizations should be ready to present all of the benefits:

Reduced temporary-disability (TD) payments. Why pay employees two-thirds of their salary (tax free) to stay home? If they are capable of doing any tasks at all, they will recover faster (State of California State Compensation Insurance Fund 2006), and the organization will benefit by keeping them on the job.

Returned control to the employer. With employees at work, even in a lesser capacity, employers can monitor their progress and can have a positive effect (Zenith National Insurance Corporation n.d.a and b) on the resolution of the claim.

An organization's internal administrator is the logical person to monitor the ERW program. Responsibilities include maintaining documentation; acting as a liaison among supervisors, workers, and medical providers; and communicating with the insurance carrier. Most importantly, the internal administrator should monitor the recovery status of the organization's most important customer—the injured worker (Olin 2003).

Policies and Procedures

It is essential that organizations set goals, plan, and put policies and procedures in place before starting an ERW program. Once policies and procedures have been approved, managers, supervisors, and employees must be trained in how the program will be applied so that there are no misunderstandings. ERW program developers should consider the following elements:

Set time limits and make them mandatory. Do not create a permanent position that accommodates an employee's temporary disability. ERW must not be confused with accommodation as provided in the ADA.

Make it clear that ERW is temporary and mandatory and those workers who refuse suitable temporary work (within their medical limitations) will not be compensated for time off by the workers' compensation carrier or the employer.

Identify available work in advance. It is important to identify transitional duty jobs for injured workers as part of the organization's standard operating procedures. This practice provides the opportunity for managers and supervisors to plan in advance productive transitional tasks that benefit the organization and the injured worker. A predetermined list of transitional assignments can also be provided to treating physicians to aid in their decision to return injured workers to their jobs with restrictions (Olin 2003).

In the authors' experience, injured workers feel more useful and their co-workers are more sympathetic if the organization creates a positive atmosphere for their recovery. Avoid make-work transitional assignments that devalue employees' self-esteem and their ability to perform. For example, assigning a person to sweep the floor in a warehouse can hinder recovery by causing him or her to develop a negative attitude. It may also create animosity among co-workers who see the person being paid for a make-work job while they have to carry their own weight.

It is common that returning workers are able to handle all but one or two tasks of their job. Employers should analyze tasks to see what elements injured workers are capable of performing without aggravating the injury. In many cases, the job can be restructured to fit employees' temporary limitations rather than putting them in a totally different, mundane, or demeaning work environment.

Putting It All Together

The following description is a real-life example from the authors' practice of how the principles described in the previous section work together to effectively resolve a claim.

An organization had a large warehouse operation. Before the organization implemented cost-containment procedures, an employee suffered a back strain and was allowed to see his family physician. He told his doctor that working in the warehouse was a physically demanding job. The doctor prescribed pain pills, muscle relaxants, and two weeks off work. The employee received workers' compensation benefits and supplemental pay from his employer. Because workers' compensation benefits are tax-free, his take-home pay was greater than his regular pay. After two weeks, the employee had a follow-up visit with the physician and complained that his back still hurt. The doctor then prescribed four more weeks off work and added physical therapy twice a week. After six weeks off, the doctor finally released the employee to go back to work. The total cost to the employer was far more than the workers' compensation and supplemental pay the worker received while he was off for six weeks because of the additional cost for finding, training, and scheduling a replacement worker. The medical and indemnity payments increased the organization's workers' compensation premium, and the injury was recorded on the company's OSHA Log 300 as a lost-time accident.

After incurring a number of similar incidents, the company was finally compelled to implement cost-containment procedures that included a designated industrial medical clinic, job descriptions that detailed the physical demands of each job, an ERW program, and a policy that required injured workers be taken to the clinic by their supervisors.

After the new policies and procedures were in place, another warehouse worker with the same job title incurred a back strain. The supervisor took the employee to the clinic, along with the employee's job description. After treatment, the treating physician reviewed the job description and made the comment that driving a forklift was "light duty" and not physically demanding. He prescribed anti-inflammatory drugs (which the clinic provided), restricted operating the forklift to one-hour increments with five-minute stretch breaks in between, and restricted lifting to under 25 pounds. The employee returned to his normal job in the warehouse without any lost time and followed the treating physician's instructions.

The result was drastically different from the previous case: the total incurred medical loss was $175. The average cost for a lost-time back injury in California at the time was $52,955 (WCIRB 2005). The company's OSHA Log 300 showed the injury as only a "restricted" case instead of a lost-time injury.

The following case illustrates the balance between providing appropriate, effective medical care to workers and controlling costs to employers.

Substance-Abuse Prevention and Workers' Compensation

According to the *2008 National Survey on Drug Use and Health* (U.S. Department of Health and Human Services), 63 percent of people who drink are full-time employees. Their national surveys show 9 percent of people who drink are "heavy drinkers," and one-third of those heavy drinkers also consume illicit drugs. It can be inferred then, that if you have ten employees who drink, there is a high probability that one employee will be a heavy drinker and use drugs. Losses due to substance abuse are well known, and many organizations have developed aggressive substance-abuse programs to combat this national problem.

The same national survey showed that 8 percent of full-time employees consumed illicit drugs. In descending order of consumption, the drugs most used were marijuana, prescription drugs (e.g., OxyContin, Vicodin, Valium, and Ritalin), cocaine (includes crack), and the fourth most-used drug, the hallucinogen Ecstasy. Prescribing medication to an injured worker with a substance-abuse history can be problematic, to say the least. If an injured worker has a known substance-abuse history, the employer should advise the treating physician so proper medication can be prescribed. Even though it is rare, if an employee becomes an active user again because of the prescribed medication, they can be treated for the addiction within the scope of the original injury. Those responsible for their workers' compensation program should always be aware that substance abuse can greatly affect the outcome of a small number of workers' compensation claims.

Many employers are subject to the Department of Transportation's (DOT) "Substance Control and Alcohol Testing," which includes post-accident testing. An injured employee testing positive under the rules is not automatically precluded from receiving workers' compensation. To be excluded from workers' compensation, the employee had to be intoxicated at the time of the accident. The DOT has set zero tolerance levels for controlled substances, meaning that testing is conducted at the lowest level scientifically possible, which is in nanograms (billionths of a gram) (DOT 2010). Intoxication is hard to prove at such low levels and the long latency period that drugs stay in the system (weeks for marijuana), makes a legal defense very difficult. The miniscule amount that can be detected in a drug test for marijuana (billionths of a gram) does not constitute intoxication (DOT 2010). In hundreds of compensation claims, the authors have not seen one employee denied benefits due to intoxication.

Provided that it is not barred by a collective bargaining agreement, mandatory post-accident drug/alcohol testing is a good control measure. Employers may develop their own policies requiring mandatory post-accident testing where there is property damage or the employee needs medical attention. If the employee tests positive, the employer can determine what action to take according to the written policies. Other enterprises, such as the trucking industry, are regulated by the Department of Transportation (DOT) and post-accident testing is mandatory in certain situations.

Another good control measure is to find suitable modified work for the employee. Keeping the substance abuser (who is currently inactive) on the job under close supervision is preferable. Having an injured employee sit at home without any type of support will lead to negative outcomes. The longer the employee is at home, the more difficult it will be to get that person back to work.

The safety professional, supervisor, or co-workers should never be in the position of diagnosing, threatening, accusing, or passing moral judgment on an employee with a substance-abuse problem. For many people, work is their only social support. According to the U.S. Census Bureau, the number of people living alone continues to increase. Over one in four people are living alone, and single parents now comprise 10 percent of all households. Employers can choose to have a positive or negative substance-abuse program. Providing the right kind of social support can lead to a human success story. Otherwise, an employee can become just another statistic.

If an employer suspects substance abuse, it is important to document what is seen and heard (see Figure 1) and to investigate rumors. It is also important to train supervisors and others in what to look

for and document. (A good sample form for use as documentation and training can be downloaded at www.teamsafetyinc.com/resources.html/forms.) If enough evidence is gathered, contact a substance-abuse professional (SAP) and get advice on how to proceed. It will be time and money well spent.

EFFECTIVE CLAIMS MANAGEMENT

Employers often believe that workers' compensation claims are the responsibility of the compensation carrier. While the carrier has an interest in keeping costs down, there are rarely enough claims adjusters to handle cases in a timely and efficient manner. For example, in 2003 in the state of Texas, the average caseload per claims adjuster was between 200 and 210 (SORM 2003). According to a February 2007 press release, an audit for the city of Los Angeles found that even the 150 claims per adjuster recommended as a best practice has impacted the quality and timeliness of services provided (Chick 2007). Without constant monitoring by the employer, claims can work their way to the bottom of the pile. The total cost and ultimate outcome of a workers' compensation claim is a direct result of the degree to which an employer is involved in the process and quickly closes the claim.

Assigning an Internal Administrator

The longer a claim is open, the higher its costs. In a data analysis of more than a million claims, 90 percent of all costs were incurred by claims that had a duration over 30 days (CWCI n.d.). A highly effective cost-control measure is to assign an internal administrator to immediately follow up on all workers' compensation claims as they occur. This person should be knowledgeable about workers' compensation, be well organized and detail oriented, and have good writing and verbal skills.

Workers' compensation claims can involve many people: the injured worker, the immediate supervisor, the treating physician, the physical therapist, the claims adjuster, the injured worker's significant other, and many more if the claim goes into litigation. Keeping the communications and paper on track takes skill and needs constant attention. The employer, not the claims adjuster, is in the best position to keep the case

DRUG / ALCOHOL USE
REASONABLE SUSPICION

Employee's Name: _____

Date of Observation: _____
                                           (month / day / year)

Time of Observation: From _____ a.m. / p.m. To _____ a.m. / p.m.

Location: _____

Observed behavior - check all appropriate items:

SPEECH   **BALANCE**   **WALKING**
❏ thick   ❏ unsteady   ❏ stumbling
❏ rapid   ❏ swaying falling   ❏ staggering
❏ slurred   ❏ grasping for support
❏ incoherent
❏ excessively talkative

PHYSICAL OBSERVATIONS
❏ dilated pupils   ❏ tremors   ❏ marijuana odor
❏ chronic red eyes   ❏ weight loss   ❏ alcohol odor
❏ cold sweats   ❏ rapid breathing
❏ loss of appetite   ❏ hygiene neglect

EMOTIONAL OBSERVATIONS   **POSSESSION OF DRUGS/ALCOHOL**
❏ depression   ❏ alcohol/containers
❏ anxiety   ❏ drugs
❏ alienation   ❏ paraphernalia
❏ moodiness
❏ withdrawal
❏ irritability

Other observed abnormal behavior: _____

_____

_____

To the best of my knowledge and belief this report represents the appearance, behavior and/or conduct of the above-named driver, observed by me and upon which I base my decision to require said driver to submit to reasonable suspicion drug/alcohol testing.

Witnessed by:

_____   _____
Signature of Supervisor or company official   Signature of Supervisor or company official

_____   _____
Date   Date

Figure 1. Sample documentation for suspicion of substance abuse (*Source:* Team Safety, Inc.)

moving forward and in a positive light. Coordinating all of the parties and keeping track of the paperwork can be taxing, but when managed effectively, this process is an effective tool for cost control.

The internal administrator has one goal: to get claims closed as quickly as possible (preferably within 30 days) with the best possible outcome for all concerned.

Prompt Accident Reporting and Investigation

A workers' compensation claim begins the moment the employer has knowledge, from any source, that an injury has occurred (California Chamber of Commerce 2006). A quick response can make the difference between a quick resolution and an ongoing, costly claim. In a study of 30,000 lost-time injuries, claims filed five or more days after the injury cost an average of 15 percent more than similar claims filed promptly (Occupational Hazards 2000). The more time that passes, the greater the chance that evidence will be lost; witnesses will forget or misstate the details of the incident; or important elements leading to the incident, such as a missing machine guard, will be corrected or concealed.

Accident Reporting Versus Accident Investigation

Accident reporting should be timely and contain sufficient detail to characterize the event, but it should not be confused with *accident investigation*. Accident investigation may take several days and has two basic purposes: to determine all root causes of the accident and to take corrective action to prevent a recurrence (Hagen et al. 2009). Facts gathered during the initial phase of the accident investigation can be used later for the full investigation.

Accident reporting must be a matter of high priority rather than simply filling out a form from the insurance carrier. The key elements of effective accident reporting are timeliness, thoroughness, and documentation. This applies to witness testimony, hearsay, and hard and circumstantial evidence.

An accident-reporting policy should clearly state who is responsible to report, when the report is re-

quired, and what details must be provided. Effective accident reporting includes the following elements:

Employee's Statement of Injury/Illness

One of the definitions of workers' compensation fraud is "false or fraudulent statement or material representation for the purpose of obtaining compensation." In the authors' experience, some employees may change their version of how the injury occurred as the claim progresses in order to obtain compensation. For this reason, a written statement *by the employee, not the immediate supervisor*, should be the first piece of documentation in any claim file (see Figure 2). A statement written in the employee's own words, recorded immediately after the incident occurs, will be the best, most irrefutable record of what happened.

Supervisor's Statement

The injured employee's immediate supervisor is in the best position to gather the initial facts and verify the employee's statement of injury. The supervisor's statement form should provide sections for validating that the supervisor has reviewed the report with the employee and sections for additional comments regarding the incident as well as for the supervisor's signature and date (see Figure 3).

KEY ELEMENTS TO REMEMBER

In the authors' experience, the following elements are essential for successful accident investigation:

1. *Begin immediately.*
2. *Get witness statements.* The more witness statements are obtained, the clearer the picture will become. Do not forget to interview people who may not have seen the incident but were involved with the injured employee just prior to it. Interviewing witnesses is a skill, and the interviewer should be trained.
3. *Take photos.* Keep photos as a permanent record in the case file. If there are conflicting statements from the injured person or witnesses, photographs will be invaluable in sorting out the truth. Digital cameras are great for this purpose.

EMPLOYEE STATEMENT OF INJURY/ILLNESS

Name_____ S.S.N _____

Res. Address_____ City: _____ Zip_____

Res. Telephone ( )_____ Date of Hire: ____/____/_____ Birth Date: ____/____/_____

Date of Injury/Death: ____/____/_____ Time _____A.M. ☐ P.M. ☐ Date Reported: ____/____/_____

Where Did Accident Occur? _____

Witness to Accident? _____

Describe How Accident Happened. Were Any Tools or Equipment Involved?_____

_____

_____

Describe what the employee was doing just before the accident;_____

Describe Injury and Part of Body_____

Did you seek medical treatment? (date/time) _____ Name of medical facility/physician:_____

Did employee provide a clearance to return to full or light duty by the treating physician: Yes ☐   No☐

PREVENTION: How Could This Accident Been Prevented_____

_____

_____

Employee Signature _____ Date ____/____/_____

Figure 2. Sample employee statement of illness or injury form (*Source:* Team Safety, Inc.)

4. *Pay attention to informal communication.* If rumors surface, follow up. Most employees are honest and hard working and do not like to see other employees take advantage of the company or the compensation system. If it is rumored that an employee on disability is working "under the table" on another job, report this immediately to the carrier. They will be happy to investigate it.

5. *Document, document, document.* Keep an on-going record of every piece of information—its source, date, and detail—even if it is in the form of hearsay.

Partnering with Your Claims Adjuster

In any claim, the third most important person, after the injured worker and the treating physician, is the insurance claims adjuster. The claims adjuster does the following:

- makes decisions about the validity of the claim
- handles the administrative details for the case
- authorizes and monitors medical services and records
- works with the defense attorney if the case is litigated
- sets reserves for the total anticipated cost of the claim, which has a direct impact on the organization's insurance premium

Think of claims adjusters as bank tellers with access to the organization's bank account. They have the authority to accept, deny, and authorize funds for claims costing tens of thousands (sometimes hundreds of thousands) of dollars. Because of large caseloads, adjusters may not have time to devote adequate attention to details, which can result in a longer period from injury to case closure, extended periods of temporary disability payments, unnecessary medical expenses, and dissatisfied patients, which could lead to litigation.

Therefore, it is important for organizations to foster open communication with the claims adjuster and not hesitate to call the claims adjuster and ask for a status report on the claim if prompt responses are not forthcoming.

At a minimum, the employer should expect the following services from the carrier:

- All necessary accident reporting forms required by the carrier should be supplied.
- A designated claims adjuster should be provided for the organization rather than any available adjuster who may not be familiar with the case or with the organization's operation.
- The carrier should show the employer how to help the adjuster close claims more efficiently.

- The carrier should provide a summary, at least quarterly, of claims for costs, litigation, and other significant information that can affect the employer's workers' compensation insurance.
- The carrier should supply a list of recommended treating physicians and clinics that specialize in workers' compensation.
- The carrier should supply a list of doctors known to consistently work for claimants' attorneys so that the employer can avoid sending employees to them.

Finally, the organization should make sure the claims adjuster has a good understanding of the employer's business and its day-to-day operation. If possible, the adjuster should visit the facility for a firsthand look at what the business does. The more adjusters know about the organizations they work with, the more help they can provide in controlling claims.

SUPERVISOR'S ACCIDENT INVESTIGATION

UNSAFE ACTS (check basic reason with "x")
- ☐ Working on moving or dangerous equipment
- ☐ Failure to wear Personal Protective Equipment
- ☐ Improper attire, jewelry, etc.
- ☐ Failure to secure or warn
- ☐ Horseplay, teasing, or distraction
- ☐ Improper use of equipment or tools
- ☐ Lifting or moving objects too heavy

- ☐ Bypassing safety devices
- ☐ Unsafe speed, haste, or short cuts
- ☐ Unsafe foot, hand, or body position
- ☐ Driving errors
- ☐ Using unsafe equipment or tools
- ☐ Failure to follow instructions or inexperience
- ☐ Unsafe act does not apply
- ☐ Other: _____

UNSAFE CONDITIONS: (check basic reason with "x")
- ☐ Defective equipment or tools]
- ☐ Inside environment unsafe
- ☐ Poor housekeeping – storage – layout, etc.
- ☐ Unsafe guarding of equipment or tools

- ☐ Unsafe condition does not apply
- ☐ Other: _____

GUIDES TO CORRECTIVE ACTIONS

What verbal direction was given to correct the unsafe condition:_____

RELEASE TO DUTY

Did employee provide a treating physician's release to full or modified duty? Yes ☐ No ☐ Modified ☐

If modified, what restrictions are required: _____

SUPERVISOR COMMENTS
I have reviewed the information on this form with the employee and verify as correct to the best of my knowledge.

Supervisor's Signature_____ Date ____/____/____

Figure 3. Sample supervisor's accident investigation form (*Source:* Team Safety, Inc.)

Periodic Claim Review

The internal claims administrator should periodically review all open claims to ensure that events are progressing in a timely manner and should continue to review them until they are closed. Periodic review will help to identify any red flags that may indicate that a claim is heading in a negative direction. As part of the review, the internal claims administrator should consider the following questions:

Is the patient getting better? The claims administrator should review progress reports from the treating physician. If it seems that the patient is not progressing, the administrator should call the doctor and get additional information not in the reports (privacy laws may prevent certain information from being disclosed). Maybe the doctor is concerned that the patient is not progressing as expected. Also, do not hesitate to call the employee to find out what is going on. Maybe the injured worker has stopped going to the physician because he or she is unhappy with the treatment.

Has there been a change in status? Has a recent medical report indicated that the employee may have a permanent disability? Will the permanent disability prevent the employee from returning to his or her usual and customary occupation? Will the employee require training in a different field? Finding answers to these difficult questions requires discussions with the claims adjuster, the treating physician, the human resources department, and organizations that provide rehabilitation services.

Are there gaps in the paper trail? Missing documentation could hurt the employer's ability to control the claim. For example, reports may be missing from the physical therapist because the employee quit going to therapy appointments. Failure to go to doctors' appointments is big red flag. In some states, failure to go to doctors' appointments and physical therapy is grounds to stop benefits such as temporary disability payments because it is assumed that the employee has been cured or relieved of the effects of the injury.

It is vital for the internal claims administrator to gather copies of correspondence between the claims adjuster and the injured worker. The claims adjuster will notify the employee of major status changes, such as starting or stopping temporary disability payments, advancing permanent disability payments, or the initiation of a vocational rehabilitation program. The internal administrator should be aware of these changes to ensure that the employee is treated fairly and equitably and to make sure that any action from the insurance company does not lead to unnecessary litigation.

Has the doctor requested an MRI? During the course of treatment, the doctor may request an MRI. This could indicate that the employee is not getting better or may be getting worse. Did the employer get the results of the MRI? There could be significant findings that indicate surgery is required, meaning that the employee could lose a significant amount of time from work—or worse.

Has the injured worker been returned to full duty? The most important thing for the internal administrator to remember is that the claim is not closed until the employer receives a written report from the treating physician indicating that the employee is recovered and ready to go back to work without any further medical treatment. In the authors' experience, the report will include language such as "returned to full duty" *and* "released from further care" (or "discharged"). If the doctor's report says the worker can "return to full duty," but the doctor continues to schedule treatment, the case is not officially closed. This situation warrants a call to the workers' compensation claims adjuster to discuss how to best close the claim.

Unit Statistical Filing

To encourage employers to decrease industrial accidents, all states use a merit-rated pricing system. Each year workers' compensation carriers must submit to their respective state rating organization a *unit statistical* (*unit stat*) *filing* that lists the organization's incurred losses. If eligible, an employer can receive an "Experience Modification Factor," which is an indication of the organization's loss experience (dollar loss on claims) compared to the average for the applicable industry. If an employer's losses are greater than the industry average, the experience modification is high; if losses are less than the industry average, the experience modification is low. Obviously, this is something that should be closely monitored, because the insurance premium an employer pays could go up or down substantially based on the experience modification. The most critical review period is just before the carrier submits its unit stat reports to the state. The unit stat report includes not only actual paid losses for each claim, but also anticipated losses, known as *reserves*, for a *total incurred cost*. For example, if, at the time of filing, a back injury claim is open, the carrier may already have paid $25,000 but may anticipate that the claim could eventually cost as much $50,000; this is the total incurred cost that would be filed with the unit stats.

Carriers are not infallible. Errors in both the actual and reserve costs on the unit stat report can increase an employer's insurance premium. Therefore it is critical for organizations to review the unit stat report with the claims adjuster prior to filing, ensure that the report is accurate, and challenge reserves if they seem excessive. A point to remember is that the experience modifier is determined by a three-year loss history. Therefore, it is advisable to review with the claims adjuster the status of open claims going back three years.

One last point: Workers' compensation laws are very complex. If internal administrators or employer representatives have any doubt about their capability to effectively review the unit stat filing report, it is recommended that they have an experienced person attend the review with the carrier.

Managing the Paper Trail

An internal administrator is in the best position to gather information and keep a running file on every detail of every case. A cut finger or foreign body in the eye may be an open-and-shut case, while a musculoskeletal injury might drag on or become a litigated claim. It is essential to have a central repository for every piece of documentation related to every case; to review each piece with an eye to accuracy, validity, and completeness; and to frequently check the recovery progress of injured workers. Internal administrators should retain all documentation required by the state, such as the claim form for workers' compensation benefits. In addition, it is helpful for administrators to create forms to make it easy to collect such informa-

tion as the employee's statement of illness or injury and the supervisor's accident investigation.

A documentation checklist should be created and attached to the front of each claim file. This will not only help to monitor the progress of the claim but also ensure that all proper documentation has been received and reviewed and call attention to missing paperwork. A sample internal claims management document checklist is presented in Figure 4.

Trend Analysis

Controlling workers' compensation costs requires a thorough analysis of the data. The major factors that help to identify trends include data for the following:

- Are back injuries the leading cause of injury?
- Do most injuries happen to new employees?
- Do most accidents occur in one department?
- Do most accidents occur under one supervisor?

The answers to these questions will help to focus direct efforts on the most critical risk areas. Once trends are identified, corrective action and control measures can be implemented.

PREVENTING FRAUD AND ABUSE

In recent years, legislators have increased their attention on workers' compensation fraud and abuse as a necessary step in reducing runaway workers' compensation costs (New York State Business Council 2007). Most states have passed legislation making it a criminal offense to file a false claim to obtain workers' compensation benefits (SB899 2004). This section explains the difference between fraud and abuse and suggests ways to protect your organization from them.

Fraud Versus Abuse

Listening to legislators, insurance companies, and employers, one would think that workers' compensation fraud is rampant. However, a 2005 California State Auditor report (State of California Workers' Compensation Fraud Division 2005) stated that the Fraud Commission and the Insurance Commissioner

---

\<Organization Name\>

Workers Compensation Case Management

Injured Employee _____

Date of Injury _____

- ☐ Employer's First Report of Injury (5020)
- ☐ Doctor's First Report of Injury
- ☐ Employee's WC Benefit Form
- ☐ Employee's Statement of Injury/Supervisor Investigation
- ☐ Doctor's Release to Work Light Duty
- ☐ Doctor's Release to Full Duties (and released from further care)
- ☐ If applicable, physical therapy reports

Date Case Closed _____ Lost Work Days ____ Light Duty Days ___

☐ First Aid   ☐ Recordable

Figure 4. Sample internal claims management documentation checklist (*Source:* Team Safety, Inc.)

"had no meaningful measure of the extent and nature of fraud in the system." Conversely, according to a California Department of Insurance report, 423 convictions out of 847 cases totaled $183,667,830 in chargeable fraud for 2005. Written premiums for that year (not including self-insured companies) amounted to $21.4 billion. If the numbers are valid, an employer can then expect that every dollar charged per one hundred dollars in premium was due to fraud. California workers file about 120,000 claims per year; based on the numbers, this creates the inference, that about one out of every one hundred claims filed is fraudulent.

Fraud can be perpetrated by workers, medical and legal providers, insurers, and employers. One type of fraud occurs when employees make false or fraudulent statements or material misrepresentations for the purpose of obtaining compensation. For example, workers may exaggerate or lie about the extent of an injury, claim that a nonwork injury is work related, or work "under the table" while collecting benefits.

Abuse of the system can add up to enormous costs over time and can involve people at all levels. For example, a disgruntled employee may stretch a minor back injury into a claim that goes on for a couple of weeks longer than it should. Or a doctor may schedule unnecessary follow-up visits or prescribe unnecessary and expensive prescription drugs. Applicants' attorneys can abuse the system by recommending numerous medical/legal exams that add significant costs to claims. These abuses are difficult to prove as fraud. In the authors' experience, a phone call to the employee or the treating physician may be enough to resolve the problem. If an employer suspects fraud or abuse, the best action is to review the claim to date, look for red flags, and contact the claims adjuster for assistance.

Ten Red Flags

A *red flag* is a warning or sense that something is not right with a claim, and it should lead to a closer look at the review process. Consider the following:

- Was there a lack of prompt reporting? In general, injured employees will report a claim on a timely basis.
- Was the claim reported on Monday, alleging the injury occurred on the previous Friday?
- Were there witnesses to the incident? Do their stories conflict with the injured worker's version?
- Has the employee been giving vague or changing statements?
- Did the injured worker refuse modified duty or early return to work?
- Is the injured worker retiring? Has he or she recently been disciplined? Is there rumor of an anticipated layoff?
- Is the worker disgruntled over perceived injustices?
- Has he or she missed doctor's appointments or physical therapy?
- When you call, can you reach the worker at home? Does he or she fail to return phone calls?
- Is the employee engaged in an activity not consistent with the injury? Is the employee alleging a back injury but playing softball or building a deck?

Policies, procedures, and claims-management practices are the primary tools for prevention of fraud and abuse. A red flag could be nothing more than poor communication, or it could be something more serious. Either way, detecting and resolving issues relating to fraud can result in cost savings as well as improve the psychosocial climate in your organization (Zenith National Insurance Corporation n.d.c). It is important to train managers, supervisors, and employees in the organization's policies and procedures regarding red flags and fraud and to review policies and procedures periodically.

HOW THE PSYCHOSOCIAL CLIMATE AFFECTS CLAIMS

The terms *culture, climate,* and *psychosocial climate* are often used interchangeably. A well-known safety consultant has said, "Culture is the way it is around here" (Mercurio and Roughton 2002). Primarily, culture

or climate refers to the morale and overall climate created by management and supervisors. According to NIOSH, job stress and low productivity can be directly linked to psychosocial climates where employees are subjected to monotonous work, have limited job control or clarity, and have limited social support from supervisors and co-workers (NIOSH 2009).

In the authors' experience, when employers get hit with a rash of claims, they are often likely to point to abuse rather than consider a poor work climate as the problem. One of the first steps in determining the root cause of increased claims is to conduct a climate survey. A good work-climate survey will tell what the current status is in the organization and give direction to efforts to improve the climate. A number of surveys are available that can help an organization get started in evaluating its climate. One of the most validated is found in *First Break All the Rules: What the World's Greatest Managers Do Differently* (Buckingham and Coffman 1999).

Since the first edition of *The Safety Professionals Handbook,* the United States has experienced the worst recession since the great depression. Home foreclosures, layoffs, and plant closings reached record levels. Longer hours, reduced job security, and part-time and temporary work are increasingly affecting the health and well-being of workers and their families.

For the second edition of the Handbook, the author interviewed private investigators, doctors, insurance executives, and claims adjustors to determine the effects of this severe recession on the workers' compensation system. They all agreed there has been a surge in stress claims (commonly referred to as "psyche claims"). Their observation is correct. In California, the second leading number of medical-legal reports, after orthopedics, were psychiatric evaluations.

Over the years, most states have enacted laws protecting employers from disgruntled or unethical employees who claimed psychiatric injury resulting from "personnel action." Depending on the state, employer protection is commonly referred to as "good faith personnel action," such as disciplinary actions, layoffs, job transfers, salary reductions, or other legitimate employer actions. However, the laws do not protect an employer found to be retaliating against an employee for refusing sexual advances, refusing to falsify payroll records, or other unlawful acts.

Defending the organization against psyche claims requires good documentation. Any personnel action taken against an employee must show "good faith or for just cause," otherwise the case could be lost. Investigate what you see and hear, including rumors. Taking early action can mitigate the situation and possibly avoid costly litigation or claims.

Organizations that consistently maintain low injury rates compared to others in their industry tend to have positive psychosocial climates (Hagen et al. 2009). Work by its very nature can be stressful; striving to create a positive psychosocial climate should be the goal of every organization. When an organization's management style and philosophy demonstrate cooperation, commitment, teamwork, and communication between labor and management, the firm has set a tone for fairness when an accident occurs. Employees in such firms tend to litigate less and abuse the system less.

THE IMPACT OF THE AGING WORKFORCE

The biggest crisis affecting today's business is the rising cost of workers' compensation and health care. One of the main cost drivers is the aging workforce. Currently, over half the workforce is over 40 (BLS 2008), the trigger point for the Age Discrimination in Employment Act of 1967 (ADEA). A natural process of aging is reduced flexibility and strength, which increases risk for injuries to backs, knees, shoulders, and necks. Even though older workers have a lower injury rate, they have three to four times the number of lost work days. The average cost of a lost-time injury is $48,000 (BLS 2008).

As people age, they become less active. Lack of exercise and a poor diet has led to an epidemic of overweight and out-of-shape people. According to the Surgeon General's "Vision for a Healthy and Fit Nation," two-thirds of American adults fall into this category and one-third of those are obese (HHS 2010). Overall, they do not exercise enough to maintain basic health. Obese people have three to five times the

incident rate for carpal tunnel syndrome (CTS) compared to slim individuals (University of Maryland 2010). Excess weight greatly increases the stress to the soft tissues of the weight-bearing joints of the lower back, knees, and feet. All of these are potential workers' compensation claims.

The dilemma for employers is, where do you draw the line between work-related and nonwork-related MSDs? In the authors' view, as baby boomers get older and less fit, it will become more difficult for courts and legislatures to sort out which injuries are the responsibility of the employer and which are due to an employee's unhealthy lifestyle, and so will eventually become another major cost-driver in the workers' compensation arena.

Efforts by public health agencies and corporate wellness programs to improve American lifestyles have failed; the American people are bigger than ever! (Drennan 2003). A whole new strategy is needed if business and society are to survive the workers' compensation and healthcare crisis.

In 2003, NIOSH held a symposium to generate discussion about integrating worker health and worker safety. The program was called *Steps to a Healthy U.S. Workforce*. It was renamed the NIOSH *WorkLife Initiative*, but is now called *Total Worker Health Initiative*. According to NIOSH, work is one of the most important determinants of a person's health (NIOSH 2010, p. 51). The goal of the initiative is to sustain and improve worker health through better coordinated or integrated wellness and safety programs. According to NIOSH director John Howard, "We can no longer accept the 'disconnect' between [those professionals] promoting healthy living and those promoting worker safety on the job."

ASSE became a co-sponsor of the symposium and participated with a member task force under the direction of Dave Heidorn, Manager of Governmental Affairs. The author and fellow task-force member Jim Ramsey (Indiana University) developed a model for meeting NIOSH's *Steps to a Healthier U.S. Workforce*. It became the lead article in the January 2006 issue of *Professional Safety*. A copy of the article is available at www.asse.org.

Integrating worker health and worker safety can create a win-win situation for employers and employees. The authors believe that NIOSH's research in this area, along with practical applications on the job by safety practitioners, will form the leading edge of best practices in injury prevention and workers' compensation management in the future. It is important for safety practitioners to be aware of the progress of studies and initiatives such as NIOSH's *Total Worker Health Initiative* and its impact on injury and illness prevention.

In the future, best practices will have to address the issues of the aging and unhealthy workforce as a major cost-driver of workers' compensation and the healthcare system. According to organizations such as Microsoft and the American Association of Retired People (AARP), many more people are delaying retirement due to lack of savings, health insurance, and pension plans (Microsoft 2006, AARP 2007).

SUMMARY

Safety professionals face many challenges in effectively managing workers' compensation, such as varying workers' compensation laws among states; frequent litigation; the prevalence and high cost of MSDs and CTDs; and the impact of an aging, overweight, out-of-shape workforce. These are tough challenges but not insurmountable ones.

Using best practices that address essential elements for cost containment and effective claims management, safety professionals can provide protection and compensation for injured workers while protecting the interest of the employer.

Essential Elements for Cost Containment

- Use a designated occupational health clinic.
- Develop job descriptions that include physical requirements.
- Use functional capacity testing for screening prospective employees.
- Implement an early return to work (ERW) program.
- Establish a substance-abuse prevention program.
- Adopt NIOSH's *Total Worker Health Initiative* to integrate employee safety and wellness (NIOSH 2010).

Effective Claims Management

- Assign an internal workers' compensation administrator.
- Require prompt accident reporting and thorough investigation.
- Actively partner with the workers' compensation carrier's claims adjuster.
- Frequently review all open claims.
- Understand and take advance measures to prevent fraud and abuse.
- Manage the paper trail.
- Analyze workers' compensation claim trends in the organization.

REFERENCES

American Association of Retired Persons (AARP). 2007. *Workforce Trends: What Older Workers Want from Work.* www.aarp.org/money/careers/employerresource center/trends/a2004-04-20-olderworkers.html

Buckingham, M., and C. Coffman. 1999. *First, Break All the Rules: What the World's Greatest Managers Do Differently.* New York: Simon and Schuster.

Bureau of Labor Statistics (BLS). 2008. *Non-Fatal Occupational Injuries and Illnesses Requiring Days Away from Work, 2007* (retrieved September 1, 2011). www.bls.gov/news.release/archives/osh2_11202008.pdf

Cable, J. 2006. "Fighting Back." *Occupational Hazards* (August). www.occupationalhazards.com/Issue/Article/38434/Fighting_Back.aspx

California Chamber of Commerce. 2006. *Workers Compensation in California* (HR Best Practice Series). Sacramento, CA: CalBizCentral.

California Workers' Compensation Institute (CWCI). *Duration of Treatment and Medical Costs in California Workers' Compensation* (retrieved March, 2007). www.cwci.org/icic/viewreport.cfm?&ReportIndex=11

Chaffin, B., B. J. Andersson et al. 1999. *Occupational Biomechanics.* New York: John Wiley & Sons.

Chick, Laura (City Controller of Los Angeles). 2007. "Chick Audit of Workers Comp: Questions Quality of Service by Outside Administrator 'What Are We Getting for $7 Million a Year?'" February 2007 press release, City of Los Angeles.

Department of Health and Human Services (HHS). 2010. *The Surgeon General's Vision for a Healthy and Fit Nation.* Rockville, MD: HHS.

Department of Transportation. 2010. 49 CFR 40, Part 40.87, *What Are the Cutoff Concentrations for Drug Testing?* (accessed September 1, 2011). www.gpoaccess.gov/cgi/text/text-idxc+ecfr=331db02490fe35d255dbc62fof483&rgn=div88&view=text&node=49:1.0.1.1.29.16.48&idno=49

Drennan, Fred. 2003. "Meeting the Needs of an Aging Workforce." *Facilities Safety Management* (December) 2003:20–22.

Hagen, Philip, John F. Montgomery, and James T. O'Reilly. 2009. *Accident Prevention Manual for Business & Industry, Administration & Programs*. 13th ed. Itasca, IL: National Safety Council.

Labor Research Association. 2003. "Workers Compensation Crisis Revisited." Oct. 24, 2003. LRA Online. www.labor research.org/story2.php/330

Mercurio, J., and J. Roughton. 2002. *Developing an Effective Safety Culture: A Leadership Approach*. Woburn, MA: Butterworth Heinemann.

Microsoft. 2006. *Shifting Workplace Demographics and Delayed Retirement*. Microsoft Accessibility. www.microsoft.com/ enable/aging/demographics.aspx

National Academy of Social Insurance (NASI). 2009. "Workers' Compensation: Benefits, Coverage, and Costs, 2007 Report Highlights." www.nasi.org/sites/ default/files/research/Workers_Comp_Highlights_ 2007.pdf

National Institute for Occupational Safety and Health (NIOSH). 1997. *Musculoskeletal Disorders and Workplace Factors: A Critical Review of Epidemiologic Evidence for Work-Related Musculoskeletal Disorders of the Neck, Upper Extremity, and Low Back*, p. 7–1.

_____. 2006. *History of the NIOSH WorkLife Initiative*. www.cdc.gov/niosh/worklife/steps/default.html

_____. 2010. *Delivering on the Nation's Investment in Worker Safety and Health*, p. 52.

_____. 2011. *NIOSH Program Portfolio: Total Worker Health* (retrieved September 1, 2011). www.cdc.gov/niosh/ programs/worklife/

National Institute on Drug Abuse (NIDA). 2005. *NIDA Workplace Facts: Workplace Trends*. National Institutes of Health. www.nida.nih.gov/about/welcome/about drugabuse/magnitude

National Safety Council (NSC). 2010. *Injury Facts*. Itasca, IL: NSC.

New York State Business Council. 2007. *Priorities for Action*. The Business Council of New York State, Inc. www.bcnys.org/inbside/prioritiesforaction.htm

New York State Insurance Fund (NYSIF). 2007. *Early Return to Work Programs*. www.nysif.com/SafetyRisk Management/Risk Management/LimitingLiability/ ReturnToWorkPrograms.aspx

Occupational Hazards. 2000. *Speed of Workers' Compensation Filing Affects Costs* (accessed March, 2007).

www.occupationalhazards.com/News//article/ 33284/

Olin. 2003. "Workers' Compensation Claims: Controlling the Cost." *Risk Alert* II(7).

Press, Irwin. 2002. *Patient Satisfaction: Defining, Measuring, and Improving the Experience of Care*. Ann Arbor, MI: Press Health Administration Press.

Putz-Anderson, V. 1997. *Cumulative Trauma Disorders: A Manual for Musculoskeletal Disorders of the Upper Limbs*. Bristol, PA: Taylor and Francis, Ltd.

State of California Department of Insurance, Workers' Compensation Fraud Division. 2004–2005. *California District Attorney's Report on Fraud*. www.insurance. ca.gov/0300-fraud-division-overview

State of California, Senate Bill 899 (SB899). 2004. California Workers' Compensation Reform Act of 2004. Sacramento. CA: California State Government.

State of California State Compensation Insurance Fund. 2006. *Developing a Successful Return to Work Program*. www.scif.com/pdf/e13088.pdf

State of California Workers' Compensation Insurance Review Board (WCIRB). 2008. *2008 Workers' Compensation Insurance Review Board, Report on 2008 California Workers' Compensation Losses and Expenses, Section 211759.1—Summary of 2008 Workers' Compensation Costs, Exhibit 16*. Workers' Compensation Insurance Rating Bureau of California.

State Office of Risk Management (SORM). 2003. Ron Josselet, ARM, CPCU, Executive Director, State Office of Risk Management, Austin, Texas. Letter to Ms. Cindy Wiley, Research Analyst, Office of the Comptroller of Public Accounts, January 27, 2003.

United States Code, Americans with Disabilities Act. 1990. 42 USC 12101.

University of Maryland. 2010. *Carpal Tunnel Syndrome: Causes* (retrieved September 1, 2011). www.umm.edu/ patiented/articlles/what_causes_carpal_tunnel_ syndrome_000034_3.htm

Zenith National Insurance Corporation. n.d.a. *Five Steps of a Return to Work Plan*, Zenith National Insurance Corp. www.thezenith.com/zenith_web/webui/ employers/emp_rty_imp.jsp

_____. n.d.b. *Return to Work Plans: A Win-Win Opportunity*. www.thezenith.com/zenith_web/webui/ employers/emp_rtw_winwin.jsp

_____. n.d.c. *Fraud Success Stories*. www.thezenith. com/zenith_web/webui/employers/emp_fraud_ stories.jsp

APPENDIX: ADDITIONAL RESOURCES

Arkansas Worker's Compensation Commission (AWCC). 2006. Arkansas Workers' Compensation Commission, Medical Cost Containment Division. Little Rock, Arkansas.

State of California Division of Labor Statistics and Research. Form 5021. www.dir.ca.gov/DLSR/dlsrform5021.pdf

State of Illinois. 2006. Illinois Workers' Compensation Act, 2006, Section 8.2. www.state.il.us/AGENCY/ IIC/8.2ff.pdf

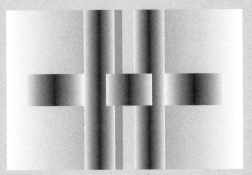

SECTION 6
FLEET SAFETY

Regulatory Issues
DOT Regulations
OSHA and Other Regulations

Applied Science and Engineering
Vehicles and Accidents
Vehicle Engineering and Ergonomics

Cost Analysis and Budgeting

Benchmarking and Performance Criteria

Best Practices

REGULATORY ISSUES: DOT REGULATIONS

Gregory L. Smith

LEARNING OBJECTIVES

▌ Be able to define the rationale and scope of the Department of Transportation (DOT) Act.

▌ Describe areas where the DOT Act has cross-jurisdictional impact.

▌ Be able to interpret the goals of the DOT Act.

▌ Know how to differentiate between state and federal requirements.

▌ Be able to formulate strategies for transportation management.

▌ Estimate the impact of successful and unsuccessful company safety programs.

BEFORE THERE WAS a Department of Transportation (DOT), transportation-related safety issues were often dealt with case by case. For example, on August 7, 1789, Congress federalized existing lighthouses built by the colonies and appropriated funds for lighthouses, beacons, and buoys. This was done to support the safety of the shipping industry by establishing a framework to provide continuity of maintenance, repair, and oversight. Shipping, and the rules governing it, grew and expanded throughout the country as expansion and population growth continued. Soon, roads and highways carried a significant portion of raw and finished goods to and from shipping points. Over time, the highway system and the regulations governing its use have grown and evolved significantly, requiring a much more comprehensive management effort than originally initiated. According to President Lyndon Johnson, when he signed the act creating the Department of Transportation on October 16, 1966 (DOT 1966):

> The Act which I sign today is the most important transportation legislation of our lifetime. . . . It is one of the essential building blocks in our preparation for the future. . . . Transportation has truly emerged as a significant part of our national life. As a basic force in our society, its progress must be accelerated so that the quality of our life can be improved.

The diversity of areas requiring oversight mandated a different approach to maintain an appropriate level of competency. This diversity was the impetus behind creating the Department of Transportation (DOT). The signing of this act marked the beginning of the national highway system as we know it today. To address growing needs, separate agencies were created within the DOT. The DOT is currently made up of several agencies with specific missions and responsibilities.

Leadership of the DOT is provided by the Secretary of Transportation, who is the principal adviser to the president in all matters relating to federal transportation programs. The secretary is assisted by the deputy secretary in this role. The Office of the Secretary (OST) oversees the formulation of national transportation policy and promotes intermodal transportation. Other responsibilities include negotiation and implementation of international transportation agreements, assuring the fitness of U.S. airlines and motor carriers, enforcing airline consumer-protection regulations, issuance of regulations to prevent alcohol and illegal drug misuse in transportation systems, and preparing transportation legislation. The following paragraphs describe the various agencies under the DOT banner.

Federal Aviation Administration

The Federal Aviation Administration (FAA) oversees the safety of civil aviation. Programs managed include Safety Hotline (maintenance improprieties, low-flying aircraft, aircraft incidents, and Federal Aviation Regulation (FAR) violations), safety advisories and alerts, data and statistics, the National Transportation Safety Board (NTSB), Security, and Awards.

Federal Railroad Administration

The Federal Railroad Administration (FRA) promotes safe and environmentally sound rail transportation with the responsibility of ensuring railroad safety throughout the nation. FRA's Office of Safety promotes and regulates safety throughout the nation's railroad industry. It employs more than 415 federal safety inspectors, who operate out of eight regional offices across the country. The inspectors specialize in five safety disciplines—hazardous materials, motive power and equipment, operating practices, signal and train control, track and structures, and industrial hygiene—and promote numerous initiatives under the Highway-Rail Grade Crossing and Trespasser Prevention programs.

Federal Transit Administration

The Federal Transit Administration (FTA) assists in developing improved mass-transportation systems for cities and communities nationwide. It currently covers areas including transit safety, emergency management, training and conferences, drugs and alcohol, safety and security, statistics, and publications.

Maritime Administration

The Maritime Administration (MARAD) is the agency within the U.S. Department of Transportation (DOT) that deals with waterborne transportation and ensures the viability of the U.S. Merchant Marine. Its programs promote the use of waterborne transportation and its seamless integration with other segments of the transportation system. The agency works in many areas involving ships and shipping, shipbuilding, port operations, vessel operations, national security, environment, and safety.

MARAD is also charged with maintaining the health of the Merchant Marine, since commercial mariners, vessels, and intermodal facilities are vital for supporting national security. Thus, the agency provides support and information for current mariners, extensive support for educating future mariners, and programs to educate Americans about the vital role the maritime industry plays in their lives.

The Maritime Administration also maintains a fleet of cargo ships in reserve to provide surge sealift during war and national emergencies, and is responsible for disposing of ships in that fleet, as well as other noncombatant government ships, as they become obsolete.

MARAD recently realigned many of its functions to revitalize its role as an industry facilitator, and to bring greater focus to the areas of environment and safety.

National Highway Traffic Safety Administration

The National Highway Traffic Safety Administration (NHTSA) is responsible for reducing deaths, injuries, and economic losses resulting from motor-vehicle crashes. NHTSA sets and enforces safety performance standards for motor vehicles and equipment, and through grants to state and local governments enables them to conduct effective local highway-safety programs. Some of the areas managed by the NHTSA include aggressive driving, bicycles, child passenger safety, disabled drivers and passengers, drowsy and distracted driving, emergency medical services, enforcement and justice services, impaired driving, motorcycles, new drivers, occupant protection, older drivers, pedestrians, programs/grants, research and evaluation, safety materials catalogs, school buses, traffic tech publications, and the Safe Communities Program.

Pipeline and Hazardous Materials Safety Administration

The Pipeline and Hazardous Materials Safety Administration (PHMSA) oversees the safety of more than 800,000 daily shipments of hazardous materials in the United States and 64 percent of the nation's energy that is transported by pipelines. Areas of focus include training and outreach, special permits, approvals, rulemaking, state and local government partnerships, enforcement, security plans, drug and alcohol programs, and a pipeline-safety program.

Research and Innovative Technology Administration

The Research and Innovative Technology Administration (RITA) coordinates DOT's research programs and is charged with advancing the deployment of crosscutting technologies to improve our nation's transportation system. RITA leads the DOT in coordinating, facilitating, and reviewing the department's research and development programs and activities; advancing innovative technologies, including intelligent transportation systems; performing comprehensive transportation statistics research, analysis, and reporting; and providing education and training in transportation and transportation-related fields.

Saint Lawrence Seaway Development Corporation

The Saint Lawrence Seaway Development Corporation (SLSDC) is a wholly owned government corporation created to construct, operate, and maintain that part of the St. Lawrence Seaway between the Port of Montreal and Lake Erie, within the territorial limits of the United States. The mission of the SLSDC is to serve the U.S. intermodal and international transportation system by improving the operation and maintenance of a safe, reliable, efficient, and environmentally responsible deep-draft waterway, in cooperation with its Canadian counterpart. The SLSDC also encourages the development of trade through the Great Lakes Seaway System.

Surface Transportation Board

The Surface Transportation Board (STB) is an independent, bipartisan, adjudicatory body organizationally housed within the DOT. It is responsible for the economic regulation of interstate surface transportation, primarily railroads, within the United States. The agency has jurisdiction over railroad rate and service issues and rail-restructuring transactions (mergers, line sales, line construction, and line abandonment); certain trucking-company, moving-van, and noncontiguous ocean shipping-company rate matters; certain intercity passenger-bus-company structure, financial, and operational matters; and rates and services of certain pipelines not regulated by the Federal Energy Regulatory Commission.

Federal Highway Administration

The Federal Highway Administration (FHWA) coordinates highway transportation programs in cooperation with states and other partners to enhance the country's safety, economic vitality, and quality of life, as well as the environment.

REGULATORY RULEMAKING

As federal entities, these agencies follow standard rulemaking processes. To create new regulations or execute revisions to existing regulations, a public notice of proposed rulemaking is published in the *Federal Register*. As an example from the DOT, the FHWA proposed a requirement for the use of high-visibility safety apparel for workers who are working within federal-aid highway right-of-ways. This was posted in the *Federal Register* on April 24, 2006, as a proposed rule. It would require workers whose duties place them on or in close proximity to a federal-aid highway to wear high-visibility safety apparel.

Each of these agencies has specific agendas and regulatory requirements. It is impossible to give detailed insights into each agency's operations within the scope of this chapter. Specific details, ranging from organizational histories and mission statements to rules and regulations, may be found on the respective agencies' Web sites. Additionally, changes to regulations and the implementation dates for those changes may be found on the Web site by searching for "rulemaking changes" or similar terms. This type of search will deliver a synopsis of reports in chronological order under the heading of the "Rulemaking Management System."

The primary agency involved with fleet safety operations, as discussed below, is the Federal Motor Carrier Safety Administration (FMCSA).

Federal Motor Carrier Safety Administration

The FMCSA was established within the DOT on January 1, 2000, pursuant to the Motor Carrier Safety Improvement Act of 1999 (FMCSA 1999). Formerly a part of the FHWA, the FMCSA's primary mission is to prevent commercial motor-vehicle-related fatalities and injuries. The FMCSA focuses heavily on commercial cartage operations, and specifically interstate commerce. The FMCSA Safety and Fitness Electronic Records (SAFER) System offers company safety data and related services to industry and the public over the Internet. Users can search FMCSA databases, register for a USDOT number, pay fines online, order company safety profiles, challenge FMCSA data using the DataQs system, access the Hazardous Material Route registry, obtain National Crash and Out of Service rates for Hazmat Permit Registration, get printable registration forms, and find information about other FMCSA Information Systems. The SAFER system may be accessed at www.safer.fmcsa.dot.gov. The remainder of this chapter will review those areas that commonly come under FMCSA oversight.

APPLICABILITY OF REGULATIONS

Operators of any of the following types of commercial motor vehicles in interstate commerce must comply with the applicable U.S. Department of Transportation (USDOT) safety regulations:

1. A vehicle with a gross vehicle weight rating or gross combination weight rating (whichever is greater) of 4537 kilograms (kg) (10,001 pounds (lb)) or more;

2. A vehicle designed or used to transport between nine and fifteen passengers (including the driver) for compensation;

3. A vehicle designed or used to transport sixteen or more passengers; or

4. Any size vehicle used in the transportation of materials that are considered hazardous under the Hazardous Materials Transportation Act and that require the motor vehicle to be placarded under the hazardous materials regulations.

These regulations include areas concerning commercial driver's licenses (CDLs): controlled substances and alcohol testing for all persons required to possess a CDL; driver qualifications (including medical exams); driving of commercial motor vehicles; parts and accessories necessary for safe operations; hours of service; and inspection, repair, and maintenance.

Pursuant to Title 49 CFR Part 107, Subpart G (§107.601–107.620), certain offerors and transporters of hazardous materials, including hazardous waste, are required to file an additional annual registration statement with the USDOT and to pay a fee.

AREAS OF INTEREST IN REGULATORY COMPLIANCE

Interstate Commerce

Interstate commerce is defined as *trade, traffic, or transportation involving the crossing of a state boundary*. Either the vehicle, its passengers, or its cargo must cross a state boundary, or the intent to cross a state boundary must exist in order for an activity to be considered interstate commerce. *Intrastate* commerce is *trade, traffic, or transportation within a single state*. Operations that include interstate commerce in addition to intrastate commerce must comply with applicable federal safety regulations and operating-authority rules in addition to state and local requirements. The state in which a vehicle is registered must be notified of the intention to operate it in interstate commerce to ensure that the vehicle is properly registered for purposes of the International Registration Plan (IRP), and International Fuel Tax Agreement (IFTA). The base state collects the appropriate fees and distributes a portion of those fees to the other states in which the commercial motor vehicle operates.

Intrastate Commerce

Companies that operate exclusively in intrastate commerce must comply with applicable state and local regulations. The only federal regulations that are applicable to intrastate operations are the commercial driver's license (CDL) for drivers operating commercial motor vehicles as defined in 49 CFR 383.5; controlled substances and alcohol testing for all persons required to possess a CDL; and minimum levels of financial responsibility for the intrastate transportation of certain quantities of hazardous materials and substances.

A USDOT number is required for vehicles over 10,000 lb if they are transporting between nine and fifteen passengers (including the driver) for compensation, if they are transporting sixteen or more passengers, or if they are hauling hazardous materials in interstate commerce. No fee is required. Carriers must complete the MCS-150, Motor Carrier Identification Report (FMCSA 2007d), and MCS-150A, Safety Certification Application (FMCSA 2007e), to obtain a USDOT number. The MCS-150 and MCS-150A can be completed online or copies can be printed, completed, and mailed to the address indicated.

For-Hire Carrier

A *for-hire carrier* is a person or company that provides transportation of cargo or passengers for compensation. In addition to the USDOT number, for-hire carriers must obtain an operating authority [motor carrier (MC) number]. Generally, for-hire motor carriers of regulated commodities or passengers in interstate commerce must also obtain an interstate operating-authority (MC) number unless the operation is limited to the transportation of exempt commodities or is within a commercial zone that is exempt from the interstate operating-authority rules. Information about commercial-zone exemptions is in 49 CFR 372. Administrative Ruling No. 119 (FMCSA n.d. a). A list of commodities that are not exempt from the operating-authority rules can be found in 49 CFR 372.115. Both

are also available online at the FMCSA's Web site (www.fmcsa.dot.gov).

Form OP-1, Application for Motor Property Carrier and Broker Authority (FMCSA 2007c), is required for a motor carrier of property. Form OP-1(P), Application for Motor Passenger Carrier Authority (FMCSA 2007b), is a proposed revision of the form designed to enhance safety for nondomestic carriers. Part of Section V (Safety Certifications) is the acknowledgment that the applicant will "maintain current copies of all U.S. DOT Federal Motor Carrier Safety Regulations, Federal Motor Vehicle Safety Standards, and the Hazardous Materials Regulations (if a property carrier transporting hazardous materials), *understands and will comply* with such Regulations, and has ensured that all company personnel are aware of the current requirements...." An Application for Motor Passenger Carrier Authority is required for motor carriers of passengers.

For-hire carriers must have an operating-authority (MC) number. Carriers must (1) complete and file the appropriate OP-1 application along with the filing fee for each type of authority requested; (2) have their insurance company file the appropriate insurance forms for the type of authority requested with the FMCSA; and (3) submit or have a process-agent service submit a BOC-3, Designation of Process Agent form (FMCSA n.d. c). (A *process agent* is a representative upon whom court papers may be served in any proceeding brought against a motor carrier, and creating this designation is one of the prelicensing requirements that must be met by the carrier before authority is issued.)

Passenger carriers who are Federal Transit Administration Grantees (Transit Benefit Operators) under 49 U.S.C. 5307, 5310, or 5311 are required to maintain liability insurance at least as high as the highest level required for any of the states in which the transit service is located. This is to ensure that both parties are protected in the event of an accident or incident. The filing fee is waived for the Transit Benefit Operator application. To travel within the United States as a for-hire motor carrier, a carrier must file for an operating authority (active MC number). The appropriate OP-1 application may be completed online at www.safer.fmcsa.dot.gov, and the required filing fee can be paid with a credit card; a copy of the application form can be downloaded from the DOT Web site, or a copy of the OP-1 application can be requested and an application will be mailed. A filing fee is currently required for each type of authority requested. No insurance information can be submitted until the carrier has been assigned its MC number.

Once the application is received and accepted, the MC number will be assigned. The applicant will receive a letter stating the MC number and detailing any additional information needed to achieve compliance. Once the carrier's insurance company has filed the correct insurance form and the process agent has filed Form BOC-3 (Designation of Process Agent), the official operating authority in the form of a certificate and/or permit will be issued (FMCSA n.d. c). Operating a carrier is not permitted until this information has been submitted and the certificate and/or permit is officially issued. Leasing of services to a for-hire carrier with a valid number is permissible if there is full compliance with the requirements under Section 376.11.

The regulations currently state that if a company operates as both for-hire and private carriage, once the USDOT number is issued, the carrier may operate as a private motor carrier. Operation as a for-hire motor carrier is not permitted, however, until an operating authority (an active MC number) is issued.

Exempt and Regulated Commodities

If a company transports exempt commodities and possesses a USDOT number, it is permitted to operate as an exempt for-hire interstate motor carrier without an MC number.

Transport of regulated commodities in interstate commerce prior to having obtained operating authority (certificate and/or permit) and received the single-state registration is not allowed. Simply applying for operating authority is not sufficient; the certificate and/or permit must be issued.

Administrative Ruling No. 119 is a guide to what is and is not exempt (FMCSA n.d. a). The booklet is no longer in print, but the information is still correct. The list of exempt commodities changes frequently, but this booklet can be used as a general guide. Also,

a list of commodities that are not exempt can be found in the FMCSR in section 372.115.

OPERATING-AUTHORITY ISSUANCE

To check whether operating authority has been issued, carriers can visit www.li-public.fmcsa.dot.gov. There is also a 24-hour automated phone verification system. FMCSA will fax the operating authority only if ten or more working days have passed since the service date and the operating authority has not yet been received. Once the operating authority has been issued, the regulations do not allow for its voluntary suspension; however, voluntary revocation of the operating authority is allowed. To accomplish a voluntary revocation, a carrier must (1) complete Form OCE-46, Request for Revocation of Registration (FMCSA n.d. b); (2) have it notarized; and (3) mail it back to the FMCSA. Upon receipt of the form, the information will be coded into the system. The date coding occurs is when the operating authority will be voluntarily revoked.

A carrier can reinstate an operating authority by requesting reinstatement of the authority and paying a fee. This can be done online at www.safer.fmcsa.dot.gov and paid for with a credit card. A carrier can also request reinstatement of the operating authority by mailing the MC number and the legal name of the carrier along with payment of the fee by check, money order, or credit card payable to FMCSA. The carrier's insurance company must file the BMC-91 (FMCSA n.d. d) or 91X (FMCSA n.d. e) and/or BMC-34 (FMCSA n.d. f), if necessary, to meet the proof-of-insurance requirement. A valid Designation of Process Agents (BOC-3) filing must also be in effect (FMCSA n.d. c). The operating authority will not be reactivated until updated insurance filings have been received and accepted. The carrier will receive a reinstatement notification from the FMCSA after the operating authority has been reinstated. To validate the reinstatement or to validate any carrier's number, check the Web site under Carrier Search. There is also a 24-hour automated system.

Common, Contract, and Broker Authority

Common carriers provide for-hire truck transportation to the general public. Common carriers must file both liability (bodily injury and property damage—BI & PD) insurance and cargo insurance. *Contract carriers* provide for-hire truck transportation to specific individual shippers based on contracts. Contract carriers must file only BI & PD insurance. A *broker* is a company that, for compensation, arranges for truck transportation of cargo belonging to others using for-hire carriers to provide the actual transportation. Brokers must file either a *surety bond* or a *trust fund agreement*. A contract carrier cannot broker loads without first applying for and receiving a license to operate as a broker of freight.

Common Carrier Authority

A common carrier of property must file Form OP-1, Application for Motor Property Carrier and Broker Authority (FMCSA 2007a), and a common carrier of passengers must file Form OP-1(P), Application for Motor Passenger Carrier Authority (FMCSA 2007b). Carriers can file for operating authority online or can download a copy of the application forms. They may also call 1-800-832-5660 and request that an application be mailed or faxed.

Carriers are also required to file an MCS-150, Motor Carrier Identification Report (FMCSA 2007d), and an MCS-150A, Safety Certification Application (FMCSA 2007e), to obtain a USDOT number. Carriers can file for the USDOT number online or call the toll-free number and request that the form be mailed or faxed.

Form OP-1(P), Application for Motor Passenger Carrier Authority (FMCSA 2007b), is required for passenger authority. This reflects more stringent rules that are in effect for the transportation of personnel. Carriers can file for this authority or download a copy of the application online. They can also call the toll-free number and request that a copy be mailed or faxed.

Transfer of Operating Authority (MC Number) and USDOT Numbers

It is important to maintain an information chain to track training and liability issues. This information can be lost if proper transfer protocols are not followed. Transfer applications can be faxed directly. A transfer application can also be requested via phone or mail.

USDOT numbers are not transferable. Carriers can file for a USDOT number online or call to request a copy of the MCS-150, Motor Carrier Identification Report (FMCSA 2007d), and the MCS-150A, Safety Certification Application FMCSA 2007e). If transporting regulated property from one state to another, for-hire carriers are required to have both a USDOT number (MCS-150 and MCS-150A) and an operating authority (active MC number, OP-1).

Brokers

To become a broker, one must file Form OP-1, Application for Motor Property Carrier and Broker Authority (FMCSA 2007c). This operating authority requires an entity to have on file with the FMCSA either a surety bond (BMC-84 form provided by an insurance company) or a trust fund. A BMC-85 form (FMCSA n.d. g) may be obtained by request to the Insurance Compliance Division at FMCSA, as well as a Designation of Agents Form BOC-3 (FMCSA n.d. c). It is important to ensure that the broker is a valid entity to maintain proper liability for shipment safety.

Freight Forwarders

A *freight forwarder* is a company that arranges for the truck transportation of cargo belonging to others, using for-hire carriers to provide the actual truck transportation. In the ordinary course of its business, a freight forwarder usually assembles and consolidates less-than-truckload (LTL) shipments at their origin and disassembles and distributes truckload (TL) shipments at their destination. The freight forwarder assumes responsibility, including responsibility for some safety issues, for the transportation from origin to destination, but it uses a for-hire carrier for the line-haul movement. Freight forwarders must register with the FMCSA by filing Form OP-1(FF), Application for Freight Forwarder Authority (FMCSA 2007a). This authority can be applied for or downloaded online or obtained by calling the toll-free number and requesting that a copy be mailed or faxed.

Apportioned Tags

License plates and stickers are state matters. Companies can contact their state department of motor vehicles for requirements but must ensure that registrations and safety inspections are current prior to allowing movement. The correct department can usually be located on the Internet home page of the state government where licensing is desired.

Information Changes for Motor Carrier Operations

Current information is important in the event of an accident or incident requiring notification of management. There are separate filing procedures for changing a carrier's name with or without a change in the ownership, management, or control of the company. There is a fee for a name change. If there is a change in ownership, management, or control of the company, a transfer application must be filed.

A company wishing to change its legal or trade name must send a letter to the FMCSA along with a check or money order. The letter must contain the current name, the new name, and a statement that there is no change in ownership, control, or management of the company. If the company is incorporated, it must send a copy of its articles of incorporation with the letter. A copy of the letter should be kept on file for verification of safety training for employees who worked under the former company name.

Some requests for name changes can be processed online, but they require additional documents for verification:

1. If an immediate family member is added or deleted, a notarized letter must be presented in order for the change to become effective. (*Immediate family member* means husband, wife, brother, sister, mother, or father.)
2. If a name is to be deleted from the operating authority because of the death of a spouse or a partner already on the operating authority, a copy of the death certificate is required.
3. If a partner is being added as a result of marriage, a copy of the marriage license must be presented.
4. If a partner currently on the operating authority is being deleted, a notarized letter from the partner being removed must be presented.

After a carrier receives a reentitlement decision, it has a 30-day window to refile the proof of insurance and designation of agents (BOC-3) in its new name (FMCSA n.d. c). Upon completion, the name will be changed on the MC number and USDOT number.

Address changes can be made online. A letter to the FMCSA Licensing Division will also be accepted. The letter must reference the MC number and include former and current addresses and telephone numbers and be signed by the applicant or applicant's representative. The address change will be updated for both the MC number and the USDOT number. No fee is currently required.

If a name change is executed, the company keeps its MC number. However, instead of receiving a new certificate or permit, it will receive a reentitlement decision that should be attached to the original operating authority.

A USDOT number may be updated by filing an MCS-150, Motor Carrier Identification Report (FMCSA 2007d). Carriers that update online need a personal identification number (PIN) and can apply for it online. The USDOT record may also be updated by filing an MCS-150 by mail. The carrier should make all necessary changes on the form and mark it "update." MCS-150 forms may be obtained by calling the toll-free number and requesting that a copy be mailed.

Insurance Requirements

To apply for common carrier authority, carriers must have on file evidence of both BI & PD and cargo insurance. This requirement promotes a greater attention to safety issues because insurance costs are directly related to recorded incidents. To apply for contract authority, carriers are required only to have evidence of BI & PD insurance on file. Common carriers hauling low-value goods (49 CFR 387.301(b)) may request exemption from cargo-insurance requirements by requesting a cargo-exemption form. The forms BMC-91 (FMCSA n.d. d) and BMC-91X (FMCSA n.d. e) are both used to make liability insurance filings with the FMCSA. The insurance company making the filing maintains its own supply of forms. In fact, many insurance carriers are set up to make the required insurance filings electronically.

CONCLUSION

The regulation of safety in transportation is constantly changing. In December 2010, FMCSA rolled out a new safety program called Compliance, Safety, and Accountability (CSA). The purpose of the program is to better identify high-risk motor carriers and drivers, then deploy a range of corrective interventions to address specific safety concerns. The centerpiece of the program is the safety measurement system (SMS), which will analyze all safety-based violations from inspections and crash data to determine a commercial motor carrier's on-road performance. The new safety measurement system uses seven safety improvement categories to examine a carrier's on-road performance and potential crash risk. The categories are:

1. unsafe driving
2. fatigued driving (hours-of-service)
3. driver fitness
4. controlled substances/alcohol
5. vehicle maintenance
6. cargo-related
7. crash indicator

This new system requires modifications to the underlying safety algorithms that will ultimately affect SAFER, and the data stored in those systems.

Companies should keep in mind that, regardless of the number and scope of regulations governing a subject, regulations are *de facto* minimums. There is no substitute for proactive pursuit of safety by the personnel involved in the tasks.

REFERENCES

Department of Transportation (DOT). 1996. Department of Transportation Act. P.L. 89-670, U.S.C. 1651–1659 (October 15, 1996).

Federal Motor Carrier Safety Administration (FMCSA). n.d. a. Administrative Ruling 119, *Composite Commodity List* (accessed Spetember 12). www.fmcsa.dot.gov/administratove.pdf

_____. n.d. b. Form OCE-46, Request for Revocation of Registration.

_____. n.d. c. Form BOC-3, Designation of Process Agents—Motor Carriers, Brokers and Freight Forwarders. www.fmcsa.gov/documents/boc

_____. n.d. d. BMC-91, Motor Carrier Bodily Injury and Property Damage Liability Certificate of Insurance.

_____. n.d. e. BMC-91X, Motor Carrier Bodily Injury and Property Damage Liability Certificate of Insurance.

_____. n.d. f. BMC 34, Motor Carrier Cargo Liability.

_____. n.d. g. Form BMC-85, Property Broker's Trust Fund Agreement Under 49 USC 13906 or Notice of Cancellation of the Agreement. www.fmcsa.gov/documents/bmc-85.pdf

_____. 1971. Transportation of Hazardous Materials; Driving and Parking Rules. Regulations, 49 CFR Subtitle B, Chapter III, subchapter B, Sections 397.1–397.225.

_____. 1990. Hazardous Materials Transportation–Uniform Safety Act. 49 U.S.C. 5101 et seq.

_____. 1999. Motor Carrier Safety Improvement Act of 1999. P. L. 106–159, 113 Stat. 1748 (December 9, 1999).

_____. 2007a. Form OP-1(FF), Application for Freight Forwarder Authority. www.documents/forms/r-1/op-1 (FF)-Instructions-and-form.pdf

_____. 2007b. Form OP-1(P), Application for Motor Passenger Carrier Authority. www.documents/forms/r-1/op-1(P)-Instructions-and-form.pdf

_____. 2007c. Form OP-1, Application for Motor Property Carrier and Broker Authority. www.documents/forms/r-1/op-1-Instructions-and-form.pdf

_____. 2007d. MCS-150, *Motor Carrier Identification Report*. www.fmcsa.dot.gov/documents/forms/r-1/MCS150-Instructions-and-Form.pdf

_____. 2007e. MCS-150A, Safety Certification Application. www.fmcsa.dot.gov/documents/forms/r-1/MCS150A-Instructions-and-Form.pdf

_____. 2010. *Compliance, Safety, Accountability*. www.csa.fmcsa.dot.gov/Documents/GeneralFactSheet.pdf

APPENDIX: RECOMMENDED RESOURCES

Federal Aviation Administration (www.faa.gov)

Federal Railroad Administration (www.fra.dot.gov)

Federal Transit Administration (www.fta.dot.gov)

Maritime Administration (www.marad.dot.gov)

National Highway Traffic Safety Administration (www.nhtsa.dot.gov)

Pipeline and Hazardous Materials Safety Administration (www.phmsa.dot.gov)

Research and Innovative Technology Administration (www.rita.dot.gov)

Saint Lawrence Seaway Development Corporation (www.seaway.dot.gov)

Surface Transportation Board Federal Highway Administration (www.stb.dot.gov)

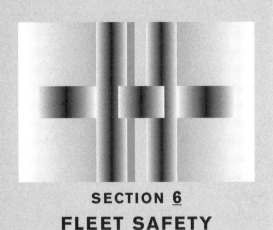

SECTION 6
FLEET SAFETY

LEARNING OBJECTIVES

▮ Identify OSHA regulations that pertain to organizations with motor-vehicle exposures.

▮ Identify other federal agencies that address motor fleet safety, including DOT, FAA, PHMSA, EPA, CDC, and NIOSH.

▮ Explain commonly cited standards for SIC 4200 (Motor Freight Transportation and Warehousing).

▮ Be familiar with the regulations for construction vehicles.

▮ Know what rollover protective structures for material-handling equipment are required for construction and agricultural vehicles.

▮ Explain what is covered under the OSHA Marine Terminal Vehicle Regulations.

▮ Understand the expanded role OSHA has taken to address motor-vehicle safety as outlined in *OSHA Motor Vehicle Guidance*.

▮ Understand how OSHA has addressed distracted driving as a special focus initiative.

REGULATORY ISSUES: OSHA AND OTHER REGULATIONS

Nancy Bendickson

ORGANIZATIONS WITH FLEET EXPOSURES are affected by a number of different regulatory agencies. This chapter will provide an overview of key regulatory issues and guidelines developed to address motor-vehicle safety. The Department of Transportation (DOT) regulations, history, and some other areas are covered in the first chapter of this section of the handbook. The primary focus of this chapter will be on the Occupational Safety & Health Administration (OSHA) and the jurisdictional role of federal agencies with regard to fleet exposures.

Data from the Bureau of Labor Statistics (BLS) showed that, in 2010, 1,766 fatal work injuries resulted from transportation incidents (BLS 2011), making them consistently the leading cause of occupational fatalities in the United States. In 2010, highway incidents accounted for one out of every five fatal work injuries—a total of 39 percent (see Figure 1). Risk of work-related motor-vehicle crashes cuts across all industries and occupations. Workers who drive on the job may be "professional" drivers whose primary job is to transport freight or passengers. Many other workers spend a substantial part of the work day driving a personal vehicle or one owned or leased by their employer. Considered to be hidden or grey, it is difficult to estimate the number of these fleets in operation. There is no specific percentage of hired/non-owned vehicle use documented in literature for the United States. Arval (a U.K. Fleet Management company) did a study within the U.K. that found one in four vehicles operated for business use was a non-owned vehicle (Road Safe Summer 2008).

Traditional fleet safety processes have typically addressed the driver of a company-owned vehicle. The historical approach to fleet safety has been to address company-owned vehicles and not to address non-owned vehicle exposures.

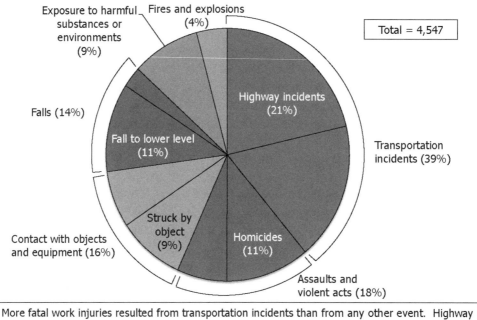

Exposure to harmful substances or environments (9%)

Fires and explosions (4%)

Total = 4,547

Falls (14%)

Highway incidents (21%)

Fall to lower level (11%)

Transportation incidents (39%)

Contact with objects and equipment (16%)

Struck by object (9%)

Homicides (11%)

Assaults and violent acts (18%)

More fatal work injuries resulted from transportation incidents than from any other event. Highway incidents alone accounted for more than one out of every five fatal work injuries in 2010.

*Data for 2010 are preliminary.
NOTE: Percentages may not add to totals because of rounding. Transportation counts are expected to rise when updated 2010 data are released in Spring 2012 because key source documentation on specific transportation-related incidents has not yet been received.

FIGURE 1. Manner in which fatal work injuries occurred, 2010 (*Source:* BLS 2011)

OSHA does not have specific standards that address passenger-vehicle operations. However, Section 5(a)(1) of the OSH Act, often referred to as the General Duty Clause, requires employers to "furnish to each of his employees employment and a place of employment which are free from recognized hazards that are causing or are likely to cause death or serious physical harm to his employees" (OSHA 1970). Occupational motor-vehicle operation does present a recognized hazard since it has been the leading cause of worker fatalities in the workplace year after year.

An initiative was launched on October 4, 2010, by the Department of Labor (DOL) and the Department of Transportation (DOT) to combat distracted driving. OSHA created a Web page directed at those employees whose workplaces are cars, vans, and trucks that deliver goods and services and their employers. The online resource provides information on workers' rights; employers' responsibilities to provide safe workplaces that extend to the operation of a motor vehicle; and best practices and policies to achieve safe workplaces in motor vehicles (OSHA 2007b).

OSHA's distracted-driving initiative addresses texting while driving. Employers are directed to prohibit

any work policy or practice that requires or encourages workers to text while driving. Allowing the practice of texting while driving will violate the OSH Act.

Additional guidance for employers on fleet safety can be found on the "Motor Vehicle Safety" page of OSHA's Web site.

Reduction in transportation crashes requires implementation of motor fleet safety-management controls that combine traffic safety principles and fleet safety-management practices.

MAJOR JURISDICTIONAL AGENCIES

OSHA has jurisdiction over off-highway loading and unloading, such as would occur at warehouses, plants, retail locations, marine terminals, wharves, piers, and shipyards (OSHA 2007c).

In addition to federal OSHA regulations, there are OSHA state plans that incorporate motor-vehicle regulations. An example of this is Washington state. The Washington Administrative Code (Chapter 296-865 WAC) has regulations for Motor Vehicle Statutory Authority (WISHA Rules–Motor Vehicles 2007). The regulations cover motor-vehicle operation, transportation of passengers, motor-vehicle equipment, trucks and trailers, dump trucks, semitruck brakes, and truck/trailer loads. Trucking companies that have operations in states with OSHA state plans need to review their specific rules to determine if there are additional regulations that would pertain to a fleet operation.

DOT has jurisdiction over interstate highway driving, hours of service, driver qualification standards, and roadworthiness of vehicles. The Environmental Protection Agency (EPA) has jurisdiction over the natural environment and pollution prevention programs. OSHA can be preempted for jurisdiction by another federal agency *only* for a specific task or activity. The ultimate responsibility for the safety and health of all employees rests with OSHA.

OSHA has developed an "OSHA Assistance for the Trucking Industry" page on its Web site that provides information about preventing occupational illness and injury in the trucking industry through links to summaries, training presentations, publications, and other resources. It also offers a one-stop location to find applicable DOT and EPA compliance requirements related to worker protection (OSHA 2007c).

OTHER AGENCIES: AN OVERVIEW

When a federal agency other than OSHA has regulated a working condition, OSHA is preempted by Section 4(b)1 from enforcing its regulations. Some examples of this are provided below:

- Department of Transportation (DOT) regulates driving over public highways, the health and safety of drivers involving their use of drugs and alcohol, hours of service, and use of seatbelts. In addition, states have additional regulations for intrastate trucking. Most states adopt many, if not all, of the federal regulations regarding a driver's qualifications, hours of service, drug and alcohol testing, and more.
- DOT also regulates the roadworthiness of trucks and trailers and has specific requirements for the safe operation of trucks.
- DOT has jurisdiction over *interstate* trucking operations, while OSHA has jurisdiction over

intrastate motor vehicles operated in the workplace and not on public roads, except those handling hazardous materials. DOT has issued regulations regarding the shipping, packaging, and handling of these materials. However, if a truck driver becomes an emergency responder in the event of a spill, then OSHA has jurisdiction.

- Interstate versus intrastate highway driving operations: DOT preempts OSHA's jurisdiction if a vehicle is traveling on public roads. OSHA has broader jurisdiction over intrastate trucking operations. Intrastate is defined as *operating strictly within a single state.* Examples of this type of trucking operation include: gravel/sand haulers, logging, agriculture, cement and concrete mixers. DOT has jurisdiction over the transportation of hazardous materials for both an interstate or intrastate trucking operation.
- Federal Aviation Administration (FAA) regulates flight crews and some aspects of the safety of ground crews. For example, if there is a working condition in an operational plan negotiated between the carrier and the FAA, FAA has jurisdiction over that working condition. Otherwise, OSHA covers most working conditions of ground crews and baggage handlers.
- Environmental Protection Agency (EPA) works with industries and all levels of government on pollution prevention programs. They have developed a number of environmental screening checklists and workbooks that can be used to screen and evaluate an industry or government agency's compliance with EPA environmental regulations. The *Environmental Screening Checklist and Workbook for the Trucking Industry* (August 2000) and *Profile of the Ground Transportation Industry: Trucking, Railroad, and Pipeline*, EPA Office of Compliance Sector Notebook Project (September 1997), provide examples of screening checklists that the transportation industry can utilize (see Figure 2).
- The Pipeline and Hazardous Materials Safety Administration (PHMSA) has public responsibilities for the safe and secure movement of

ENVIRONMENTAL CHECKLIST FOR TRUCKING INDUSTRY

1.0 WASTE MANAGEMENT***

Hazardous Waste Generation, Storage, and Transport*	Does the facility have an EPA hazardous waste generator ID number? (p. W-6)	Y ☐ N ☐ NA ☐
	Does the facility store hazardous waste in appropriate storage containers? (p. W-6)	Y ☐ N ☐ NA ☐
	Does the facility meet all hazardous waste storage (quantity and time) requirements? (p. W-7)	Y ☐ N ☐ NA ☐
	How does the facility dispose of its hazardous waste? (p. W-7)	Ships haz waste off site / Disposes of hazardous waste on site and is a RCRA-permitted TSDF / Other / NA
	Does the facility have a written contingency plan or basic contingency procedures in place for responding to spills and releases of hazardous waste? (p. W-8)	Y ☐ N ☐ NA ☐
Used Oil and Filters*	Are used oil containers/tanks and associated piping labeled "used oil?" (p. W-10)	Y ☐ N ☐ NA ☐
	Are used oil containers/tanks and associated piping leak free? (p. W-10)	Y ☐ N ☐ NA ☐
	Does the facility prevent the mixing of used oil with hazardous waste? (p. W-10)	Y ☐ N ☐ NA ☐
	How does the facility manage/dispose of used oil? (p. W-11)	Sent off site for recycling / Burned in on-site space heater / Burned off site / Other / NA
	How does the facility manage/dispose of used oil filters? (p. W-13)	Recycle / Srvc Co / Other / NA
	How does the facility manage/dispose of used fuel filters? (p. W-14)	Recycle / Srvc Co / Managed as haz waste / Other / NA
Used Antifreeze*	In terms of storage, is used antifreeze contained, segregated, and labeled? (p. W-15)	Y ☐ N ☐ NA ☐
	Has the facility determined if it generates any antifreeze that is hazardous waste? (p. W-16)	Y ☐ N ☐ NA ☐
Used Battery Storage and Disposal*	If storing used batteries, does the facility protect them from storm water contact? (p. W-19)	Y ☐ N ☐ NA ☐
	How does the facility manage/dispose of used batteries? (p. W-19)	Return to supplier/ Recycle / Srvc Co / Sent to Universal waste handler/ Sent to hazardous waste landfill/ Other/ NA
Used Shop Rags/ Towels*	How does the facility manage/dispose of used shop rags and towels? (p. W-21)	Laundry service / Burned for heat / Other / NA
Absorbents*	Does the facility determine if used absorbents are hazardous before disposal? (p. W-22)	Y ☐ N ☐ NA ☐
Used Tires	How does the facility manage/dispose of used tires? (p. W-23)	Resale / Retread / Recycle / Other / NA
Brake Repair*	How does the facility manage asbestos brake pads and asbestos-containing material (ACM) waste? (p. W-25)	Recycled off site / Disposed of by vendor / EPA-approved disposal site / Other / NA

FIGURE 2. Environmental screening checklist for the trucking industry (*Source:* Environmental Protection Agency 2000, www.epa.gov)

ENVIRONMENTAL CHECKLIST FOR TRUCKING INDUSTRY (cont.)

2.0 WASTEWATER AND STORM WATER MANAGEMENT**

Wastewater and Storm Water Management*	Can the facility identify the final destination of all its drains? (p. W-29)	Y ☐ N ☐ NA ☐
	If the facility discharges to a surface water does it have an NPDES permit? (p. W-31)	Y ☐ N ☐ NA ☐
	Does the facility have a storm water permit?	Y ☐ N ☐ NA ☐
	If Yes, does the facility have a storm water pollution prevention plan (SWPPP)? (p. W-32)	Y ☐ N ☐ NA ☐
	If discharging to a municipal sanitary sewer, has the facility notified the publicly owned treatment works (POTW) and received approval for discharges? (p. W-32)	Y ☐ N ☐ NA ☐
	If discharging to an underground injection control (UIC) well, does the facility comply with UIC program requirements? (p. W-33)	Y ☐ N ☐ NA ☐
	How does the facility manage the sludge from an oil/water separator? (p. W-34)	Off-site disposal as haz waste / Off-site disposal to other facility / On-site disposal / NA
Activities Generating Wastewater/Storm Water*	If the facility stores materials outside, are they protected from contact with storm water? (p. W-35)	Y ☐ N ☐ NA ☐
Equipment Cleaning and Spent Solvents*	If halogenated solvents are used in cleaning equipment, has the facility submitted a notification report to the air permitting agency? (p. W-39)	Y ☐ N ☐ NA ☐
	How does the facility manage/dispose of spent solvents? (p. W-40)	Third-party vendor / Permitted discharge to storm sewers or surface waters / Sanitary sewer with POTW approval / Other / NA
Fueling*	Do fuel delivery records indicate compliance with appropriate fuel requirements? (p. W-42)	Y ☐ N ☐ NA ☐
	Does the facility use overfill protection measures, spill containment methods, and spill response equipment during fueling? (p. W-44)	Y ☐ N ☐ NA ☐
Asbestos Concerns*	Has the facility assessed all buildings and structures built prior to 1980 for their potential for containing asbestos and treated accordingly? (p. W-45)	Y ☐ N ☐ NA ☐
Construction Activities*	Are there any endangered species which may be affected by construction activities? (p. W-47)	Y ☐ N ☐ NA ☐
	Has the facility obtained a Section 404 permit for any projects that may impact wetlands? (p. W-47)	Y ☐ N ☐ NA ☐
Pesticide Use*	Are restricted use pesticides (RUPs) applied only by a certified commercial applicator? (p. W-49)	Y ☐ N ☐ NA ☐
Yard Dust Control*	Does the facility prohibit the use of used oils or other liquid wastes to suppress dust? (p. W-51)	Y ☐ N ☐ NA ☐
Painting/Paint Removal*	Does the facility have air permits? (p. W-52)	Y ☐ N ☐ NA ☐
	How does the facility manage/dispose of paint stripping wastes and baghouse dusts? (p. W-53)	Municipal or hazardous landfill / Other / NA
	When not in use, does the facility store paints in labeled container? (p. W-54)	Y ☐ N ☐ NA ☐
	How does the facility manage/dispose of used paints and painting waste products? (p. W-55)	Return to supplier / Reuse / Recycle / Other / NA

FIGURE 2. Environmental screening checklist for the trucking industry (*Source:* Environmental Protection Agency 2000, www.epa.gov)

ENVIRONMENTAL CHECKLIST FOR TRUCKING INDUSTRY (cont.)

Air Conditioning Repair*	How does the facility dispose of appliances containing ozone-depleting refrigerants? (p. W-61)	Landfill / Waste hauler / Scrap metal recycler / Other / NA

4.0 STORAGE TANKS, SPCC, AND EMERGENCY RESPONSE

Underground Storage Tanks	Has the State/Tribal UST program office been notified of any USTs located on site? (p. W-64)	Y ☐ N ☐ NA ☐
	Does the facility conduct leak detection for tank and piping of all on-site USTs? (p. W-64)	Y ☐ N ☐ NA ☐
	Do USTs at the facility meet requirements for spill, overfill, and corrosion protection? (p. W-65)	Y ☐ N ☐ NA ☐
Aboveground Storage Tanks*	Does the facility inspect ASTs on a periodic basis for leaks and other hazardous conditions? (p.W-67)	Y ☐ N ☐ NA ☐
SPCC and Emergency Response*	Does the facility have a Spill Prevention, Control, and Countermeasures (SPCC) plan signed by a professional engineer? (p. W-69)	Y ☐ N ☐ NA ☐
	Is the phone number for the National Response Center posted on site for immediate reporting of oil spills? (p. W-70)	Y ☐ N ☐

5.0 RECORDKEEPING

Recordkeeping*	**NPDES:** Does the facility keep accurate records of monitoring information for the minimum requirement of 3 years? (p. W-71)	Y ☐ N ☐ NA ☐
	Air: Does the facility meet the recordkeeping requirements of its air permit(s)? (p. W-72)	Y ☐ N ☐ NA ☐
	Air: If the facility owns/operates appliances that contain ozone-depleting refrigerants, does the facility maintain all required records? (p. W-73)	Y ☐ N ☐ NA ☐
	RCRA: Does the facility keep copies of its manifests for the 3-year minimum requirement? (p. W-73)	Y ☐ N ☐ NA ☐
	USTs: Does the facility maintain leak detection records? (p. W-75)	Y ☐ N ☐ NA ☐
	USTs: Does the facility maintain corrosion protection records? (p. W-75)	Y ☐ N ☐ NA ☐

*For additional questions regarding these environmental compliance issues, refer to the workbook.

**In addition, the workbook includes environmental compliance questions regarding metal machining (p. W-26), on-site disposal of nonhazardous waste (p. W-49), and PCB-containing equipment (p. W-56).

FIGURE 2. Environmental screening checklist for the trucking industry (*Source:* Environmental Protection Agency 2000, www.epa.gov)

hazardous materials to industry and consumers by all modes of transportation, including the nation's pipeline. PHMSA is part of the U.S. Department of Transportation. This function was previously the responsibility of the Research and Special Programs Administration (RSPA). RSPA ceased operations on February 20, 2005. RSPA programs were moved to the following agencies: Pipeline and Hazardous Materials Safety Administration, Research and Innovative Technology Administration, and the Office of Emergency Transportation moved to the Office of the Secretary. The regulations governing hazardous materials are complex. Specific information about the regulations for hazardous materials can be found at www.phmsa.dot.gov.

• The Centers for Disease Control (CDC) recognize motor-vehicle-related injuries and deaths as a serious public health problem. The agency, which is part of the Department of Health and Human Services (DHHS), supports research and prevention efforts. The CDC has developed fact sheets on a number of motor-vehicle safety topics, including: child passenger safety, teen drivers, older adult drivers, impaired driving, distracted driving, Native American road safety, pedestrian safety, and global road safety (NIOSH 2010).

• National Institute of Occupational Safety and Health (NIOSH), which is a part of the CDC, was established to assure safe and healthful working conditions for working men and women by providing research, information, education, and training in the field of occupational safety and health. The NIOSH Workplace Safety and Health Topic: "Motor Vehicle Safety" offers comprehensive information on subjects such as general crash statistics and prevention, vehicle safety for fire fighters and emergency responders, highway work zones, research initiatives, and motor-vehicle injuries (NIOSH 2010).

• NIOSH Transportation Initiative: This initiative coordinates NIOSH-wide activities in all industry sectors to reduce motor-vehicle crashes, the leading cause of traumatic occupational fatalities. The initiative currently supports: (1) collaborative work with the National Center for Injury Prevention and Control (NCIPC) to address both occupational and nonoccupational issues related to motor-vehicle safety; and (2) efforts promoting global road safety, including a NIOSH-sponsored "International Conference on Road Safety at Work" (NIOSH 2008), and NIOSH participation in the United Nations Road Safety Collaboration and in the federal agency, Global Road Safety Roundtable (NIOSH 2007a), coordinated by the U.S. Department of State. NIOSH houses the global online library for resources related to the prevention of road traffic injuries and deaths while at work. Reference the Road Safety at Work Library of Training Materials and Practice Tools (Geolibrary 2005).

OSHA STANDARDS FOR THE TRUCKING INDUSTRY

OSHA regulations govern the safety and health of workers and the responsibilities of employers to ensure their safety at docks, warehouses, construction sites, and other places where truckers deliver and pick up loads. Even self-employed truckers, who are not regulated by OSHA, are covered by OSHA regulations when they enter workplaces to deliver or receive goods. Organizations that operate commercial motor vehicles need to be familiar with OSHA standards and take appropriate action to implement any relevant regulations.

Trucking companies must comply with General Industry Standard (29 CFR 1910). The ten most frequently issued citations for SIC 4200-*Motor Freight Transportation* from October 2008 to September 2009 involved (OSHA 2007c):

• Powered industrial trucks: 1910.178;
• Hazard communication: 1910.1200;
• Electrical—general requirements: 1910.303;
• Wiring methods, components, and equipment for general use: 1910.305;
• Portable fire extinguishers: 1910.157;
• Forms: 1910.29;
• Abrasive wheel machinery: 1910.215;
• Annual summary: 1910.2;
• Oxygen-fueled gas welding: 1910.253; and
• Guarding floor and wall openings and holes: 1910.23

ADDITIONAL STANDARDS COMMONLY CITED FOR THE TRUCKING INDUSTRY

In addition to the frequently cited standards discussed above, the following list highlights other standards that address common hazards in the trucking industry:

• 1910.151, Medical Services and First Aid
• 1910.176, Materials Handling, General
• 1904.7, Recordkeeping
• 1910.120, Hazardous Waste Operation and Emergency Response
• OSHA Act of 1970, General Duty Clause
• 1904.2, Log and Summary of Occupational Injuries and Illnesses
• 1910.146, Permit-Required Confined Spaces
• 1910.141, Sanitation
• 1910.106, Flammable and Combustible Liquids
• 1910.272, Grain Handling Facilities
• 1910.177, Servicing Multi-Piece and Single Piece Rim Wheels
• 1910.266, Logging Operations

These regulations can be found on the OSHA Web site at www.osha.gov/SLTC/trucking_industry/index.html (OSHA 2007a).

OSHA CONSTRUCTION-VEHICLE REGULATIONS

Motor-vehicle standards have been promulgated for the construction industry. These standards are found in CFR 1926, Subpart O, *Motor Vehicles, Mechanized Equipment, and Marine Operations* (OSHA 2007e). An overview of these regulations is provided below:

- 1926.600 Equipment – This section covers general requirements for parking unattended equipment at night, use of a safety tire rack or cage for work on tires with split rims or rims with locking devices, blocking of equipment parts when work is performed under elevated parts, parking brake use, cab glass construction, battery charging, procedures to follow when work is performed near energized power lines, and blocking of railroad cars on spur tracks.

- 1926.601 Motor Vehicles – Coverage applies to those vehicles that operate within an off-highway job site, not open to the general public. General requirements for this section include: brake systems; lighting standards; audible warning devices at operator's station; reverse alarms and use of observers for equipment with an obstructed rear view; windshields with powered wipers and defrosting system; cab shield or canopy to protect operator from falling or shifting cargo when it is loaded by crane, backhoe, or power shovel; tool securement within the cab; secured seats with adequate number for employees carried; seatbelts installed and used to meet federal motor-vehicle safety standards; means of supporting elevated dump body during inspection/maintenance; means to prevent accidental tripping of levers for dumping or hoisting devices; trip handles located so operator is in clear; fenders or mud flaps on rubber-tired equipment; and equipment inspection done before each shift to assure parts, equipment, and accessories are in safe operating condition.

- 1926.602 Earthmoving Equipment – This section applies to scrapers, loaders, crawlers or wheel tractors, bulldozers, off-highway trucks, graders, agricultural and industrial tractors, and similar equipment. Specific rules for compactors and rubber-tired, skid-steer equipment is not included in this standard, pending development of standards for this equipment. General requirements are outlined for: seatbelts, with an exemption for seatbelts when equipment is for stand-up operation or where a rollover protective structure (ROPS) is not provided; access roads and grades; brakes; fenders; audible horns; reverse alarms; and powered industrial truck rules, including operator training. The section states that equipment must meet CFR 1926, Subpart W, requirements for ROPS and overhead protection.

- 1926.1000, Subpart W – This section covers rollover protective structures (ROPS) for material-handling equipment and outlines requirements for ROPS. Key performance criteria include: ROPS shall be designed, fabricated, and installed in a manner that will support, based on ultimate strength of metal, at least two times the weight of the prime mover applied at the point of impact. The design objective is to minimize the likelihood of a complete overturn and thereby minimize the possibility of an operator being crushed as a result of a rollover or upset.

OSHA AGRICULTURAL VEHICLE REGULATIONS

Safety for agricultural motor vehicles is addressed in CFR 1928.51, *Rollover Protective Structures for Tractors Used in Agricultural Operations*. This agricultural standard defines what type of tractor is required to have ROPS and their design requirements. Where ROPS are required, employers should provide each tractor with a seatbelt, ensure that the employee tightens the seatbelt sufficiently to confine him/her to the protected area provided by ROPS, and ensure that the seatbelt meets the requirements set forth by the Society of Automotive Engineer Standard, SAE J4C,

1965 Seat Belt Assemblies (2), except when the seatbelt is used on a suspended seat. Then, the seatbelt should be fastened to a movable portion of the seat. Additional information is provided on material for seatbelt webbing, ROPS marking, different styles of tractors and ROPS requirements, operating practices, and ROPS remounting requirements (OSHA 2009).

OSHA MARINE TERMINAL VEHICLE REGULATIONS

The requirements of vehicle safety regulations for marine terminals are outlined in CFR Part 1917.44, *Marine Terminals, General Rules Applicable to Vehicles.* This is a comprehensive standard that covers signs for traffic control, distance of vehicles at check-in, securement of vehicles/trailers, employee transport-vehicle rules, servicing of multi-piece and single-piece rim wheels, and cargo securement of pipe or other rolling stock cargo while it is being loaded or unloaded from flatbed trailers (OSHA 2009).

Traffic accidents are a serious problem at marine terminals, and OSHA developed a guidance document in 2007 to help improve traffic safety in terminals. Marine terminal operations need to go beyond complying with the OSHA standards on powered industrial trucks and vehicle operations to also develop traffic safety programs for vehicle and pedestrian safety. The guidance document on the OSHA Web site is "Traffic Safety in Marine Terminals" (OSHA 2007c).

Factors that Contribute to Traffic-Related Injuries and Fatalities in Marine Terminals

There are many factors that can contribute to traffic accidents in marine terminals. Often, accidents are caused by a combination of factors. The following points illustrate common traffic safety problems:

- *Unsafe equipment.* Broken, improperly maintained, or missing safety equipment, such as lights, seatbelts, brakes, and horns, can lead to accidents and injuries.
- *Inadequate traffic controls.* Inadequate traffic controls, such as lack of proper signage or marking, may lead to accidents.

- *Condition of terminal driving surfaces.* Many marine terminals, particularly larger ones, have paved terminal driving surfaces. Paved surfaces, which are smoother, are desirable because they reduce the potential for vehicle tipovers, cargo and equipment shifting, and operator bouncing, and allow for improved road markings, such as lane markings. However, smoother driving surfaces also require heightened awareness because they can become slippery when wet and contribute to excessive vehicle speed. Road surfaces need to be maintained properly because, over time, paving material can settle and result in uneven surfaces, potholes, and sinkholes that can lead to tipovers or other vehicle accidents.
- *Driving obstacles.* Vessel equipment, stacked materials, containers, and repair crews are some of the driving obstacles that increase the risk of traffic accidents at marine terminals.
- *Weather.* Ice, fog, and rain can create hazardous conditions, including slippery surfaces and poor visibility, in marine terminals. Also, the sun may cause glare on certain types of driving surfaces and vehicle windshields.
- *Inadequate illumination.* Poor lighting, particularly at night, as well as shadows, can make it difficult for drivers to see and avoid pedestrians, hazardous driving surfaces, and other obstacles.
- *Welding.* Welding flashes can distract vehicle and crane operators.
- *Unsafe vehicle operation.* Factors such as improperly loaded equipment, speed, and distractions (such as cell phones) can contribute to traffic accidents.
- *Improper parking.* Hazards can be created by improper parking of personal or company-provided vehicles and powered industrial trucks in areas where cargo is being worked on or heavy machinery is being used.
- *Lack of communication.* Accidents often occur because of poor communication. Technicians, mechanics, and other employees fail to alert vehicle operators of their location, and

employers fail to notify employees of changes to traffic routes. In addition, noisy terminal environments can hinder effective communications. In some cases, there may be inadequate accommodations for persons with hearing impairment or language barriers.

- *Lack of training and awareness.* Accidents can occur when drivers and equipment operators do not have adequate training in the safe operation and maintenance of equipment and vehicles. Likewise, pedestrians walking in marine terminals are at risk of injury if they do not receive training on the potential for traffic accidents and how to avoid them.
- *Shift changes.* Marine terminal employers report that accidents often occur just before the end of a work shift or while employees are parking equipment at the end of the work shift.
- *Fatigue.* Marine terminal employees often work long and irregular hours, which can lead to fatigue and sleepiness. Fatigue and sleepiness can impair operator performance and contribute to workplace accidents and fatalities.
- *Substance abuse.* Substance abuse may contribute to vehicle accidents in marine terminals (OSHA 2007c).

OSHA SAFETY GUIDANCE FOR MOTOR VEHICLES

Since the roadway is a not a closed environment, employers need to develop strategies that combine traffic safety principles and sound safety-management practices. An employer cannot control the roadway condition; however, he or she can promote safe driving behavior by providing safety information to workers and by setting and enforcing driver safety policies. Crashes are *not* an unavoidable part of doing business.

OSHA highlights resources available through the National Safety Council (NSC), the National Highway Traffic Safety Administration (NHTSA), the National Institute for Occupational Safety and Health (NIOSH), the Institute for Highway Safety (IHS), and the Network of Employers for Traffic Safety (NETS).

A suggested prevention strategy for crash reduction is provided on the policies page of OSHA's Motor Vehicle Safety Web site. This prevention strategy is based on a publication by NIOSH (2004a) and includes the following steps:

- Policies
  - Assign a key member of the management team responsibility and authority to set and enforce a comprehensive driver safety policy.
  - Enforce mandatory seatbelt use.
  - Do not require workers to drive irregular hours or drive far beyond normal work hours.
  - Do not require workers to conduct business on a cell phone while driving.
  - Develop work schedules that allow employees to obey speed limits and to follow applicable hours-of-service regulations.
- Fleet Management
  - Adopt a structured vehicle maintenance program.
  - Provide company vehicles that offer the highest levels of occupant protection.
- Safety Programs
  - Teach worker strategies for recognizing and managing driver fatigue and in-vehicle distractions.
  - Provide training to workers operating specialized motor vehicles or equipment.
  - Emphasize to workers the need to follow safe driving practices on and off the job.
- Driver Performance
  - Ensure that workers assigned to drive on the job have a valid driver's license and one that is appropriate for the type of vehicle being driven.
  - Check driving records of prospective employees and perform periodic rechecks after hiring.
  - Maintain complete and accurate records of workers' driving performance.

ADDITIONAL RESOURCES FOR PREVENTION STRATEGIES

The "Best Practices" chapter within this section of the handbook provides extensive information about prevention strategies and resources, such as ANSI/ASSE Z-15.1 2006, *Safe Practices for Motor Vehicle Operations*. This standard sets forth practices for safe operation of motor vehicles owned or operated by organizations, including:

- definitions
- management, leadership, and administration
- operational environment
- driver considerations
- vehicle considerations
- incident reporting and analysis

These practices are designed for use by those having the responsibility for the administration and operation of motor vehicles. This is an excellent resource that should form the basis of an organization's fleet safety-management system (ANSI/ASSE 2006).

SUMMARY

This chapter provided an overview of OSHA and the jurisdictional role that other federal agencies have with regard to fleet safety. Motor-vehicle safety is a concern for many agencies because the risk of roadway crashes affects millions of U.S. workers and continues to be the leading cause of occupational fatalities in the United States.

The following federal agencies have initiatives or regulations that address fleet safety exposures: Department of Transportation (DOT), Federal Aviation Administration (FAA), Pipeline and Hazardous Materials Safety Administration (PHMSA), Centers for Disease Control (CDC), National Institute of Occupational Safety and Health (NIOSH), and the Environmental Protection Agency (EPA). NIOSH is involved in a global partnership on road safety at work and is housing an online library devoted to global road safety resources.

Distracted driving is the subject of several safety initiatives and regulation in 2010. OSHA considers texting to be a recognized hazard, and enforcement action will be taken against organizations that do not manage this exposure (OSHA 2007b).

Fleet safety initiatives within the regulatory agencies are changing. Safety professionals will need to monitor the Web sites of the federal agencies to stay current on motor-vehicle safety prevention strategies and regulations.

REFERENCES

American National Standards Institute (ANSI) and American Society of Safety Engineers (ASSE). 2006. *ANSI/ASSE Z-15.1 2006: Safe Practices for Motor Vehicle Operations*. Des Plaines, IL: ASSE.

Bureau of Labor Statistics (BLS). 2011. *2010 Census of Fatal Occupational Injuries--Preliminary Data* (retrieved October 31, 2011). www.stats.bls.gov/iif/oshwc/cfoi/cfch0009.pdf

Environmental Protection Agency (EPA). 2000. *Environmental Screening Checklist and Workbook for Trucking Industry* (retrieved July 10, 2010). www.epa.gov/compliance/resources/publications/assistance/sectors/truckwrkbk.pdf

Geolibrary. n.d. *Specialty Road Safety at Work Library of Training Materials and Practice Tools* (retrieved October 15, 2010). www.geolibrary.org/library/default/aspx?categoryID=627.

National Institute for Occupational Safety and Health (NIOSH). 2004a. *Work-Related Roadway Crashes: Prevention Strategies for Employers*. NIOSH Publication No. 2004-136 (retrieved July 10, 2010). www.cdc.gov/niosh/doc/2004-136/default.html

_____. 2004b. *Work-Related Roadway Crashes: Who's at Risk?* NIOSH Publication No. 2004-137 (retrieved July 10, 2010). www.cdc.gov/niosh/docs/2004-137/default.html

_____. 2007a. *Global Collaborations in Transportation, Warehousing and Utilities* (retrieved October 7, 2010). www.cdc.gov/niosh/programs/twu/global

_____. 2007b. *Motor Vehicle Safety* (retrieved October 7, 2010). www.cdc.gov/nioshtopics/motorvehicle

Occupational Safety and Health Administration (OSHA). 1970. Occupational Safety and Health Act of 1970 (retrieved October 15, 2010). www.osha.gov/pls/oshaweb/owadisp.show_document?ptable=OSHACT&p_id3359

_____. 2007a. *Safety and Health Topics: Motor Vehicle Safety* (retrieved July 10, 2010). www.osha.gov/SLTC/motorvehiclesafety/html

_____. 2007b. *Safety and Health Topics: Distracted Driving* (retrieved October 7, 2010).www.osha.gov/distracted-driving/index.html

_____. 2007c. *Safety and Health Topics: Marine Terminal* (retrieved September 11, 2010). www.osha.gov/SLTC/marineterminals/index.html

_____. 2009a. *OSHA Assistance for the Trucking Industry* (retrieved September 12, 2010). www.osha.gov/SLTC/trucking_industry/index/html

_____. 2009b. *Safety and Health Topics: Agricultural Operations* (retrieved September 11, 2010). www.osha.gov/SLTC/agriculturaloperations/index.html

_____. 2010. *Safety and Health Topics: Construction Motor Vehicles* (retrieved September 12, 2010). www.osha.gov/SLTC/constructionmotorvehicle/index.html

Pipeline and Hazardous Materials Safety Administration (PHMSA) n.d. (retrieved July 10, 2010). www.phmsa.dot.gov.index/html

Road Safe Summer. 2008. "A Grey Area of Fleet Safety" (retrieved July 28, 2011). www.roadsafe.com/magazine/2008summer/grey.html

SECTION 6
FLEET SAFETY

LEARNING OBJECTIVES

▌ Utilize vehicle-selection criteria to properly choose fleet vehicles.

▌ Establish and carry out proper vehicle maintenance programs and procedures for fleet vehicles.

▌ Understand and implement recommended practices for accident investigation.

APPLIED SCIENCE AND ENGINEERING: VEHICLES AND ACCIDENTS

Jubal Hamernik and Peter M. Himpsel

PRACTICING FLEET SAFETY is an active, ongoing process, not just a policy statement. Each step, from purchase to salvage, should be undertaken with safety concerns in mind. Fleet safety can be improved through educated vehicle selection, proper vehicle maintenance, and thorough accident investigations. This chapter seeks to address these issues and give insight into good fleet safety practices.

VEHICLE CONSIDERATIONS

For any new fleet of vehicles or addition to an existing fleet, vehicle selection is important. When selecting new fleet vehicles, issues such as safety, cost, crashworthiness, and environmental friendliness should be considered. The first step is to determine the type and class of vehicle needed. Essentially, the fleet should be tailored to use so that it can accommodate the expected range, load, and so on required of the vehicle. The Federal Motor Carrier Safety Administration's (FMCSA) Commercial Driver's License Program (CDL/CDLIS) outlines the different classes of commercial vehicles. This information may be useful in determining the class of vehicle needed and the associated license requirements for fleet drivers. Vehicle classes A through C are determined by vehicle weight, towing capacity, and passenger size. Vehicle type can be found at the Federal Highway Administration (FHA) Web site under *FHWA Vehicle Types*. Once fleet use is determined and the type and class of vehicle have been identified, the practices outlined in this chapter may be referenced to help select a specific vehicle.

Safety Features

Vehicle selection should include consideration of the following safety features: seatbelts, airbags, antilock brakes, traction and stability control, tire-pressure monitoring system, head restraints, and a design that provides visual clarity for the driver.

Seatbelt System

Seatbelts are a critical component of vehicle safety. Seatbelt type and proper seatbelt usage are both crucial factors for proper safety compliance and injury prevention. A three-point seatbelt system is preferred to a lap-only system (see Figure 1). A fleet may have more than one driver operating a vehicle. To accommodate all drivers, look for vehicles where belt height is adjustable (see Point 1 in Figure 1). If the seatbelt is comfortable, a driver may be more likely to wear it—and if it is not, the driver might be deterred from using it. Avoid passive, automatic seatbelts. Passive seatbelt systems may be by default a two-point belt system in which the lap belt must be attached separately from the shoulder belt (automatic). Sometimes the driver will not attach the lap portion; utilizing only the automatic portion increases the risk of injury. Some vehicles are equipped with an innovative seatbelt reminder system, indicating to the driver when seatbelts are not buckled. Such indicators are good for safety monitoring.

Airbags

Driver and passenger airbags have been standard equipment in all passenger vehicles since 1998 and in light trucks since 1999. In order for an airbag to function properly, the occupant must be wearing a seatbelt, and the occupant's chest should be located ten inches or more away from the steering wheel (see Figure 2). Because an airbag inflates over a short time interval, being too close to the airbag may cause injury or death. Some newer vehicles are equipped with advanced airbag systems, which utilize extra sensors to monitor vehicle and passenger characteristics and compute the specific output force of the airbag, in an attempt to reduce the chance of airbag-induced injuries. If the fleet is intended to transport children under the age of twelve, then it is recommended that the children sit only in

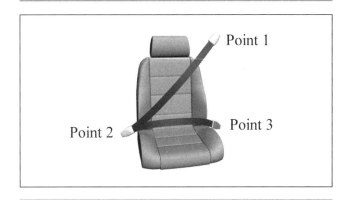

FIGURE 1. Three-point seatbelt system refers to three anchor locations for the seatbelts.

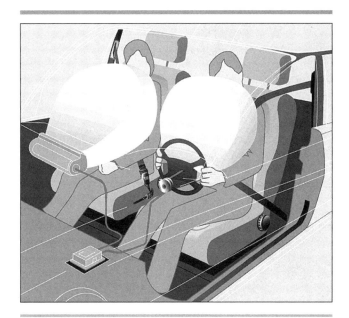

FIGURE 2. Driver and passenger airbags (*Source:* IIHS)

FIGURE 3. Side curtain airbags (*Source:* IIHS)

the rear passenger seats. The National Highway Traffic Safety Administration (NHTSA), in the "Airbags" section on its Web site (www.nhtsa.dot.gov/people/injury/airbags/airbags03/page3.html), provides useful resources on airbag safety and risks. The FMCSA does not currently have any rules or regulations mandating airbags in commercial vehicles (www.fmcsa.dot.gov/rules-regulations/rules-regulations.htm).

Vehicles equipped with side airbags offer protection to the torso and head in the event of a side-impact collision (see Figure 3). These airbags can deploy from the vehicle's roof rail, door, or seat. In addition to side-impact safety tests, many side airbag systems have been tested to determine safety in the event that the driver or occupant is out of position. Vehicles that have passed a battery of tests regarding safety in the event of out-of-position occupants are listed in NHTSA's *Buying a Safer Car* publication available for download as a pdf file at www.safercar.gov.

Antilock Brake System (ABS)

When used properly, antilock brake systems can aid in maintaining control of a vehicle on slippery surfaces and assist in retaining steering capabilities during full braking. In order for ABS to be effective, the driver must know how to properly apply the brakes. In an ABS-equipped vehicle, when the ABS system engages, it modulates brake-line pressure and causes the brake pedal to counteract a force on the driver's foot. In such instances, the driver should continue to depress the pedal as necessary to reduce speed or stop. In an ABS-equipped vehicle, the driver must not pump the brakes.

Traction Control and Stability Control

Successors to the antilock brake system, both traction and stability control systems are based on the components and concepts of the ABS system. Traction control systems available in cars today offer electronic monitoring and control of wheel spin, essentially doing for acceleration what the ABS does for braking. Traction control systems monitor wheel spin and prevent excessive wheel spin (slip) under heavy acceleration or when roadway conditions offer limited traction. When slip is sensed, the system can cut engine power and/or apply braking to maintain traction and control.

Stability control systems take this concept one step further with the addition of a yaw rate sensor. *Yaw* can be defined as the rotation about a vertical axis that passes through the car's center of gravity. The addition of a yaw rate sensor gives the stability control system the ability to sense and mitigate vehicle yaw by activating individual brakes or by applying a combination of brake and throttle in order to maintain the steering angle the driver inputs.

The presence of both traction control and stability control in a wide range of consumer vehicles continues to increase. Both systems can be useful in accident prevention and safety by assisting the driver in maintaining control of the vehicle under a variety of conditions.

Tire-Pressure Monitoring System

Tire-pressure monitoring systems, when available, work by monitoring the individual pressure of each tire. Accessible indicators can warn the driver of over- or underinflated tires. Overinflated tires can reduce vehicle traction, whereas underinflated tires can affect the vehicle's fuel efficiency and stability.

Head-Restraint Design

Head-restraint systems are important for the prevention and reduction of whiplash-type injuries, which are discussed later in this chapter. A head restraint should be sufficiently tall to reach the upper portion of the

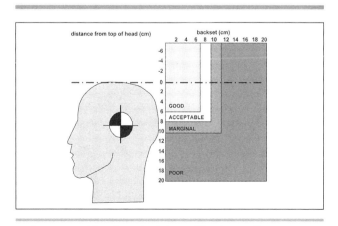

FIGURE 4. Head-restraint positioning ratings (*Source:* IIHS)

driver's or passenger's cranium (see Figure 4). Second, if possible, the head restraint should be nonadjustable. Although an adjustable head restraint may sit high on the occupant's head, in the event of a large force acting on it, the adjustable head restraint may collapse and may result in adverse loading of the head and neck.

Visual Clarity

Vehicles should be chosen so that drivers have a clear view of the roadway and surrounding areas of the vehicle (see Figure 5). Avoid placing obstructions within the driver's field of view that reduce sight capabilities (e.g., large devices mounted to the windshield). In California, a device such as a GPS unit may only be mounted at the corners of the windshield. Alternative options include dashboard mounts, vent mounts, and adhesive discs. Vehicles should be equipped with two sideview mirrors and one rearview mirror. Additional convex mirrors can be added to existing sideview mirrors for visual assistance on larger vehicles.

Crashworthiness

In selecting a vehicle, one should also consider its crashworthiness. *Crashworthiness* encompasses how a vehicle will perform in an accident, how the vehicle will protect the occupants, and how the vehicle will resist costly repairs in low- to moderate-speed accidents. The Federal Motor Vehicle Safety Standards' (FMVSS) *Quick Reference Guide to Federal Motor Safety Standards* is a set of standards and regulations to which manufacturers of motor vehicles must conform (FMVSS 2011). The adherence to and surmounting of such standards may improve the crashworthiness of a vehicle. The FMCSA's *Regulatory Guidance for Federal Motor Carrier Safety Regulations* sets out regulations for large trucks and buses. Note that when evaluating vehicle crashworthiness ratings, comparison should be made between vehicles of the same class.

Low-Speed Collisions

Low-speed collisions account for a substantial portion of all reported traffic accidents. Occupant protection and minimal vehicle damage are concerns when

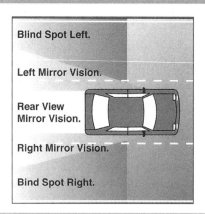

FIGURE 5. Blind spots
(*Source:* Colorado Department of Revenue)

evaluating a vehicle's low-speed crashworthiness. Vehicle bumpers can protect the vehicle from excessive damage during low-speed collisions. Quality safety belts and proper head restraints can minimize the likelihood of occupant injury during such accidents.

- *Bumpers:* Bumper systems are designed to protect the vehicle's body and structure in order to minimize expensive repair costs. Bumper systems can reduce induced damage to vehicle components such as fenders and quarter panels, which can occur by the transfer of mechanical forces. Preferably, these bumper systems and cosmetic covers should wrap around the corners of the vehicle and extend to the wheel wells, creating a larger area of protection. The FMVSS standard for passenger vehicles requires a minimum bumper strength of 2.5 miles per hour (mph), meaning at any speed below 2.5 mph, the bumper should resist permanent damage apart from minor scuffs and scraps. However, sport utility vehicles (SUVs), vans, and trucks are not required to comply with this standard. Vehicles that exceed this standard are preferred. Bumper systems that incorporate energy-absorbing material or piston isolators are preferred to simple bumpers made of stamped metal.
- *Whiplash:* Rearend-type accidents can result in biomechanical movement that leads to bodily injury. When a vehicle is hit from the

rear, the vehicle will accelerate forward. If the head of the occupant is not adequately supported by the vehicle head restraint, it will lag behind the forward motion of the torso. This unsynchronized movement (see Figure 6) will cause neck extension and may produce whiplash-type injuries. Thus proper design and positioning of the head restraint is important in reducing whiplash-type injuries.

High-Speed Collisions

In case of high-speed vehicle accidents, vehicles should be designed to aid in the protection of the occupant(s). Components such as crumple zones, occupant compartments, rollover ratings, and restraint systems are all important in protecting the occupant in the event of a high-speed collision.

- *Crumple Zones and Occupant Compartments:* Crumple zones are areas that crumple or crush upon vehicle impact in order to reduce the deceleration experienced by the occupant(s).

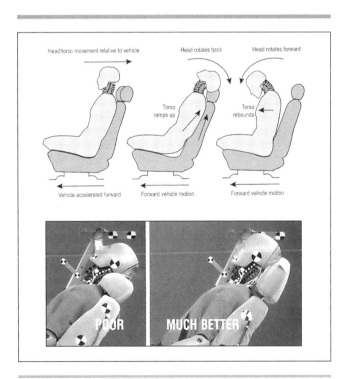

FIGURE 6. Occupant response when hit from behind with different head restraint designs (*Source:* IIHS)

By testing and design, these zones can absorb a significant amount of energy during collisions. An occupant compartment or protection cage is important in absorbing damage during a crash while keeping the occupant safe. Offset frontal crash tests performed by the Insurance Institute for Highway Safety (IIHS) are helpful in assessing the performance of vehicle structure and can be viewed at the institute's Web site.

- *Rollovers and Side Impacts:* Different vehicles have varying susceptibility to rolling, which is often termed vehicle rollover. A vehicle with a low center of gravity is preferred to reduce the chance of a rollover. The NHTSA provides rollover ratings for test vehicles based on a five-star rating system. These ratings and other information about rollovers can be viewed at the NHTSA Web site. Good rollover ratings are important for helping prevent the chance of rollover occurrence. The best form of occupant protection in the event of a rollover is proper seatbelt usage. A large percentage of occupant deaths due to rollover collisions resulted from occupants being ejected from the vehicle. Newer technology available in some vehicles includes rollover airbags or side curtain airbags, which stay inflated longer in an attempt to keep the occupant in the vehicle during a rollover.

Economic Considerations

Economic considerations almost always play a role in vehicle selection. Besides examining initial vehicle costs and overhead, attention should be paid to the long-term benefits and shortcomings of the prospective vehicle. Some considerations are outlined in the following paragraphs.

Fuel Efficiency: Estimated miles per gallon for city and highway driving should be considered with regard to the types of conditions under which the vehicle will be operating. A cost-benefit analysis should be performed to evaluate the economic impact of purchasing a more fuel-efficient vehicle. Information regarding estimated miles per gallon, fuel-saving tips, and alternatively fueled vehicles can be found at the Department of Energy Fuel Economy Web site. Also, the American Trucking Association offers a guide to fuel-saving practices for fleet managers.

Historically Low Maintenance: A good vehicle should have a reliable and low-maintenance engine, transmission, electrical system, and so on, often based on previous models or manufacturer projections. The vehicle's part-replacement costs, service fees, reliability, and expected life should also be considered.

Engine Type: The type of engine that is chosen (diesel, gasoline, or hybrid electric) will affect the overhead, maintenance, and fueling costs. Diesel engines generally have a longer life expectancy, are better suited for pulling heavy loads, and are generally more fuel-efficient in comparison with an equivalent gasoline engine. Gas engines, on the other hand, are quieter and cheaper to purchase and have a fuel supply that is more readily available. Hybrid electric vehicles may have a higher initial cost, but lower fuel consumption per mile may be preferred in stop-and-go driving environments.

Depreciation and Salvage Value: Current vehicle depreciation and salvage value projections must be considered in order to recapture capital upon fleet retirement.

Upgrades Based on Change in Usage: Vehicle upgrades should be made specific to terrain, load, mileage, and similar factors. For example, if the fleet is used in an area that is consistently snowy, then snow tires for the fleet should be considered. If the maximum vehicle load or towing capacity is insufficient, then larger, more capable vehicles should be added to the fleet, or more vehicles should break up the transportation of heavy loads. If the fleet is consistently required to travel long distances, then more fuel-efficient vehicles should be considered.

Other Considerations

Environmentally Friendly Vehicles: A vehicle should produce emissions that are below minimum Environmental Protection Agency (EPA) limits and state emission requirements while minimizing noise pollution. Emission ratings for passenger vehicles manufactured from 2000 to 2011 can be found in the EPA's *Green Vehicle Guide* (EPA 2011).

It should be noted that, for every class of vehicles, there are differences with respect to safety features, failure properties, and crashworthiness. One can reference the IIHS Web site to verify which of these safety features are included in the prospective vehicle. Consumers may also refer to other safety sources mentioned previously, along with the *Automotive Safety Handbook* (Seiffert and Wech 2003) and *Consumer Reports*, for vehicle safety, cost, and reliability information. An in-person evaluation of the vehicle being considered is recommended as well. A sample evaluation checklist is outlined here.

IN-PERSON VEHICLE EVALUATION CHECKLIST

1. Ask the manufacturer or retailer about the existence and status of the following:
   a. Airbags
   b. Antilock brake system (ABS)
   c. Tire-pressure monitoring system
   d. Stability control and/or traction control
   e. Automatic or manual seatbelt system
2. Enter the vehicle and use the seatbelt. Take note of its condition, whether it is adjustable, and whether it is comfortable.
3. See if the driver and passenger seats are adjustable in height and/or lateral distance to accommodate for different drivers. See if the steering wheel is adjustable.
4. Test-drive the vehicle.
5. Check for available warranties.
6. If the vehicle is used, hire a mechanic to perform a safety inspection.
7. If the vehicle is used, perform a vehicle history report to determine accident involvement, previous owners, and so on. (www.carfax.com).

FLEET MAINTENANCE

Fleet maintenance is important for safety, efficiency, and the cost-effective operation of a fleet. All vehicles must be properly maintained at all times. The vehicle should undergo two types of inspections: daily inspections and biannual inspections. Fleet maintenance requirements vary depending on the vehicle type. The FMCSA requires a minimum annual inspection on all operated carrier vehicles. For normal passenger vehicles, check with state regulations for applicable requirements. It is recommended for passenger and carrier vehicles alike that in-depth inspections be performed more than once a year to serve as a safety check for preventive maintenance and to determine whether a vehicle should be deemed out-of-service. An out-of-service "red flag" indicates when a fleet vehicle is in need of maintenance and is unsafe to operate.

Record Keeping

Each vehicle should have an individual record of its history that is accessible and can be easily referenced if necessary. It is important to keep records for all maintenance performed on the vehicle and previously existing problems so that diagnostics and repair are more easily addressed. For carrier vehicles, record keeping must follow part 396.3 of the FMCSA regulations. For passenger vehicles, similar applicable procedures should be followed.

Daily Inspection

Daily inspections are important. They serve as preventive measures to ensure safe daily operation of the vehicle. These inspections should become a habitual part of fleet operation. The following list outlines safety criteria that should be performed before and after operating a vehicle.

PRE-OPERATION INSPECTION LIST

1. Review the last driver inspection report; sign it if any defects were noted to indicate that the current driver has reviewed the report and verified that defects were repaired.
2. Exterior:
   a. Check for body or glass damage. If any exists, check with maintenance before

use to determine if the damage is old or new.
   b. Check the operation of all turn signals, brake lights, headlights, and taillights. Do not use the fleet vehicle until all defective lights and signals have been repaired.
   c. Examine tire condition, wear, and tire pressure. Add air if needed. If tire wear is beyond manufacturer specifications, deem the vehicle out-of-service and in need of replacement tires.
3. Safety Equipment: Make sure the vehicle's spare tire and emergency equipment are accessible and in working condition.
4. Under the Hood (after each refueling): Check fluid levels and refill as necessary. Make note of any fluid added.
5. Interior: Check for proper operation of seatbelts, starting system, fuel level, instruments, mirrors, and so on. If any problems exist, check with maintenance before use.
6. During Operation:
   a. Look for properly operating instruments.
   b. Smell for any strange or unusual odors.
   c. Listen for any unusual or abnormal sounds.
   d. Feel for any unusual vibrations or abnormal handling of the vehicle.
   e. Monitor fuel consumption and make note of any excessive or unusual fuel usage.

POST-OPERATION INSPECTION LIST

(Required for all carrier vehicles; recommended for passenger vehicles)

Check the following components:

1. Service brakes, including trailer brake connections
2. Parking (hand) brake
3. Steering mechanism
4. Lighting devices and reflectors
5. Tires
6. Horn

7. Windshield wipers
8. Rearview mirrors
9. Coupling devices
10. Wheels and rims
11. Emergency equipment

Other inspections unique to specific fleet vehicles should also be performed. If the vehicle is excessively dirty, the vehicle should be washed to ensure proper operation of instruments, full visibility of lights and signals, and ease in recognizing new damage to the vehicle. When any unusual or abnormal conditions exist, report such cases to fleet maintenance as soon as possible so that the issue can be further inspected before the vehicle is allowed back in service.

Unscheduled or Unanticipated Maintenance

Sometimes required maintenance cannot always be predicted. In the event of a roadside breakdown or tire failure, follow the procedure outlined in the driver's manual for bringing your vehicle to a stop. Make sure to turn on the emergency hazards and place triangle reflectors and flares (if visibility is poor) behind the vehicle. Call fleet management to alert them to the problem. If the fleet employee is capable, and it is safe to do so, he or she may change the vehicle's wheel. Depending on the spare tire available, it may be necessary to service the vehicle as soon as possible, in which case the vehicle should be driven to the appropriate maintenance location. If the vehicle or tire is unserviceable, tie something white to the vehicle antenna and raise the hood to let emergency personnel know you need assistance. Then stand away from the vehicle and roadway and call for assistance.

In-Depth Inspections and Maintenance

More in-depth, thorough inspections of components and systems should be performed two to three times per year by a qualified mechanic. For carrier vehicles, appendix G of part 396.6, FMCSA regulations, lists the necessary maintenance procedures. For passenger vehicles, applicable procedures based on these regulations should be followed. Thorough inspections and maintenance should be scheduled so that downtime is minimized and fleet productivity is maximized.

These inspections should assess overall vehicle condition and review feedback from driver reports and any potential problems. Maintenance should meet or exceed manufacturer recommendations. The minimum requirements for annual inspections on carrier vehicles set forth by the FMCSA are outlined in the following list. Fleet managers should perform an in-depth review of criteria for an out-of-service vehicle. The FMCSA or other professional organizations, such as the Commercial Vehicle Safety Alliance, with its *Out of Service Criteria*, provide these criteria. Certain organizations and companies, such as the state associations of the American Trucking Association, or private industry groups, such as J. J. Keller and Associates (*2011 Transport Catalog*), offer preprinted inspection forms that can assist the mechanic with inspection procedures and record keeping.

MINIMUM PERIODIC INSPECTION STANDARDS

(Required for all carrier vehicles; recommended for passenger vehicles)

Check the following:

1. Brake systems
2. Coupling devices
3. Exhaust system
4. Fuel system
5. Lighting devices
6. Safe loading
7. Steering mechanism
8. Suspension
9. Frame
10. Tires
11. Wheels and rims
12. Windshield glazing
13. Windshield wipers

If repairs are required, all manufacturer warranties that apply should be considered. It is recommended that all repairs be made using OEM or OEM-equivalent parts. After repairs have been performed, vehicles should be road-tested to check that all parts and systems operate as expected and that no other problems exist.

If a vehicle is in need of major repairs, then a cost-benefit analysis should be performed to determine whether repair or replacement is more appropriate.

Industry and Manufacturer Recalls: Check for safety- and performance-related recalls of the specific fleet vehicle on a regular basis. Information regarding recalls can be found at the NHTSA's Office of Defects Investigation Web site (www-odi.nhtsa.dot.gov). If necessary, contact the manufacturer for details so that required repairs can be performed.

ACCIDENT INVESTIGATION

When a fleet vehicle is involved in an accident, a thorough investigation should be conducted. Accident investigation is important to understand the cause(s) of the accident and to see if any preventive steps can be implemented to reduce the likelihood of reoccurrence. In the event of litigation, scene evidence collected by fleet employees can assist in assessing fault.

To aid in proper accident investigation, each vehicle should be equipped with all documentation required by law: driver's license, vehicle registration, and proof of insurance. In addition, a disposable camera, tape measure, investigation checklist (see the following list), notepad, and pen can assist in evidence collection.

Vehicles should also carry relevant contact information and emergency daytime and nighttime phone numbers for appropriate company personnel. Persons in charge of receiving accident-related calls should have easy access to all driver emergency-contact and medical history information.

Should an accident occur, depending on severity, the following procedure should be considered.

ACCIDENT PROCEDURE

1. Activate emergency four-way flashers (hazard lights), evaluate safety of vehicle's position, and move vehicle to safe location if it is safe and legal to do so.
2. Stop vehicle immediately, turn the ignition off, and set the parking brake.
3. Exit the vehicle if it is safe to do so.
4. Take reasonable precautions to prevent further accidents through proper use of emergency flares, triangle reflectors, and so on.
5. Contact authorities and emergency personnel (follow state regulations regarding accident procedures and reporting, often outlined in the state driver's manual).
6. Report accident to fleet vehicle management.
7. Collect evidence (see next section).

Evidence Collection

Initial evidence should be collected by the driver if it is safe to do so. The following information should be obtained/collected by the driver if it is safe to do so. The following information should be obtained.

EVIDENCE COLLECTION PROCEDURE

(Perform only if not injured and it is safe to do so.)

1. Write down driver name, vehicle make and model, insurance information, and license plate numbers for all vehicles involved.
2. Take notes and witness statements, with witnesses' names and contact information included.
3. Examine the vehicle where the contact or collision point occurred. Mark the damage, if any, on a diagram similar to the example in Figure 7 for all vehicles involved.

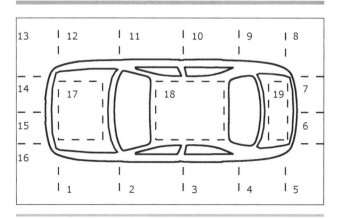

FIGURE 7. Example vehicle-damage diagram

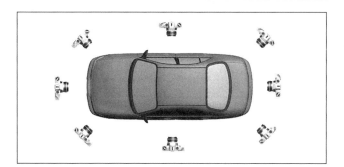

FIGURE 8. Photograph the vehicle from multiple angles.

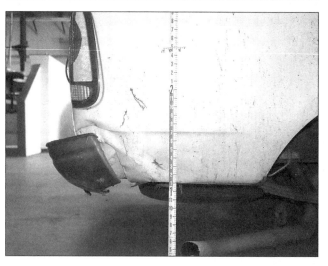

FIGURE 9. Example photo of vehicle damage

4. Examine other parts of the vehicle to determine whether other damage is related to the accident or previously existed and document any new damage.

5. Write down any damage descriptively (e.g., shattered light, 2-inch circular dent, 5-inch scrapes/scuffs).

6. Take pictures of the vehicle(s) from a distance and from multiple angles (see Figure 8), including the total roadway and intersection in the field of view.

7. Take pictures of the damaged section from multiple angles with an extended tape measure in the photos (see Figure 9).

8. Take pictures of the skid marks, starting from the beginning of the skid marks until the final vehicle location.

9. Photograph the accident scene (e.g., tire marks, gouges, obstructions, vehicle ending positions, roadway) (See examples in Figures 10–12).

10. Make note of weather and road conditions.

11. Describe the accident and events preceding and following the accident.

12. Get a copy of the police report of the accident from the local precinct for fleet records.

All of the evidence collected at the scene should be maintained by the fleet and submitted to the insurance company. The fleet vehicle involved should be checked for government or factory recalls. The driver should also document any vehicle defects or conditions that may have contributed to the accident as well as defects occurring after the accident.

FIGURE 10. Proper photographic technique
- Vehicle ending point is visible
- Total skid mark is visible
- No people in the picture

FIGURE 11. Improper photographic technique: Vehicle ending point is not visible

FIGURE 12. Improper photographic technique: Total skid mark is not visible

For serious accidents, a trained staff of independent or in-house accident investigators should be sent to the accident site as soon as possible. This is to make sure that all available scene evidence is collected and preserved. These trained investigators will be able to obtain relevant data from the roadway, vehicles, and witnesses.

Proper collection of accident-related information and, when appropriate, additional investigation and analysis will provide the best means of managing the economic impact of a motor-vehicle accident involving a fleet vehicle.

Event Data Recorders (EDRs)

Many vehicles are equipped with Event data recorders (EDRs) that may provide data relevant to an accident (www.NHTSA.gov/EDRs). Fleet vehicle management should note which vehicles are equipped with EDRs and take the appropriate steps to have a qualified technician download and evaluate any available data in the event of an accident. United States Code of Federal Regulations, Title 49, Part 563, specifies:

> . . . uniform, national requirements for vehicles equipped with event data recorders (EDRs) concerning the collection, storage, and retrievability of onboard motor vehicle crash event data. It also specifies requirements for vehicle manufacturers to make tools and/or methods commercially available so that crash investigators and researchers are able to retrieve data from EDRs.

REFERENCES

American Trucking Association. *Marketplace*. www.truck line.com

Autoliv Inc. *Illustrations* (retrieved August 2001). www.autoliv.com

Carfax Vehicle History Reports. www.carfax.com

Colorado Department of Revenue. *Colorado Driver Handbook*, Part 3 (retirieved August 2011). www.colorado. gov/cs/Satellite/Revenue-MV/RMV/1212657832969

Commercial Vehicle Safety Alliance. *Out of Service Criteria* (retrieved August 2011). www.cvsa.org

Consumer Reports. www.consumerreports.org

Federal Highway Administration (FHWA). *FHWA Vehicle Types* (retrieved August 2011). www.fhwa.dot.gov/ policy/ohpi/vehclass.html

Federal Motor Carrier Safety Administration (FMCSA). *Commercial Driver's License Program (CDL/CDLIS)* (retrieved August 2011). www.fmcsa.dot.gov/ registration-licensing/cdl/cdl.html

———. *Part 396: Inspection, Repair, and Maintenance*. www.fmcsa.dot.gov/rulesregulations/administration /fmcsr/fmcsrguidedetails.asp?menukey=396

———. *Regulatory Guidance for Federal Motor Carrier Safety Regulations* (retrieved August 2011). www.fmcsa.dot. gov/rules-regulations/administration/fmcsr/fmcsr guide.html

Insurance Institute for Highway Safety (IIHS). *A Procedure for Evaluating Motor Vehicle Head Restraints* (Volume 2), Research Council for Automobile Repairs. www.rcar. org/papers.htm

———. April 1997. *Status Report* 32(4):2.

———. October 2002. *Status Report* 37(9):2.

J. J. Keller & Associates, Inc. 2011. *2011 Transport Catalog*. www.issuu.com/jjkeller/docs_2011_transport

National Highway Traffic Safety Administration (NHTSA). Office of Defects Investigation. www-odi.nhtsa.dot.gov/cars/problems/recalls

_____. *Buying a Safer Car 2007*. www.safercar.gov/BASC2007

_____. *Airbags*. www.safercar.gov/airbags/index.html

_____. *Buying a Safer Car* (retrieved August 2011). www.safecar.gov

_____. *Event Data Recorders (EDRs)* (retrieved November 8, 2011). www.nhtsa.gov/EDRs

_____. *Rollovers*. www.safercar.gov/Rollover/Index.html

Seiffert, U., and L. Wech. 2003. *Automotive Safety Handbook*. London: Professional Engineering Publishing.

United States Department of Energy Efficiency and Renewable Energy and United States Environmental Protection Agency. *Quick Reference Guide to Federal Motor Vehicle Safety Standards* (retrieved September 23, 2005). www.fueleconomy.gov

United States Department of Transportation. *Quick Reference Guide to Federal Motor Vehicle Safety Standards* (retrieved March 2004). www.nhtsa.gov/cars/rules/standards/FMVSS-Regs/index.html

United States Environmental Protection Agency. 2011. *Green Vehicle Guide*. www.epa.gov/greenvehicles

SECTION 6
FLEET SAFETY

LEARNING OBJECTIVES

- Be able to describe the dynamics of the fleet vehicle.

- Mathematically determine the safe operations of fleet vehicles.

- Identify safe human factors for fleet operations in different environments.

- Learn defensive driving maneuvers and methods.

- Recognize the safety implications presented by a workspace environment.

- Identify safety criteria for fleet operators and drivers.

- Understand occupant protection and the biomechanics that can cause injuries.

- Learn about safe operations during the material-handling process in fleet operations.

APPLIED SCIENCE AND ENGINEERING: VEHICLE ENGINEERING AND ERGONOMICS

Dennis R. Andrews

THIS CHAPTER CONTAINS information relating to the commercial (trucks and buses) motor-vehicle fleet industry and loading and unloading facilities. The information included, while not all-inclusive, was obtained from the industry literature, articles, and the author's experience. The chapter has four major sections: Vehicle Engineering and Tests, Traffic Safety Principles, Vehicle Defensive Driving Tactics, and Ergonomic Issues.

The objective of this chapter is to supply information about and data for the fleet industry as researched by the author. Readers will gain useful new and supplementary knowledge of the fleet industry. The reference section and recommended reading section contain books and articles of interest to motor fleet operators and safety personnel concerning both fleet vehicles and fleet facilities.

The chapter includes information and data on roadway incidents (vehicle accidents), safety, and information for safety programs that will be of interest to fleet owners, fleet safety managers, fleet operations managers, fleet insurance managers, depot operations managers, and anyone else with an interest in motor-vehicle fleet operations and safety.

VEHICLE ENGINEERING AND TESTS
Vehicle Offtracking and Swept-Path Width

Special skills are required to operate commercial and fleet vehicles safely. Large vehicles such as multiaxle trucks and buses operate much differently from passenger vehicles, and their drivers must have special training and maintain concentration while driving to avoid accidents and injury. For example, drivers must learn how to turn and back up articulated vehicles because they require additional space for these maneuvers. Drivers must also be aware of *offtracking*, a term used to describe the difference between the radius of the path of the center of the steering axle and the center of the rear axle for box-type trucks. For articulated vehicles such as tractors and trailers, the spacing along the longitudinal axles of the hitch point must be considered during low-speed turns because the rear wheels do not follow the same path as the front wheels.

The *swept-path width* is the difference between the lateral distance of the inside rear wheels and outside front wheels during a turning maneuver for both box-type and articulated vehicles. The radius of the turn determines the offtracking and swept-path width. The offtracking amount is always less than the swept-path width since offtracking is a measurement from the center of the front and rear axles and the swept-path width is a measurement of the distance between the outside front wheel and the inside rear wheel during a turning maneuver. Buses and similar large vehicles have comparable maneuvering movements but smaller space requirements than do articulated vehicles such as tractors and trailers. Formulas are used to calculate the swept-path width and offtracking of large articulated vehicles and box-type trucks or buses. These formulas supply the necessary data for roadway design. They are particularly important for designing off-ramps for interstate highways and turnpikes as well as for training vehicle operators on proper turning maneuvers (see Figures 1 and 2 for more details).

The formula for low-speed offtracking of a standard two-axle, box-type truck with dual rear wheels is

$$OT \text{ (in feet)} = r_1 - r_2 \tag{1}$$

where

r_1 = the turning radius of the front axle
r_2 = the turning radius of the rear axle

To determine the rear-axle turning radius use the following formula:

$$r_2 = \sqrt{(r_1^2 - l^2)} \tag{2}$$

where

l = the wheelbase of the vehicle (the distance between the front and rear axles).

Consider a box-truck vehicle with a front-axle turning radius of 50 feet and a wheelbase of 10 feet (l), the radius of the rear axle is 49 feet (r_2). The calculated offtrack distance is equal to 1 foot (50 − 49). If the wheels of the rear axle are wider than those of the front axle, an adjustment must be made by dividing the difference in the width of the axles by two and adding that number to the result above. For example, if the outside width of the rear wheels is 8 feet and the outside width of the front wheels is 6 feet, the adjustment is 1 (8 − 6 = 2 ÷ 2 = 1). Adding this result to the 1 foot of calculated offtracking distance noted above, the offtracking amount is 2 feet. (Fricke 1990, 78-15–78-16). Since offtracking represents the difference in radius between the centers of both axles, the swept-path width is calculated by adding one-half of the width of each axle to the offtracking result.

A more complicated approach is necessary when dealing with the offtracking of large articulated tractor-trailers and similar vehicles. The formula for a tractor-trailer with ten wheels (3 axles) is

$$OT = r_1 - r_3 = r_1 - \sqrt{(r_1^2 + l_{ko}^2 - l^2 - l_2^2)} \tag{3}$$

where

r_1 = the radius of the center of the front or steering axle
r_3 = the radius of the center of the rear axle
l_{ko} = the distance of the fifth wheel (also known as the kingpin, the point at which the trailer and tractor are connected) on the tractor to the center of the drive wheels of the tractor,
l = the wheelbase of the tractor
l_2 = the wheelbase from the tractor drive wheels to the rear trailer wheels

If the front-axle turning radius is 41 feet, the tractor wheelbase is 12 feet, the trailer wheelbase is 36 feet, and the fifth-wheel offset is 1.2 feet, the offtrack distance would be approximately 25.4 feet (Fricke 1990, 78-18–78-19). As with the box-truck example, the swept path can be calculated by adding one-half the width of both the front and rear axles to the offtrack distance. If the vehicle comprises a tractor and two trailers, also known as *doubles*, additional data are needed: the rearward overhang of the *pintel hitch* (the hitch between

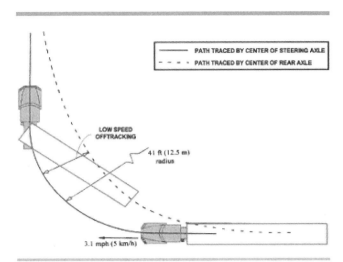

FIGURE 1. Low-Speed Offtracking
(*Source:* FHA 2007)

the first and second trailer) location, the length of the *dolly drawbar* (the attachment bar between the first and second trailer), and the wheelbase of the full trailer.

Low-speed offtracking occurs when a combination vehicle makes a low-speed turn—for example a 90-degree turn at an intersection—and the wheels of the rearmost trailer axle follow a path several feet inside the path of the tractor steering axle. Figure 1 illustrates low-speed offtracking in a 90-degree turn for a tractor-semitrailer. Excessive low-speed offtracking makes it necessary for the driver to swing wide into adjacent lanes when making a turn to avoid climbing inside curbs, striking curbside fixed objects or other vehicles. On an exit ramp, excessive offtracking can result in the truck tracking inward onto the shoulder or up over inside curbs. For single trailer combinations, this performance attribute is affected primarily by the distance of the tractor kingpin to the center of the trailer rear axle or axle group. *Kingpin setting* refers to the truck-tractor fifth wheel connection point for the kingpin, which is located to the front of the semitrailer. For multitrailer combinations the effective wheelbase(s) of all the trailers in the combination, along with the tracking characteristics of the converter dollies, dictate low-speed offtracking. In general, longer wheelbases worsen low-speed offtracking.

High-speed offtracking results from the tendency of the rear of the truck to move outward due to the lateral acceleration of the vehicle as it makes a turn at higher

speeds. Figure 2 illustrates high-speed offtracking for a standard tractor-semitrailer. The speed-dependent component of offtracking is primarily a function of the spacing between truck axles, the speed of the truck, and the radius of the turn; it is also dependent on the loads carried by the truck axles and the truck suspension characteristics (Fricke 1990).

An Analytical Approach

The Western Uniformity Scenario Analysis (DOT 2004) examines the impact that scenario truck configurations would have on freeway interchanges, at-grade intersections, mainline curves, and lane widths of the current roadway system. It determines what improvements would be needed to accommodate the new trucks, and estimates the costs of these improvements. The focus of this research is to compare the new truck configurations with the current tractor-semitrailers and LCVs operating in the scenario states.

Unlike the analysis for the *Comprehensive Truck Size and Weight (CTS&D) Study*, the base case-vehicle in this analysis varies by state, depending on that state's grandfather laws under the 1991 ISTEA freeze (DOT 2000). The chosen base case-vehicle represents the worst vehicle from an offtracking perspective currently allowed on the analyzed roadway segment. For example, if the

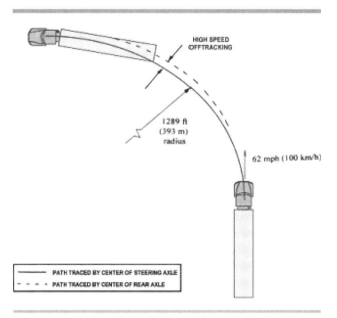

FIGURE 2. High-Speed Offtracking
(*Source:* FHA 2007)

TABLE 1

Base Case-Vehicles for the Scenario States

State	Rocky Mountain Double	Turnpike Double
Colorado	43.5 + 31	48 + 48
Idaho	35 + 20	35 + 20
Kansas	48 + 28.5	45 + 45
Montana	38 + 28	45 + 45
Nebraska	38 + 20	38 + 20
Nevada	48 + 28.5	48 + 48
North Dakota	48 + 28.5	48 + 48
Oklahoma	48 + 28.5	48 + 48
Oregon	35 + 20	N/A
South Dakota	48 + 28.5	48 + 48
Utah	48 + 28.5	48 + 48
Washington	35 + 20	N/A
Wyoming	38 + 27	N/A

(DOT 2000)

TABLE 2

Low-Speed Offtracking and Swept Path of Vehicles

Vehicle Description*	Configuration**	Performance Data (ft)	
		Low-Speed Offtracking	Swept Path
Single (53")	3-S2	16.12	24.12
STAA Double (2@28')	2-S1-2	13.52	21.52
RMD (38', 27')	3-S2-3	18.57	26.57
RMD (38', 27')	3-S2-4	22.08	30.08
RMD (38', 27')	3-S2-2	21.54	29.54
RMD (35', 20')	3-S2-2	15.78	23.78
RMD (38', 28')	3-S2-4	20.06	28.06
RMD (38', 20')	3-S3-2	18.42	26.42
RMD (38', 27')	3-S2-4	21.02	29.02
RMD (43.5', 31')	3-S2-4	20.78	28.78
RMD (38', 27')	3-S3-4	19.13	27.13
RMD (48', 28.5')	3-S2-3	21.87	29.87
Short TPD (2@45')	3-S2-4	27.98	35.98
Long TPD (2@48')	3-S2-4	30.63	38.63
Triple A-Train (3@28")	2-S1-2-2	20.38	28.38
Triple C-Train (3@28")	2-S1-2-2	20.38	28.38

*Vehicle description shows the vehicle type where RMD is a Rocky Mountain Double and TPD is a Turnpike Double. The numbers in parenthesis give the length of each trailer.

**The first number in the series indicates the number of axles on the power unit, the next set refers to the number of axles supporting the trailing unit ("s" iindicates it is a semitrailer), and the subsequent numbers indicate the number of axles associated with the remaining trailing unit.

(DOT 2000)

worst offtracking vehicle currently allowed on the roadway is a Turnpike Double (TPD), then the TPD is used as the base case-vehicle for that road segment; if the Rocky Mountain Double (RMD) is the worst off-tracking vehicle, then it is used as the base case-vehicle; and if the 53-foot tractor semitrailer has the worst offtracking, it is the base case-vehicle. Table 1 shows the base case RMD and TPD for each state. This precise framing of the base case-vehicle is an improvement to the *CTS&W Study*'s analysis that used the 48-foot trac-tor semitrailer at 80,000 pounds as the base case-vehicle for all roads (FMCSA 2000).

Table 2 shows the low-speed offtracking and swept path for the analyzed configurations. The measure is shown for a standard 90-degree, right-hand turn with a 42-foot radius, negotiated at a speed of 5 kilometers per hour. (Note that the *CTS&W Study* analyzed a 38-foot path radius.) Low-speed offtracking is the one measure where the STAA Double outperforms all the other configurations. The long TPD with twin 48-foot trailers performs the worst of the vehicles.

Vehicle Power Requirements

Large vehicles, whether articulated or not, need suf-ficient power to operate safely on highways and streets so they can maintain a safe highway speed and pass safely. *Power* is the time rate of doing work, and the *maximum power* an engine can provide is a measure of its performance capability. The power generated by large vehicles can be determined from the formula (ITE 1990, 60–63):

$$P = RV \div 3600 \qquad (4)$$

where

P = the power used in kilowatts (1 kW = 1.341 horsepower; 1 hp = 550 foot-pounds per second)

R = the total resistance to motion of the truck and trailer

V = the speed of the vehicle in ft/s

3600 = a constant representing the seconds in 1 hr

Newton's laws of physics relating to force, mass, and acceleration scientifically demonstrate the need for additional power to haul heavy loads safely. *Force* is the product of mass and acceleration, and it is necessary to overcome inertia, air resistance, tire and roadway resistance, potential energy loss due to the grade or incline of a roadway, and any other conditions that require acceleration power. More force is needed to pull an 80,000-pound trailer than to pull a 20,000-pound trailer, especially along very steep, hilly streets in cities such as San Francisco, Seattle, and Pittsburgh. The average passenger vehicle requires less force to accelerate than a heavier vehicle on the same roadway.

The mass-to-power ratio is helpful in determining and comparing levels of performance. The ratio can be in watts and kilograms or horsepower and foot-pounds. This ratio is important in determining minimum requirements of a selected power plant for a vehicle with known load-carrying capabilities. When calculating this type of power ratio, consideration should be given to the power source—diesel or gasoline. Diesel engines produce more thrust than gasoline engines since diesel fuel is ignited by compression. For both maintenance and durability, the overwhelming choice for a commercial vehicle power source is a diesel engine rather than a gasoline engine. Diesel engines are much more expensive than gasoline engines due to their heavier construction. Power-requirement considerations should include vehicle operating ranges, locations, and conditions. Driving in a more mountainous terrain requires more horsepower than driving in a typical inner city unless the city has very steep and hilly streets.

The mass-to-power ratio is the measure of a vehicle's ability to accelerate and maintain speed up grades. Mass can be thought of as an indicator of resistance to motion—the higher the mass-to-power ratio, the less the acceleration performance, and the lower the mass-to-power ratio, the greater the acceleration performance. A typical passenger vehicle's mass-to-power ratio is 1550 kg (3425 lbs) to 140 kW (188 hp) of power. A tractor semitrailer's is approximately 11,000 kg (24,310 lbs) to 240 kW (322 hp) of power (ITE 1990, 57–60). A typical passenger car has approximately 50 percent of the manufacturer's rated engine power available to travel 100 kilometers per hour (approximately 61 miles per hour); a large truck has approximately 94 percent of the manufacturer's rated engine power available. These estimates are useful in deter-

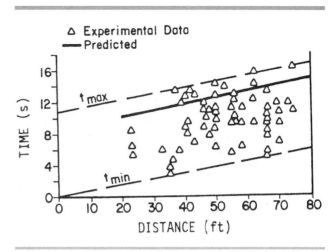

FIGURE 3. Field observations of times for 19.8-m (65-ft) tractor-trailer trucks to clear intersection distances after starting from a stop (*Source:* Transportation Research Board (TRB) 1997)

mining maximum acceleration rates and maximum speeds on grades for engine power in relation to engine speed and values of acceleration (ITE 1990, 50–54).

Acceleration is determined by the change in velocity over a period of time and is expressed as feet per second per second, or fps². Since large vehicles have more mass than average passenger cars, large vehicles accelerate more slowly than passenger cars. As a general rule, the range of acceleration for large, loaded trucks is from 0.3 to 1.6 fps² (see Figure 3).

Transit Buses

Primary human-factors considerations for public transit buses include the following (Woodson 1992, 85):

1. *Driver:* Clear visibility in all directions (360 degrees), ability to visually monitor passengers, lack of interior reflection at night, and a comfortable seat for lengthy occupancy. Figure 4 is a recommended layout for a transit bus-driver station. (Woodson 1992, 296).

2. *Onboard passengers:* Level floor with wide aisles, handrails that are easy to grasp, comfortable seating with sufficient room for knees and elbows, good visibility for seeing stops, air conditioning, minimum noise, and a reasonably comfortable ride.

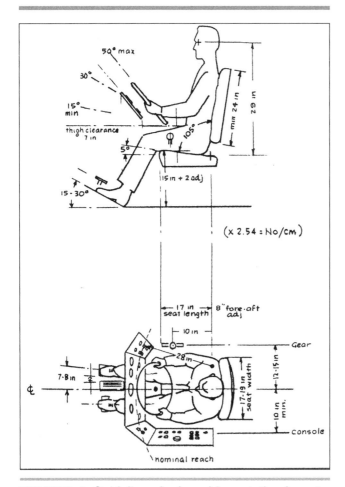

FIGURE 4. Guidelines for bus-driver-station layout (*Source:* Woodson 1992, p. 296)

3. *Boarding passengers:* Ability to identify oncoming buses from a distance and convenient entry handrails.

4. *Service personnel:* Convenient access to all maintenance components, especially those requiring frequent service.

The entry threshold for passengers must be low enough so that passengers do not have to stretch to step onto the first step from the ground or curb. It is recommended that a ramp sufficient to accommodate wheelchairs be considered for the main entrance. Aisles should be level; a grade could create a hazard for walking or standing passengers. Passenger seats are not usually fancy on intracity buses, but comfortable seats are required for buses traveling long distances. Seating on long-distance buses should be roomy so passengers don't find it necessary to stand or walk in the aisle. Arm rests should be cushioned and ergonomically designed, and reading lamps and footrests should be provided.

The primary consideration in designing intercity buses is the comfort of passengers taking long rides (Woodson 1992, 86). Intercity bus-seat dimensions can be approximately the same as those for city buses, but intercity bus seats must have headrests and reclining backs. A seat that reclines 30 degrees allows a passenger to lean back far enough to prevent his or her head from falling forward. If a seat is able to recline to 45 degrees, it should be adjusted to a horizontal position, which is more comfortable when passengers stretch their legs. The minimum clearance between the seat back in front of a passenger and the forward portion of the passenger's seat is approximately eight inches.

Transit bus companies and those who have the responsibility of locating and posting bus-stop signs must consider and document many issues:

- the safety of passengers entering and exiting the bus
- the impact on parking and adjoining landowners' traffic patterns if the stop is to be located in a business area
- the positioning of stops near intersections (whether to place the stop on the far side or near side of an intersection or midblock) (It is unsafe for a bus to stop at a stop sign, cross through the intersection, and then stop a second time at a bus stop on the opposite corner.)
- crosswalk safety (Onboard signs should direct passengers to wait until the bus departs before crossing streets, and not to cross in front of the bus. At controlled intersections, stops should be placed at a sufficient distance from crosswalks so that pedestrians are not tempted to enter the roadway from behind a stopped bus.)
- the positioning of bus stops with regard to parking areas (They should not be placed within parking areas since normal traffic may have a tendency to park near or within the bus-stop location and create a safety hazard for passengers exiting the bus) (NJ Transit Corp 1998).
- distance from other bus stops
- signage (Bus-stop signs should not be so large that they block regulatory signs or impair the view of the bus driver or other drivers. Usually local townships have regulations about

bus-stop-sign locations, and unless there are strong safety objections, signs should be placed accordingly) (Woodson 1992, 87).

All transit companies should have their own procedures and policies regarding the safety of their riders as well as methods of determining bus-stop locations with the safety of both the riding public and driving public in mind. A valuable source of information about bus-stop placement is "TCRP Report 19: Guidelines for the Location and Design of Bus Stops" (TCRP 1996). Companies must review and revise policies and procedures as circumstances change. A written policy is an excellent tool for training employees.

Braking Performance

The efficiency of braking by a vehicle is considered its *braking performance*. How well braking systems perform depends on maintenance, design, and environment. Braking performance (Ma_x) is determined by vehicle weight, linear deceleration, the braking force of the front and rear axles, aerodynamic factors, and the rate of linear elevation of the roadway. The formula for braking performance is (Gillespie 1992, 21–42):

$$Ma_x = -W/g \; D_x = -F_{xf} - F_{xr} - DA - W \sin \theta \quad (5)$$

where

W = the vehicle weight

g = the gravitational acceleration

D_x = the rate of deceleration in feet per second

F_{xf} = the front-axle braking force

F_{xr} = the rear-axle braking force

DA = the aerodynamic drag

θ = the uphill or downhill grade

The gravitational acceleration (g) is constant at 32.2 fps^2. The braking force can be determined through indices (tables) or from testing. Aerodynamic drag, which can be found in wind tunnel tables, varies among vehicles depending upon their configuration (e.g., a Corvette automobile has a lower air drag than a flat-front truck tractor). The angle of rise or fall of a hill can be determined by measurement or by estimating. Most vehicles are equipped with antilock brake systems. Constant pressure during deceleration (rather than pumping the brake pedal) will increase the per-

TABLE 3

Frontal Impact on the Test Bus

Measured Values	Bus Frontal Impact onto Rigid Wall 3,6 km/h speed 6,98 km/h speed 29,76 km/h speed		
Maximum impact force at the left longitudinal beam (k/N)	180	220	780
Maximum impact force at the right longitudinal beam (k/N)	160	190	390
Resultant impact force (k/N)	320	390	1100
Maximum acceleration on the floor above the CGV (g)	3	4	12
Maximum resultant acceleration in the Hybrid II head (g)	3	10	60
Measured maximum femur force in the Hybrid II dummy (kN)	1,1	1,3	1,6

(*Source:* FMCSA 2003)

TABLE 4

Buses Involved in Fatal Cashes by Operator Type, 1999–2005

Carrier Type	Number	Percent
School	857	3.18
Transit	731	32.5
Intercity	83	3.7
Charter/Tour	256	11.4
Other:		
Private company	20	0.9
Nonprofit Organization	62	2.8
Government	33	1.5
Personal	3	0.1
Contractor for school district	40	1.8
Other	93	4.1
Other subtotal	*251*	*11.1*
Unknown operator type	74	3.3
Total	**2252**	**100.0**

(*Source:* FMCSA 2003)

formance of antilock brakes, allowing the driver to maintain control of the vehicle.

A test bus experienced frontal impact three times with three different speeds (see Tables 3 and 4). The vehicle's dimensions were:

- length: 11,000 mm
- width: 2500 mm
- height: 2940 mm
- axle distance: 5570 mm
- front/rear overhang: 2630/2800 mm

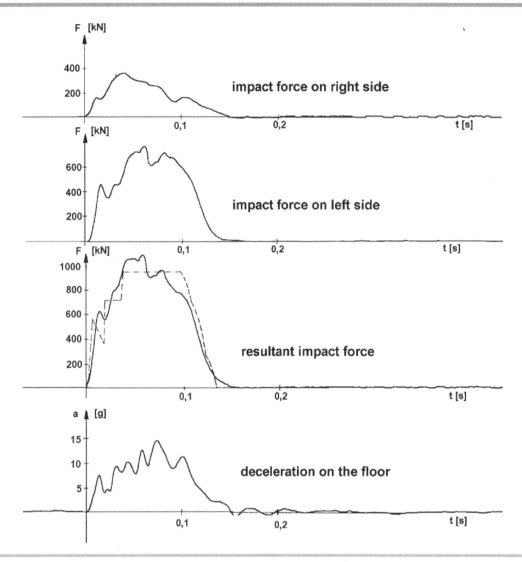

FIGURE 5. Frontal impact of 1K 411 bus; impact speed 29,76 km/h (*Source:* FMCSA 2003)

As one can see from Figure 5, in a frontal impact the right and left sides of the bus do not have the same force. Also the floor deceleration peaks at about 15 Gs.

Large tractor-trailer combinations have an engine-braking mechanism that uses the engine to retard the forward motion of the vehicle. This is commonly called a "Jake brake" after the company that invented the system—Jacob Manufacturing. The system works by retarding the speed of the vehicle through the use of the engine's exhaust system, which is able to absorb enough energy to stop a 75,000-pound gross combination vehicle without the use of the service brakes at 19 mph on a 10 percent grade (Fitch 1994, 239–254). The system can be adjusted by the vehicle operator.

The two most common types of brake systems are hydraulic and pneumatic. *Hydraulic* systems are used on typical passenger vehicles and use brake fluid to activate the brake shoes or calipers to decelerate the vehicle. Typical passenger vehicles have antilock brake systems. Hydraulic brake systems must be checked periodically to ensure that fluid has not leaked or dropped to an unacceptable level due to worn gaskets or hoses. Hydraulic systems must be cleaned (flushed) periodically and new fluid added, since it is very difficult to stop contaminants from entering the system.

Pneumatic brake systems, also known as air brakes, are usually found on large heavy vehicles, such as tractor-trailers (see Figures 6a–d). *Brake lag* is a term used to describe the time it takes for a pneumatic

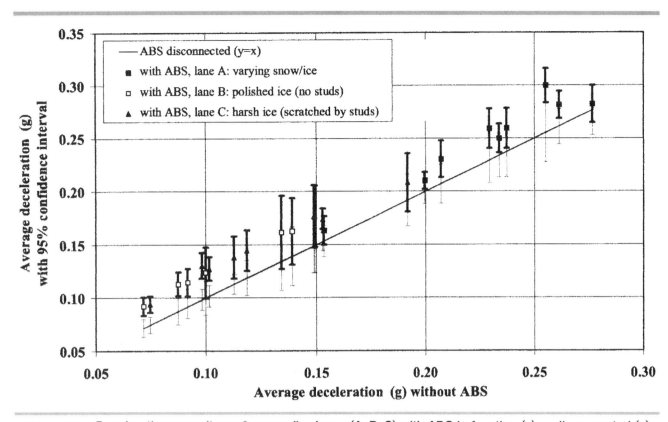

FIGURE 6a. Deceleration capacity on 3 snowy/icy lanes (A, B, C) with ABS in function (y) or disconnected (x). Each value represents one tyre type average over all drivers with 95% confidence interval. Nine tyre types on lanes A and C; 6 unstudded types on lane B (*Source:* Strandberg 1998)

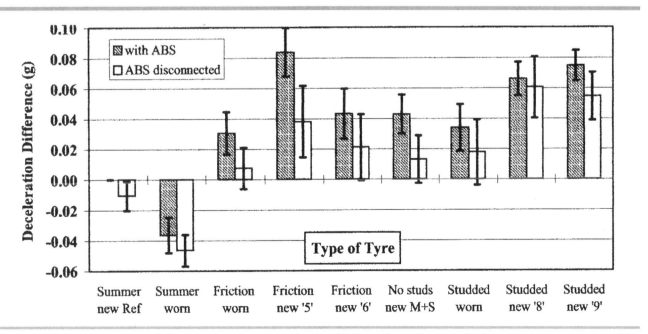

FIGURE 6b. Deceleration difference between certain tyre-ABS configurations and reference summer tyres with ABS . Paired comparisons for each driver on lane A (carrying snow and ice). Average over 24 + 24 + 18 = 66 drivers with 95% confidence interval (*Source:* Strandberg 1998)

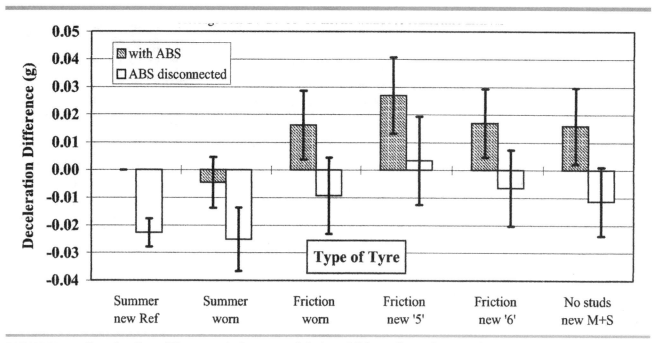

FIGURE 6c. Deceleration differences between certain tyre-ABS configurations and reference summer tyres with ABS. Paired comparisons for each driver on lane B (polished ice surface, no studs allowed). Average over 24 + 24 + 18 = 66 drivers with 95% confidence (*Source:* Strandberg 1998)

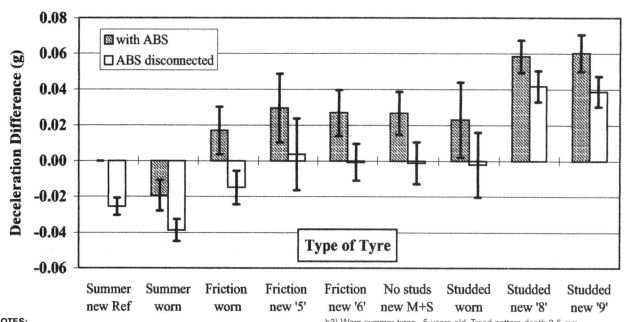

NOTES:

a1) New summer tyres–Reference type (same four-wheel individuals as b1 and c1).

a2) New "friction" tyres. Hysteresis rubber for ice and snow adhesion. Asian makes. ID no. 6.

a3) New unstuddedM+S tyres. Made for studding but without studs.

a4) New studded types. 105 studs per type. Same make and type as a3. ID no.8.

b1) New summer types–Reference type (same four-wheel individuals as a1 and c1).

b2) Worn friction tyres. 5 years old. Tread pattern depth 5 mm.

b3) Worn summer tyres. 5 years old. Tread pattern depth 3-5 mm.

b4) New studded tyres. 110 studs per tyre. Same four-wheel individuals as c4. ID no. 9.

c1) New summer tyres–Reference type (same four-wheel individuals as a1 and b1).

c2) New "friction" tyres. Hysteresis rubber for ice and snow adhesion. European. ID no. 5.

c3) New studded tyres. 5 years old. Tread pattern depth 5 mm.

c4) New studded tyres. 110 studs per tyre. Same four-wheel individuals as b4. ID no. 9.

FIGURE 6d. Deceleration differences between certain type-ABS configurations and reference summer tyres with ABS. Paired comparisons for each driver on lane C (harsh ice surface scratched by studs). Average over 24 + 24 + 18 = 66 drivers with 95% confidence interval (*Source:* Strandberg 1998)

brake system to reach full pressure and begin to lock or retard the wheels. In passenger vehicles with hydraulic systems, the brake lag is negligible—approximately 0.1 second (100 milliseconds). Some experts estimate the brake-lag time for tractor-trailer combinations at 0.5 to 1.0 second, while others estimate it at 0.25 to 0.5 second depending upon the number of trailers.

Another safety component that influences braking performance on tractor-trailer combinations and other vehicles with pneumatic brake systems is the *slack adjuster*. The term *slack adjustment* refers to the distance needed to adjust the actuation arm to fully compress the brake lining and the brake drum. If the slack adjustment is not properly set, braking performance will be greatly reduced. There are usually slack adjusters for each braking wheel. The specific ranges stated by the manufacturer should be adhered to when adjustment is done. Some pneumatic brakes have automatic adjusters, but those also must be checked for proper adjustment.

Aerodynamics and Tires

The aerodynamics of a vehicle is important for fuel economy and vehicle control. A person traveling down a roadway in a vehicle and with one hand out the window with the narrow part facing forward, will feel little resistance. But if the hand is turned so that the palm is directly forward and into the wind, he will feel greater resistance. This *aerodynamic resistance* decreases vehicle fuel mileage. The geometric design of most vehicles used to carry goods, such as semitrailers, is rectangular. The tractor or cab of a tractor-trailer combination, however, usually has a more aerodynamically efficient shape.

Lift resistance—the downward force on a vehicle due to the motion of air over and around it—varies with the geometric design of the vehicle. Lift resistance can easily be understood by watching a drag race or NASCAR race. Dragsters and NASCAR race vehicles have a wing on the rear to keep them on the road at high speeds. A Corvette has a greater lift-resistance force than an SUV or a tractor-trailer combination since the rear of a Corvette is designed to create a downward airflow. Aerodynamics also affects possible loss of control from strong crosswinds. Vehicles are aerodynamically efficient for forward movement and

are tested in a wind tunnel for centerline forces, but crosswinds are extremely difficult to counteract (Gillespie 1992, 79–103). Vehicles are not efficiently designed for crosswinds and can be very difficult to control when crosswinds are present. This is especially relevant for tractor-trailers.

Tires are extremely important to safe vehicle movement and also affect fuel efficiency. An underinflated tire creates greater rolling resistance and consequently is less fuel efficient. Overinflated tires cause uneven wear; therefore, the most important factor in tire safety, the depth of tread, is decreased, which may not be noticed until an accident occurs.

Besides inflating tires properly, one must align and balance them in order to maintain safe tire wear and fuel efficiency. Tread depth and wear are very important, since the tread disperses water on roadway surfaces and inhibits hydroplaning and loss of control.

Heavy Vehicle Tire Blowout

Tire blowout of mechanical origin involves the condition of the materials (tire, rim) and the quality of the assembly. While less spectacular than an explosion, the energy released during blowout can lead to significant injuries if people are directly in the projection trajectory of the debris. Four events of a mechanical origin that can cause a tire to blow out are (ASTE 2009):

1. *Overpressurization of the tire:* Possible causes include:
   - poorly adjusted compressor pressure
   - pressure-gauge or valve problem
   - incorrect mounting on the rim and
   - voluntary overpressurization when seating the tire on the rim.

2. *Zipper failure:* A design defect, an overloading, or an impact can cause a weakness, a cracking, or a rupture of the tire carcass (see Figure 7). The result can lead to significant air loss, the projection of tire fragments, and a sudden drop in pressure at this location, sometimes accompanied by a mark resembling an unstitched or unzipped fabric. Possible causes include:
   - deterioration of the envelope exposing the plys or the belts of the tire to contamination by air or humidity

FIGURE 7. Zipper failure in heavy truck tire blowout (*Source:* ASTE 2009)

- mechanical impact that damaged the tire's structure
- driving with an underpressurized tire, below 80% of the recommended pressure
- driving with overpressurized tires
- overloading
- loss of mechanical properties due to heat, pyrolysis, or thermo-oxidation
- significant carcass wear
- design defect in the weave of the tire cord

3. *Tire-demounting:* Tire-demounting occurs when the tire accidentally and suddenly comes off the rim with a violent release of air or other gases from inside the tire. Possible causes include:
   - mechanical impact, more or less violent, on the rim or the tire

- abnormal wear of the rim (edge)
- deformation of the rim or one of its components following overheating
- incorrect original mounting of the tire
- incompatible parts of the rim (multipiece rim)
- dimensional or other incompatibilities of the rim and tire

4. *Tire in poor condition or with a structural weakness:* A worn tire or even a new one can have a somewhat noticeable structural defect. It may then be unable to withstand normal inflation pressure.

Steady-State Cornering

Steady-state cornering is a term generally used to describe the handling characteristics of a vehicle. It is important to understand the handling of fleet vehicles since these vehicles operate in all types of environmental conditions. A tractor-trailer's cab has steering in the front axle only; the other axles of the tractor follow. In a turn, the inside front wheel has a greater steering angle than the outside front wheel, and the average of the inside and outside front wheel angles is called the *Ackerman angle*. The angle between the heading of the front wheel and the actual travel path of the wheel is known as the *slip angle*. This angle becomes greater—and the tractor becomes more difficult to control—as the friction value between the tire and the roadway surface becomes smaller (Gillespie 1992, 54–59). The *neutral steering angle* is one in which the steering angle is the same as the Ackerman angle. This occurs when the slip angle is the same for both the front and rear tires. *Understeering* occurs when the front wheels slip to a greater extent laterally than the rear wheels, and *oversteering* occurs when the rear wheels slip to a greater extent than the front wheels.

Suspension, or weight shift, plays a crucial part in cornering because the movement and displacement of the cargo can greatly affect the steering of the vehicle. Trucks that carry liquids have a baffle system within the tank so that movement of the liquid during cornering is generally stabilized. Federal transportation guidelines pertaining to cargo stabilization and securing have been established to address the issue of weight shift, as well as the possibility of personal injury during the unloading process. Suspensions are usually a trade-off between stiffness and the ability to absorb rough roadways. Steering geometry includes the understanding of and proper adjustment relating to the toe-in, caster, and camber of the wheels, especially the wheels on the steering axle. When wheels are adjusted to have *toe-in*, their front edges are closer together than their back edges. *Caster* is a backward tilting of a wheel in relation to the center of the suspension. *Camber* refers to the amount that the tops of the wheels tilt outward (Gillespie 1992, 60).

Rearward Amplification

When a combination vehicle makes a sudden lateral movement, such as to avoid an obstacle in the road, its various units undergo different lateral accelerations. The front axles and the cab exhibit a certain kind of acceleration, but the following trailer(s) have greater accelerations. This has been experimentally verified and quantified. The lateral acceleration of the first trailer may be twice that of the tractor, and the lateral acceleration of a second trailer may be four times as much.

The factors that contribute to increased lateral accelerations of the trailing units is the phenomenon known as *rearward amplification*:

- number of trailing units
- shortness of trailers (longer ones experience less amplification)
- loose dolly connections
- greater loads in rearmost trailers
- increased vehicle speeds

Quantifying rearward amplification in terms of multiples of lateral acceleration is relevant to vehicle design, but is not generally relevant to highway geometric design. The Transportation Research Board (TRB) recommended that a reasonable performance criterion would be that the physical overshoot that a following trailer exhibits during such a maneuver, relative to its final displaced lateral position, be limited to 0.8 m (2.7 ft) (TRB 1997).

Suspension Characteristics

The suspension of a heavy vehicle affects its dynamic responses in three major ways:

1. determining dynamic loads on tires
2. orienting the tires under dynamic loads
3. controlling vehicle body motions with respect to the axles

Suspension characteristics can be categorized by eight basic mechanical properties (TRB 1997):

1. vertical stiffness
2. damping
3. static load equalization
4. dynamic interaxle load transfer
5. height of roll center
6. roll stiffness
7. roll steer coefficient
8. compliance steer coefficient

Rollover

Rollover is a serious problem in commercial trucks that have a high center of gravity. The propensity for rollover greatly increases with the height of the center of mass above the ground. For example, it is widely known and has been demonstrated that SUVs have a high propensity to roll over—approximately five times that of standard passenger vehicles. The problem is exacerbated when quick movements from side to side are performed. Given the size of the typical commercial fleet vehicle, any quick movements can be hazardous and create a catastrophic event. If vehicles are carrying toxic chemicals, the hazard is multiplied many times.

Rollovers can occur if a vehicle attempts to enter a curve at a speed greater than the design speed of the curve. The cross slope or superelevation is usually a positive bank, which helps the vehicle to maintain an upright position in a curve. The radius of the curve and the cross slope are important factors and affect each other depending upon the grade of the road and the speed of the vehicle. Heavy trucks may have a rollover threshold (stability factor) of 0.4 to 0.6; in contrast, a sports car's threshold is 1.2 to 1.7. These values are unitless since they are ratios based on the height of the center of mass and the track width of the vehicles. The formula to determine the stability factor of a vehicle where there is no superelevation or roadway cross slope is

$$SF = t/2h \qquad (6)$$

where

SF = the stability factor,

t = track width

h = the height of the center of mass

If there is a cross slope, the formula is

$$SF = (t/2 + \psi h)/h \qquad (7)$$

where

ψ = the roadway's cross-slope angle (Gillespie 1992, 309–317)

Vehicles can also roll over if curbs or other low objects trip them (strike them below the center of mass) as they move laterally. These types of rollovers are generally preventable if the driver uses common sense and safe driving techniques.

The following points (McKnight and Bahouth 2009) apply to rollovers:

- Although they account for about a tenth of all large truck crashes, rollovers result from causes that are relatively unique to the vehicle and where it is driven.
- The majority of rollovers occur in curves, primarily on- and off-ramps where misjudgment and being in a hurry lead to speeds that are excessive to the vehicle's high center of gravity.
- Failure to adjust speed to the load and the stability, height, and weight of the load is a cause relatively unique to rollovers.
- Inattention, dozing, and distraction often necessitate sudden course corrections, leading to rollovers. However, they play a smaller role in crashes involving trucks than other vehicles.
- Three control errors that are relatively unique to truck rollovers are turning too sharply, turning too little to remain on the road, and overcorrecting steering errors.
- A quarter of rollovers result from problems over which drivers have no control. Half of those are the fault of other drivers, far less than is the case in other truck crashes.

TABLE 5

Speed-Related Rollovers

Cause	Number	Description
Speed	108	Speed excessive to circumstances
Curves	77	Curves taken at excessive speed
Misjudgment	67	Misjudged speed at which the curve could be taken
Hurrying	13	In a hurry and disregarded speed limitation
Anger	3	Loss of temper in response to other road users
Oversight	3	Failure to notice speed signs
Loads	26	Not adjusting speed to stability, weight, height
Brakes	15	Not adjusting speed to known poor braking
Road	11	Not adjusting speed to road conditions
Intersect	10	Not adjusting speed to sharp turn at intersection
Vehicles	5	Not adjusting speed to vehicles ahead
Tires	3	Not adjusting speed to worn tread
Sight distance	2	Not adjusting speed to limited sight distance

(*Source:* McKnight and Bahouth 2009)

TABLE 6

Control-Related Rollovers

Cause		Number	Description
Control		46	Errors in controlling motion of the truck
Steering		20	Oversteering or understeering
Overcorrection		19	Overcorrecting after error (off road, out of lane)
Following distance		7	Failing to keep distance from vehicle ahead
Avoidance maneuvers		6	Responding to vehicles/road incorrectly
Downshift		3	Failure to downshift for speed control
Braking		3	Improper braking (e.g., locked brakes)

(*Source:* McKnight and Bahouth 2009)

- Large truck instructional programs could reduce the incidence of rollover by the use of videos to expose truck drivers to situations leading to rollovers and through simulation to help drivers develop avoidance skills without being exposed to danger.

Data on speed- and control-related rollovers are presented in Tables 5 and 6.

Emergency Fleet Vehicles

Although emergency fire vehicles are not usually thought of as fleet vehicles, they have evolved in their own manner within the transportation system.

Emergency vehicles such as fire trucks may have specialized equipment such as flashing lights and sirens, may be painted special colors, and may have areas of special reflectivity. Flashing lights were invented to bring attention to persons at a distance that an emergency vehicle was approaching. The flashing intensity, duration, and ability to be detected at a distance are of prime importance. Emergency flashing lights primarily convey the message that drivers must give emergency vehicles the right of way. Since they are used among other lights, drivers must be able to identify them and respond quickly in order to avoid an accident.

Color is a key visual component in any emergency vehicle fleet accident-prevention policy. Red may not be the best choice for emergency vehicles because under normal circumstances people have difficulty seeing red objects. During the day, in fact, red is one of the most difficult colors to see, and at night everyone is practically "red blind." A range of yellow colors—from greenish-yellow to yellowish-green—is most easily detected day and night (Southhall 1961, 273). School-zone and school-crossing signs are now made with lime or yellowish-green backgrounds. Lime is also seen significantly faster than red in the peripheral (off-central) view, which is important because peripheral vision is most often responsible for early detection.

Colors and shapes that contrast with their backgrounds are essential to use in the design of emergency vehicles. NASA studied this subject and determined that the yellowish-green or greenish-yellow colors, rarely found in nature, attract more attention because they stand out more than other colors. For example, lime-yellow/white fire engines are safer than red/white vehicles. A study by Stephen Solomon published in *Firehouse Magazine* (June 1984) regarding *safety color* reported that red vehicles were involved in twice as many accidents as lime-yellow ones (see Figure 8). To understand this, the article examined the four-part reaction/perception driver-avoidance maneuver.

Use of fluorescent and retroreflective materials for the emergency vehicle fleet is another issue that must be addressed by fleet operators and safety managers. *Fluorescent* materials convert the energy from light into different color wavelengths. Fluorescent prod-

ucts are usually brighter and more eye-catching than nonfluorescent products and are used mainly during daylight hours. Fluorescent yellow-green is the most detectable color. Fluorescent signs and warnings are very noticeable when new, but their brightness diminishes over time with exposure to sunlight. Consequently, fluorescent objects must be repainted or have new striping applied. This type of material needs constant maintenance and review to be efficient throughout its lifetime (Southhall 1961, 273). Fluorescent colors do not reflect or radiate light at night.

Retroreflective materials are used for nighttime detection of signs or vehicles. They use microscopic beads, lenses, or prisms embedded in substances or added to paint. Retroreflective materials have the ability to reflect light back to its origin. As light moves away from the center of the axis of the retroreflective material, the brightness or reflectivity diminishes greatly. One of the greatest safety uses for retroreflective materials is on commercial vehicles such as tractor-trailers, where the materials can assist in reducing underride collisions. One of the problems with outlining the side of a trailer with one line of retroreflective materials is that this does not provide adequate information when the trailer is not viewed in profile. If the rear of the trailer is marked with reflective material in a right-angle pattern, vehicles approaching from the rear have more information about the size and shape of the trailer.

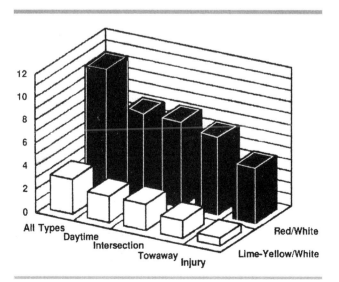

FIGURE 8. Comparison of accident incidents involving fire engines of different colors (*Source:* Solomon 1984)

Phosphorescent materials glow in the dark. They absorb light energy and radiate that energy after the light source is removed. This absorption and emission of light does not last long enough to be of value on emergency fleet vehicles.

Emergency vehicles can create a highway hazard even after they have stopped moving, so fleet operation managers must be sure that emergency vehicles have high conspicuity when stopped at a vulnerable location, such as on a highway. Proper lighting and use of warning devices must be understood by emergency vehicle operators so that the vehicle itself does not become part of the emergency scene.

Once an emergency vehicle arrives at a scene, operators should deploy all warning devices—signal arrows, signs, cones, and flares—as soon as possible.

Traffic cones have no nighttime value since they are normally unlit, so they should be used in daytime only. Highway flares are often used in close proximity to emergency scenes, but their sparks make them a hazard near flammable fuel spills. The negative characteristics of flares include not only their sparks but the amounts of smoke and red/orange flickering flames they generate. The flickering flames can detract from the overall attention demanded by emergency lighting because they may reduce or negate the effectiveness of other flashing lights. Smoke and flares contribute to a visually cluttered background and can confuse unsuspecting drivers approaching the scene (Southhall 1961, 276).

As a general rule, the longer emergency vehicles and personnel must be at a scene, the greater the possibility of injury to emergency fleet personnel, hence the more durable the traffic warning controls should be.

Creating a Risk Plan

Responding to emergencies such as fires, police calls, and accidents is a dangerous business. The danger is not limited to transportation to the scene but also at the scene and in dealing with victims. The purpose of a risk-management plan is to control the risk as best as possible to minimize the danger. Risk management is not static; it is a fluid process. At the end of the process, continual review and updating is crucial to maintaining an effective and efficient health and safety program.

Losses have an effect on personnel, property, legal liability, and time. The most important of these is the personnel. Because the responders must enter into or about buildings, crashed vehicles, or dangerous scenes, personnel may be, and at times are, lost through injury or death. While fatalities or injuries are always to be avoided if possible, they do happen and, as a consequence, are costly to the emergency organizations and the team. These costs can be controlled through risk-management planning and recovery planning. Property losses include damage to the emergency organization's property, such as vehicles, which are very expensive since they are usually custom-made equipment. The loss includes cost of a replacement for repair. In recent times, legal liability has become a substantial portion of the insurance premium package and also a large part of the planning. It is no longer to be taken for granted that the victim will feel fortunate to survive; sometimes, the victim and his or her family need someone to blame, and an attorney may be readily available to exploit raw emotions. The time element is the fourth possible loss category and includes the cost of renting equipment or the time damaged equipment cannot be used until it is repaired.

During risk-management planning, there are many choices to be made, some of which are difficult, while others are clear and precise. The best method of making choices is to have as much data and research information as possible about the subject. There are times when the data will be clear, but the choice may not be clear. All choices involve responsibilities and consequences and, since a decision must be made and implemented through training or a written standard operating procedure, all consequences must be thoroughly examined. The personnel or procedure most affected by a new decision or a changing decision must be considered, and discussion with the appropriate personnel should occur so that all sides of the issues and possible circumstances are delineated prior to implementation.

Some of the results obtained from a sound risk-management program include (Andrews 2004):

- The emergency organization may survive a major loss rather than be put out of business.
- The organization achieves a bottom line where the income is still greater than the expenses.

Even though most emergency organizations are nonprofit-based, they still need to handle their expenses just as if they were a for-profit organization. Contributions and charity events are usually the main source of income if the local government has problems devoting operating funds through real estate taxes.

- Emergency service organizations must be available 24 hours a day, 7 days a week. Keeping equipment in good repair means that no emergencies may need to be rerouted to another organization for help until lost or damaged equipment is returned to service.

- The risk-management program is similar to a for-profit corporation's budget. The emergency organization needs to prepare and anticipate any stable expenses for its operating year.

- The management of losses will not impede the growth of the organization, and the organization should maintain good relations with the public it serves.

- As with any process of risk management, all critical areas such as laws, regulations, and standards must be included in the finished program. Compliance is a major factor in any completed and implemented risk-management program.

When starting a risk management plan (RMP), a company must begin by consulting with all applicable parties to obtain their input, such as the legal department, the safety department, and drivers (and the union if warranted). If the business is local or regional, the state's regulations must be considered; if it is national, all appropriate regulations must be included.

TRAFFIC SAFETY PRINCIPLES
Highway Safety and Roadway Geometry

Highway safety is the responsibility of everyone, and safety elements must be reviewed, updated when necessary, and used for training. Management must begin by setting standards, showing employees how to meet the standards, evaluating the safety efforts, and giving recognition or additional training when needed.

Roadway geometry plays an important part in safety and must be considered each time roads are built or improved. Roadway design usually includes the travel portion of the roadway, shoulders or emergency escape path, alignment, and intersecting roadway safety. There are many references on the subject, including the American Association of State Highway and Transportation Officials' "Policy on Geometric Design of Highways and Streets" (AASHTO 1990), the *Manual on Uniform Traffic Control Devices* (DOT 2000), and the *Traffic Engineering Handbook* (ITE 1999). These publications provide detailed standards and best practices relating to roadway geometry. Design guides should also be used as references for driver training.

A railroad-track grade crossing is a special type of highway intersection where three elements converge: the driver, the vehicle, and the physical intersection. At a typical motor-vehicle intersection, drivers take turns yielding to opposing traffic, but at railroad grade crossings, trains are the opposing traffic, and they rarely yield right-of-way to motorists. Motor-vehicle operators can change their path and alter their speed, whereas trains have a fixed path and change speed much more slowly. Fleet-vehicle operators must be aware of the difference between a typical roadway intersection and a railroad grade crossing. At a railroad grade crossing, the vehicle operator bears most of the responsibility for avoiding a collision with a train. The railroad crossing crossbuck is a yield sign, and the motor-vehicle operator must interpret it as such (Southhall 1961, 273).

The Uniform Vehicle Code (NCUTLO 2000) is a model for motor-vehicle laws that indicates actions drivers are required to take at railroad crossings. This code states, in section 11/701, that when a driver of a motor vehicle approaches a rail highway crossing under the following circumstances, he or she shall stop the vehicle within fifty feet of but not less than fifteen feet from the nearest rail and shall not proceed until it is safe to do so (Southhall 1961, 275):

- A clearly visible electric or mechanical signal indicates the approach of a train.

- A crossing gate is lowered or the presence of a human flagman gives or continues to give the signal of an approaching train.

- A train approaching within 1500 feet of the highway crossing gives an audible signal.

- The approaching train is clearly visible and presents a hazardous condition.

Fleet drivers must also be aware of the various decision zones relating to railroad crossing hazards:

- The *approach zone* is an area in which drivers must begin to formulate their actions in order to avoid a collision. In this zone drivers look ahead and determine whether a train is nearby or present.
- The *nonrecovery zone* is the area in which drivers begin to stop if a train is crossing or approaching as well as being cautious and looking left and right for additional information if a train is not immediately perceived.
- The final zone is the *hazard zone*. In this zone, drivers must stop if a train is crossing or approaching and also must decide whether or not to go across the tracks. If there is no train present, drivers must look both ways before crossing the tracks.

Vehicle type is another component of decisions made at railroad crossings. A passenger vehicle that has acceleration and deceleration superior to that of a truck can cross railroad tracks much more quickly than a truck. The length of the truck, its braking ability, and its acceleration are important in determining whether a truck driver can cross tracks safely. Longer and heavier trucks must be considered when designing railroad crossings with respect to these factors:

- *Sight distance* (A longer sight distance is needed for trucks due to their slower deceleration and handling compared to passenger vehicles.)
- *Placement of advanced warning signs* (They must be far enough away that trucks have time to stop.)
- *Train warning whistles* (Whistles must be sounded in time for trucks to hear them and stop.)
- *Sight lines of approach and departure grates* (Truck drivers must be able to see them in time to react and stop.)

When approaching railroad crossings, truck operators must consider the type of road, the traffic volume, the angles and geometry of the crossing, the presence of nearby intersecting roadways, and the illumination. They must never be impatient or attempt to cross in front of an oncoming train.

Passing Sight Distance

Greater sight distance is required for one vehicle to pass another in the lane normally reserved for opposing traffic on a two-lane highway than is required simply to bring a vehicle to a stop before reaching an object in the road. Table 7 presents the passing sight-distance criteria used in geometric design, and the criteria used in marking of passing and no-passing zones on two-lane highwaysis shown in Table 8. The geometric design criteria are more conservative than the marking criteria, but neither is based on a completely consistent set of assumptions.

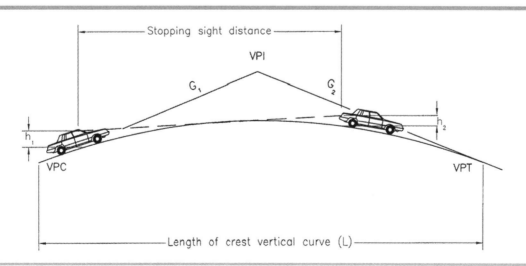

FIGURE 9. Application of stopping sight distance to crest vertical curves (*Source:* TRB 2008)

TABLE 7

Design Speed (mi/h)	Minimum Stopping Sight Distance Used in Design (ft)
15	80
20	115
25	155
30	200
35	250
40	305
45	360
50	425
55	495
60	570
65	645
70	730
75	820
80	910

Note: Brake reaction distance predicated on a time of 2.5 s; deceleration rate of 11.2 ft/s^2 used to determine calculated sight distance

(*Source:* TRB 1997)

TABLE 8

Design and Marking Criteria for Passing Sight Distance

Design or Prevailing Speed (mi/h)	Highway Design[a]	Marking of Passing and No-Passing Zones[b]
25	900	450
30	1090	500
35	1280	550
40	1470	600
45	1625	700
50	1835	800
55	1985	900
60	1985	900
65	2285	1100
70	2480	1200

[a]*Based on AASHTOGreen Book.*
[b]*Based on MUTCD.*

(*Source:* TRB 1997)

The current passing sight-distance criteria shown in Table 7 were derived on the basis of passenger-car behavior and do not explicitly consider heavy vehicles. Using a new sight-distance model with more consistent assumptions, Harwood et al. derived sight-distance requirements for various passing scenarios involving passenger cars and trucks, as shown in Figure 9 (TRB 2008). The figure indicates that all passing scenarios are accommodated within the current geometric design criteria. Furthermore, Harwood et al. also found that a truck can safely pass a passenger car on any crest vertical curve on which a passenger car can safely pass a truck (see Figure 10). The current marking criteria for passing and no-passing zones do not necessarily accommodate all passing maneuvers that truck drivers might wish to make (TRB 2008).

However, there is currently no indication that the passing and no-passing zone markings lead truck drivers to make poor passing decisions, or that trucks are over-involved in passing-related accidents. Thus, there is no indication that a change in marking criteria to better accommodate trucks would have safety benefits. There is concern that such a change could eliminate some passing zones that are currently used effectively by passenger cars. Further research on this issue is needed.

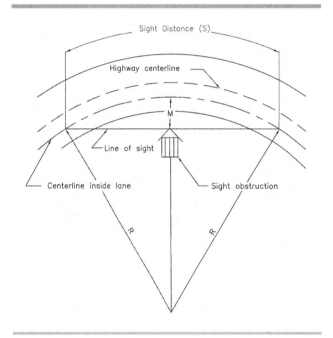

FIGURE 10. Application of stopping sight distance to horizontal curves (*Source:* TRB 1997)

Fleet Statistics

It is important for fleet managers to keep statistics because they can demonstrate the proficiency of fleet drivers with regard to avoidable and unavoidable accidents. Statistics also assist the maintenance department in creating vehicle maintenance schedules. Accident and injury statistics such as data compiled for large trucks and buses in the State of New Jersey for 2001–2005 (Tables 9 and 10) can also demonstrate the effects of efforts toward safety; but, in and of themselves, they cannot achieve a reduction in injuries. Statistics are a snapshot taken at one point in time that can guide safety managers in continuing or developing fleet safety programs. These programs can include regular driver-safety updates as well as safety at loading and unloading docks and warehouse facilities. According to the National Safety Council, there was a reduction in motor-vehicle deaths for 2001–2002 but an increase for 2002–2003 (NSC *Injury Facts* 2004). Statistical graphs of the type

shown in Figures 11–16 for large trucks and buses are a valuable asset for review and are especially useful in determining whether a company is keeping up with or doing better than its state or the nation in controlling injuries and deaths. These statistics are for New Jersey, but statistics for each state and the nation are available online at www.ai.volpe.dot.gov/crashprofile/crashprofilemainnew.asp. [*NOTE:* For Tables 9 and 10 and Figures 11 through 16, Fatality Analysis Reporting System (FARS) and Motor Carrier Management Information System (MCMIS) data are from March 2006. FARS data from 2005 are not available.]

TABLE 9

Summary of Large Trucks Involved in Crashes
(New Jersey)

Number of Large Trucks Involved in:	Year				
	2001	2002	2003	2004	2005
Fatal and nonfatal crashes (FARS & MCMIS)	7735	6928	7741	7893	NA
Fatal crashes (FARS)	76	69	85	87	NA
Fatal crashes (MCMIS)	73	39	61	87	66
Nonfatal crashes (MCMIS)	7659	6859	7656	7806	6680
Injury crashes (MCMIS)	3653	3176	3547	3500	2851
Towaway crashes (MCMIS)	4006	3683	4109	4306	3829
HM placard crashes (FARS & MCMIS)	0	0	2	3	NA
Fatalities (FARS)	77	72	75	79	NA
Injuries (MCMIS)	5358	4694	5171	4979	4154

The MCMIS crash file is intended to be a census of trucks and buses involved in fatal, injury and towaway crashes; however, some states do not report all FMCSA-eligible crashes. FMCSA continues to work with the states to improve data quality and reporting of all eligible truck and bus crashes to the MCMIS crash file.

(*Source*: FMCSA Analysis and Information Online 2006)

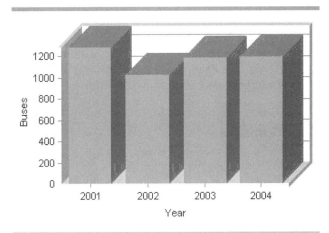

FIGURE 11. Number of buses involved in fatal and nonfatal crashes (FARS and MCMIS) (*Source:* FMCSA Analysis and Information Online 2006)

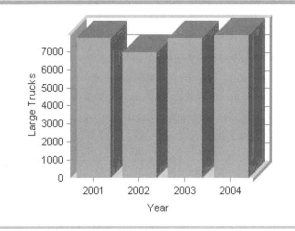

FIGURE 12. Number of large trucks involved in fatal and nonfatal crashes (FARS and MCMIS) (*Source:* FMCSA Analysis and Information Online 2006)

TABLE 10

Summary of Buses Involved in Crashes
(New Jersey)

Number of Buses Involved in:	Year				
	2001	2002	2003	2004	2005
Fatal and nonfatal crashes (FARS & MCMIS)	1282	1024	1182	1197	NA
Fatal crashes (FARS)	10	13	10	10	NA
Fatal crashes (MCMIS)	7	8	6	8	8
Nonfatal crashes (MCMIS)	1272	1011	1172	1187	1034
Injury crashes (MCMIS)	713	574	624	656	554
Towaway crashes (MCMIS)	559	437	548	531	480
HM placard crashes (FARS & MCMIS)	0	0	0	0	NA
Fatalities (FARS)	12	14	11	11	NA
Injuries (MCMIS)	1379	1149	1223	1309	990

The MCMIS crash file is intended to be a census of trucks and buses involved in fatal, injury and towaway crashes; however, some states do not report all FMCSA-eligible crashes. FMCSA continues to work with the states to improve data quality and reporting of all eligible truck and bus crashes to the MCMIS crash file.

(*Source*: FMCSA Analysis and Information Online 2006)

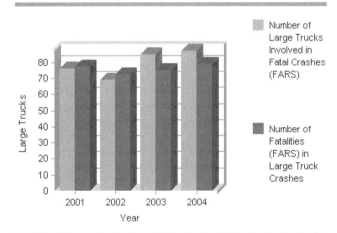

FIGURE 13. Number of large trucks involved in fatal crashes (*Source:* FMCSA Analysis and Information Online 2006)

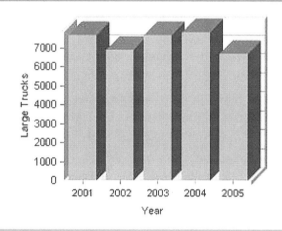

FIGURE 15. Number of large trucks involved in nonfatal crashes (MCMIS) (*Source:* FMCSA Analysis and Information Online 2006)

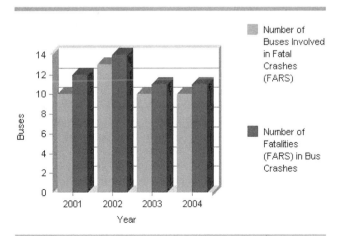

FIGURE 14. Number of buses involved in fatal crashes (*Source:* FMCSA Analysis and Information Online 2006)

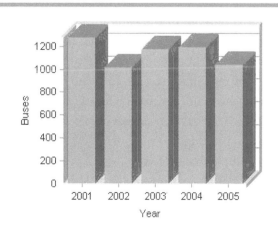

FIGURE 16. Number of buses involved in nonfatal crashes (MCMIS) (*Source:* FMCSA Analysis and Information Online 2006)

Injury Crashes

From 1994 to 2004, the number of large trucks involved in injury crashes per 100 million vehicle miles traveled declined by 32 percent, while the rate for passenger vehicles dropped by 30 percent (see Figure 17).

One notable statistic shows that passenger vehicles far surpass large trucks in injuries per million miles traveled, but large trucks outnumber passenger cars in deaths (Figure 18). It is no surprise that large-truck death figures surpass those of passenger vehicles since the results of an impact between a large truck and a passenger vehicle normally are weighted against the passenger vehicle. Statistics such as these are of great importance to a safety analysis, and statistics generated regarding a company's own fleet are even more meaningful. Committees that decide whether accidents are preventable or not can use statistical information such as this along with specific facts surrounding the accidents.

Work-related roadway accidents kill more employees each year than any other occupational cause of death. In addition to the devastating human toll to employees, communities, and families, companies face massive productivity losses and soaring medical and workers' compensation costs. Michael Deak, safety director at DuPont in Wilmington, Delaware, stated, "If a worker is injured driving their own vehicle or driving a fleet vehicle, the cost is the same to us." In an attempt to counter the high productivity cost as a result of accidents, OSHA is bringing more agency resources to bear on the problem of occupational driving fatalities (Deak 2004, 44–48).

Increasingly, employers are instituting their own internal driving standards, procedures, and regulations covering subjects from seatbelts to fleet vehicle selection and use of personal vehicles on company business. DuPont has outlined driving standards for vehicle safety which include procedures for driver training as well as for auditing and measuring the results (Deak 2004, 44–48). Some believe that statistically, the more moving violations or preventable crashes a driver has, the greater the chance he or she will be involved in a catastrophic crash (Deak 2004, 44–48). It is believed that people with no moving violations on their driving

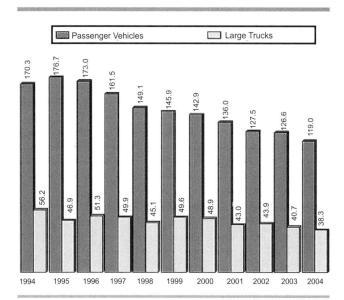

FIGURE 17. Vehicles involved in injury crashes per 100 million vehicle-miles traveled (*Source:* NSC 2004)

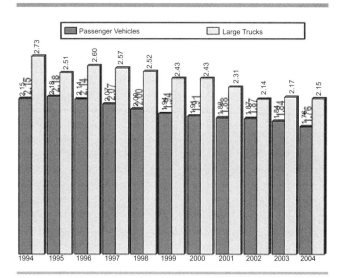

FIGURE 18. Vehicles involved in fatal crashes per 100 million vehicle-miles traveled (*Source:* NSC 2004)

record have been careful. Some insurance carriers check driving records of those who drive company-owned vehicles quarterly and assign a point system for moving violations and preventable crashes. When a driver reaches a certain level of points, action is taken to improve his or her performance.

A study completed by the National Institute of Occupational Safety and Health (NIOSH) in 2004 determined that 28 percent of workers fatally injured while driving a vehicle were wearing seatbelts, and 56 percent were unbelted or had no seatbelt available. OSHA, in its movement toward creating driving standards, indicates that in 2001 approximately 4.2 million workers drove a motor vehicle on the job. They ranged from long-haul truckers to pizza deliverers and from school bus drivers to salespersons. Between 1992 and 2001 over 13,000 workers died in crashes. The statistics bear out the need for fleet training as well as constant monitoring of drivers and driver records (see Tables 11 and 12 and Figures 19 through 24).

Nighttime Driving and Vision

Safety issues when it is dark involving nighttime driving require special evaluation and action since the visibility and acuity is are critical to safe driving. Reaction time is considerably slower at night than during the day

TABLE 11

National Summary of Large Trucks Involved in Crashes

Number of Large Trucks Involved in:	Year				
	2004	2005	2006	2007	2008
Fatal and nonfatal crashes (FARS & MCMIS)	139,345	147,202	147,149	147,697	132,791
Fatal crashes (FARS)	4902	4951	4766	4633	4066
Fatal crashes (MCMIS)	4848	5240	4967	4808	4169
Nonfatal crashes (MCMIS)	134,433	142,251	142,383	143,064	128,725
Injury crashes (MCMIS)	60,796	61,777	60,248	58,089	51,147
Towaway crashes (MCMIS)	73,647	80,474	82,135	84,975	77,578
HM placard crashes (MCMIS)	2453	2574	2278	2296	2630
Number of:					
Fatalities (FARS)	5235	5240	5027	4822	4229
Injuries (MCMIS)	85,023	86,642	84,199	80,098	70,567

The MCMIS Crash File is intended to be a census of trucks and buses involved in fatal, injury and towaway crashes; however, some States do not report all FMCSA-eligible crashes. FMCSA continues to work with the States to improve data quality and reporting of all eligible truck and bus crashes to the MCMIS crash file.

(*Source*: FMCSA Analysis and Information Online 2009)

TABLE 12

National Summary of Buses Involved in Crashes

Number of Large Trucks Involved in:	Year				
	2004	2005	2006	2007	2008
Fatal and nonfatal crashes (FARS & MCMIS)	9181	11,148	12,514	13,529	14,089
Fatal crashes (FARS)	279	280	305	281	247
Fatal crashes (MCMIS)	210	5240	273	260	257
Nonfatal crashes (MCMIS)	8902	249	12,209	13,248	13,842
Injury crashes (MCMIS)	5224	10,868	6912	7143	7491
Towaway crashes (MCMIS)	3678	6140	5297	6105	6351
HM placard crashes (MCMIS)	0	8	10	11	11
Number of:					
Fatalities (FARS)	315	340	337	325	307
Injuries (MCMIS)	12,368	14,426	15,466	15,633	16,935

The MCMIS Crash File is intended to be a census of trucks and buses involved in fatal, injury and towaway crashes; however, some States do not report all FMCSA-eligible crashes. FMCSA continues to work with the States to improve data quality and reporting of all eligible truck and bus crashes to the MCMIS crash file.

(*Source*: FMCSA Analysis and Information Online 2009)

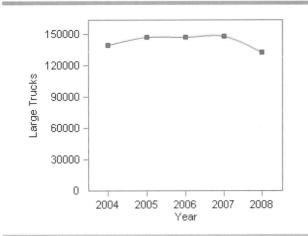

FIGURE 19. Number of large trucks involved in fatal and nonfatal crashes (*Source:* FARS and MCMIS 2009)

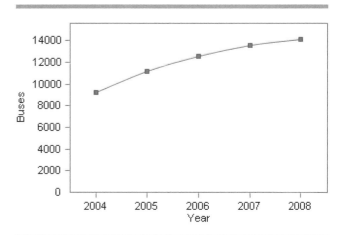

FIGURE 20. Number of buses involved in fatal and nonfatal crashes (*Source:* FARS and MCMIS 2009)

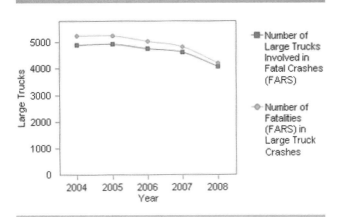

FIGURE 21. Number of large trucks involved in fatal crashes (*Source:* FARS and MCMIS 2009)

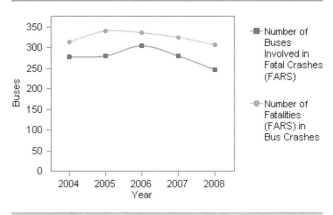

FIGURE 22. Number of buses involved in fatal crashes (*Source:* FARS and MCMIS 2009)

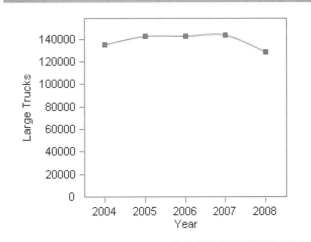

FIGURE 23. Number of large trucks involved in nonfatal crashes (*Source:* FARS and MCMIS 2009)

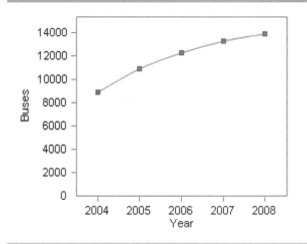

FIGURE 24. Number of buses involved in nonfatal crashes (*Source:* FARS and MCMIS 2009)

Note: Although efforts have been made to provide the most accurate and complete MCMIS crash data possible, data quality can vary from state to state. Please use caution when interpreting MCMIS crash data.

(Allen 1996, 201–238). The human eye sees using rods and cones. *Rod* vision is known as *scotopic* vision, while *cone* vision is *photopic* vision. Scotopic vision is the vision a driver uses during nighttime driving. Photopic vision is used for acuity and to distinguish between colors. The level of nighttime lighting on roadways is below what is necessary for photopic vision. At night the human eye relies on the more sensitive 125 million rod cells, usually seeing shades of gray or black, which explains why it is difficult for someone to see an object that is not fully illuminated. Daytime vision is performed with cones, which comprise approximately 5.5 million cells. They allow for quicker identification of colors and possible hazards than rods, which do not distinguish between colors except for shades of gray and black.

State traffic regulations require visibility at certain distances when using illuminated headlamps: 250 feet on low beam and 500 feet on high beam. Therefore, on low beam a driver needs to know what is ahead within the next 250 feet, and in order not to overdrive the headlights he or she must consider the vehicle's speed, the road conditions, and his or her own acuity. Perception and reaction times are believed by some to be a minimum of 1.5 seconds for a single emergency maneuver. This 1.5-second perception-reaction time is controversial because some perception-reaction studies allow drivers to know that they will be expected to react to an object, and consequently their attention is high— usually higher than that of a typical driver with no idea a hazard may lie ahead. The 1.5 seconds may be accurate for one reaction, such as braking, to an expected emergency, but it does not include more complicated perception, evaluation, and reaction sequences in reaction to different types of unexpected hazards, so nighttime perception and reaction times could be much greater than this value.

The *Manual on Uniform Traffic Control Devices* (DOT 2000, 2A-19) uses a standard of 2.5 seconds for simple reaction and perception times. Of course all drivers are different, and to use an exact figure would be inconsistent with good engineering judgment. It would be best to use a range for perception and reaction times depending upon the specific accident issues being investigated. For example, one would not use the same time for a simple emergency braking maneuver for a driver who requires more information to make an appropriate safety maneuver and is traveling closer to the hazard while acquiring the information.

Nighttime visibility involves many factors, including brightness and contrast. *Brightness* is the reflection off an object from light falling on the object, and *contrast* is the difference in brightness between an object and its background. At night, if pedestrians wear dark clothing and there is no backlighting, even an alert driver will find it difficult to spot them soon enough to avoid impact. There are many other reasons for poor nighttime visibility, including dirt on the inside and outside of the windshield, dirty headlamps, inattention, and so on.

Research has been a valuable tool in alerting drivers to the problems of nighttime driving. It has found that light clothing is preferable to dark clothing and that visibility is better if some portion of the clothing is made of reflective material. Tests have also shown that fog creates a substantial driving hazard because light reflects off the water droplets and returns directly to the eye of the driver. The driver's level of expectancy or attention also plays a critical part in detection of hazards during nighttime driving (Shinar 1985, 243–245).

The driver's limit of vision varies outside of the accurate vision area (one degree on either side of the centerline of the eyes). The word recognition limit for signs occurs between 5 and 10 degrees, and the symbol recognition limit is between 5 and 30 degrees from the centerline of the driver's eyes while facing forward. Limits for locating emergency controls within the truck cab are between 30 and 60 degrees. Cleaning the cab interior, especially the lens caps of instruments, as well as a routine maintenance program for replacing instrument bulbs, adds to the safety of the driver (Marshall 2000, 376–380).

Sensitivity to contrast is the ability of the human eye to perceive a small difference in luminance. Visual acuity—the ability to detect small details and small objects—decreases with age: the visual acuity of an 80-year-old is approximately 50 percent that of a 20-year-old. Contrast sensitivity is more important than visual acuity for many jobs such as inspection and product control. Speed of perception and contrast sensitivity are closely connected to each other and must be maintained for safe driving at night (Kroemer 1999, 275–282).

On December 10, 1992, the National Highway Traffic Safety Administration (NHTSA) published a final rule requiring that trailers manufactured on or after December 1, 1993, which have an overall width of 2032 mm (80 inches) or more and a gross vehicle weight rating (GVWR) of more than 4536 kg (10,000 pounds), except pole trailers and trailers designed exclusively for living or office use, be equipped on the sides and rear with a means for making them more visible on the road.

The NHTSA rule allows trailer manufacturers to install either red and white retroreflective sheeting or reflex reflectors. Manufacturers of retroreflective sheeting or reflectors are required to certify compliance of their product with Federal Motor Vehicle Safety Standard (FMVSS) No. 108 (49 CFR 571.108), whether the product is for use as original or replacement equipment. The manufacturer's certification will consist of one of the following markings, depending on the type of conspicuity material:

- DOT-C: Rectangular reflex reflectors certified as meeting the standard.
- DOT-C2: 50 millimeter (mm) wide retroreflective sheeting material certified as meeting the standard.
- DOT-C3: 75 mm wide retroreflective sheeting certified as meeting the standard.
- DOT-C4: 100 mm wide retroreflective sheeting certified as meeting the standard.

Currently, Section 393.11 requires that all lamps and reflective devices on motor vehicles placed in operation after March 7, 1989, meet the requirements of FMVSS No. 108 in effect on the date of manufacture. Therefore, trailers manufactured on or after December 1, 1993, must have reflective devices of the type and in the locations specified by FMVSS No. 108, including the conspicuity treatments.

If you plan on driving after the sun goes down, it is important to remember that driving at night presents different challenges than driving during the day. Traffic death rates are three times greater at night, yet many of us are unaware of the hazards that night driving poses or of effective ways to handle them.

At night, vision is severely limited. Drivers lose the advantage of color and contrast that are available during the day, and depth perception and peripheral vision are also diminished.

To improve night vision and driving ability after sunset, the Motor Vehicle Lighting Council (MVLC) offer drivers these tips (MVLC 2009):

1. *Use your lights courteously.* Turn your headlights on one hour before sunset to make it easier for other drivers to see you in early twilight. Keep your headlights on at least one hour after sunrise. Refrain from flashing your high beams at a vehicle with its high beams on; this will only increase the chance that drivers will not be able to see. In fog, use low-beam headlights; high beams reduce your own ability to see and may temporarily blind other drivers. If your vehicle is equipped with fog lamps, use them with your low beams only when there is fog or inclement weather.

2. *Make it easy for others to see you.* Be sure that all exterior vehicle lights work properly. In case of a vehicle breakdown, pull completely off the road beyond the end of the guardrail, if possible, and turn on the emergency flashers.

3. *Avoid glare.* Instead of looking at oncoming headlights, look toward the right side of the road and watch the white line marking the outside edge of the traffic lane. When headlights from vehicles following you reflect in your rearview mirror, use the "day-night" feature on the mirror or adjust your mirror to cut out as much of the light as possible.

4. *Adjust your vehicle's interior lighting.* If streetlights cause a lot of glare, dim your dashboard lights and use your sun visor. Avoid using any other light inside your vehicle.

5. *Keep all windows and headlights clean.* Dirty windows can increase glare, making it more difficult to see, while dirty headlights can reduce efficiency by as much as 90 percent. Be sure to clean the inside and outside of your windshield as well as your headlights.

6. *Keep your eyes moving.* Look for flashes of light at hilltops, curves, and intersections that may indicate the headlights of other vehicles.

7. ***Increase your following distance.*** Increasing your distance by four to five seconds can make it easier to spot potential problems on the roadway and gives you more time to respond. In addition, proper lighting will enable you to react quicker and stop at a safe distance from the vehicle in front of you.

8. ***Regulate speed.*** Driving too fast is more dangerous after dark than during the day because of decreased visibility. Traveling at high speeds does not allow you enough time or distance to stop when you see something dangerous on the road ahead.

9. ***Prevent fatigue.*** Night driving can be tiring, so ensure good ventilation inside the vehicle and take frequent refreshment breaks to give your eyes a chance to recover. Take a short nap or a brisk walk, or have some caffeine to help you stay alert.

10. ***Use vehicle mirrors to your advantage.*** Exterior mirrors that are properly aligned not only reduce blind spots, they also reduce glare from vehicles behind you. The outside rearview mirrors should be adjusted so that the bodywork of the vehicle is just outside of the driver's view. In addition, the rearview mirror can be flipped to its "day-night" setting, which changes the angle of the reflective surface and appears to dim the mirror.

In addition, there are also some general practices one can follow to help ensure safe night driving:

1. ***Align your headlights correctly.*** Properly aligned headlights will help you see the road better and will help other drivers avoid glare. If you live in a state that requires regular safety inspections, ask the service technician to check and correct the aim of your headlights. If your state does not require such an inspection, take your vehicle to a dealer or repair shop at least once a year for a headlight checkup.

2. ***Have your vision checked regularly.*** The American Optometric Association recommends that everyone under the age of 40 have a thorough eye exam at least every three years; drivers 41–60, every two years; and drivers over 60, every year. Age can make eyes more sensitive to glare. In addition, certain medical conditions, such as encroaching cataracts, will increase eye sensitivity.

3. ***Look into antireflective eyeglass coating.*** Many eye-care professionals strongly recommend eyeglasses that have an antireflective (AR) coating. This ultra-thin film reduces internal reflections in the lenses. AR-coated glasses actually transmit more light than regular lenses, which improves vision at night and helps distinguish fine details during the day.

Work Zone Safety

Good safety professionals are acutely aware of safety in roadwork zones. Safety is also an important consideration when the work involves closing lanes or complete roadways due to emergency events. Safety in work zones is and has been crucial to the protection of public employees and emergency responders. Work-zone setup or design is based on the regulations found in the *Manual on Uniform Traffic Control Devices* (DOT 2000, ch. 6) and 29 CFR 1926.21 and .200. These regulations define and guide the proper placement of signs, markings, barriers, flaggers, and so on.

Safety professionals should be cognizant of three terms used throughout these manuals and regulations:

- *Shall* means that use of a device or practice is mandatory.
- *Should* means the device or practice is recommended but not mandatory.
- *May* means the device or practice is not required by regulation.

Work zones are planned and designed according to the type of work to be done, the location, characteristics of the roadway, and the length of time the work will take. For example, if a work zone requires closing one lane of a multilane roadway, signs of different kinds are installed at various distances before and after the actual work area. Regulations are specific regarding the use of the devices mentioned earlier, and the placement of warning devices is also dictated by regulation. The purpose of the warnings is to allow drivers to pass work areas safely and without incident. In some locations, such as on interstate highways, the first notice of the impending work area is a sign approximately one mile from the traffic cones that taper the traffic into other lanes if one lane is closed.

Typical equipment used at a work zone includes standard orange cones, lighted and flashing signs, crash-cushion trucks, and human flaggers. Flaggers are normally used on single-lane roadways where traffic is stopped in one direction to allow traffic from the opposite direction to pass through the work area. Alternating traffic through this work area is the prime concern of the flagger. The placement of traffic-control devices such as signs is important, since they can create hazards within the roadway and can be hazards themselves. Signs must be temporary in work zones of short duration or be made to break away in more permanent installations. Traffic-control devices used in work zones are different from those used for standard traffic control, but the goal is the same: safety of the traveling public and pedestrians.

Several principles and procedures must be considered when designing a safe work zone. If the work is to continue for a number of days or weeks, traffic-control devices are more permanent in nature, especially if the roadway remains in repair over this period of time! Many accidents that occur in work zones are contributed to by inattentive drivers. Work zones must be planned well in advance so that proper notice and guides for drivers are in place. One of the most common violations of work-zone design is the lack of appropriate advanced notice to drivers of the impending work area. Work-zone design for nighttime driving must include more highly visible warnings, such as lighted signs, so the attention of nighttime drivers will be drawn to the warnings.

The following factors are important for work-zone safety:

- Traffic safety is a high priority in every emergency or work zone. Every element regarding planning and design must be thoroughly

analyzed and a sound and safe plan properly implemented.

- Traffic movement is the main element to consider when designing a work zone since the traffic that must pass through the work zone is the number one hazard to both workers and other traffic.

- *Traffic guidance* is the method whereby motorists are guided on a safe travel path through and around a work zone. The guidance must include daytime and nighttime traffic-control devices and must consider the human factors of the majority of drivers.

- Inspection of the work zone is imperative for continuous safe operation. Once a work zone is designed and the design is implemented, the traffic-control devices must be constantly monitored for consistent expectancy and safe operation. The work zone must be inspected during both daytime and nighttime operation.

- Maintenance of the work zone needs constant attention during the period the work zone is active because hazards may change from time to time.

Work zones must be analyzed by considering the type and location of work being performed, the expected life of the work zone, the type of roadway, and the traffic speed and volume. The location of the work zone is important because the design for a highway is not applicable to all situations, especially inner-city work zones. Shoulders and lane widths must be considered in the design of new traffic patterns as well as traffic volume during various times of day.

Signs and other control devices should be consistent for all work-zone areas so that drivers know what to expect. The colors and sizes of signs specified by regulation must be adhered to since drivers expect certain types of signs to be a certain size and color. Various types of tubular markers and barricades are designed to alert drivers at various stages as traffic flows through a work zone. Flaggers should be used when traffic is compressed into a single lane so that traffic congestion and accidents are reduced or eliminated.

The training of flaggers must be consistent with regulations, and any deviation from the standards and expectancies of the traveling public should be eliminated. Flashing traffic-control devices that alter traffic patterns must be set up at the minimum distance required. If the warning distance is insufficient for drivers to alter their travel pattern in time, accidents and congestion can develop. During any traffic-pattern change, traffic signs, especially route signs and detour signs, become crucial.

DEFENSIVE DRIVING TACTICS
Weather-Related Safety

In addition to darkness, weather (high winds, snow and rain, dust storms, and so on) is a key factor contributing to accidents and injuries. Under the best dry conditions, posted speed limits can be used to regulate speed, but when weather conditions are adverse, speed limits no longer should be used as a guideline. Large tractor-trailers are especially vulnerable to poor weather conditions; they may jackknife under slippery surface conditions or be blown off the road during high winds. During long hauls, driver fatigue sets in, and if this is coupled with adverse weather, the driver's attention and precision are drastically reduced. Frequent stops will help with fatigue, and drivers should stop and sleep when necessary.

Weather can affect the mechanics of vehicles too:

- Moisture in air-brake bleed-off tanks (drain moisture) can freeze and lock the brakes if not drained properly.
- Antifreeze must be appropriate for anticipated temperatures; it should be adequate for a lower temperature range than anticipated in case there is an extreme cold snap.
- During winter months when snow or slush is on the roadway, windshield wipers and washers must work properly, and washer fluid must be antifreeze protected. Dirty windshields may cause vision problems and accidents.
- Headlamps must be kept clear during nighttime use, and if the roadway is covered with

rain or snow, they must be cleaned periodically during a long trip.
- On slippery surfaces, it is easy to lose traction, so drivers must accelerate slowly and with light foot pressure.
- Most commercial vehicles, state regulations permitting, may use chains or studded tires on their drive axle. They work well on snowy roadways, but on dry roadways, they produce less friction (stability) than standard tires do.
- During adverse weather conditions, stopping and braking efficiency are reduced. Adjusting speed will improve these problems, but increasing the following distance behind other vehicles is also critical in order to stop safely.
- During turns in poor weather, a gentler and slightly wider turn, if possible, should be made since cutting a turn sharply in adverse weather will exacerbate poor handling and possibly cause accidents and injuries.
- Drivers must not drive through water above the vehicle's brake lining, since wet brakes will dramatically reduce stopping distance.

Pretrip Vehicle Examination

A pretrip inspection should be performed each time a driver begins a trip. A thorough pretrip inspection to catch operational problems is a defensive driving practice since it is an active step compared to waiting until a problem arises. Drivers doing pretrip inspections may identify defective safety devices or worn parts prior to driving on the road, thereby avoiding an accident or injury. Inspections are designed so that the operator can spot system problems prior to an actual failure. Specifically, the following items should be checked to make sure they are working properly prior to starting out on a trip (ATA 1996, 46):

1. Service brakes, including couplings between tractors and trailers, should be inspected for cracks or holes. The hoses can rupture or crack because of changes between one climate and another, and the ensuing loss of brake fluid or air pressure could be critical.

2. The parking brake should be inspected to determine whether it is working properly. If the service brakes do not function, this is the driver's last line of defense.

3. The steering mechanisms must be examined for unusual noise or friction, and if there is a problem, a determination must be made regarding its seriousness. An examination of the steering mechanism by a garage mechanic is not warranted at the start of each trip; this type of detailed inspection is done during regular maintenance.

4. The horn, windshield wipers, and rearview mirrors must all be in proper working order prior to the start of a trip. If any of these devices are not working or are damaged, they must be replaced prior to the start of the trip.

5. Wheels, rims, and emergency equipment (flares, reflective triangles, communication radio, and so on) must be inspected for damage and defects. Wheels and rims, if damaged, must be replaced, because they can cause loss of control and accidents. Emergency equipment must be carried and maintained on every commercial vehicle. The required number of flares, reflective triangles, and radios must be present, and they must be in proper working order and have working batteries. It is prudent to carry extra batteries. Emergency equipment may include extreme cold-weather clothing in case of a breakdown or being stranded.

During inspections, the cargo must be examined to be sure tie-downs or other securing methods have not become loose. The cargo must be thoroughly inspected for shifting that could cause a loss of cargo and possibly cause the truck to overturn on a curve. If cargo has shifted and the driver cannot correct the problem, the truck must be taken out of service until the load can be secured properly. When trailers are security sealed and the driver cannot inspect the cargo for shifting, unusual noises could indicate shifted cargo,

and the driver should warn unloading personnel of a possible hazard as they open the trailer door.

Figure 25 is an example of an inspection record. It can be modified to accommodate different fleet vehicle types and other information needed. The author suggests that vehicle trip sheets be kept for approximately one year and reviewed to determine whether retraining is necessary.

Driver Distraction

The specific sources of distraction among distracted drivers are listed in Table 13.

Percentages for the different types of distractions should be viewed as preliminary estimates that are likely biased by differential underreporting. These are research results that will be useful in building a broader understanding of driver distraction. The percentages for the different types of distractions should not be used to guide policy development.

Young drivers (under 20 years of age) were most likely to be involved in distraction-related crashes. In addition, certain types of distractions were more prominent in certain age groups: adjusting the radio, CD, or MP3 player among the under 20-year-olds; other occupants (e.g., young children) among 20–29 year-olds; and outside objects and events, among those age 65 and older. Variations by the gender of

TABLE 13

Specific Driver Distractions

Specific Distraction	% of Drivers
Outside person, object, or event	29.4
Adjusting radio, cassette, CD	11.4
Other occupant in vehicle	10.9
Moving object in vehicle	4.3
Other device/object brought into vehicle	2.9
Adjusting vehicle/climate controls	2.8
Eating or drinking	1.7
Using/dialing cell phone	1.5
Smoking related	0.9
Other distrction	25.6
Unknown distraction	8.6
	100.0

(AAA Foundation 2001)

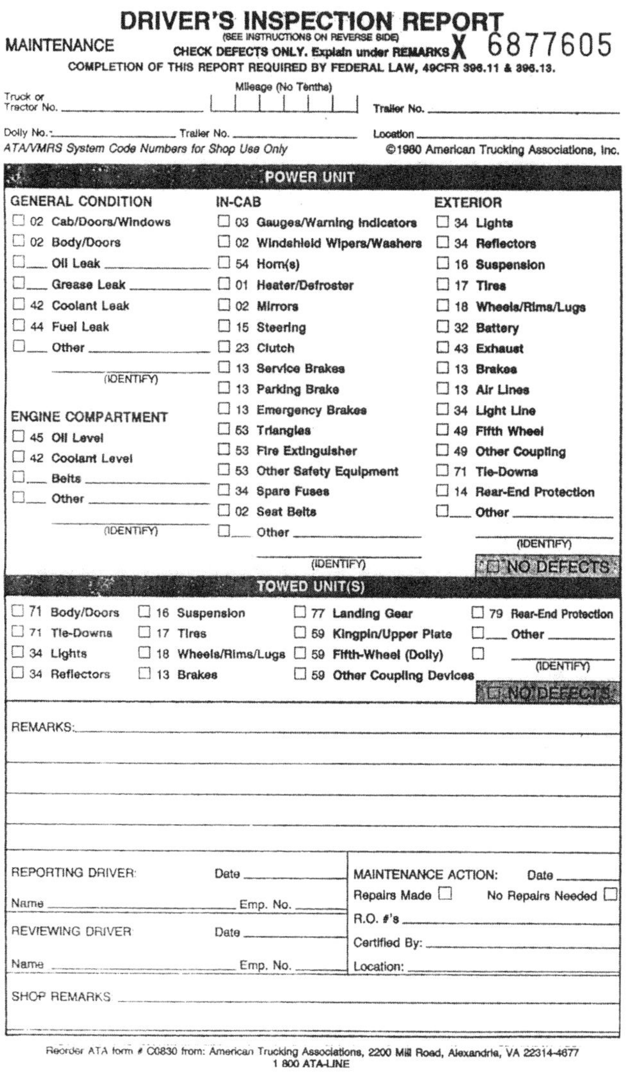

FIGURE 25. Example of an inspection record
(*Source*: ATA 1996, 19-1–19-12)

the driver were less pronounced, although males were slightly more likely than females to be categorized as distracted at the time of their crash (AA Foundation 2001).

Drivers see more poorly at night, and pedestrians overestimate how visible they are to motorists, according to Richard Tyrell, a Clemson University psychology professor and researcher who has been studying night driving for 20 years. Tyrell has conducted more than 30 experiments to find ways to keep both drivers and pedestrians safer after dark (Tyrrell et al. 2009).

Over the weekend, two pedestrians in Aiken County died after being hit by cars while trying to cross a highway at night, and a Walhalla man died after he was struck by a Greenville County sheriff deputy's car while crossing a street early in the morning.

Each year about 5000 pedestrians are hit and killed in traffic accidents. "Most of those incidents happen at night even though there are fewer drivers," Tyrrell said. Tyrrell's research has found that drivers steer pretty well at night, which may lead to not slowing down. Most drivers also rely too heavily on low-beam headlights (Tyrrell 2006).

Most pedestrians wear dark clothing, making them harder to see and when they do wear reflective material, it usually consists of a vest. Reflective material would be better if people wore it on their joints so it would move more. "Humans are good at seeing humans in motion" (Tyrell 2006).

Tyrrell and another Clemson psychology professor, Johnell Brooks, use a driving simulator to study how drivers of different ages perform at night. They have found that while drivers stay in their lanes well, they overestimate how well they see in the dark. Older drivers have more difficulty seeing at night but then also tend to be more aware of the problem. The simulator allows researchers to put people into what might be dangerous situations and record how they react (Balk et al. 2008).

In another experiment, a volunteer pedestrian walks in place in a low-traffic area in a Clemson neighborhood. Sometimes the volunteer wears only dark clothing, other times reflective material. Student volunteers then are driven through the area and push a button when they first see the pedestrian. The study found that if people are going to wear reflective material, the best place is on the ankles because they move as you walk and the low beams will shine on the ankles first. Tyrrell said people need to be educated about the hazards of night driving and hopes pedestrians will wear more reflective clothing and stay away from busy traffic areas. If such warnings "can get into their heads before they decide to step into an intersection, I've succeeded," he said (Balk et al. 2008).

Driver Training

Driver training begins with a driver's application for a commercial driver's license and should never stop. The interviewing, hiring, and training of transit bus drivers in particular should be taken very seriously, since dozens of passengers will be exposed to unsafe situations if the bus driver is not properly evaluated and trained. Even when drivers have commercial driver's licenses (CDLs), a safety-conscious transportation organization will continually provide them with updated training and critique their driving records. At the time drivers are being considered for hiring, transit companies should order a motor-vehicle driving license abstract to determine whether any moving violations appear on their record. With constant monitoring and continuing driver education, insurance carriers may reduce premiums if companies demonstrate a serious commitment to employing safe drivers and maintaining driving safety. If fleet operators are not able to teach defensive driving in-house, there are trucking associations [such as the American Trucking Association (ATA) and regional or state trucking associations] that offer defensive driving courses. Drivers should be instructed about stopping distances and following distances and participate in emergency warning-device exercises. Transit companies should have written policies on conducting accident analyses and thoroughly review accidents to determine whether they were unavoidable or avoidable. This type of analysis can help to determine whether drivers need refresher courses.

During driver training, issues relating to vehicle size should be discussed thoroughly, including methods of performing emergency maneuvers. Safe driving requires qualified drivers, and professional drivers should have as their objectives the desire and pride to improve professional driving knowledge and awareness, good driving judgment, foresight, and skill. Driver training must encompass pretrip inspections, fatigue and stress, handling emotions, and having a good attitude, as well as the effects of age on a driver's vision, hearing, and mobility. Driver retraining is a good time to spot bad habits and correct them. People who drive more than one type of vehicle must also be in-structed on the unusual aspects of safe operation for each type of vehicle they will be expected to operate.

Buses must be driven with a high degree of safety because they carry a very precious commodity: human passengers. Specific considerations must be incorporated into the decisions bus drivers make regarding where to stop buses in relation to parked vehicles, high curbs, pedestrian hazards, crosswalks, and so on. Safely picking up passengers is also crucial, since passengers boarding buses can be seriously injured. Bus drivers should be instructed that they are authorized to pick up and drop off passengers only at designated bus stops.

Bus drivers must constantly evaluate their surroundings. They must be sure the bus is safe to operate in the existing environment given the bus's width, length, and height. They must be sure there are no overhead hazards that can hit the top of the bus and jolt the occupants. One way to prevent this type of incident is for drivers to know the height of the bus. Choosing appropriate locations for bus stops is extremely important and is usually done by transit companies in cooperation with local towns and law enforcement. Locations have good points and bad points and must be evaluated in total context for the good of the overall ridership.

Accident Avoidance and Anticipation

The motor fleet industry must consider and create a system to control accidents and injuries. The core aspects of an efficient system include record keeping, analysis, prevention activities, and evaluation. Records that reveal what types of accidents typically occur must be kept so that avoiding them can become part of a teaching program. Records also indicate injuries sustained by employees and can be a means to analyze the cost of injuries to the fleet company. A simple accident register can be prepared using the Department of Transportation (DOT) Federal Highway Administration (FHWA) requirements in 49 CFR Part 390.15. This information can be found online at the U.S. Department of Transportation's Web site (www.dot.gov). Two important aspects of accident analysis are specifics of the cause of the accident and recommendations for what can be done to eliminate the same type of accident in the future. An accident review should include the following data (ATA 1996, 56–59):

- the *employee's name* (Repeated problems involving the same individual will come to the surface, and appropriate action can be taken.)
- the *time of day, lighting conditions, and other conditions* that may or may not have contributed to the accident.
- the *day of the week* (Patterns may emerge that indicate solutions. For example, if records show that accidents occur more frequently on the first and last day of the week, this could be an indication of preoccupation by employees.)
- *hours driver had been on duty at the time of the accident* (This information must be recorded by regulation, but can also be critical in evaluating driver fatigue.)
- *weather and road conditions* (They can indicate the conditions that most often cause accidents, and steps can be taken to work around them.)
- the *type of vehicle*, including handling characteristics and whether the vehicle was being loaded or unloaded
- the *speed and condition of the vehicle* (These are usually looked at first as primary accident causes.)
- the *type of accident* (For example, if the driver's back was turned when the accident occurred, this may indicate that the driver needs additional training.)
- *what the employee was doing at the moment of injury, body part(s) injured, and other pertinent information that will help to analyze the accident*

Accident avoidance and anticipation are major factors in safe driving. Avoiding an accident requires anticipation and the proper choice of an evasive action. In order to anticipate a possible hazard in the roadway ahead, the driver must be attentive—not distracted. Accident avoidance is a learned process—not an inborn one. For example, many drivers, when confronted with a vehicle entering their travel path from the right, steer to the left in an effort to avoid impact. If, under these circumstances, the driver steers to the right, the encroaching vehicle will usually pass through the driver's original travel path and an impact will be avoided. This is a quick response that can be learned.

Anticipation requires more than attention; it requires training and a conscious desire to understand what constitutes a developing hazard. A hazard could develop when another vehicle slows to a stop from either the left or right or when traffic ahead becomes congested. Drivers should always enter intersections with their foot off the accelerator and hovering over the brake so that their reaction time is cut to a minimum. An accident has been said to be an unfortunate event resulting from unavoidable causes. While some may think this definition is true, others question the term *unavoidable*. Accidents can be unfortunate, but they should never be accepted as the cost of doing business. Many can be avoided, depending upon the circumstances and the drivers involved. A term used by many, *preventable collision*, is defined as a collision in which the driver failed to do every reasonable thing. While litigators may latch onto this terminology, there is much more to the term preventable. Drivers should be aware of some preventable causes of collisions:

- slowing down too late
- failing to scan the road
- failing to check blind spots
- not driving at the appropriate speed given an adverse condition, regardless of the posted speed limit
- following too closely
- not focusing on the driving task

Other factors contribute to accidents, such as the condition of the roadway, work-zone traffic, and heavy vehicle loads. Factors can generally be categorized into three areas: driver factors, vehicle factors, and condition factors. Avoiding accidents requires training in recognizing hazards, understanding proper defensive maneuvers, and deciding and acting correctly in time to prevent an impact. One anticipation training tip is for drivers to ask themselves "What if?" To plan ahead, drivers can be driving down a roadway, looking for an escape route. A constant "what if" strategy can help drivers predetermine accurate evasive maneuvers when faced with specific hazards.

Turning and Maneuvering

Drivers of large trucks must use extreme care when turning and maneuvering. The large mass and length of commercial and fleet vehicles demand vigilance and caution that is referred to as managing space—in other words, operating, parking, and maneuvering fleet vehicles. If drivers are not thoroughly familiar with the space and rear vision limitations of the vehicles they operate, they will be at a disadvantage and may become involved in avoidable incidents. Understanding the length and turning ability of large vehicles is crucial when learning how to drive them. Space is limited on highways and must be preserved during parking and limited-space maneuvering. Braking maneuvers require drivers to be familiar with the weight of their vehicles, their cargo, and the distance needed to safely brake and come to a complete stop. Drivers also must be aware of the spacing between their vehicle and the one in front of them—the *following distance*. This is a crucial factor in avoiding rear-impact accidents. Some transportation engineers the author has spoken with understand and acknowledge that roadways in the United States are built and designed mainly for passenger vehicles, not for fleet or commercial vehicles. Lanes are normally eleven to twelve feet wide. Although curves are designed for speeds greater than the posted speed limit, drivers of commercial trucks must be aware of design limitations and know that speed limits on curves should not be exceeded.

Overhead space is another factor drivers must consider when operating large vehicles in close spaces or on open roadways. Overpasses are generally fourteen feet high. It is important for drivers of closed-end trailers to know their trailer's height and for drivers of flatbed trailers to know the height to the top of their cargo in relation to the height of each overpass they drive under (ATA 1996, 85-87) so that overpass collisions can be avoided. Drivers must also be aware that strong winds can force trailers out of travel lanes

and that vehicles could hit overpass abutments or other vehicles passing in adjacent lanes.

Making right turns in urban areas may be very difficult since vehicles in the right lane of the intersection may not give trucks sufficient turning space. Signaling long before starting the turn is crucial. Attempts to squeeze by in limited roadway spaces, especially in city driving, can cause impacts with other vehicles and pedestrians. To make a proper turn, a driver must keep the vehicle in its own lane and make a wide turn into the two lanes of the street he or she is turning onto (NJDOT 1988, 2-22–2-25). All turns must be approached with caution. Before starting a left turn, drivers should keep the vehicle in the center of the intersection and not cut the corner.

When backing into a dock, drivers must be prepared to use a spotter. Sometimes—usually at loading or unloading docks, not on roadways—the trailer will be parked and the tractor will be in a jackknifed position.

Tanker trucks and their cargo are constantly moving during transit. Tanker trucks are designed with a baffle system that slows displacement of the liquids in the tank compartment. These trucks are especially susceptible to rollover since the baffles are sometimes lateral and liquids shift to the outside during a turn. The suspension of tanker trucks is usually stiffer than that of other trucks to allow for very little compression during turns so that liquid cargo remains stable.

ERGONOMIC AND INJURY BIOMECHANICAL ISSUES
Investigating Employee Injuries

The musculoskeletal system is quite complicated and is very vulnerable at times. The *musculoskeletal system* includes tendons, ligaments, fascia, cartilage, bone, and muscle. Soft-tissue injuries usually relate to tendons, ligaments, fascia, and muscle. Soft-tissue injuries can occur in an occupational environment as well as a nonoccupational environment, such as motor-vehicle impact and so on. Functional units or joints are a necessary connecting point that allows linear body segments to move and interact.

Ligaments connect bone to bones, which provide stability through the joints, and tendons attach muscle to bone, which transmits force. The *fascia* is also a connective tissue that covers organs or parts of organs and keeps them separate within the body cavity. The fibers run parallel in tendons, nonparallel in ligaments, and irregularly in the skin. Each group of fibers creates strength of its own, which is based upon the structure of the fibers. Collagen fibers, while under tension, first stretch slightly and then become stiffer until failure. The fibers have a wavy pattern, which accounts for the initial slight stretching until the wavy pattern is eliminated. Elastic fibers are weakened and become brittle as they stretch greater than collagen fibers and can deform more than at higher degrees. As the elastic fibers stretch, they reach a point where they stiffen, and failure occurs with little warning. Connective tissue as one conceding gets its strength, depending upon the number of collagen or elastic fibers contained in the tissue.

Bone can be molded or change in size and shape based upon the stress and the duration of the stress. The relationship between change and stress is still unknown but could be described mathematically. The skeletal system reaches its maximum mass (strength) at about age 30, after which bone loss occurs continuously. Gradual aging changes normal bone into osteoporotic bone at an accelerating rate. In the early 30s, there is little change in bone loss between men and women, but it sharply increases for women after menopause. Changes relating to aging produce the following results:

- continuing decrease in mineral content
- cortical bone becomes thinner
- increasing diameter of long bones, which increase the moment arm
- decreasing trabeculae (inner core of cancellous bone) in cancellous bone

For these reasons, the bones are weaker and fracture more often after trivial trauma in older people, especially women.

Disc compression studies have shown the discs are flexible at low loads and resistance increases at higher loads (Backaitis 1993a). This study also indicates the discs are particularly at risk from lateral bending and rotation, and portion is especially harmful to the disc and responsible for failure when combined with compression. Compressive loads to the lumbar-supplied failure occur in the end plates, then in the vertebrae bodies and, lastly, in the discs proper. There is great variation among individuals and age groups in equating moment rotation and force deformation of the motion disc segments.

Muscle strength is of great importance, since many jobs in industry require workers to exceed their strength or at least approach their limit. Muscular strength is defined as the strength muscles can produce during maximum exertion. *Muscular strength* is separate from *muscular endurance*. The latter is a measurement of the amount of muscular strength over time intervals. Naturally, the initial exertion of muscular strength is greater for a short time but, over a longer time, the measured muscular strength is reduced. This correlation is important when creating jobs requiring muscular strength over a worker's shift. *Isokinetic strength* is determined by controlling the movement of the joints. *Isotonic strength* requires continuing muscle activity while the velocity of the muscle changes. *Static strength* involves fixed postures (holding an object) and is usually associated with isometric contractions or exercises. Isokinetic, isotonic, and isoinertial are considered dynamic muscular movement, such as lifting or pushing. Strength and force curves can be developed and analyzed upon obtaining data from subjects. This information is valuable for matching the worker with the required task.

Sitting while performing tasks saves energy and is generally best for close and precise work. The lumbar curve is *lordotic* (backward curve), since the vertebrae and discs are thicker in front than in the back. This is the posture that creates the upright torso, which is what all of our mothers meant when they said "sit up straight." The lumbar spine articulates, or moves, while the sacrum is fused with the pelvis. This feature creates a rotation about the pelvis and shapes the lumbar spine. In a sitting posture, the pelvis rotates forward, which creates lordosis in the lumbar. When a person is sitting in a relaxed posture, the lumbar may be either straight or in a slight *kyphosis* (forward curve) position. The spine is comprised of four segments: (1) the cervical with seven vertebrae; (2) the thoracic, with twelve vertebrae; (3) the lumbar, with five vertebrae; and (4) the sacrum, also with five vertebrae that are not articulated. The posture shape of a seatback can influence the curvature of the spine. Normally, the cervical is in slight lordosis, along with the lumbar, and the thoracic is in slight kyphosis when a person is standing.

There are times when an injury claimed by an employee is investigated; either in response to a workers' compensation claim or civil or criminal litigation. The claimed injury can occur while driving a fleet truck or fleet passenger vehicle. Your attorney will usually take the lead in this scenario but you will still be expected to assist in the claim defense and process.

Injury biomechanics includes the analysis, research, and calculations relating to a specific accident (motor vehicle, slip, trip, fall, etc.). The conclusion of injury biomechanics is to determine from the evidence if there exists a mechanism of injury to support the claim. The mechanism is crucial in determining the probability of injury. Biomechanics does not conclude an injury could or could not have occurred, only that a mechanism is present or not. Studies are used to quantify forces of an impact of an accident to help evaluate the probability of the claimed injury. The accuracy of the injury biomechanical analysis is directly dependant on the evidence, testimony, and available replicate research.

Injuries to employees may include upper and lower extremities, neck, back, and so on. All claimed injuries have a mechanism of injury and must be accurately analyzed using the appropriate scientific principals (Rivers 2001, 53–57).

Occupants in vehicles are subject to injuries and fatalities if safety is not of prime importance, and of course, occupants must actually use seatbelts in order for them to prevent injury or death. It is easy to understand that, in a collision between a large commercial truck and a typical passenger vehicle, the truck occupants will probably be injured less seriously than those in the passenger vehicle.

Seatbelts use two types of mechanical systems: (1) *gravity* or (2) a *pretensioner*. In the gravity-operated seatbelt, a mechanism in the spooling portion simply rotates upon emergency braking. When the front of

the vehicle dips, the mechanism locks the seatbelt in place. The disadvantage of this type of seatbelt is that unless the occupant has the seatbelt properly positioned and tight against his or her body, the slack in the seatbelt remains on impact. The pretensioner system resolves this problem: the pretensioner automatically takes up the slack and usually presses the occupant against the back of the seat.

Occupant protection in motor fleet and commercial vehicles is usually more of a concern with passenger vehicle fleets or small vans than with large tractor-trailers. Usually during impacts, drivers of tractor-trailers or large trucks do not sustain serious injury due to the large mass of the vehicle. If the vehicle rolls over, however, drivers of such vehicles could be severely injured or killed if they did not use a seatbelt.

While today it may be difficult to believe, until the 1950s seatbelts were not even considered an option on most vehicles, apparently because the public was not demanding safety items on vehicles they purchased. Research into the safety of seatbelts was not widely understood or demanded. However, occupant protection in standard passenger vehicles requires understanding and proper use of seatbelts. seatbelts should be adjusted so that the shoulder portion passes between the middle of the shoulder and the neck. The belt must be snug so that the wearer cannot move forward or side to side upon impact. Figure 26 is a diagram of a side view of a typical seat-belt locking mechanism without a pretensioner. Diagram B-2 is the position of the locking mechanism upon impact. If occupants move out of position during an impact while

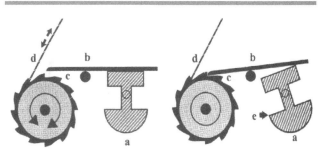

B-1 NORMAL CONDITIONS   B-2 EMERGENCY CONDITIONS

FIGURE 26. Side view of a typical seatbelt locking mechanism without a pretensioner (*Source:* Rivers 2001, 53–57)

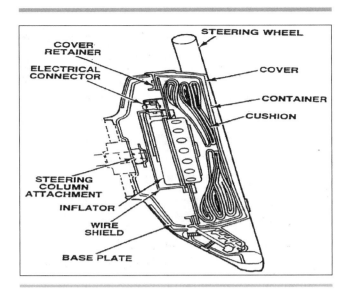

FIGURE 27. A cutaway showing the manner in which an airbag is folded inside the steering wheel (*Source:* Rivers 2000, 55–60)

an airbag deploys, more severe injuries could occur. Figure 27 shows a folded airbag ready to be deployed.

One of the most prevalent types of injury in motor-vehicle impacts is the whiplash (cervical spine) injury, which is a severe problem in the United States. Even though most people survive this type of injury, the cost from lost work and medical treatment is a burden on the U.S. economy and on productivity. Accurate prediction of this type of injury is crucial if prevention devices are to be invented and proper medical diagnosis and treatment is to be effective through the understanding of the mechanisms of the injury.

Statistics concerning whiplash (Croft 1995, 86–98) include:

- Most injuries occur at crash speeds below 12 mph.
- Most cars withstand 8–12-mph impacts without vehicle damage.
- More than half of all low-speed, rear-impact collision (LOSRIC) injuries occur without vehicle damage.
- There is no correlation between vehicle damage and injury outcome.
- During impact, the peak acceleration of the occupant's head is much greater than the peak acceleration of the vehicle.

- In a 5-mph crash the occupant's head typically experiences 10–12 g of acceleration.
- More than three million Americans sustain whiplash injuries every year.
- The reported risk (probability) of injury in a LOSRIC is 35 percent to 68 percent. The Japanese Auto Insurance Rating Association reports a 50 percent risk of injury.
- About 10 percent of those injured become permanently disabled.
- *Minor* neck injuries account for up to 60 percent of all permanent impairment claims.
- For every 6 million occupants in LOSRICs,
  - about three million will be injured (approximately the population size of South Carolina)
  - about 1.5 million will have chronic pain (approximately the population size of Nebraska)
  - about 400,000 of those with chronic pain will become disabled, usually due to pain (approximately the population size of Wyoming) (Microsoft Encarta 2006).
- Nearly half of all chronic neck pain in America is due to car crashes—mostly LOSRICs.
- About 9 percent of all Americans suffer from chronic neck pain due to LOSRICs.
- Children are two to three times more likely to suffer whiplash injuries than adults.

A conservative estimate of the cost of spinal cord injuries to the health and insurance industries due to medical costs and lost productivity is $97 million annually (Nahum 2002, 324–330).

The number of spinal cord injuries, including whiplash, in the United States continues to climb and is a major concern of the automobile, insurance, and health industries as evidenced by the following data (Shands 1993, 75–79):

- The number of new injuries in the United States in 2007 was about 10,000.
- The gender breakdown for whiplash is 82 percent male, 18 percent female.
- The highest per-capita rate of injury occurs between the ages of 16 and 30.

- The leading causes of spinal cord injury are
  - motor-vehicle accidents: 44 percent
  - acts of violence: 24 percent
  - falls: 22 percent
  - sports: 8 percent (two-thirds from diving)
  - other: 2 percent.

Whiplash analysis does not seem to be consistently accurate, and the true mechanisms are still not fully understood. The mechanisms and their predictability must be thoroughly understood by the medical community and automobile manufacturers in order for proper treatment to be given and prevention methods instituted. See "Important Terms" at the end of this chapter for definitions of biomechanical injury anatomy terms.

As previously noted, the mechanisms that cause whiplash are not fully understood. Kornhauser of EM Systems Inc., concluded "it is apparent that the injury threshold, the approximate level of trauma to cause injury, is above 8 kph, or 5 mph, *even for subjects with mild preexisting spinal degeneration*" [author's emphasis] (Kornhauser 1993, 1–14). Further uncertainty is evidenced by Nielsen, et al., who tried to accurately predict the human response to delta-v (severity of impact) using mathematical modeling. They concluded "further work is required to explore the validity of the model used to calculate delta-v" (Nielsen et al. 1997, 23–28). Delta-v is a widely used measurement for determining the probability of injury. It is a measurement of the change of velocity over time. For example, decelerating from 50 mph to 0 mph in 0.1 second is more severe than decelerating from 50 mph to 0 mph in 0.5 second. The probability of injury depends on both the change of force and the amount of time over which the change of force takes place. Astronauts, for example, are not injured when accelerating from zero to approximately 18,000 mph because of the length of time it takes for this change to occur. It is the opinion of the author that, while the mechanisms of whiplash injury are controversial and not totally understood, diagnosis of whiplash without a full understanding of the mechanisms involved is often given.

Whiplash injury has a great potential for insurance fraud and can greatly increase the cost of insurance for all consumers. This problem is worldwide, as evidenced by Cupid's research, which concluded that "there is urgent need to introduce accident reconstruction in the Caribbean [to counter insurance fraud]. Insurance companies continue to receive a level of practice that needs to be brought up to international standards" (Cupid 2002, 1–16). The research associated with this type of problem is of paramount importance. Millions of dollars in healthcare and insurance costs could be saved and devoted to designing better and more efficient safety equipment to reduce the problem and costs. The United States is not the only country with widespread insurance fraud, and we may be able to learn from other countries how to prevent or at least greatly reduce insurance fraud.

Pintar states a need for "further research to better understand the biomechanics and mechanisms of [motor-vehicle injuries]" (Cupid 2002, 1–26). Learning how to accurately and reliably diagnose whiplash and understanding the mechanisms that cause it, can aid in the fight against insurance fraud. The research of Lawrence et al. concluded that "it is not known if the conclusions drawn from [research] testing can be applied to higher severity collisions" (Kornhauser 2002, 1–15).

It is the opinion of the author that future studies should focus on determining how to accurately predict the occurrence of whiplash injuries, beginning with a review of present research in assessing whiplash probability. In order to fight whiplash fraud, determining injury thresholds for the general population is critical. Fraud from rear-end motor-vehicle accidents, according to insurance advertising, has increased dramatically over the past few years. Research can assist in preventing fraud by developing a more accurate understanding of the mechanism of injury and the probability of injury.

Driver Work Space and Vision

The interior of a truck's cab can be considered a closed environment, and as such must be controlled for the driver's comfort. Air temperature, temperature of surrounding surfaces, humidity, air movement or ventilation, and air quality must all be controlled. The temperature of the human body is not a constant

98.6°F throughout. This temperature, also known as *core temperature*, is found only in the interior of the brain and other organs. There is great temperature variation in the muscles, the limbs, and the skin—called the *shell temperature*. The body automatically attempts to regulate body heat by either conserving or dissipating it. The rule of thermodynamics states that energy always flows from a warm location to a cold location. As a driver's body begins to suffer from excessive heat or cold, his or her safety and the safety of passengers and other motorists becomes jeopardized (Kroemer 1999, 355–369).

The temperature of adjacent surfaces within a truck's cab should not fluctuate more than two to three degrees. Humidity does not affect temperature substantially, but air begins to feel stuffy within the range of 80 percent humidity at 18°C (64.4°F) and 60 percent humidity at 24°C (75.2°F). Conditions also become unpleasant when air movement is below 0.5 meters per second (m/s), even when the air is warm. Air currents from behind are more unpleasant than frontal currents, and the neck and feet are especially sensitive to drafts; a cool draft is less welcome than a warm one. Seat occupants have reported finding air movement unpleasant at more than 0.2 m/s. Recommended temperatures for comfort are 20–21°C in the winter and 20–24°C in the summer for sedentary work such as driving (Kroemer 1999, 370–377).

The driver's environment is important for both comfort and safety. The ergonomics of the various dials and switches contributes to driver comfort by reducing fatigue and to driver safety by reducing unnecessary movement or distraction. When drivers take over-the-road trips in large trucks with large trailers, sleeping accommodations must be considered as well as aspects of driver comfort in all climates. It is also important to consider ease and safety of entering and exiting the cab. The number and placement of footholds and handholds and the distance between each pair are important because some tractors are high enough above the ground that a slip could cause a serious injury (Woodson 1992, 82-85).

Driver limitations must be considered during interviewing for, hiring for, and operation of motor-vehicle fleets. The ability of operators to drive in inclement weather should be strongly analyzed since they will be expected to drive in all types of environments and with different types of cargo. Important assets for professional truck drivers are good judgment and not taking chances. Drivers limit themselves by using poor safety practices and having avoidable accidents. Vision is one of the most important factors of safety since it is mandatory for the safe operation of fleet vehicles. Poor visibility, whether due to poor roadway design, weather, an obstructed windshield, or a poor driving position, must be dealt with immediately.

Limitations placed upon drivers also come from the type of truck being driven and the cargo being carried. If the truck is a tractor with two trailers, it will be more difficult to drive and have more limitations than a tractor with one trailer. Drivers must understand, realize, and consider these limitations when making maneuvers.

Visibility, both front and rear, is important, since without good, clear visibility the operation of fleet vehicles is extremely compromised. Visibility is directly affected by seating placement and window size and shape. Visibility is also affected by the placement of dashboard dials and switches; if they are placed incorrectly, viewing them could take the driver out of safe visibility range for operating the vehicle. If the numbers on the dials are too small or the lighting within the dials is too dim, the driver will have difficulty instantly determining the position of the hands. Dials should be placed so that they are not partially or totally blocked by the steering wheel or another fixed object in the tractor's cab. Dials should be designed and installed so that drivers do not have to move their head or torso to read them. Drivers should also be able to read any dial on the dashboard without staring or removing their eyes from the roadway for an unsafe period of time, usually more than one second. Visibility to the back of the trailer must be unrestricted, because the cargo may become loose and the driver must stop when he sees that the cargo needs to be tightened.

The interior of the tractor must be an ergonomically friendly environment, since over-the-road or other long trips can easily fatigue drivers and create unsafe situations. Special attention should be paid to temperature, ventilation, noise, and vibration. Over time, vibration—the oscillating motion of the body and its limbs and organs—will cause fatigue and produce an unsafe driving situation. *Free vibration* is caused by internal forces, and *forced vibration* is caused by external forces. Truck drivers are constantly subjected to vibration forces since they sit on a relatively stiff seat in a vehicle with a relatively stiff suspension. Harmful vibration usually occurs at the lower end of the vibration frequency scale (Chaffin 1999, 463–473).

The vibration and frequency of noise is harmful to the human ear. Humans are sensitive to vibration of the *vestibular* (hearing) system at low frequencies—1 to 2 hertz (Hz), such as vibrations generated by ships, cranes, or aircraft. Humans are also sensitive to vibration of the body at frequencies of 2 to 20–30 Hz, the middle frequency range, which is generated by vehicles and aircraft. At high frequencies—greater than 20 Hz, the receptors in muscles, tendons, and skin are highly sensitive. This high-frequency vibration is generated by tools or machines (Chaffin 1999, 485–488).

Designing driver and passenger spaces in buses requires special consideration. Drivers must be able to see nearby hazards or objects as well as necessary gauges and dials. They must also be able to see onboard passengers in case one falls or needs assistance. Seeing passengers is very important during the operation of the bus as well as during stopping and starting. Boarding passengers must also be visible to drivers since injuries can occur when drivers prematurely close access doors or pull away when all passengers are not properly seated.

Material Handling

Commercial fleet operators must be concerned with material-handling injuries when loading and unloading their vehicles. Forklifts, cranes, and hoists are used regularly at truck depots, and rules for operating these types of equipment can be found in OSHA regulations 29 CFR parts 1910.179 and 1926.550. Any time large machines are used, space is at a premium. Minimum width of warehouse aisles is 36 inches when small hand trucks are used and 10 feet if forklifts are used (Marshall 2000, 372–375). NIOSH offers the following statistics:

- Over 60 percent of lower back pain is caused from overexertion.
- Overexertion injuries of the lower back account for a significant loss of work time, and less than one-third of injured employees return to work.
- Overexertion injuries account for one-fourth of all reported occupational injuries in the United States, with some industries reporting that over 50 percent of their total injuries are due to overexertion.

Many characteristics of containers affect material-handling systems, including the load dimensions, distribution of the load, handling the load, and stability of the load. There are physiological limits to lifting based upon size and weight of the load and the frequency of lifting. The more often a load is lifted, the less weight a worker can safely handle. People who lift should consider the following NIOSH recommendations (Marshall 2000, 376–386):

- Lifting should be smooth, with no sudden acceleration.
- Objects lifted should be of moderate width— less than approximately 75 centimeters.
- The lifting path should be unrestricted, with no need to brace the torso with a hand.
- Handles should be secure and in good shape, and temperatures should be favorable to lifting (not too cold or too hot).

NIOSH uses the following formula to determine the recommended weight limit (RWL) for lifting:

$$RWL = LC \times HM \times VM \times DM \times AM \times FM \times CM \quad (8)$$

where

LC = the load constant,
HM = the horizontal multiplier,
VM = the vertical multiplier,
DM = the distance multiplier,
AM = the asymmetric multiplier,
FM = the frequency multiplier, and
CM = the coupling multiplier

These values can be obtained from D. Chaffin's *Occupational Biomechanics* (1999, 315–324).

When material handling is done with equipment such as a forklift or lift truck, the forklift/lift truck operators must be trained, and if they are involved in an accident or near-miss, they must be retrained. Forklift operators must pay special attention to moving in and out of open trailers from a dock since there may not be a smooth transition between the two and there may be a gap that could cause an accident. Usually a large metal sheet is placed over the gap for safety. Forklift operators must also never go around corners without sounding the horn to alert possible pedestrians (NSC 1999, 22–25).

A maintenance schedule must be kept so that fleet vehicle maintenance is performed regularly. If items need to be replaced, they should be replaced promptly even if they are approaching the end of their useful life. If safety items are not replaced but allowed to be used beyond their useful life expectancy, they could fail and cause an accident. Fleet vehicles should be equipped with all necessary parts and equipment that will assist drivers to safely reach a location for permanent repairs.

Loading and unloading should be done in a safe and efficient manner. The shifting of cargo on an open trailer is easy to spot, but on a closed trailer the cargo may shift without the driver knowing it. On a closed trailer, if the cargo has shifted it may fall when the trailer doors are opened, or the cargo may have been jostled to the point that it is unsafe to begin removing packages or boxes for fear that the rest of the cargo will fall. Loading is not only labor-intensive and time-consuming, but is also an art and must be thoroughly thought through prior to the start of the loading process. When cargo is organized by stops, it is convenient for the driver to check it for possible shifting prior to leaving each stop.

Determining the proper method for performing tasks requires planning and forethought. A preferred method, standard practice, and a time standard should be considered when attempting any job function. Training the worker is of utmost importance, since the worker must not only be trained in what the job function is but also how to safely complete the daily tasks. Several methods must be used to determine the safest way to perform a task, which include using

accepted practice and safety scientific data for the subject task at hand. During the interview for the job position, the best worker in relation to experience, knowledge, safety, and physical criteria should be selected. A spirit of cooperation between management and the worker must exist so that the worker does not feel safety is only his responsibility or that management does not care about injuries. It has been clearly shown that a low number of injuries usually provide a higher profit. Another aspect of safety is dividing the workload as equally as possible, so that one worker does not have to perform his task faster and, consequently, in a less safe manner.

Biomechanical safety begins with knowledge of unsafe stress factors, which should be identified by the worker along with his or her supervisor. Trained persons who either perform the task or supervise the task performance can easily identify these stress factors. To analyze safe performance of tasks, one must be able to separate and evaluate each movement of a particular task. Each task has a minimum, median, and maximum time limit for performing the task safely. The evaluation of the worker and the subject task is required to set safe time limits for a particular job function. This motion can be predetermined for a specific task. Some of the movements include reach, position for most efficient movement, the release factor after the motion is completed, rebound as when pulling pieces apart on an assembly line, grasping or controlling an object, eye movement and focus, turning or manipulation of tools as parts, body segment motion, and motion of all or some of these movements simultaneously.

During lifting, the load should be kept as close to the body, lumbar spine, as possible, which results in a much smaller moment arm than if the weight was held outward. Figure 28 demonstrates the compression on the male back at various stages of the distance that the horizontal load (constant 650 kg) is from the spine at L5/S1. The spine must be supported by its own structure, along with the specific muscles; if it is not, it becomes unstable and can buckle under a very low compression force of approximately 20 newtons. The individual muscles exert lateral or front to back forces on the spine to prevent injury from bending and compression buckling. Loading on the disc is less

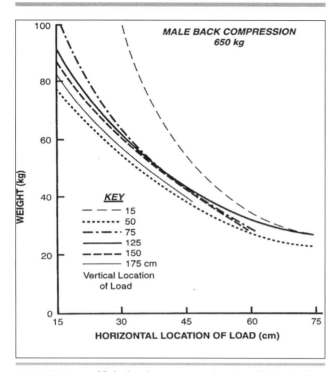

FIGURE 28. Male back compression in relation to the distance of a horizontal load from the spine at L5/S1 (*Source:* Chaffin et al. 1999)

during pushing than pulling, which is why material handlers are usually told to push instead of pull. Minimizing internal disc pressure can be achieved by having the backrest recline at approximately 120 degrees, and the lumbar support at approximately 5 cm. The greatest disc pressure was observed when the backrest was at 90 degrees with no lumbar support. Lumbar support affected lordosis, or backward banding, when the angle of the backrest affected disc loads (Andrews 2005).

There are a number of techniques for lifting. Many are described in other literature; the following are some of the more common techniques (Andrews 2005):

- Select strong people, based on testing, for heavy lifting.
- Bend the knees when in a squat in position, leaving the back straight.
- Do not slip, jerk, or twist during the strongest part while lifting.
- Use machines when possible.
- Divide the weight into smaller, more manageable parts.
- Use a good grip rather than a less secure one.

- If the load consists of smaller pieces, find a container, which will place the load in a more compact state, making sure that the weight is not excessive.
- Keep the load close to the body, since that will greatly reduced the moment arm and reduce the force on the spine.
- If possible, work at knuckle height; avoid lifting loads below the knees and above the shoulders.

Vehicle Design and Driving in the Future

In the author's opinion, about every three to four years there is usually a major design change for family passenger vehicles, and the change is usually based on customers' wants and safety regulations. The future of fleet vehicle design is one in which efficiency, economy, and safety are paramount. Current roadways limit the size of fleet vehicles and consequently limit the size of their cargo. Fuel is one of the main expenses for large truck fleets. The price of fuel may continue to rise, if history is any reference, and a more efficient combustion engine will be required to hold down or at least mitigate the high cost of fuel. Reduction in wind resistance, the rolling resistance of tires, and friction of mechanical parts will be of increasing importance since they directly relate to fuel savings.

Various inventions, such as forward-looking radar, self-parking, and so on, called intelligent transportation systems (ITS), are currently being researched. Another useful system of the future uses infrared to spot pedestrians or animals on roadways long before the driver can see them, especially in adverse weather conditions. Some fleet systems currently use the global positioning system (GPS) to track the speed and location of their tractors and trailers so that it is more difficult for drivers to be off schedule or speeding.

Ride and Vibration

Seating plays an important function in riding performance and vibration dampening. Seat design should be ergonomically correct. The seat's back should be flat vertically and somewhat concave horizontally. Sling-type seats should be avoided because they could cause the weight of the torso and upper legs to be pinched, and the resulting decrease in blood flow could create numbness. Very soft or thickly cushioned seats should also be avoided, since they may cause drivers to become too relaxed when fatigued, compromising safety. The seat back must be inclined so that drivers will be comfortable yet able to keep safety uppermost in their minds (Woodson 1992, 82–85). The seat material should be breathable for air circulation and comfort and have a pattern that will help the driver avoid slipping. It should also be nonflammable, highly resistant to friction and wear, and easy to clean. Foam used in seats should be sufficient to maintain comfort yet not impede visibility or cause *submarining* (sliding forward toward the dashboard) in a frontal collision. Seatbelts must be made of standard materials and must be kept clean and functioning. The seat position must be appropriate for clear and unobstructed vision yet maintain comfort.

It is important to reduce vibration not only for safe vehicle operation but also to avoid driver injury. Usually vibration injuries are subtle at first and become increasingly severe until the source of vibration is eliminated. The smoothness of the vehicle's ride and the construction of the driver's seat play important roles in dampening harmful vibration. The dynamics of vibration begin with an excitation source such as road roughness, tires and wheels, or the engine. The response of the vehicle to this stimulus is the severity of the vibration. A rough road would normally be of short duration while subtler but higher cycles of vibration would usually be over a longer period. Tires can create vibration when their shape is elongated during high-velocity operation. The more misshapen the tire is, the more intense the vibration will be, and the greater the probability of injury is (Kumar 1999, 233–237).

The smoothness of the ride depends on the equilibrium and center of the mass as the mass is rotated. A vehicle's suspension is the main factor in dampening harmful vibration and creating a smooth ride. Dampening consists of both compression and extension of the vehicles' suspension system. Suspension includes the shock-absorber system, which reduces harmful rebounding and extends the time between cycles, effectively dampening or softening vibration. Evidence of

wheel hopping are bumps on the tread surfaces of tires. It is caused when the dampening effect of the suspension is not operating properly but allows wheels to rise and fall very quickly and with great force. Since compression and extension usually are not equal, the spatial frequency of this type of dynamic is best when the frequency is further apart rather than close together.

Vibrations can be injurious to the human body, especially if it is exposed to them over a period of time. *Vibration* is the movement back and forth of a body or mass. Any body that is elastic is subject to vibration. *Free vibration* occurs from internal forces only, such as the vibration of an electric hand tool. *Forced vibration* is a result of external forces, such as motor vehicles riding over bumps. Forced vibration is considered to be more harmful. Regular repetition is referred to as *periodic motion*, and the repetition rate is called *frequency*. Normal frequency is determined using a time value, such as per second. Oscillating movements can be repeated regularly or irregularly. A simple periodic or regular repetition is what is known as a *sine wave* or *harmonic wave*. These types of vibrations, which are regular, can be easily determined in a given period of time. Stochastic or random vibrations cannot be so easily determined, except by means of averaging over time. Vibrations can be small or large; the large vibrations are usually considered peak. These vibrations can be considered strong or a weak by their displacement, velocity, or acceleration. The displacement is the movement over time; the velocity is the speed over time, while the acceleration is the change of velocity over distinctive periods of time.

Acceleration is usually determined in metric terms as meters per second per second or in standard units, such as feet per second. The easiest way to describe oscillations is by the terms *peak* and *average*. This can be easily seen on an oscilloscope. An oscilloscope is similar to a television screen, but rather than entertaining pictures, harmonic vibration is seen as wavy lines of different displacement over time. Vibration can be measured in various ways; the most accurate method is the root mean square value, which is between the average and peak values. The human response to vibration is dependent upon the frequency of such vibration. The greater the cycle of peaks and average is over time (i.e., one second), the more harmful the vibration. The greater occurrence of vibration that applies to a human body is a random motion, as opposed to a regular or periodic motion.

This motion, when analyzed, is split into spectrums, and the most used spectrum for human analysis is the third octave bandwidth. *Accelerometers* are used to measure human exposure to vibration. The data from the accelerometers is broken down into displacement and velocity, which are more easily understood and analyzed. Vibration is a vector quantity, and the human body has mechanical properties that vary with the direction of the vibration. Vibration is usually measured along three directors, which are classified as the x, y, and z axes. The specific direction of the vibration depends upon the hand tool or other source of vibration such that any harmful vibration effects followed the vector and access of the tool and body region.

The human body does allow absorption of certain amounts of vibration; however, beyond this threshold, vibrations become mechanisms of injury and, in extreme cases, may cause death. We have all become familiar with vibrators that, when used on the back of the neck, have a calming and soothing effect. If this same vibration is kept on the skeletal system for any duration, injury could occur. Injury vibrations depend mainly on their frequency, amplitude, or direction, as well as exposure time (Chaffin et al. 1999).

Occupational Stress

Occupational stress is the reaction of an individual to a threatening or pressing situation (Kroemer 1999, 211–215). Stress comes from many sources and could lead to injury or death depending upon the work being performed. Humans are better than machines at (Kroemer 1999, 157–160):

- detecting low levels of light and sound
- detecting a wide variety of stimuli
- perceiving patterns and the formulation of their general makeup
- detecting signals when the noise level is high

- storing large amounts of information for long periods of time and recalling the appropriate information at the right moment
- using judgment when all of the necessary facts or information are not available
- being flexible when inflexibility is a hazard
- reacting to sudden or unexpected problems and hazards
- solving problems when ingenuity and new methods must be employed
- learning from experience and mistakes
- performing human reasoning

To overcome boredom and fatigue, workers need to be satisfied and challenged. They should be challenged to use their skills—not just be human machines assembling parts. Workers must also feel that the work they perform is meaningful and that they are responsible for the outcome.

Stress may mean different things for different people even within the same field. Stress generally refers to physiological and emotional effects that come with job performance, worry and pressures of the job, and family problems. Stress may include physical problems such as ulcers and cardiovascular problems as well as emotional ones such as fear, jealousy, and moodiness. Stress can also be caused by an overload of work activities acting upon the sensory organs of the body. One well-known, overloaded, computer-like organ is the brain. If workers' brains become overloaded from stress, their training or skill becomes secondary to the handling of the stress or problem. There are times when a human brain receives or perceives one billion bits of information per second, but it is estimated that only about three billion bits can actually be transmitted to the nervous system for action. Of these, approximately sixteen per second become conscious thought in the brain and an even smaller number, one bit per second, is retained by memory.

When the brain becomes overloaded due to a massive influx of information, it is said to be under stress. If it is overloaded with data bits that cannot be processed, the bits are held until the brain can absorb them. If they cannot be absorbed within a relatively short period, the information is no longer accurate and will be distorted, and a possible harmful action could result. Everyone at one time or another exhibits mental fatigue—burnout—when he or she can no longer think clearly or absorb the information necessary to safely perform a task (Kroemer 1999, 191–194).

As with physical fatigue, human movement can also become stressed from mental fatigue, which is complex and has different elements that must be dealt with. A feeling of tiredness when sufficient rest has been received is a sign of mental fatigue, and with the tiredness comes slowed reactions and a slow thought process. It is thought that tiredness is a warning sign. Yawning appears to be a mechanism that increases oxygen intake to the lungs. Oxygen is a crucial element in worker performance, since the brain needs it to survive, and when muscle exertion occurs, oxygen is needed to replenish necessary chemicals. Blood carries oxygen to muscles and also takes waste products such as carbon dioxide and water from the system. Normal basal metabolism is usually sufficient during light physical activities, but when strenuous work is necessary it soon becomes insufficient. To improve the situation, breathing and heart rate increase, and physiological changes in the body can occur since the mind controls body functions. A reduction in output or reduced efficiency of work performance is a sign of mental fatigue, but it can also represent other areas that must be investigated and improved.

Mental fatigue is caused by brain overload, and this overload is more difficult to recover from than physical overload. Mental fatigue appears to be correlated with psychological and emotional stress, while physical overload is caused by work exertion. A factor that may help to increase resistance to mental fatigue is a good mental attitude toward the work performed. Education, experience, good working conditions, and contact with other workers are crucial ways to hold off mental fatigue. A worker's ability to perform a task varies based upon mental stress, fatigue, and distractions. Given the fact that the work function also varies, a combination of mental stress, physical fatigue, distractions, and varying work functions can be a recipe for injury. A worker's ability to perform a specific task should exceed the demand of that task. Boredom is said to be a reaction to a situation where there are too few stimuli, causing a decrease in baseline activity in the human central nervous system and can degrade efficiency and safety. Different people react differently when faced with a monotonous, prolonged task. Monotonous tasks breed boredom and should be interspersed with numerous short breaks and, if possible, a slight change of pace from usual activities.

There are many stressors in the work environment, some of which include the following (Kroemer 1999, 219–225):

- *Lack of job control.* If workers cannot participate in determining their own work routines, boredom and stress can occur.
- *Lack of supervisor support.* Support of supervisors appears to reduce the effects of stress on workers and should be encouraged whenever possible.
- *Heavy workload.* Job distress can be caused by a heavy workload. Too much stress and a heavy workload results in job dissatisfaction and possible loss of employees. If a job has a high rate of turnover, this is usually the reason.
- *Tasks and demands of the job such as deadlines, efficiency ratings, and so on.* These play a very important part as stressors and can reduce efficiency.
- *Lack of job security.* Lack of job security itself is not usually a problem, but when combined with other stress factors, it becomes a very highly important issue and consequently a high source of job stress.

Fatigue and Shift Work

Stress and fatigue are recipes for disaster, or at least injury. Mental stress and fatigue are as dangerous as their physical partners. Mental activity occurs in any job where incoming information must be processed by the brain. Some brain work, such as thinking, does not involve physical movement. Sometimes brain work can involve a link between a human and a machine. Brain work includes the ability to formulate ideas without acting on them. Humans require perception, interpretation, and the processing of information transmitted by the body's organs. Workers or commercial drivers have an obligation to maintain the highest level of alertness over long periods and to be responsible for making decisions involving the safety of people and equipment while fighting off occasional monotony. The mind may become stressed when more than two bits of information need to be classified and sequenced simultaneously. Fleet drivers run into this type of information overload every time they take the wheel and enter the roadway (Kroemer 1999, 219–225). Bits of information constantly bombard drivers' minds and compete for time. Over a long period this can become quite exhausting. Mental fatigue may take over and, consequently, safety is compromised.

The phases of the human cycle fall into daytime (*ergotropic*) and nighttime (*trophotropic*) categories. A *circadian rhythm* (24-hour cycle) is necessary in order for humans to recycle and regenerate for the next working and relaxation cycles. The cycles are triggered by changes from light to dark, social contacts, work and its associated events, and changes in time as shown on clocks. These events occur on a routine basis, and, consequently, circadian periods are considered routine.

The human body changes during different periods of the circadian cycle:

- Body temperature, heart rate, and blood pressure may fluctuate.
- Respiratory volume and adrenaline production vary.
- Mental ability changes.

During daytime activities all bodily functions and organs are ready for activity and the mind is rested. During nighttime activities, most of these functions are dampened, but they can be regenerated with recuperation and renewal of energy for the next cycle. It is believed that humans are oriented toward daytime performance and nighttime rest. Organizations can perform their own research on this by plotting the number of injuries or near-misses during various time periods and noting whether they occur near the beginning or the end of a shift. Some shift-work studies have found that workers report illnesses 2.5 times more often on evening and night shifts than on day shifts. These illnesses include stomach problems, ulcers,

nervous disorders, and intestinal problems. Some can be directly correlated with the type of food ingested during the second or third shift. These problems occur because of disturbances in the sleeping and eating habits of the worker. There is a correlation between chronic fatigue and unhealthy eating habits and increased nervous disorders and stomach ailments. The symptoms of chronic fatigue are loss of appetite, disturbed sleeping, and digestive problems (Kroemer 1999, 191–201).

Younger workers may not sustain illness or injury as often as older workers and may be able to handle disturbance of their circadian rhythm better than older workers. Older workers already have higher probabilities of injury or illness and, coupled with the circadian periods, usually suffer stress more often than younger workers.

Effect of Noise and Vibration

Vibration is the rapid oscillation of waves and can cause injuries to the auditory system as well as to the rest of the body. Vibrations experienced when working with hand power tools can injure the nervous and skeletal systems; the seriousness of the injury depends upon the severity of the vibration and the length of exposure. Vibration is the motion or oscillation of bodies containing mass and elasticity that can move short distances at very fast velocities. *Free vibration* is caused by internal forces of the system, while *forced vibration* is caused by external forces. An example of free vibration is the ear receiving sound waves and the eardrum and the inner ear reacting. There is a limit to the decibels (dB) human ears can withstand over a period of time without permanent injury. Sound waves react with the natural frequency (HZ), resonance occurs and creates *motion amplitude*. Large amplitude within a system is harmful—for example, crystal can be shattered in the presence of very loud sound waves (Kroemer 1997, 320–324).

Motion during vibration can be *harmonic*, meaning that it can be represented by a simple sine wave and is predictable. These predictable motions or frequencies are called *deterministic* if they can be calculated mathematically. *Stochastic* or random vibration is the opposite of deterministic. Random vibration can be determined by averaging the waves. *Oscillation* has magnitude, displacement velocity, and acceleration. For this reason vibration is usually measured with accelerometers. Accelerometers are used to determine the value of the magnitude and are measured in meters per second squared (m/s^2). The quantifying value is so small that it is usually signified by thousands or millions or even greater values of a second squared. Gravity provides an example; at the earth's surface it is approximately 32.2 feet per second squared.

Frequency is the repetitive rate or oscillations per second. These wavelengths of vibration have peak values and average values, which indicate stress relationships. *Peak values* indicate maximum stress but do not consider the time duration, and consequently they are used to determine short-term motion such as shock or impact loading. Average acceleration is mathematically determined by considering cycle time and instantaneous amplitude. *Root mean square* (RMS) is the square root of the mean squared values of the motion of the body. RMS is proportional to the energy of the vibration and is usually between the peak and average values.

How the human body reacts to vibration depends on its frequency. Normally vibrations are applied to the human body randomly. Vibrations act as vectors, and the biomechanical properties of the human body are different depending on the direction of vibration. Therefore, measurement of vibrations must be along the three whole-body axes—*z*-axis (top to bottom), *y*-axis (side to side), and *x*-axis (front to back). These axes must be carefully determined so that the correct threshold of injury can be determined. It should be remembered that vibration is rarely unidirectional and consequently may cause confusion during an analysis if not properly understood.

Injury is caused from the frequency, amplitude, and direction of the vibration over time. If any one of these changes, the probability of injury can decrease or increase. Sensitivity of the human body is as follows:

- A low frequency—1 to 2 Hz—creates sensitivity in the vestibular system—the sensory receptors of the inner ear. This type of vibration may come from ships, cranes, or aircraft.

- A medium frequency—2 to 20–30 Hz—creates sensitivity from a biomechanical standpoint of body resonance. This resonance takes place in body tissues. This type of vibration is caused by vehicles or aircrafts.

- A high frequency—above 20 Hz—creates sensitivity in receptors of the muscles, tendons, and skin. This type of vibration is seen in tools and machinery.

Individual injuries and effects of vibration are based not only on the strength of the vibration and length of time someone is exposed to it but also on the physical condition of the individual. All individuals do not have the same susceptibility to injury, and consequently healthy individuals should adhere to safety guidelines regarding vibration. Vibration in and of itself may not produce injury, but in combination with noise, temperature, posture, or exertion of force, it can create a hazard or injury. Everyone is familiar with motion sickness, either in a motor vehicle or on a ship. Motion sickness is caused by low-frequency vibration and affects the vestibule or receptors of the ear. There are two receptors, the semicircular canal, which is sensitive to angular accelerations, and the otolith organs, which have linear acceleration sensitivity. Motion sickness is believed to occur when these two sensors conflict with each other in relation to head motion.

The human body is said to be a dynamic biomechanical system, but it also models as a linear system within specific ranges of spine oscillations, up to approximately 100 Hz when body tissues have small deformations. The body can be considered a nonlinear model and is said to be better for predicting effects of random and shock vibrations. Vertical vibrations from 5 to 10 Hz cause resonance in the thoracic or abdomen area; vibrations from 20 to 30 Hz affect the head, neck, and shoulders, and vibrations from 30 to 60 Hz affect the eyeballs. Generally, there is less motion in body segments as the frequency increases above 10 Hz.

It is well known that spinal fractures can be caused by compression from large vertical accelerations. Vibrations at lower acceleration levels may cause fatigue fractures in different spinal components. These vibrations also interfere with the nutrition of spinal discs and predispose them to degenerative changes. Normally, degenerative changes are not one-time events but occur over a long period of time, which is one reason older people are more likely to suffer from degenerative discs than younger people. The physiological effects when people are exposed to vibrations include changes in heart rate, blood pressure, ventilation rate, oxygen intake, and so on. The vibrations necessary to produce simple effects are moderate to high in magnitude and in the middle of the frequency range. Vibration applied to a seated person increases the activity of back muscles from the lumbar, thoracic, and cervical regions.

Noise and vibration are harmful over a long period of time and can be harmful even over a short period, depending upon the frequency and level. Vibration affects different areas based upon different frequencies. Various peak-to-peak accelerations affect arm and hand steadiness, which could create a significant hazard. Vibration tolerance limits are classified in vertical or horizontal planes and the following tolerance limits for vertical vibration demonstrate the effects:

- Eight hours can be tolerated for a frequency of 1 Hz to maintain levels of proficiency with an acceleration of 0.6 Gs.
- Four hours can be tolerated for the same frequency with an acceleration of 1.

IMPORTANT TERMS

Basic Definitions of Biomechanical Injury Anatomy Terms (Stedman's Medical Dictionary 1997)

Cervical: referring to a segment of the spine, C1 through C7 (vertebrae beginning at the occipital bone and ending at thoracic vertebra T1)

Disc: a jellylike substance between each pair of vertebrae of the spine

delta-v: the change of velocity over time

herniated disc: a disc that protrudes either anteriorly or posteriorly from the vertebrae

LOSRIC: low-speed rear-impact collision

lumbar: referring to a segment of the spine having five vertebrae, L1–L5, between T12 and S1

occipital bone: the bone at the rear base of the skull just above C1

sacrum: an area of the spine with five vertebrae, S1 through S5, between T12 and the coccyx; the buttocks area

thoracic: referring to twelve vertebrae, T1 through T12, between C7 and S1; the upper trunk section

vertebra: a segment of the spinal column. There are seven cervical vertebrae, twelve thoracic, five lumbar, and five sacral.

The following terms and their positions are accepted and used consistently (Andrews 2001, Nahum and Melvin 2002):

- Anterior—Ventral—Forward
- Posterior—Dorsal—Back
- Flexion—Bend forward
- Extension—Bend rearward
- Mid Sagittal Plane—The right and left halves of the body
- Superior—Cranial—Toward the head
- Inferior—Caudal—Toward the feet
- Coronal Plane—The front and rear halves of the body
- Medial—Lateral—Side
- Palmar—Palm side of the hand
- Dorsal—Back of the hand
- Abduction—Movement away from the center of the body
- Adduction—Movement toward the center of the body

Terminology for body position:

- Sagittal—Divides the body into right and left
- Medial sagittal—Close to the center; lateral away from medial
- Corona—Divides the body into the front and back
- Anterior front or ventral side—Posterior back or dorsal side
- Transverse—Divides the body into top and bottom
- Superior—Closest to the head

- Posterior—Closest to the feet
- Limbs, proximal—Closer to the torso
- Limbs, distal—Farther from the torso

Wrist and hand motions:

- Flexion—Bend down
- Extension—Bend up
- Radial deviation—Bend the hand horizontal towards the thumb
- Ulnar deviation—Bend the hand horizontal towards the little finger
- Pronation—Rotation toward palm down
- Supination—Rotation toward palm up

REFERENCES

Allen, Merrill. 1996. *Forensic Aspects of Vision and Highway Safety*. Tucson, AZ: Lawyers & Judges Pub. Co.

American Association of State Highway and Transportation Officials (AASHTO). 1990. *Policy on Geometric Design of Highways and Streets*. Washington DC: AASHOC.

American Trucking Association (ATA). 1996. *Motor Fleet Safety Supervision: Principles and Practices*. 5th ed. Alexandria, VA: ATA.

ASTE. 2009. "Heavy Truck Tire Blowout." France: ASTE.

Backaitis, Stanley H., ed. *Biomechanics of Impact Injury and Injury Tolerances of the Extremities*. Warrendale,PA: SAE International, 1993.

Backaitis, Stanley H., ed. *Biomechanics of Impact Injury and Injury Tolerances of the Thorax and Shoulder Complex*. Warrendale, PA: SAE International, 1993.

Balk, S. A., R. A. Tyrrell, J. O. Brooks, and T. L. Carpenter. 2008. "Highlighting Human Form and Motion Information Enhances the Conspicuity of Pedestrians at Night." *Perception* 37, pp. 1276–1284.

Chaffin, D. 1999. *Occupational Biomechanics*. 3d ed. New York: Wiley-Interscience Publication.

Croft, Art. 1995. "Mechanisms." Whiplash Biomechanics Seminar. Spine Research Institute of San Diego. March 13–17. www.srisd.com

Cupid, Carl. 2002. "Application of Collision Deformation Classification to Compute a Numerical Value Called 'Extent of Collision Damage' (ECD) for Motor Vehicles Involved in Accidents." SAE Technical Paper 2002-01-2133. Warrendale, PA: Society of Automotive Engineers (SAE) International.

Deak, Mike. 2004. "Fleet Injuries." *Safety and Health Magazine* (June 2004), pp. 44–48.

Department of Transportation (DOT), Federal Highway Administration (FHWA). 2000. *Manual on Uniform Traffic Control Devices*. www.mutcd.fhwa.dot.gov/kno_millenium_12.08.01.htm

Federal Motor Carrier Safety Administration (FMCSA). 2003. *Commercial Truck and Bus Safety*. Washington, D.C.: FMCSA.

_____. Federal Motor Carrier Safety Administration. (FMCSA). Information and Analysis Online. www.fmcsa.dot.gov

Fitch, James. 1994. *Motor Truck Engineering Handbook*. 4th ed. Warrendale, PA: SAE.

Fricke, Lynn B. 1990. *Traffic Accident Reconstruction*. Evanston, IL: Northwestern University Traffic Institute.

Gillespie, Thomas T. 1992. *Fundamentals of Vehicle Dynamics*. 4th ed. Warrendale, PA: SAE.

Institute of Transportation Engineers (ITE). 1999. *Traffic Engineering Handbook*. 5th ed. Washington, DC: ITE.

Kornhauser, Murray. 1993. "Delta-V Thresholds for Cervical Spine Injury." SAE Technical Paper 960093. Warrendale, PA: SAE International.

Kroemer, K.H.E. 1997. *Engineering Physiology: Bases of Human Factors/Ergonomics*. 3d ed. New York: Van Nostrand Reinhold.

_____. 1999. *Fitting the Task to the Human: A Textbook of Occupational Ergonomics*. 5th ed. London; Bristol, PA: Taylor & Francis.

Kumar, Shrawan, ed. 1999. *Biomechanics in Ergonomics*. London; Philadelphia, PA: Taylor & Francis.

Lawrence, J. 2002. "The Accuracy and Sensitivity of Event Data Recorders in Low-Speed Collisions." SAE Technical Paper 2002-01-0679. Warrendale, PA: SAE International.

Marshall, Gilbert. 2000. *Safety Engineering*. 3rd ed. Des Plaines, IL: American Society of Safety Engineers.

McKnight, A. James, and George T. Bahouth. "Analysis of Large Truck Rollover Crashes." *Traffic Injury Prevention*, 2009.

Microsoft Encarta. 2006. MS XP Software. "State Populations."

Nahum, Alan, and John W. Melvin, eds. 2002. *Accidental Injury: Biomechanics and Prevention*. 2nd ed. New York: Springer.

National Committee on Uniform Traffic Laws and Ordinances (NCUTLO). 2000. *Uniform Vehicle Code*. Alexandria, VA: National Committee on Uniform Traffic Laws and Ordinances. www.ncutlo.org

National Safety Council (NSC). 1999. *Coaching the Lift Truck Operator*. Itasca, IL: NSC.

_____. 2004. Injury Facts CD. www.nsc.org

New Jersey Department of Transportation (NJDOT). 1998. *Commercial Driver Manual*. Trenton, NJ: State of New Jersey.

Nielsen, G., et al. 1997. "Repeated Low Speed Impacts with Utility Vehicles and Humans." *Accident Reconstruction Journal* (Jan.-Feb. 1997), pp. 23–28.

Pintar, Frank. 2002. "Biomechanics of Inertial Head-Neck Trauma: Role of Cervical Components." SAE Technical Paper 2002-01-1445. Warrendale, PA: SAE International.

Pike, J. 2008. *Forensic Biomechanics*. Warrendale, PA: SAE.
_____. 2002. *Neck Injury*. Warrendale, PA: SAE.

Rivers, R. 2001. *Seat Belt and Air Bag Systems Manual for Traffic Crash Investigation and Reconstruction*. Jacksonville, FL: Institute of Police Technology and Management.

Shands, 1993. "Health Care Spinal Cord Injuries." *Spine* (October 1993).

Shinar, David. 1985. "Effects of Expectancy, Clothing Reflectance, and Detection Criterion on Nighttime Pedestrian Visibility." *Human Factors and Ergonomics Society* (HFES) (June) 27:327–333.

Solomon, Stephen.1984. "The Safety Color." *Firehouse Magazine*. (June 1984) 9:106.

Southhall, J. P. 1961. *Introduction to Psychological Optics*. New York: Dover Publications.

Stedman's Medical Dictionary for Health Professionals. 3d ed.1997. Philadelphia: Lippincott Williams & Wilkins.

Strandberg, L. 1998. *Winter Brake Tests 1998*. Tokyo, Japan: National Research Institute of Police Science.

Transit Cooperative Research Board (TCRP). 1996. "TCRP Report 19, Guidelines for the Location and Design of Bus Stops." Washington, D.C.: National Academy Press. www.trb.org/onlinepubs/trcp/trcp_rpt_19a.pdf

Transportation Research Board (TRB). 1997. *Physical and Performance Characteristics of Heavy Vehicles*. Washington, D.C.: TRB.

Tyrrell, R. A., J. M. Wood., A. Chaparro, T. P. Carberry, B. S. Chu, and R. P. Marszalek. 2009. "Seeing Pedestrians at Night: Visual Clutter Does Not Mask Biological Motion." *Accident Analysis & Prevention*, 41, pp. 506–512.

U.S. Department of Transportation, Federal Highway Administration (FHWA). 2007. Roadway Geometry VI. Washington, D.C.: DOT.

Woodson, Wesley E. 1992. *Human Factors Design Handbook: Information and Guidelines for the Design of Systems, Facilities, Equipment, and Products for Human Use*. 2nd ed. New York: McGraw Hill.

APPENDIX: RECOMMENDED READING

Backaitis, Stanley H., ed. *Biomechanics of Impact Injury and Injury Tolerances of the Head-Neck Complex*. Warrendale, PA: SAE International, 1993.

Commercial Vehicle Safety Alliance (CVSA). 1996. "Out of Service Criteria." www.regscan.com

Hyde, Alvin S. 1992. *Crash Injuries: How and Why They Happen: A Primer for Anyone Who Cares about People in Cars*. Key Biscayne, FL: Hyde Associates.

International Traffic Medicine Association (ITMA). *Traffic Injury Prevention*. London: Taylor & Francis. www.traffic medicine.org

International Society of Biomechanics. *Journal of Applied Biomechanics*. www.humankinetics.org/JAB/journal/About.htm

New Jersey Transit Corp. 1998. *Manual for Locating Bus Stops, Bus Stop Sign Installation and Shelter Installation*. Trenton New Jersey: New Jersey Transit Corp.

Ozkaya, Nihat, and Margareta Nordin. *Fundamentals of Biomechanics: Equilibrium, Motion, and Deformation*. 2d ed. New York: Springer, 1999.

Spine Research Institute of San Diego. 1999. *Whiplash Injury Statistics*. www.srisd.com

Watts, Alan J., Dale R. Atkinson, and Corey J. Hennessy. *Low Speed Automobile Accidents: Accident Reconstruction and Occupant Kinematics, Dynamics, and Biomechanics*. Tucson, AZ: Lawyers & Judges Pub. Co., 1999.

Whiplash Associated Disorders Conference. World Congress Convention. Vancouver Canada, 1999.

SECTION 6
FLEET SAFETY

LEARNING OBJECTIVES

- Understand the problem of traffic crashes and the types of loss analyses needed to identify and minimize the problem.

- Determine a cost-benefit-analysis methodology for fleet safety initiatives.

- Be able to provide useful guidelines regarding what to include in budgeting for fleet safety

- Learn how to analyze the cost of driver training.

- Understand the factors that influence the cost of vehicle maintenance (inspection and repair).

COST ANALYSIS AND BUDGETING

Fran Sehn

IN APRIL 2006, U.S. Transportation Secretary Norman Y. Mineta declared that highway traffic deaths were a "national tragedy" and called on all Americans to respond by wearing safety belts, using motorcycle helmets, and driving sober. According to a report from the Department of Transportation's National Highway Traffic Safety Administration (NHTSA), 43,200 people died on the nation's highways in 2005, up from 42,636 in 2004. Injuries dropped from 2.79 million in 2004 to 2.68 million in 2005, a decline of 4.1 percent. Fifty-five percent of passenger-vehicle occupants who died in 2005 were unbelted, despite the fact that overall safety-belt use is at an historic high of 82 percent nationwide (NHTSA 2006).

When NHTSA reported safety-belt use at 82 percent, Mineta stated, "Every year this country experiences a national tragedy that is as preventable as it is devastating . . . We have tools to prevent this tragedy—every car has a safety belt, every motorcycle rider should have a helmet, and everyone should have enough sense to never drive while impaired" (NHTSA 2006).

This NHTSA report also projected an eighth-straight year of increased motorcycle fatalities. In 2005, 4315 motorcyclists died, a 7.7 percent increase over 2004, when there were 4008 fatalities.

A NHTSA study, based on 2006 Centers for Disease Control (CDC) data, claimed that motor-vehicle crashes are the leading cause of death for those between the ages of 3 and 34.

Traffic crashes come at an enormous cost to society, Mineta noted. NHTSA estimates show that highway crashes cost society $230.6 billion a year, about $4820 per person (NHTSA 2006).

Significantly, 2009 fatality and injury data, coming from U.S. Transportation Secretary Ray LaHood in September 2010, show highway deaths fell to 33,808 in that year—the lowest fatality record since 1950. This meaningful decline occurred while the estimated vehicle miles traveled in 2009 increased by 0.2 percent from 2008.

The data for 2009 reflected the lowest fatality and injury rates ever recorded: 1.13 deaths per million miles traveled in 2009 (1.26 deaths were reported for 2008). In addition, fatalities declined in all categories of vehicles, including motorcycles, with fatalities there falling by 850 from 2008. The number of people injured in motor-vehicle crashes in 2009 also declined for the tenth straight year, falling an estimated 5.5 percent from 2008.

According to NHTSA Administrator David Strickland, alcohol-impaired driving fatalities in 2009 stood at 10,839, down from 11,711 in 2008 (a decline of 7.4 percent). Overall, 33 states and Puerto Rico saw a decline in the number of alcohol-impaired driving fatalities between 2008 and 2009.

> Today's numbers reflect the tangible benefits of record seat-belt use and strong antidrunk-driving enforcement campaigns. But we are still losing more than 30,000 lives a year on our highways, and about a third of these involve drunk driving. We will continue to work with our state partners to strictly enforce both seat belt use and anti-drunk driving laws across this nation, every day and every night. (NHTSA 2010)

How Business Views Traffic Safety

Guidelines for Employers to Reduce Motor Vehicle Crashes, funded by the Occupational Safety and Health Administration (OSHA), NHTSA, and the Network of Employers for Traffic Safety (NETS) state (OSHA, NHTSA, and NETS 2006):

> Motor vehicle crashes cost employers $460 billion annually in medical care, legal expenses, property damage, and lost productivity. They drive up the cost of benefits such as Workers' Compensation, Social Security, and private health and disability insurance. In addition, they increase the company overhead involved in administering these programs."

The Bureau of Labor Statistics (BLS), in 2010 preliminary data, indicated that more work-related fatalities resulted from transportation incidents than from any other type of event. Highway incidents alone accounted for nearly one of every five fatal work injuries in 2010. Drivers/sales workers and truck drivers accounted for 683 fatalities in 2010. This is a rate of 21.8 per 100,000 employed. Transportation incidents accounted for 50 percent of the workers killed in multiple-fatality events (BLS 2010).

NHTSA has determined that "the average crash costs an employer $16,500. When a worker has an on-the-job crash that results in an injury, the cost to their employer is $74,000. Costs can exceed $500,000 when a fatality is involved. Off-the-job crashes are costly to employers as well" (OSHA, NHTSA, and NETS 2006).

These costs are highlighted in a final report for the Federal Motor Carrier Safety Administration. The report noted (Zaloshnja and Miller 2002):

- The cost of crashes with two or more trailers involved was the highest among all crashes— $88,483 per crash.
- Among crashes of all types of trucks (including a single large truck, tractor-trailer or multiple trailers, and buses), bus-involved crashes had the lowest cost—$32,548 per crash. (*NOTE: large trucks* means tractor-trailers, single-unit trucks, and some cargo vans over 10,000 pounds.)
- The cost per crash with injuries averaged $164,730 for large-truck crashes and $477,043 for bus crashes.
- The crash cost per 1000 truck miles was $157 for single-unit trucks, $131 for single combination trucks (tractor and trailer), and $63 for multiple combinations—tractor and multiple trailers.
- The average annual cost of large-truck crashes from 1997–1999 exceeded $19.6 billion, including $6.6 billion in productivity losses, $43.4 billion in resource costs, and $419.6 billion in quality-of-life losses.

These cost estimates exclude mental healthcare costs for crash victims, roadside repair costs, cost of cargo delays, earnings lost by family and friends caring for the injured, and the value of schoolwork lost. These data are prime examples of the hidden costs of crashes and their related outcomes.

Social Media Accident Causation

The use of cell phones has become as common as any other human activity in many countries, including the United States. This wireless communication device is both a benefit and a hinderance to driving activities. The cell phone can be used for emergency contact, but it is often involved in distracting the driver. The National Safety Council (NSC) research shows cell-phone use while driving has been associated with quadrupling the crash risk. The NSC estimated that 28 percent of all crashes per year involve talking on cell phones and texting while driving—accounting for 1.6 million crashes (NSC 2010). According to the the NHTSA, an estimated 11 percent of drivers in 2008 were talking on cell phones at any given time. The NHTSA statistics also show that, in 2008, approximately 5870 people were killed and an estimated 515,000 were injured in crashes in which there was at least one reported form of driver distraction. Drivers younger than 20 years of age accounted for about 16 percent of those deaths (NHTSA 2011).

The same article indicated that, in 1999, only 3 percent of NSC members reported any type of cell-phone ban. Ten years later, nearly 50 percent reported either handheld or full cell-phone bans.

Is banning cell-phone use the answer? In a recent visit to California for business, this author witnessed the impact of no use of handheld cell phones in the Los Angeles area on three major highways used during the business trip. Asking a client what has encouraged nonuse the most, the simple answer was "the fine if caught."

Overview of Distracted Driving

The NHTSA states that driver distraction could pose a serious and potentially deadly danger. In 2009, 5474 people were killed on U.S. roadways and an estimated 448,000 were injured in motor-vehicle crashes that were reported to have involved distracted driving. *Distracted driving* is any nondriving activity that a person engages in, which has the potential to distract him or her from the primary task of driving and increases the risk of crashing.

Distracted driving comes in various forms, such as cell-phone use, texting while driving, eating, drinking, talking with passengers, as well as using in-vehicle technologies and portable electronic devices. Daydreaming and dealing with strong emotions are less obvious forms of distractions.

There are three main types of distraction:

- *Visual:* Taking your eyes off the road
- *Manual:* Taking your hands off the wheel
- *Cognitive:* Taking your mind off what you are doing

Texting while driving is alarming because it involves all three types of distraction (NHTSA n.d.).

The Federal Motor Carrier Safety Administration (FMCSA) states (FMCSA 2010):

New technologies are available that provide objective measures of driver behavior. These in-vehicle technologies are able to provide continuous measures on a wide variety of driving behaviors previously unavailable to the fleet safety manager . . . If behavioral approaches can be integrated with technologies that monitor behavior, fleet safety managers would have an effective tool to improve safety-related behaviors.

This concurs with the information in this chapter that commercial truck and bus drivers typically work alone and in relative isolation, and therefore require alternative strategies.

Using Telemetrics as a Tool to Solve the Problem

In *An Introduction to Telematics*, Tam states (Tam n.d):

The data captured by the devices commonly include the vehicles location, speed, driver behavior, and vehicle diagnostics data determined by the telematics system. The fleet safety manager can in advanced solutions view data in real time. . . . Virtually any fleet operation can benefit from adoption of fleet safety telematics solutions. These solutions enable drivers and companies to proactively reduce costs, improve fleet safety and increase productivity. Some fleet safety solutions also involve installation of an in-vehicle video camera to capture evidence of collisions and other important driving events. The data obtained can be combined with other in-depth analytics to help identify root causes and driving behavior. The fleet safety reports, viewed over an extended period of time are excellent tools for supervisors to use in conducting targeted driver training and counseling programs.

LOSS ANALYSIS METHODS

The employee's cost due to a crash can be significant. The loss of wages and medical costs beyond what Workers' Compensation Insurance pays, as well as pain and suffering, are a burden to the employee, the employee's family, and the employer.

National Safety Council

MOTOR TRANSPORTATION
DRIVER'S ACCIDENT REPORT
READ CAREFULLY – FILL OUT COMPLETELY

FORM VEHICLE 1

(For office use)
File No. ____
☐ Preventable
☐ Not Preventable
☐ Reportable
☐ Not reportable

COMPANY ____
DIVISION ____ ADDRESS ____

ACCIDENT INFORMATION

DATE OF ACCIDENT ____, 19__
DAY OF WEEK ____
TIME ____ A.M. P.M.

MOVING: ☐ Another com'l vehicle ☐ Passenger car ☐ Pedestrian ☐ ____

FIXED: ☐ Building or fixture ☐ Parked vehicle ☐ ____

TYPE: ☐ Head On ☐ Sideswipe ☐ Right Angle ☐ Rear End ☐ Other (Describe) ____ ☐ Front End ☐ Non Collision (Describe) ____

LOCATION

PLACE WHERE ACCIDENT OCCURED:
ADDRESS OR STREET ON WHICH ACCIDENT OCCURED: ____
☐ AT INTERSECTION WITH: ____
CITY/TOWN, STATE ____, ____
☐ NOT AT INTERSECTION: ____ FEET N ☐ S ☐ E ☐ W ☐ OF ____
Nearest Intersecting Street/Road; House Number, or Landmark: Bridge, Milemarker, etc.

POLICE PRESENT? ☐ YES ☐ NO
Name of Force ____
☐ Local ☐ County ☐ State
Officers Name ____
Badge No. ____
Report No. ____
Tickets/Arrests Driver 1 ☐ 2 ☐
Other ____

FIGURE 1A. **Accident information** (*Source: Driver's Accident Report*, with permission of the National Safety Council 1996)

DRIVER / PASSENGER / PEDESTRIAN INFORMATION

DRIVER VEHICLE ONE	DRIVER VEHICLE TWO
Driver's Name: / Company I.D. Number:	Driver's Name: / Phone No.:
Driver's Address: / City/State:	Driver's Address: / City/State:
Phone No.: / Driver's License Number:	Driver's Occupation: / Driver's License Number:
Vehicle Number(s): / Run: / Route:	Age: / Insurance Co.:
Date Of Birth: / Employment Date As Driver: / Hours Since Last 8 Hours Off:	Make Of Vehicle: / Year: / Type: / Vehicle License No.:
Parts Of Vehicle Damaged:	Registered Owner:
Was Street Lighted? ☐ Yes ☐ No / Was Vehicle Lighted? ☐ Yes ☐ No	Owner's Address:
	Parts Of Vehicle Damaged:
	Others In Vehicle:
	Was Vehicle Lighted? ☐ Yes ☐ No

PASSENGER / PEDESTRIAN

PASSENGER ☐ PEDESTRIAN ☐ NO. 1	Name	Address, City, Zip	Home Phone
	Passenger In Vehicle # / Date Of Birth	Sex	What Was Pedestrian/Passenger Doing:
PASSENGER ☐ PEDESTRIAN ☐ NO. 2	Name	Address, City, Zip	Home Phone
	Passenger In Vehicle # / Date Of Birth	Sex	What Was Pedestrian/Passenger Doing:

INJURIES

	INJURED: YES	NO	DESCRIBE INJURIES	INJURED TAKEN TO/BY
DRIVER VEHICLE 1				
DRIVER VEHICLE 2				
PASSENGER VEH___				
PASSENGER VEH___				
PEDESTRIAN 1				
PEDESTRIAN 2				
OTHER				

Driver's Accident Report.

FIGURE 1B. **Driver/passenger/pedestrian information** (*Source: Driver's Accident Report*, with permission of the National Safety Council 1996)

Methods of determining employer costs are varied. Several tools are available to fleet safety professionals to analyze these costs. The goal of analysis should be to determine problem areas, gaps in the safety program, and initiatives needed to minimize future crashes.

When a crash occurs, an initial investigation to determine the cause of the incident should take place. One method employers use for this inquiry includes an incident investigation form (see Figures 1A–E) (NSC 1996).

VEHICLES/PEDESTRIANS/PASSENGERS

(CHECK ONE OR MORE FOR EACH DRIVER)—YOU ARE No. 1

	PREVIOUS TO ACCIDENT	WHEN FIRST IN DANGER	AT IMPACT
	No. 1 No. 2	No.1 No. 2	No. 1 No. 2
Going straight ahead			
Slowing			
Stopped in traffic			
Park or stopped in zone			
Backing			
Starting			
Passing			
Being passed			
Changing lanes			
Turning left			
Turning right			
Entering zone/Pulling to curb			
Leaving zone/Pulling from curb			
Other (explain)			

YOUR SPEED ___ MPH ___ MPH ___ MPH
SPEED OF OTHER VEHICLE ___ MPH ___ MPH ___ MPH

DISTANCE YOUR VEHICLE FROM OTHER VEHICLE ___ FEET ___ FEET

DID YOU SOUND HORN? ☐ YES ☐ NO HOW FAR AWAY? ___ FEET
DID YOU APPLY BRAKES? ☐ YES ☐ NO HOW FAR AWAY? ___ FEET

AFTER IMPACT—VEHICLE MOVED ___ FEET
AFTER IMPACT—OTHER VEHICLE MOVED ___ FEET

GIVEN CONDITIONS, WHAT WAS SAFE SPEED FOR:

VEH. 1 ___ MPH   VEH. 2 ___ MPH

VEHICLE 1 2
- Did not have right-of-way
- Following too closely
- Failure to signal intentions
- Speed too fast for conditions
- Disregarded traffic signs or signals
- Improper passing
- Improper turning
- Improper backing
- Improper traffic lane
- Improper parking
- No improper driving
- Defective brakes
- Defective steering
- Defective lights
- Defective tires
- No defects
- _____
- _____ (Specify other)

PEDESTRIAN
- Walking with traffic
- Walking against traffic
- Coming from behind parked vehicle
- Crossing at intersection
- Crossing not at intersection
- Alighting from a vehicle
- Working in roadway
- Playing in roadway
- _____ (Specify other)

PASSENGER
- Boarding vehicle
- Alighting from vehicle
- Caught in doors
- Seated
- In motion in vehicle
- Other (describe)

FIGURE 1C. Vehicles/pedestrians/passengers information (*Source: Driver's Accident Report*, with permission of the National Safety Council 1996)

ENVIRONMENTAL CONDITIONS (CHECK ALL THAT APPLY)

WEATHER (check one)	SURFACE (check one)	TRAFFIC CONTROL (check one)	LIGHT (check one)	ROADWAY (No. of Lanes)	ALIGNMENT (check one)	
☐ CLEAR	☐ DRY	☐ STOP SIGN	☐ DAWN	☐ DIVIDED ___	☐ STRAIGHT	☐ OVERPASS
☐ CLOUDY	☐ WET	☐ YIELD SIGN	☐ DAY	☐ UNDIVIDED ___	☐ CURVE	☐ UNDERPASS
☐ RAINING	☐ ICY	☐ TRAFFIC SIGNAL	☐ DUSK	☐ ASPHALT ___	☐ BRIDGE	☐ LEVEL
☐ SNOWING	☐ SNOWY	☐ FLAGMAN	☐ DARK-NO LIGHTS	☐ CONCRETE ___	☐ INTERSECTION	☐ UPHILL
☐ FOGGY	☐ OTHER	☐ NO CONTROL	☐ ARTIFICIAL LIGHT	☐ GRAVEL ___	☐ RAMP	☐ DOWNHILL
☐ OTHER		☐ OTHER	☐ OTHER	☐ OTHER ___	☐ RAILROAD	

FIGURE 1D. Environmental conditions information (*Source: Driver's Accident Report*, with permission of the National Safety Council 1996)

INDICATE ON THIS DIAGRAM WHAT HAPPENED
Use one of these outlines to sketch the scene of your accident, writing in street or highway names or numbers.
1. Number each vehicle and show direction of travel by arrow:
2. Use solid line to show path before accident; dotted line after accident
3. Show pedestrian by:
4. Show railroad by:
5. Show distance and direction to landmarks; identify landmarks by name or number.
6. Indicate north by arrow, as:

INDICATE NORTH BY ARROW

ACCIDENT DESCRIPTION

DRIVER'S ACCOUNT OF ACCIDENT ___

This report is accurate to the best of my knowledge   DRIVER(S) ___   DATE ___

FIGURE 1E. A schematic or diagram of the collision/crash (*Source: Driver's Accident Report*, with permission of the National Safety Council 1996)

An effective investigation or analysis of a crash/incident will provide fleet safety professionals with information that can be used to determine

- the root cause of the crash/incident
- its preventability
- appropriate countermeasures to prevent a recurrence

Safety Measurement System (SMS)

In 2010, the FMCSA introduced the safety measurement system (SMS), a new risk-control measurement system that replaced its older SafeStat system. SMS quantifies the on-road safety performance of carriers and drivers. The primary intent is to identify candidates for interventions, determine the specific safety problems the carrier or driver exhibits, and monitor whether safety problems are improving or worsening. SMS is integral to the compliance, safety, and accountability operational model.

SMS uses the motor carrier's data from roadside inspections, including all safety-based violations, state-reported crashes, and the federal motor carrier census to quantify performance in the following behavior analysis and safety improvement categories (BASICs):

1. **Unsafe Driving:** Operation of commercial motor vehicles (CMVs) by drivers in a dangerous or careless manner. Example violations include speeding, reckless driving, improper lane change, and inattention (FMCSR Parts 392 and 397).

2. **Fatigued Driving:** (Hours of Service): Operation of CMVs by drivers who are ill, fatigued, or in noncompliance with the hours-of-service (HOS) regulations. This BASIC includes violations of regulations pertaining to logbooks, as they relate to HOS requirements, and the management of CMV driver fatigue. Examples of violations include exceeding HOS, maintaining an incomplete or inaccurate logbook, and operating a CMV while ill or fatigued (FMCSR Parts 392 and 395).

3. **Driver Fitness:** Operation by drivers who are unfit to operate a CMV due to lack of training, experience, or medical qualifications. Examples of violations include failure to have a valid and appropriate commercial driver's license (CDL) and being medically unqualified to operate a CMV (FMCSR Parts 383 and 391).

4. **Controlled Substances or Alcohol:** Operation of CMVs by drivers who are impaired due to alcohol, illegal drugs, and misuse of prescription, or over-the-counter medications. Examples of violations include the use or possession of controlled substances or alcohol (FMCSR Parts 382 and 392).

5. **Vehicle Maintenance:** Failure to properly maintain a CMV. Examples of violations include brakes, lights, and other mechanical defects, and failure to make required repairs (FMCSR Parts 393 and 396).

6. **Cargo-Related Failures:** Failure to properly prevent shifting loads, spilled or dropped cargo, overloading, and unsafe handling of hazardous materials on a CMV. Examples of violations include improper load securement, cargo retention, and hazardous material handling (FMCSR Parts 392, 393, 397, and hazardous material violations).

7. **Crash Indicator:** Histories or patterns of high crash involvement, including frequency and severity. It is based on information from state-reported crashes.

A carrier's measurement for each BASIC depends on the following:

- the number of adverse safety events (violations related to that BASIC or crashes)
- the severity of violations or crashes
- when the adverse safety events occurred (more recent events are weighted more heavily)

After a measurement is determined, the carrier is then placed in a peer group (e.g., other carriers with a similar number of inspections). Percentiles from 0 to 100 are then determined by comparing the BASIC measurement of the carrier to the measurements of other carriers in the peer group. A percentile of 100 indicates the worst performance.

TABLE 1

Fleet Loss Run (Policy Effective Date: 5/15/2010 to 5/14/2011)							
Claim Number	Date of Loss	Claimant Name	Claim Status Description	Accident Narrative	Paid Total	Reserved Total	Net Incurred Total
166123	09/01/2011	S. Jones	Closed	IV was rear ended by CV	$2235.46	$0.00	$98.00
166124	05/01/2011	J. Smith	Closed	Insured was driving north on Rt. 219 when tire blew	$2834.86	$0.00	$2834.86
166125	04/22/2011	F. Washington	Closed	Claimant vehicle hit IV at driver side doors	$1587.95	$0.00	$1587.95
166126	09/05/2011	A. Kennedy	Closed	IV was rear- ended by CV	$0.00	$0.00	$0.00
166127	05/05/2011	R. Jefferson	Closed	Insured was driving on Rt.19 when vehicle struck a deer	$4234.36	$0.00	$4293.36
TOTAL					$10,892.63	$0.00	$8814.17

Note: IV indicates insured vehicle, CV indicates claimant vehicle or the vehicle of others.

Additional Loss-Source Information for the Fleet Safety Professional

Fleet safety professionals have many potential loss sources at their disposal. Insurance carriers and their brokers and agents regularly produce and provide loss runs to assist in the analysis process. A loss run is a historical report of crash/incident information that has been given to an insurance carrier. A typical loss run will include, but not be limited to, the following:

1. date of the incident
2. driver/employee name
3. a brief description of the incident (e.g., "backing" or "struck fixed object")
4. location of the incident
5. anticipated cost or dollars reserved for future costs
6. costs to date

The loss run in Table 1 provides only an overview of needed information—the information it contains is limited by the input data and the ability of the software used to assemble and present the information. A fleet safety professional will need additional information and data in order to determine preventability. One of the goals of a successful fleet safety program is to propose appropriate countermeasures to minimize the possibility of a recurrence.

Exposures and Controls of the "Grey Fleet"

The *grey fleet* is a reflection of business miles traveled by employees using their own vehicles. Sales and service are two categories of employment most frequently associated with this group. These employees are typically paid a fixed mileage allowance for business purposes to cover the cost of operating their own car or truck. The employer has the advantage of minimizing the costs associated with purchasing or leasing a vehicle for this use, but not all costs of risk are eliminated.

While there is very limited data regarding the cost of incidents related to this business risk, the fact that employees are driving on company business presents both liability and worker's compensation exposures that may be significant.

In order to manage this aspect of the business risk, the fleet safety manager should include the following controls at a minimum:

- A copy of the valid insurance certificate should be obtained, including coverage for business use.
- A copy of the employee's driver's license should be obtained.
- A signed declaration should be obtained that the vehicle is fully serviced and maintained to the manufacturer's standards.

The same safety training provided to operators of company-owned vehicles should be mandated for these drivers. There are many appropriate defensive driving courses that are available for this purpose (Businesslink n.d.).

DIRECT AND INDIRECT COSTS OF ACCIDENTS

The image of an iceberg has been used by safety professionals to depict the direct and indirect costs of accidents. The direct costs are easily visible, similar to the section of an iceberg above the water. The indirect costs are buried below the surface of the water. The OSHA $afety Pays eTool discusses the cost of workplace injuries and illnesses in terms of the iceberg model (OSHA 1996).

"Accidents are more expensive than many of us realize. Why? Because there lots of hidden costs. Some are obvious—your workers' compensation claims cover medical and indemnity (lost wages) for an injured or ill worker. These are the direct costs of accidents. But what about the costs to train and compensate a replacement worker, repair damaged property, investigate the accident, and implement corrective action? Even less apparent are the costs related to schedule delays, added administrative time, lower morale, increased absenteeism, and poorer customer relations. These are the indirect costs and the bulk of the iceberg. Studies show that the ratio of indirect costs to direct costs varies widely, from a high of twenty-to-one to a low of one-to-one. We've taken a conservative approach that says that the lower the direct costs of an accident, the higher the ratio of indirect to direct costs" (OSHA 1996).

A worksheet is provided so that fleet safety professionals can determine the direct and indirect costs of accidents (see Figure 2). This worksheet also provides information that can determine the impact of injuries and illnesses on profitability.

These costs, in the context of this chapter, apply to employees of a fleet operator, including drivers, mechanics, sales personnel, administrative personnel, and management. The Federal Motor Carrier Safety Administration's (FMCSA) Accident Cost Table

---

WORKSHEET
How to Estimate the Impact of Accidents on Profits and Sales

Use this worksheet to determine costs of injuries and illnesses and their impact on business operations.

DIRECT COST

To calculate the direct cost, enter the following information:

• Total value of the insurance claim (medical costs and indemnity payments) for the injury or illness $_____

INDIRECT COST

To calculate the indirect cost of this injury or illness, multiply the direct cost by a cost multiplier. The cost multiplier to use depends on the size of the direct cost.

If your direct cost is:	Use this cost multiplier:
$0–$2999	4.8
$3000–$4999	1.6
$5000–$9,999	1.2
$10,000 or more	1.1

• Direct Cost   ×   Cost Multiplier   =   Indirect Cost
  $_____   _____   = $_____

TOTAL COST

• Direct Cost   +   Indirect Cost   =   Total Cost
  $_____ $_____   = $_____

FIGURE 2. How to estimate the impact of accidents on profits and sales (*Source:* OSHA 1996)

TABLE 2

Accident Cost Table

THIS TABLE SHOWS THE DOLLARS OF REVENUE REQUIRED TO PAY FOR DIFFERENT AMOUNTS OF COSTS FOR ACCIDENTS

It is necessary for a motor carrier to generate an additional $1,250,000 revenue to pay the cost of a $25,000 accident, assuming an average profit of 2%. The amount of revenue required to pay for losses will vary with the profit margin.

Yearly Accident Costs	Profit Margin				
	1%	2%	3%	4%	5%
$1,000	100,000	50,000	33,000	25,000	20,000
5,000	500,000	250,000	167,000	125,000	100,000
10,000	1,000,000	500,000	333,000	250,000	200,000
25,000	2,500,000	1,250,000	833,000	625,000	500,000
50,000	5,000,000	2,500,000	1,667,000	1,250,000	1,000,000
100,000	10,000,000	5,000,000			
150,000		7,500,000	3,333,000	2,500,000	2,000,000
200,000	15,000,000	10,000,000			
			5,000,000	3,750,000	3,000,000
	20,000,000				
			6,666,000	5,000,000	4,000,000
REVENUE REQUIRED TO COVER LOSSES					

(*Source*: FMSCA 2006)

(see Figure 2 and Table 2) shows revenue dollars required to pay for different amounts of costs of accidents from a fleet's standpoint. Table 2 includes the following accident costs that could be considered in relation to a crash (FMCSA 2006).

Direct and Indirect Costs

Direct costs include:

- repair of cargo damage
- repair of vehicle damage
- medical treatment
- loss of revenue
- administrative
- police report
- possible effect on the cost of insurance
- possible effect on the cost of Workers' Compensation Insurance
- towing
- storage of damaged vehicles

Indirect costs include:

- revenue from clients or customers
- revenue from sales
- meetings missed
- salaries (wages) paid to employees in the accident
- lost time at work
- cost to hire and train replacement employees
- supervisor's time
- loss of personal property
- replacement vehicle rental
- damaged equipment downtime
- accelerated depreciation of equipment
- accident reporting
- medical costs paid by the company
- poor public relations/publicity
- increased public relations costs
- government agency costs

If this worksheet is applied to fleet accidents and coupled with the Revenue Required to Pay for an accident chart, it is apparent that even a $5000 accident can impact profitability.

For example, an accident involving $5000 in direct costs would result in $6000 in indirect costs, so the

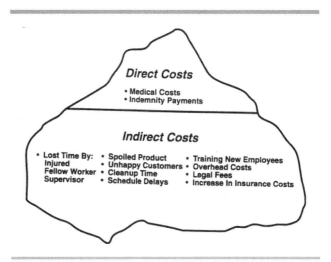

FIGURE 3. Direct/indirect costs iceberg (*Source: OSHA 1996*)

total cost would be $11,000. If a company operates at a 4 percent profit margin, it would need to generate over $250,000 in additional sales to cover the cost of this accident/incident. This example assumes a $5000 deductible by the carrier on a per accident/incident basis. The *iceberg* in Figure 3 "demonstrates the relationship between direct and indirect costs of accidents" (OSHA 1996) and the Accident Cost Table (Table 2) sets out the revenue necessary to pay for accident losses. According to the FMCSA average, indirect costs exceed direct costs by a four-to-one ratio.

ACCIDENT REGISTER

An additional source of information for fleet safety professionals conducting analyses of incidents and crashes is the Accident Register. Part 390.15 of the Federal Motor Carrier Safety Regulations (FMCSR) is reproduced in the sidebar.

A sample accident register is shown in Figures 4A and B.

Fleet safety professionals should use all of the tools detailed in this chapter to conduct regular analyses of their fleets' losses. Detailed analyses will provide opportunities for continuous improvement of safety efforts. An accident register can be used to determine trends, which in turn will provide information for future needs and initiatives for driver selection, equipment, safety training, and related information.

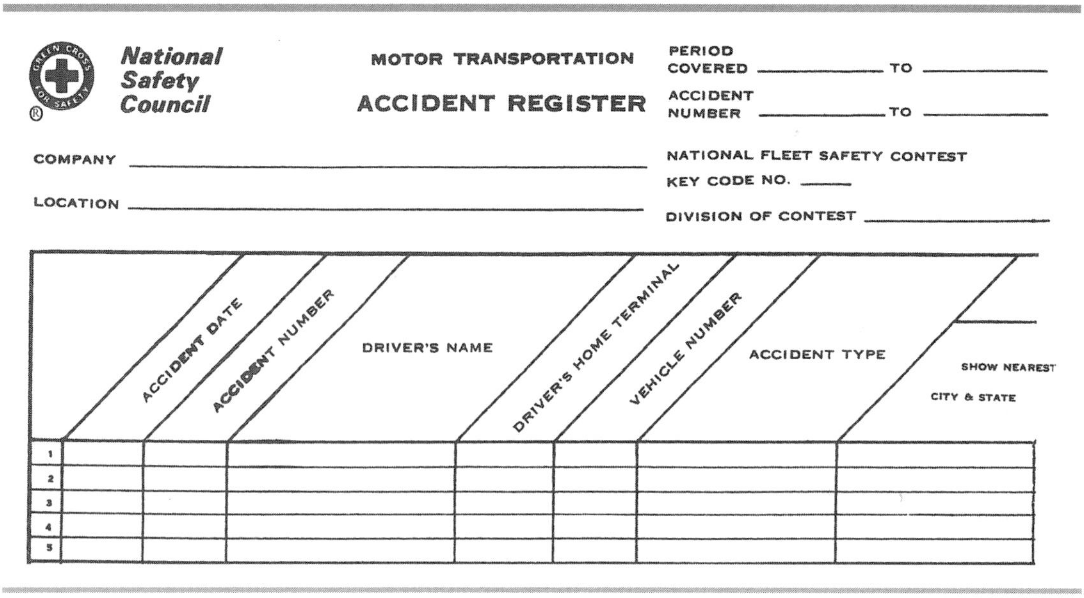

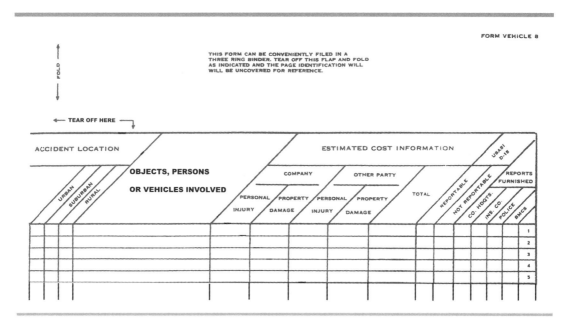

FIGURE 4A. Sample accident register (*Source:* NSC 1996)

FIGURE 4B. Sample accident register (*Source:* NSC 1996)

COST-BENEFIT ANALYSIS

An effective fleet safety program can produce benefits to the employer, employee/driver, and the customer or client. Well-managed fleets also benefit the community or communities in which they operate.

The National Safety Council (NSC 1996) indicates that some benefits of an effective safety program are:

- reduced costs of operations
- reduced insurance premiums and related costs
- improved customer satisfaction
- lower employee turnover
- improved employee morale

While all of these benefits would be considered logical to anyone operating a fleet, the safety program alone may not achieve them. It is essential that all drivers be aware that the safe operation of vehicles is very important. The standard explains that organizations should periodically evaluate driver performance.

FMCSR, PART 390.15

"Assistance in investigations and special studies.

"(a) A motor carrier must make all records and information pertaining to an accident available to an authorized representative or special agent of the Federal Motor Carrier Safety Administration, an authorized State or local enforcement agency representative, or authorized third party representative, upon request or as part of any investigation within such time as the request or investigation may specify. A motor carrier shall give an authorized representative all reasonable assistance in the investigation of any accident including providing a full, true, and correct response to any question of the inquiry.

"(b) For accidents that occur after April 29, 2003, a motor carrier must maintain an accident register for three years after the date of each accident. For accidents that occurred on or prior to April 29, 2003, motor carriers must maintain an accident register for a period of one year after the date of each accident. Information placed in the accident register must contain at least the following:

"(b)(1) A list of accidents as defined at 390.5 of the chapter containing, for each accident:

"(b)(1)(i) Date of accident.

"(b)(1) (ii) City or town, or most near, where the accident occurred and the State where the accident occurred.

"(b)(1)(iii) Driver name.

"(b)(1)(iv) Number of injuries.

"(b)(1)(v) Number of fatalities.

"(b)(1)(vi) Whether hazardous materials, other than fuel spilled from the fuel tanks of motor vehicle involved in the accident, were released.

"(b)(2) Copies of all accident reports required by State or other governmental entities or insurers."

Many types of safety initiatives may have an impact on a company's cost of operations. One is direct observation and feedback from the general public regarding vehicles that are clearly identified with either a company phone number or a commercial safety hotline call-in program. Anyone who drives has probably seen decals on commercial vehicles asking "How is my driving?" along with a vehicle identification number and toll-free phone number. Two companies that provide this early warning service indicate that insurance companies have studied the financial impact of these programs. The Safety Alert Network states that clients have reported a vehicular accident-frequency reduction in excess of 40 percent when using the program (Safety Alert 2006).

Safety Alert charges a one-time fee of $3.95 to place a decal on a trailer plus an annual per-vehicle charge based on the number of vehicles. The company provides this estimated benefits information:

frequency rate of accidents × million miles driven
= number of accidents   (1)

number of fleet accidents × $9000/accident
= cost of accidents   (2)

cost of accidents × 0.10 (a conservative reduction in accident savings) = minimum net savings (3)

For example, if a fleet operates 50 vehicles and 100 trailers, the cost of the program is estimated at $5000 for the first year, and $1400 for subsequent years (50 vehicles at approximately $20 per vehicle and 100 trailers at $4 per trailer).

According to the ROI calculator provided on the Safety Alert Network Web site, the ANSI vehicular accident rate for over-the-road vehicles in 1995 was 2.0 per million miles. If the fleet in our example drives 5 million miles per year, the savings would be estimated as follows:

2.0 × 5 = 10 accidents
10 × $9000 = $90,000 in accident costs
$90,000 × 0.10 = $9000 in avoided accident costs

$9000 in avoided accident costs – $5000 cost of service = $4000 net savings   (4)

This is a very conservative estimate.

Paul Farrell of Safety First, which also operates a hotline program, has conducted numerous studies on the benefits of these monitoring programs and has determined that savings can be as high as 20 percent of the cost of accidents.

While Safety Alert and Safety First are only two examples of safety initiatives that produce encouraging results, the use of technology is changing daily and will ultimately be used to improve safe driving habits and reduce risky behaviors. Additional studies are needed to determine the impact of safety training and initiatives similar to those noted above.

BUDGETING FOR FLEET SAFETY

The fleet safety professional or the person responsible for fleet safety in a company should consider the cost of three major components of the safety program in order not only to ensure compliance but also to operate in a safe and efficient manner. These cost components are:

1. record keeping
2. fleet safety training
3. fleet maintenance

In 2008, ORC Worldwide (now Mercer) engaged eighteen occupational health, safety, and environmental professionals and others to provide a comprehensive look at investment decisions and to answer important questions, such as:

- What health and safety or environmental investments should we make?
- When should we make a particular investment?
- Which health and safety of health investments create the greatest value to the organization?
- How do we compare an operational investment decision to an HS&E decision?
- How do we know we are doing the "right things" in the "right way?"
- To which projects should we allocate our human resources?
- How can we demonstrate the business value of our organization?

The return on the health, safety, and environmental investment process and software tools facilitates and encourages a team approach and calculates financial metrics in a common language. This type of tool, along with others referred to in this section, provides the fleet safety manager with the information to make informed decisions for the control and minimization of risk.

Record Keeping

The ANSI/ASSE Standard Z15.1-2006, *Safe Practices for Motor Vehicle Operations*, states, "Organizations shall maintain documentation of the qualifications and driving records of drivers." The data or documents needed for this aspect of fleet safety are noted in the section below.

Either a specific budget for an outside consultant should be established for these compliance efforts or the fleet safety professional should allow ample time in his or her regular work activities to complete these review and administrative activities.

From a driver perspective, the driver file is a critical component for compliance. A small fleet can be audited just as readily as a large one. The driver file and its related documents are a significant aspect of any compliance review. The Federal Motor Carrier Safety Regulations are found in the Code of Federal Regulations (49 CFR) 300–399.

The documents contained in each driver's file must include

- employment application
- current medical certificate
- DOT medical waiver, if applicable
- certificate of road test or equivalent, such as a CDL
- past employment verifications
- motor vehicle record
- annual review of driving record
- annual list of driver violations
- other documents, such as safety training records, pertinent to the driver's ability to operate a commercial motor vehicle

In accordance with 49 CFR 396.3(b), the vehicle maintenance file must contain

- an identification of the vehicle
- a method or document to indicate the nature and due dates of inspections and maintenance

- a record of inspections, repairs, and maintenance, indicating their date and nature or type
- a record of tests conducted on push-out windows, emergency doors, and emergency-door marking lights on buses

In addition to the costs associated with the review and maintenance of these records, fleet safety professionals are responsible for and may incur costs for keeping the written programs, policies, and procedures for the overall safety process current. This could require attendance at seminars or training sessions in order to stay up to date on changes in the regulations. Many organizations offer such seminars throughout the United States.

Fleet Safety Training

The Z15 standard also states, "Organizations shall establish a driver training program. The driver training program shall address requirements for new drivers, continuing education of existing drivers, and instances where remedial training shall be required" (ANSI/ASSE 2006).

The standard further states, "The training should include both classroom and behind-the-wheel training" (ANSI/ASSE 2006). The following topics should be considered for the training sessions:

- defensive driving
- substance abuse
- distracted driving (e.g., cell-phone use)
- aggressive driving (e.g., tailgating)
- vehicle inspection
- commodity-specific training (e.g., hazardous materials, material handling, cargo securement)
- safety regulations
- security procedures
- emergency equipment
- post-incident procedures
- vehicle inspection/maintenance

There are numerous software solutions for the fleet safety manager to consider to manage the data associated with the record-keeping requirements and safety training, as well as other aspects of the operation of a fleet of vehicles. FleetMentor from J. J. Keller, an online toolbox and advisor to assist the fleet safety manager with the myriad of tasks that impact fleet safety, provides tools and resources that include the following (J. J. Keller, Inc. n.d.):

- accident register
- best practices for fleet operations
- cargo securement
- driver and supervisor training
- motor-carrier safety audits
- online safety training
- PM service schedule
- roadside inspection tracking
- repair and maintenance costs
- scoring MVRs

These tools follow the CSA requirements and provide additional resources to adequately manage the fleet's needs. The fleet safety manager is encouraged to review the software products available from J. J. Keller and others.

Evaluating the Risks of Driving

In September 2003, the Health and Safety Executive (HSE) published a pamphlet entitled *Driving at Work: Managing Work Related Road Safety*. A significant portion of this publication is devoted to assessing the risks involved with road safety, including but not limited to the driver, training, vehicles, and the journey itself. The pamphlet suggests that working through a section on evaluating these risks will answer many questions that the fleet safety manager may not have considered. The "Training" section asks, "Are you satisfied that your drivers are properly trained?" The following questions help in the risk assessment:

- Do you evaluate whether those who drive at work require additional training to carry out their duties safely?
- Do you provide induction training for drivers?
- Do you arrange for drivers to be trained, giving priority to those at higher risk (i.e., those with high annual mileage, poor crash records, or young drivers)?
- Do drivers know how to correctly adjust safety equipment (i.e., seat belts and head restraints)?

- Do drivers know how to use antilock brakes properly?
- Do drivers know how to check washer-fluid levels before starting a journey?
- Do drivers know how to ensure safe load distribution (i.e., when undertaking multidrop operations)?
- Do drivers know what actions to take to ensure their own safety following the breakdown of a vehicle?
- Do you need to provide a handbook for drivers, giving advice and information on road safety?
- Are drivers aware of the dangers of fatigue?
- Do they know what to do if they feel sleepy?
- Are drivers fully aware of the height of their vehicle, both laden and empty?

The final question of the assessment is appropriate and a great lead-in to the next section of this chapter, "Has money been budgeted for training? To be effective training needs should be periodically assessed, including the requirements for refresher training" (HSE 2003).

The Cost of Driver Training

Several types of safety or driver training sessions are used by fleet safety professionals.

Initial Training

When new employees are hired, a supervisor or a fleet safety professional should communicate the company's safety expectations. The time for this training will depend on the nature of the vehicle to be operated, the experience of the employees, and the organization's level of sophistication with regard to safety. *Many companies find that the more time they spend on initial training, the more likely it is that new hires realize the importance of safety.* The cost of initial training is usually part of the cost of the new-hire orientation process.

Calculating the cost for each hour of orientation should include:

- employee's hourly rate and benefits
- trainer's hourly rate and benefits

- clerical and administration time (hourly rate and benefits)

For example, *The Occupational Outlook Handbook* (BLS 2006–2007) states that in 2004 the median hourly pay for heavy-truck and tractor-trailer drivers was $16.11. If a trainer earns $50,000 per year ($25 per hour) and an administrative employee earns $25,000 per year ($12.50 per hour) and benefits for each category cost approximately 30 percent of earnings, a single hour of orientation would cost

Driver	$16.11 plus $4.83 = $20.94
Trainer	$25.00 plus $15.60 = $40.60
Administrative employee	$12.50 + $3.75 = $16.25
Total cost:	$77.79 for one hour of orientation

Annual Training

Due to the nature of fleet operations, many companies conduct annual safety meetings lasting from as little as one hour to an entire day. In addition to updating drivers on policy or equipment changes, this is an opportunity to review the importance of safe driving techniques and safe behaviors. Often guest speakers are invited to participate in the sessions to provide a new or fresh perspective on safety. This type of meeting/training (if held annually) may also include a *safety awards* recognition program in which drivers are rewarded for years of driving without a preventable accident. The American Trucking Association (ATA) published a study highlighting exceptional approaches to safety management by some of the country's safest carriers, including some that won safety awards. The study notes that the average spent on safety for all surveyed carriers was $1060 per powered unit, but for the award-winning carriers the average was $2500 per powered unit. These expenditures included costs of driver training, compliance, safety awards, and safety meetings (ATA 1999).

- The cost of safety training includes wages and benefits paid to drivers while they are attending training sessions as well as the cost of speakers, video equipment and facilities, refreshments and meals, and rewards (ATA 1999).

Remedial Training

Remedial training may be necessary if employees have safety violations or a certain number of *chargeable* or preventable accidents during a specified time period. During this training, an effort is made to modify employees' behavior or to determine whether they have special needs that should be addressed. The cost of remedial training is an hourly rate for the driver plus the cost of the trainer's time (ATA 1999).

Ongoing Training

Computers have made this type of training readily available and affordable. A search of the Internet using the phrase "fleet safety training" reveals literally thousands of resources, many of which offer online training. The cost of the training depends on several factors, including the number of drivers to be trained and the number of training modules chosen.

Is there a cost benefit for this type of training? AlertDriving provides an example of the return on investment (ROI) on its Web site with an ROI calculation scenario showing that if eight training modules are presented to 125 drivers, the cost of the program per driver is $43. Several companies that have used the training have reduced their accidents per million miles by an average of 20 percent with a potential savings of $145,000 each. The ROI is over 30 percent per carrier (AlertDriving 2006).

Boorman notes that Occupational Health Services, which operated 48 vehicles in 1994, reduced its average net cost per claim by £1500 over four years and reduced its overall cost by £65,000 in the same time period. The training consisted of a three-pronged approach: (1) raising driver awareness, (2) identifying higher-risk drivers, and (3) providing advanced driver training and providing targeted support to drivers after an incident. The cost per driver was estimated at £125 (Boorman 1999).

Fleet safety professionals are encouraged to find safety training that meets the needs of the fleet and should evaluate the ROI over a three- to four-year period.

The many aspects of ongoing training will also be discussed in the "Best Practices" chapter later in this section of the handbook.

Cost of Vehicle Maintenance

The Federal Motor Carrier Safety Regulations, Part 396.3, require motor carriers to "inspect, repair, and maintain all motor vehicles" under their control (FMCSA 2006). It is considered good business practice to comply with these regulations. In fact, Standard Z15.1 states, "The purpose of the Standard is to provide organizations with a document for the development of policies, procedures, and management processes to control risks associated with the operations of motor vehicles. It is not intended to be a mandate for its use; it has been developed to assist organizations in defining and developing an effective risk management program for their vehicle operations" (ANSI/ASSE 2006).

In Section 6, "Vehicles," Standard Z15.1 states, "Organizations shall institute formal maintenance procedures and record-keeping procedures that meet or exceed the vehicle manufacturer's recommendations, giving consideration to the operating environment" (ANSI/ASSE 2006). The standard also addresses scheduled maintenance, repairs, qualified automotive service personnel, automotive service facilities, and vehicle replacement:

- *Scheduled Maintenance.* All vehicles shall be maintained by qualified automotive service technicians at regular intervals based on miles driven, hours of operation, and/or calendar time.
- *Repairs.* When defects are reported, the vehicle shall be repaired by a qualified automotive service technician. Safety-related defects shall be repaired before the vehicle is placed back in service, with appropriate records maintained.
- *Qualified Automotive Service Personnel.* All personnel performing maintenance, repair, modifications, or inspections shall possess the requisite skills and be qualified through experience and training.
- *Automotive Service Facilities.* Organizations performing their own vehicle maintenance shall have appropriate facilities and automotive service equipment to perform the required tasks. When maintenance is performed by

vendors, the organization shall assess each vendor's ability to adequately perform the required service.

- *Vehicle Replacement.* Organization-operated vehicles shall be replaced according to formal procedures. Factors that affect the need for replacement include total mileage, maintenance cost, condition, operating requirements, operating environment, hours of service, and safety. Additional information below regarding life-cycle costing notes similar considerations and methods of determining these criteria (ANSI/ASSE 2006).

All of the above maintenance considerations are costly to an organization. *Vehicle Maintenance: A Comprehensive Guide to Improved Operations & Compliance* (J. J. Keller and Associates 2001) provides some insight on the expense associated with the maintenance aspect of fleet operations. The section entitled "Organizing Maintenance Programs" emphasizes the importance of tracking costs, stating:

> Operating costs are all the expenses directly related to running a vehicle on the road. Generally, driver expenses amount to about 50 percent or even more of the total costs of operating a vehicle. Vehicle expenses and indirect expenses (clerical staff, office supplies, etc.) make up the rest. Driver expenses include wages and benefits, but for the fleet that employs its drivers, rather than leases them, all employer-paid items must be included.

The guide notes that vehicle expenses are the second major category of costs. They include fixed costs: interest, depreciation, licenses, taxes (federal and state), permits, and insurance (vehicle and cargo) and variable costs: maintenance (labor and parts), fuel, oil, tires, tolls, and other miscellaneous road expenses. While variable costs are difficult to predict, they can be controlled (J. J. Keller and Associates 2001).

The cost per mile is the total dollar amount that it takes to run one truck for one mile. The guide states that cost per mile is the best and most convenient measure of trucking costs and is an easy indicator to use for comparison between vehicles (J. J. Keller and Associates 2001).

In statistics developed by Transportation Services of Fredericksburg, Virginia, (cited in J. J. Keller and

TABLE 3

Cost Per Mile	
Labor Costs	**Nonlabor Costs**
Driver—$0.445	Fuel—$0.138
Repair Wages—$0.049	Fuel Taxes—$0.059
Supervision—$0.025	Highway Taxes—$0.028
Other Labor—$0.013	Repair/Parts—$0.059
Fringes—$0.153	Tires/Tubes—$0.026
	Insurance—$0.032
	Depreciation—$0.083
	Other—$0.052
TOTAL—$0.684	TOTAL—$0.476

(*Source*: J. J. Keller and Associates 2001)

Associates 2001, 5) from reports of 46 large general freight carriers, all with revenues above $20 million, the cost of operating a truck over the road was approximately $1.16 per mile. Of that total, 47.6 cents was spent on nonlabor costs and 68.4 cents was spent on labor costs. The study included primarily unionized drivers; this cost could be higher than in nonunion operations. The breakdown is found in Table 3.

Although this study was completed in 1990, it is a good model for determining cost per mile. These formulas can be used to determine the cost per mile and revenue per mile.

$$\text{total cost/total miles} = \text{cost per mile} \qquad (5)$$

$$\text{total revenue/total miles} = \text{revenue per mile} \qquad (6)$$

Fleet safety professionals are encouraged to use this data to determine areas where operating costs can be controlled using good risk-management practices.

Life-Cycle Costing

The decision to replace a truck should be based on life-cycle costing (J. J. Keller and Associates 2001). Life-cycle costing can also indicate the need for component replacements. Ideally, fleets replace vehicles the moment it costs more to keep them than to replace them. The guide suggests that the following vehicle records are important in determining when this moment occurs:

- the truck's initial cost and component specifications (which become the vehicle's history)

- the fuel/oil/lube/filter data (from purchase records)
- the vehicle utilization data (from driver reports and mileage logs)
- the maintenance data (from repair orders)

A tracking system can aid in determining the cost of operating a fleet and is a key component of vehicle-replacement decision making. A computerized tracking system also simplifies record keeping for fleet management.

A search of the Internet for "Fleet Maintenance" reveals numerous computerized tracking systems that fleet safety managers can use to determine fixed and variable costs. These systems assist in determining the cost of operating an individual vehicle in the fleet as well as the cost of operating the overall fleet. As noted in the Z15 standard, maintenance procedures and record-keeping procedures must meet or exceed the manufacturer's recommendations (ANSI/ASSE 2006).

Tracking systems provide data necessary for deciding when vehicles should be replaced. The Z15 standard states that "organization-operated vehicles shall be replaced upon formal procedures" (ANSI/ASSE 2006). The standard explains that the factors involved in a decision to replace a vehicle include total mileage, maintenance costs, vehicle condition, operational requirements, operating environment, its hours of service, and vehicle safety (ANSI/ASSE 2006).

For a discussion of software for tracking FMCSA CSA requirements, see the end of the section on record keeping earlier in this chapter.

Conclusion

Fleet safety will continue to evolve with the advent of improved training methods, in-cab monitoring, driver professionalism, and maintenance practices. The primary responsibility for these improvements lies in the hands and wallets of the owners and managers of fleets and motor carriers. Without management commitment to safety and adequate resources, little progress will occur. Fleet safety professionals must be creative and innovative in their day-to-day activities in order to lead a safety process that will minimize crashes and prevent injuries.

There is still a need for additional research into this topic. A study of both regulated and nonregulated fleets should be conducted with the conclusions presented as a business case for driver training in all organizations that place drivers at risk on our nation's roads.

References

American National Standards Institute (ANSI) and the American Society of Safety Engineers (ASSE). 2006. Z15.1-2006, *Safe Practices for Motor Vehicle Operations*. Des Plaines, IL: ASSE.

AlertDriving. *ROI Calculations Scenarios* (accessed March 17, 2007). www.alertdriving.com

American Trucking Association (ATA) Foundation with Parker-Young. 1999. "SafeReturns, A Compendium of Injury Prevention and Safety Management Practices of Award Winning Carriers." Arlington, VA: ATA.

Boorman, S. 1999. "Reviewing Car Fleet Performance After Advanced Driver Training." *Occupational Medicine* 49(8):558–591.

Brodbeck, J., ed. 1996. *Motor Fleet Safety Manual*. 4th ed. Itasca, IL: National Safety Council.

Bureau of Labor Statistics (BLS). 2006–2007. Bulletin 2600, *Occupational Outlook Handbook*. 2006–2007 ed. Washington, D.C.: BLS.

———. 2010. *Census of Fatal Occupational Injuries*. www.bls.gov/iif/oshwc/cfoi/cfch0009.pdf

BusinessLink. n.d. *The Grey Fleet—Using Private Cars for Business Travel* (accessed November 16, 2011). www.businesslink.gov/uk/bdotg/action/detail

Code of Federal Regulations (CFR). Federal Motor Carrier Safety Administration. Title 49, Subtitle B, Chapter III, Parts 390–399. www.fmcsa.dot/rules-regulations

———. Hazardous Materials Regulations, 49 CFR Chapter I, Subchapter C. www.fmcsa.dot/rules-regulations

Federal Motor Carrier Safety Administration (FMCSA). 2006. "Accident Cost Table, Revenue Necessary to Pay for Accident Losses." www.fmcsa.dot.gov/facts-figures/analysis-statistics/Revenue.htm

———. 2010. *Evaluating the Safety Benefits of a Low Cost Driving Behavior Management System in Commercial Vehicle Operations* (accessed November 22, 2011). www.fmcsa.dot.gov/facts-research/research-technology/report/FMCSA-RRR-10-333.pdf

———. n.d. *Compliance, Safety, Accountability* (CSA). "About CSA—What Is It?" (retrieved November 13, 2011). www.csa.fmcsa.for/about/basics.aspx

Health and Safety Executive (HSE). 2003. *Driving at Work: Managing Work-Related Road Safety*. Sudbury, Suffolk, UK: HSE

J. J. Keller, Inc. 2001. *Vehicle Maintenance Manual: A Comprehensive Guide to Improved Operations.* Neenah, WI: J. J. Keller and Associates, Inc.

_____. n.d. *FleetMentor* (accessed November 20, 2011). www.fleetmentor.com

National Highway Traffic Safety Administration (NHTSA). 2006. *Transportation Secretary Mineta Calls Highway Fatalities National Tragedy.* www.nhtsa.dot.gov/portal/ site/nhtsa/template

_____. 2010. *U.S. Transportation Secretary LaHood Announces Lowest Traffic Fatalities in Six Decades* (retrieved October 1, 2010). www.nhtsa.gov/PR/ DOT-165-10.

_____. 2011. *Statistics and Facts About Distracted Driving* (retrieved November 13, 2011). www.distraction.gov/ stats-and-facts/index.html

National Safety Council (NSC). 1996. "Driver's Accident Report." Itasca, IL: NSC.

_____. 2010. "Employers Focus Efforts to Prevent Distracted Driving." *Safety & Health*, June 2010.

Occupational Safety and Health Administration (OSHA). 1996. "Safety Pays: Do You Know How Much Accidents Are Really Costing Your Business?" (Includes the direct and indirect costs of accidents, iceberg and worksheet.) www.osha.gov/SLTC/etools/safetyhealth/ images/safpay1.gif

OSHA, NHTSA, and NETS (Network of Employers for Traffic Safety). 2006. "Guidelines for Employers to Reduce Motor Vehicle Crashes." www.osha.gov/ Publications/motor_vehicle_guide.html

Safety Alert Network. 2006. "Cost Benefit Analysis" (accessed November 25, 2007). www.safetyalert.com/ costbenefit.asp

Tam, Joyce. n.d. *An Introduction to Telematics* (accessed November 16, 2011). www.zurich.com/insight/ insightmagazine/fleet/telematics.htm

Zaloshnja, E., and T. Miller. 2002. *Revised Cost of Large Truck and Bus-Involved Crashes.* Calverton, MD: Pacific Institute for Research and Evaluation (PIRE); prepared for FMCSA (November 18, 2002).

SECTION 6
FLEET SAFETY

LEARNING OBJECTIVES

▮ Be able to develop and administer a fleet accident/incident reporting system.

▮ Be able to develop and administer a fleet accident/incident record-keeping system.

▮ Understand the benchmark selection process.

▮ Be able to perform statistical analysis of fleet accident/incident data, including the ability to calculate incidence rates and to prepare a control chart.

▮ Understand the importance of accident statistical reporting.

▮ Understand the uses and limitations of incentive programs.

▮ Understand the legal implications associated with accident records.

BENCHMARKING AND PERFORMANCE CRITERIA

Edward Musal

BENCHMARKING AND PERFORMANCE appraisal are as important to fleet safety as they are to any other safety program; indeed, they are important in any management activity. Using benchmarking and performance appraisal will provide a "report card" that can be used to measure the effectiveness of any safety program. The statistical information that supports this activity can also be useful in identifying weaknesses in a safety program so that resources can be allocated for maximum effectiveness. In addition, the incident-reporting and record-keeping framework may be useful in evaluating the effect of proposed activities related to fleet safety.

One must be careful in choosing benchmarks in fleet safety. Choosing them is often quite difficult (see discussion in Benchmarking section). While *Injury Facts*, put out by the National Safety Council (NSC), provides a wealth of statistics for all areas of safety, including fleet safety, safety professionals must consider the unique characteristics of their fleets when choosing a benchmark. Important considerations include the size of the fleet, the type(s) of vehicles that comprise the fleet, and the area in which the fleet operates (road conditions, traffic conditions, weather, and so on).

Much of the information presented in this chapter is based on the author's experience. Where there is no citation in the text to support a specific item, the item is based on the author's experience. At this point it is appropriate for the author to summarize his experience in fleet benchmarking and performance appraisal so the reader may understand the background of the viewpoints presented. He was employed by the New York City Transit Authority, currently Metropolitan Transportation Authority-New York City Transit (NYCT), for 23 years (1973–1996). During most of this time his main function was related to all aspects of accident record keeping, including employee, motor vehicle, and passenger accidents record keeping. His responsibility began with classification. At the end of his career with NYCT, he managed a work unit of five professional employees whose sole responsibility was accident record keeping, analysis, and report preparation. During this period, accident record keeping and analysis at NYCT evolved from a manual system with minimal analysis to a complex computer-based system using sophisticated statistical techniques.

During the author's tenure at NYCT, the Manhattan and Bronx Surface Transit Operating Authority (MaBSTOA), which operates most of the bus service in the Bronx and Manhattan, was integrated into NYCT, which operates most of the bus service in the other three boroughs of New York City. In addition to buses, NYCT operates a fleet of maintenance vehicles for both rapid transit and bus operations as well as supervisory patrol cars. At the time of his employment, NYCT also maintained its own police force. This transit police force was subsequently absorbed into the New York City Police Department. The fleet accident record-keeping system managed by the author included vehicles supporting all of these operations. All the examples presented in this chapter are drawn from his experiences with NYCT.

SOURCES

A list of references is provided at the end of this chapter. As an introduction, however, it is appropriate to identify the four most pertinent sources in the United States. Two American National Standards Institute (ANSI) standards relate to fleet benchmarking and performance appraisal:

- ANSI Z15.1 *Safe Practices for Motor Vehicle Operations* (2006) §6.0 ff presents requirements for incident reporting, record keeping, and analysis.
- ANSI D16.1 *Manual on Classification of Motor Vehicle Traffic Accidents* (1996) provides a classification system that may be used in accident record keeping and analysis.

As indicated earlier, the National Safety Council's *Injury Facts* (previously *Accident Facts*) provides a wealth of accident statistics, including fleet accident statis-

tics, for possible use in benchmarking. The Network of Employers for Traffic Safety (NETS) also provides benchmarking information (www.trafficsafety.org).

In addition to these general sources, there are quite a few industry-specific sources. Some types of motor vehicle fleets are required to report accident statistics to a governmental agency. Statistics on public transit accidents are available from the Federal Transit Administration of the Department of Transportation (DOT). The Bureau of Transportation of the DOT also maintains accident statistics.

Various trade groups catering to specific industry segments also have potentially useful information. These include the American Trucking Association, the American Public Transit Association, the School Bus Information Council, the United Motorcoach Association (which performed a benchmarking study in 2001), and the American Bus Association (which has a 2000 census of the motorcoach industry). A Web site dedicated to fleet safety benchmarking has been set up in the United Kingdom at www.fleetsafetybenchmarking. net. In addition, an Internet search for a specific type of fleet could be rewarding.

ACCIDENT REPORTING

The foundation on which a fleet's benchmarking and performance appraisal system is built is its accident-reporting system. If this system is not properly designed and implemented, benchmarking and performance appraisal are valueless. People in the computer programming business have an acronym that precisely describes this: GIGO—garbage in, garbage out. It is absolutely necessary to precisely define the criteria for a recordable incident. It is also necessary to implement controls to be sure that all recordable incidents will be captured in the system. These issues will be dealt with in more detail later in this section. The first focus is on the methodology of accident reporting.

There are several means by which fleet management may obtain information about an incident. The usual first report is from the driver of the fleet vehicle involved in the accident. However, the driver may not be aware of an accident or may choose to avoid reporting it (especially if there is minor or no damage to the fleet vehicle), hoping it will be overlooked. Depending on the seriousness of the accident and the fleet's policy, a supervisor may be dispatched to the scene to perform a detailed investigation. It is also possible that a field supervisor may witness the accident. The driver of the other vehicle (if there is one) may be interviewed as part of the supervisor's investigation or may independently contact fleet management. A bystander (or passenger on the fleet vehicle) may be interviewed or may independently contact fleet management. Depending on fleet procedures, the first report of an accident may come after the driver turns in the vehicle from maintenance personnel (or another operator) who inspects the vehicle and notes damage not previously present. Finally, the first notice of an accident might be a lawsuit filed by an aggrieved party. This could occur many months after the alleged incident. The accident-reporting system should provide for all of these potential sources of information. Recent developments in computer technology have allowed several fleets to develop methods of allowing incidents to be reported by computer over the Internet. This provides more timely and accurate accident information as data transcription is eliminated. Several such systems can be found through an Internet search.

If a fleet is large enough to have more than one vehicle dispatch location, such as a nationwide trucking company, its accident-reporting system may be centralized or decentralized. If there is more than one dispatch location, should each location have a person or unit responsible for collecting information about incidents and providing the information to a single fleet location (decentralized), or should the entire fleet have a single unit (centralized) responsible for collecting incident information and providing information to the appropriate dispatch locations? There are certain advantages to each of these methodologies.

The *decentralized* method has the advantage of being closer to the incident. Accordingly, more detailed information can be acquired more quickly, so the initial report of the accident is likely to be more complete and accurate than if a centralized system were used. The major advantage of the *centralized* system is that fewer people collect information and prepare initial accident reports, providing a greater degree of consistency. The

centralized system also provides an easier way of incorporating accidents first reported to fleet management (calls to the main office and lawsuits filed) than the decentralized system. Another advantage of the centralized system is that it takes the system out of the control of local management, which may unfairly benefit from not having some accidents reported.

Especially with larger properties, accident reporting may overlap with other reporting systems. If a fleet employee is injured in the accident, the accident may be reported through the employee accident-reporting system, the Workers' Compensation system, and/or the medical reporting system (if the employee sees a physician and the fleet pays for the visit or has its own physician). If a lawsuit is filed with regard to the accident, the accident may be entered into a system used to track lawsuits. It is prudent for people responsible for accident reporting to establish a liaison with people responsible for other reporting systems to see that all systems receive the proper incident reports.

To avoid duplication of effort within an organization, it may be appropriate to expand the accident-reporting system to include nonaccident events of interest to management. As mentioned earlier, the usual sources of accident-reporting information are fleet vehicle drivers, who are also the usual source of information about other incidents related to vehicles and their operation, such as

- criminal activity involving a fleet vehicle (robbery, hijacking, and so on)
- accidents not involving fleet vehicles that are witnessed by fleet drivers
- injuries to a driver or passenger due to nonvehicular accidents
- illnesses of a driver or passenger
- vehicle breakdowns
- other miscellaneous incidents

Even though these events may not be of interest for fleet benchmarking and performance appraisal, they are of interest to other areas of fleet management, and consideration might be given to expanding the fleet accident-reporting system to become a fleet incident-reporting system. Case Study 1 describes a sample fleet accident-reporting system.

CASE STUDY 1

Overview of a Sample Accident-Reporting System

This case study presents the NYCT's fleet accident-reporting system for its bus operation and is based on an unpublished master's thesis by the author (1994).

The first verbal report of the incident is directed to the accident desk located within the fleet's centralized communications center, which is manned 24 hours a day, 365 days a year. The report is usually transmitted by radio immediately after the incident by the driver of the fleet vehicle. Occasionally the first report to the accident desk may come from another fleet employee, such as a maintenance employee discovering vehicle damage, a public affairs person taking a complaint from the public, or an attorney receiving notification of a lawsuit. The person at the accident desk enters the information constituting the initial incident report into a structured database (the specific data elements will be discussed later in the Accident Record Keeping section). If appropriate, the accident desk notifies the vehicle dispatch location to send a supervisor to the incident scene to conduct an investigation. More serious incidents (multiple injuries/fatalities) are reported to the fleet safety unit for more thorough investigation.

After completion, the written initial report (referred to as a *brief* because it contains only basic information; see Figure 1 for a sample brief and Figure 2 for an explanation of the information that is included) and a short description of the incident (a few sentences) are immediately transmitted electronically to the dispatch location (both operations and maintenance) responsible for the fleet vehicle involved and to certain fleet management personnel. The briefs are packaged daily and transmitted to the fleet training office, the torts division of the fleet law department, and the safety department. It is important to note that the brief contains only summary information about the incident before any investigation has taken place. It does not contain information regarding fault or preventability. In the NYCT, the safety department has responsibility for fleet benchmarking and performance appraisal as well as internal and external statistical reporting. The brief is the primary data source for this function.

If subsequent investigation determines that any of the information recorded in the brief is incorrect or incomplete, a revised brief is created that replaces the original brief. Revised briefs are necessary relatively infrequently (for fewer than 5 percent of incidents).

The person responsible for fleet benchmarking and performance appraisal must determine which of the reported incidents are to be recorded in the accident record-keeping system.

Before moving on to a discussion of accident record keeping, it is appropriate to discuss the establishment of criteria for including reported incidents in an accident record-keeping system.

One of the pioneers of the industrial safety movement in the United States, H. W. Heinrich, introduced the concept of the accident pyramid in 1931. According to Heinrich, for every major accident (serious injury or death) there were 29 minor-injury accidents and 300 no-injury accidents (property damage or disruption) (Heinrich 1969).

As the subject of his doctoral dissertation in 1963, William E. Tarrants added a new, broader-base layer to Heinrich's pyramid. Tarrants realized that analysis of the number of accidents was not an effective preventive technique for small work units. Due to statistical constraints, several years' worth of accident records would have to accumulate before any meaningful statistics could be generated. Tarrants interviewed workers in a small work unit to identify critical incidents— events that could have resulted in an accident but by luck did not. He gathered sufficient information about critical incidents to perform meaningful statistical analysis so that he could direct efforts to prevent accidents (Tarrants 1963).

The main purpose of fleet benchmarking and appraisal should be to direct accident prevention efforts so they will have maximum effectiveness. Comparison of fleet accident experience with appropriate benchmarks shows how safe a specific fleet is compared to similar fleets. This will show the need for additional accident-prevention efforts. Only through accident record keeping and analysis can comparisons be made of accidents experienced before and after a safety initiative so that the effectiveness of that initiative can be determined. The more incidents in the accident record-keeping system, the more precise statistical analyses can be, so there is a rationale for including as many accident or near-miss events in the accident record-keeping system as possible.

There are other factors to consider. A conscientious operator or supervisor who meticulously reports every critical incident may be considered to have a poor safety record compared to that of a colleague who successfully hides many accidents. There is a strong incentive for both operators and local supervisors to avoid reporting accidents if they think they can get away with it. Above all, the accident-reporting and record-keeping system must be fair.

Reporting of critical incidents may be especially useful in a small fleet where the emphasis is on safety and not discipline. The practice of examining each fleet vehicle for damage every time it returns to the dispatch location or changes drivers is a good way to ensure that every accident is reported.

Whatever threshold is set for recording incidents, it is always possible to maintain nonrecordable incidents in the record-keeping system for use in statistical analyses even if they are not counted for internal and external reporting purposes. Knowing that critical incidents will not count against their safety record is an incentive for operators and supervisors to report them.

Some fleet safety officers (in the author's experience) believe that preventability by the fleet operator should be a criterion in determining whether an accident is recorded. There is certainly a strong incentive for both the safety officer and fleet management to not record incidents unless the fleet operator is found to be at fault, because if fewer accidents are recorded, the fleet's safety record appears to be better. The author disagrees with this position, because even accidents the fleet operator could not prevent might result in injury, damage, and disruption of fleet activity, and the elimination of preventability by the fleet operator as

---

BRIEF NO: ENY01177   ACC CODE: 2AAAAAAA   DATE OCC: 05/28/87   TIME: OCC: 1100

DIVISION: Brooklyn   ROUTE: B10 - New Lots Avenue   RUN NO: 5

DEPOT: East New York   DESTIN: HOPKINS ST & SUMNER AVE   SIDE: Near Side

ON: New Lots Avenue   AT: Livonia Avenue

PRIM VEH: 1266   SCHOOL TRIP NO. ____   TOUR OF DUTY: ____

VISIB: Daylight   ROAD COND: Dry   DELAY TO SER: 12   DELAY TO BUS: 35

OP NAME: Smith   OP PASS: 812345   OP BADGE: 44354   OP BIRTH: 03/23/55

TITLE (IF NOT OP):_____ POLICE : (NAS)   OP HIRE: 08/12/79

STUDENT: _____   ST PASS: _____   ST BADGE: _____   ST BIRTH: __/__/__

SUV PASS: 455987   SUV: (AS)   ST HIRE: __/__/__

SUV TITLE: SLD   BUS: GARAGE   NOTIFIED: Control Desk   NO. PSNGR.: 22

DAM PRIM VEH: Slight   DAM SEC. VEH: Moderate   SEC VEH LIC # ABC123   NY

RECD DAT/TIM: 05/28/87   1230   TRAN DAT/TIM: 05/28/87   1300   INITIAL: ABC

Collision-Vehicle

ACTION OF PRIMARY VEHICLE / Forward / Moving in lane

ACTION OF SECONDARY VEHICLE / Forward / Moving in lane

RELATIVE POSITIONS / Other vehicle ahead

CONTACT POINT ON PRIMARY VEHICLE / Front

CONTACT POINT ON SECONDARY VEHICLE / Front

TYPE OF PRIMARY VEHICLE / Bus

TYPE OF SECONDARY VEHICLE / Auto (Jimmy, and so on)

*TOT INJURY: 2

M/23 – Primary Veh. – Treated at scene

F/45 – Sec. Veh. or Ped. – Removed to hosp

*Tot Fat: 1

M/55 – Sec. Veh. or Ped. –

Secondary vehicle failed to observe red signal and entered intersection as bus was entering intersection.

FIGURE 1. Example of a brief (*Source:* Musal 1994)

a criterion removes a subjective variable from statistical analysis and makes the accident record-keeping system more complete. Also, recording the accident but noting that the operator was not at fault puts the fleet in a stronger legal position should a lawsuit follow an incident.

ACCIDENT RECORD KEEPING– DESIGNING A SYSTEM

The author's first involvement with accident record keeping occurred before personal computers were introduced into the office environment. He vividly remembers being part of a team of five employees searching through piles of paper accident reports to determine how many of a certain type of vehicle accident happened in the previous year to answer a top management question.

Development of a computer-based accident record-keeping system is necessary with a large fleet, because manual searches through accident records are very time-consuming. While it would be possible to use a spreadsheet program such as Microsoft Excel to record incidents, a database program such as Microsoft Access is more suited for use when organization policies require report generation, statistical analysis, and searching for incidents or trends. Both of these programs are frequently provided as part of the software package on office computers. The person responsible for accident record keeping must become familiar with the capabilities and basic operations of the database program selected to support the accident record-keeping system.

The first step in creating an accident record-keeping system is choosing the data elements to be recorded. Figure 2 provides a suggested list of data elements to consider. This list should not be considered comprehensive; additional elements may be added or removed depending on the scope of the system (see discussion below).

No matter how much thought is put into developing an accident record-keeping system, some odd incident will occur that will provide a record-keeping challenge. The data elements in Figure 2 are intended to capture information about a typical two-vehicle collision, but what if more than two vehicles are involved? A suggestion is to collect information on the first vehicle to collide with the fleet vehicle (no matter where that vehicle falls in the chain of events in the overall accident). Include the total other vehicle injuries and fatalities in the secondary vehicle numbers. If the fleet vehicle collides with two or more other vehicles simultaneously, pick the one with the most serious injuries or damage to record. Other potential events to consider are pedestrian accidents, collisions with objects, non-collision accidents involving passengers on the fleet vehicle, and employee accidents on the fleet vehicle.

As was previously mentioned, there is a possibility that information gathered within the fleet accident record-keeping system may overlap information in other record-keeping systems. It is also possible that information reported, such as crimes, witnessing of events, and other miscellaneous occurrences, while not useful to the fleet safety benchmarking and performance appraisal system, might be useful to other areas of fleet management. The administrator of the fleet accident record-keeping system should communicate with the administrators of other record-keeping systems within the fleet and coordinate management of information sources and record keeping for mutual benefit. Case Study 2 presents a sample fleet accident record-keeping system. The details of the coding system are provided in the Appendix.

BENCHMARKING

Perhaps the most difficult task of fleet benchmarking and performance appraisal is to determine what benchmark, or benchmarks, to use. ANSI Z15.1 *Safe Practices for Motor Vehicle Operations* (ANSI 2006) establishes incidents per million miles as a standard rate for comparing motor fleet accidents, but what does the person responsible for fleet safety performance appraisal compare against? There are many possible answers to this question.

The National Safety Council's *Injury Facts*, published annually, provides a wealth of accident statistics for possible use in benchmarking. Incidence rates per million miles are presented in it for many types of fleets. In addition, industry-specific organizations may provide statistics for benchmarking comparisons. Membership in the Network of Employers for Traffic Safety (NETS) allows fleet participation in their benchmarking

Data Element	Explanation
Date	Date of incident
Time	Time of incident (suggest using 24-hour time)
Work unit	Dispatch location of fleet vehicle
Driver	Identity of operator of fleet vehicle (employee number or name)
Driver demographics	Date of birth, date of hire, gender, and so on, for possible use in statistical analyses. This information might be acquired by linking with a personnel database.
Primary vehicle number	Identity of the fleet vehicle
Primary vehicle type	E.g., bus, truck, car
Primary vehicle point of impact	E.g., left front, front, right front. Consider using a numbered diagram instead of wording to identify.
Primary vehicle action	What the fleet vehicle was doing at the time of the incident (e.g., stopped in traffic, stopped at curb, starting forward, moving forward, turning left)
Driver of secondary vehicle/pedestrian	Identity of other vehicle operator
Registered owner of secondary vehicle	Identity of other vehicle owner
Secondary vehicle/object type	E.g., bus, truck, car, emergency vehicle, other fleet vehicle, bicycle, pedestrian
Secondary vehicle point of impact	E.g., left front, front, right front. Consider using a numbered diagram instead of wording to identify.
Secondary vehicle/pedestrian action	What the other vehicle/pedestrian was doing at the time of the incident
Relative position of vehicles/object/pedestrian	E.g., other vehicle ahead, other vehicle behind, other vehicle overtaking and passing, other vehicle approaching from left
Fleet employees injured, primary vehicle	Number of employees injured
Fleet employees killed, primary vehicle	Number of employees killed
Other injuries, primary vehicle	Number of passengers injured
Other fatalities, primary vehicle	Number of passengers killed
Injuries secondary, vehicle/pedestrian	Number in other vehicle injured
Fatalities secondary, vehicle/pedestrian	Number in other vehicle killed
Damage, primary vehicle	Estimated dollar value or subjective estimate (e.g., none, minor, moderate, severe)
Damage, secondary vehicle/object	Estimated dollar value or subjective estimate (e.g., none, minor, moderate, severe)
Geographical location	E.g., nearest intersection, milepost. Consider using a mapping program to provide precise longitude/latitude.
Number of passengers on primary vehicle	To assist law department; occasionally more lawsuits are filed claiming injury than there were passengers on the bus
Demographics on injured persons	Age, gender (to assist law department)
Identity of responders	E.g., police, ambulance
Detailed narrative of accident	Include potentially useful information that doesn't fit elsewhere.

FIGURE 2. Vehicle accident record-keeping system data elements (*Source:* Musal 1994)

efforts. Even within the same industry, the selection of benchmarks may be difficult. Is it fair to compare a fleet of eighteen-wheelers with a fleet of smaller trucks? Is it fair to compare a fleet of articulated buses with a fleet

without such vehicles? What about a fleet with mixed vehicle types?

Can the fleet accident rate of a post office delivering primarily to RFD routes with dirt roads be compared

CASE STUDY 2

Overview of a Sample Accident Record-Keeping System

This case study presents the fleet incident record-keeping system of the bus operation of NYCT and is based on an unpublished master's thesis by the author (1994).

A database was set up to accept most of the information suggested in Figure 2. Rather than establish multiple fields or have a narrative to describe the incident, an eight-character coding system occupying one field in the database was established for accident classification. The details of this coding system are provided in the Appendix. The structure of the coding system is summarized in the table.

The structure of this coding system makes it easy to select accidents when either responding to inquiries or performing detailed statistical analyses. For example, pedestrian accidents may be found by selecting all records with a first character of "1." Collisions with taxis would

		Coding System							
		Character							
Type	1	2	3	4	5	6	7	8
Collision pedestrian	1	Primary vehicle action	Pedestrian action	--	Primary vehicle contact point	--	Primary vehicle type	--
Collision vehicle	2	Primary vehicle action	Secondary vehicle action	Relative positions	Primary vehicle contact point	Secondary vehicle contact point	Primary vehicle type	Secondary vehicle type
Collision object	3	Primary vehicle action	--	--	Primary vehicle contact point	--	Primary vehicle type	Object type
Passenger	4	Primary vehicle action	Passenger action	Passenger location	Event	--	--	--
Crime	5	Crime category	Crime details	--	--	--	--	--
Misc.	6	Misc. category	Misc. details	--	--	--	--	--

be found by selecting all records with the eighth character "J." Collisions involving the right front of the fleet vehicle

would be found by selecting all records with the first character "1," "2," or "3" and the fifth character "F."

with a suburban post office delivering to town houses on well-paved roads? Traffic density is another issue. NYCT accident rates for Queens and Staten Island depots, which have relatively low traffic density as well as express routes on superhighways that provide many miles to the denominator of the equation, always have significantly lower accident rates than Manhattan depots providing crosstown service, where it may take as much as an hour to traverse the two-mile-wide island in very dense stop-and-go traffic. Is it fair to use a Queens or Staten Island accident rate as a benchmark for a Manhattan bus depot? Of course not.

Another confounding variable in using accident rates from other fleets as a benchmark is the use of different accident record-keeping methodologies. (In the Accident Reporting section of this chapter, this issue was raised during the discussion of preventability being used as a factor in determining whether an incident should be recorded.) While the NYCT did

not use preventability as a factor in determining whether to record bus traffic accidents, the author discovered that several other transit properties in the United States did not report accidents that they determined were not their fault. NYCT accident rates are compared directly with the accident rates of other fleets in American Public Transit Association (APTA) safety contests and are published alongside the rates of other fleets by the Federal Transit Administration (FTA).

The most accurate benchmark is often a fleet's own prior history unless the fleet changes its accident record-keeping methodology. Many of the variables mentioned above are eliminated if a work unit's own history is selected as a benchmark. There are, however, still variables that must be looked at in considering a fleet's own history as a benchmark. Seasonality is one important factor. Aside from weather conditions, there may be other seasonal issues. For example, as birds migrate, so do some people, and traffic conditions in the southern parts of the United States may be heavier in the winter than in the summer. When school is in session, the presence of school buses may appreciably increase traffic density. Special factors, such as a heavy snowstorm, temporary construction traffic patterns, or the occurrence of a special activity, such as a political convention, may drastically alter accident statistics. Such issues should be addressed in the notes presented with statistical reports.

While the most accurate benchmark may be the fleet's own prior experience, totally neglecting the experience of other fleet operators would be a serious mistake. Continued comparison of a fleet that has an abysmal safety record with its own record alone would provide little incentive to improve. Such benchmarking would perpetuate poor safety performance. Selection of benchmarks outside the fleet must be made with care, understanding the limitations of using such benchmarks.

The United States has adequate fleet accident-reporting systems, public and nonprofit, as described earlier. There is, however, little fleet safety benchmarking information available for many other countries (P.A.U. Education 2005). Case Study 3 shows how one company developed fleet safety benchmarking information where little was available.

Even where international data is available, it may be difficult to make proper comparisons due to differences in data-collection methodologies, population distribution, and traffic conditions. This is illustrated in "Benchmarking Australian Bus Safety" (Hildebrand and Geoff 2002), a study that compared bus accident rates in Australia with those in the United States and Canada. This study found that the bus fatality rate per kilometer in Australia is about 50 percent of that in Canada or the United States. However, the population-based fatality rate among bus passengers is more than ten times that in the United States or Canada. Lumley General Insurance of Australia provides statistical information on fleet accidents to clients. Included is information on how each client compares to other clients. Lumley also provides training materials and safety giveaways to clients, but believes the benchmarking initiative is their most effective tool (Haworth et al. 2000).

Prompted by unusually high fleet accident costs in 2006–2007, the British Royal Mail conducted a benchmarking audit, comparing their fleet safety practices to British Telecom, British Gas, and other organizations. They found that while they had good vehicle safety practices and reporting of accident information, they were deficient in driver assessment. Subsequently, they improved driver risk assessment, including license checks and installing telemetry in vehicles to identify driver performance (Murray and Keeler 2008).

The preceding discussion of benchmarking has been confined to vehicle accidents. It should be noted that ANSI Z15.1 provides a means for calculating incidence rates for other fleet operations. For example, delivery vehicles or dump trucks might use the *number of incidents per 10,000 deliveries made* or *number of incidents per 10,000 loads carried*, and fleets carrying passengers might use the *number of incidents resulting in passenger injury per million passengers carried*.

CASE STUDY 3

Fleet Safety Benchmark Survey: Europe, Middle East, and Africa

The Europe, Middle East, and Africa (EMEA) division of the Johnson & Johnson Company realized there was little data available for fleet safety benchmarking in their geographic area, so it conducted a survey to develop such data. Initially pharmaceutical companies in the area were included, but the scope was expanded to include medical and consumer products companies. In all, 23 multinational companies participated in the survey.

For the calendar year 2004, vehicle mileage and accident data, safe driving programs, and environmental and risk management issues were included in the survey for all of the respondents' operations in Europe, the Middle East, and Africa.

The survey was initiated with three conference calls during which the questionnaire was explained and questions responded to. A second similar survey, which is global in scope, was begun in May 2006 (P.A.U. Education 2005).

Benchmarking must be done with caution. While a fleet's own previous accident experience may be the most accurate benchmark, other benchmarks should also be considered, comparing judiciously and taking confounding factors into account.

STATISTICAL ANALYSIS

An intensive study of statistical analytical methods is beyond the scope of this book. Many statistical tests have been developed to perform all sorts of different analyses. It is important for the statistician to understand exactly what is to be measured and the limitations of the statistical test proposed. It is quite possible for different statistical tests to result in what appear to be contradictory findings. Having said this, it is necessary to use some statistical analysis techniques when carrying out performance appraisals.

Whether it is intended to compare one work unit with another within the fleet or to compare the fleet's accident experience with that of another fleet, it is necessary to consider the activity of the fleet as well as the number of accidents.

The most frequently used standard rate for comparing fleet accidents is *accidents per million miles traveled*. This is calculated by multiplying the number of accidents recorded (see discussion on recordable accidents in the Accident Reporting section of this chapter) by one million and dividing the result by the number of miles traveled by all vehicles in the work unit (see Case Study 4 for a sample calculation). Other rates noted in the Benchmarking section are similarly calculated using the appropriate incidents and the constant specified in the rate instead of 1,000,000.

Now that an accident rate has been calculated, the accident experience of one fleet work unit (or a whole fleet) may be directly compared with that of another. Such comparisons should be considered carefully, as there are many possible confounding variables, such as traffic conditions, weather, and different vehicle types, that would make the comparison invalid.

One note of caution: it is not statistically proper to add or average rates. Once rates have been calculated for subsidiary work units, do *not* add or average the rates. Each accident rate must be calculated

CASE STUDY 4

To calculate the standard rate for comparing fleet collision accidents, first, determine the work unit for which the rate is to be calculated. Almost any work unit may be selected; it could be one vehicle, one driver, one route, one dispatch point, or the whole fleet. Next determine the time period for which the rate will be collected: a day, a month, a year, and so on. Then identify the number of recordable collision accidents and the cumulative number of miles all vehicles in that work unit traveled.

For example, for a given work unit and time period, assume that there were three recordable collision accidents and the total number of miles traveled was 50,000. These numbers are put in the following equation:

$$\text{accidents per million miles} = \frac{\text{accidents} \times 1,000,000}{\text{miles traveled}} =$$

$$\frac{3 \times 1,000,000}{50,000} = 60 \text{ accidents per million miles}$$

separately using the incidents and miles traveled (or deliveries made or passengers carried) for the work unit being examined.

As has been noted in the Benchmarking section, the author recommends a work unit's own accident record as an appropriate benchmark because it is likely that using it will introduce the fewest confounding variables. The use of the unit's own record as a benchmark facilitates an ongoing analysis of the effectiveness of accident prevention efforts within that unit. One very useful tool to perform this analysis is the *control chart*.

Accident occurrences vary daily. This variation may be due to chance or some extraneous factor, such as a snowstorm or the implementation of a safety initiative that may have caused the accident rate to go up or down. A control chart uses statistical techniques to measure each individual time unit (day, month, and so on) against all other similar time units included within the calculation. A statistical technique is used to set control limits at levels of statistical significance [e.g., 95 percent confidence interval—approximately two standard deviations (actually 1.96) above and below the mean, or 99 percent confidence interval—approximately three standard deviations (actually 2.576) above and below the mean]. After application of this statistical technique, the user may state that any data point above the upper control limit or below the lower control limit was influenced by a factor other than chance with 95 percent (or 99 percent) certainty. Regular use of the control-chart technique is especially useful in measuring the continued effect of a particular safety initiative. Does the initiative result in a permanent accident reduction, or is its effect temporary?

A word of caution: before attempting to use a control chart, one should understand some fundamental statistical concepts, such as a normal distribution, probability distribution, and standard deviation.

Before introducing the preparation of a control chart, a brief discussion of time intervals and statistical significance is helpful. Statistical calculations by their nature are estimates. For example, in the previous paragraph the reader was given choices of 95 percent or 99 percent certainty; statistical analysis used as an estimating tool does not provide 100 percent accuracy. The more data points within a statistical analysis, the more accurate it will be, because the number of values is one of the factors used in determining the accuracy of the statistical calculation. Thus, a weekly analysis (with seven days of accidents) will be more accurate than a daily analysis (with only one day of accidents), and a monthly analysis (with 28 to 31 days of accidents) will be more accurate than a weekly analysis. Using longer time periods reduces variability, thereby allowing control limits to be tighter so that developing trends may be identified earlier.

Besides selecting the time period measured (day, week, month), it is also necessary to select the time interval used to establish the control limits. This selection should be made based on what the chart is intended to show. If the intention is to show the long-term effectiveness of the implementation of a safety initiative started several years in the past, it may be appropriate to create a control chart showing yearly accident rates over a period of twenty or more years. If the effectiveness of a current safety program is being evaluated, it may be more appropriate to start the control chart after the previous safety initiative was fully implemented and use monthly intervals. If the intention is just to watch accident statistics to see if any trends develop, 24 months is suggested, with monthly data points.

The formulas for calculating the upper control limit (UCL) and the lower control limit (LCL) at the 95 percent confidence level are

$$UCL = \bar{p} + 1.96\sqrt{\frac{\bar{p}(1-\bar{p})}{n}} \qquad (1)$$

$$LCL = \bar{p} - 1.96\sqrt{\frac{\bar{p}(1-\bar{p})}{n}} \qquad (2)$$

where

$$\bar{p} = \text{sum of } \frac{\text{accidents}}{n}$$

n = sum of miles traveled

Depending on the accident rate used, the value for n might also be the sum of passengers carried, deliveries made, and so on. Should the 99 percent confidence level be desired, substitute 2.576 for 1.96 in the above equations (Tarrants n.d.). The numbers 1.96 and 2.576 are used because those are the numbers of standard deviations required for the 95 percent and 99 percent confidence intervals, respectively. These numbers are derived from the standard normal (z) distribution table, which shows the areas under a normal curve for different numbers of standard deviations from the mean. Any number of standard deviations may be selected based on the degree of accuracy desired.

Case Study 5 is presented to show the calculations necessary to prepare a control chart with a 95 percent confidence level for vehicle accidents based on miles traveled in a work unit. The data are fictitious. An interpretation of the control chart is also presented with fictitious events used to explain any anomalies.

The primary purpose of accident record keeping and analysis is for performance appraisal and benchmarking. Occasionally, however, it is necessary to use these tools to evaluate the effectiveness of accident-

CASE STUDY 5

Preparing a Control Chart

This case provides a chart showing fictitious data for a fleet unit and the calculations necessary to prepare the control chart.

The individual monthly data points as well as the upper and lower control limits may then be plotted on a line graph.

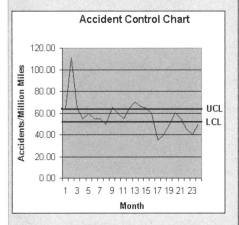

Time Interval	No. of Accidents	Miles Traveled	Accidents Per Million Miles
1	13	200,923	64.70
2	21	190,013	110.52
3	13	201,198	64.61
4	11	200,201	54.94
5	12	201,989	59.41
6	11	200,805	54.78
7	11	199,879	55.03
8	10	199,987	50.00
9	13	200,113	64.96
10	12	201,198	59.64
11	11	200,098	54.97
12	13	201,175	64.62
13	14	200,123	69.96
14	13	197,013	65.99
15	13	201,213	64.61
16	12	200,197	59.94
17	7	201,112	34.81
18	8	200,891	39.82
19	10	199,979	50.01
20	12	199,998	60.00
21	11	200,250	54.93
22	9	201,213	44.73
23	8	200,118	39.98
24	10	201,200	49.70
Sum	278	4,800,886	57.91
$\bar{p}$	5.7906E-05		
$\dfrac{\bar{p}(1-\bar{p})}{n}$	1.20608E-11		
$\sqrt{\dfrac{\bar{p}(1-\bar{p})}{n}}$	3.47287E-06		
$1.96\sqrt{\dfrac{\bar{p}(1-\bar{p})}{n}}$	6.80682E-06		
UCL	6.47128E-05		64.71
LCL	5.10992E-05		51.10

It is now necessary to interpret the control chart in light of (fictitious) events that happened related to the work unit under examination. Months 1 through 24 represent January of the first year through December of the second year. The spike in month 2 represents a very snowy February of year 1 with icy road conditions through much of the month resulting in more accidents than usual. The ticks below the lower control limit in month 8 and above the upper control limit in month 9 are unexplained. A 95 percent confidence level was chosen, so it is possible that some points outside the control limits are due to chance. Had a 99 percent confidence level been used in the calculations, both of these points would have been within the control limits. Note that due to the relatively small size of the work unit, only about three accidents separate the lower control limit from the upper control limit. Had the monthly number of accidents varied more widely than those presented here, the control limits would have been farther apart because the standard deviation would have been greater. Months 13 and 14 represent January and February of year 2 with snow and ice again, but not as severe as in year 1. In month 17, the safety director implemented an incentive program focusing on accident reduction. There was a significant reduction in accidents for three months, but the novelty of the program wore off (see discussion of incentive programs) and things were back to normal in month 20.

In month 22 the traffic department installed a traffic light at an especially dangerous intersection that most fleet vehicles had to pass through. This resulted in a permanent drop in traffic accidents to a new lower plateau. Month 22 would be a logical starting point for a future control chart because it represents a permanent change in traffic conditions that makes prior data a poor benchmark.

prevention efforts. The accident record-keeping database becomes a useful tool in performing these analyses. Depending on the situation, it may be necessary to perform a prospective or retrospective study, and the appropriate statistical tests must be selected. A prospective study is one in which the ground rules of the study are set and participants are selected before the study is begun. A retrospective study is one in which preexisting data is used for the study. Care must be taken in establishing the ground rules of the study to eliminate or reduce confounding variables and to ensure the validity and reliability of the findings.

Case Study 6 presents an analysis of the effectiveness of an accident-prevention effort. No documentation of this study remains; its description is based on the author's memory only. The presentation focuses on the methods followed in setting up the study rather than the exact statistical techniques used in the study.

CASE STUDY 6

Analysis of the Effectiveness of an Accident-Prevention Effort

This case study presents a real accident-prevention effort at the NYCT. It is drawn from memory, as no documentation of the study remains.

Statistics showed that collisions involving the bus rear represented a significant number of accidents. A suggestion was made that if the bus rear were to be more visible, fewer vehicles might collide with it. Further investigation revealed two possible ways to make the bus rear more visible. One was to paint the rear with chevron-shaped alternating yellow and black stripes ("zebra stripes"), as is done with some construction vehicles. A second was to install a third brake light (a "cyclops light") below the rear window of the bus and centered above a horizontal line drawn between the two existing brake lights.

Discussions were initiated with the bus operations and maintenance departments. They agreed on a preliminary test protocol for a prospective matched control study calling for participation by four bus depots: one each in Queens and Staten Island, which serve areas with relatively light traffic conditions, and one each in Brooklyn and the Bronx, which serve areas with heavy traffic volume. Thirty regular buses were to be chosen at random from each depot. (This test excluded high-mileage express routes that used a different type of bus and included significant amounts of highway travel.) All 120 buses were to have rear advertising signs removed because the signs were a potentially confounding variable. Ten buses at each depot were to be repainted with zebra stripes, ten were to have the cyclops light installed, and ten were to remain as is (with the advertising signs removed). The study was to last one year.

The concept of removing the advertising signs from the buses brought vehement objections from the real estate department, which produced revenue from renting space for the signs. Negotiations resulted in an agreement that only the 20 zebra-striped buses would have their advertising signs removed, and the signs would remain in place on the other 40 buses. Should the zebra stripes prove effective in reducing rear-end accidents, further discussion would take place with the real estate department.

After the buses were prepared, the study began. The test buses were randomly assigned to routes and drivers using regular procedures at the depots. Test buses withdrawn from service for more than a few days due to accident damage or mechanical breakdown were replaced by other regular buses selected at random from the same depot and prepared appropriately. On a monthly basis all accidents involving the test buses where the point of impact was either left rear, rear, or right rear (see the Appendix for coding structure) were abstracted from the accident record-keeping system, and copies of the accident brief were maintained in a separate file for the duration of the study. Special procedures were established to obtain monthly mileage counts from each depot for the buses in the study.

At the end of the first month of the study it was noted that the zebra-striped test buses had more rear accidents than the other test groups. Approximately four months into the study, sufficient data had been collected to indicate that the zebra-striped test buses had significantly more rear accidents than the other test groups. At that point a decision was made to withdraw the zebra-striped buses from the study, have them repainted, and have the advertising signs remounted. This resolved issues with the real estate department.

The study continued with only two test groups. Analysis of the results at the conclusion of the twelve-month test period showed the cyclops-light-equipped buses had significantly fewer rear collisions than the control group. The study results were presented to management. Management determined that all future new bus orders would include the requirement that a cyclops light be factory installed. Moreover, management directed that all existing buses be retrofitted with a cyclops light.

It would not be appropriate to conclude this discussion of statistical analysis without touching on nonstatistical analysis—specifically, the human element. People processing accident reports sometimes notice odd things or come up with ideas that can be very productive in reducing accidents. Hence, Case Study 7 is presented.

Statistical Reporting

Maintaining accident statistics is valueless unless something is done with them. Their use in initiating and measuring accident-reduction efforts has already been discussed. Accident statistics are also reported as a measure of work-unit safety. Such reports may be made to entities outside the organization as well as those inside the organization.

Certain motor fleets may be required to report accident statistics to regulatory agencies. For example, public transit properties are required to submit annual statistical reports to the Federal Transit Administration (FTA). Most business organizations are also required to make annual reports of employee accident statistics to the Occupational Safety and Health Admin-

istration (OSHA). Local public agencies often must report employee accident statistics to regulatory bodies similar to OSHA.

Members of the National Safety Council (NSC) are requested to voluntarily report their accident statistics to the NSC. These statistics are amalgamated and presented in the NSC's annual publication *Injury Facts*, previously mentioned in this chapter. Members with especially noteworthy accident records receive recognition from the NSC. Industry groups, such as the American Public Transit Association (APTA), also collect accident statistics from members for publication within the industry. Again, fleets with excellent safety records receive recognition.

Publications from and inquiries for statistical information from all of these organizations become sources of information fleets can use to develop benchmarking criteria to measure their overall safety. Care must be taken in selecting benchmarking criteria (see the discussion on benchmarking earlier in the chapter).

Finally, and perhaps most importantly, accident statistics are reported internally to management. They become a tool local management can use to measure their success in safety. Statistical reports may also be

CASE STUDY 7

Bus Operators Falling from Doors

This case study presents a real event at the NYCT. It is related from memory, as no documentation remains.

The person responsible for classifying employee accidents noted that several incidents had been classified as "bus operator falling from door." This was identified from the NYCT employee accident record-keeping system, which has not been described here but was fully described in *The Development of an Accident Record-Keeping System at the New York City Transit Authority* (Musal 1994). Why do bus operators fall from the door of a bus? Interest was piqued and further investigation of accident records and a visit to a bus depot resolved the mystery.

For safe driving, it is necessary that both right and left outside rearview mirrors be properly adjusted for the height and seat position of the driver. Accordingly, when drivers enter a bus, the first thing they adjust is the seat and the second is the mirrors. It is easy to adjust the left outside mirror by opening the window and manually moving it. The right outside mirror is more difficult. The driver sits in the seat, looks at the mirror, estimates how it must be adjusted, and then opens the front door of the bus and places his or her left foot on the door hinge while grasping a railing with his or her left hand. The right hand adjusts the mirror while the right foot moves in the air, trying to maintain balance. The driver then returns to the seat to check the mirror position and repeats the adjustment process as necessary.

As is known from ladder safety rules, three points of secure contact are required for safety. Drivers have two secure points: left foot and left hand, making mirror adjusting less than safe. Two additional factors make the mirror-adjusting operation even more unsafe. A properly maintained door hinge is well oiled or greased, and therefore slippery. Also, quite often bus drivers relieve other drivers on the road, not in the depot, and in winter ice and snow tend to accumulate on the door hinge.

The findings of this study were presented to management along with a recommendation that small servomotors be attached to the right outside mirrors to permit them to be adjusted by the driver from the seat. Management directed that all future bus orders have servomotors factory installed.

among the measures used to rate managers for promotions and possible bonuses. For these reasons it is especially important that accident-reporting, record-keeping, and analysis systems be above reproach (see the discussion on criteria for recording accidents in the Accident Reporting section of this chapter).

An internal fleet accident statistical reporting system may include charts and graphs showing accidents geographically by fleet unit and showing accident trends by time. Accidents may be presented as raw numbers and/or as rates (see Case Studies 4 and 5).

INCENTIVE PROGRAMS

The use of incentive programs as accident-prevention tools is somewhat controversial in the safety profession. Because such programs raise safety awareness, they do prevent some accidents. Their continued effectiveness requires constant effort to keep employees interested. Where funding is limited, incentive programs must take second place to efforts to ameliorate unsafe conditions.

The effectiveness of incentive programs has come to be linked to an industrial research phenomenon known as the "Hawthorne effect." From 1927 to 1932, Elton Mayo and Fritz Roethlisberger conducted research on methods of enhancing employee productivity at the Hawthorne Works of the Western Electric Company (now Alcatel-Lucent) near Chicago. The key experiment in the series occurred in the relay assembly test room, where six female employees were isolated and working conditions could be controlled. The researchers measured productivity under various working conditions: rest breaks were provided or withheld; the length of the workday was changed; temperature and lighting levels were increased and decreased. After a year of experimentation, no correlation could be discovered between the varying working conditions and the women's productivity, but productivity increased throughout the experiment. Finally, interviews with the women uncovered the secret to their enhanced productivity. They felt special because they had been chosen from all other workers in the plant. They appreciated the communications and openness to questions by the researchers. A degree of team cohesiveness developed among these six women, who became fast friends. Productivity increases had nothing to do with the test conditions. They related directly to the attention given to the employees as part of the research study and the cohesiveness and dedication that developed as a result of it (Rieger 1995).

Similarly, an incentive program as an accident-prevention tool succeeds only to the extent that employees are genuinely interested in the program and modify their behaviors to align with those promoted by the program. When that interest wanes, money spent on incentive programs is as good as thrown away.

Case Study 8 describes an incentive program in use in 1988 and 1989 at NYCT to promote employee safety.

Several studies have found that a significant number of fleets use driver incentive programs as part of their accident-reduction efforts. One study found that 70 percent of trucking firms surveyed use them (Barton and Tardiff 1998). Another found that 41 percent of surveyed fleets and 66 percent of award-winning

CASE STUDY 8

A Safety Incentive Program

This case study presents a safety incentive program used in 1988 and 1989 at the NYCT and is reconstructed from the author's memory.

It began as an annual program recognizing the bus maintenance shop with the best lost-time accident record. Suitable publicity announced the program before it began. After the annual accident records were compiled, a ceremony was held at the winning work location. A trophy was presented by the chief executive officer followed by coffee and cake. Coffee mugs imprinted with the winning maintenance shop's name, year, and achievement were presented to all employees.

During the second year of the program a second award was added to recognize the maintenance shop with the most improved lost-time accident record. A similar presentation ceremony was held at each winning maintenance shop. After the 1989 awards were presented, in 1990 that particular program was brought to a close and another safety initiative was implemented.

fleets use them (American Trucking Associations Foundation 1999). Still another found that 73 percent use them (Knipling et al. 2003).

LEGAL IMPLICATIONS

Vehicle accidents often result in legal action by injured parties. To protect the interests of the employer, the custodian of vehicle accident records must be very careful in responding to requests for accident information from outside the organization.

Public agencies are especially at risk. Many public bodies are required by various freedom-of-information laws to provide their internal information to members of the public upon request, and accident information is included. Accident information may also be useful to researchers doing academic investigations. As such information is accessible to anyone, it is quite possible, and not illegal, for a person to submit a request as a private citizen without indicating in the request that he or she is an attorney representing a client. Accordingly, it is prudent for all freedom-of-information requests to be funneled through an agency's legal department.

Both public and private fleet operators may receive subpoenas requiring the presentation of accident records as part of the discovery process of a lawsuit. Upon receiving a subpoena, it is likewise important to consult with the fleet's attorney to determine how it will be handled.

The custodian of the accident records and the fleet's attorney can determine how best to handle the issue to protect both the employer and the custodian. For example, the author remembers one freedom-of-information request submitted by an attorney suing the NYCT. The request sought information to show that the specific type of accident suffered by the attorney's client had previously occurred and that the NYCT was negligent in not correcting the hazard that caused the accident. The request was worded quite broadly, requesting information for all accidents occurring during a particular period of time. After consultation with the legal department's freedom-of-information officer, the attorney was provided with precisely what he asked for, not what he wanted. The accidents he was searching for were scattered throughout the hundreds of printed pages he was given precisely in the order in which they had been entered into the computer. The NYCT successfully defended this particular lawsuit.

CONCLUSION

Benchmarking and performance appraisal are critical parts of an effective fleet safety program. There are several components of a benchmarking and performance appraisal system. An accident/incident-reporting system must be established to ensure that incidents are reported with adequate details. A record-keeping system must maintain easy availability of all of the accident data to facilitate analysis and reporting. Appropriate benchmarks must be selected so that fleet performance can be adequately judged. Proper statistical tools must be used to meaningfully analyze accident data. Appropriate methodologies must be used to create understandable reports of statistical results. All of the above should be accomplished with an understanding of how the total benchmarking and appraisal system might be used to prosecute or defend fleet management should legal action be commenced.

Without an effective accident-reporting and record-keeping system, there can be no safety management. Benchmarking and performance appraisal are the tools used to identify problem areas for accident-reduction efforts and to evaluate the effectiveness of those efforts.

Acknowledgements

The author acknowledges Robert J. Crain, P.E., who worked for many years with the author in developing the computer-based accident record-keeping systems at the NYCT that were used in most of the case studies presented in this chapter. The author also thanks Bram D. Weiser, M.S., who was intimately involved in the evolution and operation of the fleet accident record-keeping and analysis system and kindly consented to review a draft of this chapter.

REFERENCES

American National Standards Institute (ANSI). 1996. Standard ANSI D16.1. In *Manual on Classification of Motor Vehicle Traffic Accidents*. Washington, D.C.: ANSI.

_____. 2006. Standard ANSI Z15.1. In *Safe Practices for Motor Vehicle Operations*. Washington, D.C.: ANSI.

American Trucking Associations Foundation. 1999. *Safe Returns: A Compendium of Injury Reduction and Safety Management Practices of Award Winning Carriers*. Alexandria, VA: American Trucking Associations.

Barton, R., and L. P. Tardiff. 1998. *Incentive Programs for Enhancing Truck Safety and Productivity*. Montreal, CAN: Transportation Development Centre.

Haworth, Narelle, Claes Tingvall, and Naomi Kwadlo. 2000. *Review of Best Practice Road Safety Initiatives in the Corporate and/or Business Environment*. Melbourne: Monash University.

Heinrich, H. W. 1969. *Industrial Accident Prevention*. New York: McGraw-Hill.

Hildebrand, Eric, and Rose Geoff. 2002. "Benchmarking Australian Bus Safety." *Road & Transport Research*. Vermont South, Victoria, Australia: ARRB Group Ltd.

Knipling, Ronald R., Jeffrey S. Hickman, and Gene Bergoffen. 2003. *Commercial Truck and Bus Safety Synthesis Program, Synthesis 1: Effective Commercial Truck and Bus Safety Management Techniques*. Washington, D.C.: Transportation Research Board.

Murray, Will, and Cathy Keeler. 2008. *Summary Report from the Fleet Safety Benchmarking Seminar*. London, 16 January 2008. (accessed April 28, 2011) www.virtualriskmanager.net/main/news/Benchmarking-Workshop-Report-Jan-08.pdf

Musal, Edward A. 1994. "The Development of an Accident Record-Keeping System at the New York City Transit Authority." Unpublished master's thesis. New York: Hunter College.

National Safety Council (NSC). 2010. *Injury Facts* (previously titled *Accident Facts*) Itasca, IL: NSC.

P.A.U. Education. (Barcelona, Spain.) 2005. *European Road Safety Charter—Sharing of Best Practices*. (Retrieved January 14, 2007.) www.paueducation.com/comm/transport/roadsafety/charger/media/media1252.doc

Rieger, Bradley J. 1995. "Lessons in productivity and people." *Training & Development* 49:56–58.

Tarrants, William E. Undated, approximately 1960. *Measurement of Safety Performance*. Unpublished manuscript used as text for course. New York: New York University.

_____. 1963. "An Evaluation of the Critical Incident Technique as a Method for Identifying Industrial Accident Causal Factors." Unpublished doctoral dissertation. New York: New York University.

APPENDIX: BUS FLEET INCIDENT CODES

Character 1: Incident Type

1	Collision-Pedestrian
2	Collision-Vehicle
3	Collision-Object
4	Passenger
5	Crime
6	Miscellaneous
7	Industrial (employee) accident

Collision

Character 2: All Collisions (Pedestrian/Vehicle/Object) – Action of Primary Vehicle

Forward/Reverse

A/B	Moving in lane
C/D	Changing lanes
E/F	Turning right
G/H	Turning left
I/J	U-turn
K/L	Pulling into curb
M/N	Pulling out from curb
O/P	Starting (not from curb)
Q/R	Stopping (not from curb)
S	Standing in traffic
T	Standing/parked at curb
X	Unknown

Character 3: Pedestrian Collision – Pedestrian Action

A	In street
B	On sidewalk
C	In crosswalk—crossing from left
D	In crosswalk—crossing from right
E	Not in crosswalk—crossing from left
F	Not in crosswalk—crossing from right
X	Unknown

Character 3: Vehicle Collision – Secondary Vehicle Action

Forward/Reverse

A/B	Moving in lane
C/D	Changing lanes

E/F   Turning right
G/H   Turning left
I/J   U-turn
K/L   Pulling into curb
M/N   Pulling out from curb
O/P   Starting (not from curb)
Q/R   Stopping (not from curb)
S   Standing in traffic
T   Standing/parked at curb
X   Unknown

Character 4: Vehicle Collision – Relative Positions

A   Other vehicle ahead
B   Other vehicle behind
C   Other vehicle overtaking and passing left
D   Other vehicle overtaking and passing right
E   Primary vehicle overtaking and passing left
F   Primary vehicle overtaking and passing right
G   Other vehicle approaching from left
H   Other vehicle approaching from right
I   Other vehicle approaching from opposite direction
J   Both vehicles standing (e.g., slide on ice, open door)
X   Unknown

Character 5: All Collisions (Pedestrian/Vehicle/Object) – Contact Point on Primary Vehicle

A   Front
B   Left front
C   Left side
D   Left rear
E   Rear
F   Right front
G   Right side
H   Right rear
I   Left open door (including engine door)
J   Right open door (including engine door)
X   Unknown

Character 6: Vehicle Collision – Contact Point on Secondary Vehicle

A   Front
B   Left front
C   Left side
D   Left rear

E   Rear
F   Right front
G   Right side
H   Right rear
I   Left open door (including engine door)
J   Right open door (including engine door)
X   Unknown

Character 7: All Collisions (Pedestrian/Vehicle/Object) – Primary Vehicle Type

A   Bus
B   Van
C   Truck
D   Auto (e.g., Jimmy)
E   Industrial truck (e.g., forklift)

Character 8: Vehicle Collision – Secondary Vehicle Type

A   Auto (e.g., Jimmy)
B   Van
C   Truck
D   Fleet bus
E   Fleet auto
F   Fleet truck
G   Fleet industrial truck (e.g., forklift)
H   School bus
I   Nonfleet bus
J   Taxi
K   Emergency vehicle (e.g., police, fire, ambulance)
L   Motorcycle
M   Moped
N   Bicycle or tricycle
O   Other person-powered vehicle (e.g., pushcart)
P   Animal-drawn vehicle
Q   Nonfleet industrial truck (e.g., forklift)
X   Unknown

Character 8: Object Collision – Object Type

A   Fixed object (e.g., abutment, pole, building, tree, curb)
B   Movable object on roadway
C   Movable object on sidewalk
D   Movable object elsewhere (e.g., depot)
E   Animal
X   Other

Passenger Accident

Character 2: Passenger Accident – Bus Action

Forward/Reverse

A/B   Moving in lane
C/D   Changing lanes
E/F   Turning right
G/H   Turning left
I/J   U-turn
K/L   Pulling into curb
M/N   Pulling out from curb
O/P   Starting (not from curb)
Q/R   Stopping (not from curb)
S   Standing in traffic
T   Standing/parked at curb
X   Unknown

Character 3: Passenger Accident – Passenger Action

A   Boarding
B   On board standing
C   On board walking
D   On board seated
E   On board sitting down
F   On board arising
G   On board action unknown
H   Alighting
X   Unknown

Character 4: Passenger Accident – Passenger Location

A   Front door/steps
B   Near fare box
C   Front seat area
D   Rear door/steps
E   Rear seat area
X   Unknown

Character 5: Passenger Accident – Event

A   Slipped/tripped/fell
B   Bumped into object/person
C   Struck by doors
D   Caught by doors and dragged
E   Struck by vehicle/object (part of body extended through window)
F   Object through window (not thrown)
G   Defective equipment

H   Bus fire
I   Actions of other passengers (not assault)
X   Unknown

Crime

Character 2: Crime Category

A   Robbery/larceny (theft)
B   Assault (injury or intent to injure person)
C   Criminal mischief (damage or intent to damage property)
D   Violation (no damage or injury intended)

Character 3: Crime Details – A. Robbery/Larceny

A   Robbery operator (theft with force or threat of force)
B   Robbery passenger (theft with force or threat of force)
C   Larceny operator (theft without force, e.g., pickpocket)
D   Larceny passenger (theft without force, e.g., pickpocket)
E   Larceny fleet property (theft without force)
F   Larceny fleet revenue (theft without force)
G   Larceny non-fleet property (theft without force)

Character 3: Crime Details – B. Assault

A   Other operator assault
B   Other passenger assault
C   Assault by operator
D   Operator struck by thrown object
E   Passenger struck by thrown object

Character 3: Crime Details – C. Criminal Mischief

A   Missiles
B   Graffiti
C   Other

Character 3: Crime Details – D. Violations

A   Harassment
B   Hitching (no injury)
C   Hitching (injury)
D   Hitching (fatal)
E   Other violation

Miscellaneous

Character 2: Miscellaneous Category

A   Person leaving after alighting
B   Person approaching to board
C   Equipment damage or failure
D   Involvement—passenger/other person
E   Miscellaneous other
F   Incident observed

Character 3: Miscellaneous Details – A. Person Leaving after Alighting

A   Other fall in roadway or on adjacent ground
B   Fall in bus stop zone
C   Struck by vehicle in roadway—other
D   Struck by vehicle in roadway—alongside bus
E   Miscellaneous other and indeterminate

Character 3: Miscellaneous Details – B. Person Approaching to Board

A   Other fall in roadway or on adjacent ground
B   Fall in bus stop zone
C   Struck by vehicle in roadway—other
D   Struck by vehicle in roadway—alongside bus
E   Miscellaneous other and indeterminate

Character 3: Miscellaneous Details – C. Equipment Damage or Failure

A   Window/bus damage—no injury, not a crime
B   Bus fire

Character 3: Miscellaneous Details – D. Involvement – Passenger/Other Person

A   Illness/death on bus including sick employee
B   With passenger—fare or transfer
C   With passenger—other reason
D   Between passengers
E   With person other than passenger
F   Miscellaneous other and indeterminate

Character 3: Miscellaneous Details – E. Miscellaneous Other

A   Clothing soiled or damaged on bus
B   Other property damaged on bus
C   Miscellaneous other and indeterminate— also denial by operator

Character 3: Miscellaneous Details – F. Incident Observed

A   Vehicles colliding
B   Vehicle striking person
C   Person falling
D   Injury off bus
E   Other

Industrial (Employee) Accident

Character 2: Cause

A   Animal or insect
B   Contact—e.g., electricity, surface, molten metal, liquid
C   Fall—elevation
D   Fall—surface
E   Falling object
F   Flying object
G   Flying particle—source unknown (wind, dust)
H   Gas, fume, compressed air, heat
I   Handling object
J   Striking object (including pothole)
K   Stepping on object
L   Struck by object
M   Struck by train or vehicle
N   Dropped operator seat (seat collapses)
O   Miscellaneous
R   Trip, slip, or stumble boarding or alighting from bus

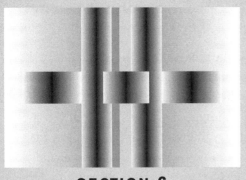

LEARNING OBJECTIVES

- Understand what *best practices* means for fleet operations.

- Be able to define the risk elements associated with fleet operations.

- Know the ten steps used to develop a fleet operations' driver-safety initiative.

- Be able to define *reportable* crashes.

- Understand the classes of Commercial Driver's Licenses (CDLs) and the use of endorsements and restrictions.

- Summarize the hours-of-service rules that were revised in 2005.

- List three types of provisions of laws pertaining to CDL drivers that regulate the use of drugs and alcohol.

BEST PRACTICES

Phil Moser, Carmen W. Daecher, and Amy Stewart

THE TERM *best practices* is often heard in organizations today. In this chapter, *best practices* describes consistently applied principles and activities that have produced consistently positive results in fleet management.

Over time, many misconceptions or myths have crept into our collective thinking regarding vehicle fleets. This chapter will discuss two such myths as a prelude to the discussion of best practices. The first is that fleet managers manage vehicles. If that is all they did, fleet management would be less challenging than it is. After all, vehicles cannot talk back or offer criticism to make the fleet manager's job more challenging.

The second myth is that the lowest-cost vehicle is best for an organization. While cost is always an important consideration, the quality of the ride and the vehicle's safety features are fundamentally important to its effective and efficient use and to the employee/driver being able to operate it safely and remaining safe while in it.

Most of the myths associated with fleet management overlook a critical element in fleet operations—the driver. Most fleet-operations management systems do not fully encompass all of the risk elements associated with the operation of vehicle fleets. Because of this, the term *fleet management* is inaccurate if an organization has employees who operate fleet vehicles. *Fleet operations management* is a far better general description of the process and its challenges.

BEST PRACTICES FOR RISK MANAGEMENT OF FLEET OPERATIONS

Managing fleet operations is managing risk. Best practices for managing these risks start with the identification of risk elements associated with fleet operations. They are drivers, vehicles, and operations associated with the use of vehicles.

These three elements comprise the core around which any effective management program for fleet operations is built. Not addressing any one of these elements allows risk to be uncontrolled.

Based upon this author's twenty years of experience in studying and assisting fleet operations of all sizes and types, three key management principles are important in effectively managing fleet operations:

- *Hiring the best person for the job.* The job description, if it includes driving a vehicle, should include consideration of driving abilities or the ability to learn the driving task effectively.
- *Training people to succeed.* Providing employees with the knowledge to effectively drive vehicles and understand critical behaviors associated with vehicle operations is essential to managing fleet operations. Fleet managers must ensure proficiency through repetition and/or testing during training.
- *Managing consistently.* With the knowledge that new employees receive, they should be expected to behave consistently according to the standards provided to them during training. Celebrating consistently good behavior and addressing unacceptable behavior are critical to keeping employees focused on behaviors that are critical in mitigating risk associated with fleet operations.

Too often, some or all of these principles are compromised. People are hired because of need rather than ability. Training is minimized or overlooked, and management is personal rather than objective. By objectively implementing and using these three key management principles, an effective and successful process of fleet operations management can be established.

A subtle but fundamentally important difference in managing fleet operations compared to other types of operations is the environment in which critical behaviors occur. In most situations, a supervisor is with employees on the floor or in the field and can identify critical behaviors and address them on the spot. Or, because of the interconnectivity between many job tasks, one employee's unsafe behavior is viewed as dangerous to the health and well-being of other employees. Thus, employees also assist in identifying and changing unacceptable behaviors.

This type of environment hardly ever exists while an employee is driving a vehicle. Usually, the driver is the captain of the ship. He or she is also the chief cook and bottle-washer. Drivers control their own destinies as well as those of others on the roadway with no direct supervision or oversight while operating the vehicle. The old paradigm *management by walking around* (MBWA) is not applicable in fleet operations. Rather, a new paradigm must be established for successful fleet operations: *management by driving around* (MBDA).

Expected Outcomes of Best Practices

With all of this in mind, best practices for management of fleet operations occur after the following components are in place:

- Enhancement of existing policies or establishment of new policies directed at fleet operations and critical behaviors associated with vehicle operations.
- Provision of adequate training to ensure that people have the proper skills to operate and maintain vehicles and understand critical behaviors and the importance of attitude and alertness while driving.
- Establishment of a progressive system of discipline for those who fail to behave acceptably. This system should attempt to refocus and retain employees rather than be purely negative in consequence. However, if employees cannot maintain consistently acceptable behavior, the company must limit the risk and liability associated with the unacceptable behavior.

- Implementation of a positive behavior-reinforcement strategy that is intended to celebrate good behavior on a regular basis and as soon as possible after such behavior is observed or acknowledged. Safety bonus programs by themselves are not always the best answer. A more fluid and interactive approach to positive reinforcement and a system in which all employees are focused on critical behaviors is more effective. The intended result of these programs is to keep people conscious of their own actions and behaviors as they drive. Positive communication may also take on the form of reminding employees of what is important as well as rewarding good behaviors after they are performed.

- Implementation of an improved fleet-efficiency program. By properly selecting and maintaining vehicles and establishing standards for their use (maximum speed, fuel usage, and so on) a more efficient and effective use of the vehicle fleet—in conjunction with vehicle performance standards that incorporate safe operation—can be established and measured.

- Revisions to organizational operations as they relate to critical behaviors and fleet efficiency. Through reassessment and adjustment to company operations that affect safe vehicle-fleet operations (such as scheduling, routing, and provisions for replacing vehicles), company employees other than drivers and service technicians become involved in safe fleet operations. Through this process, others who influence safe fleet operations are aware of the company's commitment to safe fleet operations in combination with customer service and satisfaction and profitability.

- Establishment of a measurement and accountability process to monitor results and to help safety records to continue to improve. Regular reporting and analyzing will identify processes, policies, personnel, and other key performance items that may need change or improvement.

After an effective fleet-operations management system is in place, what should be expected? A consistently applied, effective fleet management program should produce the following sequence of results:

- elimination of poor performers
- reduced turnover
- improved communication regarding performance
- higher-quality training
- a more efficient vehicle fleet
- improved customer services and profitability
- more consistent and effective management of fleet operations

References that Can Help the Fleet Manager

The following standards, in addition to referenced publications, offer guidelines that organizations can use to shape and implement a fleet improvement program:

- ANSI Z15.1-2006, *Safe Practices for Motor Vehicle Operations* (ANSI/ASSE 2006) (for all fleet operations)
- Code of Federal Regulations (CFR) Title 49 (Parts 40, 171–180, 325, 380–399) (for commercial fleet operations)

These standards define the framework for achieving best management practices for fleet operations and detail regulatory requirements for commercial fleets. By implementing a well-defined and measurable risk-management process that also complies with all applicable regulations, an organization can achieve best practices for fleet operations.

A TEN-STEP OUTLINE FOR CREATING A FLEET SAFETY INITIATIVE

Year in and year out, traffic crashes are the leading cause of death for American workers. Annually, approximately 21 percent of worker fatalities occur as a result of motor-vehicle collisions (BLS 2011). Nevertheless, driver safety has rarely received the same level of attention as other areas of employee safety, but this is changing. Since the ANSI Z15.1-2006 standards on driver safety were published, the awareness level for driver safety has been elevated. This is great news, because in order for a problem to be corrected, there must be an awareness that the problem exists. The ANSI Z15.1-2006 standard is just one source that can be used by organizations to achieve their driver-safety goals. While many of the suggested strategies for achieving success with a driver-safety initiative are discussed in ANSI Z15.1-2006. (ANSI/ASSE 2006), the information covered in this chapter originated from the author's experiences, training, and knowledge regarding driver safety.

Many safety professionals are not familiar with the steps necessary to create a comprehensive fleet safety initiative within their organization. The following ten-step best-practices approach will help them to create a driver-safety initiative for their organization.

Step 1: Understand the Problem

In order to justify taking on a major driver-safety initiative, it is first necessary to understand the problem. This justification can begin at the national level. In 2008, according to the *Fatality Analysis Reporting System Encyclopedia* on the NHTSA Web site (NHTSA 2008), there were 34,017 fatal motor-vehicle traffic

crashes. That is an average of 93 people dying every day. Early estimates for 2009 are that 33,963 people died in motor-vehicle traffic crashes, a decline of 8.9 percent from 2008, in which 37,261 people died.

Looked at in terms of risk factors, this means that one average American driver in fifteen will be involved in a motor-vehicle collision during the next year. One average American driver in forty-five will be involved in an injury collision during the next year. And one average American driver in sixty-five will be involved in a fatal collision during his or her driving lifetime. The term used for these statistics is *average American driver*. People who drive as part of their job may not be considered average. Chances are they drive quite a bit more than the *average* driver.

A National Household Travel Survey (NHTS) conducted from 2001 to 2002 by the Bureau of Transportation Statistics found that contrary to the stereotypical image of the business traveler heading off to catch a cross-country flight, the majority of long-distance business trips in the United States are taken to destinations within 250 miles of home and are by automobile. The personal vehicle is the dominant travel mode for business travel, comprising 81 percent of all trips. Air travel accounts for about 16 percent of all business trips (BTS

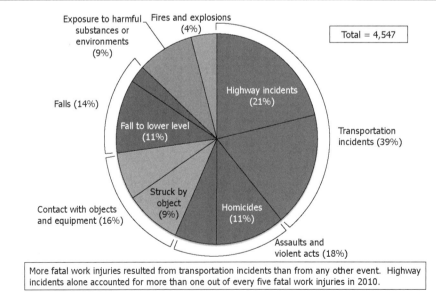

More fatal work injuries resulted from transportation incidents than from any other event. Highway incidents alone accounted for more than one out of every five fatal work injuries in 2010.

*Data for 2010 are preliminary.
NOTE: Percentages may not add to totals because of rounding. Transportation counts are expected to rise when updated 2010 data are released in Spring 2012 because key source documentation on specific transportation-related incidents has not yet been received.

FIGURE 1. Manner in which U.S. workplace fatalities occurred, 2010 (*Source:* BLS 2011)

2003). The average driver logs approximately 10,000 to 12,000 miles a year. The typical business driver logs approximately 25,000 miles a year. The exposure of business drivers to collisions and all of their associated risks is greater than that of the average driver—they are not *average*.

In fact, data analysis by the U.S. Department of Labor, Bureau of Labor Statistics (BLS), has shown that transportation incidents cause more work-related deaths in the United States (at 39 percent) than any other single incident type (BLS 2011). As illustrated in Figure 1, motor-vehicle crashes were responsible for 21 percent of all worker fatalities in 2010, causing over one in five work-related deaths. The next most frequent cause of worker fatalities—contact with objects and equipment—accounted for less than half as many fatalities.

To fully understand the problem, it is necessary to look at more than just national statistics. Each organization should determine its own crash rate as well as the number of crash-related injuries, lost workdays, and workers' compensation claims that resulted from motor-vehicle collisions.

Step 2: Set Achievable Goals

The ultimate goal is to create a safe driving culture throughout an organization. Organizations that have created such a culture have had great success. As an example, in the manufacturing environment, there are some areas employees would never think of entering without the proper safety equipment, such as hard hats or eye protection, because, in this work environment, wearing protection is part of the culture. Nobody questions it. Employees adhere to these safety practices as a matter of course. This is the type of culture that must be achieved when it comes to driver safety. To reach this important overall goal, it is necessary to set achievable goals along the way. Each step listed in this chapter should be viewed as an incremental goal that is necessary to achieve a successful driver-safety initiative.

Another important goal is setting timelines for reducing the number of crashes. Quarterly, semiannual, and annual goals can be set. They should be realistic but not too easy to achieve. If an organization does not ask for quality, it will not achieve quality.

Step 3: Enlist Help

Safety professionals should seek help from people in various divisions of their organization, such as human resources, fleet management, risk management, and legal department personnel.

Human resources personnel can provide information that can justify a safe-driving initiative. They have an obvious understanding of the human element of such an initiative and can be very beneficial in trying to move it forward.

Fleet personnel see the damages and lost assets that result from motor-vehicle collisions and can also be of great assistance.

Risk-management personnel should work hand in hand with safety professionals on this initiative because managing risk is what it is all about. If an organization is insured, a reduced number of vehicle crashes has benefits in the form of reduced insurance rates. If an organization is self-insured, the savings from a reduced crash rate will improve its bottom line.

Involving the legal department provides a couple of benefits. The first is they will make sure that the initiative is within legal guidelines. The second is legal advisers can emphasize the benefits of a comprehensive driver-safety initiative from the viewpoint of exposure to litigation.

Step 4: Obtain Management Buy-In

No initiative will work if upper management is not behind it. They control the purse strings, but they also set the tone of the organization. If it is important to the boss, it will be important to the employee.

Most managers understand that creating a safe work environment is a fundamental requirement of running a successful business. Many organizations have mission statements that express the need for a safe work environment for all employees, and the driving environment should be no exception. With upper-management support, much can be done to create the safest work environment possible for employees who drive as part of their job.

In order to obtain upper-management support, it is important to look at the human element. This is where a relationship with human resources personnel

TABLE 1

Results of a Fleet Driver Training Program

Year	Training (in $)	Number of Claims	Fleet Size	Crash Rate
Year 1	75,860	632	1664	38%
Year 2	41,442	576	1747	33%
Year 3	91,860	517	1847	28%
Year 4	141,890	525	1945	27%
Year 5	100,612	492	2054	24%
Year 6	90,412	483	2198	22%

TABLE 2

Claims Reduction and Direct Cost Savings

Year	Reduction in Claims	Average Claim Cost (in $)	Savings (in $)
Year 1	Year program started	--	--
Year 2	56	3224	180,544
Year 3	115	2695	309,925
Year 4	107	2971	317,897
Year 5	140	2851	399,140
Year 6	149	2889	430,461

is helpful. They can provide information about workers' compensation, lost workdays, and quality-of-life issues as they relate to employee motor-vehicle collisions.

The human element aside, all organizations look for ways to save money. The return on investment from a successful driver-safety initiative can be tremendous. Safety professionals should create mathematical models that take into consideration all losses caused by motor-vehicle collisions, including workers' compensation, lost productivity, litigation, and vehicle repairs and replacement, and contrast them with the savings that can be achieved with a reduced crash rate. The fiscal benefits of a driver-safety initiative will soon become apparent. A number of companies in the United States have achieved tremendous savings as a result of their reduced crash rates (OSHA 2006).

Table 1 depicts an actual case study and Table 2 shows the savings the organization achieved.

During this six-year period, Company A's fleet grew by 534 vehicles—32 percent. At a time when the fleet's total number of claims might have been expected to increase, it actually decreased by 16 percent. In fact, during each year of the driver training, the number of claims diminished.

Total reduction in claims = 567
Total direct savings = $1,637,967

Table 2 shows the program savings . The total cost of Company A's driver training program was $542,076. The total direct savings that Company A realized were $1,637,967. This represents a savings of $1,095,891, approximately a 62 percent return on the investment.

The average cost per crash is $16,500 [quoted from the Web site for the Network of Employers for Traffic Safety (NETS)]. Another $4000 can conserva-

tively be added to each incident to cover medical costs, lost time on the job, workers' compensation, and claims and litigation resulting from the collisions. Multiplying that number ($20,500) by the number of claims Company A avoided (567), the estimated total savings is $11,623,500.

Step 5: Develop Fair and Comprehensive Policies

Safety professionals must help their organizations to create fair and comprehensive driver-safety policies. These policies will evolve over time, but it is important to set a base from which to start. Policies should include driver's license requirements, standards for driver's license records checks, hiring standards, an action plan for problem drivers, training requirements, and safety incentives.

Step 6: Require Drivers' License Records Checks and Set Consequences for At-Risk Drivers

It is absolutely imperative to run drivers' license records checks on employee drivers, and systems must be in place to manage these records. The organization must also be prepared to take immediate action regarding drivers with poor driving records.

There are fifty states, and each has a different motor-vehicle code. Organizations must have systems in place that interpret their state's driving records and provide a point-scoring system for various violations. This scoring system should assign points that are appropriate to the seriousness of each infraction. For instance, a driver who has a stop-sign violation might receive two points, but one who drives under the influence of drugs or alcohol would receive ten points. There are vendors that offer this type of system.

All crash data must be recorded on employee drivers' records. Only *reportable* crashes will show up on a driver's record check. Reportable crashes are those that involve injury or death and those in which vehicles must be towed. Crashes in which nobody is hurt and the cars drive away will not show up in a driver's record check, but there are vendors that can help collect all crash data, even the data that does not show up in the records.

Once drivers receive a certain number of points, an intervention should take place that is equivalent to their level of risk. Organizations should classify drivers in three risk groups based on the number of violation points on their records. Suggested interventions are:

- Level I (smallest number of points): Consider an intervention that includes a computer-based training program.
- Level II: Consider a more active intervention such as a classroom program and a behind-the-wheel program.
- Level III: Consider termination or one-on-one training.

Step 7: Educate Drivers

Step 6 will identify and help drivers who are having problems—and encourage driver accountability. It is not possible to hold drivers accountable if they do not have a base of knowledge regarding safe driving. Just because drivers are licensed does not mean they are safe drivers. If drivers are unaware of basic safe-driving principles, it is difficult to hold them accountable for collisions that might have been avoided had they been aware of those principles.

Organizations should provide all drivers with basic safe-driving information and keep records documenting that they received this knowledge. Once this is accomplished, drivers should be held accountable for driving safely.

Step 8: Begin at the Beginning

Statistics prove that new hires are involved in more crashes than established employees (Volpe 1998). According to this report, the crash rate for employees within their first twelve months of employment is higher than for employees who have been driving for a company longer. This stands to reason, because many of these new employees are learning new jobs in unfamiliar vehicles, possibly in unfamiliar areas.

Also, many of these newly hired drivers are young people who fall within an age range that statistically has a higher crash rate than other age ranges.

For this reason, new hires should be provided with safe-driver training right from the start. This accomplishes two things: (1) they will gain some very important information that will help them to stay safe when they get behind the wheel, and (2) they will understand the tone of the organization from the beginning—that safe driving is considered very important.

Step 9: Ensure that Field-Level Managers Convey the Right Message

People who have direct managerial responsibility for an organization's drivers can make or break a driver-safety initiative. Some managers tell drivers to GO, GO, GO; others say, SAFETY, now GO, GO, GO. If safe driving is not important to a driver's immediate manager, it will not be important to that driver.

Managers should be taught that they play a vital role in helping to keep employees safe. They should have instruction on how to conduct safety ride-alongs and be required to conduct ride-alongs at least twice a year. The results of ride-alongs should be an important part of each employee's performance review. This is an extremely important part of any driver-safety initiative.

Step 10: Sustain What Is Achieved

Organizations should not waste time, money, and effort putting together a driver-safety initiative if they do not plan to sustain it. They may identify problem drivers and provide drivers with some initial training with great results, but unless they keep driver safety in front of their drivers, their results will diminish with time.

Sustaining a safe-driving initiative can be done very cost effectively. Newsletters, e-flashes, periodic testing, and recognition of safe driving are all effective measures that can be taken to help an organization maintain a safe driving record.

Addressing Safe Driving Is Worth the Effort

Addressing driver safety is a formidable but very achievable task. For organizations that have addressed driver safety and are still looking for ways to improve, this chapter will provide some assistance. Safety professionals in an organization can make a big difference in this area of safety.

DRIVER-SAFETY POLICY GUIDELINES

The following sections should be included in a comprehensive driver-safety policy. Some may not apply to all organizations, and additional sections may be necessary for some organizations.

1.0 Purpose

This section provides reasons for the policies that help to ensure the safe operation of vehicles, including those owned or leased by the organization and those used to conduct business for the organization.

- The ultimate goal of these policies is to promote and maintain the well-being of the employees.
- By reducing the number of collisions, the risks of employee injury and death are reduced.

2.0 Scope

In this section the organization explains to whom the policy applies and what vehicles are affected. It should include company-owned, leased, and rented vehicles as well as those that are used to conduct business for the organization.

3.0 Definitions

Some definitions may clarify which employees and vehicles are affected by the policy. Others may describe serious infractions and immediate-action incidents.

4.0 Hiring Requirements

These are clear guidelines that are to be followed regarding employee license requirements and driving history, and how they affect the consideration of those applying for employment.

5.0 Driver Records Checks

Organizations must spell out Department of Motor Vehicle (DMV) check timelines. Wording should be included that makes it clear that DMV checks will be run on a regular basis and at other times when determined necessary. Wording should cover the Fair Credit and Reporting Act regulations.

6.0 Violation Point Assessments

Organizations should develop point codes that rate violations and crashes. Point codes are utilized to determine level of discipline/retraining. The point codes should reflect the severity of each type of incident.

7.0 Risk Levels

Organizations should develop a system that rates the number of points accumulated by drivers and defines risk levels based on the number of points.

8.0 Risk-Level Interventions

This policy describes the interventions that will take place for each level of risk.

9.0 Dispute of Findings

This policy sets a time during which a driver can dispute the findings of a DMV driver records check. It should specify that no record can be changed internally until the governing body that issued the record has changed the official record.

10.0 General Compliance

A general policy should be included that states all employee drivers must comply with all laws related to the legal operation of motor vehicles.

11.0 Family Members Operating Organization Vehicles

This policy states whether family members (spouses, common-law spouses, life partners, and driver-age children) may operate the organization's vehicles. If family members are sometimes allowed to operate company vehicles, the policy must specify how DMV-check regulations affect family members and how their driving records will affect whether they may operate the organization's vehicles.

12.0 Collision Reporting

This policy describes employees' responsibilities for reporting work-related collisions and other collisions involving the organization's vehicles. It should define the steps that employees must take when a collision occurs, including notification of the proper authorities and notification of the employer.

13.0 Violation Reporting

This policy should require that all moving violations be reported to the employer within a given time period, both those that occur during work time and those that occur during personal time. The reasoning behind this is that any violation that affects a person's driving record affects the person's ability to drive for the organization.

14.0 Personal Vehicle Use

Some organizations allow employees to use personal vehicles for work-related activities. This policy defines insurance and vehicle maintenance requirements and describes reimbursement policies. The organization's tax department should make sure the policy complies with all applicable tax codes.

15.0 Collision Classifications

Many organizations determine whether an employee driver could have prevented a collision. There is a distinct difference between fault and preventability. It may be found that a driver is not at fault for a collision but could have prevented it from happening.

16.0 Collision Deductibles

Some employers charge a deductible to employees who are involved in preventable collisions in organization vehicles. Some states regulate this practice and may prohibit it.

SAMPLE POLICY

The following policy is a blueprint for a comprehensive fleet safety policy. Items covered in this sample policy may not apply to every organization, and some organizations may need to add policies to address their specific needs.

1.0 Purpose

(Organization Name) is committed to promoting the safe, proper, and professional operation of all motor vehicles that it owns, leases, or rents, and any other vehicles used for (Organization Name) business. These vehicles are operated by its employees, client employees, vendors, and other authorized operators for business and personal use.

(Organization Name) has an obligation to make sure anyone driving an (Organization Name)-owned or -leased vehicle, or anyone driving on (Organization Name) business has a valid driver's license. (Organization Name) also has an obligation to make sure that its drivers do not have a history of unsafe driving.

(Organization Name) has enacted a policy for the purpose of implementing procedures for drivers' license records checks. This policy also institutes an action plan for drivers who have a history of unsafe driving. This policy will be referred to as the *DMV Policy*.

2.0 Scope

The DMV Policy is applicable to the following:

- All persons who drive an (Organization Name)-owned or -leased vehicle for business or personal use
- All spouses who, in accordance with this policy, are permitted to drive an (Organization Name)-owned or -leased vehicle
- All persons who drive personal vehicles for (Organization Name) business
- All persons who drive any other vehicles for (Organization Name) business

3.0 Definitions

The following definitions apply to the DMV Policy:

3.1 (Organization Name) Motor Vehicles includes all motor vehicles that are owned, leased, or rented by (Organization Name) and any other vehicles used for (Organization Name) business.

3.2 Drivers refers to all persons described in section 2.0 of the DMV Policy.

3.3 Administrative Suspension of Driving Privileges includes any suspension of a driver's operating license as the result of administrative actions. They include nonpayment of child support, nonpayment of taxes, and any other instance that does not involve a motor-vehicle violation.

3.4 *Suspension of Driving Privileges* includes any suspension, revocation, or other loss of a driver's operating privileges as a result of a motor-vehicle violation(s).

3.5 *Preventable Collision:* A collision is preventable when it is determined that a driver's actions (or inactions) put him or her into a position in which a collision occurred.

3.6 *Nonpreventable Collision:* A collision is nonpreventable when no matter what action the driver took, he or she could not have avoided a collision.

3.7 *At-Fault Collision:* A collision is at-fault with respect to a driver when the investigating authority determines that the driver was responsible for at least 51 percent of the cause of the collision.

3.8 *Not-at-Fault Collision:* A collision is considered not-at-fault with respect to a driver when the investigating authority determines that the driver was responsible for less than 51 percent of the cause of the collision.

3.9 *Serious Driving Infractions* include the following:

- any suspension of driving privileges
- any driving-under-suspension violation
- any driving-under-the-influence violation
- any offense involving fleeing or evading police, or related actions
- any violation involving leaving the scene of a motor-vehicle collision
- any reckless driving violation*
- any homicide-by-vehicle or vehicular manslaughter violation
- any speeding violation of 30 or more miles per hour (mph) over the speed limit
- any vehicle-related misdemeanor or felony violation

*Reckless driving is included under *Serious Driving Infractions* because it is defined as "The willful and wanton disregard for safety of persons or property" (Pennsylvania Consolidated Statutes, Vehicle Code, Title 75). It is not the same as inattentive driving.

4.0 Requirements for Consideration of Employment

4.1 Scope

This section of the DMV Policy is applicable to all persons who operate vehicles within the scope of their employment with (Organization Name) and is a consideration of employment to any person who has been given a conditional offer of employment by (Organization Name).

4.2 General Requirements

- Any person who falls under the scope of this section must possess a current and valid driver's license that is issued by the controlling authority where the applicant currently resides.
- Persons who fall under the scope of this section must give written permission to conduct a check of their motor-vehicle record (MVR). The federal Driver's Privacy Protection Act (DPPA) of 1994 is the primary law governing a fleet manager's ability to collect and use employees' MVRs. Under this law, state DMVs are restricted from disclosing personally identifiable driver records without first obtaining the driver's expressed written consent (Alaniz 2008). This is a condition of employment.

4.3 Considerations

Persons who have received a conditional offer of employment will not be eligible for employment if, within the past three years, they

- received a conviction for any serious driving infraction as defined by the DMV Policy, such as collisions for which they were convicted of driving under the influence (DUI)/driving while intoxicated (DWI).
- received three or more convictions for a speeding violation in excess of 20 mph.
- received four or more convictions for moving violations.
- were involved in more than two preventable collisions.

5.0 Driver License Records Checks

On an annual basis, or more frequently, (Organization Name) will run a check on the drivers' licenses of all individuals who fall under the scope of the DMV Policy Violations, and collisions that have occurred over a rolling three-year period will be considered for the purposes of these checks.

6.0 Risk-Level Classifications

In order to effectively manage drivers with motor-vehicle violations and/or collisions, the following risk-level classifications will be used to determine which interventions will result in accordance with each driver's activities:

> 0–3 points—No risk
> 4–6 points—Level I
> 7–9 points—Level II
> 10-plus points—Level III

7.0 Risk-Level Interventions

All interventions must be communicated to the drivers with a clear expectation for improvement.

7.1 Level I

Drivers will complete a computer-based training program that addresses the specific problems they are experiencing. This training will include testing to document the results of the training.

7.2 Level II

Drivers will complete an instructor-led, eight-hour classroom and behind-the-wheel training program that addresses the specific problems they are experiencing.

7.3 Level III

Drivers will participate in a one-on-one, full-day training session that addresses the specific problems they are experiencing. A comprehensive report will be filed that details the driver's driving habits. Level III drivers also face further disciplinary action up to and including termination of employment.

7.4 Spouse/Domestic Partner Risk-Level Drivers

Spouses or domestic partners of (Organization Name) employees who receive violations that put them in any of the risk levels outlined in this policy will not be permitted to operate (Organization Name)-owned or -leased vehicles until they have proven that they are no longer risk-level drivers.

8.0 Dispute of Findings

Once a risk-level driver is notified of the findings from a driver's license records check, he or she has 30 days to dispute the findings. To be removed from a risk-level category, a driver's violation(s) must be removed from the driver's license records by the issuing authority that posted them. If, within the 30 days, a driver notifies (Organization Name) that the violation(s) have been removed, (Organization Name) will conduct another driver's license records check. If the driver no longer falls under a risk-level category, no further action will be taken. If the driver still falls under a risk-level category, the appropriate action will take place.

(Organization Name) may remove the driver from all (Organization Name) driving responsibilities during the 30-day dispute period.

9.0 Violation Point Assessments

The following is an example of a violation-point system to classify motor vehicle violations and collisions:

9.1 No Points

Nonmoving violations, including equipment violations
Other nonmoving actions

9.2 Two Points

One preventable collision in a year
Windshield/window obstruction
Speeding (one to ten mph over speed limit)
Driving with expired driver's license
Stop-sign violations
Driving while fatigued
Red/yellow light violations
Backing-up violation
Failure to yield
Seatbelt violation
Improper lane change
Following too closely
Improper turn
Improper lane use
Improper passing
Headlight violation (nonequipment)
Disobedience of traffic devices
One-way street violation
Blocking intersection
Failure to obey police officer

Improper signaling
Littering from vehicle
Obstructing traffic
Other moving violation
Vehicle license class violation

9.3 Four Points

Driving too fast for conditions
Passing school bus
Speeding (eleven to twenty mph over speed limit)
Failure to yield to emergency vehicle
Speeding (school zone)
Unrestrained child
Inattentive driving

9.4 Six Points

Two preventable collisions in a year
Speeding (twenty-one to thirty mph over speed limit)

9.5 Ten Points

Three preventable collisions in a year
Fleeing or evading police and related offenses
Speeding (thirty-one to forty mph over speed limit)
Driver's license suspension
DWI/DUI and other alcohol-use violations
Driving while license is suspended
Hit-and-run violations
False reports
Reckless driving

9.6 Twenty Points

Four preventable collisions in a year
Any misdemeanor or felony charge except DUI/DWI
Speeding (forty-one or more mph over speed limit)

10.0 Driver's License Requirements

Drivers who fall under the scope of the DMV Policy must, at all times, possess a valid driver's license issued by the authority that has jurisdiction where the driver resides. The license class must be appropriate for the class of vehicle the person drives for (Organization Name).

11.0 Vehicle-Law Compliance

Persons who fall under the scope of the DMV Policy must, at all times, comply with all traffic laws that pertain to the area where they are driving.

12.0 Spouse Use of (Organization Name) Vehicles

The spouse or domestic partner of an (Organization Name) employee may operate a vehicle that has been assigned to that employee. This policy pertains to (Organization Name)-owned or -leased vehicles and does not include vehicles that bear (Organization Name) decals.

13.0 Reporting Violations

Drivers who fall under the scope of the DMV Policy must report to their immediate manager when they are charged with motor-vehicle violations as follows:

- Within 72 hours of their first reporting workday, they must report any moving violations they have been charged with.
- They must immediately report any suspension of driving privileges.
- Within 24 hours of their first reporting workday, they must report any serious motor-vehicle infraction as defined by this policy.

Any violation that affects a person's driver's license status affects the person's ability to legally operate a vehicle for (Organization Name). Therefore, reporting of violations includes violations that occur during either company or personal time and includes incidents that involve either company or personal vehicles.

13.1 Managers' Responsibility

Managers who receive a self-reported notification of a violation from an employee will, as soon as possible, report this information to the (Organization Name) Fleet Services and/or Risk Management Department.

14.0 Motor-Vehicle Collision Reporting

Persons who are involved in motor-vehicle collisions while operating any vehicle on (Organization Name) business or at any time while operating an (Organization Name)-owned or -leased vehicle must immediately report the collision to the (Organization Name) Fleet Services Department or its designee.

15.0 Seatbelt Usage

Drivers and passengers traveling in vehicles that are being driven on (Organization Name) business or in vehicles owned or leased by (Organization Name) must properly wear seatbelts while vehicles are in operation.

16.0 Vehicle Maintenance

Vehicles that fall under the scope of the DMV Policy must be properly maintained as described by the (Organization Name) Fleet Services Department.

17.0 Privately Owned Vehicles Used for Business

Persons who, with the approval of (Organization Name), use a privately owned vehicle for (Organization Name) business will receive a predetermined per-mile reimbursement for this use.

18.0 Collision Classifications

It is the responsibility of the (Organization Name) Fleet Services Department or its designee to determine whether an (Organization Name)-related motor-vehicle collision was preventable or nonpreventable as defined under sections 3.5 and 3.6 of the DMV Policy.

19.0 Driver Deductibles

19.1 If, within a three-year period, an employee is involved in a preventable collision while operating an (Organization Name) vehicle or while driving on (Organization Name) business, that employee will be charged a deductible fee of ???. [The fee is determined by individual organizations and typically increases with each offense.]

19.2 If, within a three-year period, an employee is involved in two preventable collisions while operating an (Organization Name) vehicle or while driving on (Organization Name) business, that employee will be charged a deductible fee of ???. [The fee is determined by individual organizations and typically increases with each offense.]

19.3 If, within a three-year period, an employee is involved in three preventable collisions while operating an (Organization Name) vehicle or while driving on (Organization Name) business, that employee will be charged a deductible fee of ???. [The fee is determined by individual organizations and typically increases with each offense.]

19.4 If, within a three-year period, an employee is involved in more than three preventable collisions while operating an (Organization Name) vehicle or while driving on (Organization Name) business, that employee will be charged a deductible fee of ??? and will face possible termination. [The fee is determined by individual organizations and typically increases with each offense.]

COMMERCIAL VEHICLES
Department of Transportation (DOT) Regulations

The regulations covering commercial vehicles are extensive. Areas covered in these regulations include, but are not limited to, driver licensing; hours of service; weight, height, and length restrictions; vehicle inspection; and driver alcohol and drug violations.

For the purposes of this chapter, the focus will be on hours of service, alcohol and drug regulations, and driver licensing requirements.

Visit the Federal Motor Carrier Safety Administration (FMCSA) Web site at www.fmcsa.dot.gov for a complete view of commercial vehicle regulations.

Figure 2 is an excerpt of the Commercial Motor Vehicle Safety Act of 1986; it is taken from the Federal Motor Carrier Safety Administration Web site (FMCSA 2008).

CDLIS CLEARINGHOUSE

States must be connected to the Commercial Driver's License Information System (CDLIS) and the National Driver Register (NDR) in order to exchange information about CMV drivers, traffic convictions, and disqualifications. A state must use both the CDLIS and NDR to check a driver's record, and the CDLIS to make certain that the applicant does not already have a CDL. Members of the law-enforcement community seeking access to CDLIS data should visit the

COMMERCIAL MOTOR VEHICLE (CMV) SAFETY ACT OF 1986

The Commercial Motor Vehicle Safety Act of 1986 was signed into law on October 27, 1986. The goal of the Act is to improve highway safety by ensuring that drivers of large trucks and buses are qualified to operate those vehicles and to remove unsafe and unqualified drivers from the highways. The Act retained the State's right to issue a driver's license, but established minimum national standards which States must meet when issuing CDLs.

The Act addresses circumstances that existed prior to 1986 by making it illegal for CDL holders to possess more than one license, requiring States to adopt knowledge and skills testing to ensure that individuals required to have a CDL are qualified to operate heavy trucks and buses, and establishing minimum licensing standards and information requirements for the CDLs.

It is important to note that the Act does not require drivers to obtain a separate Federal license; it merely requires States to upgrade their existing testing and licensing programs, if necessary, to conform to the Federal minimum standards.

The CDL program places requirements on the CMV driver, the employing motor carrier and the States.

THE DRIVER

Drivers have been required to have a CDL in order to drive certain CMVs since April 1, 1992.

The Federal Motor Carrier Safety Administration (FMCSA) has developed and issued standards for testing and licensing CDL holders. These standards require States to issue CDLs to certain CMV drivers only after the driver passes knowledge and skills tests administered by the State and related to the type of vehicle the driver expects to operate. Drivers are expected to obtain and hold a CDL if they operate in interstate, intrastate, or foreign commerce if they drive a vehicle that meets any of the classifications of a CDL:

Classes of License:

The Federal standard requires States to issue a CDL to drivers according to the following license classifications:

Class A -- Any combination of vehicles with a gross vehicle weight rating, GVWR, of 26,001 or more pounds provided the GVWR of the vehicle(s) being towed is in excess of 10,000 pounds.

Class B -- Any single vehicle with a GVWR of 26,001 or more pounds, or any such vehicle towing a vehicle not in excess of 10,000 pounds GVWR.

Class C – Any single vehicle, or combination of vehicles, that does not meet the definition of Class A or Class B, but is either designed to transport 16 or more passengers, including the driver, or is transporting material designated as hazardous under 49 U.S.C. 5103 and is required to be placarded under subpart F of 49 CFR Part 172 or is transporting any quantity of a material listed as a select agent or toxin in 42 CFR Part 73.

Endorsements and Restrictions:

Drivers who operate special types of CMVs also need to pass additional tests to obtain any of the following endorsements on their CDL:

- T - Double/Triple Trailers (Knowledge test only)
- P - Passenger (Knowledge and Skills Tests)
- N - Tank Vehicle (Knowledge Test only)
- H - Hazardous Materials (Knowledge Test and TSA Threat Assessment)
- X - Combination of Tank Vehicle and Hazardous Materials
- School Bus (Knowledge and Skills Tests)

If a driver either fails the air brake component of the general knowledge test or performs the skills test in a vehicle not equipped with air brakes, the driver is issued an air brake restriction, restricting the driver from operating a CMV equipped with air brakes.

THE STATES

Knowledge & Skills Tests:

States develop their own tests, which must meet the Federal standards provided for in Subpart G and H of 49 CFR Part 383. Model driver and examiner manuals and tests have been prepared and distributed to the States to use, if they wish.

- Each basic knowledge test, i.e., the test covering the areas referred to in 49 CFR 383.11 for the applicable vehicle group, shall contain at least 30 items, exclusive to the number of items testing air brake knowledge.
- To pass the knowledge tests (general and endorsement), applicants must correctly answer at least 80 percent of the questions.
- To pass the skills test, applicants must successfully perform all the required skills (listed in 49 CFR 383.113 through 49 CFR 383.123). The skills test must be taken in a vehicle representative of the type of vehicle that the applicant operates or expects to operate.

Third-Party Skills Testing:

A State may authorize a person (including another State, an employer, a private driver training facility or other private institution, or a department, agency, or instrumentality) to administer the skills tests, if the following conditions are met:

- Tests must be the same as those given by the State.
- Examiners must meet the same qualifications as State examiners.
- The third party has an agreement with the State containing, at a minimum, provisions that:
  - States must conduct an on-site inspection at least yearly.
  - At least annually, State employees must evaluate the programs by taking third party tests as if they were test applicants, or by testing a sample of drivers tested by the third party and then comparing pass/fail rates.
- The State's agreement with the third-party skills tester must allow the FHWA and the State to conduct random examinations, inspections, and audits without prior notice.

FIGURE 2. Excerpt from Commercial Motor Vehicle Safety Act of 1986

Exemption of Skills Testing Requirements:

States have the option to exempt certain individuals with good driving records from the skills testing requirements (commonly known as "grandfathering"). The State shall impose conditions and limitations to restrict the applicants from whom a State may accept alternative requirements for the skills test described in 49 CFR 383.11. Such conditions must require at least the following:

Driver has a current license at time of application; and Driver has a good driving record and previously passed an acceptable skills test; or driver has a good driving record in combination with certain driving experience.

"Good driving record" means:

A driver can certify that, during the 2-year period immediately prior to applying for a CDL he/she:

- Has not had more than one license;
- Has not had any license suspended, revoked, or canceled;
- Has not had any convictions in any type of motor vehicle for major disqualifying offense;
- Has not had more than one conviction for any type of motor vehicle for a serious traffic violation;
- Has not had any violation of State or local law relating to motor vehicle traffic control arising in connection with any traffic accident, and has no record of an accident in which he/she was at fault.

"Driving experience" means:

A driver can certify and provide evidence that:

- He/she is regularly employed in a job requiring operation of CMV, and that either:
- He/she has previously taken and passed a skills test given by a State with a classified testing system, and that the test was behind-the-wheel in a representative vehicle for that applicant's driver's license application; or
- He/she has operated a representative vehicle for at least 2 years immediately preceding application for a CDL.

Commercial Driver's License Document:

A State determines the license fee, the license renewal cycle, most renewal procedures, and continues to decide the age, medical and other driver qualifications of its intrastate commercial drivers. Interstate drivers must meet the longstanding Federal driver qualifications (49 CFR 391).

All CDLs must contain the following information:

- The words "Commercial Driver's License" or "CDL";
- The driver's full name, signature, and address;
- The driver's date of birth, sex, and height
- Color photograph or digitized image of the driver;
- The driver's State license number;
- The name of the issuing State;
- The date of issuance and the date of the expiration of the license;
- The class(es) of vehicle that the driver is authorized to drive;
- Notation of the "air brake" restriction, if issued;
- The endorsement(s) for which the driver has qualified.

States may issue learner's permits for purposes of behind-the-wheel training on public highways as long as learner's permit holders are required to be accompanied by someone with a valid CDL appropriate for that vehicle and the learner's permits are issued for limited time periods.

Waiver Provisions:

All active duty military drivers were waived from the CDL requirements by the Federal Highway Administrator. A State, at its discretion, may waive firefighters, emergency response vehicle drivers, farmers and drivers removing snow and ice in small communities from the CDL requirements, subject to certain conditions.

In addition, a State may also waive the CDL knowledge and skills testing requirements for seasonal drivers in farm-related service industries and may waive certain knowledge and skills testing requirements for drivers in remote areas of Alaska. The drivers are issued restricted CDLs. A State can also waive the CDL hazardous materials endorsement test requirements for part-time drivers working for the pyrotechnics industry, subject to certain conditions.

OTHER REQUIREMENTS

There are a variety of other requirements related to this legislation which affect the commercial drivers, their employing motor carriers and the States.

Penalties:

The Federal penalty to a driver who violates the CDL requirements is a civil penalty of up to $2,500 or, in aggravated cases, criminal penalties of up to $5,000 in fines and/or up to 90 days in prison. An employer is also subject to a penalty of up to $10,000, if he or she knowingly uses a driver to operate a CMV without a valid CDL.

CDLIS Clearinghouse:

States must be connected to the Commercial Driver's License Information System (CDLIS) and the National Driver Register (NDR) in order to exchange information about CMV drivers, traffic convictions, and disqualifications. A State must use both the CDLIS and NDR to check a driver's record, and the CDLIS to make certain that the applicant does not already have a CDL. Members of the law enforcement community seeking access to CDLIS data should visit the FMCSA Technical Support Web site. Carriers needing CDLIS data should seek a commercial company that provides a clearinghouse service for this information, or contact the driver's State of licensure.

FIGURE 2. Excerpt from Commercial Motor Vehicle Safety Act of 1986 (cont.)

2003 Rule Property-Carrying CMV Drivers (compliance through 09/30/05)	2005 Rule Property-Carrying CMV Drivers (compliance on and after 10/01/05)
May drive a maximum of eleven hours after ten consecutive hours off duty	No change
May not drive beyond the fourteenth hour after coming on duty following ten consecutive hours off duty	No change
May not drive after 60/70 hours on duty in a seven/eight-consecutive-day period after taking 34 or more consecutive hours off duty	No change
CMV drivers using a sleeper berth must take ten hours off duty, but may split sleeper berth time into two periods provided neither is less than two hours.	CMV drivers using the sleeper berth provision must take at least eight consecutive hours in the sleeper berth or off duty or any combination of the two.

Passenger-carrying carriers/drivers are not subject to the new hours-of-service rules. These operators must continue to comply with the hours-of-service limitations specified in 49 CFR 395.5.

FIGURE 3. Hours-of-service regulations (*Source: FMCSA 2005*)

FMCSA Technical Support Web site. Carriers needing CDLIS data should seek a commercial company that provides a clearinghouse service for this information, or contact the driver's state of licensure.

HOURS OF SERVICE REGULATIONS

The rules governing hours of service were changed in 2005. The last changes had been made in 2003. Figure 3 offers a snapshot of the new regulations.

Short-Haul Hours-of-Service Provisions

Short-haul drivers are drivers of property-carrying CMVs who do not require a commercial driver's license for operation and who operate within a 150 air-mile radius of their normal work-reporting location. They

- may drive a maximum of ten hours after coming on duty following ten or more hours off duty
- are not required to keep records of duty status (RODS)

- may not drive after the fourteenth hour after coming on duty five days a week, or after the sixteenth hour after two days a week

In place of RODS, these employers must maintain and retain accurate time records for six months that show what time duty periods began and ended and the total hours on duty each day.

Drivers who use this short-haul provision are not eligible to use the 100 air-mile provision (395.1(e)) or the current sixteen-hour exception in 395.1(o).

DRUG AND ALCOHOL REGULATIONS FOR CDL DRIVERS

The laws regulating the use of drugs and alcohol are much more stringent for CDL drivers than for drivers with standard licenses. Preemployment testing, testing on the job, and lower blood-alcohol-concentration allowances are a few examples of these stricter provisions. The regulations are extensive and complicated. To obtain the full text of these regulations, visit this section of the FMCSA Web site: (www.fmcsa.dot.gov/safety-security/safety-initiatives/drugs/drug-guidelines.htm).

Figure 4 provides an overview of the laws regarding blood-alcohol-concentration (BAC) limitations for CDL drivers.

Result:	Action:
Less than 0.02%	No action required under CFR Part 40
0.02%–0.039%	Varies among DOT agencies. For example, FMCSA states that a driver may not resume safety-sensitive functions for twenty-four hours (382.505), while the Federal Railroad Administration (FRA) requires eight hours (219) .101 (a)(4). The Federal Transit Administration (FTA) and Pipeline and Hazardous Materials Safety Administration (PHMSA) require only that a driver test below 0.02%. A driver who does not pass that test cannot work until the next scheduled duty period, which cannot be less than eight hours from the time of the test (655.35 and 199.237 respectively).
0.04% or greater	Drivers must immediately be removed from safety-sensitive functions and may not resume them until they successfully complete the return-to-duty process.

FIGURE 4. BAC finding and subsequent actions

REFERENCES

Alaniz, Richard. 2008. "Striking the Balance: MVR Checks and Privacy Laws." *Automotive Fleet* (retrieved February 9, 2008). www.automotivefleet.com

American National Standards Institute/American Society of Safety Engineers (ANSI/ASSE). 2006. ANSI Z15, *Safe Practices for Motor Vehicle Operations*. Des Plaines, IL: ANSI/ASSE.

Bureau of Labor Statistics (BLS). 2011. *Census of Fatal Occupational Injuries, 2010* (retrieved November 3, 2011). www.bls.gov/iif/oshwc/cfoi/cfc0009.pdf

Bureau of Transportation Statistics (BTS). 2003. *U.S. Business Travel*. www.bts.gov/publications/america_on_the_go/us_business_travel/

Code of Federal Regulations (CFR) Title 49 (Parts 40, 171–180, 325, 380–399).

Federal Motor Carrier Safety Administration (FMCSA). 2008. "Commercial Driver's License Program (CDL/CDLIS)" (retrieved February 8, 2008). www.fmcsa.dot.gov/registration-licensing/cdl/cdl.htm

John A. Volpe National Transportation Systems Center (Volpe). 1998. "New Entrant Safety Research." Report prepared for the Federal Highway Administration.

Cambridge, MA: Economic Analysis Division, Volpe National Transportation Systems Center.

National Highway Traffic Administration, 2008. *Fatality Analysis Reporting System Encyclopedia* (retrieved June 29, 2010). www-fars.nhtsa.dot.gov/Main/index.aspx

National Highway Traffic Safety Administration (NHTSA). 2007. *The Economic Burden of Traffic Crashes on Employers: Costs by State and Industry and by Alcohol and Restrain Use*. www.nhtsa.dot.gov/people/injury/airbags/EconomicBurden/pages/WhatDoTCCost.htm
_____. 2009. *Traffic Safety Facts*. DOT HS 811 291. Washington, D.C.: NHTSA's National Center for Statistics and Analysis (retrieved June 29, 2010). www-nrd.nhtsa.dot.gov/Pubs/811291.pdf

National Safety Council (NSC). 2010. *Injury Facts, 2010 Edition*. Itasca, IL: NSC (www.nsc.org).

Occupational Safety and Health Administration (OSHA). 2006. "Guidelines for Employers to Reduce Motor Vehicle Crashes." www.osha.gov/Publications/motor_vehicle_guide.html

Pennsylvania Consolidated Statutes. 2007. *The Vehicle Code* (Title 75). www.law.onecle/pennsylvania/vehicles/index.html

APPENDIX: RECOMMENDED RESOURCES

There is a growing awareness in the once-forgotten area of driver safety. Because of this, numerous organizations, both private and government, provide information that can help with driver safety programs. The sources below provide a wealth of information.

U.S. Bureau of Labor Statistics, U.S. Department of Labor.

Network of Employers for Traffic Safety (NETS). www.trafficsafety.org

Occupational Safety and Health Administration (OSHA). www.OSHA.gov

Mothers Against Drunk Driving (MADD). www.MADD.org

Federal Transit Administration. www.fta.dot.gov

Traffic Accident Reconstruction Origin (TARO). www.tarorigin.com

U.S. Department of Transportation (US DOT). www.DOT.gov

AAA Foundation for Traffic Safety. www.aaafoundation.org

Transportation Research Board (TRB). www.trb.org

Transit Cooperative Research Program, www.trcponline.org

Appendix: Formulas, Computations, and Rules-of-Thumb

Ben Cranor and Matthew Elam

English and Metric Units of Measure

Abbreviations

a	ampere, amperes
atm	atmosphere
bar	bar
Btu	British thermal unit
C	Centigrade
c	candle
cal	calorie, calories
cd	candela
cfm	cubic feet per minute
cm	centimeter, centimeters
cu	cubic
dB	decibels
deg	degree, degrees
E	volt, volts
EE	base 10
erg	erg
F	Fahrenheit
fL	footlambert
fpm	feet per minute
fps	feet per second
ft	foot, feet
g	gravitational constant
gal	gallon, gallons
gpm	gallons per minute
h	height
Hg	mercury
hp	horsepower
hr	hour, hours
I	electrical current
in	inch, inches
j	joule, joules
k	kilo
K	Kelvin
kg	kilogram, kilograms
kgf	kilogram of force
km	kilometer, kilometers
kPa	kilopascal
kw	kilowatt, kilowatts
L	liter, liters, litre, litres
lb	pound, pounds
lbf	pound of force
lbm	pound-mass
lm	lumens
Ln	linear
lx	Lux
μ	micro, micron
μF	microfarads
M	million
m	meter, meters, metre, metres
mi	mile, miles
min	minute, minutes
mm	millimeter, millimeters
mph	miles per hour
MW	molecular weight

N	Newton, Newtons	mm	= 0.03937 in
Nm	newton meter		= 25.4 × in
NTP	normal temperature and pressure		
oz	ounce, ounces		

English

Pa	Pascal, Pascals
pcf	pounds per cubic foot
pF	picofarads
psi	pounds per square inch
psig	pounds per square inch gauge
psf	pounds per square foot
pt	pint, pints
qt	quart, quarts
R	Rankine
rad	radian, radians
rev	revolution, revolutions
rpm	revolutions per minute
rps	revolutions per second
s, sec	second, seconds
sq	square
sr	steradins
thm	therm
vol	volume
W	Watt, Watts
WC	water column
wg	water gage (syn. gauge)
yd	yard, yards

mi	= 5280 ft
	= 1.609 km
	= ft × 1.894 EE–4
	= 0.6214 (0.62) × km
yd	= 0.914 m
ft	= 0.3048 (0.3) m
	= 30.48 cm
	= 3.28 × m
	= 3280 × km
	= 3.28 EE–2 × cm
in	= 25.4 mm
	= 2.54 (2.5) cm
	= 3.937 EE–2 × mm
	= 0.3937 × cm

Some common values (approximations)

1/32 in	0.8 mm
1/16 in	1.6 mm
1/8 in	3.2 mm
3/16 in	4.8 mm
1/4 in	6.4 mm (6) mm
3/8 in	9.5 mm (10) mm = 1 cm
1/2 in	12.7 (13) mm
17/32 in	13.5 mm
5/8 in	15.9 (16) mm
7/10 in	17.8 (18) mm
3/4 in	19.0 mm = 1.9 cm
1 in	25.4 (25) mm
9/8 in	28.6 (29) mm
1 1/4 in	31.8 (32) mm
1 1/2 in	38.1 (38) mm
1 3/4 in	44.5 (45) mm
2 in	50.8 (51) mm = 5 cm
2 1/4 in	57.2 (57) mm
2 1/2 in	63.5 (64) mm
3 in	76 mm
3 1/2 in	89 mm = 8.9 (9) cm
4 in	102 mm
4 1/2 in	114 mm
5 in	127 mm

EQUIVALENTS AND CONVERSION FACTORS

Length and Distance

Units: m, cm, mm—all dimensions

Equivalents*/conversion factors (use to convert)

Metric

m	= 3.28 ft
	= 39.37 in/mi × 1609.34
	= yd × 0.9144
	= ft × 0.3048
	= in × 2.54 EE–2
	= μ × EE–6
cm	= 0.3937 in
	= ft × 30.48
	= 2.54 × in

6 in	152 mm
7 1/2 in	191 mm
8 in	203 mm = 20.3 cm
10 in	254 mm
12 in	305 mm = 30.5 cm
13 in	330 mm
16 in	406 mm
18 in	457 mm
20 in	508 mm
22 in	559 mm
24 in	610 mm
28 in	711 mm = 71 cm
30 in	762 mm
32 in	813 mm
36 in	914 mm = 91 cm
38 in	965 mm
42 in	1067 mm = 106.7 (107) cm
44 in	112 cm = 1.1 m
48 in	122 cm = 1.2 m
60 in	152 cm = 1.5 m
72 in	183 cm = 1.8 m
6 1/2 ft	198 cm = 2.0 m
7 ft	213 cm = 2.1 m
7 1/2 ft	229 cm = 2.3 m
8 ft	244 cm = 2.4 m
10 ft	3.1 m
12 ft	3.7 m
12 1/2 ft	3.8 m
15 ft	4.6 m
20 ft	6.1 m
25 ft	7.6 m
30 ft	9.1 m
40 ft	12.2 m
50 ft	15.2 (15) m
60 ft	18.3 m
75 ft	22.9 (23) m
100 ft	30.5 (31) m
120 ft	36.6 m
150 ft	45.7 m
200 ft	61.0 m
250 ft	76.2 (76) m
275 ft	83.8 m
300 ft	91.4 m
350 ft	106.7 (107) m
400 ft	121.9 (122) m
500 ft	152.4 (152) m
1000 ft	304.8 (305) m

Area

Units: m^2, cm^2, mm^2—all areas
Equivalents*/conversion factors (use to convert)

Metric

m^2	= 10.76 sq ft
	= 1.55 EE3 sq in
	= 0.0929 × sq ft
	= 6.452 EE–4 × sq in
cm^2	= 0.155 sq in/6.452 × sq ft
mm^2	= 0.00155 sq in/645.2 × sq ft

English

sq ft	= 0.0929 m^2
	= 10.76 × m^2
	= 1.076 EE–3 × cm^2
sq in	= 645.2 mm^2
	= 0.00155 × mm^2
	= 0.155 × cm^2

Some common values (approximations)

1 sq in	645.2 mm^2
10 sq in	6452 mm^2
100 sq in	0.065 mm^2
1 sq ft	0.093 m^2
3 sq ft	0.28 m^2
10 sq ft	0.93 m^2
60 sq ft	5.6 m^2
80 sq ft	7.4 m^2
100 sq ft	9.3 m^2
130 sq ft	12.1 m^2
225 sq ft	20.9 (21) m^2
300 sq ft	27.9 (28) m^2
500 sq ft	46.5 m^2
800 sq ft	74.3 m^2
1000 sq ft	92.9 (93) m^2
1500 sq ft	139 m^2
1950 sq ft	181 m^2
2000 sq ft	186 m^2

2500 sq ft	232 m²
3000 sq ft	279 m²
4000 sq ft	372 m²
5000 sq ft	465 m²
10,000 sq ft	929 m²
20,000 sq ft	1858 m²
25,000 sq ft	2323 m²
40,000 sq ft	3716 m²
52,000 sq ft	4831 m²
100,000 sq ft	9290 m²

Volume and Capacity

Units: m^3, cm^3, L—volumes
Equivalents*/conversion factors (use to convert)

Metric

m^3	= 35.32 cu ft
	= 1000 L
	= 0.02832 × cu ft
	= 3.785 EE–3 × gal
	= 0.001 × L
	= 1.639 EE–5 × cu in
cm^3	= 1000 × L
	= 473.18 × pt
	= 16.378 × cu in
	= EE6 × m^3
L (cubic decimeters)	
	= 0.26417 gal
	= 1.057 qt
	= 0.03532 cu ft
	= 61 cu in
	= 2.113 pt
	= 28.32 × cu ft
	= 3.785 × gal
	= 0.94635 × qt
	= 1.639 EE–2 × cu in
	= 0.001 × cm^3
	= 1000 × m

English

gal	= 3.785 (3.8) L
	= 3.785 EE–3 m^3
	= 0.1337 cu ft
	= 231 cu in
	= 0.2642 × L
	= 0.125 × pt
	= 7.481 × cu in
	= 264.17 × m^3
	= 8.33 lb (water)
	= 3.78 kg (water)
pt	= 16 oz
	= 0.473 L
	= 28.875 cu in
	= 0.5 qt
	= cm^3 × 2.113 EE–3
cu ft	= 0.028 m^3
	= 7.84 gal
	= 28.32 L
	= 1728 cu in
	= 0.075 lb (air)

Some common values (approximations)

1 gal	3.785 (3.8) liters
40 gal	151 liters
60 gal	227 liters
100 gal	379 liters
120 gal	454 liters
150 gal	568 liters
275 gal	1041 liters = 1 m^3
500 gal	1893 liters = 1.9 m^3
660 gal	2498 liters = 2.5 m^3
750 gal	2839 liters = 2.8 m^3
1000 gal	3.785 (3.8) m^3
5000 gal	18.9 (20) m^3
50,000 gal	189 (190) m^3
75,000 gal	284 (290) m^3
100,000 gal	379 (380) m^3
150,000 gal	568 (570) m^3
200,000 gal	757 (760) m^3
263,000 gal	996 (1000) m^3
500,000 gal	1893 (2000) m^3
750,000 gal	2839 (3000) m^3
1 M gal	3785 (4000) m^3

Weight and Mass

Units: kg
Equivalents*/conversion factors (use to convert)

Metric

kg	= 0.06854 slugs
	= 2.2 lb
	= 0.4536 × lb
MW	= kg/kg mole

English

lbm	= 0.4536 (0.45) kg
	= 2.205 × kg
	= 32.17 × slugs
1 slug	= 32.17 pound-mass

Some common values (approximations)

1 lb	453 (0.45) kg
10 lb	4.54 kg
50 lb	22.7 kg
100 lb	45.4 kg
150 lb	68 kg
200 lb	91 kg
250 lb	113 kg
300 lb	136 kg
350 lb	159 kg
500 lb	227 kg
1000 lb	454 kg
4000 lb	1814 kg

Density

Units: kg/m³
Equivalents*/conversion factors (use to convert)

Metric

kg/m³	= 0.0624 pcf
	= 16.02 × lb/cu ft
	= 2.768 EE4 × lb/cu in
	= 119.8 × lbm/gal
1 g mole	= 22.41 L

English

62.4 lb/cu ft	
	= 1000 kg/m³
	= 0.0361 lb/in
	= 8.33 lbm/gal
lb per cu ft	
	= 16.02 kg/m³
	= 0.1337 lbm/gal
1 lbm mole = 359 cu ft	

Weight and Force

Units: N, kgf—force
Equivalents*/conversion factors (use to convert)

Metric

Newton (j/m)	
	= 0.1020 kgf
	= 0.2248 lbf
	= 4.448 × lbf
	= 9.807 × kgf
	= EE-5 × dyne
kgf	= 2.2 lbf
	= 0.4536 × lbf
g	= 9.81 m/sec/sec

English

lbf	= 4.448 N
	= 1.36 Nm
	= 0.2248 × N
dyne	= N × EE5

Some common values (approximations)

1 lbf	0.048 kPa = 4.44 N
10 lbf	0.48 kPa = 44.4 N
15 lbf	0.72 kPa = 67 N
30 lbf	1.44 kPa= 133 N
50 lbf	2.4 kPa = 222 N
100 lbf	4.8 kPa = 444 N
135 lbf	6.5 kPa = 600 N
180 lbf	8.6 kPa = 800 N
200 lbf	9.6 kPa = 888 N
258 lbf	12.4 kPa = 1148 N
300 lbf	14.4 kPa = 1334 N

Pressure

Units: Pa, kgf/cm² — pressure
Equivalents*/conversion factors (use to convert)

Metric

Pa (N/m²) = 20.89 EE–3 psf
$\qquad$ = 0.145 EE–3 psi
$\qquad$ = 1.02 EE–5 kgf/cm²
$\qquad$ = 0.0075 mm Hg
$\qquad$ = 2.953 EE–4 in Hg
$\qquad$ = 1.013 EE × atm
$\qquad$ = 47.88 × psf
$\qquad$ = 6894.76 × psi
$\qquad$ = 2.491 EE2 × in H_2O
$\qquad$ = 0.981 EE3 × m (H_2O)
$\qquad$ = 3 EE3 × ft (H_2O)

kgf/cm² = 9.807 EE4 Pa
$\qquad$ = 735.6 mm Hg
$\qquad$ = 393.7 in H_2O
$\qquad$ = 32.81 ft H_2O
$\qquad$ = 28.96 in Hg
$\qquad$ = 14.22 psi
$\qquad$ = 0.9678 atm

H (m) (water) = 0.102 kPa

English

psi $\qquad$ = 0.0689 bar
$\qquad$ = 6.895 kPa
$\qquad$ = 0.0703 kg/cm²
$\qquad$ = 27.67 in H_2O
$\qquad$ = 6.944 EE–3 × psf
$\qquad$ = 0.145 × kPa
$\qquad$ = 14.5 × bar
$\qquad$ = 0.4335 × h (ft)
$\qquad$ = 0.0193 × mm Hg

psig $\qquad$ = in Hg × 0.4912

bar $\qquad$ = EE5 Pa
$\qquad$ = EE2 kPa
$\qquad$ = Mdynes/cm²
$\qquad$ = 14.50 psi
$\qquad$ = 0.9869 atm

atm $\qquad$ = 14.7 psia
$\qquad$ = 29.9 in Hg
$\qquad$ = 1.013 EE5 N/m (Pa)
$\qquad$ = 2116.22 psf

$\qquad$ = 1.01325 bar
$\qquad$ = 101.3 kPa
$\qquad$ = 406.8 in H_2O
$\qquad$ = 33.90 ft (water)
$\qquad$ = 10.35 m (water)
$\qquad$ = 760.5 mm Hg
$\qquad$ = 0.08072 lbm/cu ft (air)
$\qquad$ = 1.033 kgf/cm

Torr $\qquad$ = 133.3 Pa
$\qquad$ = 1 mm Hg
$\qquad$ = 1.316 EE–3 atm
$\qquad$ = 0.00136 kgf/cm²
$\qquad$ = 0.5353 in H_2O
$\qquad$ = 0.01934 psi

in WC $\qquad$ = 249.1 Pa
$\qquad$ = 0.25 kPa
$\qquad$ = 1.868 mm Hg
$\qquad$ = 0.00246 atm
$\qquad$ = 0.0361 psi
$\qquad$ = 0.07355 in Hg
$\qquad$ = 0.0833 ft (water)
$\qquad$ = 4.015 EE–3 × Pa

H (ft) (water)
$\qquad$ = 0.4335 psi
$\qquad$ = 3 kPa
$\qquad$ = 0.88 in Hg
$\qquad$ = 0.0295 atm
$\qquad$ = 12 in H_2O
$\qquad$ = 0.03048 kgf/cm²
$\qquad$ = 22.24 mm Hg

Some common values (approximations)

0.052 in H_2O	13 Pa
0.064 in H_2O	16 Pa
0.22 in H_2O	55 Pa
0.35 in H_2O	87 Pa
1.0 in H_2O	250 Pa
1 psi	0.0689 bar = 6.89 (7) kPa
5 psi	0.345 bar = 35 kPa
7 psi	0.48 (0.5) = 48 kPa
10 psi	0.7 bar = 69 kPa
15 psi	1.0 bar = 103 kPa
18 psi	1.2 bar = 124 kPa
20 psi	1.4 bar = 138 kPa
25 psi	1.7 bar = 170 kPa
30 psi	2.1 bar = 207 kPa

40 psi	2.8 bar = 276 kPa		
50 psi	3.5 bar = 345 kPa		
60 psi	4.1 bar = 414 kPa		
65 psi	4.5 bar = 450 kPa		
68 psi	4.7 bar = 469 kPa		
70 psi	4.8 bar = 483 kPa		
75 psi	5.2 bar = 517 kPa		
80 psi	5.5 bar = 552 kPa		
100 psi	6.9 bar = 689 kPa		
140 psi	9.7 bar = 966 kPa		
150 psi	10.3 bar = 1034 kPa		
175 psi	12.1 bar = 1208 kPa		
200 psi	13.8 bar = 1380 kPa		
250 psi	17.3 bar = 1723 kPa		
300 psi	20.7 bar = 2070 kPa		
350 psi	24.2 bar = 2413 kPa		
1000 psi	6.9 MPa = 6895		
10,000 psi	69 MPa		
15,000 psi	103 MPa		

165°F	74°C	347°K
175°F	79°C	352°K
190°F	88°C	361°K
200°F	93°C	366°K
212°F	100°C	373°K
286°F	141°C	414°K
300°F	149°C	422°K
500°F	260°C	533°K
600°F	315°C	588°K
1000°F	538°C	811°K
1100°F	593°C	866°K
1500°F	816°C	1089°K
2000°F	1093°C	1366°K
2500°F	1371°C	1644°K
3000°F	1649°C	1922°K

Temperature

Units: K, C—temperature
Equivalents*/conversion factors (use to convert)

Metric

K $\quad = °C + 273.15$ (273)

English

C $\quad = 5/9 \,(°F - 32)$
R $\quad = °F + 459.69$ (460)
F $\quad = 32 + (9/5) \,°C$

Some common values (approximations)

−40°F	−40°C	233°K
−20°F	−20°C	244°K
0°F	−18°C	255°K
20°F	−6.7°C	266°K
32°F	0°C	273°K
40°F	4°C	277°K
68°F	20°C	293°K
70°F	21°C	294°K
77°F	25°C	298°K
100°F	38°C	311°K
135°F	57°C	330°K
150°F	66°C	339°K

Power

Units: Watt
Equivalents*/conversion factors (use to convert)

Metric

W (n × m/sec) = 1 j/sec
$\quad\quad = 2.26 \text{ EE–2} × \text{ft-lbf/min}$
$\quad\quad = 0.2931 × \text{Btu/hr}$
$\quad\quad = 745.7 × \text{hp}$
$\quad\quad = \text{EE–7} × \text{erg/sec}$
$\quad\quad = E × I$
kw $\quad = 0.948 \text{ Btu/min}$
$\quad\quad = 1.341 \text{ hp}$
$\quad\quad = 1.758 \text{ EE–2} × \text{Btu/min}$
$\quad\quad = 0.7457 × \text{hp}$
$\quad\quad = 1.055 × \text{Btu/sec}$

English

Btu/hr $\quad = 0.393 \text{ W}$
$\quad\quad = \text{Btu/min} × 60$
$\quad\quad = 2.546 \text{ EE3} × \text{hp}$
Btu/min $= 17.58 \text{ W}$
$\quad\quad = 1.758 \text{ EE–2 kw}$
$\quad\quad = 42.41 × \text{hp}$
$\quad\quad = 56.88 × \text{kw}$
$\quad\quad = \text{MBtu/hr} × 1.667 \text{ EE4}$
Btu/sec $= 1.055 \text{ kw}$
$\quad\quad = \text{Btu/min} × 1.667 \text{ EE–2}$
Btu/ft²/hr$= 0.317 × \text{W/m}^2$

Btu/ft^2 = 11.35 kw/m² (heat flux)

         = 1.135 W/m²

$Btu/ft/sec$ = 2.889 EE–4 × W/m

$ft\text{-}lbf/min$ = 33,000 × hp

$ft\text{-}lbf/sec$ = 550 × hp

         = 737.46 × kw

hp   = 550 ft-lbf/sec

         = 746 W

         = 1.341 × kw

         = 3.989 EE–4 × Btu/hr

         = 1.341 EE–3 × W

Some common values (approximations)

1 kw	56.88 (57) Btu/min	0.948 Btu/sec
10 kw	568.8 (570) Btu/min	9.5 Btu/sec
20 kw	1138 Btu/min	19 Btu/sec
50 kw	2844 Btu/min	47 Btu/sec
100 kw	5688 (5700) Btu/min	95 Btu/sec
120 kw	6826 (6800) Btu/min	114 Btu/sec
150 kw	8532 (8500) Btu/min	142 Btu/sec
300 kw	17,064 Btu/min	284 Btu/sec
325 kw	18,500 Btu/min	308 Btu/sec
450 kw	25,600 Btu/min	427 Btu/sec
1000 kw	57,000 = (3.4) MBtu/hr	950 Btu/sec
1055 kw	60,000 = (3.6) MBtu/hr	1000 Btu/sec
1.1 Mw	62,600 = (3.7) MBtu/hr	1043 Btu/sec
1.17 Mw	66,000 (4.0) MBtu/hr	1108 Btu/sec
1.5 Mw	85,000 (5.0) MBtu/hr	1417 Btu/sec
2 Mw	114,000 (6.8) MBtu/hr	1900 Btu/sec
2.1 Mw	7	1983 (2000) Btu/sec
4.2 Mw	14	3983 (4000) Btu/sec
5 Mw	17	4733 Btu/sec
8.4 Mw	29	7976 (8000) Btu/sec
17 Mw	58	16,117 (16,000) Btu/sec
50 Mw	171	47,400 Btu/sec
100 Mw	341	94,800 Btu/sec

Energy

Units: joule

Equivalents*/conversion factors (use to convert)

Metric

joule (Watt-sec, N m)

         = 0.7376 ft-lbf

         = 0.9478 EE–3 Btu

         = 0.2778 EE–6 kw-hr

         = 1.356 × ft-lbf

         = 1055.1 × Btu

         = 3.6 EE6 × kw-hr

         = 2.684 EE6 × hp-hr

         = 4.184 × cal

kw-hr   = 2.931 EE–4 × Btu

         = 2.778 EE–8 × erg

         = 2.778 × j

kgf-m   = 0.13826 × ft-lbf

erg   = EE7 × j

kj/kg (heat)

         = 0.43 Btu/lb

         = 5.1 Mj/L

         = 2.33 × Btu/lb h (Mj/kg) + Mj/mole

English

Btu   = 778 ft-lbf

         = 252 cal

         = 1055 j

         = 1.055 EE–3 Mj

         = 1.285 EE–3 × ft-lbf

         = 9.478 EE–4 × j

         = 3412 × kw-hr

Btu/ft^2 = 11.356 kj/m²

Btu/cu ft = 0.0373 Mj/m³

         = 26.8 × Mj/m³

ft-lbf   = 7.367 EE-8 erg

         = 778 × Btu

         = 2.655 EE6 × kw-hr

         = 0.7376 × j

hp-hr   = 3.725 EE–7 × j

         = 3.930 EE4 × Btu

therm   = EE–5 × Btu

Velocity

Units: m/sec

Equivalents*/conversion factors (use to convert)

Metric

m/sec   = 2.237 mph

         = 196.85 fpm

         = 3.281 fps

         = 3.6 km/hr

         = 0.44704 × mph

$= 5.1\ EE{-}3 \times fpm$

$= 3.048 \times fps$

$= EE{-}2 \times cm/sec$

cm/sec $= 0.508 \times fpm$

English

mph $= 1.467\ fps$

$= 0.4470\ m/sec$

$= 0.68182 \times fps$

fpm $= 0.011364\ mph$

$= 0.0051\ m/sec$

$= 196.85 \times m/sec$

$= 88 \times mph$

fps $= 0.305\ m/sec$

$= 18.29\ m/min$

$= 3.28 \times m/sec$

Some common values (approximations)

100 fpm	0.51 m/sec
200 fpm	1.02 m/sec
300 fpm	1.53 m/sec
500 fpm	2.55 m/sec
1000 fpm	5.10 m/sec

Flow Rates

Units: m^3/sec, L/sec, and L/min

Equivalents*/conversion factors (use to convert)

Metric

m^3/sec $= 2118.8\ cfm = $ vol flow, viscosity

$= 1000\ L/sec$

$= 1.6\ EE4\ gpm$

$= 35.31\ ft^3/sec$

$= 4.7\ EE{-}4 \times cfm$

$= 6.31\ EE{-}5 \times gpm$

m^3/min $= 0.0283 \times cfm$

$= EE{-}3 \times L/min$

$= 3.785\ EE{-}3 \times gpm$

m^2/min $= $ diffusivity

$= 9.29\ EE{-}2 \times ft^2/sec$

L/min $= 26.42\ EE{-}2\ gpm$

$= 3.785 \times gpm$

$= 1000 \times m^3/min$

L/sec $= 15.85\ (16)\ gpm$

$= 2.118\ ft^3/min$

$= 0.0631 \times gpm$

$= 0.472 \times cfm$

$= EE3 \times m^3/sec$

kg/sec $= $ mass flow/mass loss rate

$= lbs/min \times 7.56\ EE{-}6$

English

cu ft/hr $= 8.0208 \times gpm$

$= 35.3 \times m^3/hr$

cu ft/min (cfm)

$= 2.83\ EE{-}2\ m^3/min$

$= 0.472\ L/sec$

$= 7.48\ gpm$

$= 4.72\ EE{-}4\ m^3/sec$

$= 35.34 \times m^3/min$

cu ft/sec $= 28.32\ L/sec$

$= 0.0283\ m^3/sec$

$= 0.002228 \times gpm$

lb (water)/min $= 62.43 \times ft^3/min$

dynamic viscosity $= slugs/ft\text{-}sec$

gpm $= 0.0631\ L/sec$

$= 3.785\ L/min$

$= 6.3\ EE{-}5\ m/sec$

$= 448.83 \times ft^3/sec$

$= 0.2642 \times L/min$

gpm/Ln ft $= 12.3\ L/min/m$

Some common values (approximations)

5 gpm	19 L/min	
13 gpm	49 L/min	
15 gpm	57 L/min	
18 gpm	68 L/min	
20 gpm	76 L/min	
25 gpm	95 L/min	
26 gpm	98 L/min	
30 gpm	114 L/min	
32 gpm	121 L/min	
36 gpm	136 L/min	
50 gpm	190 L/min	
54 gpm	204 (200) L/min	
100 gpm	378 L/min	0.38 m³/mj
250 gpm	946 L/min	0.95 m³/mj
500 gpm	1892 (1900) L/min	1.89 m³/mj
700 gpm	2650 L/min	2.65 m³/mj

750 gpm	2840 L/min	2.84 m³/mj
850 gpm	3217 L/min	3.21 m³/mj
1000 gpm	3785 (3800) L/min	3.79 m³/mj
1500 gpm	5678 L/min	5.68 m³/mj
2000 gpm	7570 L/min	7.75 m³/mj
2500 gpm	9463 L/min	9.46 m³/mj
3000 gpm	11,355 L/min	11.36 m³/mj

cfm	m³/min	m³/sec	L/sec
2000	56.6 (57)	0.94	944
5000	142	2.4	2360
10,000	283	4.7	4720
15,000	425	7.1	7080
20,000	566	9.4	9440
22,000	623	10.5	10,384
35,000	991	16.5	16,520
67,000	1896	31.5	31,624
100,000	2830	47.0	47,200

Flow Densities

Units: m³/min, L/min, L/sec
Equivalents*/conversion factors (use to convert)

Metric

$L/sec/m^2 = 0.679 \times gpm/sq\ ft$

$L/min/m^2$
$\qquad = 0.0245\ gpm/sq\ ft$
$\qquad = 40.75 \times gpm/sq\ ft$

English

gpm/sq ft
$\qquad = 40.75\ L/min/m^2$
$\qquad = 0.0245 \times L/min/m^2$
$\qquad = 1.473 \times L/sec/m^2$

Some common values (approximations)

gpm/sq ft	L/sec/m²	L/min/m²
0.1	0.0679	4.07
0.15	0.1	6.1
0.19	0.13	7.8
0.2	0.14	8.2
0.25	0.17	10.2
0.28	0.19	11.4
0.3	0.20	12.2
0.32	0.22	13.1
0.38	0.26	15.5
0.4	0.27	16.3
0.45	0.31	18.3
0.5	0.34	20.4
0.6	0.41	24.5
0.7	0.48	28.6
0.8	0.54	32.6
0.9	0.61	36.7
1.0	0.68	40.7

Other Units of Measure

sec	$= min \times 60$
1/sec	$= 1/min \times 1.667\ EE{-}2$
min	$= hr \times 60$
cd	$= c = lm/sr$
rad	$= deg \times 1.74\ EE{-}2$
	$= min \times 2.909\ EE{-}4$
	$= rpm \times 6.283$
coulombs	$= a\text{-}hr \times 3600$
	$= faradays \times 9.649\ EE{-}4$
	$= 1\ a\text{-}sec$
1 ft-c	$= 10.76\ lux$
	$= 1\ lm/sq\ ft$
	$= 10.76\ lm/m^2$
1 lux	$= 0.093\ ft\text{-}c$
5 ft-c	$= 54\ lux$
1 fL	$= 3.426\ cd/m^2$
	$= 3.1416 \times cd/sq\ ft$
	$= 0.2919 \times cd/m^2$
rpm	$= °/sec \times 0.1667$
	$= 6°/sec$
	$= 0.01667\ rps$
deg	$= rad \times 57.3$
min	$= rad \times 3437.7$
sec	$= 2.06\ EE5 \times rad$
rev	$= 0.159 \times rad$

MOST COMMON ENGLISH-METRIC CONVERSIONS

Length

m	$= 0.3048 \times ft$
cm	$= 2.54 \times in$
mm	$= 25.4 \times in$

Area

m²	= 0.0929 × sq ft
cm²	= 6.452 × sq ft
mm²	= 645.2 × sq ft

Volume

m³	= 3.785 EE–3 × gal
	= 0.02832 × cu ft
	= 1.639 EE–5 × cu in
	= 16.387 × cu in
L	= 3.785 × gal
	= 28.32 × cu ft
	= 1.639 EE–2 cu in

Mass and Weight

kg	= 0.4536 × lb

Density

kg/m³	= 16.02 × lb/cu ft

Weight and Force

N	= 4.448 × lbf
kgf	= 0.4536 × lbf

Pressure

Pa	= 2.491 EE2 × in H_2O
	= 6894.76 × psi
	= EE5 × bar
kPa	= 0.0479 × lbf
kgf/cm²	= 0.0703 × psi

Temperature

K	= °C + 273.15

Power

W	= 0.2931 × Btu/hr
	= 745.7 × hp
kw	= 1.758 EE–2 × Btu/min
	= 1.055 × Btu/sec
metric hp	= 0.001843 × ft-lbf/sec = 1.0139

Energy

j	= 1.356 × ft-lbf
	= 1055.1 × Btu
kgf-m	= 0.1383 × ft-lb

Velocity

m/sec	= 5.1 EE–3 × fpm
	= 0.3048 × fps
cm/sec	= 0.51 × fpm

Flow Rates

Water

m³/sec	= 6.31 EE–5 × gpm
m³/min	= 3.785 EE–3 × gpm
L/sec	= 0.0631 × gpm
L/min	= 3.785 × gpm

Air

m³/sec	= 4.7 EE–4 × cfm
m³/min	= 0.0283 × cfm
L/sec	= 0.47 × cfm

Water Flow Densities

L/sec/m² = 0.679 × gpm/sq ft
L/min/m²
$\qquad$ = 40.75 × gpm/sq ft

STATISTICS

Sample Mean

If the observations in a sample mean of size n are $X_1, X_2, \ldots X_n$, then the sample mean is:

$$\bar{X} = \frac{X_1 + X_2 + \ldots X_n}{n} = \frac{\sum_{i=1}^{n} X_i}{n}$$

The sample mean is a point estimate of an unknown population mean (μ).

The Microsoft Excel function for calculating this result is AVERAGE(cell range), where the cell range is the range of cells containing the sample.

If the sample is 16.2, 12.8, 13.3, 10.7, 12.8, 11.0, 14.5, 11.9, 15.2, 12.6, for example, and these numbers are entered into cells A1 through A10, respectively, of an Excel worksheet, then from typing "=AVERAGE(A1:A10)" into a blank cell of the same Excel worksheet, the answer is calculated to be 13.1.

Sample Median

Let $X_1, X_2, \ldots X_n$ denote a sample arranged in increasing order of magnitude; that is, X_1 denotes the smallest observation, X_2 denotes the second smallest observation, . . ., and X_n is the largest observation.

If n is odd, the sample median $\hat{X}$ is defined as the middle or $\left[\left(\frac{n+1}{2}\right)\right]$th observation. If n is even, the sample median is defined as the mean of the two middle observations, the $\left[\left(\frac{n}{2}\right)\right]$th observation and the $\left[\left(\frac{n}{2}\right)+1\right]$th observation.

$$\hat{X} = \begin{cases} X_{(n+1)/2}; \text{ if } n \text{ is odd} \\ \dfrac{X_{n/2} + X_{(n/2)+1}}{2} ; \text{ if } n \text{ is even} \end{cases}$$

The sample median is a less popular point estimate of an unknown population mean (μ).

The Microsoft Excel function for calculating this result is MEDIAN(cell range), where the cell range is the range of cells containing the sample.

If the sample is 16.2, 12.8, 13.3, 10.7, 12.8, 11.0, 14.5, 11.9, 15.2, 12.6, for example, and these numbers are entered into cells A1 through A10, respectively, of an Excel worksheet, then from typing "=MEDIAN(A1:A10)" into a blank cell of the same Excel worksheet, the answer is calculated to be 12.8.

Sample Mode

The sample mode is the observation that occurs most frequently in the sample. It is a less popular point estimate of an unknown population mean (μ).

The Microsoft Excel function for calculating this result is MODE(cell range), where the cell range is the range of cells containing the sample.

If the sample is 16.2, 12.8, 13.3, 10.7, 12.8, 11.0, 14.5, 11.9, 15.2, 12.6, for example, and these numbers are entered into cells A1 through A10, respectively, of an Excel worksheet, then from typing "=MODE(A1:A10)"

into a blank cell of the same Excel worksheet, the answer is calculated to be 12.8.

Sample Variance

If $X_1, X_2, \ldots X_n$ is a sample of n observations, then the *sample variance* is calculated to be:

$$s^2 = \sum_{i=1}^{n} \frac{(X_i - \bar{X})^2}{n-1}$$

The sample variance is a point estimate of an unknown population variance (σ^2).

The Microsoft Excel function for calculating this result is VAR(cell range), where the cell range is the range of cells containing the sample.

If the sample is 16.2, 12.8, 13.3, 10.7, 12.8, 11.0, 14.5, 11.9, 15.2, 12.6, for example, and these numbers are entered into cells A1 through A10, respectively, of an Excel worksheet, then from typing "=VAR(A1:A10)" into a blank cell of the same Excel worksheet, the answer is calculated to be 3.118.

Sample Standard Deviation

The sample standard deviation (s), is the positive square root of the sample variance.

It is a point estimate of an unknown population standard deviation (σ).

The Microsoft Excel function for calculating this result is STDEV(cell range), where the cell range is the range of cells containing the sample.

If the sample is 16.2, 12.8, 13.3, 10.7, 12.8, 11.0, 14.5, 11.9, 15.2, 12.6, for example, and these numbers are entered into cells A1 through A10, respectively, of an Excel worksheet, then from typing "=STDEV(A1:A10)" into a blank cell of the same Excel worksheet, the answer is calculated to be 1.766.

Descriptive Statistics

The sample mean, median, mode, variance, standard deviation, and other statistics may be obtained using the Descriptive Statistics menu option in Excel. In the 2003 version of Excel, it is located in the Tools menu under Data Analysis. If the Data Analysis menu option is not available, then it needs to be installed. This is accomplished by choosing Add-Ins from the Tools menu and selecting Analysis ToolPak and then OK in the resulting window. In the 2007 version of Excel, the Data Analysis menu option is located under the Data menu option. To install the Data Analysis menu option, select the Windows icon in the upper left-hand corner of the Excel window, select Excel Options, then Add-Ins, then the Go button, then Analysis ToolPak, and then the OK button.

For example, consider the sample 16.2, 12.8, 13.3, 10.7, 12.8, 11.0, 14.5, 11.9, 15.2, 12.6 entered into a column of an Excel worksheet. The Descriptive Statistics menu options used are Input Range (the cell range containing the sample), Grouped By Columns, and Summary Statistics. The following output was generated:

Mean	13.1
Standard Error	0.558370646
Median	12.8
Mode	12.8
Standard Deviation	1.765723018
Sample Variance	3.117777778
Kurtosis	−0.512836418
Skewness	0.424149685
Range	5.5
Minimum	10.7
Maximum	16.2
Sum	131
Count	10

Probability Distributions

The normal probability distribution is a necessary assumption for populations in many statistical inference procedures, such as confidence intervals and hypothesis tests. The normal probability distribution is bell-shaped, symmetric about its mean (μ), and converges to the x-axis as $x\to\infty$ and as $x\to-\infty$. Approximately three standard deviations ($\mu - 3\sigma$, $\mu + 3\sigma$) from its mean, the normal probability distribution appears to sit on the x-axis (see the Figure 1). A normal probability distribution with $\mu = 0$ and $\sigma = 1$ is a standard normal probability

distribution, which is denoted with the letter Z in statistical inference.

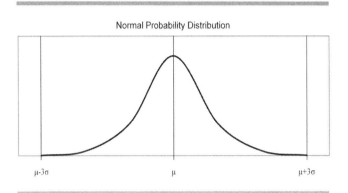

Normal Probability Distribution

μ-3σ   μ   μ+3σ

FIGURE 1. Normal probability distribution

For small sample sizes, say $n < 40$, the t probability distribution is used in place of the standard normal probability distribution. The t probability distribution is shaped similarly to the standard normal probability distribution, except it has more area in the tails and is shorter at its peak. It is meant to model the additional uncertainty in the results of statistical analyses due to the smaller sample sizes. As $n\to\infty$, the t probability distribution converges to the standard normal probability distribution.

Shapes of probability distributions are also described by the terms skewness and kurtosis. *Skewness* refers to the lack of symmetry in the probability distributions's graph. *Kurtosis* refers to the amount of peakedness in the probability distribution's graph.

Single-Sample Statistical Inference

A $100(1 - \alpha)\%$ confidence interval on the population mean (μ) of a normal population when n is small is given by:

$$\bar{X} - t_{\alpha/2,\, n-1}\left(\frac{S}{\sqrt{n}}\right) \leq \mu \leq \bar{X} + t_{\alpha/2,\, n-1}\left(\frac{S}{\sqrt{n}}\right)$$

For example, consider the sample 16.2, 12.8, 13.3, 10.7, 12.8, 11.0, 14.5, 11.9, 15.2, 12.6 entered into a column of an Excel worksheet. The Descriptive Statistics menu options used are Input Range, Grouped By Columns, Summary Statistics, and 95% Confidence Level for Mean. The following output was generated:

Mean	**13.1**
Standard Error	0.558370646
Median	12.8
Mode	12.8
Standard Deviation	1.765723018
Sample Variance	3.117777778
Kurtosis	−0.512836418
Skewness	0.424149685
Range	5.5
Minimum	10.7
Maximum	16.2
Sum	131
Count	10
Confidence Level(95.0%)	**1.263122153**

The 95% confidence interval on the population mean (μ) of a normal population is calculated as $13.1 - 1.263 < \mu < 13.1 + 1.263$, which results in $11.837 < \mu < 14.363$.

Hypothesis testing on the mean (μ) of a normal population may also be performed using the confidence interval above. The null (H_0) and alternative (H_1) hypotheses are $H_0: \mu = \mu_0$ and $H_1: \mu \neq \mu_0$. If the hypothesized value for μ, which is μ_0, is in the confidence interval, then H_0 is not rejected; otherwise, H_0 is rejected. Rejecting the null hypothesis when it is true is defined as a type-I error, the probability of which is denoted as α ("alpha"). Failing to reject the null hypothesis when it is false is defined as a type-II error, the probability of which is denoted as β ("beta").

If n is large (say $n \geq 40$), then $t_{\alpha/2, n-1}$ can be replaced with $Z_{\alpha/2}$ in the above confidence interval. However, it is not necessary as long as the population follows a normal probability distribution. $Z_{\alpha/2}$ can be calculated by typing the following Excel function into a cell of an Excel worksheet: "=−NORMSINV($\alpha/2$)."

Two-Sample Statistical Inference

The following are the null and alternative hypotheses for hypothesis tests on the difference in population means:

$$H_0: \mu_1 - \mu_2 = \Delta_0$$
$$H_1: \mu_1 - \mu_2 \neq \Delta_0 \text{ or } \mu_1 - \mu_2 > \Delta_0 \text{ or } \mu_1 - \mu_2 < \Delta_0$$

When at least one of the two sample sizes is small and both populations have a normal probability distribution, the Data Analysis menu option in Excel gives the following three options for performing the hypothesis test:

- *t*-Test: Paired Two-Sample for Means
  This is used when the two populations are dependent on each other, such as in a before and after study.
- *t*-Test: Two-Sample Assuming Equal Variances
  This is used when the two populations are independent and the population variances may be assumed equal.
- *t*-Test: Two-Sample Assuming Unequal Variances
  This is used when the two populations are independent and the population variances may be assumed unequal.

Regardless of the choice, the menu options require the user to enter the variable 1 range (the cell range containing the first sample), the variable 2 range (the cell range containing the second sample), the hypothesized mean difference (Δ_0), and alpha (the significance level for the test).

For example, consider the following two samples.

Sample 1	Sample 2
9.700	13.233
8.722	8.975
10.244	13.530
11.276	13.658
11.198	14.253
11.733	15.597
7.816	9.750
9.766	12.562
11.095	13.412
8.913	11.770

The two-sample *t*-test, assuming the unequal variances menu option with the variable 1 range as the range of cells containing sample 1, the variable 2 range as the range of cells containing sample 2, the hypothesized mean difference as zero, and alpha as 0.05, generated the following output:

	Variable 1	Variable 2
Mean	10.04648518	12.67401334
Variance	1.670303701	4.073474954
Observations	10	10
Hypothesized Mean Difference	0	
df	15	
t Stat	−3.466957598	
$P(T \le t)$ one-tail	**0.001724841**	
t Critical one-tail	1.753050325	
$P(T \le t)$ two-tail	**0.003449683**	
t Critical two-tail	2.131449536	

If the alternative hypothesis has ≠, then alpha is compared to 0.00345 (the *p*-value). Since 0.00345 is less than alpha, the null hypothesis is rejected. If the alternative hypothesis has > or <, then alpha is compared to 0.00173 (the *p*-value). Since 0.00173 is less than alpha, the null hypothesis is rejected.

When both sample sizes are large, in which case no assumption is necessary about the probability distributions for the two populations, the Data Analysis menu option in Excel gives the "*z*-Test: Two-Sample for Means" option for performing the hypothesis test. The menu options require the user to enter the variable 1 range, the variable 2 range, the hypothesized mean difference, the variable 1 variance (S_1^2), the variable 2 variance (S_2^2), and alpha.

MATHEMATICS

A safety professional applies math knowledge and skills on a routine basis in analyzing and evaluating data, in preparing studies of quantifiable subjects, and in normal administrative duties. Thus, a basic competence in mathematics is expected for safety professionals and is required for applicants for the BCSP Safety Fundamentals examination.

In every mathematical operation, the unit terms (pounds, feet, miles, seconds, and so on) must be carried along with the numbers and must undergo the same mathematical operations as the numbers. Quantities cannot be added or subtracted directly unless they have the same units. However, any number of quantities can be combined in multiplication or division when the units as well as the numbers obey the algebraic laws of squaring, cancellation, and so on. For example, in converting 75 feet per second to miles per hour, notice that the minutes, seconds, and feet units cancel out, leaving miles and hours:

$$\frac{75 \text{ ft}}{1 \text{ sec}} \cdot \frac{1 \text{ mile}}{5280 \text{ ft}} \cdot \frac{60 \text{ sec}}{1 \text{ min}} \cdot \frac{60 \text{ min}}{1 \text{ hour}} = 51.14 \text{ mph}$$

Scientific Notation

Very large and very small numbers can be expressed and calculated efficiently by means of scientific notation, a method that depends primarily on the use of exponents.

A number is said to be expressed in scientific notation when it is written as the product of an integral power of 10 and a rational number between 1 and 10. For example:

$$253 = 2.53 \times 10^2$$

The procedure for expressing a number using scientific notation is:

- Place the decimal point to the right of the first nonzero digit to obtain a number between 1 and 10.
- Multiply this number by a power of 10 whose exponent is equal to the number of places the decimal point was moved. The exponent is positive if the decimal point was moved to the left and negative if it was moved to the right.

By use of the laws of exponents and scientific notation, computations involving very large or very small numbers are simplified. For example:

$$\frac{378{,}000{,}000 \times 0.000004}{2000} = \frac{(3.78 \cdot 10^8)(4 \cdot 10^{-6})}{2 \cdot 10^3}$$

$$= 7.56 \cdot 10^{-1} = 0.756$$

Engineering Notation

Engineering notation is a form of scientific notation in which the exponent of 10 is positive or negative 3 or a multiple of 3 expressed as follows:

10^9 giga-

10^6 mega-

10^3 kilo-

10^{-3} milli-

10^{-6} micro-

10^{-9} nano-

For example:

10^3 watts = 1 kilowatt

10^{-6} watts = 1 microfarad

Significant Digits

Measurements, in contrast to discrete counts, often result in approximate numbers. As an indication of the accuracy of numbers, the scientific community has adopted the convention of significant digits.

The significant digits in a number are:

- Nonzero digits.
  In 241: 2, 4, and 1 are significant.
- A zero between 2 significant digits.
  In 1087: 1, 0, 8, and 7 are significant.
- A zero that is terminal on the right side of a decimal.
  In 1.0: 1 and 0 are significant.
- A zero that is known to be reliable or in some way significant.
  In 530: 5 and 3 are significant, 0 may not be significant unless proven so.

Computational Accuracy and Precision

In any computation involving sums and differences of approximations, the number with the smallest number of digits following the decimal point determines the number of decimal places to be used in the answer.

For example, for this sum:

```
   2883.00
     43.46
 +    0.1376
   2926.5976
```

the answer should be reported as 2927. Since 2883 has been rounded to the nearest integer, the answer should also be rounded to the nearest integer.

With products or quotients, the *accuracy* of the result depends on the number of significant digits in the component measurements. Thus, the number of significant digits to be retained in the result is the smallest number of significant digits in any of the components.

When comparing the *precision* of two or more approximate numbers, the number with the most significant digits to the right of the decimal point is the most precise.

Rounding

In performing computations, it is recommended that rounding be done after the calculation has been performed. This practice incurs the least possible error. The rules of rounding are:

- Add 1 if the succeeding digit is more than 5.
- Leave it unchanged if the succeeding digit is less than 5.
- If the succeeding digit is exactly 5, round off the number so that the final digit is even.

Exponents and Logarithms

Laws of Exponents

Exponents provide a shorthand method of writing the product of several like factors. If b is any number and n is a positive integer, the product of b multiplied by itself n times is denoted symbolically:

$$\underbrace{b \cdot b \ldots b}_{n \text{ factors}} = b^n$$

where n is the exponent and b is the base. It is read "b to the nth power." This definition can be extended to include exponents other than positive integers.

LAW I (Multiplication): When multiplying two or more factors with the same base, add the exponents and place the sum as an exponent on the same base.

$$A^m \cdot A^n = A^{m+n}$$

LAW II (Division): When dividing two quantities with the same base, subtract the exponent of the divisor from the exponent of the dividend and place the difference as an exponent on the same base.

$$A^m \div A^n = A^{m-n}$$

LAW III (Raising powers to powers): When raising a number with an exponent to a power, multiply the exponents and place the product as an exponent on the same base.

$$(A^m)^n = A^{mn}$$

ZERO EXPONENT: Any value (except 0) raised to the zero power is equal to 1.

$$A^0 = 1$$

NEGATIVE EXPONENT: A quantity raised to a negative power is equal to the reciprocal of that quantity with the corresponding positive exponent.

$$A^{-4} = \frac{1}{A^4}$$

SQUARE ROOT:

$$\sqrt{A} = A^{\frac{1}{2}} = A^{0.5}$$

Logarithms

Logarithms are exponents and behave accordingly. Hence, multiplication problems become addition of logarithms, division becomes subtraction, raising to a power becomes multiplication, and computing a root becomes division.

To perform calculations by means of logarithms, only a table of logarithms and a basic knowledge of algebra is needed.

DEFINITION: The logarithm of a number N to the base a is the exponent x to which the base must be raised to equal the number N.

$\log_a N$ = the logarithm of N to the base a

Then the definition states:

Properties of Logarithms

PROPERTY I: The logarithm of a product is equal to the sum of the logarithms of its factors.

PROPERTY II: The logarithm of a quotient is equal to the logarithm of the numerator minus the logarithm of the denominator.

PROPERTY III: The logarithm of the kth power of a number equals k times the logarithm of the number.

PROPERTY IV: The logarithm of the qth root of a number is equal to the logarithm of the number divided by q.

Common Logarithms

Logarithms that use 10 as a base are called *common logarithms*. Usually, these are written simply as log x, without any base indicated.

Note: Log 1 = 0 and log 10 = 1, since $10^0 = 1$ and $10^1 = 10$.

Thus, the integer portion of the logarithm of any number between 1 and 10 will be 1. Similarly, the integer portion of the logarithm of any number greater than 10 and less than 100 will be 2, and so on.

The integer portion of a logarithm is called the *characteristic*. The decimal portion is called the *mantissa*.

When finding the logarithm of a number using logarithmic tables, the characteristic is the exponent of 10, and the mantissa corresponding to the first part is taken from the table of logarithms. For example:

$$
\begin{aligned}
\text{Log } 52 &= \log(5.2 \times 10) \\
&= \log 5.2 + \log 10 \\
&= 0.7160 + 1 \\
&= 1.7160
\end{aligned}
$$

This same rule applies to numbers less than 1, although a characteristic with a negative value can be written as a digit with a line over it instead of as a negative number. The characteristic is normally written after the mantissa with a negative sign between them.

Prior to the popular use of calculators, lengthy tables were required to compute logarithms, especially when working backward to solve the original value of a logarithm (called an *antilog*). If a table is used, the number must be restated as a decimal minus a whole number. To use the previous problem as an example:

Find the antilog –2.2725:

$$= \text{antilog } (0.7275 - 3)$$
$$= \text{antilog } 0.7275 \times \text{antilog } (-3)$$
$$= 5.34 \times 10^{-3}$$
$$= 0.00534$$

Natural Logarithms

The *natural*, or *Napierian*, system of logarithms has as its base the irrational number *e*, whose decimal expansion is 2.71828. Natural logarithms are denoted by the symbols *ln x* or *log_ex*. Natural logs occur in nearly all natural mathematical relationships.

Algebra

Algebra is a generalized form of arithmetic. It uses representative symbols and a few fundamental principles for reducing, or transforming, equations in order to determine a specific number in a specific problem.

Algebra uses signed numbers (+ or –) to identify positive or negative numbers.

Equations are the primary unit of expression of mathematical thought in algebra. Letters are used to represent numbers. By naming letters and mathematical symbols, short algebraic statements replace lengthy verbal statements.

The four steps of algebraic problem solving are:

1. *Representation* of unknowns by letters.
2. *Translation* of relationships about unknowns into equations.
3. *Solution* of equations to find the values of unknowns.
4. *Verification* of the value found to see if it satisfies the original problem.

Laws and Assumptions

Commutative Law: The result of addition of terms or multiplication of terms in an equation is the same in whatever order the terms are added or multiplied (but not both).

Associative Law: The sum of three or more terms, or the product of three or more factors, is the same in whatever manner they are grouped.

Distributive Law: The product of an expression of two or more terms by a single factor is equal to the sum of the products of each term of the expression by the single factor.

Algebra assumes:

- The sign preceding the product of two quantities is plus if the quantities have like signs, minus if unlike signs.
- Quantities equal to the same thing or equal things are equal.
- If equals are added to equals, the sums are equal.
- If equals are subtracted from equals, the remainders are equal.
- If equals are multiplied by equals, the products are equal.
- If equals are divided by equals, the quotients are equal. Division by zero is not permissible.
- If equals are raised to the same power, the results are equal.
- Like roots of both members of an equation are equal.
- A quantity may be substituted for its equal in any expression.

Order of Operations in Algebra

Order of Operations

The following is the order in which the operations in an algebraic expression are to be performed:

First, perform all operations within grouping symbols.

Second, perform all multiplications and divisions.

Third, perform all additions and subtractions.

Equations

Linear (one unknown, *X*):

$$AX + B = 0$$

Representation = straight line

Quadratic (one variable, *X*):

$$AX^2 + BX + C = 0$$

Representation = parabola

Quadratic (two variables, *X* and *Y*):

$$AX^2 + BXY + XY^2 + DX + EY + F = 0$$

Representation = curve

TRIGONOMETRY

Laws of Cosines and Sines

These two laws give the relations between the sides and angles of any plane triangle (see Figure 2). In any plane triangle with vertices *A*, *B*, and *C*, and sides opposite *a*, *b*, and *c*, respectively, the following relations apply:

Law of Cosines

$$a^2 = b^2 + c^2 - \frac{2bc}{\cos A}$$

$$b^2 = a^2 + c^2 - \frac{2ac}{\cos B}$$

$$c^2 = a^2 + b^2 - \frac{2ab}{\cos C}$$

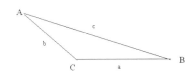

FIGURE 2. Relationship between sides and angles of any plane triangle

Law of Sines

$$\frac{\sin A}{a} = \frac{\sin B}{b} = \frac{\sin C}{c}$$

or

$$\frac{\sin A}{\sin B} = \frac{a}{b} \quad \frac{\sin A}{\sin C} = \frac{a}{c} \quad \frac{\sin B}{\sin C} = \frac{b}{c}$$

These laws apply to any triangle, right-angled or not. In case the angle is between 90 degrees and 180 degrees, as in the case of angle *C* in the diagram above, then these rules can be applied:

$\sin 0 = \sin (180 - 0) = 0.00$
$\sin 120 = \sin (180 - 120) = \sin 60 = 0.866$
$\cos 120 = -\cos (180 - 120) = -\cos 60 = -0.500$
$\cos 0 = -\cos(180 - 0) = 1.000$

Solutions of Triangle Problems

Procedure in solving a triangle:

1. Construct a figure.
2. Label the figure, introducing single letters to represent unknown angles or lengths.
3. Outline the solution and clearly indicate the formulas that are used.
4. Arrange a good computation schematic and perform the arithmetic.

ENGINEERING ECONOMY

Present Value of Future Dollar Amount

$$P = F(1 + i)^{-n}$$

Terms and Units

P = present value ($)
F = future value ($)
i = interest rate (%) compounded annually
n = number of years

Example

What is the present value of $2000 to be received in 6 years, if it is invested at 4% compounded annually?

The Microsoft Excel function for calculating this result is PV(*i*%, *n*, , −*F*). From typing "=PV(4%, 6, , −2000)" into a cell of an Excel worksheet, the answer is calculated to be $1580.63.

Therefore, the present value of $2000 to be received in 6 years, if it is invested at 4% compounded annually, is $1580.

Note that the time units on the interest rate (annual) and *n* (years) must match in order to use correctly the PV(*i*%, *n*, , −*F*) function in Excel.

Future Value of a Present Dollar Amount

$$F = P(1 + i)^{n}$$

Terms and Units

F = future value ($)
P = present value ($)
i = interest rate (%) compounded annually
n = number of years

Example

If $6000 is invested for 8 years at 10% compounded annually, what will the investment be worth at the end of the 8 years?

The Microsoft Excel function for calculating this result is FV(*i*%, *n*, , −*P*). From typing "=FV(4%, 8, , −6000)" into a cell of an Excel worksheet, the answer is calculated to be $12,861.53.

Therefore, the future value of $10,000 if invested for 8 years at 10% interest compounded annually will be $12,861.53.

Note that the time units on the interest rate (annual) and n (years) must match in order to use correctly the FV($i\%$, n, , $-P$) function in Excel.

Present Value of Equal Annual Dollar Amounts

$$P = A\left(\frac{(1 + i)^n - 1}{i(1 + i)^n}\right)$$

Terms and Units

P = present value ($)
A = equal annual investment or payment ($)
i = interest rate (%) compounded annually
n = number of years

Example

How much must be invested today at 5% compounded annually so that annual returns of $1000 will be made from the investment for 10 years?

The Microsoft Excel function for calculating this result is PV($i\%$, n, $-A$). From typing "=PV(5%, 10, -1000)" into a cell of an Excel worksheet, the answer is calculated to be $7,721.73.

Therefore, $7,721.73 invested today at 5% compounded annually will provide annual returns of $1000 in each of the next 10 years.

Note that the time units on the interest rate (annual), n (years), and frequency of cash flows (annual) must match in order to use correctly the PV($i\%$, n, $-A$) function in Excel.

Equal Annual Payment from a Present Dollar Value

$$A = P\left(\frac{i(1 + i)^n}{(1 + i)^n - 1}\right)$$

Terms and Units

A = equal annual investment or payment ($)
P = present value ($)
i = interest rate (%) compounded annually
n = number of years

Example

How much will an investment of $10,000 yield annually over 5 years at an interest rate of 15% compounded annually?

The Microsoft Excel function for calculating this result is PMT($i\%$, n, $-P$). From typing "=PMT(15%, 5, $-10,000$)" into a cell of an Excel worksheet, the answer is calculated to be $2,983.16.

Therefore, $10,000 invested at 15% compounded annually for 5 years will yield an annual payment of $2983.16.

Note that the time units on the interest rate (annual), n (years), and frequency of cash flows (annual) must match in order to use correctly the PMT($i\%$, n, $-P$) function in Excel.

Future Value of Equal Annual Dollar Amounts

$$F = A\left(\frac{(1 + i)^n - 1}{i}\right)$$

Terms and Units

A = equal annual investment or payment ($)
F = future value ($)
i = interest rate (%) compounded annually
n = number of years

Example

If annual investments of $400 are made for 6 years, and invested at 8% compounded annually, what will the value of the investment be at the end of the 6-year period?

The Microsoft Excel function for calculating this result is FV($i\%$, n, $-A$). From typing "=FV(8%, 6, -400)" into a cell of an Excel worksheet, the answer is calculated to be $2,934.37.

Therefore, the value at annual investments of $400 made for 6 years at 8% compounded annually will be $2934.37 at the end of the 6-year period.

Note that the time units on the interest rate (annual), n (years), and frequency of cash flows (annual) must match in order to use correctly the FV($i\%$, n, $-A$) function in Excel.

Equal Annual Payment from a Future Dollar Value

$$A = F\left(\frac{i}{(1 + i)^n - 1}\right)$$

Terms and Units

A = equal annual investment or payment ($)
F = future value ($)
i = interest rate (%) compounded annually
n = number of years

Example

How much must be invested annually over a period of 8 years at 5% compounded annually to be worth $10,000 at the end of the 8-year period?

The Microsoft Excel function for calculating this result is PMT(i%, n, $-F$). From typing "=PMT(5%, 8, –10,000)" into a cell of an Excel worksheet, the answer is calculated to be $1,047.22.

Therefore, an annual investment of $1,047.22 for each of the next 8 years will be worth $10,000 at the end of the 8-year period if the interest rate is 5% compounded annually.

Note that the time units on the interest rate (annual), n (years), and frequency of cash flows (annual) must match in order to use correctly the PMT(i%, n, $-F$) function in Excel.

ERGONOMICS

Lifting Index

$$LI = \frac{LW}{RWL}$$

Terms and Units

LI = lifting index
LW = loading weight
RWL = recommended weight limit

Example

Calculate the lifting index for a task with the following factors:

LW = 65 lb
RWL = 35 lb

$$LI = \frac{LW}{RWL}$$

$$LI = \frac{65}{35}$$

$$LI = 1.857$$

NIOSH Lifting Equation (English Units)

$$RWL = LC \times HM \times VM \times DM \times AM \times FM \times CM$$

$$RWL \ (\text{lb}) = (51)(10/H)[1 - (0.0075\,|V - 30|)][0.82 + (1.8/D)](1 - 0.0032A)(FM)(CM)$$

Terms and Units

RWL = recommended weight limit
LC = load constant
HM = horizontal multiplier
VM = vertical multiplier
DM = distance multiplier
AM = asymmetric multiplier
FM = frequency multiplier
CM = coupling multiplier

Example

Calculate the recommended weight limit (RWL) in pounds for a given task with the following factors:

LC = 60 lb
H = 15 in
V = 25 in
D = 45 in
A = 30°

frequency = 6 lifts/min
work duration = 2 hr
coupling type = fair

$$RWL = LC \times HM \times VM \times DM \times AM \times FM \times CM$$
$$FM = 0.50 \ (\text{from table})$$
$$CM = 0.95 \ (\text{from table})$$

$$60 \times \frac{10}{H} \times \left(1 - (0.0075|V - 30|)\right) \times \left(0.82 + \frac{1.8}{D}\right) \times$$
$$(1 - 0.0032A) \times FM \times CM$$

$$60 \times \frac{10}{H} \times \left(1 - (0.0075|25 - 30|)\right) \times \left(0.82 + \frac{1.8}{45}\right) \times$$
$$\left(1 - (0.0032 \times 30)\right) \times 0.50 \times 0.95$$

$$60 \times 0.667 \times 0.962 \times 0.860 \times 0.904 \times 0.50 \times 0.95$$

$$RWL = 14.217 \ \text{lb}$$

NIOSH Lifting Equation (Metric Units)

$$RWL = LC \times HM \times VM \times DM \times AM \times FM \times CM$$

$$RWL \text{ (kg)} = (23)(25/H)[1 - (0.003\,|V - 75|)][0.82 + (4.5/D)](1 - 0.0032A)(FM)(CM)$$

Terms and Units

RWL = recommended weight limit

LC = load constant

HM = horizontal multiplier

VM = vertical multiplier

DM = distance multiplier

AM = asymmetric multiplier

FM = frequency multiplier

CM = coupling multiplier

Example

Calculate the recommended weight limit (RWL) in kilograms for a given task with the following factors:

LC = 30 kg

H = 28 cm

V = 60 cm

D = 86 cm

A = 105°

frequency = 3 lifts/min

work duration = 4 hr

coupling type = poor

$$RWL = LC \times HM \times VM \times DM \times AM \times FM \times CM$$

FM = 0.55 (from table)

CM = 0.90 (from table)

$$30 \times \frac{25}{H} \times (1 - (0.003|V - 75|)) \times \left(0.82 + \frac{4.5}{D}\right) \times$$

$$(1 - 0.0032A) \times FM \times CM$$

$$30 \times \frac{25}{28} \times (1 - (0.003|60 - 75|)) \times \left(0.82 + \frac{4.5}{86}\right) \times$$

$$(1 - (0.0032 \times 105)) \times 0.55 \times 0.90$$

$$30 \times 0.892 \times 0.955 \times 0.872 \times 0.664 \times 0.55 \times 0.90$$

$$RWL = 7.324 \text{ kg}$$

GENERAL SCIENCE

Lower Flammability Limit for Mixtures

$$LFL_m = \frac{1}{\dfrac{f_1}{LFL_1} + \dfrac{f_2}{LFL_2} + \cdots \dfrac{f_n}{LFL_n}}$$

Terms and Units

LFL_m = lower flammability limit of a mixture (%)

$F_{1\ldots n}$ = the decimal fraction of the substance present for materials $1 \ldots n$ (unitless)

$LFL_{1\ldots n}$ = the lower flammability limits for materials $1 \ldots n$ (%)

Example

Determine the lower flammability limit of a mixture containing 25% toluene, 30% ethyl ether, and 45% acetone. The LFLs are: toluene 1.1%, ethyl ether 1.9%, and acetone 2.5%.

$$LFL_m = \frac{1}{\dfrac{f_1}{LFL_1} + \dfrac{f_2}{LFL_2} + \cdots \dfrac{f_n}{LFL_n}}$$

$$LFL_m = \frac{1}{\dfrac{0.25}{1.1\%} + \dfrac{0.30}{1.9\%} + \cdots \dfrac{0.45}{2.5\%}}$$

$$LFL_m = \frac{1}{0.565\%}$$

$$LFL_m = 1.769\%$$

Parts per Million: Pressure/Pressure

$$ppm = \frac{P_v}{P_{atm}} \times 10^6$$

Terms and Units

P_{atm} = atmospheric pressure (mm Hg)

ppm = parts per million (ppm)

10^6 = conversion factor to express answer in ppm

P_v = vapor pressure of agent or contaminant at a specified temperature (mm Hg)

Example

Calculate the equilibrium (saturation) concentration for xylene at 68°F and normal atmospheric pressure. The vapor pressure of xylene at 68°F is 9 mm Hg.

$$ppm = \frac{P_v}{P_{atm}} \times 10^6$$

$$ppm = \frac{9 \text{ mm Hg}}{760 \text{ mm Hg}} \times 10^6$$

$$ppm = 11{,}842 \; ppm$$

Parts Per Million to mg/m³ Conversion

$$ppm = \frac{\text{mg/m}^3 \times 24.45}{\text{MW}}$$

Terms and Units

ppm = parts per million (*ppm*)
MW = molecular weight of contaminant
24.25 = molar volume of any gas or vapor at NTP
mg/m³ = milligrams of contaminant per cubic meter of air (mg/m³)

Example

Convert 2570 mg/m³ of acetone to *ppm*. The MW of acetone is 58.1.

$$ppm = \frac{\text{mg/m}^3 \times 24.45}{\text{MW}}$$

$$ppm = \frac{2570 \text{ mg/m}^3 \times 24.45}{58.1 \text{ g}}$$

$$ppm = 1081 \; ppm$$

General Gas Law

$$\frac{P_1 V_1}{n R T_1} = \frac{P_2 V_2}{n R T_2}$$

Terms and Units

n = number of moles of gas or vapor (unitless)
T = absolute temperature Rankine (°R); Kelvin (K)
V_1; V_2 = gas or vapor volume under conditions 1 and 2 (1)

R = gas constant for air (0.082 liters atmosphere/moles K)
P_1; P_2 = gas or vapor pressure under conditions 1 and 2 (mm Hg)

Example

An acetone/air mixture is collected in an impervious 5-L gas-sampling bag at 80°F and 710 mm Hg. Calculate the new volume for the bag when it is at NTP.

$$\frac{P_1 V_1}{n R T_1} = \frac{P_2 V_2}{n R T_2}$$

$$\frac{720 \text{ mm Hg} \times 5 \text{ liters}}{(80°\text{F} + 460)} = \frac{760 \text{ mm Hg} \times V_2}{(77°\text{F} + 460)}$$

$$\frac{3600}{540} = \frac{760 \, V_2}{537}$$

$$V_2 = 4.7 \; L$$

TLV of Mixture (Liquid Composition)

$$TLV_{mix} = \frac{1}{\dfrac{F_1}{TLV_1} + \dfrac{F_2}{TLV_2} + \cdots \dfrac{F_n}{TLV_n}}$$

Terms and Units

$F_{1\ldots n}$ = weight % of chemical in liquid (unitless decimal)
$TLV_{1\ldots n}$ = threshold limit value of the contaminant (mg/m³)
TLV_{mix} = threshold limit value of a mixture of chemical with additive effects (mg/m³)

Example

Determine the threshold limit value of a mixture containing 25% toluene, 40% xylene, and 15% hexane. The TLVs are: toluene 188 mg/m³, xylene 434 mg/m³, and hexane 176 mg/m³.

$$TLV_{mix} = \frac{1}{\dfrac{F_1}{TLV_1} + \dfrac{F_2}{TLV_2} + \cdots \dfrac{F_n}{TLV_n}}$$

$$TLV_{mix} = \cfrac{1}{\cfrac{0.25}{188 \text{ mg/m}^3} + \cfrac{0.40}{434 \text{ mg/m}^3} + \cfrac{0.15}{176 \text{ mg/m}^3}}$$

$$TLV_{mix} = \frac{1}{0.00310 \text{ mg/m}^3}$$

$$TLV_{mix} = 323 \text{ mg/m}^3$$

HEAT STRESS

Wet-Bulb Globe Temperature Index (No Solar Load)

WBGT = 0.7WB + 0.3GT

Terms and Units

WBGT = wet-bulb globe temperature index, °C
WB = wet-bulb temperature, °C
GT = globe temperature, °C

Example

Two temperature measurements are taken of the air surrounding an indoor task:

wet-bulb temperature = 30°C
globe temperature = 15°C

Calculate the wet-bulb globe temperature index.
WBGT = 0.7WB + 0.3GT
WBGT = 0.7(30) + 0.3(15)
WBGT = 21.0 + 4.5
WBGT = 25.5°C

The wet-bulb globe temperature is 25.5°C.

Wet-Bulb Globe Temperature Index (Solar Load)

WBGT = 0.7WB + 0.2GT + 0.1DB

Terms and Units

WBGT = wet-bulb globe temperature index, °C
WB = wet-bulb temperature, °C
GT = globe temperature, °C
DB = dry-bulb temperature, °C

Example

Three temperature measurements are taken of the air surrounding an outdoor task on a sunny day:

wet-bulb temperature = 30°C
globe temperature = 15°C
dry-bulb temperature = 45°C

Calculate the wet-bulb globe temperature index.
WBGT = 0.7WB + 0.3GT + 0.1DB
WBGT = 0.7(30) + 0.3(15) + 0.1(45)
WBGT = 21.0 + 4.5 + 4.5
WBGT = 30°C

The wet-bulb globe temperature is 30°C.

NOISE

Distance and Sound Pressure Level

$$dB_1 = dB_0 + 20 \log \frac{d_0}{d_1}$$

Terms and Units

dB_0 = noise level at distance d_0 (dB)
dB_1 = noise level at distance d_1 (dB)
d_0, d_1 = distance (any consistent units, e.g., m)

Example

A noise survey at a work station 6 m from a noise shows a reading of 124 dB. What will be the reading if the work station is moved further away, to 12 m?

$$dB_1 = dB_0 + 20 \log \frac{d_0}{d_1}$$

$$dB_1 = 124 \text{ dB} + 20 \log\left(\frac{6}{12}\right)$$

$$dB_1 = 124 + (-6)$$

$$dB_1 = 118$$

Sound Power Level

$$L_W = 10 \log_{10} \frac{W}{W_0}$$

or

$$W = W_0 \text{ antilog}_{10} \frac{L_W}{10} = W_0 \times 10^{\frac{L_W}{10}}$$

where

dB is the reference quantity for W_0
W is the sound power in Watts
W_0 is the reference sound power in Watts

Sound Intensity Level

$$L_1 = 10 \log \frac{I}{I_0} \text{ dB}$$

Terms and Units

L_1 = sound pressure level (dB)
I = sound intensity (W/m²)
I_0 = reference sound intensity (W/m²)

Example

What is the sound power level for a measured intensity of 5^{-10} W/m² where the reference intensity is 14^{-8} W/m²?

$$L_1 = 10 \log \frac{I}{I_0} \text{ dB}$$

$$L_1 = 10 \log \left(\frac{5^{-10}}{14^{-8}} \right)$$

$$L_1 = 22 \text{ dB}$$

Sound Pressure Level

$$L_P = 20 \left(\log \frac{P}{P_0} \right)$$

Terms and Units

L_P = sound pressure level (dB)
P = measured sound pressure (Pa)
P_0 = reference sound pressure (Pa)

Example

What is the sound pressure level in dB when the measured sound pressure is 0.2 Pa?

$$L_P = 20 \left(\log \frac{P}{P_0} \right)$$

$$L_P = 20 \left(\log \frac{0.15 \text{Pa}}{0.00002 \text{ Pa}} \right)$$

$$L_P = 78 \text{ dB}$$

Total Sound Pressure Level

$$L_{Pt} = 10 \log \left(\sum_{i=1}^{N} 10^{\frac{L_{Pi}}{10}} \right)$$

Terms and Units

L_{Pt} = total sound pressure level generated by N sources (dB)

L_{Pi} = individual sound pressure level of ith source (dB)
N = number of sound pressure levels

Example

Three machines will be situated in close proximity. Given their individual sound pressure levels, L_P, of 42, 54, and 78 dB, what is the approximate total sound pressure level, L_{Pt}?

$$L_{Pt} = 10 \log \left(\sum_{i=1}^{N} 10^{\frac{L_{Pi}}{10}} \right)$$

$$L_{Pt} = 10 \log \left(10^{\frac{42}{10}} + 10^{\frac{54}{10}} + 10^{\frac{78}{10}} \right)$$

$$L_{Pt} = 78 \text{ dB}$$

TWA Calculated from % Dose

$$\text{TWA} = 16.61 \log \left(\frac{D}{100} \right) + 90$$

Terms and Units

D = dose for noise exposure in percent
TWA = equivalent time-weighted average exposure in dB based on percent dose (D) for a shift

Example

The percent dose for a shift is determined to be 50%. What is the TWA exposure?

$$\text{TWA} = 16.61 \log \left(\frac{D}{100} \right) + 90$$

$$\text{TWA} = 16.61 \log \left(\frac{50}{100} \right) + 90 \text{ dBa}$$

$$\text{TWA} = 85 \text{ dBa}$$

MECHANICS

Bending Moment (Concentrated Load at Center)

$$M = \frac{Pl}{4}$$

Terms and Units

M = maximum bending moment (ft-lb)

P = concentrated load applied at center of beam (lb)

l = length of beam (ft)

Example

A 5-ton hoist is suspended at the midpoint of a 12-ft beam that is supported at each end. What is the maximum bending moment in this beam?
(*Note:* Neglect the weight of the beam.)

P = 5 tons = 10,000 lb

l = 12 ft

$$M = \frac{Pl}{4}$$

$$M = \frac{(10,000 \text{ lb})(12 \text{ ft})}{4}$$

$$M = 30,000 \text{ ft-lb}$$

Bending Moment (Concentrated Load Off-Center)

$$M = \frac{Pab}{l}$$

Terms and Units

M = the maximum bending moment (ft-lb)

P = concentrated load on beam (lb)

$a \neq b$ = respective distances from left and right supports of beam (ft)

l = length of beam (ft)

Example

A 10-ft beam supported at each end is loaded with a weight of 1400 lb at a point 3 feet left of its center. What is the maximum bending moment in this beam? (*Note:* Neglect the weight of the beam.)

P = 1400 lb

a = 3 ft

b = 7 ft

l = 10 ft

$$M = \frac{Pab}{l}$$

$$M = \frac{(1400 \text{ lb})(3 \text{ ft})(7 \text{ ft})}{10 \text{ ft}}$$

$$M = 29,400 \text{ ft-lb}$$

Bending Moment (Uniform Loading)

$$M = \frac{wl^2}{8}$$

Terms and Units

M = maximum bending moment (ft-lb)

w = uniform weight loading per foot of beam (lb/ft)

l = length of beam (ft)

Example

A 12-ft beam supported at two points, one at each end, is uniformly loaded at a rate of 400 lb/ft. What is the maximum bending moment in this beam?

w = 400 lb/ft

l = 12 ft

$$M = \frac{wl^2}{8}$$

$$M = \frac{(400 \text{ lb/ft})(12 \text{ ft})^2}{8}$$

$$M = 7200 \text{ ft-lb}$$

Capacitance (Electrical in Parallel Circuits)

$$C_{parallel} = C_1 + C_2 + \ldots C_n$$

Terms and Units

$C_{parallel}$ = equivalent capacitance of n capacitors wired in parallel in a circuit (farads or microfarads)

$C_{1, 2\ldots n}$ = equivalent capacitance of individual capacitors in a circuit (farads or microfarads)

Example

Find the equivalent capacitance of a circuit having three capacitors wired in parallel if

C_1 = 10 μF

C_2 = 75 μF

C_3 = 54 μF

$$C_{parallel} = C_1 + C_2 + C_3$$

$$C_{parallel} = (10 + 75 + 54)\ \mu\text{F}$$

$$C_{parallel} = 139\ \mu\text{F}$$

Capacitance (Electrical in Series Circuits)

$$\frac{1}{C_{series}} = \frac{1}{C_1} + \frac{1}{C_2} + \dots \frac{1}{C_n}$$

Terms and Units

C_{series} = equivalent capacitance in farads of n capacitors wired in series (farads or microfarads)
$C_{1,2\dots n}$ = individual capacitance (farads or microfarads)

Example

What is the equivalent capacitance of a circuit having four capacitors wired in series if

$C_1 = 80 \; \mu F$
$C_2 = 35 \; \mu F$
$C_3 = 42 \; \mu F$
$C_4 = 72 \; \mu F$

$$\frac{1}{C_{series}} = \frac{1}{C_1} + \frac{1}{C_2} + \frac{1}{C_3} + \frac{1}{C_4}$$

$$\frac{1}{C_{series}} = \frac{1}{80 \; \mu F} + \frac{1}{35 \; \mu F} + \frac{1}{42 \; \mu F} + \frac{1}{72 \; \mu F}$$

$$C_{series} = 0.079 \; \mu F$$

Electrical Resistance Length and Area of Conductor

$$R = \rho \frac{L}{A}$$

Terms and Units

R = resistance (ohms)
ρ = resistivity* (ohm-ft)
L = length of conductor (ft)
A = conductor's cross-sectional area (ft)

*Note: ρ / A is resistivity in ohm/ft

Example

What is the resistance of 50 ft of #14 gauge copper wire? (*Note:* From table, we find the resistivity, ρ, for #14 gauge copper wire to be 2.525 ohms/1000 ft.)

$\rho / A = 2.525 / 1000 \; ft = 0.002525 \; ohms/ft$
$L = 50 \; ft$

$$R = \rho \frac{L}{A}$$

$R = (0.002525 \; ohm/ft)(50 \; ft)$
$R = 0.126 \; ohms$

Flow Calculation for Water Supplies (approximate)

$$Q_2 = Q_1 \left[\frac{(S - R_2)^{0.54}}{(S - R_1)^{0.54}} \right]$$

Terms and Units

R = residual pressure for predicted flow rate (psi)
Q_1 = known flow rate from a group of open hydrants with a measured residual pressure, R_1 (gpm)
Q_2 = predicted flow rate at a different residual pressure, R_2, usually 20 psi (gpm)
S = static pressure in a hydrant system with no flow from any hydrants (psi)
R_1 = the residual pressure measured at a nonflowing hydrant during a flow test (psi)

Example

The static pressure of a hydrant system is 75 psi. When the flow from several hydrants combined reaches 3500 gpm, the pressure at the nonflowing hydrant reduces to 30 psi. (a) What is the expected flow for a residual pressure of 40 psi? (b) What would the static pressure need to be to obtain a flow of 5000 gpm at 30 psi?

Question a

$S = 75 \; psi$
$Q_1 = 3500 \; gpm$
$R_1 = 30 \; psi$
$R_2 = 40 \; psi$

$$Q_2 = Q_1 \left[\frac{(S - R_2)^{0.54}}{(S - R_1)^{0.54}} \right]$$

$$Q_2 = 3500 \left[\frac{(75 \; psi - 40 \; psi)^{0.54}}{(75 \; psi - 30 \; psi)^{0.54}} \right]$$

$$Q_2 = 3500 \left(\frac{(35)^{0.54}}{(45)^{0.54}} \right)$$

$$Q_2 = 3500 \left(\frac{6.82}{7.81} \right)$$

$$Q_2 = 3500(0.87)$$

$$Q_2 = 3056.34 \text{ gpm}$$

Question b

It is known from question *a* that

$$\frac{Q_1}{(S - R_1)^{0.54}} = \frac{Q_2}{(S - R_2)^{0.54}} = \text{constant}$$

The constant for this system is 550.
The equation can be rewritten as

$$(S - R_2)^{0.54} = \frac{Q_2}{\text{constant}}$$

$$S = \left(\frac{Q_2}{\text{constant}} \right)^{1.85} + R_2$$

$$S = \left(\frac{5000}{550} \right)^{1.85} + 30$$

$$S = 89.4 \text{ psi}$$

Hydraulic Flow-Pressure Relationship (approximate)

$$\frac{Q_1}{Q_2} = \frac{\sqrt{P_1}}{\sqrt{P_2}}$$

Terms and Units

P = pressure in psi
Q = flow in gpm

Example

A sprinkler system was hydraulically designed so that 1450 gpm at 30 psi was needed at the top of the riser to meet a certain storage arrangement demand. The warehouse manager would like to rearrange the storage in such a way that 2000 gpm will be required over the same area to satisfy the increase in the density of the demand. What will the pressure requirement be at the top of the riser to deliver the new flow requirement?

$P_1 = 30$ psi
$Q_1 = 1450$ gpm
$Q_2 = 2000$ gpm

$$P_2 = P_1(Q_2 / Q_1)^2$$

$$P_2 = (30 \text{ psi})(2000 \text{ gpm}/1450 \text{ gpm})^2$$

$$P_2 = 57.1 \text{ psi}$$

Hydraulic Friction Loss Formula (approximate)

$$P_d = \frac{4.52 Q^{1.85}}{C^{1.85} d^{4.87}}$$

Terms and Units

Q = flow rate (gpm)
C = coefficient of friction
d = inside diameter of pipe (in)
P_d = pressure in lb per sq in per ft of pipe (psi)

Example

What is the friction loss in psi per ft for a 5-in pipe having a C of 85 with a 250 gpm flow?

$Q = 250$ gpm
$C = 85$
$d = 5$ in

$$p = 4.52 Q^{1.85} / C^{1.85} d^{4.87}$$

$$p = (4.52)(250)^{1.85} / (85)^{1.85}(5)^{4.87}$$

$$p = 0.131 \text{ psi per foot}$$

Ideal Gas Law

$$PV = nRT$$

Terms and Units

P = absolute pressure (psia)
V = volume (ft^3)
n = the number of moles of gas (lb-moles)
R = the Universal Gas Constant (10.73 psi-ft^3/lb mole-°R)
T = absolute temperature (°R)

Example

A 40-lb cylinder of propane (C_3H_8 MW = 44) is mounted on a forklift truck that is garaged in a room having dimensions of 15 ft × 30 ft × 45 ft. If the cylinder is full (20 lb of gas in the tank) and the room temperature is 80°F at the time a leak develops, will a dangerous situation develop? Assume there is excellent air movement in the room to cause complete mixing of the gases with the air-handling system in a 100% recirculation mode with no leakage to the outside. The LEL for propane is 2.15%.

Or

Is the volume of 40 lb of propane at 80°F greater than 15 ft × 30 ft × 45 ft × 0.0215 = 435.4 ft^3?

V = ft^3 of 40 lb of propane at 80°F, 14.7 psia
n = 40 lb/44 lb/lb-mole = 0.9090 lb-moles
R = 10.73
T = 80°F + 460 = 540°R
P = 1 atm = 14.7 psia

$$PV = nRT$$

$$V = (0.9090)(10.73)(540)/14.7$$

$$V = 358.3 \ ft^3$$

A dangerous situation.

Kinetic Energy

$$\text{K.E.} = \frac{mv^2}{2}$$

Terms and Units

K.E. = the kinetic energy (ft-lbf)
m = the mass of an object (slugs = W/g*)
v = the velocity of an object (ft/s)

*Note: In order for the units of K.E. to come out correctly, if the weight (W) of an object is known [commonly stated as pounds (lbf)] it needs to be divided by g, which has the value and units of 32.2 ft/s^2, to get the equivalent "slugs."

Example

How much work can be done by a 200-lb weight moving at a velocity of 60 mph?

m = 200 lb ÷ 32.2 ft/s^2 = 6.2 slugs
v = 60 mi/hr × 5280 ft/mi × hr/3600 s = 88 ft/s

$$\text{K.E.} = 1/2 \ mv^2$$

$$\text{K.E.} = 1/2(3.1 \text{ slugs})(88 \text{ ft/s})^2$$

$$\text{K.E.} = 12,003.2 \text{ ft-lb}$$

OHM's Law

$$V = IR$$

Terms and Units

V = voltage
I = current in amperes
R = resistance in ohms

Example

What is the current in an 18-gauge wire plugged into a 120-volt outlet that supplies a saw that has a resistance of 75 ohms?

V = 120 volts
R = 75 ohms

$$I = V/R$$

$$I = 120/75$$

$$I = 1.6 \text{ amperes}$$

Pipe Head Pressure

$$h_p = \frac{p}{w}$$

Terms and Units

h_p = pressure head (ft)
p = pressure (lb/ft^2 or psf)
w = density (lb/ft^3 or pcf)

Example

A pressure gauge at the base of a gravity tank reads 80 psi. How high is the level of the water in the tank?

$p = 80 \text{ psi} \times 144 \text{ si/sf} = 11{,}520 \text{ psf}$
$w = 62.4 \text{ pcf}$

$h_p = p/w$

$h_p = 11{,}520 \text{ psf}/62.4 \text{ pcf}$

$h_p = 184.6 \text{ ft}$

Potential Energy

$\text{P.E.} = mgh$

Terms and Units

P.E. = potential energy (ft-lb)
m = mass $\left(\text{slugs} = W \,(\text{lb})/g^{(\text{ft/s}^2)}\right)$
g = gravitational constant (32.2 ft/s²)
h = height or elevation (ft)

Note: mg can be replaced by *W*, which simplifies the formula to P.E. = *Wh*.

Example

How much potential energy is stored in a 90,000-gal water gravity tank whose average elevation above ground level is 125 ft? (*Note:* Density of water = 62.4 lb/ft³; 7.48 gal = 1 ft³)

$W = (62.4 \text{ lb/ft}^3)(90{,}000 \text{ gal}) \div 7.48 \text{ gal/ft}^3 = 750{,}802 \text{ lb}$
$h = 125 \text{ ft}$

$\text{P.E.} = mgh$

$\text{P.E.} = mgh = Wh$

$\text{P.E.} = (750{,}802)(125)$

$\text{P.E.} = 6006.4 \text{ ft-lb}$

Friction

$F = \mu N$

Terms and Units

F = force (lb)
μ = the coefficient of friction, which is dimensionless

N = the force acting normal (i.e., perpendicular) to the surface in pounds (lbf)

Example

How much force is required to move a 500-lb box if the static coefficient of friction between it and the horizontal surface upon which it is resting is 0.90?

$F = (0.90)(500 \text{ lb}) = 450 \text{ lb}$

Or

A 300-lb box is placed on a plane incline at a 30° angle from horizontal. The plane has a static coefficient of friction of 0.80. What is the minimum push or pull force required to move the box down the plane?

Force required to overcome friction:

$F = (0.80)(300 \times \cos 30)$

$= (0.80)(300 \text{ lb} \times 0.866)$

$= (0.80)(259.8 \text{ lb}) = 207.84 \text{ lb}$

Note: Due to gravity, there is a preexisting force acting in the downward direction of the incline, which is equal to *W* sin 0 or 300 × 0.80 = 240 lb. Therefore, the push/pull force required to begin the box's movement is 240 lb – 207 lb = 33 lb.

Force (Newton's Second Law)

$F = ma$

Terms and Units

F = force (lb)
m = mass (slugs; 1 slug = 32.2 lb) = W/g_c (lb ÷ 32.2 ft/s²)
a = acceleration (ft/s²)

Example

How much force must a seat belt be capable of withstanding to safely restrain a 130-lb woman when her car comes to a sudden (i.e., 1.0-second) stop if initially traveling at 60 mph? [Assume a safety factor (S.F.) of 3.]

$m = 130 \text{ lb} \div 32.2 \text{ ft/s}^2 = 4.03 \text{ slugs}$
$a = v/t = (60 \text{ m/hr})(5280 \text{ ft/m})(\text{hr}/3600 \text{ s}) \div 1.0 \text{ s} = 88 \text{ ft/s}^2$

$F = ma \times$ S.F. of 3

$F = (4.03)(88)$ lb $\times 3 = 354.64$ lb

Weight

$W = mg$

Terms and Units

W = weight in pounds—force (lb)
m = mass in slugs (1 slug = 32.2 lb)
g = acceleration of gravity (lb $\div$ 32.2 ft/s^2)

Example

An object weighs 100 lb when measured at sea level. What is its mass?

$W = 100$ lb
$g = 32.2$ ft/s^2

$W = mg$

$m = W/g$

$m = 100$ lbf $\div 32.2$ ft/s$^2 = 3.01$ slugs

Resistance (Electrical in Series Circuits)

$R_{series} = R_1 + R_1 + \ldots R_n$

Terms and Units

R_{series} = equivalent resistance of n resistances wired in series (ohms)
$R_{1,\,2\ldots n}$ = resistance (ohms)

Example

There are three resistors in a series circuit having a 50-volt battery as a power source. Resistor A is a resistance of 30 ohms, resistor B is 25 ohms, and resistor C is 15 ohms. What is the voltage drop across resistor B?

$\Delta V_B = R_b I$

$R_B = 25$ ohms

$I = V/R_{series} = V/\left(R_A + R_B + R_C\right)$

$I = 50/23 = 2.17$ amps

$\Delta V_B = (25$ ohms$)(2.17$ amps$)$

$\Delta V_B = 54.24$ volts

Power (Electric)

$P = VI$

Terms and Units

P = power (Watts)
V = voltage (volts)
I = current (amperes)

Example

An electric heater is rated as 10.8 kw wired at 220 volts. What current draw will dictate minimum wire sizing and fuse protection for this appliance?

$P = 10.8$ kw $= 10,800$ W
$V = 220$ volts

$P = VI$

$I = P/V = 10,800$ W$/220$ volts

$I = 49.1$ amps

VENTILATION

Effective Ventilation

$Q' = \dfrac{Q}{K}$

Terms and Units

Q' = effective ventilation rate (cfm)
Q = actual ventilation rate (cfm)
K = safety factor, ranging from 1 to 10

Example

What would be the actual ventilation rate if it were determined that 4000 cfm would control a contaminated concentration to the permissible exposure limit (PEL) under ideal conditions? Assume a safety factor of 4.

$Q' = \dfrac{Q}{K}$

$Q = Q'K$

$Q = 4000$ cfm $\times 4$

$Q = 16,000$ cfm

Total Pressure in a Duct

$$TP = VP + SP$$

Terms and Units

TP = total pressure within a duct ("wg)
VP = velocity pressure within a duct ("wg)
SP = static pressure within a duct ("wg)

Example

Calculate the static pressure of a duct if the velocity pressure is 5 "wg and the total pressure on the inlet side of the fan measures 0.9 "wg.

$$TP = SP + VP$$

$$SP = TP - VP$$

$$SP = -0.9 - 5.0$$

$$SP = -5.9 \text{ "wg}$$

Note: The static and total pressures on the inlet/upstream/intake side of a fan are always negatively signed; therefore, the negative designation indicates the duct pressures are below atmospheric pressure.

Hood Flow Rate and Static Pressure

$$Q = 4005 C_e A \sqrt{SP}$$

Terms and Units

Q = volumetric flow rate (cfm)
A = area of the duct (ft^2)
4005 = constant
SP = hood static pressure ("wg)
C_e = hood entry coefficient (unitless)

Example

A static pressure tap was installed on an 8-in-diameter duct (A = 0.35 ft^2) with a plain opening. The manometer read 4.0 "wg. What was the flow rate of the hood?

$$Q = 4005 C_e A \sqrt{SP}$$

$$Q = 4005(0.72) \, 0.35 \text{ ft}^2 \sqrt{4}$$

$$Q = 2018.52 \text{ cfm}$$

Note: C_e for a flanged hood is 0.82 or 82% efficient, and for a plain opening it is 0.72 or 72% efficient.

Coefficient of Entry

$$C_e = \sqrt{\frac{VP}{|SP_h|}}$$

Terms and Units

C_e = hood entry coefficient (unitless)
VP = velocity pressure ("wg)
$|SP_h|$ = absolute value of the hood static pressure ("wg)

Example

What is the hood entry coefficient for a flanged hood opening if the average velocity pressure for the duct is 0.50 "wg and the hood static suction measures 2.15 "wg?

$$C_e = \sqrt{\frac{VP}{|SP_h|}}$$

$$C_e = \sqrt{\frac{0.50 \text{ "wg}}{2.15 \text{ "wg}}}$$

$$C_e = \sqrt{0.23}$$

$$C_e = 0.48$$

RULES-OF-THUMB FOR THE SAFETY PROFESSIONAL

A *rule-of-thumb* is a principle with broad application that is not intended to be strictly accurate or reliable for every situation. It is an easily learned and easily applied procedure for approximately calculating or recalling some value, or for making some determination.

Tom Parker wrote in the introduction to his book, *Rules-of-Thumb*, "A rule-of-thumb is a homemade recipe for making a guess. It is an easy-to-remember guide that falls somewhere between a mathematical formula and a shot in the dark."

Concrete

Rule-of-thumb: *Expansion Joint Cut Depth*
Expansion control joints in a concrete slab should be cut to a depth of one-fourth of the slab's thickness.

Noise

Source: Noise Control: A Guide for Employees and Employers. Chicago, IL: National Safety Council, 1986. Print.

Rule-of-thumb: *Rule of Three* (*Adding noise sources*)
Application: Adding noise sources
Limitation: (1) Accuracy is limited to ±1 dB.
(2) Noise sources operate in a near free field.
(3) Noise sources must have similar frequency profiles.

In lieu of using the equation for adding decibels, a table of adding decibels can be utilized to approximate the addition of multiple noise sources.

$$L_{total} = 10 \log \left(\sum_{i=1}^{N} 10^{L_i/10} \right)$$

Or

Difference in Decibel Values	Add to Higher Value
0 or 1 dB	3 dB
2 or 3 dB	2 dB
4 to 9 dB	1 dB
10 dB or more	0 dB

Example

Four similar noise sources have the following individual dB values: 90, 88, 82, and 79.

90 − 88 = 2

From the table, add 3 to the higher value 90, which equals 93. Then use 93 in the next step.

93 − 82 = 11

From the table, add 0 to the higher value 93, which equals 93. Then use 93 in the next step.

93 − 79 = 14

From the table, add 0 to the higher value 93, which equals 93.

The sum of the four noise sources 90, 88, 82, and 79 is 93 using the *Rule of Three*, or using the calculation method:

$$L_p = 10 \log \left(10^{9.0} + 10^{8.8} + 10^{8.2} + 10^{7.9} \right) = 92.7$$

Rule-of-thumb: *Rule of Six* (*Sound reduction by distance*)
Application: Decreasing sound with distance
Limitation: Sound spreading in open air and measured at a certain distance from the source is reduced by about 6 dB for each doubling of that distance. Sound is reduced less when spreading inside a room.

If a small sound source produces a sound level of 96 dB at a distance of 1 meter, the sound level at 2 meters is approximately 90 dB (96 dB − 6dB). Doubling the distance again, to 4 meters, the sound level will be approximately 84 dB (90 dB − 6 dB).

Rule-of-thumb: *Rule of Ten* (*Adding ten similar noise sources*)
Application: Adding ten similar noise sources
Limitations: (1) Noise sources must have similar frequency profiles. (2) It is based upon the use of the *Rule of Three* above. (3) The ten noise sources must have the same sound pressure level (e.g., ten identical pressure pumps).

Difference in Decibel Values	Add to Higher Value
0 or 1 dB	3 dB
2 or 3 dB	2 dB
4 to 9 dB	1 dB
10 dB or more	0 dB

Example

Adding the sound level of ten near-identical noise sources with individual sound levels of 80 dB.

80 − 80 = 0

From the table, add 3 to the higher value 80, which equals 83. This is for two of the ten noise sources. Then use 83 in the next step.

$83 - 80 = 3$

From the table, add 2 to the higher value 83, which equals 85. This is the sound contribution of source number 3. Then use 85 in the next step.

$85 - 80 = 5$

From the table, add 1 to the higher value 85, which equals 86. This is the sound contribution of source number 4. Then use 86 in the next step.

$86 - 80 = 6$

From the table, add 1 to the higher value 86, which equals 87. This is the sound contribution of source number 5. Then use 87 in the next step.

$87 - 80 = 7$

From the table, add 1 to the higher value 87, which equals 88. This is the sound contribution of source number 6. Then use 88 in the next step.

$88 - 80 = 8$

From the table, add 1 to the higher value 88, which equals 89. This is the sound contribution of source number 7. Then use 86 in the next step.

$89 - 80 = 9$

From the table, add 1 to the higher value 89, which equals 90. This is the sound contribution of source number 8. Then use 86 in the next step.

$90 - 80 = 10$

From the table, add 0 to the higher value 90, which equals 90. This is the sound contribution of source number 9.

If you add a tenth noise source with a sound level of 80 dB, as with the first 9 noise sources, the sum of the ten sources (actually nine) cannot become any higher than 10 dB above the common sound level. In this example, ten noise sources, each generating a sound level of 80 dB, cannot total more than 10 dB above the 80 dB, or a total of 90 dB. This is referred to as the *Rule of Ten*.

Rule-of-thumb: *Rule of 20*
If you move ten times further away from a noise source, the sound intensity will fall by a factor of 100 because of the effects of the inverse square law. A factor of 100 is a drop of 20 dB. For example, a 90-dB source measured at 6 meters would have a 20-dB reduction at 60 meters (ten times further away).

Rule-of-thumb: *Protecting Your Hearing*
If you need to raise your voice to talk to people only three feet away, you probably need to be wearing hearing protection.

Rule-of-thumb: *Practical Adjustment of Noise Reduction Rating* (NRR)
Reduce the NRR value shown on the packaging of hearing protection devices by one-half the value to approximate the "real world" hearing protection versus the "ideal laboratory" conditions used to obtain the NRR value posted on the packaging.

Organic Solvents

Rule-of-thumb: *Vapors Heavier than Air*
If an organic solvent is a liquid at room temperature, its vapors are heavier than air.

Temperature Conversions

Rule-of-thumb: *°C to °F Conversion in Your Head*
To quickly convert Centigrade to Fahrenheit, double the °C temperature and add 30. The exact formula is $°C = 5/9 \ (°F - 32)$. Using this rule-of-thumb, 10°C is 50°F and 20°C is 40°F.

Rule-of-thumb: *°F to °C Conversion in Your Head*
To quickly convert Fahrenheit to Centigrade, subtract 30 from the °F value and divide by 2. The exact formula is $°F = 9/5 \ (°C + 32)$. Using this rule-of-thumb 60°F is 15°C and 80°F is 25°C.

Respiratory Protection

Rule-of-thumb: *Organic Vapor Cartridge Respirator Service-Life Adjustments*
OSHA's respiratory eTool offers some schedule change rules-of-thumb. It is acknowledged that

these rules came from Chapter 36 of the American Industrial Hygiene Association (AIHA) publication *The Occupational Environment—Its Evaluation and Control*. The publication suggests that

- If the chemical's boiling point is > 70°C and the concentration is less than 200 ppm, you can expect a service life of 8 hours at a normal work rate.
- Service life is inversely proportional to work rate.
- Reducing concentration by a factor of 10, will increase service life by a factor of 5.
- Humidity above 85 percent will reduce service life by 50 percent.

These generalizations should only be used in concert with one of the other methods of predicting service life for specific contaminants.

Sling Angle

Rule-of-thumb: *NO Sling Angles Less than 30 Degrees*
Sling angles of less than 30° are not recommended even if loading can be calculated for sling angles less than 30°.

Walking-Working Surfaces

Rule-of-thumb: *Slope of a Ladder*
The bottom of a ladder should be 1 foot away from the wall for every 4 feet of vertical height.

Rule-of-thumb: *Ladder Overreach or the Belt Buckle Rule*
Do not overreach from a ladder, or lean too far to one side; always keep your belt buckle inside the rails of a ladder.

Rule-of-thumb: *Rise and Tread of Stairs*
Between the incline angles of 30 to 50 degrees, any combination of riser height plus the tread width that adds up to 17 1/2 inches will be comfortable to use and will be in compliance with 29 CFR 1910.24(e).

Weather

Rule-of-thumb: *1-2-3 Rule*
The National Hurricane Center of the National Oceanic and Atmospheric Administration (NOAA) states that the *1-2-3 Rule* is the single most important aid in accounting for hurricane forecast track errors (FTE). The *1-2-3 Rule* establishes a minimum recommended distance to maintain for a hurricane in the Atlantic.

1-2-3 Rule-of-Thumb

1–100 mile error radius for 24-hr forecast

2–200 mile error radius for 48-hr forecast

3–300 mile error radius for 72-hr forecast

Rule-of-thumb: *Wipers and Headlights*
If it is raining hard enough to use your windshield wipers, then you should turn on your headlights as well.

Welding

Estimate the initial amperage selection based upon electrode size. Once the electrode has been selected, the correct amperage may be estimated at one amp per thousandth of an inch of the electrode's diameter. Thus, an electrode 1/4-inch thick would require 250 amps (1/4 = 250/1000).

ADDITIONAL RULE-OF-THUMB RESOURCES AND REFERENCES

Barnett, R., and P. Poczynok. 1996. "Safety Rules-of-Thumb." Triodyne Inc, Niles, IL. *Safety Bulletin* Volume 2, No. 4. www.triodyne.com/SAFETY~1/B_V2N4.pdf

Belle, G. 2008. *Statistical Rules-of-Thumb*, 2d ed. Hoboken, NJ: Wiley.

Branan, C. 2005. *Rules-of-Thumb for Chemical Engineers*, 4th ed. Oxford, UK: Gulf Professional Publishing.

Electronics and Electrical Web Directory. July 18, 2004. *Electrical Safety: Rules-of-Thumb* (retrieved December 19, 2009). elecdir.com/press_release/store/95/index.html

Fisher, D. 1988. *Rules-of-Thumb for Physical Scientists*. Brookfield, VT: Trans Tech Publications.

Gibillisco, S. 2001. *Mathematical and Physical Data, Equations, and Rules-of-Thumb*. Blue Ridge Summit, PA: Tab Books.

McAllister, E. 2005. *Pipeline Rules-of-Thumb Handbook*. Maryland Heights, MO: Elsevier Science & Technology.

Parker, T. 2008. *Rules-of-Thumb: A Life Manual*. New York, NY: Workman Publishing.

Pope, J. 1996. *Rules-of-Thumb for Mechanical Engineers*. Oxford, UK: Gulf Professional Publishing.

Rajapakse, R. 2008. *Geotechnical Engineering Calculations and Rules-of-Thumb*. Oxford, UK: Butterworth-Heinermann.

Rich, G. n.d. *Environmental Rules-of-Thumb*. Des Plaines, IL: Cahners Publishing Co.

Silverman, J., E. Hughes, and D. Wienbroer. 2007. *Good Measures: A Practice Book to Accompany Rules-of-Thumb*, 7th ed. New York, NY: McGraw-Hill.

Smith, R., and R. Mobley. 2007. *Rules-of-Thumb for Maintenance and Reliability Engineers*. Oxford, UK: Butterworth-Heinermann.

Woods, D. 2007. *Rules-of-Thumb in Engineering Practice*. Hoboken, NJ: John Wiley & Sons.

INDEX